C000056150

ALL NEW MERRILL EARTH SCIENCE

OPENS STUDENTS' EYES TO THE NATURAL PROCESSES OF EVERYDAY LIFE

AT LAST—AN EARTH SCIENCE PROGRAM THAT TRULY IMPACTS STUDENTS' LIVES

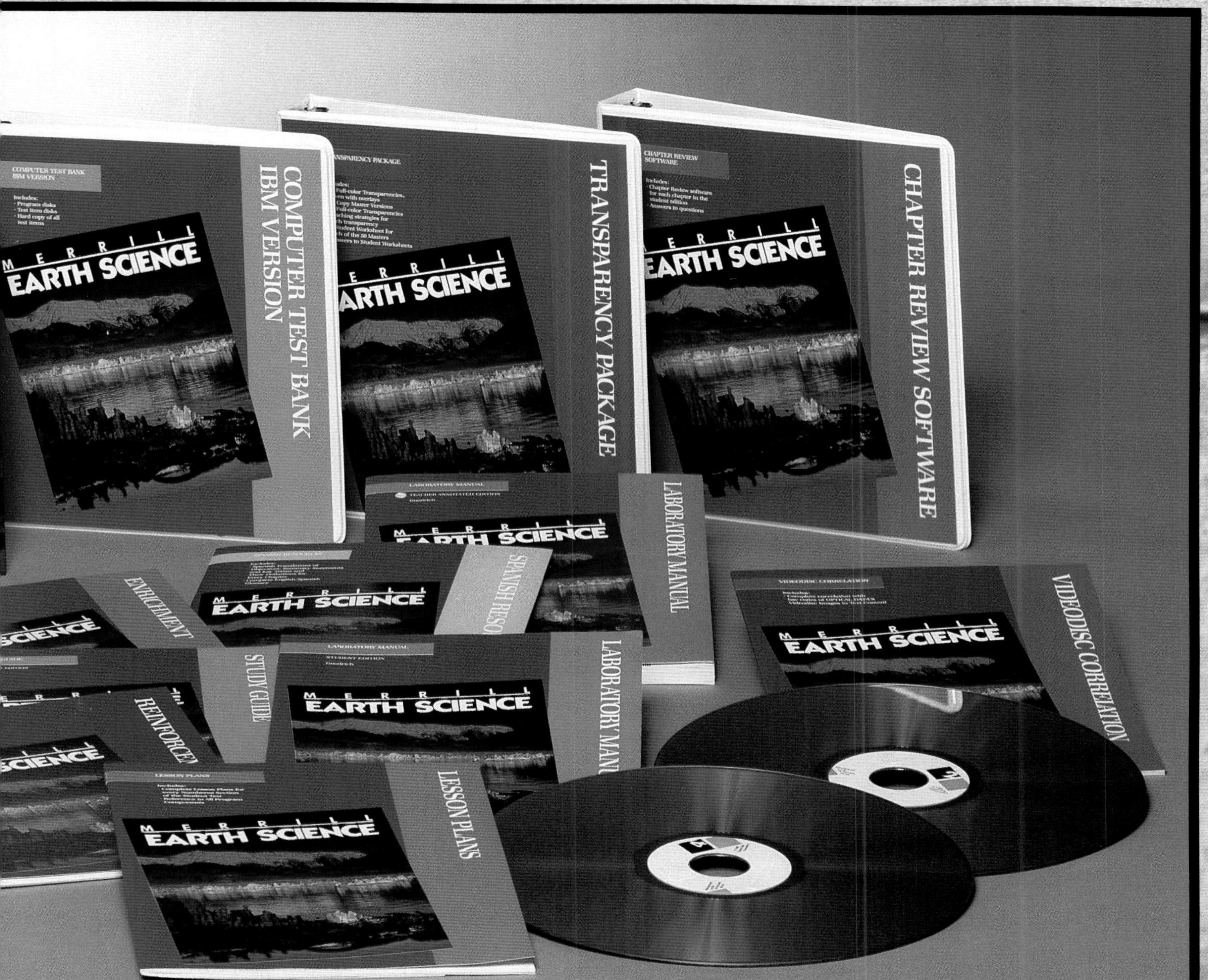

Earth science is a subject all students should be familiar with because every activity they do depends on their natural environment. The all new ***Merrill Earth Science*** *opens students' eyes to the many natural processes occuring around them everyday. It uses familiar analogies, such as the motion of ocean water and sunlight shining through a car window, to explain such principles as erosion and the greenhouse effect. With* ***Merrill Earth Science,*** *your students will gain an understanding and appreciation of our precious planet Earth. And they will learn about the many things they can do to help preserve it for the future.*

The ***Merrill Earth Science*** *comprehensive learning and teaching program provides everything you need to make earth science an* ***active learning experience.*** *Your students will learn through:*

- ***Solid concept development,*** *thematically structured to focus on the principle ideas of earth science.*
- ***Hands-on activities*** *that actively involve students in the subject matter.*
- ***Strong skill development*** *which leads to student success in science and the real world.*
- ***Fascinating, real-world applications*** *that will make the study of earth science come alive in your classroom.*

As for teacher's classroom support, the new ***Merrill Earth Science*** *provides a wealth of resource materials in the* ***Teacher Wraparound Edition*** *and* ***Teacher Resource Package.*** *Teaching suggestions, background information, reinforcement activities, and extension activities are just a few of the valuable tools we provide to help enrich your program and reduce your preparation time.*

ACTIVITIES HELP STUDENTS SEE THE WORLD AT WORK

*To really understand the principles of earth science, students need to implement them. The all new **Merrill Earth Science** offers a variety of stimulating activities that give your students plenty of opportunities to apply topics covered in class. These activities not only help students to better understand earth science, they help them to relate the principles to everyday life. Plus they help them to build the skills needed to become responsible decision makers and critical thinkers in our society.*

Two full-page **Activity** features, in each chapter, give your students opportunities to learn by doing. Each encourages the use of scientific methods of investigation.

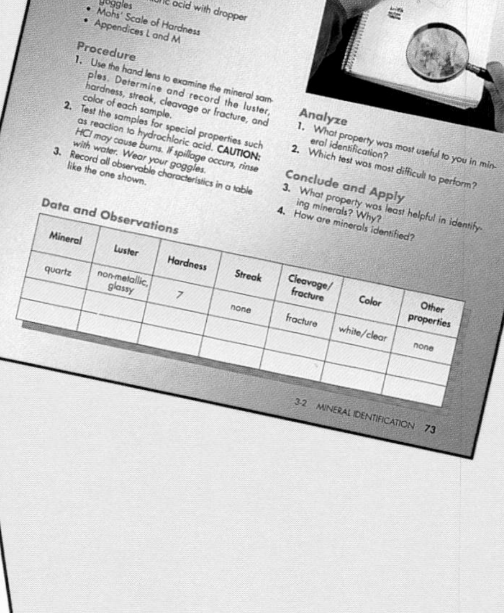

ACTIVITY 3-2
Mineral Identification

Problem: How are minerals identified?

Materials
- mineral samples
- hand lens
- pan balance
- graduated cylinder
- water
- copper penny
- glass slide
- steel file
- streak plate
- 5% hydrochloric acid with dropper
- goggles
- Mohs' Scale of Hardness
- Appendices L and M

Procedure
1. Use the hand lens to examine the mineral samples. Determine and record the luster, hardness, streak, cleavage or fracture, and color of each sample.
2. Test the samples for special properties such as reaction to hydrochloric acid. **CAUTION:** *HCl may cause burns. If spillage occurs, rinse with water. Wear your goggles.*
3. Record all observable characteristics in a table like the one shown.

Analyze
1. What property was most useful to you in mineral identification?
2. Which test was most difficult to perform?

Conclude and Apply
3. What property was least helpful in identifying minerals? Why?
4. How are minerals identified?

Data and Observations

Mineral	Luster	Hardness	Streak	Cleavage/ fracture	Color	Other properties
quartz	non-metallic, glassy	7	none	fracture	white/clear	none

3-2 MINERAL IDENTIFICATION 73

Some of the planets in the solar system have systems of rings around them. The image at the left is a photo collage of several planets in the solar system. The rings of Saturn are seen in the center. From Earth, planetary rings look like solid bands that circle the planet. Actually, planetary rings are made up of millions of individual particles of dust, rock, and ice that are orbiting around some planets in bands.

FIND OUT!

Do this simple activity to find out about planetary rings.

Bring in some color comics from your local newspaper. First, examine the color while holding the comics at arm's length from your eyes. The colors of areas within the lines seem solid and made up of just one color, don't they? Now examine the comics up close with a magnifying glass. Try to observe tan or orange colors in the comics. What does the magnifying glass reveal? Are all of the colors really solid? What does this comparison help to explain about planetary rings?

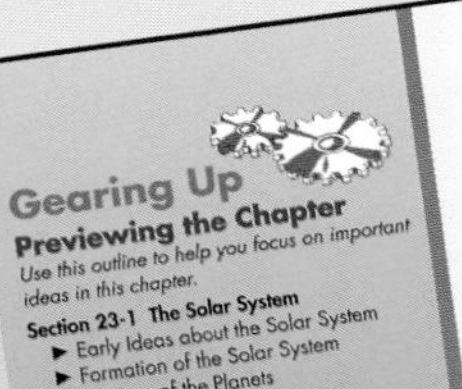

Gearing Up
Previewing the Chapter

Use this outline to help you focus on important ideas in this chapter.

Section 23-1 The Solar System
- Early Ideas about the Solar System
- Formation of the Solar System
- Motions of the Planets

Section 23-2 The Inner Planets
- Inner Planets

Section 23-3 Science and Society
Mission to Mars
- Who Should Explore Mars—Humans or Robots?

Section 23-4 The Outer Planets
- Outer Planets

Section 23-5 Other Objects in the Solar System
- Other Objects in the Solar System
- Comets
- Meteoroids, Meteors, and Meteorites
- Asteroids

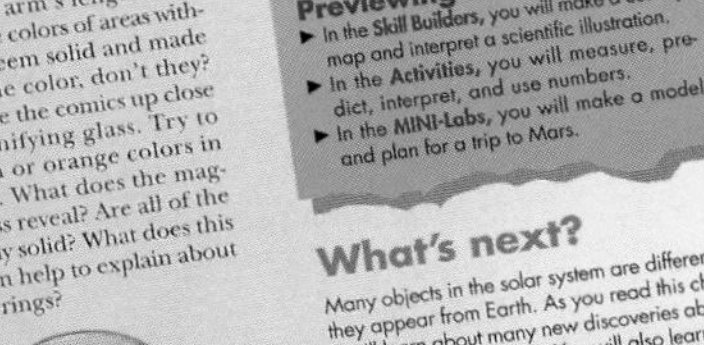

Previewing Science Skills
- In the **Skill Builders**, you will make a concept map and interpret a scientific illustration.
- In the **Activities**, you will measure, predict, interpret, and use numbers.
- In the **MINI-Labs**, you will make a model and plan for a trip to Mars.

What's next?

Many objects in the solar system are different than they appear from Earth. As you read this chapter, you'll learn about many new discoveries about the planets and their moons. You will also learn about other objects that are part of our solar system.

598 599

Chapter Openers offer fun, interesting ways to get your students excited about the upcoming lesson.
- A unique **Find Out** activity entices students to make observations and raise questions about upcoming content.
- **Gearing Up** previews key concepts and skills.
- **What's Next** provides an intriguing transition into the chapter's main ideas.

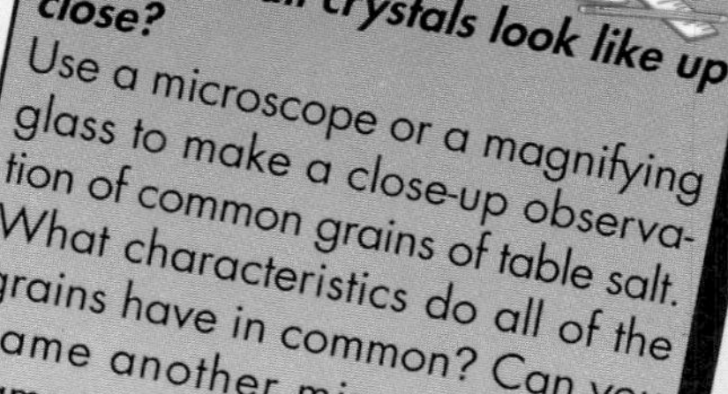

MINI-Lab
What do salt crystals look like up close?

Use a microscope or a magnifying glass to make a close-up observation of common grains of table salt. What characteristics do all of the grains have in common? Can you name another mineral with the same crystal system as salt? What is the name of this crystal system?

Mini-Labs are quick hands-on activities that give your students additional opportunities to practice important process skills. Great for in-class instruction or take-home exercises.

As you learned in Chapter 2, dense materials sink below less dense materials. In the ocean, denser water around the North Pole and the South Pole sinks and travels along the ocean floor toward the equator. At the same time, less dense water at the equator rises and moves toward the poles along the surface. These two events form a continuous cycle that circulates ocean water.

What is one reason that cold ocean water is more dense than warm ocean water?

What can make seawater denser and sink? The cold air near the poles chills the water, causing its molecules to be less active and closer together. This decreases the volume of the water and makes it denser, so it sinks. Also, the cold climate freezes some of the water. This concentrates the salts in the remaining unfrozen water, which increases its mass, makes it denser, and causes it to sink. Once this happens, the colder, saltier, denser water moves as a mass along the ocean bottom.

You made a density current in the Find Out activity at the beginning of this chapter. As the ice cube melted, its cold water was denser than the warm water in the pan, so the cold water sank to the bottom. This created a density current which moved the food coloring.

PROBLEM SOLVING

Testing the Water

Parul decided that her dog, Grover, needed a bath. She got a metal washtub and began filling it with water from the garden hose. She filled it three-fourths full. When she tested the temperature with her hand, she thought it was just too cold to put Grover into. So, she decided to heat some water on the stove and add that to the washtub. She did this, then retested the water. To her surprise, the surface of the water was very hot, but the bottom three-fourths of the water was still quite cold.

Think Critically: Why wasn't all the water in the tub the same warm temperature?

290 OCEAN WATER

Problem Solving features are real-life stories about kids. A critical thinking question engages the student in solving an everyday problem linked to the chapter content.

Flex Your Brain blends critical thinking and problem solving. Students use a step-by-step method to explore a topic while they learn to develop good problem solving skills.

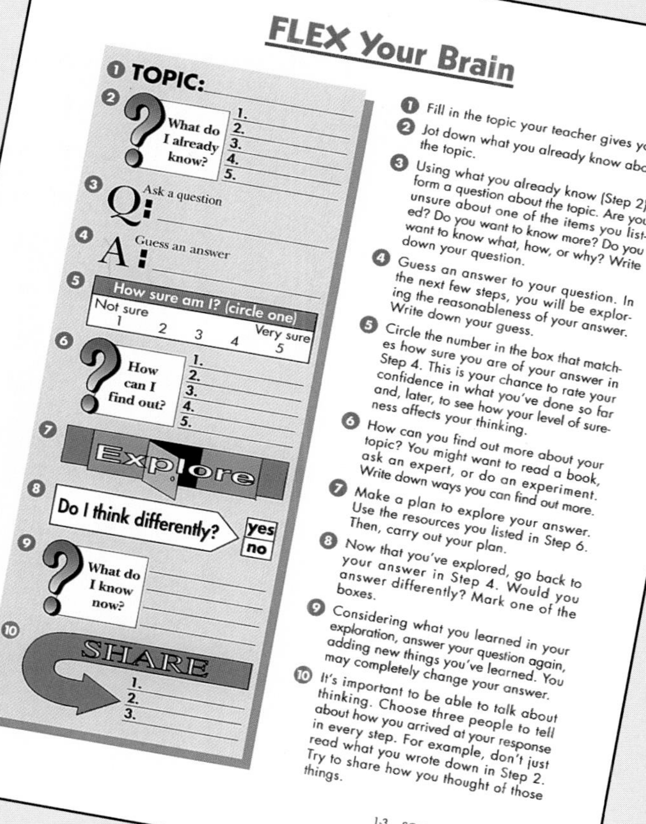

FLEX Your Brain

1 TOPIC:

2 What do I already know? 1. 2. 3. 4. 5.

3 Q: Ask a question

4 A: Guess an answer

5 How sure am I? (circle one)
Not sure 1 2 3 4 5 Very sure

6 How can I find out? 1. 2. 3. 4. 5.

7 Explore

8 Do I think differently? yes no

9 What do I know now?

10 SHARE 1. 2. 3.

1. Fill in the topic your teacher gives you.
2. Jot down what you already know about the topic.
3. Using what you already know (Step 2), form a question about the topic. Are you unsure about one of the items you listed? Do you want to know more? Do you want to know what, how, or why? Write down your question.
4. Guess an answer to your question. In the next few steps, you will be exploring the reasonableness of your answer. Write down your guess.
5. Circle the number in the box that matches how sure you are of your answer in Step 4. This is your chance to rate your confidence in what you've done so far and, later, to see how your level of sureness affects your thinking.
6. How can you find out more about your topic? You might want to read a book, ask an expert, or do an experiment. Write down ways you can find out more.
7. Make a plan to explore your answer. Use the resources you listed in Step 6. Then, carry out your plan.
8. Now that you've explored, go back to your answer in Step 4. Would you answer differently? Mark one of the boxes.
9. Considering what you learned in your exploration, answer your question again, adding new things you've learned. You may completely change your answer.
10. It's important to be able to talk about thinking. Choose three people to tell about how you arrived at your response in every step. For example, don't just read what you wrote down in Step 2. Try to share how you thought of those things.

1-3 SOLVING PROBLEMS 15

Another nonfoliated metamorphic rock is marble. Marble forms from the sedimentary rock limestone which is composed of calcite. The calcite crystals give marble its glassy, shiny luster that makes it a popular material for sculpturing. Usually, marble contains several other minerals besides calcite which color it. For example, hornblende and serpentine give it a greenish tone whereas hematite makes it red.

So far, we've traveled through only a portion of the rock cycle. We still haven't observed how sedimentary rocks are formed and how igneous and metamorphic rocks evolve from them. The next section will complete our investigation of the rock cycle.

SECTION REVIEW

1. How is the formation of igneous rock different from that of metamorphic rock?
2. How are metamorphic rocks classified? What are the characteristics of rocks in each of these classifications?
3. Marble rarely contains fossils even though limestone does. Explain.
4. **Apply:** Slate is sometimes used as roofing tiles for houses. What properties of slate make it useful for this purpose?

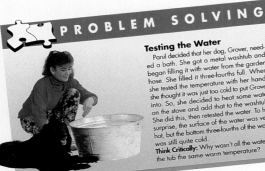

Figure 4-11. Sculptors often work with marble because it's soft and easy to shape. Its calcite crystals also give it a glassy, shiny luster.

Skill Builder

Sequencing

Put the following events in a sequence that could explain how a metamorphic rock might form from an igneous rock. (HINT: Start with igneous rock forms.) Use each event just once. If you need help, refer to Sequencing in the **Skill Handbook** on page 681.

Events: sedimentary rock forms, weathering occurs, heat and pressure is applied, igneous rock forms, metamorphic rock forms, erosion occurs, sediments are formed, deposition occurs

98 ROCKS

A **Skill Builder,** at the end of each section, challenges students to use basic process skills. The activity also directs the students to the **Skill Handbook,** located at the back of the text, for a step-by-step overview on how to accomplish that particular skill.

STUDENTS DISCOVER HOW EARTH SCIENCE TOUCHES THEIR EVERYDAY LIVES

Earth Science is around us. It impacts everything we do, see, and feel. Reading the poetic words of Langston Hughes "In Times of Silver Rain" teaches students more than the basic principles of earth science. It teaches them how our natural environment impacts people and places around the world. This is what makes the study of earth science real. And it's what makes ***Merrill Earth Science*** *more enriching than any other earth science program currently available.*

The **Science and Society** lesson in each chapter challenges students to make decisions and formulate their own viewpoints about issues facing them and their community.

SCIENCE & SOCIETY 10-4

Can We Slow Down Global Warming?

New Science Words

greenhouse effect
deforestation

Objectives

- Describe the greenhouse effect.
- List causes of global warming.

The Greenhouse Effect

Do you remember the last sunny day you got into a car that had the windows up? It was really hot inside. Do you know why? When sunlight shines through the car windows, it is absorbed by the seats and other materials inside the car. Some of this energy is then radiated from the seats as heat. Heat radiation cannot pass through glass, so the temperature inside the car got hotter and hotter. This also happens in glass greenhouses. Sunlight penetrates the glass and heat that is reflected by the plants in the greenhouse can't escape back through the glass. This warms the air in greenhouses.

This process of warming also happens to Earth. As you learned in Chapter 9, much of the heat radiated from Earth's surface is reflected back down to Earth by gases in the atmosphere. This causes Earth's atmosphere to warm up. This process by which heat is trapped by gases

Incoming solar energy
Greenhouse Gases
Deforestation
Industry
Rice paddies
Vehicle exhaust
Cows

274 WEATHER AND CLIMATE

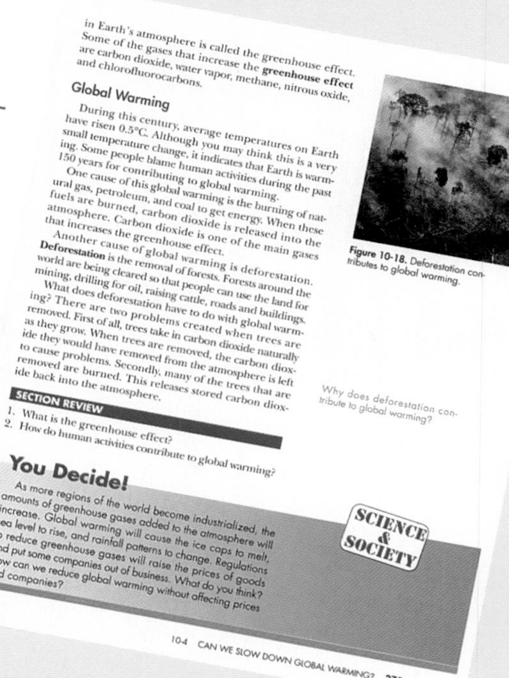

in Earth's atmosphere is called the greenhouse effect. Some of the gases that increase the **greenhouse effect** are carbon dioxide, water vapor, methane, nitrous oxide, and chlorofluorocarbons.

Global Warming

During this century, average temperatures on Earth have risen 0.5°C. Although you may think this is a very small temperature change, it indicates that Earth is warming. Some people blame human activities during the past 150 years for contributing to global warming.

One cause of this global warming is the burning of natural gas, petroleum, and coal to get energy. When these fuels are burned, carbon dioxide is released into the atmosphere. Carbon dioxide is one of the main gases that increases the greenhouse effect.

Another cause of global warming is deforestation. **Deforestation** is the removal of forests. Forests around the world are being cleared so that people can use the land for mining, drilling for oil, raising cattle, roads and buildings.

What does deforestation have to do with global warming? There are two problems created when trees are removed. First of all, trees take in carbon dioxide naturally as they grow. When trees are removed, the carbon dioxide they would have removed from the atmosphere is left to cause problems. Secondly, many of the trees that are removed are burned. This releases stored carbon dioxide back into the atmosphere.

Figure 10-18. Deforestation contributes to global warming.

Why does deforestation contribute to global warming?

SECTION REVIEW

1. What is the greenhouse effect?
2. How do human activities contribute to global warming?

You Decide!

As more regions of the world become industrialized, the amounts of greenhouse gases added to the atmosphere will increase. Global warming will cause the ice caps to melt, sea level to rise, and rainfall patterns to change. Regulations to reduce greenhouse gases will raise the prices of goods and put some companies out of business. What do you think? How can we reduce global warming without affecting prices and companies?

SCIENCE & SOCIETY

10-4 CAN WE SLOW DOWN GLOBAL WARMING? 275

EcoTip

Will the fossils you leave behind pollute the environment? Plastic foam cups and plates last up to 500 years in a landfill. Reduce waste by washing and reusing cups and plates whenever possible.

Ecotips enhance students' environmental awareness by suggesting simple changes in their own behavior that can have positive effects on the environment.

Two **Careers** are featured in every unit to expose students to the interesting and wide range of career choices available for those with a knowledge of science.

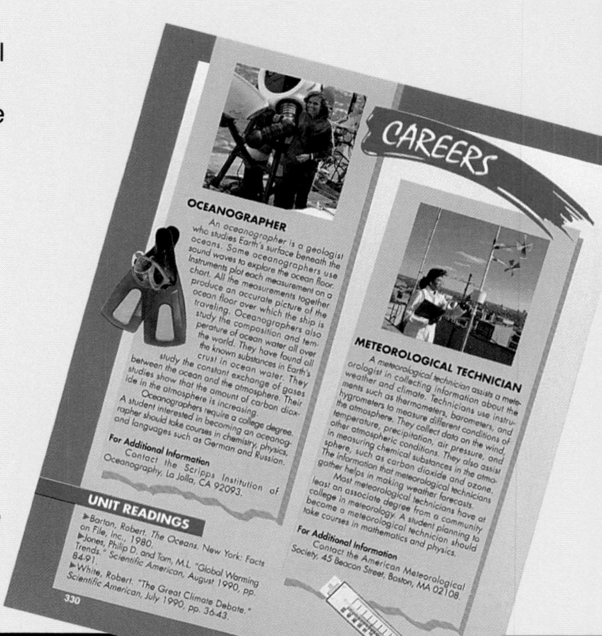

CAREERS

OCEANOGRAPHER

An oceanographer is a geologist who studies Earth's surface beneath the oceans. Some oceanographers use sound waves to explore the ocean floor. Instruments plot each measurement on a chart. All the measurements together produce an accurate picture of the ocean floor over which the ship is traveling. Oceanographers also study the composition and temperature of ocean water all over the world. They have found all the known substances in Earth's crust in ocean water. They study the constant exchange of gases between the ocean and the atmosphere. Their studies show that the amount of carbon dioxide in the atmosphere is increasing.

Oceanographers require a college degree. A student interested in becoming an oceanographer should take courses in chemistry, physics, and languages such as German and Russian.

For Additional Information

Contact the Scripps Institution of Oceanography, La Jolla, CA 92093.

METEOROLOGICAL TECHNICIAN

A meteorological technician assists a meteorologist in collecting information about the weather and climate. Technicians use instruments such as thermometers, barometers, and hygrometers to measure different conditions of the atmosphere. They collect data on the wind, temperature, precipitation, air pressure, and other atmospheric conditions. They also assist in measuring chemical substances in the atmosphere, such as carbon dioxide and ozone. The information that meteorological technicians gather helps in making weather forecasts.

Most meteorological technicians have at least an associate degree from a community college in meteorology. A student planning to become a meteorological technician should take courses in mathematics and physics.

For Additional Information

Contact the American Meteorological Society, 45 Beacon Street, Boston, MA 02108.

UNIT READINGS

- Barton, Robert. *The Oceans*. New York: Facts on File, Inc., 1980.
- Jones, Philip D. and Tom, M.L. "Global Warming Trends." *Scientific American*, August 1990, pp. 84-91.
- White, Robert. "The Great Climate Debate." *Scientific American*, July 1990, pp. 36-43.

330

UNIT 3

GLOBAL CONNECTIONS

The Changing Surface of Earth

In this unit, you studied processes that change Earth's surface. Now find out how these processes are connected to other subjects and places around the world.

CHEMISTRY

CARLSBAD CAVERNS
Carlsbad, New Mexico
Water percolating through soil picks up carbon dioxide, forming a weak acid capable of dissolving limestone. When a droplet with limestone reaches the airfilled chamber of a cave, the limestone is precipitated from the water and left on the ceiling, wall, or floor, as calcite crystals. These grow to form stalactites or stalagmites. Are the crystal formations the result of weathering or deposition?

HISTORY

WEATHERING AT MOUNT RUSHMORE
Mount Rushmore, South Dakota
In 1989, a study was begun to see how weathering is affecting the Mount Rushmore National Memorial. When the study is completed, those in charge of the monument will decide which cracks should be filled with putty and which cracks will need to be supported with steel pins. What kinds of weathering may be affecting the monument? What presidents are represented by the monument?

OCEANOGRAPHY

EROSION OF COASTLINES
Southwest Coast of England
The ocean is always moving. The jagged coastline of southwest England is clear evidence of the remarkable power of water to eat away and reshape rock. The motion of the water also mixes the minerals flowing from the land, making the chemical composition of seawater constant all over the world. What motions in the ocean help to reshape the coastline?

SOCIAL STUDIES

PRE-AGRICULTURAL COMMUNITIES
Nile Delta, Egypt
About 18 500 years ago, people in Egypt exploited the valley when the Nile River overflowed its banks. From July to September they camped on high ground to catch catfish trapped in ponds. When the ponds dried up, they sowed wheat, barley, and chick peas in the mud. They returned to harvest the grain when it was ripe. Why was the floodplain of the Nile a good place to grow crops?

221

SCIENCE & ART

Native American Pottery

In Chapters 3 and 4, you read about the properties of rocks and minerals. As you read the following paragraphs about Maria Martinez and her pottery, you'll discover that rocks and minerals can be used to fashion works of art.

The Pueblo people of the Southwest had one of the most highly developed civilizations to ever inhabit North America. Like other Native Americans, the Pueblos have always had a good understanding of how to make use of the natural resources of their environment. They employed minerals and rocks to produce useful and artistic products. Of particular interest are the beautiful hand-painted pieces of pottery fashioned by Pueblo craftspeople.

In the twentieth century, modern utensils have replaced pottery for kitchen use. So now Native Americans are producing pottery that is treasured mostly for its artistic value. One Pueblo artist whose works are in many museums of the world was Maria Martinez. Most of her long life of ninety-nine years was dedicated to producing the exquisite black-on-black pottery such as the pieces shown on this page.

Black pottery had not been produced by Native Americans for over 700 years until an archaeologist discovered some black pottery shards in an excavation of an ancient Native American village near San Ildefonso. He brought them to Maria who had already become well known for her multicolored pottery. Maria began working with a clay, rich in several minerals, found near her home, hoping to find the secret of how to make black pottery. Then one day she and her husband smothered the flames while the clay pots were being fired. When they removed the pots, they found that the clay had blackened! They had finally discovered how to duplicate the ancient black pottery.

Maria later devised a way to make the black pots shine by polishing the surface with a smooth stone before firing. After awhile, she combined polished designs with a flat finish called matte.

When demands for her black-on-black pottery exceeded her ability to produce them, Maria taught others in her village the secret. Soon Maria Martinez's black-on-black pottery replaced the earlier styles in several villages. Other Native Americans, influenced by Maria, have received recognition for their artistic pottery: Grace Medicine Flower, Cristina Naranjo, Joy "Frogwoman" Navasie, Blue Corn, and Nampeyo (a Hopi artist).

In Your Own Words

▶ Maria Martinez's rediscovery of an ancient skill came after many trials and errors. Write an essay to compare and contrast the techniques of artists and scientists. Explain how both must experiment, observe, and analyze results to achieve their goals.

117

Global Connections, at the end of every unit, relate the concepts studied in the unit to other subjects and events around the world. Each vignette raises important questions for further study in such areas as history, oceanography, astronomy, and biology.

The natural world has inspired artists, authors, sculptors, and musicians to express their creativity. **Science and Literature** and **Science and Art** features promote students' appreciation of the value and importance of science to the humanities.

STRATEGIES AND RESOURCES ARE RIGHT AT YOUR FINGERTIPS

*As a teacher, you will thoroughly enjoy all the valuable information **Merrill Earth Science** provides in our **Teacher Wraparound Edition.** Everything is well organized, highly visible and positioned, at the point of instruction, to give you the most teaching value.*

The **Three-Step Teaching Cycle** includes **Motivate, Teach,** and **Close.** It provides various strategies for developing your individual lesson plans plus highlights optional activities and program resources for enhancing your presentation.

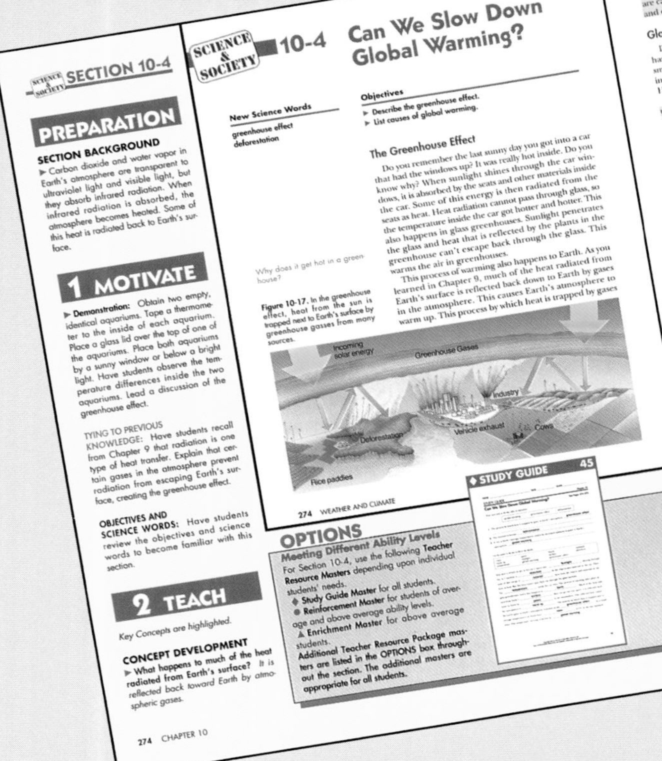

SCIENCE & SOCIETY SECTION 10-4

PREPARATION

SECTION BACKGROUND

▶ Carbon dioxide and water vapor in Earth's atmosphere are transparent to ultraviolet light and visible light, but they absorb infrared radiation. When infrared radiation is absorbed, the atmosphere becomes heated. Some of this heat is radiated back to Earth's surface.

1 MOTIVATE

▶ **Demonstration:** Obtain two empty, identical aquariums. Tape a thermometer to the inside of each aquarium. Place a glass lid over the top of one of the aquariums. Place both aquariums by a sunny window or below a bright light. Have students observe the temperature differences inside the two aquariums. Lead a discussion of the greenhouse effect.

TYING TO PREVIOUS KNOWLEDGE: Have students recall from Chapter 9 that radiation is one type of heat transfer. Explain that certain gases in the atmosphere prevent radiation from escaping Earth's surface, creating the greenhouse effect.

OBJECTIVES AND SCIENCE WORDS: Have students review the objectives and science words to become familiar with this section.

2 TEACH

Key Concepts are highlighted.

CONCEPT DEVELOPMENT

▶ What happens to much of the heat radiated from Earth's surface? *It is reflected back toward Earth by atmospheric gases.*

274 CHAPTER 10

SCIENCE & SOCIETY 10-4 Can We Slow Down Global Warming?

New Science Words

greenhouse effect
deforestation

Objectives

▶ Describe the greenhouse effect.
▶ List causes of global warming.

The Greenhouse Effect

Do you remember the last sunny day you got into a car that had the windows up? It was really hot inside. Do you know why? When sunlight shines through the car windows, it is absorbed by the seats and other materials inside the car. Some of this energy is then radiated from the seats as heat. Heat radiation cannot pass through glass, so the temperature inside the car got hotter and hotter. This also happens in glass greenhouses. Sunlight penetrates the glass and heat that is reflected by the plants in the greenhouse can't escape back through the glass. This warms the air in greenhouses.

This process of warming also happens to Earth. As you learned in Chapter 9, much of the heat radiated from Earth's surface is reflected back down to Earth by gases in the atmosphere. This causes Earth's atmosphere to warm up. This process by which heat is trapped by gases

Why does it get hot in a greenhouse?

Figure 10-17. In the greenhouse effect, heat from the sun is trapped next to Earth's surface by greenhouse gasses from many sources.

274 WEATHER AND CLIMATE

OPTIONS

Meeting Different Ability Levels

For Section 10-4, use the following **Teacher Resource Masters** depending upon individual students' needs.

◆ **Study Guide Master** for all students.
● **Reinforcement Master** for students of average and above average ability levels.
▲ **Enrichment Master** for above average students.

Additional Teacher Resource Package masters are listed in the OPTIONS box throughout the section. The additional masters are appropriate for all students.

◆ STUDY GUIDE 45

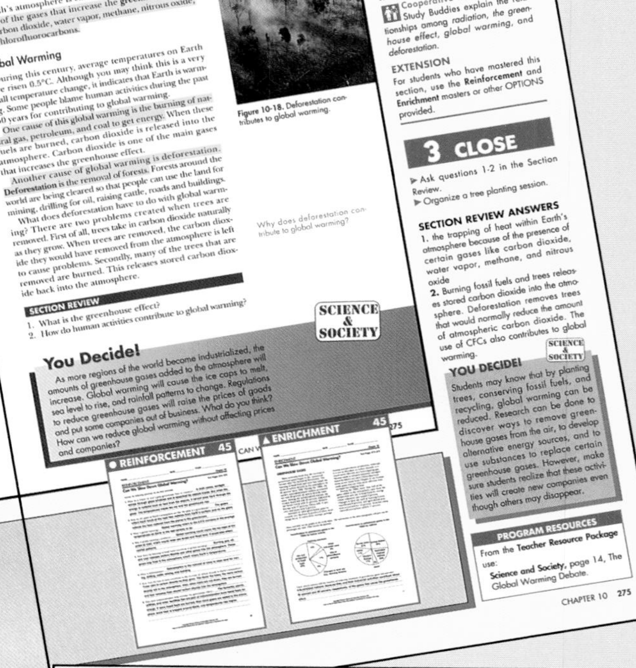

in Earth's atmosphere is called the greenhouse effect. Some of the gases that increase the **greenhouse effect** are carbon dioxide, water vapor, methane, nitrous oxide, and chlorofluorocarbons.

Global Warming

During this century, average temperatures on Earth have risen 0.5°C. Although you may think this is a very small temperature change, it indicates that Earth is warming. Some people blame human activities during the past 150 years for contributing to global warming.

One cause of this global warming is the burning of natural gas, petroleum, and coal to get energy. When these fuels are burned, carbon dioxide is released into the atmosphere. Carbon dioxide is one of the main gases that increases the greenhouse effect.

Another cause of global warming is deforestation. **Deforestation** is the removal of forests. Forests around the world are being cleared so that people can use the land for mining, drilling for oil, raising cattle, roads and buildings.

What does deforestation have to do with global warming? There are two problems created when trees are removed. First of all, trees take in carbon dioxide naturally as they grow. When trees are removed, the carbon dioxide they would have removed from the atmosphere is left to cause problems. Secondly, many of the trees that are removed are burned. This releases stored carbon dioxide back into the atmosphere.

Figure 10-18. Deforestation contributes to global warming.

Why does deforestation contribute to global warming?

SECTION REVIEW

1. What is the greenhouse effect?
2. How do human activities contribute to global warming?

SCIENCE & SOCIETY

You Decide!

As more regions of the world become industrialized, the amounts of greenhouse gases added to the atmosphere will increase. Global warming will cause the ice caps to melt, sea level to rise, and rainfall patterns to change. Regulations to reduce greenhouse gases will raise the prices of goods and put some companies out of business. What do you think? How can we reduce global warming without affecting prices and companies?

● REINFORCEMENT 45

▲ ENRICHMENT 45

CHECK FOR UNDERSTANDING

Ask students to explain how the greenhouse effect causes global warming.

RETEACH

Cooperative Learning: Have Study Buddies explain the relationships among radiation, the greenhouse effect, global warming, and deforestation.

EXTENSION

For students who have mastered this section, use the **Reinforcement** and **Enrichment** masters or other OPTIONS provided.

3 CLOSE

▶ Ask questions 1-2 in the Section Review.
▶ Organize a tree planting session.

SECTION REVIEW ANSWERS

1. the trapping of heat within Earth's atmosphere because of the presence of certain gases like carbon dioxide, water vapor, methane, and nitrous oxide
2. Burning fossil fuels and trees releases stored carbon dioxide into the atmosphere. Deforestation removes trees that would normally reduce the amount of atmospheric carbon dioxide. The use of CFCs also contributes to global warming.

SCIENCE & SOCIETY

YOU DECIDE!

Students may know that by planting trees, conserving fossil fuels, and recycling, global warming can be reduced. Research can be done to discover ways to remove greenhouse gases from the air, to develop alternative energy sources, and to use substances to replace certain greenhouse gases. However, make sure students realize that these activities will create new companies even though others may disappear.

PROGRAM RESOURCES

From the **Teacher Resource Package** use:

Science and Society, page 14, The Global Warming Debate.

CHAPTER 10 275

CROSS CURRICULUM

▶ **Mathematics:** The Sierra Nevadas formed about 10 million years ago. Mt. Whitney is one of the many peaks in the range that stand 4000 m above sea level. Have students compute an average annual rate of uplift.

Preceding each chapter is a two-page **Planning Guide** which gives you quick access to chapter content, features, activities, skill exercises, and all other program components.

Cross Curriculum strategies provide unique ways to connect earth science to other sciences and other disciplines such as math, reading, writing, fine arts, and health.

ALTERNATIVE TEACHING STRATEGIES HELP YOU MEET THE ABILITY NEEDS OF ALL YOUR STUDENTS

Student masters, designed to help you address different learning abilities, are shown in reduced form in the bottom margins. They include **Study Guide** worksheets, a great review for those students who need a little extra help; **Reinforcement** worksheets, ideal for enhancing student understanding of key concepts; and **Enrichment** worksheets, the best way to challenge your above average students.

Meeting Different Ability Levels

For Section 4-1, use the following **Teacher Resource Masters** depending upon individual students' needs.

◆ **Study Guide Master** for all students.

● **Reinforcement Master** for students of average and above average ability levels.

▲ **Enrichment Master** for above average students.

Additional Teacher Resource Package masters are listed in the OPTIONS box throughout the section. The additional masters are appropriate for all students.

TYING TO PREVIOUS KNOWLEDGE: Have students recall from Chapter 2 the physical properties used to identify minerals. Explain that rocks are grouped and named according to the processes that form them and the minerals they contain.

OBJECTIVES AND SCIENCE WORDS: Have students review the objectives and science words to become familiar with this section.

2 TEACH

Key Concepts are highlighted.

CONCEPT DEVELOPMENT

Cooperative Learning: Using the Numbered Heads Together strategy, have students answer the following questions. **If a geologist finds a sedimentary rock composed of pieces of igneous rock, what conclusion might he or she draw?** *Weathering has broken the igneous rock into pieces, which became cemented to form a sedimentary rock.* **Where do the different processes of the rock cycle occur?** *Melting occurs deep within Earth. Metamorphic changes can occur in the crust or deep within the mantle. Weathering and erosion occur at Earth's surface.*

CHECK FOR UNDERSTANDING

Use the Mini Quiz to check for understanding.

MINI QUIZ

Use the Mini Quiz to check students' recall of chapter content.

1. **A mixture of one or more minerals is a(n) ____.** *rock*
2. **Granite is a mixture of which minerals?** *quartz, feldspar, hornblende, and mica*
3. **The processes that a rock undergoes to change into another rock is the ____.** *rock cycle*

Figure 4-2 is a model of the rock cycle. It shows how one rock changes into another. Notice that rocks are classified as igneous, metamorphic, or sedimentary. You will learn more about each of these groups of rocks in this chapter.

Rocks are changed by processes such as weathering, erosion, compaction, cementation, melting, and cooling. For example, the minerals of a sedimentary rock can melt and later cool to form an igneous rock. The

CHAPTER 4 87

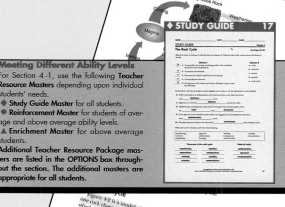

Multicultural Awareness puts students in touch with a medley of events and people from around the world and their contributions to the advancement of earth science.

Multicultural Awareness

Have students collect photographs and articles of volcanoes and earthquakes from around the world. Have students make a collage of the photographs and discuss the cultural effects each volcano or earthquake might have had on the people living there.

For Your Gifted and Talented Students and **For Your Mainstream Students** provide activity-based suggestions that reinforce chapter content. These features stimulate critical thinking, and/or tie together current material with previous chapter content.

OPTIONS

For Your Gifted Students

Have students use toothpicks to design earthquake-resistant buildings and bridges. Have them experiment with shapes and reinforcements. When structures are completed, they can be glued onto posterboard supported by wooden frames. An earthquake can be simulated by applying force to the posterboard. Then have students attach fishing line through the posterboard so that the line freely moves up and down. Have them use spring scales to measure the amount of force applied by lifting or pulling on the line. Structures can be evaluated, compared, and modified.

For Your Mainstreamed Students

Have students conduct research to find out about major earthquakes that have occurred during recorded history. Have them construct timelines of these earthquakes from the earliest to the most recent. The magnitude of each earthquake should be included. Students can also use a world map to mark the locations of these earthquakes. Have students hypothesize why certain areas have more earthquakes than others.

A FULL RANGE OF SUPPORT MATERIALS

*When you purchase the **Merrill Earth Science** program, you'll get everything you have come to expect in support materials plus a whole lot more! Not only do you receive a **Teacher Classroom Resources** that contains 13 exciting theme booklets, you have the opportunity to purchase a variety of additional resources sure to motivate your students and further enliven their learning experience.*

Teacher Resource Guide contains a program planning guide, lab design and equipment, safety instruction, a media worksheet, and a Flex Your Brain worksheet in one convenient booklet.

Activity Worksheets include worksheets for every Mini-Lab and full-page Activity in the chapters.

Study Guide Worksheets are tailored to the needs of students who need a little extra help. They reinforce understanding of the topics and vocabulary found in each chapter.

Reinforcement Worksheets provide a variety of interesting activities to help students of average ability levels retain the important points in every chapter.

Enrichment Worksheets challenge your students of above average ability to design, interpret, and research scientific topics based on the text in each lesson.

Critical Thinking/Problem Solving helps your students develop important critical thinking and problem solving skills as they work through additional problems related to chapter topics.

Concept Mapping masters reinforce learning by having students complete a concept map for each chapter.

Cross-Curriculum Connections are interdisciplinary worksheets. They emphasize learning by doing and provide valuable insight into the connection earth science has with other disciplines.

Science And Society worksheets encourage further involvement with Science and Society lessons in the student text.

Technology masters explore recent developments in science and technology or explain how familiar machines, tools, or systems work.

Transparency Masters include blackline reproductions and student worksheets for each of the program's full-color transparencies.

Chapter Review masters are two-page review worksheets consisting of 25 questions for each chapter. Ideal for test preparation, alternative test, and vocabulary review.

Chapter Test Masters provide comprehensive tests for each chapter.

ADDITIONAL RESOURCES GIVE YOU CONVENIENT WAYS TO PROMOTE GREATER UNDERSTANDING

Lab Partner is a spreadsheet program that allows you and your students to record, collect, and graph data from laboratory activities. A user guide is also available to assist students through the programs.

Chapter Review Software presents chapter-end review questions in random order and provides feedback, for incorrectly answered questions, by noting the textbook page where the answer is found.

Lesson Plan Book is a complete lesson planning resource for teachers. It is a correlation of lessons, objectives, features, and program resources.

Spanish Resources provides Spanish translations of chapter objectives, glossary terms, and definitions. Ideal for bilingual classrooms.

Laboratory Manual contains at least 2 hands-on laboratory activities for each chapter. Students get more chances to acquire scientific knowledge while you get more opportunities to reinforce and apply chapter concepts. A **Teacher Edition** provides suggestions for alternate materials, teaching tips, sample data, and answers to all student questions.

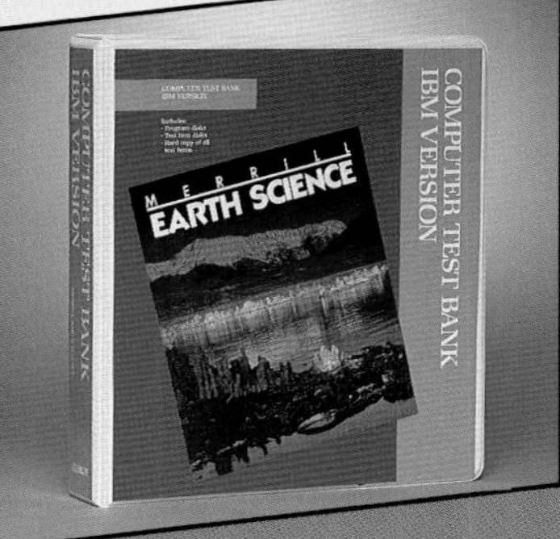

Computer Test Bank Package, available in Apple and IBM versions, provides a convenient tool for creating your own chapter test. The software allows you to add your own problems or edit the existing questions.

Color Transparency Package includes 50 full-color transparencies, some with overlays, in a three-ring binder with a resource book of blackline masters and student worksheets for each transparency. Excellent for direct instruction, reteaching, and review.

Study Guide, Reinforcement, and Enrichment workbooks provide activities for every ability level.

Videodisc Correlation Booklet uses a bar code reader to correlate the colorful diagrams, movie clips, and thousands of photographs, found in Optical Data's Videodiscs, with the pages in ***Merrill Earth Science.*** This booklet is available from your Glencoe representative. Videodiscs are available direct from Optical Data:

Earth Science Videodiscs
Optical Data Corporation
30 Technology Drive
P.O. Box 4919
Warren, NJ 07060

ALL NEW MERRILL EARTH SCIENCE BUILDS UNDERSTANDING AND APPRECIATION THROUGH EVERYDAY APPLICATIONS

Student Edition	0-675-16744-2
Teacher Wraparound Edition	0-675-16745-0
Teacher Classroom Resources	
Activity Worksheets	0-675-16832-5
Chapter and Unit Tests	0-675-16842-2
Chapter Review	0-675-16841-4
Concept Mapping	0-675-16837-6
Critical Thinking/ Problem Solving	0-675-16836-8
Cross-Curriculum Connections	0-675-16838-4
Enrichment Worksheets	0-675-16835-X
Reinforcement Worksheets	0-675-16834-1
Science and Society	0-675-16839-2
Study Guide Worksheets	0-675-16833-3
Teacher Resource Guide	0-675-16747-7
Technology	0-675-16843-0
Transparency Masters	0-675-16840-6
Study Guide SE	0-675-16750-7
Reinforcement SE	0-675-16751-5
Enrichment SE	0-675-16798-1
Laboratory Manual SE	0-675-16748-5
Laboratory Manual TE	0-675-16749-3
Color Transparency Package	0-675-16752-3
Spanish Resources	0-675-16754-X
Lesson Plan Book	0-675-16800-7
Computer Test Bank (Apple)	0-675-16755-8
Computer Test Bank (IBM)	0-675-16757-4
Chapter Review Software (Apple)	0-675-16756-6
Chapter Review Software (IBM)	0-675-16758-2
Lab Partner Software Package (Apple)	0-675-02487-0
Lab Partner Software Package (IBM)	0-675-17271-3
Videodisc Correlation Booklet	0-675-16801-5

Optical Data Videodiscs:
Order Direct from
Optical Data Corporation
30 Technology Drive
P.O. Box 4919
Warren, NJ 07060

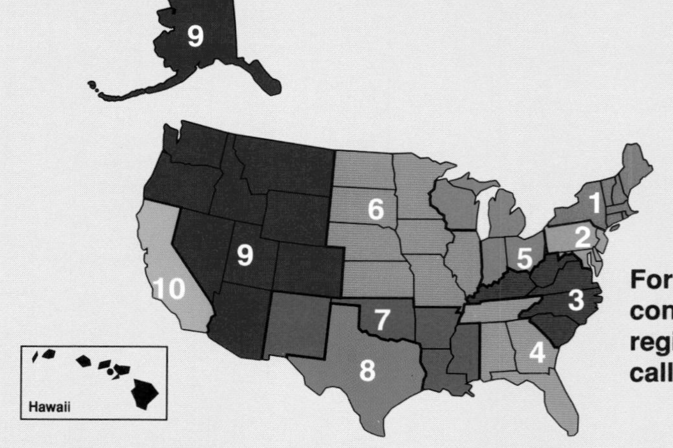

For more information contact your nearest regional office or call 1-800-334-7344.

1. Northeast Region
GLENCOE
17 Riverside Drive
Nashua, NH 03062
603-880-4701
800-424-3451

2. Mid-Atlantic Region
GLENCOE
5 Terri Lane, Suite 5
Burlington, NJ 08016
609-386-7353
800-553-7515

3. Atlantic-Southeast Region
GLENCOE
Brookside Park
One Harbison Way, Suite 101
Columbia, SC 29212
803-732-2365

4. Southeast Region
GLENCOE
6510 Jimmy Carter Boulevard
Norcross, GA 30071
404-446-7493
800-982-3992

5. Mid-America Region
GLENCOE
4635 Hilton Corporate Drive
Columbus, OH 43232
614-759-6600
800-848-1567

6. Mid-Continent Region
GLENCOE
846 East Algonquin Road
Schaumburg, IL 60173
708-397-8448
800-762-4876

7. Southwest Region
GLENCOE
320 Westway Place, Suite 550
Arlington, TX 76018
817-784-2100
800-828-5096

8. Texas Region
GLENCOE
320 Westway Place, Suite 550
Arlington, TX 76018
817-784-2100
800-828-5096

9. Western Region
GLENCOE
610 East 42nd Street, #102
Boise, ID 83714
208-378-4002
800-452-6126
Includes Alaska

10. California Region
GLENCOE
15319 Chatsworth Street
P. O. Box 9609
Mission Hills, CA 91346
818-898-1391
800-423-9534

Canada
Maxwell Macmillan Cana
1200 Eglinton Avenue, E
Suite 200
Don Mills, Ontario M3C
Telephone: 416-449-603
Telex: 069.59372
Telefax: 416-449-0068

Overseas and Hawaii
Macmillan/McGraw-Hill
International
866 Third Avenue
New York, NY 10022-62
Telephone: 212-702-327
Telex: 225925 MACM U
Telefax: 212-605-9377

Glencoe Catholic School Region
GLENCOE
25 Crescent Street, 1st F
Stamford, CT 06906
203-964-9109
800-551-8766

GLENCOE

MacMillan/McGraw-Hill
936 Eastwind Drive
Westerville, OH 43081

MERRILL

EARTH SCIENCE

TEACHER WRAPAROUND EDITION

GLENCOE

Macmillan/McGraw-Hill

New York, New York Columbus, Ohio Mission Hills, California Peoria, Illinois

MERRILL EARTH SCIENCE

Student Edition
Teacher Wraparound Edition
Teacher Resource Package
Study Guide Student Edition
Reinforcement Student Edition
Enrichment Student Edition
Transparency Package
Laboratory Manual
Laboratory Manual, Teacher Annotated Edition
Spanish Resources
Chapter Review Software
Computer Test Bank
Videodisc Correlation
Lesson Plan Book

AUTHORS

Ralph M. Feather Jr.
Susan Leach Snyder
Dale T. Hesser

Send all inquiries:
GLENCOE DIVISION
Macmillan/McGraw-Hill
936 Eastwind Drive
Westerville, Ohio 43081

ISBN 0-675-16744-2 (Student's Edition)
ISBN 0-675-16745-0 (Teacher's Edition)

Printed in the United States of America

5 6 7 8 9 RRW 00 99 98 97 96 95 94

Table of Contents

Merrill Earth Science

Goals and Philosophy

Merrill Earth Science is designed to help students with a wide range of backgrounds and abilities to learn earth science.

Over the last several years there has been significant dialogue about reforming the science curriculum. Catalysts for the reform movement are the many recent reports that rank American students at or near the bottom in math and science performance when compared to other developed nations. Of the numerous reform-oriented proposals Project 2061: Science for All Americans (sponsored by AAAS) and Scope, Sequence, and Coordination (sponsored by National Science Teacher's Association) have attained national prominence.

These two projects suggest sweeping changes in what, when, and how science is taught. In response to the science curriculum reform movement, ***Merrill Earth Science*** presents solid, accurate content, a thematic orientation, hands-on activities that employ scientific thinking, science process skills methods of inquiry emphasis, and integration of science concepts across the curriculum.

Themes

The themes of science are broad, unifying ideas that integrate the major concepts of many disciplines. They are an important part of any teaching strategy because they help students see the importance of truly understanding concepts rather than simply memorizing isolated facts. Themes help students see connections between earth science and other science courses.

Several unifying themes pervade ***Merrill Earth Science.*** These themes serve as a conceptual framework for an earth science course and provide a rationale for the sequence of topics in the text. Major themes in the text are

- energy
- evolution
- patterns of change
- scale and structure
- systems and interactions

Integration of Science Concepts Across the Curriculum

Because no subject or skill can be taught in isolation and subject areas naturally interweave and overlap, ***Merrill Earth Science*** connects science learning to many other disciplines.

Each of the seven units closes with a two-page Global Connections feature. Students see geographic connections to the content of the unit as well as five examples of connections to other disciplines. Each example with its geographic connection to physical science ends with an extension activity to engage students in the other disciplines. These features have a strong multicultural perspective.

Science and Literature and Science and Art features help students understand the value and importance of science to the arts. Science and Math, Science and Reading, and Science and Writing integrate earth science with those subjects. Ecotips relate chapter concepts to the environment; many Did You Know features offer historical connections.

Learning Science naturally develops interactive, cooperative group skills as students work in teams to complete activities. The implementation of cooperative learning in ***Merrill Earth Science*** is discussed on pages 26T to 29T.

Text Features

Chapter Opener

Each chapter opens with a striking full-page photograph illustrating a concept introduced in the chapter. The chapter introductory paragraph establishes a relationship between the photo and the chapter. **FIND OUT,** an inquiry activity, is featured at each chapter's beginning. Designed to give students an opportunity to make observations and raise questions about upcoming chapter content, these brief activities require few materials. **FIND OUT** provides a hands-on introduction to the chapter content. **Gearing Up,** an outline of the chapter sections, assists students in previewing the chapter and focusing on its most important ideas. **What's Next** leads students into the body of the chapter.

Teaching Sections

Each chapter is divided into three to five sections, with student objectives listed at the beginning of each. When appropriate, major sections are divided into subsections, making it easier for students to organize material and giving them better insight into the hierarchy of topics. **Objectives** provide the framework for the review questions, chapter review, review worksheets (in the *Teacher Resource Package*), and chapter tests. At the beginning of each section, **New Science Words** for that section are listed to help students preview the vocabulary words they will learn in that section.

Narrative Features

Presenting concepts in a comfortable, conversational style, this text is user friendly. Concepts are personalized and made relevant to students' lives with the use of familiar examples and analogies. To match the developmental and conceptual needs of the middle or junior high student, concepts are presented in logical order moving from the concrete to the abstract.

Special Text Features

Science and Society

Each chapter has a **Science and Society** section that shows the impact of society on current societal issues and problems. The impact of technology on the environment and economics is included, and some sections are controversial, but all provide facts on both sides of the issue discussed. Concluding each of these lessons is a **You Decide** feature that provides students an opportunity to practice critical thinking and problem-solving skills as they formulate opinions on the issue discussed.

Flex Your Brain

Flex Your Brain is a self-directed activity students use while investigating content areas. **Flex Your Brain** occurs as a one-page activity in Chapter 1 accompanying a text section discussing critical thinking and problem solving. The Teacher Resource Guide of the *Teacher Resource Package* provides a master with spaces for students to write their responses.

Flex Your Brain is a tool for developing problem-solving and critical thinking skills. It provides students with an opportunity to explore a topic in an organized, self-checking way and to discover how they arrived at their responses during each step of their investigation. It helps students to think about their own thinking and learn about thinking from their peers.

Technology

Technology features show "real-life" applications of the science concepts. Some topics are high-tech; some are low, but all are of high interest to students. A color photograph helps students visualize the application. *Think Critically* at the end of the feature provides for student involvement in real-life applications of science principles.

Problem Solving

Problem Solving features are stories about kids who are confronting a problem linked to the chapter content. The feature's real-life application question engages students in the solving of the problem.

Activities

Activities provide students with opportunities to learn by doing and to actively engage in learning concepts by using the scientific method. Each chapter has two full-page laboratory activities that can each be done in one laboratory period. Each **Activity** includes a problem statement, materials list, step-by-step procedures, and questions to help students review their observations, form hypotheses, draw conclusions, and apply what they've learned. The accompanying color illustrations either show the steps of the procedure or are used by the students in the **Activity.** Additional information about lab safety and equipment and supplies can be found in this Teacher Guide. A worksheet for each activity for recording data and answering questions is available in the Activities Worksheets book of the *Teacher Resource Package.*

Margin Features

MINI-Labs provide students with another opportunity to practice science process skills while using the scientific method. Observing scientific phenomena engages students in science content. **MINI-Labs** are hands-on activities that students can complete in a short amount of time. Required materials are easily accessible. A worksheet for reporting results and conclusions is in the Activities Worksheets component of the *Teacher Resource Package.*

Science and Reading, Science and Writing, Science and Math are features that provide problems or projects that require reading, writing, or math calculations to further explore the science concept discussed on the text page.

Did You Know? features present students with interesting facts related to the content being developed; they occur at least once per chapter. As students react with an "I didn't know that!" feeling, they experience the wonder of science and their curiosity is excited.

EcoTips relate to the content of each chapter. **EcoTips** suggest small changes in students' lifestyles that will have positive effects on the environment. **EcoTips** extend the environmental theme of the book, make the text relevant to students' lives, and increase their sense that their actions have an effect in the world.

Student notes are blue margin questions about main ideas; they serve as a study guide for students.

Section and Chapter End

Following each numbered section are three to five **Section Review** questions, including an **Apply** question that demands a higher level of thinking to answer. One question correlates to each objective for the section. Answers to these questions are provided in the margin of the *Teacher Wraparound Edition.*

The three-page chapter-end material begins with a **Summary** that concisely reviews the major concepts and principles of the chapter. Each summary statement is numbered to correspond to a section objective.

- **Key Science Words** list the chapter's vocabulary terms in alphabetical order.
- **Understanding Vocabulary** is an exercise in matching definitions to key terms.
- **Checking Concepts** provides multiple choice recall questions.
- **Understanding Concepts** provides sentence completion exercises.
- **Think and Write Critically** provides higher level thinking questions.
- **Apply** questions require application of chapter concepts.
- **More Skill Builders** require students to use process skills as they answer content-related questions.
- **Projects** provide ideas for researching, creating, or investigating topics based on chapter concepts.

Answers to all chapter end questions are provided in the margin of the *Teacher Wraparound Edition.*

Unit Introductions and Closures

What's Happening Here? photographs and text combine for an inquiry strategy to introduce each unit. A two-page full-color photo picturing a dramatic scene, a puzzling situation, or an intriguing relationship and a smaller photo connected to it opens each unit. The text will connect the photos with each other and with the upcoming concepts of the unit. The *Teacher Wraparound Edition* provides more background on the relationships set up in the photographs and inquiry questions to engage students in unit topics.

The units close with four-page features that include **Global Connections, Careers, Readings,** and **Science and Literature** or **Science and Art. Global Connections** features a two-page world map with topics from five or six places that relate to the chapter content. Each topic is also related to another discipline and each engages the student in the topic with an extension activity. These features provide a strong multicultural perspective.

In the **Careers,** students see real-world applications of science knowledge acquired in the unit. Because one career in each unit requires a college degree and the other does not, students can see the range of careers available for people with a science background. **Readings** provides three or four books or magazine articles related to the unit content.

Closing each unit is a **Science and Literature** or **Science and Art** feature that connects science concepts to literature or art and promotes understanding of the value and importance of science to the humanities. Included may be fiction or nonfiction book excerpts, paintings, sculpture, photos, or music related to the unit. Students are actively engaged at the close of the feature as they respond to application or critical thinking questions.

Skill Reinforcement

Skills are reinforced throughout *Merrill Earth Science.* Each section ends with a **Skill Builder** feature that challenges students to practice basic process skills on a specific science concept. The skill to be learned or practiced is explained in the **Skill Handbook,** a fourteen-page illustrated reference in the back of the student text. Specific examples are used to guide students through the steps of acquiring skills. **More Skill Builders** in the **Chapter Review** material also reference the **Skill Handbook.**

Appendices

There are 13 appendices that may be used to expand student learning or application of concepts. The Appendix begins on page 662.

Glossary and Index

The **Glossary** provides students with a quick reference to key terms and their pronunciations within the text. Page references are provided for all New Science Words from each chapter so students can easily locate the page on which a word is defined. Because it is complete and cross-referenced, the **Index** allows text material to be found quickly and easily.

Features of the Teacher Wraparound Edition

The *Teacher Wraparound Edition* is designed to make teaching ***Merrill Earth Science*** as easy as possible. Two pages of planning charts precede every chapter. The Chapter Planning Guide lists the objectives, activities, and chapter features for every section. Also correlated to each section is all material in the *Teacher Resource Package* and other components, including the *Laboratory Manual* and *Color Transparency Package.* The equipment and materials required for the chapter's Activities and MINI-Labs are listed; commercially available software and audiovisuals such as films, filmstrips, and slide sets are also referenced.

The majority of the teacher material is conveniently placed in the margin right next to the student page. At the beginning of each chapter, a **Theme Development** section describes how one or all of the themes of the book are incorporated into the chapter. A **Chapter Overview** lists and describes the material in the sections of the chapter; **Chapter Vocabulary** lists boldface terms as they will occur in the chapter.

Introducing the Chapter and **FIND OUT** provide suggestions for an inquiry approach to starting the chapter. **Gearing Up** helps direct students in previewing the Chapter and **What's Next** helps make the connection between the FIND OUT inquiry activity and the topics to follow. Each lesson, or section, starts with **PREPARATION** containing **Section Background** and **Preplanning** sections. **MOTIVATE** follows; it contains several ideas to grab students' interest in the coming section. It can include **Demonstrations, Tying to Previous Knowledge,** and **Objectives and Science Words** all correlated to the section.

TEACH sections include a multitude of teaching suggestions for **Concept Development** and **Check for Understanding** ideas, which may include a **MINI Quiz.** MINI Quizzes are three to five recall questions to use in assessing students' mastery of the material. The answers are provided in the margin and are also keyed by numbers in blue circles next to the place where they occur in the student text. **Reteach** and **Extension** ideas provide alternate ways for teachers to present a particular concept. **Teacher F.Y.I.** includes interesting extensions or applications of the science content. **Revealing Misconceptions** provides suggestions for eliciting and/or correcting student misconceptions. **Cross Curriculum** strategies connect earth science with another science or other subject areas. **Flex Your Brain** and **Cooperative Learning** strategies appear whenever applicable throughout the chapter. Answers to and teaching strategies for Problem Solving, Technology, Science and Reading, Science and Math, Science and Writing occur next to the student page feature.

CLOSE sections consist of two or three ideas for bringing closure to a lesson. The closure activity summarizes the section, bridges to the next lesson, or provides an application of the lesson.

Information for teaching each **Activity** and **MINI-Lab** is included in the margins where these activities occur. Time needed to complete each Activity, objectives, process skills, teaching suggestions, troubleshooting ideas, alternate materials, and answers to questions are included for each.

OPTIONS material, located directly below the page on which it is to be used, includes strategies **For Your Gifted Students** that are activity-based as are strategies **For Your Mainstreamed Students,** which are suggestions for students who are physically or emotionally challenged in some way or for those with learning disabilities.

Inquiry Questions are suggested critical-thinking questions that teachers may use for stimulating class discussions. Possible student responses are in italic type. Suggestions for **Enrichment** activities or articles to read will further students' content knowledge of the content covered or of tangential concepts. **Program Resources** contain references to other instructional materials coordinated to the section.

Major concepts are highlighted in yellow on the reduced student pages, and blue circles point out locations on the student pages of answers to MINI Quiz questions.

Misconceptions

How do students learn science? Decades ago, many educators believed students were empty vessels into which one could pour the pure wisdom gained by humans over centuries. Now, we understand that students come to science class with firmly-held beliefs about how the world works. Students themselves have formed these views of the world and found them to be consistent with everyday life.

Students interpret lectures, books, and even demonstrations and experiments in the light of this world-view. Since what we say in class is interpreted by the student in light of his or her own world view, a student may internalize an idea in a form completely different from what we intend. Each student's adoption of a false perspective becomes a misconception.

Refer to the problem-solving concept map on page 13T. Notice the interactive arrow between misconceptions and critical thinking. Misconceptions may result from a student not using appropriate critical thinking skills. For example, a student may jump to a conclusion, disregarding inconsistencies that may or may not be apparent. Misconceptions may interfere with a student's effectively applying critical thinking skills. A false premise that a student may incorporate while otherwise using sound critical thinking processes may lead to wrong conclusions and new misconceptions.

Misconceptions are complicated by increased vocabulary without conceptual understanding. Students attempt to explain concepts by using words that they really don't understand. Questions may be concisely and satisfactorily answered, however, students' lack of understanding lays the groundwork for misconceptions.

Strategies to treat misconceptions include

- using free recall, word association, structured questioning, and recognition to elicit background knowledge and misconceptions.
- using concept mapping.
- clarifying and interviewing.
- modeling questioning techniques.
- using Activities and MINI-Labs.
- collecting a chapter's misconceptions for review use at its conclusion.
- using Merrill's Flex Your Brain activity (see page 19T).

In the ***Merrill Earth Science*** *Teacher Wraparound Edition,* "Misconceptions" suggests strategies for eliciting misconceptions about specific content in the student edition. "Tying to Previous Knowledge" strategies will also prove useful in identifying and treating misconceptions.

Supplementary Materials

Teacher Resource Package

The *Teacher Resource Package* for ***Merrill Earth Science*** provides background information and comprehensive teaching material to aid in the effective teaching of earth science. The following worksheet masters are provided: Activity, MINI-Lab, Study Guide, Reinforcement, Enrichment, Critical Thinking/Problem Solving, Concept Mapping, Cross-Curricular Connections, Science and Society, Transparency, Technology, Chapter Review, Chapter Test, and Unit Test.

For each section, three worksheets for students of different ability levels are provided. The **Study Guide** worksheets are suitable for all students; they are closely tied to the text and require recall of text content. **Reinforcement** worksheets are for students of average and above average ability; a variety of formats are used to reinforce each text lesson. **Enrichment** worksheets are tailored for students with above average ability; a wide range of formats allows students to design, interpret, research, and create based on the text of each lesson. The three types of worksheets are also available in consumable books—Study Guide, Reinforcement, and Enrichment.

For every text **Activity** and **MINI-Lab** there is a worksheet that reproduces the complete text for the Activity or MINI-Lab, provides charts for data collection, and illustrates the procedures.

Critical Thinking/Problem Solving worksheets consist of a reading selection related to a chapter topic and questions that help to develop critical thinking skills while applying important concepts learned in the classroom to new situations.

Concept Mapping masters challenge students to construct a visual representation of relationships among particular chapter concepts. This booklet is developmental in its approach; early concept maps are nearly complete; later ones provide only a skeleton and linking words.

Cross-Curricular Connections masters are interdisciplinary worksheets that relate science to other disciplines. There is one worksheet per chapter; the emphasis is on "doing" the related discipline whenever possible.

Science and Society worksheets show the impact of science on current societal issues and problems. There is one worksheet for each chapter; each ends with a question requiring students to draw conclusions and/or make decisions.

Transparency Masters are blackline versions of the 50 color transparencies. For each transparency there is a student worksheet and a teacher guide with instructions.

Chapter Review masters are two-page review worksheets consisting of 25 questions for each chapter. They can be used to prepare for tests, as alternate tests, and as vocabulary review. **Chapter and Unit Test masters** test the concepts of each chapter.

Technology masters explain how something works and/or integrate the sciences. The topics are tied to the student text.

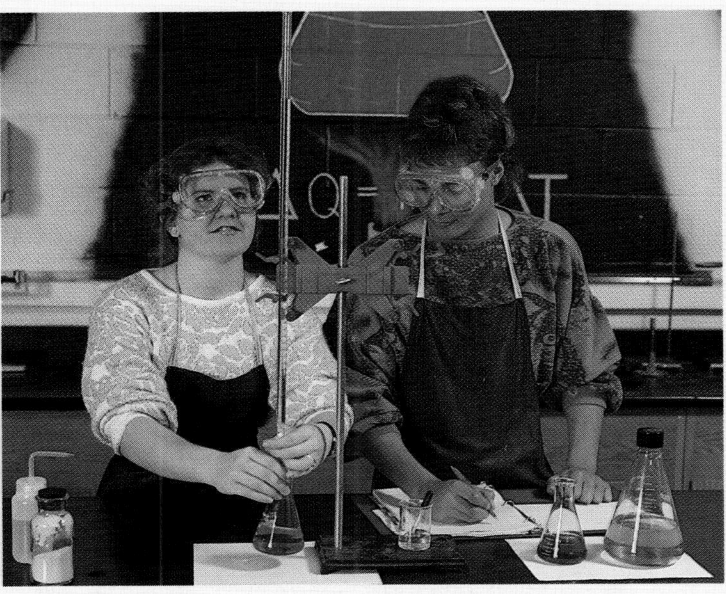

Laboratory Program

The *Laboratory Manual* is a learning-through-doing program of activities. Based on the philosophy that scientific knowledge is acquired through individual activity and experimentation, the manual consists of many, varied laboratory activities designed to reinforce concepts presented in ***Merrill Earth Science.*** Laboratory investigations for each student edition chapter require students to work through a problem by observing, analyzing, and drawing conclusions. The *Laboratory Manual, Teacher Edition* consists of the student edition pages with teacher answers on reduced pages in the back. The reduced pages include suggestions for alternate materials, teaching tips, sample data, and answers to all student questions.

Transparency Package

The **Color Transparency Package** contains 50 full-color transparencies, as well as a book containing a blackline version of each transparency, a student worksheet, and instructions for using the transparencies. The book is also part of the **Teacher Resource Package.** The color transparencies and book are conveniently packaged in a 3-ring binder.

Computer Software

Two types of software have been created to correlate with the ***Merrill Earth Science*** program.

The *Chapter Review Software* provides chapter-end review questions for student use. Based on the review questions found in the textbook at the end of the chapter, the software presents questions in random order. Feedback for incorrectly-answered questions provides the textbook page where the answer is found.

The *Computer Test Bank* provides the teacher with a tool to design a test from a bank of questions. Features include selection of sections to be tested, number of questions for each section, total number of questions on a test, inclusion or exclusion of specific questions, and multiple test forms.

Lesson Plan Booklet

The **Lesson Plan Booklet** contains complete lesson plans for every lesson in the Student Text. Also included are references to all program components of ***Merrill Earth Science.***

Spanish Resources

The **Spanish Resources** book provides Spanish translations of objectives, summary statements, and key terms and their definitions for every chapter. Also included is a complete English/Spanish glossary to ***Merrill Earth Science.***

Videodisc Correlation

The **Videodisc Correlation** book contains the complete correlation with bar codes of OPTICAL DATA'S Videodisc images to the content of ***Merrill Earth Science.***

Thinking in Science

What *are* thinking skills? How are thinking skills developed? We educators know that learning involves a crucial awareness followed by an evaluation and judgment.

Throughout the ***Merrill Earth Science*** program are experiences that help students develop, practice, and apply thinking process skills. The process skills are carefully introduced and developed through the use of higher level divergent questions, controlled experiments, problem-solving activities, critical thinking questions, and creative activities. The Flex Your Brain critical thinking matrix introduced in Chapter 1 provides a method for self-directed problem solving that can be used throughout the course.

Shown below is a concept map that explains the relationships of the thinking skills developed and reinforced in ***Merrill Earth Science*** and the ways they are incorporated in the text.

Thinking extends and refines knowledge and can lead to problem solving. As our concept map shows, effective problem solving relies on the integration of three types of thinking. The first, critical thinking, is characterized by

- a search for clarity and accuracy.
- open-mindedness.
- taking and defending a position.
- sensitivity to others' knowledge and feelings.

The next type of thinking, creative thinking, is characterized by

- engaging in tasks when answers are not apparent.
- pushing the limits of one's knowledge and abilities.
- generating and following one's own standard of evaluation.
- generating new ways of viewing situations.

The third type of thinking, self-regulated thinking, consists of

- planning.
- sensitivity to feedback.
- using available resources.
- awareness and evaluation of the effectiveness of one's own thinking.

Critical, creative, and self-regulated thinking skills contribute to successful problem solving. These skills help one to evaluate accuracy and worth, to construct logical arguments, and, finally, to determine truth. The developmental goal of the ***Merrill Earth Science*** skill strand is to help you produce discriminating, disciplined, questioning problem solvers.

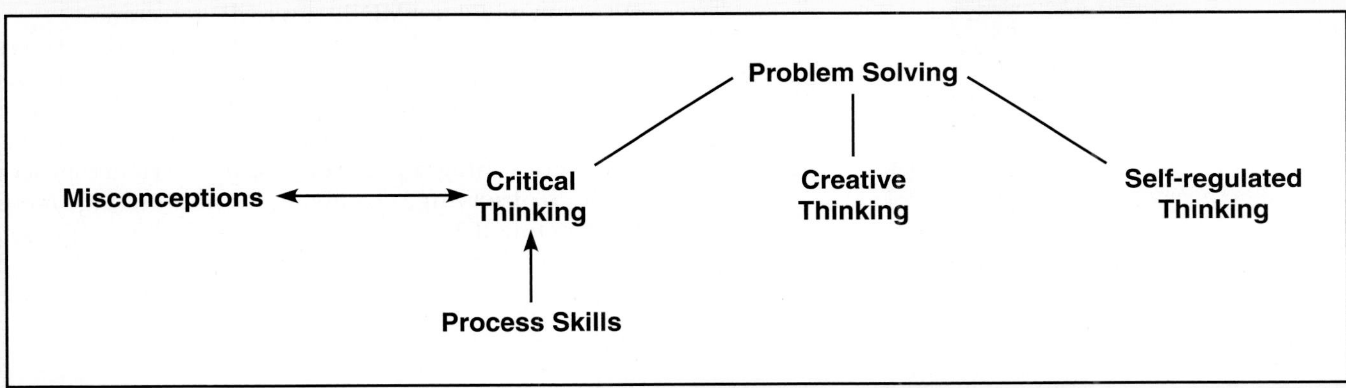

Developing and Applying Thinking Skills

Merrill Earth Science provides a wide range of experiences that help students develop and apply thinking process skills. **Apply** questions that require higher level, divergent thinking appear in every Section Review. Problem-Solving features ask students to solve real-life problems. **Think Critically** questions provide students an opportunity to reflect on issues related to technology.

Critical thinking skills developed in the text include

- observing and inferring
- comparing and contrasting
- recognizing cause and effect
- defining operationally
- formulating models

Refer again to the Thinking in Science concept map on page 13T. It shows diagrammatically that the process skills help develop and reinforce critical thinking.

The fourteen-page illustrated **Skill Handbook** includes specific examples to guide students through the steps of acquiring skills. As students complete each section, a **Skill Builder** gives them a chance to reinforce the concepts just learned as they practice a particular skill explained in the handbook.

FIND OUT inquiry activities that open each chapter allow students to start generating questions about the concepts to come, make observations as they do "hands-on" work, and share prior knowledge about the chapter content. Student misconceptions often surface during this activity.

Activities and MINI-Labs provide the "learn by doing" experiences necessary for acquiring safe, efficient laboratory techniques, learning and applying the scientific method, and practicing all of the thinking skills.

The Activities and MINI-Labs are designed to help you provide an engaging, diverse, active program for learning and practicing process skills.

The MINI-Labs provide short, quick hands-on experiences that require a minimum of equipment. You might make students responsible for their organization and execution. Also, you might use MINI-Labs as demonstrations.

Activities in ***Merrill Earth Science*** provide students experiences that develop and reinforce or restructure concepts as well as develop the ability to use process skills. The format is structured to guide students to make discoveries using a scientific method. Science process skills such as observing, classifying, hypothesizing, measuring, interpreting data, analyzing, and concluding are learned and reinforced as they do the Activities.

Process skills developed and reinforced in the text are

- Organizing Information
  - classifying
  - sequencing
  - outlining
- Thinking Critically
  - observing and inferring
  - comparing and contrasting
  - recognizing cause and effect
  - defining operationally
  - formulating models
- Experimentation Skills
  - measuring in SI
  - hypothesizing
  - using variables, constants and controls
  - collecting and organizing data
  - interpreting data
  - experimenting
  - analyzing
- Graphic Organizers
  - concept mapping
  - making and using tables
  - making and using graphs
  - interpreting scientific illustrations
- Others
  - communicating
  - using numbers
  - recognizing spatial relationships

A chart showing chapter-by-chapter development of skills is on page 16T. Several features to aid teachers in skills assessment have been built into ***Merrill Earth Science.*** **Think and Write Critically, Apply,** and **More Skill Builders** sections of the Chapter Review material ask students questions that relate the chapter material to the skill from that chapter, as well as to skills learned in previous chapters. Questions relating to the skill developed in the chapter are included in each of the chapter tests found in the **Teacher Resource Package.**

Questioning Strategies that Support Critical Thinking

The following categories of questions and examples can help you devise critical thinking strategies for handling class discussion.

Clarifying Questions

- What is the main issue?
- How does this relate to our discussion?
- Can you summarize in your own words?

Questioning Assumptions

- Are you taking this for granted?
- Is this always the case?
- Why do you think this assumption is correct?

Questioning Reasons and Evidence

- Give an example.
- What reasons do you have to doubt the evidence?
- How did you come to that conclusion?
- How could we find out whether that is true?
- How does this apply in this case?

Questioning Viewpoints or Perspectives

- How do you think other groups or types of people would respond? Why?
- If you disagreed what would you say?
- Give an alternative.

Probing Implications and Consequences

- If that happened, what else might happen and why?
- How might that affect the situation?
- Given the situation, would that always happen?
- If this is the case, then what else must be true?

Questioning the Question

- Why is this important?
- What other questions can we ask?
- Why do we need to know this?

THINKING IN SCIENCE

Skills Map

	Chapters 1	2	3	4	5	6	7	8	9	10	11	12	13	14	15	16	17	18	19	20	21	22	23	24
Classifying		•	•	••	••						•	•			••	•			•	••	•			
Sequencing	•			•	•	•	•	•							•		••	•			••		•	•
Outlining		•	•		•	•	•	•			•		••	•		•	•		•	•	•			
Observing & Inferring		••	•••	••	••	••	••	••	•••	•••	••	•••	••	••	•••	••		•	••	••	••	•••	•	•••
Comparing & Contrasting	••			•		•	•		•	••	••	••	•		••			•	••			•		•
Recognizing Cause & Effect				•	••					•	••		•			•	••		•	•		•	•	••
Defining Operationally									•		•			••							•			
Formulating Models						•	••		•		••		•			•	•				•	•	•	•
Measuring in SI	•••	••	•	•	•		•	••••	••	•		••	••	•	••		•	•	••		••	•	•••	•
Hypothesizing	•	••		•	•	•••	•		•	•••	•		•		••		••	•		•		••	••	••
Using Variables, Constants, and Controls	•		•	•	••	•	••	•	••	•		•		•				•			•	•	•	
Interpreting Data	•	••	••	••	••	••	•••	•••	•	••	•••	••	••	••	••	••	••	•		••	••	••	•••	••
Experimenting			••		•	••	••		•	•	••							•		•	••	••		
Analyzing																	••		•					
Concept Mapping	••	••	••	•	••	••	•	••	••	•	•	••	••	•	••	•		••		••	••	•	••	•
Making & Using Tables		••				•	•			•				•		•	•	•	•	•	•		•	•
Making & Using Graphs		•	•				•		••		•			•		•			•••					
Interpreting Scientific Illustrations				•		••		•		•				•			•	•	•	•			•	•
Communicating	•	•	••	••	•	••	•					••		•	••		•	••		•	••	•		
Using Numbers		•			•				••	•		•	•	••			••	•	•	•			••	•
Recognizing Spatial Relationships													•			•						•		

• Activity • SKILL BUILDER/More SKILL BUILDERS

THINKING IN SCIENCE

Concept Maps

Concept maps are visual representations of relationships among particular concepts. In science they make abstract information more concrete and useful, improve retention of information, and show students that thought has shape. Concept maps can be generated by individual students, small groups, or an entire class. ***Merrill Earth Science*** develops and reinforces three types of graphic organizers—the **network tree, events chain,** and **cycle concept map** that are most applicable to studying science. Examples of the three types and their applications are shown below.

Students can learn how to construct each of these types of concept maps by reading pages 688 and 689 of the Skill Handbook. They will practice this skill throughout the course.

Events Chain

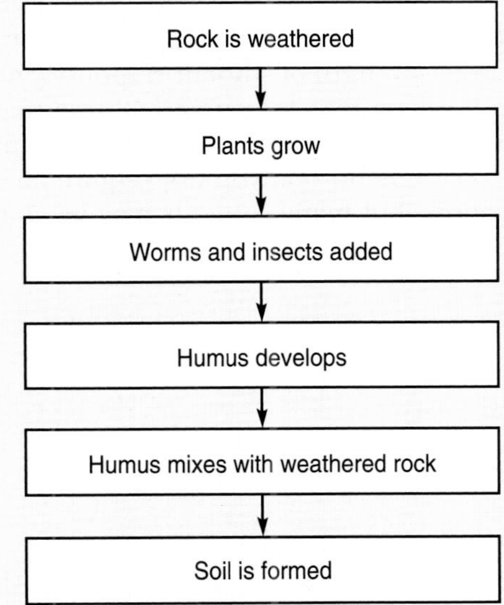

Applications: describes the stages of process, the steps in a linear procedure, a sequence of events

Network Tree

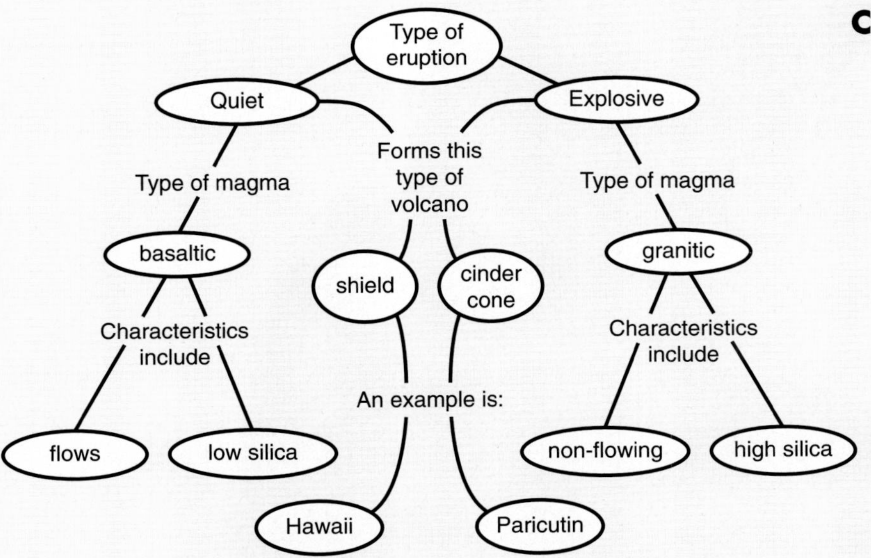

Applications: shows causal information, a hierarchy, and branching procedures.

Cycle

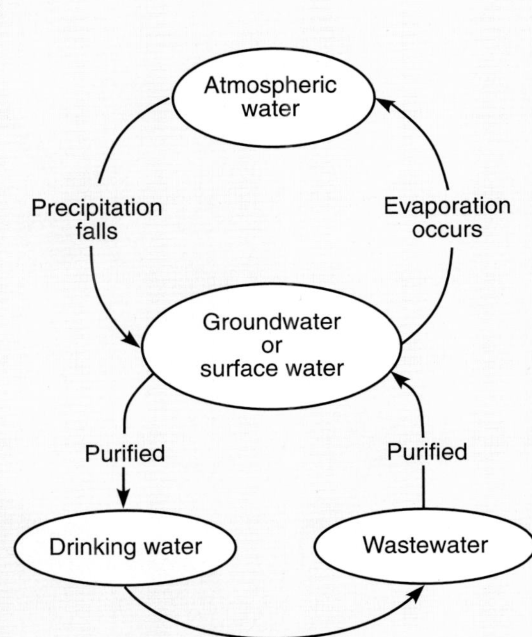

Applications: shows how a series of events interacts to produce a set of results again and again.

The section-ending Skill Builders and the More Skill Builders section of Chapter Reviews in early chapters direct students to make a specific type of concept map and in most cases concept terms to be used are provided. Later, in a developmental approach, students are given general guidelines. For example, concept terms to be used may be provided and students are required to select the appropriate model to apply or vice-versa. Finally students may be asked to provide both the terms and type of concept map to explain relationships among concepts. When students are given this flexibility, it is important for you to recognize that sample answers are provided, but student responses may vary. Look for the conceptual strength of student responses, not absolute accuracy. You'll notice that most network tree maps provide connecting words that explain the relationships between concepts. We recommend that you not require all students to supply these words, but many students may be challenged by this aspect.

More Skill Builders in the Chapter Reviews that ask students to make a concept map usually provide the concept map format and the specific concept terms to use. This will ensure you more consistent student responses, making grading easier, than when students are asked to make more determinations about their concept maps.

The Concept Mapping book of the *Teacher Resource Package,* too, provides a developmental approach for students to practice concept mapping.

As a teaching strategy, generating concept maps can be used to preview a chapter's content by visually relating the concepts to be learned and allowing the students to read with purpose. Using concept maps for previewing is especially useful when there are many new key science terms for students to learn. As a review strategy, constructing concept maps reinforces main ideas and clarifies their relationships. Construction of concept maps using cooperative learning strategies as described on pages 26T-29T of this Teacher Guide will allow students to practice both interpersonal and process skills.

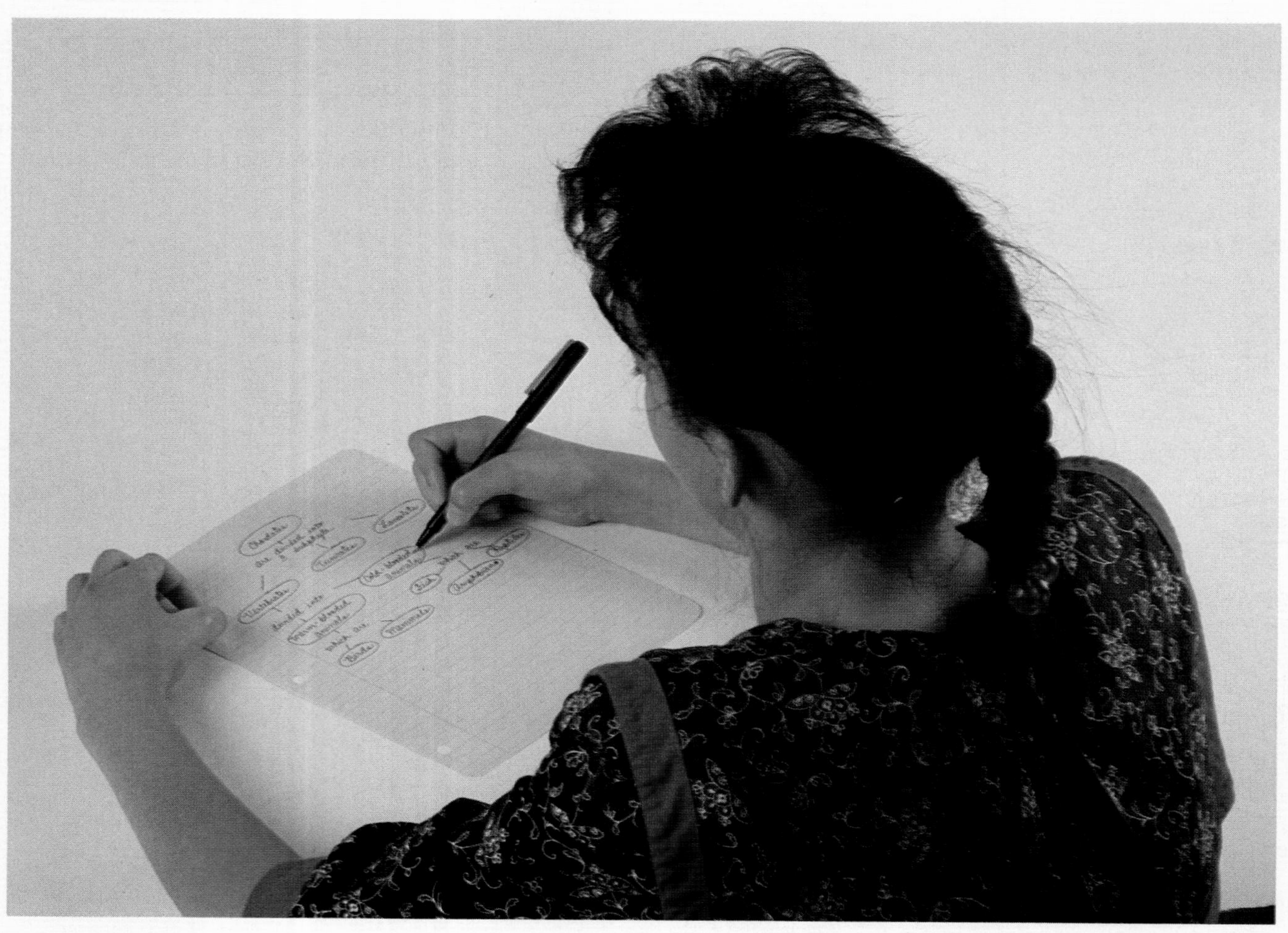

THINKING IN SCIENCE

Flex Your Brain

A key element in the coverage of problem solving and critical thinking skills in ***Merrill Earth Science*** is a critical thinking matrix called **Flex Your Brain.**

Flex Your Brain is a self-directed activity intended to assist students in developing critical thinking skills while investigating content areas.

Flex Your Brain provides students with an opportunity to explore a topic in an organized, self-checking way and then identify how they arrived at their responses during each step of their investigation. The activity incorporates many of the skills of critical thinking. It helps students to think about their own thinking and learn about thinking from their peers.

In a step-by-step way, Flex Your Brain asks students to:

(1) focus on a single topic;
(2) consider their prior knowledge of the topic;
(3) pose questions regarding the topic;
(4) hypothesize answers to their questions;
(5) evaluate their confidence in their answer;
(6) identify ways to investigate the topic to prove, disprove, or amend their responses;
(7) follow through with their investigation;
(8) evaluate their responses to their questions, checking for their own misconceptions or lack of understanding;
(9) rewrite their question responses, incorporating new knowledge gained; and
(10) review and share the thinking processes that they used during the activity.

Where is FLEX YOUR BRAIN found?

In Chapter 1, page 15, of the student text is an introduction to the topics of critical thinking and problem solving. Flex Your Brain accompanies the text section as a one-page activity in Chapter 1. Brief student instructions are given, along with the matrix itself. A two-page version of Flex Your Brain appears as a worksheet in the Teacher Resource Guide of the *Teacher Resource Package.* This version provides spaces for students to write in their responses.

In the *Teacher Wraparound Edition,* suggested topics are given in each chapter for the use of Flex Your Brain. You can either refer students to Chapter 1 for the procedure or photocopy the worksheet master from the Teacher Resource Guide.

Use of Flex Your Brain is certainly not restricted to those topics suggested in the *Teacher Wraparound Edition.* Feel free to use it for practice in critical thinking about any concept or topic.

Using FLEX YOUR BRAIN

Flex Your Brain can be used as a whole-class activity or in cooperative groups, but is primarily designed to be used by individual students within the class. There are three basic steps.

1. Teachers assign a class topic to be investigated using Flex Your Brain.
2. Students use Flex Your Brain to guide them in their individual explorations of the topic.
3. After students have completed their explorations, teachers guide them in a discussion of their experiences with Flex Your Brain, bridging content and thinking processes.

Flex your Brain can be used at many different points in the lesson plan.

▶**Introduction:** Ideal for introducing a topic, Flex Your Brain elicits students' prior knowledge and identifies misconceptions, enabling the teacher to formulate plans specific to student needs.

▶**Development:** Flex Your Brain leads students to find out more about a topic on their own, and develops their research skills while increasing their knowledge. Students actually pose their own questions to explore, making their investigations relevant to their personal interests and concerns.

▶**Review and Extension:** Flex Your Brain allows teachers to check student understanding while allowing students to explore aspects of the topic that go beyond the material presented in class.

FLEX YOUR BRAIN
Annotated Directions

To assist teachers in using Flex Your Brain, an annotated version of the directions appearing on the student page is given below.

1. **Fill in the topic your teacher gives you.**
   Focus students by providing a topic that you need to introduce, develop, or review. Topics should be fairly broad and stated in only a few words; for example, "frog life cycle" or "weathering." Later, when students are familiar with Flex Your Brain, you may want students to select the topic.
2. **Jot down what you already know about the topic. If you know more than five things, write them on another sheet of paper.**
   As a class or cooperative group, this could be a brainstorming process. Otherwise, students should recall individually what they know about the topic. Set a reasonable time limit for this step.
   As you track student progress through this step, look for evidence of misconceptions. Encourage students to draw knowledge from their own experiences as well as from academic sources.
3. **Using what you already know (Step 2), form a question about the topic. Are you unsure about one of the items listed? Do you want to know more about anything? Do you want to know what, how, or why? Write down your question.**
   Students can pose their own questions about the topic and pursue their answers independently; or as a class or group, they can generate several questions. Groups may choose one of these questions to investigate, or the entire class can select one question for all to research.
4. **Guess an answer to your question. In the next few steps, you will be exploring the reasonableness of your answer. Write down your guess.**
   The significance of this step is to get students to think, not just know the right answer. Based on what they already know about the topic, students should form hypotheses about their questions in Step 3. The correctness of their answers at this point is not as important as the means by which they arrive at them.
   Guessing is not a poor means to arrive at an answer if students first consider the facts they know about the topic. Still, students may hesitate to write down answers that they aren't sure of. Encourage students to provide a "best guess."
5. **Circle the number in the box that matches how sure you are of your answer in Step 4. This is your chance to rate your confidence in what you've done so far and, later, to see how your level of sureness affects your thinking.**
   Students should evaluate their feelings at this point and begin to recognize the extent to which they are confident of their answers. Self-evaluation is critical to successful problem solving. This step becomes especially important when students review their thinking process in Step 10. Make sure students know that emotions and intuition are important aspects of problem solving.
6. **How can you find out more about your topic? You might want to read a book, ask an expert, or do an experiment. Write down ways you can find out more.**
   The first time through this activity, you may want to have the class brainstorm ways to explore topics. Discuss the usefulness and appropriateness of the different means of investigation.
   Evaluating the appropriateness of sources is an important skill to emphasize at this step. Encourage students to gain knowledge from the world at large, not just from expert sources. Be sure to bring out in your discussion that checking with a friend may be appropriate in some situations, but not in others.
7. **Make a plan to explore your answer. Use the resources you listed in Step 6. Then, carry out your plan.**
   Students should use at least three resources before drawing conclusions. Encourage them to consider and use resources that might provide different perspectives on the topic in question.
   Experimenting should be encouraged as a means of exploration. Review the scientific method when introducing this step and emphasize the science process skills.
8. **Now that you've explored, go back to your answer in Step 4. Would you answer differently? Mark one of the boxes.**
   Students should consider whether they want to change their original answers. If their original answers require modifying in any way, they should mark the "yes" box.
   At this step, students should begin to recognize their original misconceptions regarding the topic.
9. **Considering what you learned in your exploration, answer your question again. You may want to add new things you've learned or completely change your answer.**
   If students' original answers were correct, request that they restate their answers incorporating new knowledge gained from their explorations. Otherwise, students should correct or modify their answers as needed.
   This step leads students to draw conclusions. Help students to recognize how even a wrong answer in Step 4 contributed to the new answer by giving them a basis for exploration. Wrong answers are an important part of the scientific process.
10. **It's important to be able to talk about thinking. Choose three people to tell about how you arrived at your response in every step. For example, don't just read what you wrote in Step 2. Try to share how you thought of those things.**
    The process of sharing ensures that students will reflect on what they have done. Encourage students to review each preceding step to determine how they arrived at their responses. Make sure students know that this is not an easy task and that they may struggle to put their process into words.

Planning Guide

CLASS SESSIONS			
Chapter	Full-Year Course	Semester ES	Semester G
1	7	3	3
2	8	3	4
3	7	3	4
4	8	4	5
5	7	4	4
6	8	4	5
7	8	5	4
8	7	—	3
9	8	6	4
10	8	6	4
11	7	5	4
12	8	4	5
13	7	3	5
14	7	3	4
15	7	3	4
16	8	4	4
17	8	4	4
18	7	6	4
19	7	7	—
20	7	7	—
21	7	2	—
22	7	2	3
23	8	2	6
24	9	—	7
TOTALS	**180**	**90**	**90**

Teaching Cycle

The ***Merrill Earth Science*** *Teacher Wraparound Edition* delivers the collective teaching experience of its authors, consultants, and reviewers. By furnishing you with an effective teaching model, this book saves you preparation time and energy. You, in turn, are free to spend that time and energy on your most important responsibility—your students.

As a professional, you will be pleased to find that this program provides you with readily available activities that will engage your students for the entire class period. Each major section of every chapter may be considered an individual lesson that includes a preparation section followed by a comprehensive three-part teaching cycle that, when utilized consistently, will result in better cognitive transfer for your students.

Each chapter begins with a section called **Theme Development** that describes how one or all of the themes of the book are incorporated into the chapter. Following Theme Development is a **Chapter Overview** that lists and describes the material in each of the sections of the chapter. The **Chapter Vocabulary** is then listed for you in the order in which the words occur in the chapter.

Each chapter opens with a **FIND OUT** activity that helps you focus the students' attention on the chapter and get them into the material immediately. Everything you will need to help the students complete the **FIND OUT** is given along side the student page. Any advanced preparation and materials needed are listed for you. A **Cooperative Learning** strategy is suggested and teaching tips are given to help you conduct the activity smoothly.

In the **OPTIONS** section of the chapter opener, activity-based strategies are given to help you with any gifted or mainstreamed students you may have in your class.

PREPARATION

Preparation is an extremely important part of teaching any lesson. The **PREPARATION** section contains **SECTION BACKGROUND** which will provide you with science content that is relevant to the section. Also provided for you in PRE**PLANNING** is a list of things you may wish to do to prepare for the section in advance. The **PREPARATION** section will give you the foundation for keeping your lesson instructionally sound.

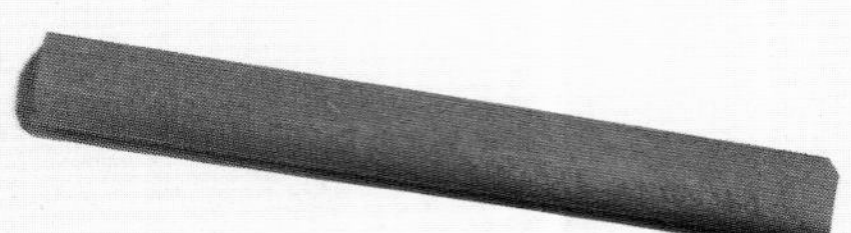

1 MOTIVATE

The first step to teaching any lesson is to motivate the students. Several **Motivate** ideas are provided for each section. The ideas may include demonstrations, cooperative learning techniques, audiovisuals, brainstorming, or other ideas that help motivate and focus the class so the lesson can begin. You may pick one of the motivate ideas listed or alternate them among your classes according to student need. One unique way to get students interested in the section content is by using the FLEX YOUR BRAIN activity. This activity will give students confidence to begin learning section content by helping them find out what they already know and don't know about a certain topic.

Another important way to help motivate students is by connecting the current lesson with previous lessons or to common knowledge possessed by most students. The **Tying to Previous Knowledge** section helps you do this. Research has shown that connecting ideas provides for greater concept retention among students.

2 TEACH

The primary aim of the ***Merrill Earth Science*** *Teacher Wraparound Edition* is to give you the tools to accomplish the task of getting concepts of earth science across to your students. Many teaching suggestions are given to you under a series of clearly defined headings. Each section contains, under the **CONCEPT DEVELOPMENT** heading, ways for you to develop the content of the section. This may include a series of questions for you to ask students followed by possible student responses. These questions are a tool for you to use to develop the concepts in the section. Demonstration ideas also appear in Concept Development when they can help you develop student interest in the concepts to be taught.

To help you monitor and adjust your teaching to what students are learning a **CHECK FOR UNDERSTANDING** idea is provided for you in each section where it seems the most appropriate. For students who are having trouble, a **RETEACH** suggestion immediately follows the CHECK FOR UNDERSTANDING hint. The RETEACH tip is a way to teach the same concepts or facts differently to adjust to students' individual learning styles. For those students in the class who do not need additional help understanding the lesson, there are suggestions for **ENRICHMENT** to allow these students to go on while others are reviewing the section. These ENRICHMENT ideas are provided for you in the **OPTIONS** boxes at the bottom of the *Teacher Wraparound Edition* pages.

The **TEACH** step of the *Teacher Wraparound Edition* provides many other strategies to help you teach the content of the section. In each section you will find a way to connect earth science to another discipline in the **CROSS CURRICULUM** teaching tip. A **MINI QUIZ** is provided for you to use in assessing students' mastery of the material. These can also be used as CHECK FOR UNDERSTANDING activities. An annotation key is provided with each of these to help you refer students to the page on which the answer is found.

Many times students have misconceptions about a particular concept you are teaching. The **REVEALING MISCONCEPTIONS** teaching tip suggests questions you may ask to elicit student misconceptions about section content or provides you with a possible misconception held by students and a method of correcting that misconception.

There are **TEACHER F.Y.I.** tips that give you additional information to help you teach the section. These may be everyday applications or connections to other disciplines. Answers are given in the margin to any text questions to be answered by students. Also, for your convenience we have highlighted the key concepts.

COOPERATIVE LEARNING suggestions are given in various locations of the *Teacher Wraparound Edition.* They are found in the FIND OUT activities, in the lab activities and when appropriate within the Teach section. In each COOPERATIVE LEARNING tip, a specific cooperative grouping strategy is given to help you make the most of these activities.

You are also provided with information needed to teach each of the special features of the student edition such as; **MINI-Labs, Science and..., TECHNOLOGY, PROBLEM SOLVING, and ACTIVITIES.**

And There's More

Our special *Teacher Wraparound Edition* has been designed to provide you with the most meaningful teacher information in the most convenient way. At the bottom of most pages is an OPTIONS Box containing a variety of items. The OPTIONS Box on the Chapter Opener pages provides you with ideas to help you teach the Gifted students and the Mainstreamed students in your class. Both of these groups pose a challenge to any teacher and these tips are designed to help you teach the content of the chapter to these exceptional students.

Every classroom contains students with a variety of different ability levels. The OPTIONS box on the first two pages of each section shows you reduced copies of pages in the *Teacher Resource Package* to help you deal with all of the different ability levels. The Study Guide Master can be used by all students to review the basic content of the section. For the average students, the Reinforcement Master will allow them to go beyond the basic concepts of the chapter while reinforcing them. The Enrichment Master will provide those students who quickly master section content with an additional challenge to explore the ideas in the section more fully.

On the pages in the chapter, the OPTIONS Boxes provide you with Inquiry Questions and additional Enrichment activities to use with all students. The Inquiry Questions are suggested questions you may ask that require critical thinking on the part of the students. The questions relate specifically to the content of the page on which they are located.

With the materials present in the TEACH step of the teacher edition your efficiency and productivity as a teacher will increase. The TEACH section brings together the major elements that form a sound teaching approach.

3 CLOSE

Closing the lesson is the last but one of the most important steps of teaching any lesson. This step is the complement in many ways to the MOTIVATE step. While the motivate step helps students become involved in the lesson, the close step helps students bring things together in their minds to make sense of what went on in the lesson. The ***Merrill Earth Science*** *Teacher Wraparound Edition* gives you a variety of ways to provide effective closure to a lesson. The close options are activities that summarize the section, bridge to the next lesson, or provide an application of the lesson.

As you review the ***Merrill Earth Science*** *Teacher Wraparound Edition,* you will discover that you and your students are considered very important. With the enormous number of teaching strategies provided by the teacher edition, you should be able to accomplish the goals of your curriculum. The materials allow adaptability and flexibility so that student needs, and curricular needs can be met.

Cooperative Learning

What is Cooperative Learning?

In cooperative learning, students work together in small groups to learn academic material and interpersonal skills. Group members are responsible for the *group* accomplishing an assigned task as well as for learning the material themselves. When compared to competitive or individual learning situations in which students either work against each other or alone, cooperative learning fosters academic, personal, and social success for all students. Recent research shows that cooperative learning results in

- development of positive attitudes toward science.
- choosing to take more science courses as electives.
- positive attitudes toward science carrying over to positive attitudes toward school.
- lower drop-out rates for at-risk students.
- building respect for others regardless of race, ethnic origin, or sex.
- increased awareness of diverse perspectives.
- increased capability for problem solving in sciences.
- increased realization of potential for girls in science classes.
- development of kindness, sensitivity, and tolerance.

What is the Teacher's Role in Cooperative Learning?

Before teaching the lesson, the teacher must decide the academic task and interpersonal skills students will learn or practice in groups. Students can learn most any academic objective in cooperative groups.

The teacher should also specify what interpersonal behaviors are necessary for a group to work cooperatively. When first starting out, it is wise to list and discuss with students basic interpersonal skills needed for people to work together. Basic interpersonal skills you might discuss include being responsible for your own actions, staying on task, listening while others are speaking, and respecting other people and their ideas. Students can learn and practice other interpersonal skills such as using quiet voices, encouraging other group members to participate, summarizing, checking for understanding, disagreeing constructively, reaching a group consensus, and criticizing ideas rather than people.

Cooperative groups usually contain from two to six students. If students are not experienced working in groups, start with small groups. You might consider grouping students in pairs and then joining pairs later to form groups of four or even six.

Generally, it is best to assign students to heterogeneous groups. Be certain that each heterogeneous group contains a mixture of abilities, genders, and ethnicity. The use of heterogeneous groups exposes students to ideas different from their own and helps them learn how to work with persons different from themselves.

Students may also be randomly assigned to groups, or they can be allowed to select their own groups. Consider using random grouping to let students get acquainted at the beginning of the year or for students to learn to work with all students in the class. As a general rule, it is not good to allow students to choose groups until students have experience with cooperative learning. Have student-selected groups work together when students have interests in common.

Initially, cooperative learning groups should only work together for a day or two. After the students are more experienced, they can do group work effectively for longer periods of time. Some teachers change groups every week, while others keep groups of students together during the study of a unit or chapter. Regardless of the duration you choose, it is important to keep groups together long enough for each group to experience success and to change groups often enough that students have the opportunity to work with others.

You can structure the learning task to promote the participation of each group member by the arrangement of your classroom and the provision of materials. Limiting the materials needed to accomplish the assigned task forces students to share them. Also, consider assigning students roles that contribute to accomplishing the group task. Student roles should be rotated so each group member has the opportunity to perform each role.

Finally, you must decide on how you will evaluate the learning task and how well the students worked together in learning groups. Since students are responsible for themselves and other group members learning the material, you can evaluate group performance during a lesson by frequently asking questions to group members picked at random. Other forms of group evaluation include having each group take a quiz together or having all students write and choosing one student's paper at random to grade. Individual learning can be assessed by traditional tests and quizzes.

To assess the learning of interpersonal skills, you can observe their use during the lesson. Or, you or a group member could tally the use of a specific interpersonal skill. Groups can assess themselves by rating themselves on a scale from one to ten; they then list ways group members used interpersonal skills and ways to improve group performance.

Teaching the Lesson

Explain the day's lesson before students start group work. Do so by writing the following headings on the chalkboard or a transparency and discussing each.

- ▶**Academic Task:** Prepare students for the academic task by teaching any material they might need to know and by giving specific instructions for the task.
- ▶**Criteria for Success:** Instruct students that they are responsible for their own learning as well as the learning of other members of the group. Explain the sharing of materials and assuming of roles. Explain your criteria for evaluating group and individual learning.
- ▶**Interpersonal Skills:** Specify the interpersonal skills students will be working on, and list what behaviors look and sound like. Explain how you will evaluate interpersonal skills.
- ▶**Group Formation:** Divide the class into groups. Assign roles or divide materials.
- ▶**Provide Assistance with the Academic Task:** Make certain each student can see and hear all other group members. When students are having trouble with the task, answer questions, clarify the assignment, reteach, or provide background as needed. When answering questions, make certain that no students in the group can answer the question before you reply.
- ▶**Monitor Student Behavior:** Spend most of your time monitoring the functioning of groups. Praise group cooperation and good use of interpersonal skills.
- ▶**Intervene to Teach Interpersonal Skills:** Whenever possible, allow groups to work out their own problems. When groups are having problems, ask group members to figure out how the group can function more effectively. Record your observations of the use of interpersonal skills; share your observations with the groups.
- ▶**Provide Closure to the Lesson:** Reinforce student learning by having groups share their products or summarize the assignment. Answer any questions about the lesson.
- ▶**Evaluate Group and Individual Learning:** Use the criteria discussed before the lesson began to evaluate and give feedback on how well the academic task was mastered by the groups. Assess individual learning by your traditional method.
- ▶**Assess How Well Groups Functioned:** Have students analyze how well their groups functioned and how well they used interpersonal skills. Groups can list what they did well and what they could do to improve. Have groups share their analysis with the class, and summarize the analyses of the whole class.

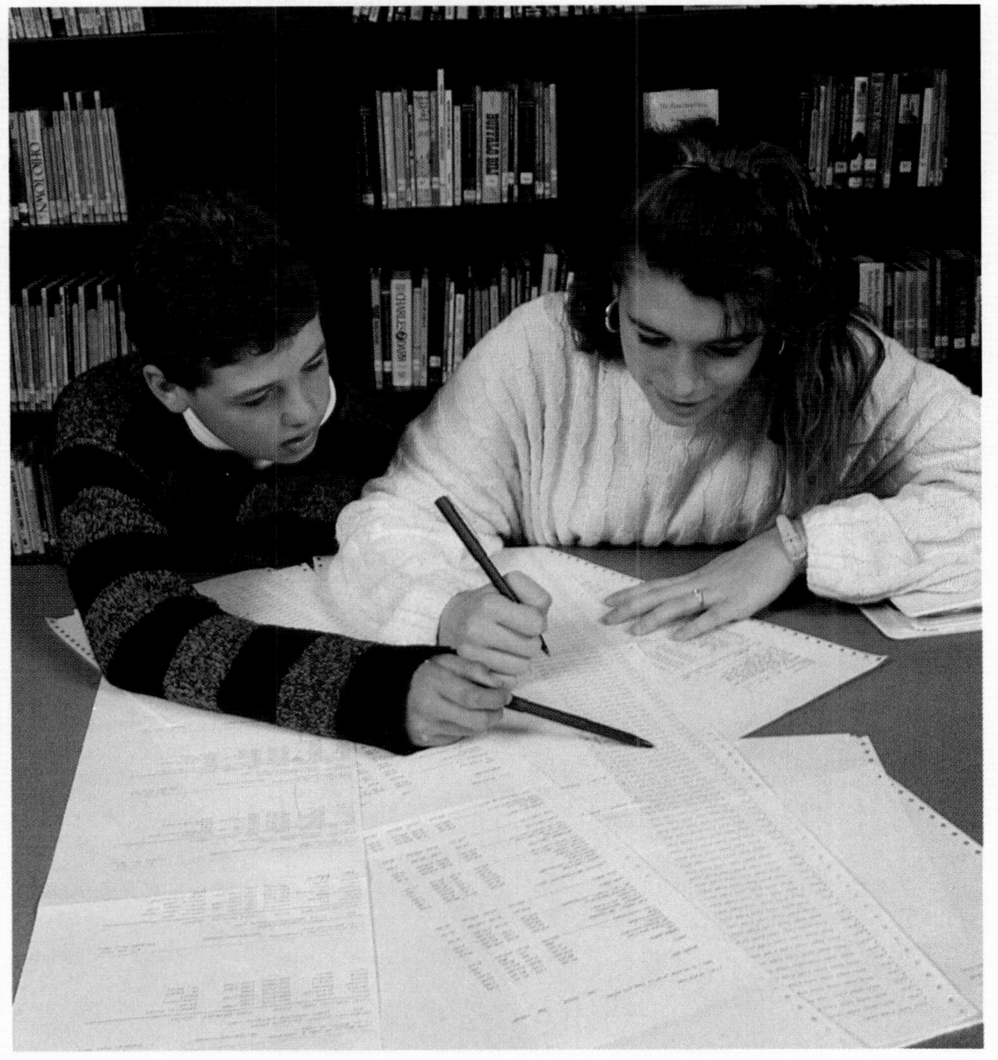

Using Cooperative Learning in *Merrill Earth Science*

In ***Merrill Earth Science*** *Teacher Wraparound Edition,* Activities, MINI-Labs, Find Outs, and Chapter Reviews contain specific suggestions for Cooperative Learning. In addition, cooperative learning groups can be used with section reviews and problem solving, concept mapping, and skill builder features. The following cooperative learning strategies are referenced in the *Teacher Wraparound Edition.*

Paired Partners

Assign each student a partner, and ask a question or present a problem for them to solve. Each student composes an answer or solution; the pair then shares answers with each other. If partners disagree, they explain and discuss the issues until they agree. When both agree and can explain the answer, partners raise their hands to signify both agree and can explain the answer. After determining if groups have the correct answer, some teachers use thumbs up to indicate "correct" and thumbs down to indicate "incorrect." Students can also write their answers on the chalkboard or on response cards. Paired Partners can be used for problem solving, concept mapping, and Skill Builder features.

Expert Teams

Form students into groups of two to six. Give each group member a different part of an assignment to study and master. Send group members with the same part of the assignment from the different teams to work together to become experts on their parts. Bring the experts back to their original groups. Each group member teaches his or her part of the assignment to other members of the original group until everyone has mastered all the material. Expert Teams can be used for section and chapter reviews.

Study Buddies

Study Buddies work together to help one another study for tests or to create concept maps. Group students in fours. After a chapter is completed, give students one class period to work in groups to master the material in the Chapter Review before giving the end of chapter test. If you wish, Study Buddies can be divided into Expert Teams to study and then teach the material. To have Study Buddies create concept maps, give each group member a different colored pen. Group members pass the concept map around the table adding to the map on each pass with their colored pens.

Numbered Heads Together

Form groups of three to five and have students number off. Then, ask a question or give an assignment. Have students in each group either agree on an answer or, for higher level thinking skills, name an example, make a prediction, or state an application. When students have agreed on an answer, call a number at random. Students with that number raise their hands and wait to be called on. Select one student to provide an answer. Determine if other students with that number have the correct answer by indicating thumbs up or down or by having them write their responses on index cards or on the chalkboard. Numbered Heads Together can be used for section and chapter reviews, problem solving, concept mapping, and Skill Builders.

Problem Solving Team

Form groups of four students, and assign roles. The reader reads the problem; the clarifier restates it; the solver suggests answers. If the group agrees on answers, the recorder writes the answers on a paper that all members sign. Review the answers and discuss the problem by calling on any group member. Use thumbs up or down, responses on response cards or the chalkboard to determine if all groups have the same answers. This strategy can be used for problem solving and Skill Builder features.

Science Investigation

Science Investigation group members work together to perform hands-on science investigations. The Science Investigation strategy is used for Activities, MINI-Labs, and FIND OUT features. In Science Investigation, each group member has a different role and duties to perform for the investigation. Some roles are working roles to accomplish the investigation, while others are interpersonal skill roles that help the group function effectively. Following are possible roles for Science Investigation groups.

Working Roles

Reader: reads the activity directions out loud

Materials Handler: obtains, dispenses, and returns all materials

Safety Officer: informs group of safety precautions; ensures group handles equipment safely

Recorder: records data collected during the activity; writes answers to activity questions; has all group members sign data collection and answer sheets

Reporter: reports data collected and answers to activity questions

Timekeeper: keeps group on task; and manages the group's time

Calculator: performs activity calculations and measurements

Interpersonal Skill Roles

Monitor: ensures each group member participates and encourages participation

Praiser: compliments group members on fulfilling their assigned tasks; compliments group members on use of interpersonal skills

Checker: checks on learning of group members; ensures each group member can summarize the results of the activity and answer activity questions.

Applications

The following chart provides strategies for applying cooperative learning during ***Merrill Earth Science*** activities.

Merrill Earth Science features	Applicable Cooperative Learning Strategies
Find Out	Science Investigation, Paired Partners, Numbered Heads Together
Concept Mapping	Study Buddies, Paired Partners, Numbered Heads Together
Problem Solving	Problem Solving Teams, Paired Partners, Numbered Heads Together
Skill Builder	Problem Solving Team, Paired Partners, Numbered Heads Together
Section Review	Study Buddies, Expert Teams, Paired Partners, Numbered Heads Together
Chapter Review	Study Buddies, Expert Teams, Paired Partners, Numbered Heads Together
MINI-Lab	Science Investigation, Paired Partners, Numbered Heads Together
Activity	Science Investigation, Paired Partners, Numbered Heads Together

Resources

Adams, D.M., and M.E. Hamm. *Cooperative Learning, Critical Thinking, and Collaboration Across the Curriculum.* Springfield, IL: Charles C. Thomas Publisher, 1990.

Association for Supervision and Curriculum Development. *Educational Leadership,* Volume 47, Number 4, December, 1989-January, 1990.

Foot, H.C., M.J. Morgan, and R.H. Shute. *Children Helping Children.* New York: John Wiley & Sons, 1990.

Johnson, D.W., and R.T. Johnson. *Learning Together and Alone: Cooperative, Competitive, and Individualistic Learning.* Englewood Cliffs, NJ: Prentice-Hall, 1987.

Johnson, D.W., and R.T. Johnson., E.J. Holubec, and P. Roy. *Circles of Learning: Cooperation in the Classroom.* Alexandria, VA: Association for Supervision and Curriculum Development, 1984.

Kagan, S. *Cooperative Learning: Resources for Teachers.* Riverside, CA: University of California, 1988.

Shlomo, S. *Cooperative Learning Theory and Research.* Westport, CT: Praeger, 1990.

Slavin, R. *Cooperative Learning Theory, Research, and Practice.* Englewood Cliffs, NJ: Prentice Hall, 1990.

Slavin, R. *Using Student Team Learning.* Baltimore, MD: The John Hopkins Team Learning Project, 1986.

Meeting Individual Needs

	DESCRIPTION	SOURCES OF HELP/INFORMATION
Learning Disabled	All learning disabled students have an academic problem in one or more areas, such as academic learning, language, perception, social-emotional adjustment, memory, or attention.	*Journal of Learning Disabilities* *Learning Disability Quarterly*
Behaviorally Disordered	Children with behavior disorders deviate from standards or expectations of behavior and impair the functioning of others and themselves. These children may also be gifted or learning disabled.	*Exceptional Children* *Journal of Special Education*
Physically Challenged	Children who are physically challenged fall into two categories—those with orthopedic impairments and those with other health impairments. Orthopedically impaired children have the use of one or more limbs severely restricted, so the use of wheelchairs, crutches, or braces may be necessary. Children with other health impairments may require the use of respirators or have other medical equipment.	Batshaw, M.L. and M.Y. Perset. *Children with Handicaps: A Medical Primer.* Baltimore: Paul H. Brooks, 1981. Hale, G. (Ed.). *The Source Book for the Disabled.* NY: Holt, Rinehart & Winston, 1982. *Teaching Exceptional Children*
Visually Impaired	Children who are visually disabled have partial or total loss of sight. Individuals with visual impairments are not significantly different from their sighted peers in ability range or personality. However, blindness may affect cognitive, motor, and social development, especially if early intervention is lacking.	*Journal of Visual Impairment and Blindness* *Education of Visually Handicapped* American Foundation for the Blind
Hearing Impaired	Children who are hearing impaired have partial or total loss of hearing. Individuals with hearing impairments are not significantly different from their hearing peers in ability range or personality. However, the chronic condition of deafness may affect cognitive, motor, and social development if early intervention is lacking. Speech development also is often affected.	*American Annals of the Deaf* *Journal of Speech and Hearing Research* *Sign Language Studies*
Limited English Proficiency	Multicultural and/or bilingual children often speak English as a second language or not at all. Customs and behavior of people in the majority culture may be confusing for some of these students. Cultural values may inhibit some of these students from full participation.	*Teaching English as a Second Language Reporter* R.L. Jones, ed., *Mainstreaming and the Minority Child.* Reston, VA: Council for Exceptional Children, 1976.
Gifted	Although no formal definition exists, these students can be described as having above average ability, task commitment, and creativity. Gifted students rank in the top 5% of their class. They usually finish work more quickly than other students, and are capable of divergent thinking.	*Journal for the Education of the Gifted* *Gifted Child Quarterly* *Gifted Creative/Talented*

TIPS FOR INSTRUCTION

1. Provide support and structure; clearly specify rules, assignments, and duties.
2. Establish situations that lead to success.
3. Practice skills frequently—use games and drills to help maintain student interest.
4. Allow students to record answers on tape and allow extra time to complete tests and assignments.
5. Provide outlines or tape lecture material.
6. Pair students with peer helpers, and provide classtime for pair interaction.

---

1. Provide a clearly structured environment with regard to scheduling, rules, room arrangement, and safety.
2. Clearly outline objectives and how you will help students obtain objectives. Seek input from them about their strengths, weaknesses, and goals.
3. Reinforce appropriate behavior and model it for students.
4. Do not expect immediate success. Instead, work for long term improvement.
5. Balance individual needs with group requirements.

---

1. Openly discuss with student any uncertainties you have about when to offer aid.
2. Ask parents or therapists and students what special devices or procedures are needed, and if any special safety precautions need to be taken.
3. Allow physically disabled students to do everything their peers do, including participating in field trips, special events, and projects.
4. Help nondisabled students and adults understand physically disabled students.

---

1. As with all students, help the student become independent. Some assignments may need to be modified.
2. Teach classmates how to serve as guides.
3. Limit unnecessary noise in the classroom.
4. Encourage students to use their sense of touch. Provide tactile models whenever possible.
5. Describe people and events as they occur in the classroom.
6. Provide taped lectures and reading assignments.
7. Team the student with a sighted peer for laboratory work.

---

1. Seat students where they can see your lip movements easily, and avoid visual distractions.
2. Avoid standing with your back to the window or light source.
3. Using an overhead projector allows you to maintain eye contact while writing.
4. Seat students where they can see speakers.
5. Write all assignments on the board, or hand out written instructions.
6. If the student has a manual interpreter, allow both student and interpreter to select the most favorable seating arrangements.

---

1. Remember students' ability to speak English does not reflect their academic ability.
2. Try to incorporate the student's cultural experience into your instruction. The help of a bilingual aide may be effective.
3. Include information about different cultures in your curriculum to aid students' self-image—avoid cultural stereotypes.
4. Encourage students to share their cultures in the classroom.

---

1. Make arrangements for students to take selected subjects early and to work on independent projects.
2. Let students express themselves in art forms such as drawing, creative writing, or acting.
3. Make public services available through a catalog of resources, such as agencies providing free and inexpensive materials, community services and programs, and people in the community with specific expertise.
4. Ask "what if" questions to develop high-level thinking skills; establish an environment safe for risk taking.
5. Emphasize concepts, theories, ideas, relationships, and generalizations.

Performance Objectives

Books on science education list many valid reasons for teaching science. These reasons range from general to more specific goals. A general goal might be to help students acquire habits of critical thinking. A specific goal might be to teach these students the definition of an element and a compound. How do you know if you are accomplishing these goals in your teaching? Herein lies the value of performance objectives—the behaviors that you, the teacher, can observe and which indicate that students are achieving the goals of science education.

In many cases, several types of behaviors will indicate that the students are achieving the objectives. For example, how do you determine that the students are acquiring habits of critical thinking? Some student behaviors you might observe include:

1. asking related questions.
2. gathering data or offering evidence that supports their answers.
3. questioning or expressing doubt about the hypotheses posed by others.

Other behaviors will indicate if students are learning other things. These behaviors can be written as performance objectives to aid you in assessing student accomplishment. A good performance objective is written in three parts:

1. the condition,
2. the performance or criterion, and
3. the criterion measure.

The condition tells what causes, stimulates, or motivates the student to perform the behaviors, or under what circumstances those behaviors will be performed. The performance or criterion tells exactly what behavior you are looking for. A good performance objective would avoid using such terms as *know about, appreciate,* or *sense the relationship between.* The criterion measure tells how many of the students have achieved the objective, or to what degree of accuracy or level of performance the behavior should be performed for you to know the students have actually achieved the objective.

In other words, a good performance objective uses verbs that express some type of observable action. Here are some examples of action verbs that describe observable behaviors: states orally, identifies, watches, matches, lists, states, distinguishes, manipulates, hypothesizes, measures, constructs.

Performance objectives are related to the four broad goals of science education:

Attitudes: To develop students' attitudes of curiosity and involvement with occurrences in their environment; to develop an appreciation for the contributions of science; and to recognize the value of solving problems in a scientific manner.

Processes: To develop those intellectual processes of inquiry by which scientific problems and occurrences are explained, predicted, and/or controlled.

Knowledge: To develop knowledge of facts, terminology, concepts, generalizations, and principles that help students confront and interpret occurrences in their environment.

Skills: To develop students' abilities to handle, construct, and manipulate materials and equipment in a productive and safe manner; and to develop the ability to measure, organize, and communicate scientific information.

Performance objectives are listed for students at the beginning of each section of ***Merrill Earth Science.*** Review questions located at the end of each major text section and the chapter review questions test students' mastery of the objectives. The Chapter Review and Chapter Tests of the *Teacher Resource Package* are correlated with the section objectives.

Laboratory Safety

Safety is of prime importance in every classroom. However, the need for safety is even greater when science is taught. Outlined below are some considerations on laboratory safety that are intended primarily for teachers and administrators.

The activities in ***Merrill Earth Science*** are designed to minimize dangers in the laboratory. Even so, there are no guarantees against accidents. However, careful planning and preparation as well as being aware of hazards can keep accidents to a minimum. Numerous books and pamphlets are available on laboratory safety with detailed instructions on preventing accidents. However, much of what they present can be summarized in the phrase, *Be prepared!* Know the rules and what common violations occur. Know the Safety Symbols used in this book (see p. 34T). Know where emergency equipment is stored and how to use it. Practice good laboratory housekeeping and management by observing these guidelines.

Classroom/Laboratory

1. Store chemicals properly.
   - **a.** Separate chemicals by reaction type.
   - **b.** Label all chemical containers. Include purchase date, special precautions, and expiration date.
   - **c.** Discard chemicals when outdated, according to appropriate disposal methods.
   - **d.** Do not store chemicals above eye level.
   - **e.** Wood shelving is preferable to metal. All shelving should be firmly attached to walls. Anti-roll lips should be placed on all shelves.
   - **f.** Store only those chemicals that you plan to use.
   - **g.** Flammable and toxic chemicals require special storage containers.
2. Store equipment properly.
   - **a.** Clean and dry all equipment before storing.
   - **b.** Protect electronic equipment and microscopes from dust, humidity, and extreme temperatures.
   - **c.** Label and organize equipment so that it is accessible.
3. Provide adequate workspace.
4. Provide adequate room ventilation.
5. Post safety and evacuation guidelines.
6. Be sure safety equipment is accessible and works.
7. Provide containers for disposing of chemicals, waste products, and biological specimens. Disposal methods must meet local guidelines.
8. Use hot plates whenever possible as a heat source. If burners are used, a central shut-off valve for the gas supply should be available to the teacher. Never use open flames when a flammable solvent is in the same room.

First Day of Class/Labs (with students)

1. Distribute and discuss safety rules, safety symbols, first aid guidelines, and safety contract found in the Teacher Resource Guide. Have students refer to Appendices C and D on pages 664-665, to review safety symbols and guidelines.
2. Review safe use of equipment and chemicals.
3. Review use and location of safety equipment.
4. Discuss safe disposal of materials and laboratory cleanup policy.
5. Discuss proper laboratory attitude and conduct.
6. Document students' understanding of above points.
   - **a.** Have students sign the safety contract and return it.
   - **b.** Administer the safety assessment found in the *Teacher Resource Package.* Reteach those points that students do not understand.

Before Each Investigation

1. Perform each investigation yourself before assigning it.
2. Arrange the lab in such a way that equipment and supplies are clearly labeled and easily accessible.
3. Have available only equipment and supplies needed to complete the assigned investigation.
4. Review the procedure with students, emphasizing any caution statements or safety symbols that appear.
5. Be sure all students know proper procedures to follow if an accident should occur.

During the Investigation

1. Make sure the lab is clean and free of clutter.
2. Insist that students wear goggles and aprons.
3. Never allow a student to work alone in the lab.
4. Never allow students to use a cutting device with more than one edge.
5. Students should not point the open end of a heated test tube toward anyone.
6. Remove broken glassware or frayed cords from use. Also clean up any spills immediately. Dilute solutions with water before removing.
7. Be sure all glassware that is to be heated is of a heat-treated type that will not shatter.
8. Remind students that hot glassware looks cool.
9. Prohibit eating and drinking in the lab.

After the Investigation

1. Be sure that the lab is clean.
2. Be certain that students have returned all equipment and disposed of broken glassware and chemicals properly.
3. Be sure all hot plates and electrical connections are off.
4. Insist that each student wash his or her hands when lab work is completed.

The ***Merrill Earth Science*** program uses safety symbols to alert you and your students to possible laboratory dangers. These symbols are explained below. Be sure your students understand each symbol before they begin an investigation or skill.

Safety Symbols

 **DISPOSAL ALERT** This symbol appears when care must be taken to dispose of materials properly.	 **ANIMAL SAFETY** This symbol appears whenever live animals are studied and the safety of the animals and the students must be ensured.
 **BIOLOGICAL HAZARD** This symbol appears when there is danger involving bacteria, fungi, or protists.	 **RADIOACTIVE SAFETY** This symbol appears when radioactive materials are used.
 **OPEN FLAME ALERT** This symbol appears when use of an open flame could cause a fire or an explosion.	 **CLOTHING PROTECTION SAFETY** This symbol appears when substances used could stain or burn clothing.
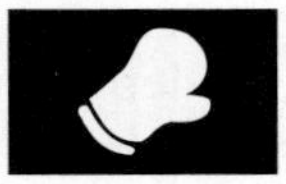 **THERMAL SAFETY** This symbol appears as a reminder to use caution when handling hot objects.	 **FIRE SAFETY** This symbol appears when care should be taken around open flames.
 **SHARP OBJECT SAFETY** This symbol appears when a danger of cuts or punctures caused by the use of sharp objects exists.	 **EXPLOSION SAFETY** This symbol appears when the misuse of chemicals could cause an explosion.
 **FUME SAFETY** This symbol appears when chemicals or chemical reactions could cause dangerous fumes.	 **EYE SAFETY** This symbol appears when a danger to the eyes exists. Safety goggles should be worn when this symbol appears.
 **ELECTRICAL SAFETY** This symbol appears when care should be taken when using electrical equipment.	 **POISON SAFETY** This symbol appears when poisonous substances are used.
 **PLANT SAFETY** This symbol appears when poisonous plants or plants with thorns are handled.	 **CHEMICAL SAFETY** This symbol appears when chemicals used can cause burns or are poisonous if absorbed through the skin.

Chemical Storage and Disposal

General Guidelines

Be sure to store all chemicals properly. The following are guidelines commonly used. Your school, city, county, or state may have additional requirements for handling chemicals. It is the responsibility of each teacher to become informed as to what rules or guidelines are in effect in his or her area.

1. Separate chemicals by reaction type. Strong acids should be stored together. Likewise, strong bases should be stored together and should be separated from acids. Oxidants should be stored away from easily oxidized materials and so on.
2. Be sure all chemicals are stored in labeled containers indicating contents, concentration, source, date purchased (or prepared), any precautions for handling and storage, and expiration date.
3. Dispose of any outdated or waste chemicals properly according to accepted disposal procedures.
4. Do not store chemicals above eye level.
5. Wood shelving is preferable to metal. All shelving should be firmly attached to all walls and have anti-roll edges.
6. Store only those chemicals that you plan to use.
7. Hazardous chemicals require special storage containers and conditions. Be sure to know what those chemicals are and the accepted practices for your area. Some substances must even be stored outside the building.
8. When working with chemicals or preparing solutions, observe the same general safety precautions that you would expect from students. These include wearing an apron and goggles. Wear gloves and use the fume hood when necessary. Students will want to do as you do whether they admit it or not.
9. If you are a new teacher in a particular laboratory, it is your responsibility to survey the chemicals stored there and to be sure they are stored properly or disposed of. Consult the rules and laws in your area concerning what chemicals can be kept in your classroom. For disposal, consult up-to-date disposal information from the state and federal governments.

Disposal of Chemicals

Local, state, and federal laws regulate the proper disposal of chemicals. These laws should be consulted before chemical disposal is attempted. Although most substances encountered in high school biology can be flushed down the drain with plenty of water, it is not safe to assume that is always true. It is recommended that teachers who use chemicals consult the following books from the National Research Council.

Prudent Practices for Handling Hazardous Chemicals in Laboratories, Washington, DC: National Academy Press, 1981.

Prudent Practices for Disposal of Chemicals from Laboratories, Washington, DC: National Academy Press, 1983.

These books are useful and still in print, although they are several years old. Current laws in your area would, of course, supersede the information in these books.

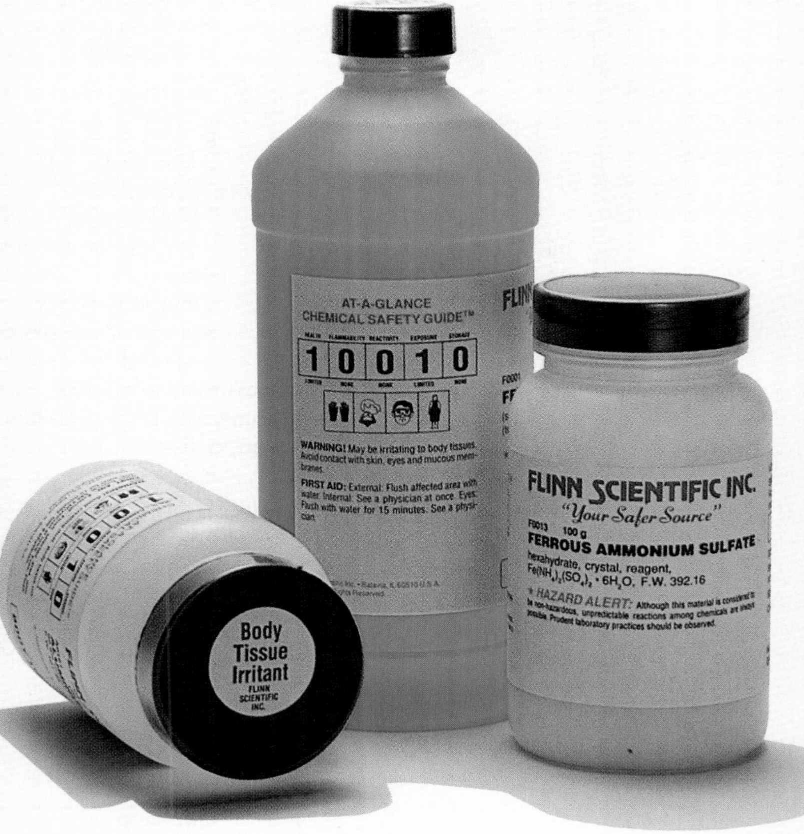

Earth Science Materials List

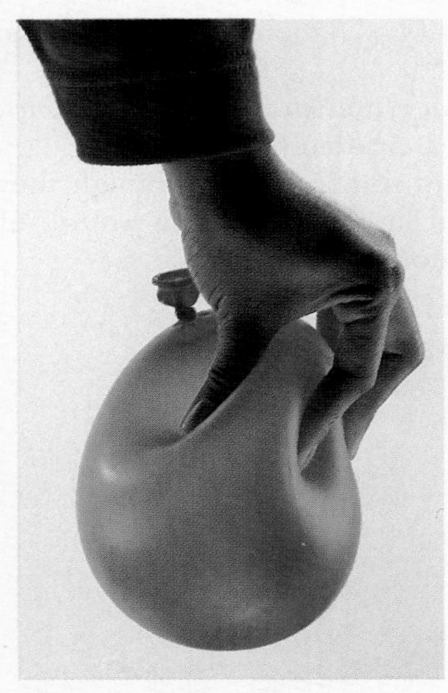

NONCONSUMABLES			
ITEM	**ACTIVITY**	**MINI LAB**	**FIND OUT**
Balance	2-1		
Balance, pan	2-2, 3-2 5-1, 11-1	232	
Ball, basketball or volleyball		582	
inflatable		232	
polystyrene	22-2		
Balloon,			627
rubber	9-1		
Beaker,	7-2, 8-1		
100-mL	2-2		
250-mL (2)		184	
250- or 400-mL	19-1		
500-mL (2)	11-1		
clear glass		246	
large		173	
small		173	
Block, metal, small	2-2		
wood (3)	6-1, 7-1		
wood, small	2-2		
Books, (4)	7-1, 24-2		
Bottle, hot-water		259	
plastic, with cap	5-1		
2-liter plastic (4)	19-2		253, 305
Boxes, clear plastic,	9-2		
or glass baking dish		294	
or glass or pie plate		291	
shoe	1-1		
shoe, with lid	16-2		
storage, clear plastic,	11-2		
with lid	8-1		
Brass fasteners (100)	16-2		
Camera, instant, and film	21-2		
Can, coffee	9-1		
metal		227	
Candle	21-1		
Cardboard,	3-1, 10-1 11-1, 24-2		
21.5 cm × 28 cm	23-1		
pieces of			171
white, 50 cm × 60 cm	21-1		
Carton, milk			417
Chalk,		644	
or water-soluble marker	14-2		
Clay,	2-2, 5-2 6-2	314	
modeling			387
slabs 10 cm × 5 cm × 1 cm (2)			359
Clipboard	24-2		
Clock, or watch	11-2		
Cloth			523
Clothespin			627
Compasses, drawing		614	
small magnetic (2)	13-1		
Container, plastic		529	
small (2)		538	

NONCONSUMABLES

ITEM	ACTIVITY	MINI LAB	FIND OUT
Cork,		294	
small	7-1		
Cups,			61
paper or 50-mL beakers (11)	19-1		
Dishes, clear glass or plastic (3)	18-2		
Dishpans			281
Dissecting probe		129, 405	
Dropper	3-2, 4-2		
eye			171, 305
Dust			523
Electric fan, 3-speed	11-2		
Electric hot plate	3-1, 11-1 20-1	246, 353	227
File, steel	3-2		
Filters, colored, (3 different)			551
Flashlight (4)	21-1		551
Flask, 1000-mL	11-1		
Freezer		46	
Funnel	7-2		
Gauze, piece (2cm2)	10-1		
Globe,	2-1, 14-2 22-2	582	575
or world map		203, 465	195
Goggles, safety	3-2, 4-2 6-2, 11-1	339	
Graduated cylinder,	3-2	46, 184	
100-mL	1-1		
100-mL or larger	2-1		
250-mL	2-2		
Gravel	5-2, 6-2	150	141
(100 mL)		184	
Hair dryer	6-2		
Hammer		339	
Hand lens	3-1, 3-2 4-1, 5-2 10-2, 20-1		
Ice block containing sand,			
clay, and gravel	6-1		
Lamp, 200-watt, with reflector			
and clamp	18-2		
without shade			575
Leaf, shell or bone			417
Lids, plastic (4)	20-1		
plastic coffee can, (3)	5-2		
Light source,	11-2	129	
overhead with			
reflector	6-1, 9-2		
unshaded	22-2		
Limestone, or shale, samples,			
(100 g)	5-1		
Magnets,	12-1		
bar	13-1		
Magnifying glass	21-1	72	85, 599
Marbles		173, 569	
Marker,	20-1		
felt-tip			627
glass	18-2		
transparency	8-1		
Metersticks, (10)	2-1, 7-1 17-2, 23-2 24-1	437, 465 644, 650	

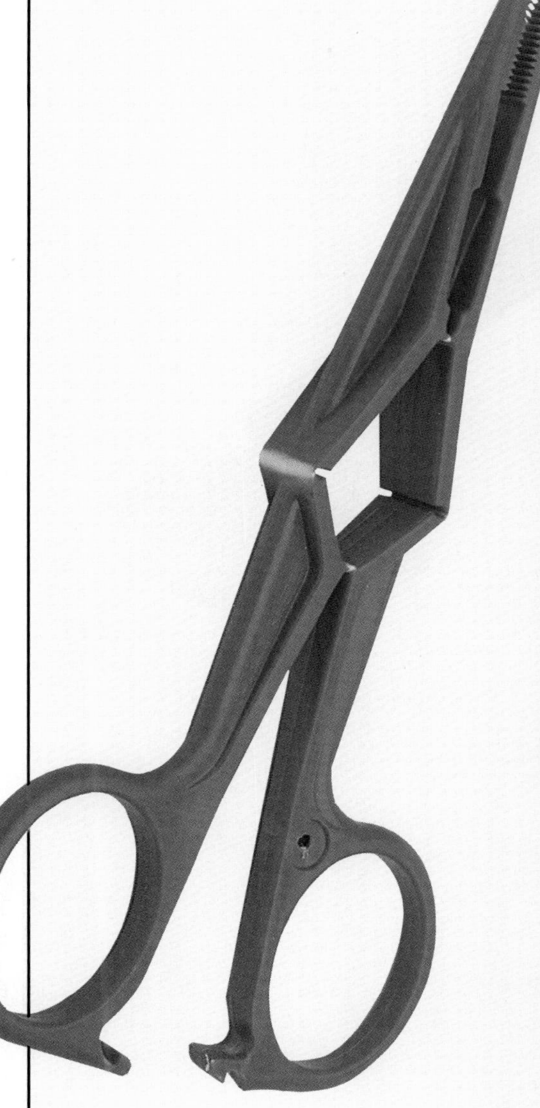

NONCONSUMABLES			
ITEM	**ACTIVITY**	**MINI LAB**	**FIND OUT**
Microscope,		319,405	
binocular	20-1		
or magnifying glass		64,129	
stereo	12-1		
Mineral samples,	3-2		
transparent, of calcite, muscovite, gypsum, halite, or quartz		72	
Mirror, concave	21-1		
convex	21-1		
plant	21-1		
Mitt, thermal	3-1, 20-1	353	
Newspaper,		314	
color comics from			599
Objects, small, of uniform shape (dried beans, corn kernels, etc.)	19-1		
Pail	6-1		
plastic (2)	7-1		
Pans, flat	6-2		61
large		147, 150	
shallow (4)	3-1, 11-1	126	
Paper,	5-2, 8-2 13-1, 14-2 15-2, 18-1 23-1	101, 198 203, 419 459, 479 609, 614	501
construction,		569	
green			445
drawing	24-2		
graph	1-1, 9-2 12-2, 14-1 16-2, 18-2 19-2	198	
heavy	9-1		
large sheet		650	
notebook		20	5
thin, white			335
tracing	15-1		
waxed			171
white	11-2	129	551
Paper clips (100)	16-2		
Paper plates (2)		399	
Paper towel	4-2	126	
Paper-towel roll, empty	21-1	558	
Pen, marking	4-2		
or marker	13-1		
Pencils,	13-2, 15-2 17-2, 18-1 23-1, 23-2	20, 198 203, 419 437, 459 609, 614	479, 501
blue and brown	12-2		
colored (6)	9-2, 16-2 18-2		
Penny, copper	3-2		
(100)	16-2		
Petroleum jelly			417
Pin		405	
Plaster of paris		399	417
Plastic bags		129	
Plastic food wrap	19-2	173	
Plastic model landform	8-1		
Playing cards, (1 deck)	17-1		

NONCONSUMABLES			
ITEM	ACTIVITY	MINI LAB	FIND OUT
Protractor	6-2, 7-2 11-2	399	
Putty, silicon, or taffy		339	
Quartz, piece of	2-2		
Record, phonograph, LP		569	
Refracting telescope, small	24-2		
Refrigerator	20-1		
Remote controlled car	21-2		
Ring stand	9-2, 11-2 18-2		
Rocks, large, 30 cm	21-2		
(4)		85	
igneous	4-1		
metamorphic (4)		97	
nonmetamorphic (4)		97	
sample	2-1		
volcanic ejecta		405	
several samples of different for each student			121
sediments of		101	
small	1-1		
unknown sedimentary samples	4-2		
Rubber band	9-1, 19-2	173	
Ruler, metric	1-1, 6-1 6-2, 8-1 9-1, 9-2 11-2, 13-1 13-2, 14-2 18-2, 23-1 24-1	198, 614	627
Sand,	5-2	150	141
beach, different types (3)	12-1		
fine	6-2		
moist		147	
or cereal		399	
(100 mL)		184	
Saucepan, metal		353	
Scissors	5-2, 7-2 9-1, 11-1 17-2, 23-2 24-2	569	335
Screen, portable	21-2		
Sheet, cardboard	6-2		
plastic	7-1		
Sink	7-2		
Slide, glass	3-2		
Soil,	9-2, 19-2	150	
dry black	18-2		
dry brown	18-2		
dry white sandy	18-2		
samples	5-2	129	
Spoon,		294	
aluminum or silver	21-1		
Sprinkling can	6-2		
Steel wool, piece of		126	
Stick	2-1		
Stopper, 1-hole rubber	11-1		
Stopwatch	7-1, 21-2		
Strainer, wire	5-1		
Straw, drinking	9-1		
Streak plate	3-2		
Stream table with sand	6-1, 7-1		

NONCONSUMABLES

ITEM	ACTIVITY	MINI LAB	FIND OUT
String	1-1, 2-1 10-1, 14-2 23-1	582	627
(125 cm)		644	
cotton	3-1		
Tape,	7-2, 8-1 10-1,13-1	294	253
adding machine	17-2, 23-2	437	
masking	9-2, 21-1 24-1	46, 569	
transparent	9-1		
Test tube, large	3-1		
Test-tube holder	3-1		
Thermometers, (9)	2-1, 9-2 10-1, 18-2 19-2	257	
Thumbtacks, or pins	23-1		
Toothpicks	3-1		281
Towel	11-1		
Transparency	8-1		
Tripod, small	24-2		
Tubing, glass, bent at right angle	11-1		
rubber	7-1, 11-1		
rubber or plastic (30 cm)	7-2		
Turntable, phonograph		569	
Tweezers		101	445
Washers	11-1		
Watch, or clock with second hand	18-2	5	
Water meter, home	20-2		
Yarn, 3-cm green, orange, and blue, (15 pieces each)		445	

CONSUMABLES			
ITEM	**ACTIVITY**	**MINI LAB**	**FIND OUT**
Egg, raw	22-1		
Gelatin, small box, plain	20-1		
Ice,	11-1		
crushed		257	
cubes		259	281
Sugar, cubes			27
granulated	3-1		
Tea, cold (1 cup)			27
warm (1 cup)			27

CHEMICAL SUPPLIES			
ITEM	**ACTIVITY**	**MINI LAB**	**FIND OUT**
Food coloring,		246, 291 353	281
Garbage	19-2		
Glycerine	11-1		
Hydrochloric acid, 5%	3-2, 4-2		
pH ion paper		529	
Rain, or snow		529	
Salt, solution	3-1		
table	3-1,11-1	291	
(2 teaspoons)			61
Soap,			523
dishwashing			253
liquid		538	
Sugar solution	3-1		
Water,	1-1, 2-1 2-2, 4-2 5-1, 5-2 6-2, 7-1 7-2, 8-1 9-2, 10-1 11-1, 11-2	46, 126 150, 173 184, 257 291, 294 353	171, 227 253, 305 523
distilled		538	
fresh or ocean		319	
(1 glass)	21-1		
(1 pan)	20-1		

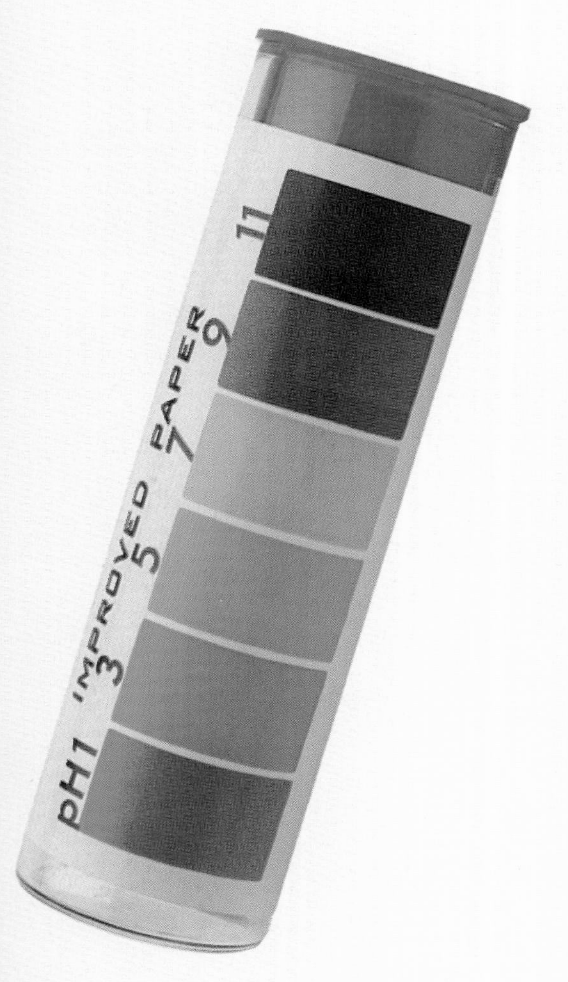

Preparation of Solutions

The following text gives some general hints on solution preparation and some safety tips to keep in mind.

For best results, the preparation of each solution is tailored to the requirements of the Activity, Mini-Lab, or Find Out activity in which it is used. Directions for preparing needed solutions are given in the margin of the *Teacher Wraparound Edition* adjacent to each activity. It is not recommended that solutions be made far in advance. Rather, they should be prepared fresh as needed.

Unless otherwise specified, solutions are prepared by adding the solid to a small amount of water and then diluting with water to the volume listed. Use distilled water for the preparation of solutions. For example, to make a 0.1*M* solution of aluminum sulfate, dissolve 34.2 g of $Al_2(SO_4)_3$ in a small amount of distilled water and dilute to a liter with water. If you use a hydrate that is different from the one specified in a particular preparation, you will need to adjust the amount of the hydrate to obtain the required concentration.

It is most important to use safe laboratory techniques when handling all chemicals. Many substances may appear harmless but are, in fact, toxic, corrosive, or very reactive. Always check the hazard information on the reagent bottle. If in doubt, check with the manufacturer or with Flinn Scientific Inc., (312) 879-6900. Chemicals should never be ingested. Be sure to use proper techniques to smell solutions or other reagents. Always wear safety goggles and an apron. The following general cautions should be used.

1. *Liquid and/or vapor poisonous/corrosive. Use in the fume hood.*
   acetic acid — hydrochloric acid
   ammonium hydroxide — nitric acid
2. *Poisonous and corrosive to eyes, lungs, and skin.*
   acids — limewater — iron(III) chloride
   bases — silver nitrate — potassium permanganate
   iodine
3. *Poisonous if swallowed, inhaled, or absorbed through the skin.*
   acetic acid, glacial — copper compounds
   barium chloride — lead compounds
   chromium compounds — lithium compounds
   cobalt(II) chloride — silver compounds
4. *Always add acids to water, never the reverse.*
5. *When sulfuric acid and sodium hydroxide are added to water, a large amount of thermal energy is released. Sodium metal reacts violently with water. Use extra care if handling any of these substances.*

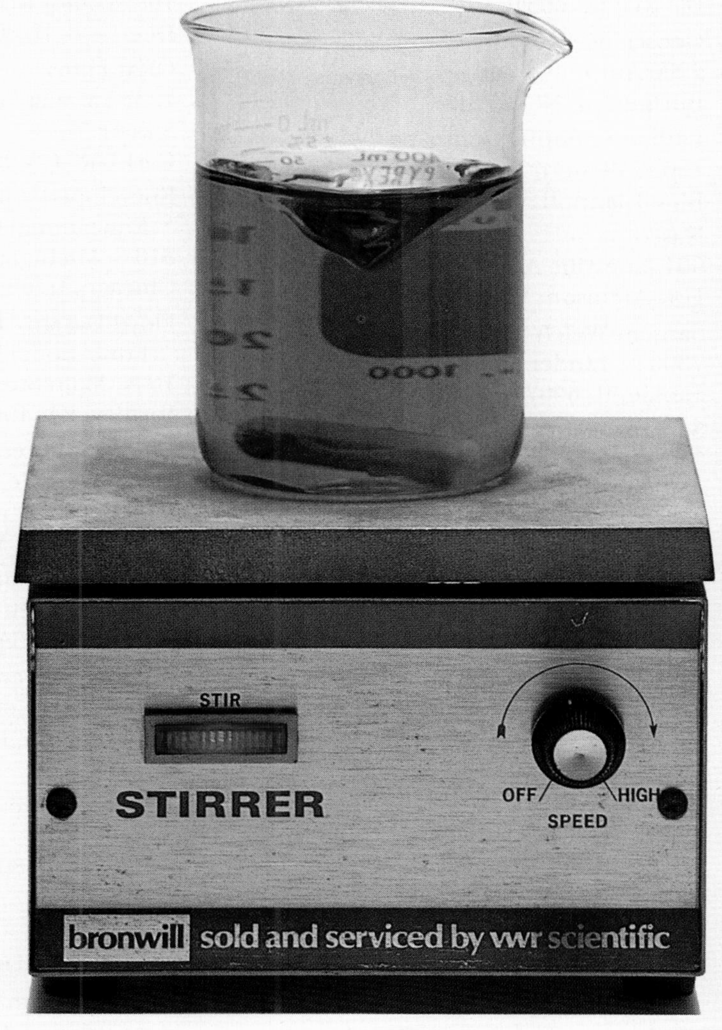

Supplier Addresses

EQUIPMENT SUPPLIERS

Central Scientific Company
11222 Melrose Avenue
Franklin Park, IL 60131

Fisher Scientific Company
4901 W. LeMoyne Avenue
Chicago, IL 60615

Flinn Scientific Inc.
P.O. Box 219
Batavia, IL 60510

Geoscience Resources
2990 Anthony Road
Burlington, NC 27215

LaPine Scientific Company
13636 Western Avenue
Blue Island, IL 60406-0780

Nasco
901 Janesville Avenue
Fort Atkinson, WI 53538

Sargent-Welch Scientific Co.
7300 N. Linder Avenue
Skokie, IL 60077

Sargent-Welch Scientific of Canada, Ltd.
285 Garyray Drive
Weston, Ontario,
Canada M9L 1P3

Science Kit and Boreal Labs
777 E. Park Drive
Tonawanda, NY 14150

Turtox/Cambosco
8200 S. Hoyne Avenue
Chicago, IL 60620

Ward's Natural Science Establishment, Inc.
5100 W. Henrietta Road
Rochester, NY 14692

AUDIOVISUAL DISTRIBUTORS

Aims Media
9710 Desoto Avenue
Chatsworth, CA 91311-4409

BFA Educational Media
468 Park Avenue S.
New York, NY 10016

Coronet/MTI Film and Video Distributors of LCA
108 Wilmot Road
Deerfield, IL 60015

CRM Films
2233 Faraday Avenue
Suite F
Carlsbad, CA 92008

Encyclopedia Britannica Educational Corp. (EBEC)
310 S. Michigan Avenue
Chicago, IL 60604

Floyd Design/Turner Educational Services
10 N. Main Street
Yardley, PA 19067

Health EduTech, Inc.
10800 Lyndale Avenue S.
Suite 200
Bloomington, MN 55420

Image Entertainment
9333 Oso Avenue
Chatsworth, CA 91311

Indiana University
Audiovisual Center
Bloomington, IN 47405-5901

Lumivision
1490 Lafayette
Suite 305
Denver, CO 80218

NASA
Code FAM
Washington, DC 20546

National Earth Science Teacher's Association (NESTA)
c/o Art Weinle
733 Loraine
Grosse Point, MI 48230

National Geographic Society
Educational Services
17th and "M" Streets, NW
Washington, DC 20036

National Weather Service (NOAA)
8060 13th Street
Silver Springs, MD 20910

Optical Data Corporation
30 Technology Drive
Warren, NJ 07059

PBS Video
1320 Braddock Place
Alexandria, VA 22314-1698

Pyramid Film & Video
Box 1048
Santa Monica, CA 90406

Science Software Systems
11890 W. Pico Blvd.
Los Angeles, CA 90064

Singer Media Corporation
3164 Tyler Avenue
Anaheim, CA 92801

Society for Visual Education Inc. (SVE)
Dept. VM
1345 Diversey Parkway
Chicago, IL 60614-1299

Sterling Educational Films, Inc.
241 E. 34th Street
New York, NY 10016

Time-Life Videos
Time and Life Building
1271 Avenue of the Americas
New York, NY 10020

Universal Education & Visual Arts (UEVA)
100 Universal City Plaza
Universal City, CA 91608

US Army Corps of Engineers
1000 Independence Avenue, SW
Washington, DC 20314

US Bureau of Mines
Cochrans Mill Road
P.O. Box 18070
Pittsburgh, PA 15236
Attn: Film

US Geological Survey (USGS)
National Center
Reston, VA 22092

The Voyager Company
1351 Pacific Coast Highway
Santa Monica, CA 90401

SOFTWARE DISTRIBUTORS

American Peripherals
122 Bangor Street
Lindenhurst, NY 11757

Aquarius Instructional
P.O. Box 128
Indian Rocks Beach, FL 34635

Cambridge Development Lab (CDL)
1696 Massachusetts Avenue
Cambridge, MA 02138

(Classroom Consortia Media Inc.)
Gemstar
P.O. Box 050228
Staten Island, NY 10305

COMPress
P.O. Box 102
Wentworth, NH 03282

Datatech Software Systems
19312 E. Eldorado Drive
Aurora, CO 80013

Earthware Computer Services
P.O. Box 30039
Eugene, OR 97403

Educational Courseware
3 Nappa Lane
Westport, CT 06880

Educational Materials and Equipment Company (EME)
P.O. Box 2805
Danbury, CT 06813-2805

Focus Media, Inc.
839 Stewart Avenue
P.O. Box 865
Garden City, NY 11530

D.C. Heath and Company
2700 Richardt Avenue
Indianapolis, IN 46219

Human Relations Media (HRM)
175 Tompkins Avenue
Pleasantville, NY 10570

IBM Educational Systems
Department PC
4111 Northside Parkway
Atlanta, GA 30327

McGraw-Hill Webster Division
1221 Avenue of the Americas
New York, NY 10020

Micro-ED, Inc.
P.O. Box 24750
Edina, MN 55424

Micro Learningware
Route No. 1
Box 162
Amboy, MN 56010-9762

Minnesota Educational Computing Corporation (MECC)
3490 Lexington Avenue N.
Saint Paul, MN 55126

Queue, Inc.
562 Boston Avenue
Bridgeport, CT 06610

Rand McNally
8255 N. Central Park Avenue
Skokie, IL 60076

Soft-Kat Inc.
20630 Nordhoff Street
Chatsworth, CA 91311

Sunburst Communications
39 Washington Avenue
Pleasantville, NY 10570

Sunshine Computer Software
1101 Post Oak Blvd.
Suite 9-493
Houston, TX 77056

Teach Yourself by Computer Software
349 W. Commercial
Suite 1000
East Rochester, NY 14445

Texas Instruments, Data Systems Group
P.O. Box 1444
Houston, TX 77251

John Wiley and Sons, Inc.
1 Wiley Drive
Somerset, NJ 08875

Photo Credits

4T, Brent Turner/BLT Productions; 5T ©Ken Frick; 7T, 8T, Doug Martin; 9T, Tim Courlas; 10T, ©Ken Frick; 11T, Cobalt Productions; 12T, file photo; 14T, Les Losego/Crown Studios; 15T Doug Martin; 18T, Les Losego/Crown Studios; 19T-21T, ©Ken Frick; 22T, LloydLemmermann; 25T, ©Ken Frick; 27T, Ted Rice; 32T, 35T, Les Losego/Crown Studios; 36T, file photo; 37T, 38T, Doug Martin; 39T, ©Ken Frick; 40T-41T, 42T, Doug Martin; 43T, Les Losego/Crown Studios.

We want your opinions!

We at Merrill Publishing feel that with this edition of ***Merrill Earth Science***, we have produced a quality textbook program—but the final proof of that rests with you, the teachers who have had the opportunity to put our materials to use in your classrooms. That's why we would appreciate it if you would take the time to respond to any part of this questionnaire that is appropriate for you. In doing so, you will be letting us know how good a job we've done and where we can work to improve.

Please note: (1) you need not have used all of the program components to respond to this questionnaire; and (2) we encourage you to give us your honest and most candid opinions.

Excellent				Poor	Student Text
5	4	3	2	1	Organization
5	4	3	2	1	Narrative style
5	4	3	2	1	Readability
5	4	3	2	1	Visual impact
5	4	3	2	1	Usable Table of Contents
5	4	3	2	1	Accuracy of content
5	4	3	2	1	Coverage of science principles
5	4	3	2	1	Reduced number of bold-face terms
5	4	3	2	1	Skill builder questions
5	4	3	2	1	Skill Handbook
5	4	3	2	1	Mini Labs Activities
5	4	3	2	1	Problem Solving features
5	4	3	2	1	Technology features
5	4	3	2	1	Science & Society Sections
5	4	3	2	1	Glossary and Index
5	4	3	2	1	Appendices
5	4	3	2	1	Global Connections features
5	4	3	2	1	Unit End features

Excellent				Poor	Teacher Edition
5	4	3	2	1	Teachability
5	4	3	2	1	Planning charts
5	4	3	2	1	Organization of teaching cycle
5	4	3	2	1	Performance objectives
					Supplements
5	4	3	2	1	Teacher Resource Package
5	4	3	2	1	Laboratory Manual
5	4	3	2	1	Color Transparency Package
5	4	3	2	1	Test Bank
5	4	3	2	1	Chapter Review Software

Comments (general or specific):

Please feel free to include additional comments on a separate sheet.

School Information

1. What is the grade level of the students you teach? 6 7 8 9
2. Total number of students in that grade? 1-50 51-100 101-200 200+
3. Average class size? 25 or less 26-30 31-40 41 or more
4. Total school enrollment? 1-200 201-500 501-1000 1000+
5. Ability level of your average class? Basic Average Advanced
6. How appropriate is this text for your class? Too easy On level Too difficult
7. How many years have you used this text? 1 2 3 4 5
8. What text were you using *before* adopting this program? (Title/publisher/copyright year)

Fold

Please feel free to include additional comments on a separate sheet.

Name ______________________ Date ______________

School ______________________________________

Street ______________________________________

City ______________________ State __________ Zip __________

Fold

NO POSTAGE
NECESSARY
IF MAILED
IN THE
UNITED STATES

BUSINESS REPLY MAIL

FIRST CLASS PERMIT NO 284 COLUMBUS OHIO

POSTAGE WILL BE PAID BY ADDRESSEE

GLENCOE

SCIENCE PRODUCT MANAGER

PO BOX 508

COLUMBUS OHIO 43272-6174

M E R R I L L

EARTH SCIENCE

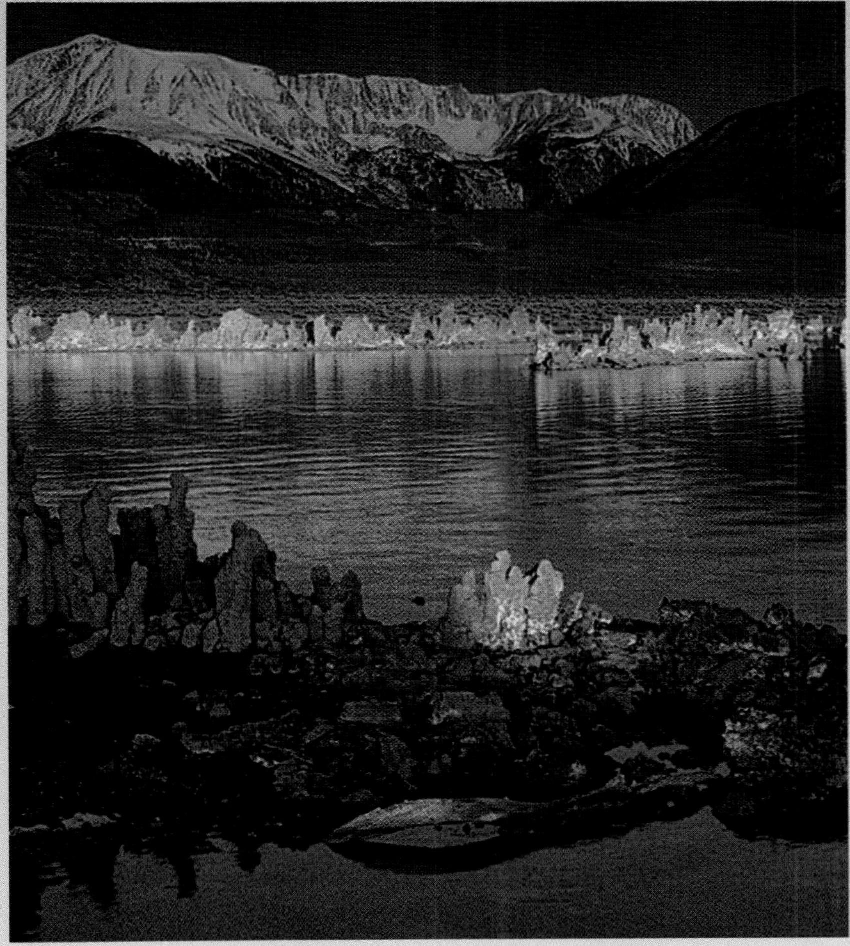

GLENCOE

Macmillan/McGraw-Hill

New York, New York Columbus, Ohio Mission Hills, California Peoria, Illinois

A GLENCOE PROGRAM

MERRILL EARTH SCIENCE

Student Edition
Teacher Wraparound Edition
Teacher Resource Package
Study Guide, Student Edition
Reinforcement, Student Edition
Enrichment, Student Edition
Transparency Package
Laboratory Manual
Laboratory Manual, Teacher Annotated Edition
Spanish Resources
Chapter Review Software
Computer Test Bank
Videodisc Correlation

REVIEWERS

Marilyn W. Miles
Nowlin Middle School
Independence, Missouri

Ellis Eugene Underkoffler
1989 Recipient, Presidential Award for Excellence in Science and Math Teaching
Talley Junior High School
Wilmington, Delaware

Jeffery W. Tolhurst
1989 Recipient, Outstanding Earth-Science Teacher Award
San Benito High School
Hollister, California

Larry G. Friedrichs
1989 Recipient, Presidential Award for Excellence in Science and Math Teaching
Palmer High School
Colorado Springs, Colorado

David M. Barlow
1989 Recipient, Outstanding Earth-Science Teacher Award
Mooresville High School
Mooresville, North Carolina

Susan Tarwick Roberts
Wirt County High School
Elizabeth, West Virginia

Edward Wayne Gordon, Jr.
President, Science Teachers Association of Texas
San Antonio, Texas

Priscilla Jane Lee
Venice High School
Los Angeles, California

John A. Fradiska, Jr.
Gov. Thomas Johnson Middle School
Frederick, Maryland

Tracy Day
Nevis School
Nevis, Minnesota

James Michael Henry
Kazen Middle School
San Antonio, Texas

Joyce Rowland Johnson
Miller Intermediate School
Pasadena, Texas

Michael Scott Goodrich
Lake Oswega High School
Lake Oswega, Oregon

Cover Photograph: Mount Dana at dawn over Mono Lake by Galen Rowell

Send all inquiries to:
GLENCOE DIVISION
Macmillan/McGraw-Hill
936 Eastwind Drive
Westerville, OH 43081

ISBN 0-675-16744-2

Printed in the United States of America.

4 5 6 7 8 9-RRD-W-99 98 97 96 95 94 93

AUTHORS

Ralph M. Feather, Jr. is a teacher of geology, astronomy, and earth science, and serves as Science Department Chair in the Derry Area School District in Derry, PA. He holds a B.S. in Geology and a M.Ed in Geoscience from the Indiana University of Pennsylvania, and is currently working on his Ph.D. at the University of Pittsburgh. Mr. Feather has more than 20 years of teaching experience in secondary science and has supervised student teachers for over 15 years. He is a past recipient of the Outstanding Earth Science Teacher Award from the National Association of Geology Teachers and the Keivin Burns Citation from the Spectroscopy Society of Pittsburgh. In 1989, Mr. Feather was nominated for Excellence in Science Teaching. He is also a member of the Geological Society of America, the National Science Teachers Association, the American Association for the Advancement of Science, and the Association for Supervision and Curriculum Development.

Susan Leach Snyder is a teacher of earth science at Jones Middle School, Upper Arlington School District, Columbus, Ohio. She serves on the Board of Trustees of North American Astrophysical Observatory and has served on the Boards of Directors for state and national science organizations. Ms. Snyder received a B.S. in Comprehensive Science from Miami University, Oxford, Ohio, and an M.S. in Entomology from the University of Hawaii. She has 18 years of teaching experience and is author of various educational materials. Ms. Snyder, in addition to receiving Exemplary Earth Science and Career Awareness in Science Teaching Team awards from NSTA, was the 1987 Ohio Teacher of the Year, and one of four finalists for the 1987 National Teacher of the Year.

Dale T. Hesser currently serves as the Assistant Superintendent of Schools in North Syracuse, New York. A past recipient of the Outstanding Earth Science Teacher award from the National Association of Geology Teachers, Mr. Hesser received his B.S. in earth science from Buffalo State College, New York, and holds an M.S. and Certificate of Advanced Studies in Science Education from Syracuse University. He has over 20 years of classroom teaching experience in the earth sciences ranging from junior/senior high school through college astronomy, and numerous pre-service and in-service teacher training institutes. Mr. Hesser currently serves as an adjunct instructor for Syracuse University in Earth Science Teaching.

CONSULTANTS

Dr. Gerald H. Newsom
Professor of Astronomy
The Ohio State University
Columbus, Ohio

Dr. Robert C. Howe
Professor of Geology
Indiana State University
Terre Haute, Indiana

Dr. James B. Phipps
Professor of Geology and Oceanography
Grays Harbor College
Aberdeen, Washington

Dr. Allan A. Ekdale
Professor of Geology
University of Utah
Salt Lake City, Utah

Eric Danielson
Associate Professor of Meteorology
Hartford College for Women
Hartford, Connecticut

Dr. George Moore
Professor Emeritus, Geology
The Ohio State University
Columbus, Ohio

Reading:
Barbara Pettegrew, Ph.D.
Director of Reading/Study Center
Assistant Professor of Education
Otterbein College
Westerville, Ohio

Safety
Robert Tatz, Ph.D.
Instructional Lab Supervisor
Department of Chemistry
The Ohio State University
Columbus, Ohio

Special Features:
Stephen C. Blume
St. Tammany Pubic School System
Slidell, Louisiana

Gifted and Mainstreamed:
Barbara Murdock
Elementary Consultant For Instruction
Gahanna - Jefferson Public Schools
Gahanna, Ohio

Judy Ratzenberger
Middle School Science Instructor
Gahanna Middle School West
Gahanna, Ohio

CONTENTS

IV

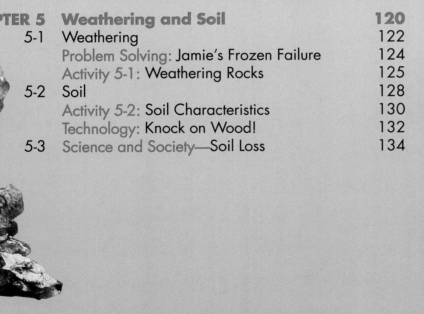

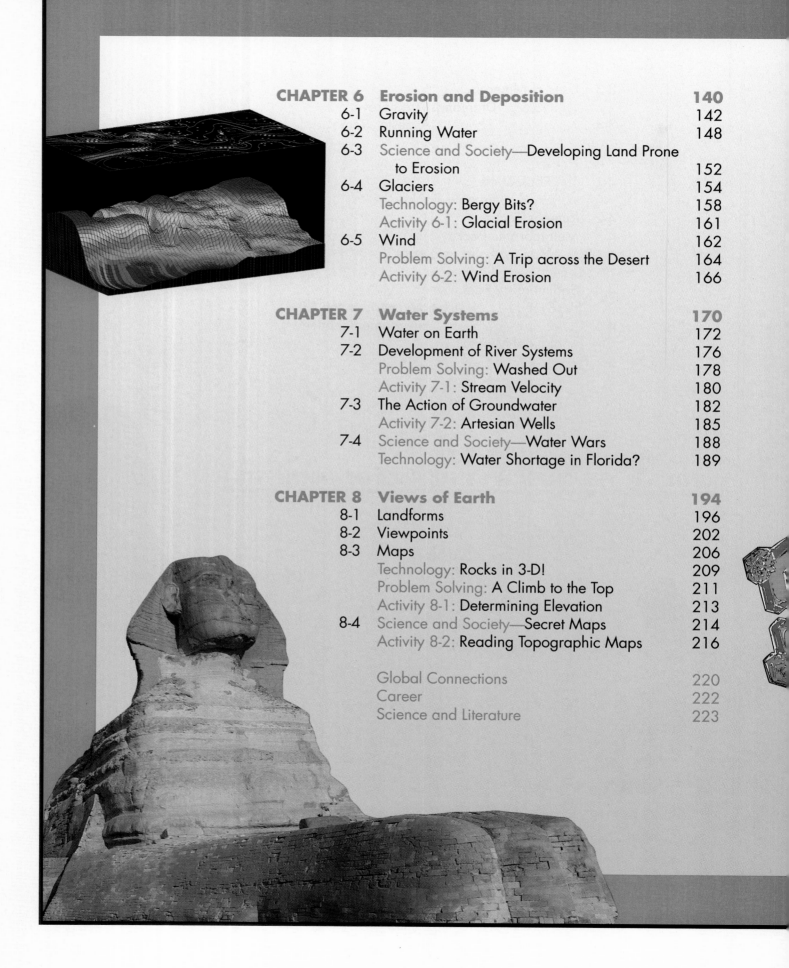

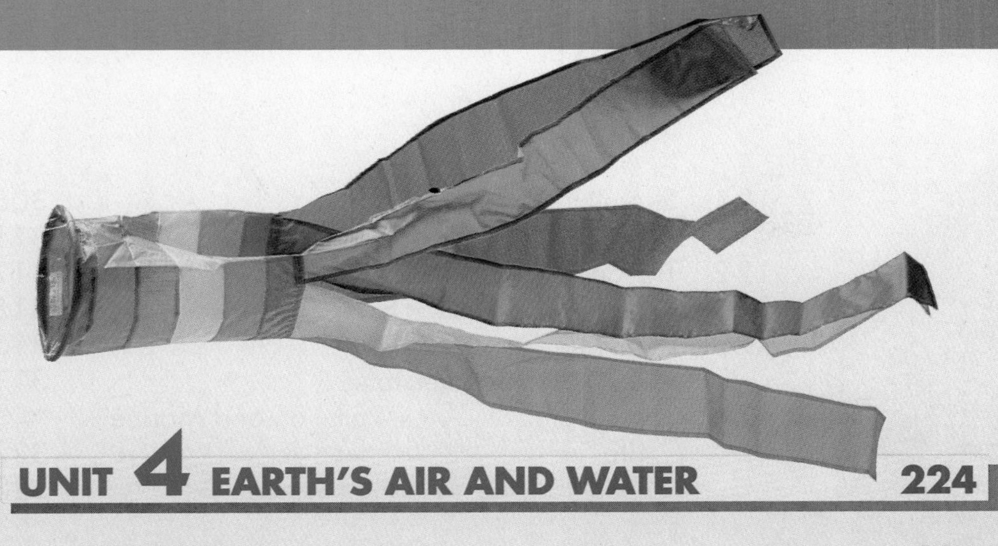

UNIT 4 EARTH'S AIR AND WATER 224

VII

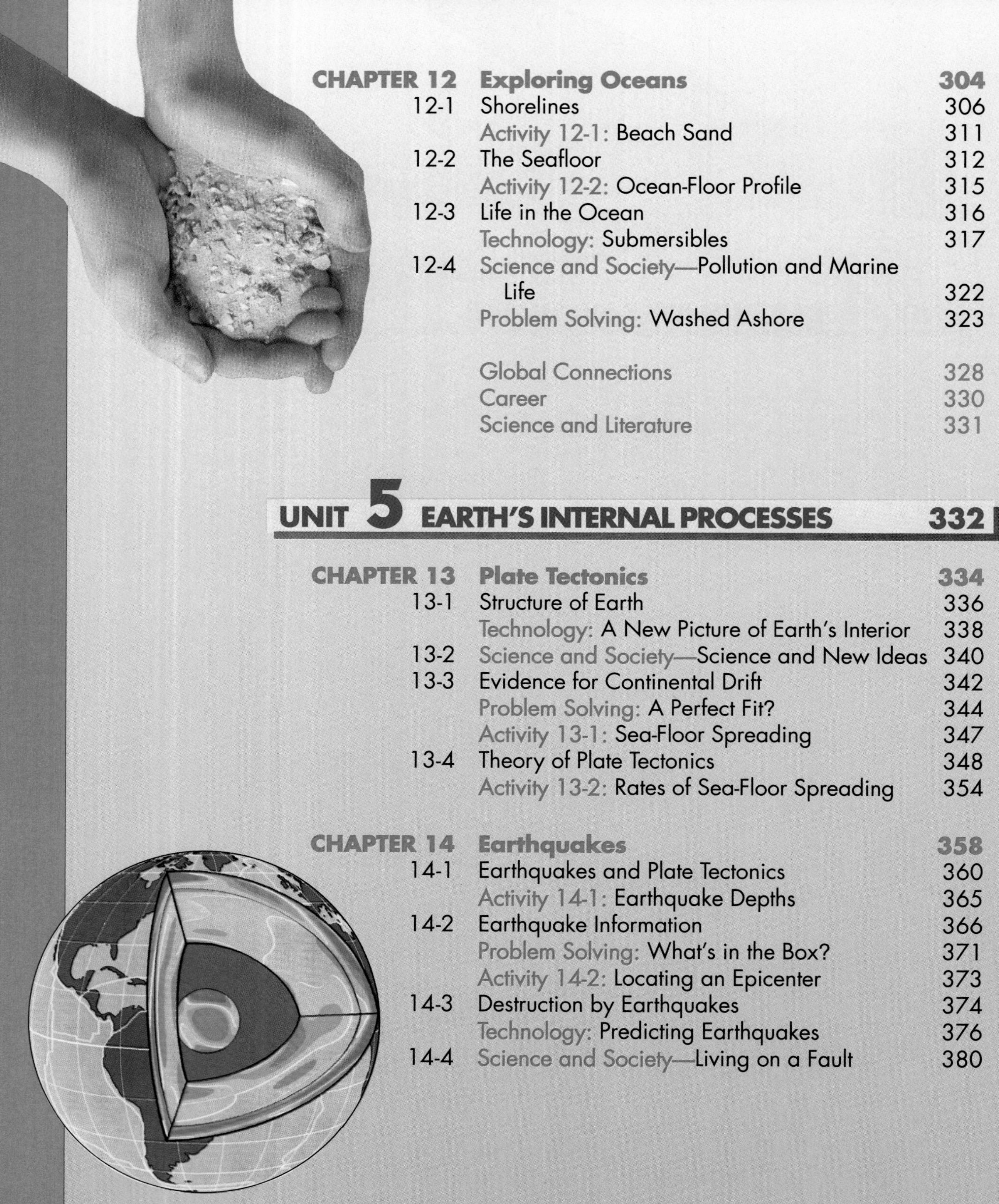

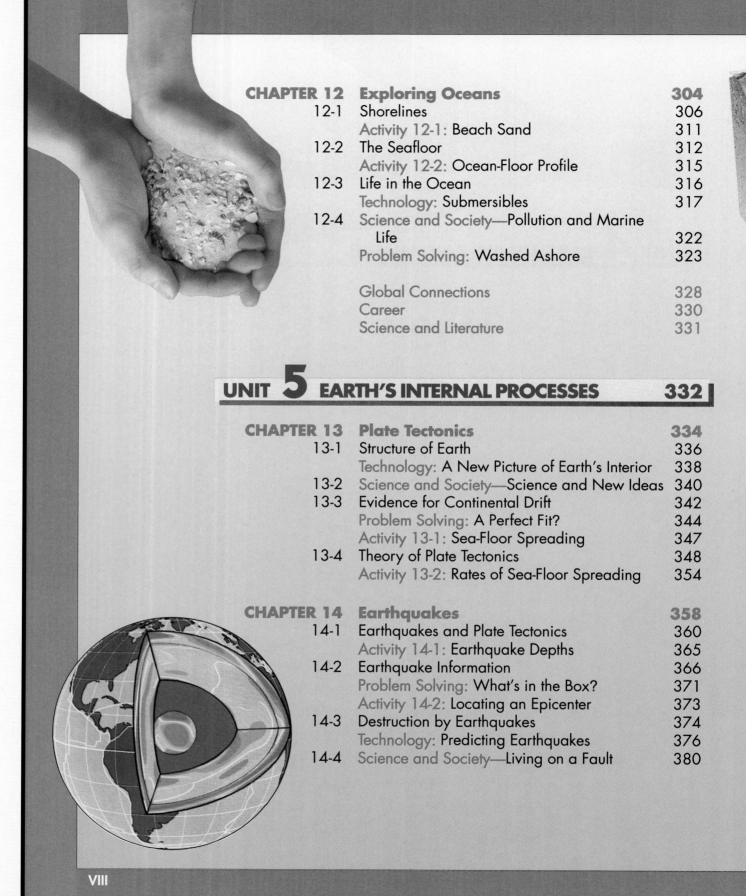

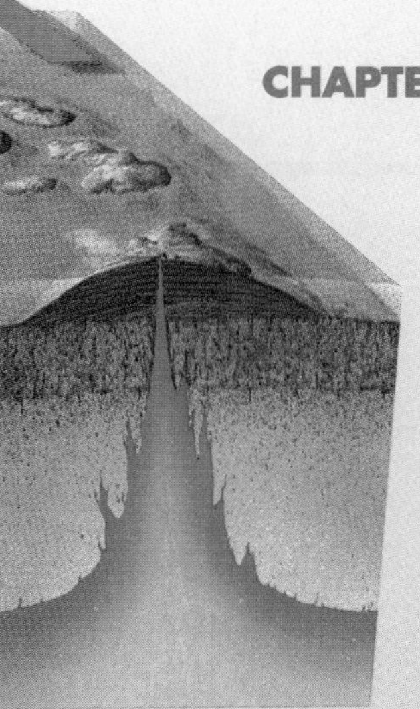

IX

UNIT 7 EARTH'S RESOURCES 476

UNIT 8 ASTRONOMY 548

XI

ACTIVITIES

XIII

MINI-Labs

XIV

PROBLEM SOLVING

TECHNOLOGY

SKILL BUILDERS

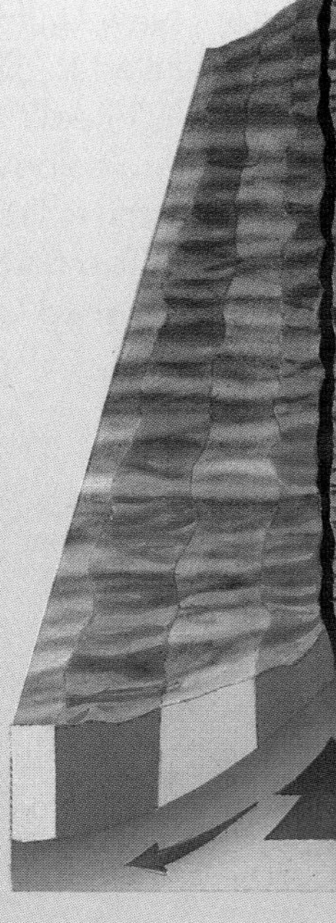

XVI

GLOBAL CONNECTIONS

CAREERS

SCIENCE AND LITERATURE/ART

XVII

USING MERRILL EARTH SCIENCE

Earth Science is a subject you're familiar with because your every activity depends on the natural environment around you. The types of clothes you wear depend on the weather and every item you buy is produced from natural resources. Your link to Earth and its environment is an important one. How you view your world is determined by your understanding of how it works. **Merrill Earth Science** will help you understand the many natural processes occurring around you. And once you've learned about your own planet, you'll explore other worlds and objects in the universe. As you read this text, you'll discover much about your natural environment and how you can help preserve it for your future.

a quick tour of your textbook

What's happening here? Why have we built a model of planet Earth? Each unit begins with thought-provoking photographs that will make you wonder. The unit introduction then explains what is happening in the photographs and how the two relate to each other and to the content of the unit. Why is this model of Earth important to your future? Read the opener to Unit 7 to find out.

UNIT 7 EARTH'S RESOURCES

What's Happening Here?

Could you build a scale model of Earth? Biosphere II, located near Oracle, Arizona, is a glass-enclosed structure covering 10 000 m^2 of land. It encases a human habitat and five connected biomes. Teams of humans, living in Biosphere II, conduct research on bio-farming and recycling techniques. Biosphere II is shown in the larger photograph. Biosphere I, Earth, is shown in the smaller photograph below. As you study the chapters in this unit, you'll learn about some of the environmental problems that we face and what you can do to help save Biosphere I.

UNIT CONTENTS

Chapter 18 Energy
Chapter 19 You and the Environment
Chapter 20 You, Air, and Water

476 477

XVIII

It's clearly organized to get you started and keep you going.

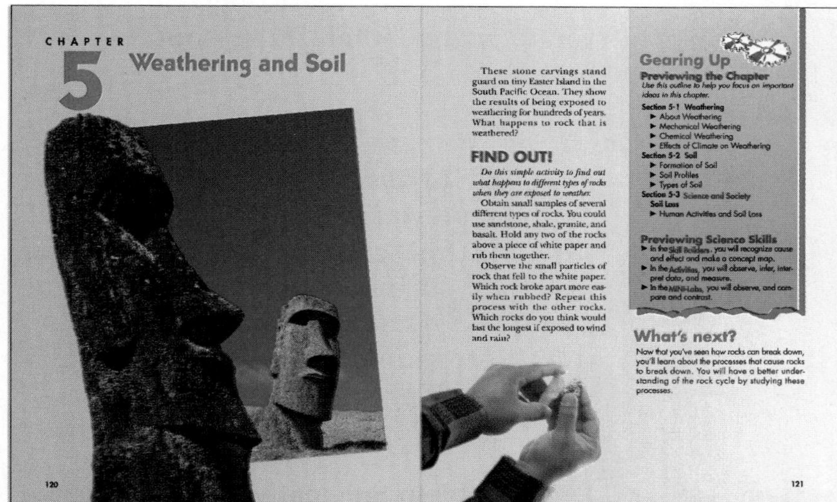

CHAPTER

5 Weathering and Soil

These stone carvings stand guard on tiny Easter Island in the South Pacific Ocean. They show the results of being exposed to weathering for hundreds of years. What happens to rock that is weathered?

FIND OUT!

Do this simple activity to find out what happens to different types of rocks when they are exposed to weather.

Obtain small samples of several different types of rocks. You could use sandstone, shale, granite, and basalt. Hold any two of the rocks above a piece of white paper and rub them together.

Observe the small particles of rock that fell to the white paper. Which rock broke apart more easily when rubbed? Repeat this process with the other rocks. Which rocks do you think would last the longest if exposed to wind and rain?

Gearing Up

Previewing the Chapter

Use this outline to help you focus on important ideas in this chapter.

Section 5-1 Weathering
- About Weathering
- Mechanical Weathering
- Chemical Weathering
- Effects of Climate on Weathering

Section 5-2 Soil
- Formation of Soil
- Soil Profiles
- Types of Soil

Section 5-3 Science and Society
Soil Loss
- Human Activities and Soil Loss

Previewing Science Skills
- In the Skill Builders, you will recognize cause and effect and make a concept map.
- In the Activities, you will observe, infer, interpret data, and measure.
- In the MINI-Labs, you will observe, and compare and contrast.

What's next?

Now that you've seen how rocks can break down, you'll learn about the processes that cause rocks to break down. You will have a better understanding of the rock cycle by studying these processes.

120 121

As you begin each new chapter, use the **Gearing Up** to preview what topics are covered and how they are organized. You will also preview the skills you will use in this chapter.

After you've performed the **FIND OUT** activity and previewed the chapter, you're ready to further explore the topics ahead. Read **What's Next** to see what's ahead.

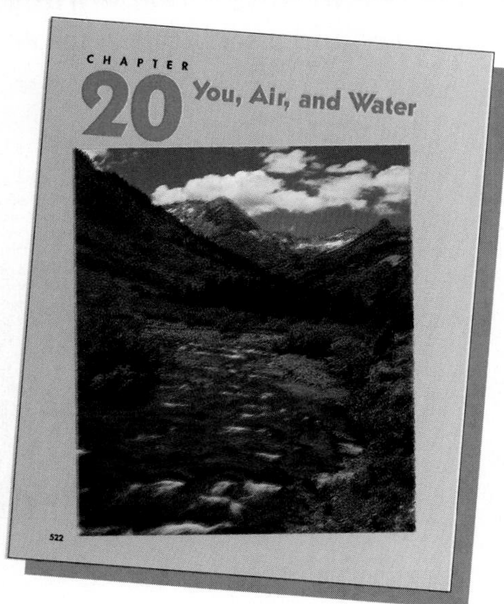

CHAPTER

20 You, Air, and Water

522

Chapters are organized into three to five numbered sections. The **Objectives** at the beginning of the numbered section tell you what major topics you'll be covering and what you should expect to learn about them. The **New Science Words** are also listed in the order in which they appear in the section.

XIX

Experience science by observing, experimenting, and asking questions.

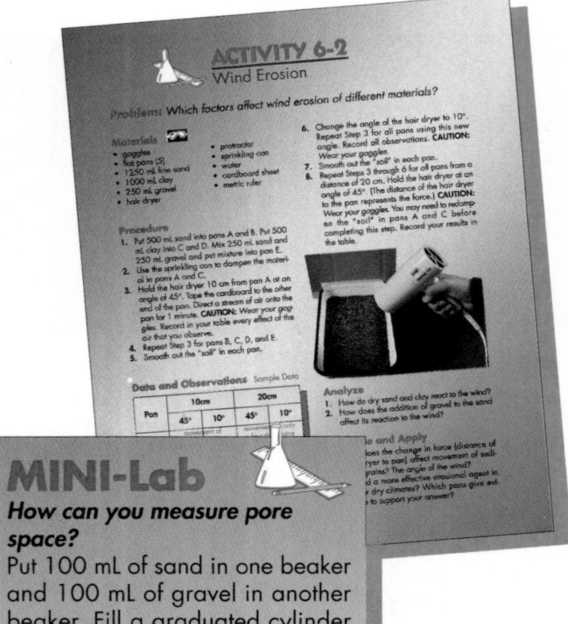

ACTIVITY 6-2
Wind Erosion

Problem: Which factors affect wind erosion of different materials?

Materials
- goggles
- flat pans (5)
- 1250 mL fine sand
- 1000 mL clay
- 250 mL gravel
- hair dryer
- protractor
- sprinkling can
- water
- cardboard sheet
- metric ruler

Procedure
1. Put 500 mL sand into pans A and B. Put 500 mL clay into C and D. Mix 250 mL sand and 250 mL gravel and put mixture into pan E.
2. Use the sprinkling can to dampen the material in pans A and C.
3. Hold the hair dryer 10 cm from pan A at an angle of 45°. Tape the cardboard to the other end of the pan. Direct a stream of air onto the pan for 1 minute. **CAUTION:** Wear your goggles. Record in your table every effect of the air that you observe.
4. Repeat Step 3 for pans B, C, D, and E.
5. Smooth out the "soil" in each pan.
6. Change the angle of the hair dryer to 10°. Repeat Step 3 for all pans using this new angle. Record all observations. **CAUTION:** Wear your goggles.
7. Smooth out the "soil" in each pan.
8. Repeat Steps 3 through 6 for all pans from a distance of 20 cm. Hold the hair dryer at an angle of 45°. (The distance of the hair dryer to the pan represents the force.) **CAUTION:** Wear your goggles. You may need to redampen the "soil" in pans A and C before completing this step. Record your results in the table.

Data and Observations Sample Data

Pan	10cm		20cm	
	45°	10°	45°	10°

Analyze
1. How do dry sand and clay react to the wind?
2. How does the addition of gravel to the sand affect its reaction to the wind?

MINI-Lab

How can you measure pore space?

Put 100 mL of sand in one beaker and 100 mL of gravel in another beaker. Fill a graduated cylinder with 100 mL of water. Pour the water slowly into the gravel and stop when the water just covers the top of the gravel. Record the volume of water used. Repeat the procedure with the sand. Which substance has more pore space—gravel or sand? Why?

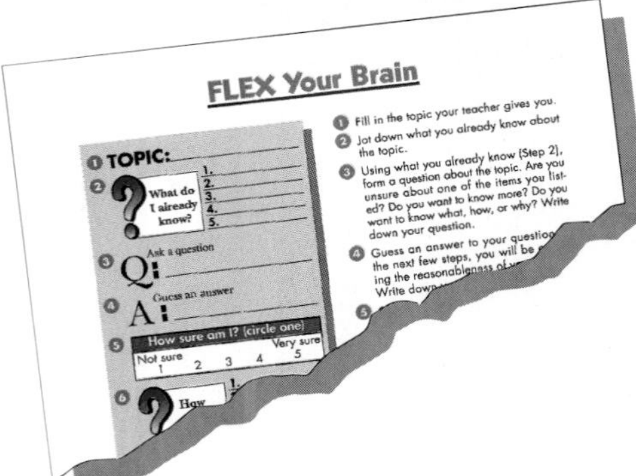

FLEX Your Brain

TOPIC:
What do I already know?
Q:
A:
How sure am I? (circle one)
Not sure 1 2 3 4 5 Very sure

1. Fill in the topic your teacher gives you.
2. Jot down what you already know about the topic.
3. Using what you already know (Step 2), form a question about the topic. Are you unsure about one of the items you listed? Do you want to know more? Do you want to know what, how, or why? Write down your question.

Flex Your Brain is a unique activity you can use to sharpen your critical thinking skills. Starting from what you already know about a science topic, you will apply a simple ten-step procedure to extend your knowledge about the topic from a perspective that interests you.

Science is more than words in a book. The two Activities and the MINI-Labs in each chapter give you the chance to further explore and investigate the science topics covered in your textbook.

In the **Activities,** you'll use household items and laboratory equipment as you follow the easy, step-by-step procedure. At the end of each Activity are questions that ask you to analyze what you've done.

Most **MINI-Labs** are designed so you can do them on your own or with friends outside of the science classroom using materials you find around the house. Doing a MINI-Lab is an easy and fun way to further your knowledge about the topics you're studying.

Each **Problem Solving** feature gives you a chance to solve a real world problem or understand a science principle.

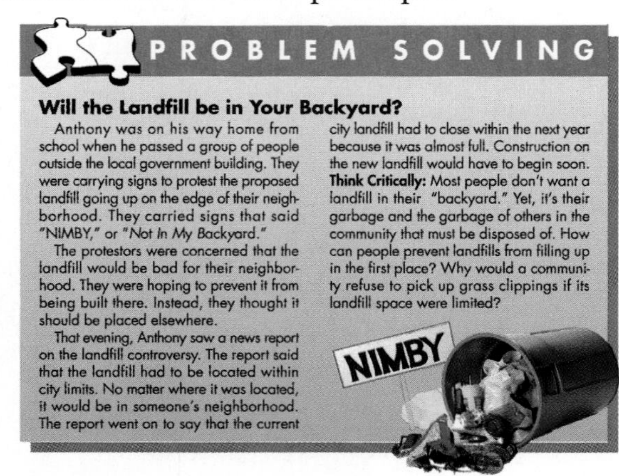

PROBLEM SOLVING

Will the Landfill be in Your Backyard?

Anthony was on his way home from school when he passed a group of people outside the local government building. They were carrying signs to protest the proposed landfill going up on the edge of their neighborhood. They carried signs that said "NIMBY," or "*Not In My Backyard.*"

The protestors were concerned that the landfill would be bad for their neighborhood. They were hoping to prevent it from being built there. Instead, they thought it should be placed elsewhere.

That evening, Anthony saw a news report on the landfill controversy. The report said that the landfill had to be located within city limits. No matter where it was located, it would be in someone's neighborhood. The report went on to say that the current city landfill had to close within the next year because it was almost full. Construction on the new landfill would have to begin soon.

Think Critically: Most people don't want a landfill in their "backyard." Yet, it's their garbage and the garbage of others in the community that must be disposed of. How can people prevent landfills from filling up in the first place? Why would a community refuse to pick up grass clippings if its landfill space were limited?

XX

Explore news-making issues, concerns about the environment, and how science shapes your world through technology.

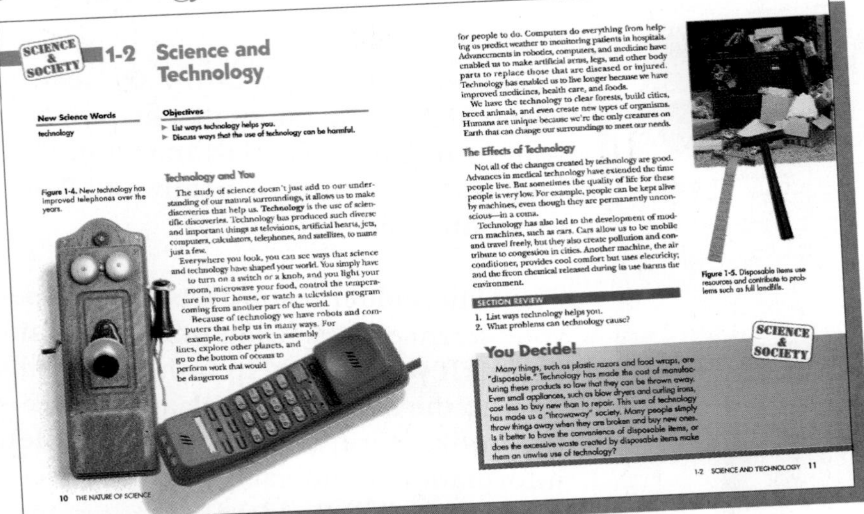

SCIENCE & SOCIETY **1-2 Science and Technology**

New Science Words

technology

Objectives

- List ways technology helps you.
- Discuss ways that the use of technology can be harmful.

Technology and You

The study of science doesn't just add to our understanding of our natural surroundings, it allows us to make discoveries that help us. **Technology** is the use of scientific discoveries. Technology has produced such diverse and important things as televisions, artificial hearts, jets, computers, calculators, telephones, and satellites, to name just a few.

Everywhere you look, you can see ways that science and technology have shaped your world. You simply have to turn on a switch or a knob, and you light your room, microwave your food, control the temperature in your house, or watch a television program coming from another part of the world.

Because of technology we have robots and computers that help us in many ways. For example, robots work in assembly lines, explore other planets, and go to the bottom of oceans to perform work that would be dangerous for people to do. Computers do everything from helping us predict weather to monitoring patients in hospitals. Advancements in robotics, computers, and medicine have enabled us to make artificial arms, legs, and other body parts to replace those that are diseased or injured. Technology has enabled us to live longer because we have improved medicines, health care, and foods.

We have the technology to clear forests, build cities, breed animals, and even create new types of organisms. Humans are unique because we're the only creatures on Earth that can change our surroundings to meet our needs.

Figure 1-4. New technology has improved telephones over the years.

The Effects of Technology

Not all of the changes created by technology are good. Advances in medical technology have extended the time people live. But sometimes the quality of life for these people is very low. For example, people can be kept alive by machines, even though they are permanently unconscious—in a coma.

Technology has also led to the development of modern machines, such as cars. Cars allow us to be mobile and travel freely, but they also create pollution and contribute to congestion in cities. Another machine, the air conditioner, provides cool comfort but uses electricity, and the freon chemical released during its use harms the environment.

Figure 1-5. Disposable items use resources and contribute to problems such as full landfills.

SECTION REVIEW

1. List ways technology helps you.
2. What problems can technology cause?

You Decide!

Many things, such as plastic razors and food wraps, are "disposable." Technology has made the cost of manufacturing these products so low that they can be thrown away. Even small appliances, such as blow dryers and curling irons, cost less to buy new than to repair. This use of technology has made us a "throwaway" society. Many people simply throw things away when they are broken and buy new ones. Is it better to have the convenience of disposable items, or does the excessive waste created by disposable items make them an unwise use of technology?

SCIENCE & SOCIETY

10 THE NATURE OF SCIENCE

1-2 SCIENCE AND TECHNOLOGY 11

The impact of science on society directly affects you. In the **Science and Society** section in each chapter, you'll learn about an issue that's affecting the world around you. The topics you'll read about are controversial, and you'll explore them from several sides. Then, you'll have a chance to express your opinion in the You Decide feature that follows.

In the **Technology** feature in each chapter, you'll read about recent discoveries, newly developed instruments, and applications of technology that have shaped our world and furthered our knowledge.

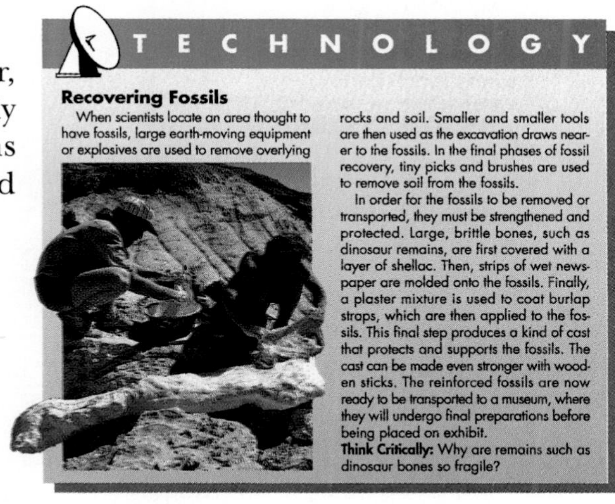

TECHNOLOGY

Recovering Fossils

When scientists locate an area thought to have fossils, large earth-moving equipment or explosives are used to remove overlying rocks and soil. Smaller and smaller tools are then used as the excavation draws nearer to the fossils. In the final phases of fossil recovery, tiny picks and brushes are used to remove soil from the fossils.

In order for the fossils to be removed or transported, they must be strengthened and protected. Large, brittle bones, such as dinosaur remains, are first covered with a layer of shellac. Then, strips of wet newspaper are molded onto the fossils. Finally, a plaster mixture is used to coat burlap straps, which are then applied to the fossils. This final step produces a kind of cast that protects and supports the fossils. The cast can be made even stronger with wooden sticks. The reinforced fossils are now ready to be transported to a museum, where they will undergo final preparations before being placed on exhibit.

Think Critically: Why are remains such as dinosaur bones so fragile?

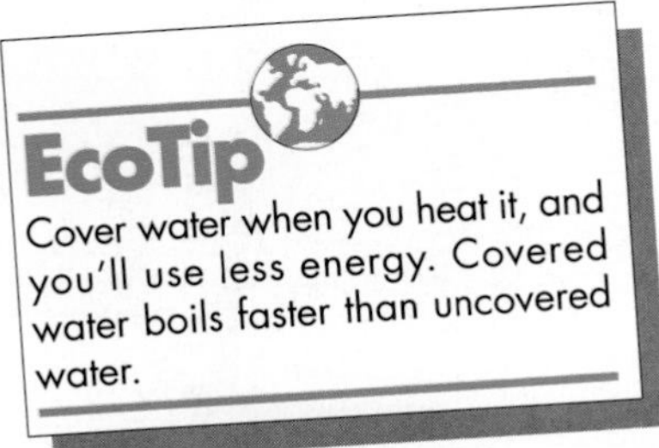

EcoTip

Cover water when you heat it, and you'll use less energy. Covered water boils faster than uncovered water.

Each **EcoTip** suggests a simple step you can take to help improve the environment. EcoTips explain how you can get involved in making Earth a better place to live.

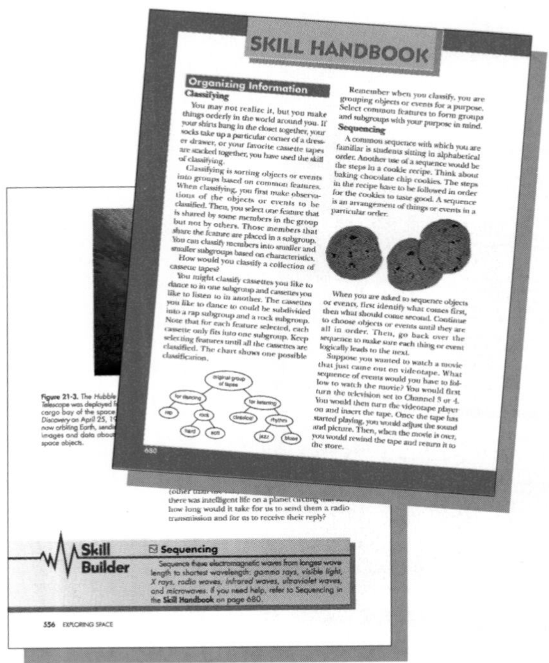

Discover that you can apply what you've learned as you answer questions and practice your science skills.

At the end of each section are several Section Review questions that help you test your knowledge. The last question challenges you to think critically and **Apply** what you've learned.

The **Skill Builder** feature lets you sharpen your science skills using only paper and pencil. If you need help with these skills, refer to the **Skill Handbook** at the back of the book. Here, you can find complete information about each type of skill covered in the Skill Builders

Science and MATH

Earth is about 150 000 000 km from the sun. The radiation coming from the sun travels at 300 000 km/second. About how long does it take for the radiation leaving the sun to reach Earth?

Science is related to every other subject you study. The **Science And** features challenge you to solve math problems, read literature excerpts, and to write about topics you're studying as you make the connections between science and other disciplines.

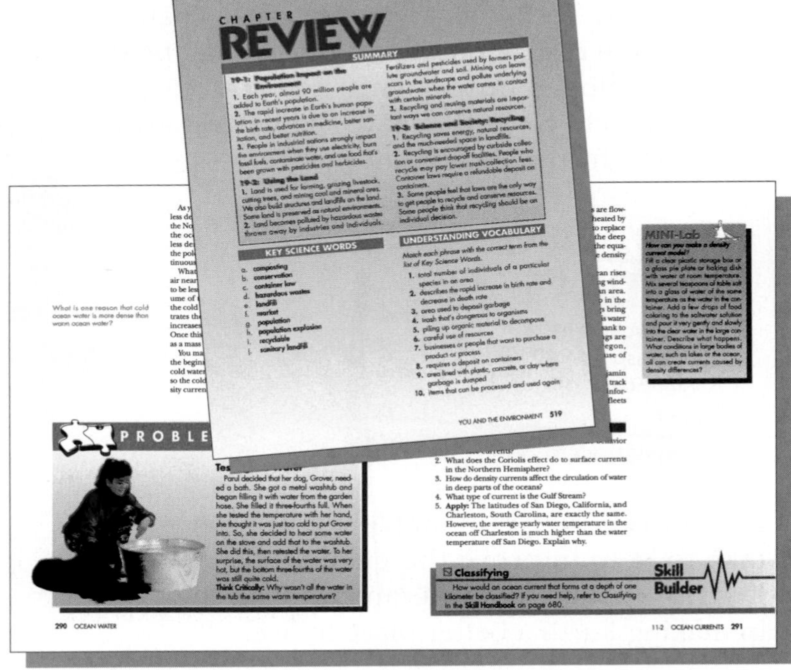

The **Chapter Review** starts with a summary so you can review the major concepts from each section. Then, you'll apply your knowledge and practice thinking skills as you answer the questions that follow.

XXII

Discover how earth science topics relate to people and places all over the world.

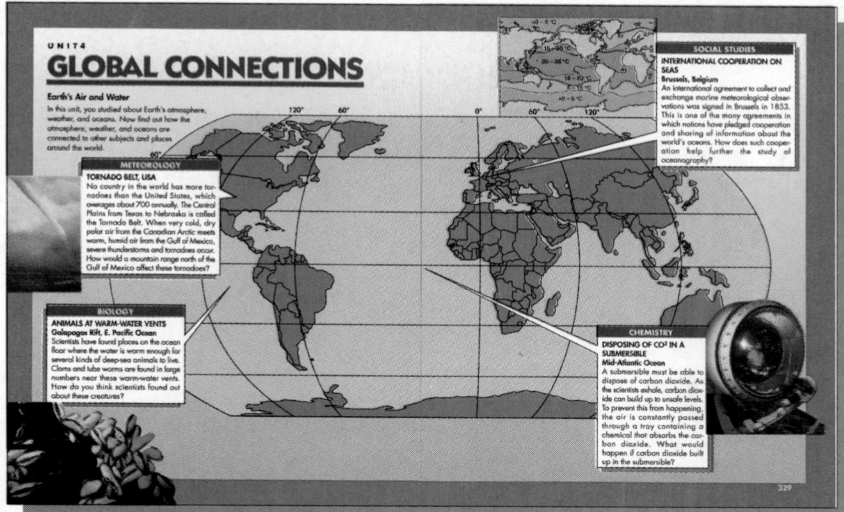

UNIT 4

GLOBAL CONNECTIONS

Earth's Air and Water

In this unit, you studied about Earth's atmosphere, weather, and oceans. Now find out how the atmosphere, weather, and oceans are connected to other subjects and places around the world.

METEOROLOGY

TORNADO BELT, USA

No country in the world has more tornadoes than the United States, which averages about 700 annually. The Central Plains from Texas to Nebraska is called the Tornado Belt. When very cold, dry polar air from the Canadian Arctic meets warm, humid air from the Gulf of Mexico, severe thunderstorms and tornadoes occur. How would a mountain range north of the Gulf of Mexico affect these tornadoes?

BIOLOGY

ANIMALS AT WARM-WATER VENTS

Galapagos Rift, E. Pacific Ocean

Scientists have found places on the ocean floor where the water is warm enough for several kinds of deep-sea animals to live. Clams and tube worms are found in large numbers near these warm-water vents. How do you think scientists found out about these creatures?

SOCIAL STUDIES

INTERNATIONAL COOPERATION ON SEAS

Brussels, Belgium

An international agreement to collect and exchange marine meteorological observations was signed in Brussels in 1853. This is one of the many agreements in which nations have pledged cooperation and sharing of information about the world's oceans. How does such cooperation help further the study of oceanography?

CHEMISTRY

DISPOSING OF CO² IN A SUBMERSIBLE

Mid-Atlantic Ocean

A submersible must be able to dispose of carbon dioxide. As the scientists exhale, carbon dioxide can build up to unsafe levels. To prevent this from happening, the air is constantly passed through a tray containing a chemical that absorbs the carbon dioxide. What would happen if carbon dioxide built up in the submersible?

329

Global Connections help you to see how earth science is related to other sciences as well as social studies, history and health.

Also at the end of each unit you will find two **Careers** that relate to the material in the unit you just read. What jobs may be related to Earth's air and water? Read the careers at the end of Unit 4 to find out.

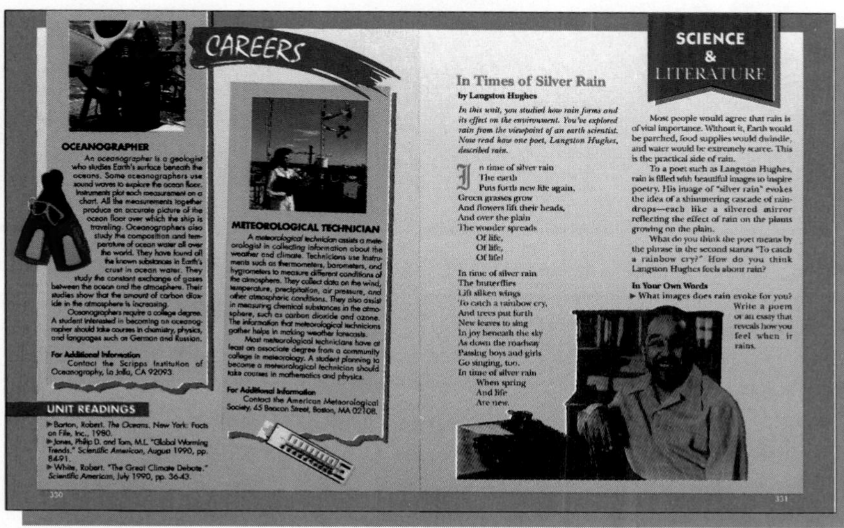

CAREERS

OCEANOGRAPHER

An oceanographer is a geologist who studies Earth's surface beneath the oceans. Some oceanographers use sound waves to explore the ocean floor. Instruments plot each measurement on a chart. All the measurements together produce an accurate picture of the ocean floor over which the ship is traveling. Oceanographers also study the composition and temperature of ocean water all over the world. They have found all the known substances in Earth's crust in ocean water. They study the constant exchange of gases between the ocean and the atmosphere. Their studies show that the amount of carbon dioxide in the atmosphere is increasing.

Oceanographers require a college degree. A student interested in becoming an oceanographer should take courses in chemistry, physics, and languages such as German and Russian.

For Additional Information

Contact the Scripps Institution of Oceanography, La Jolla, CA 92093.

METEOROLOGICAL TECHNICIAN

A meteorological technician assists a meteorologist in collecting information about the weather and climate. Technicians use instruments such as thermometers, barometers, and hygrometers to measure different conditions of the atmosphere. They collect data on the wind, temperature, precipitation, air pressure, and other atmospheric conditions. They also assist in measuring chemical substances in the atmosphere, such as carbon dioxide and ozone. The information that meteorological technicians gather helps in making weather forecasts.

Most meteorological technicians have at least an associate degree from a community college in meteorology. A student planning to become a meteorological technician should take courses in mathematics and physics.

For Additional Information

Contact the American Meteorological Society, 45 Beacon Street, Boston, MA 02108.

UNIT READINGS

- Barton, Robert. *The Oceans*. New York: Facts on File, Inc., 1980.
- Jones, Philip D. and Tom, M.L. "Global Warming Trends." *Scientific American*, August 1990, pp. 84-91.
- White, Robert. "The Great Climate Debate." *Scientific American*, July 1990, pp. 36-43.

330

SCIENCE & LITERATURE

In Times of Silver Rain

by Langston Hughes

In this unit, you studied how rain forms and its effect on the environment. You've explored rain from the viewpoint of an earth scientist. Now read how one poet, Langston Hughes, described rain.

In time of silver rain
The earth
Puts forth new life again,
Green grasses grow
And flowers lift their heads,
And over the plain
The wonder spreads
Of life,
Of life,
Of life!

In time of silver rain
The butterflies
Lift silken wings
To catch a rainbow cry,
And trees put forth
New leaves to sing
In joy beneath the sky
As down the roadway
Passing boys and girls
Go singing, too.
In time of silver rain
When spring
And life
Are new.

Most people would agree that rain is of vital importance. Without it, Earth would be parched, food supplies would dwindle, and water would be extremely scarce. This is the practical side of rain.

To a poet such as Langston Hughes, rain is filled with beautiful images to inspire poetry. His image of "silver rain" evokes the idea of a shimmering cascade of raindrops—each like a silvered mirror reflecting the effect of rain on the plants growing on the plain.

What do you think the poet means by the phrase in the second stanza "To catch a rainbow cry?" How do you think Langston Hughes feels about rain?

In Your Own Words

- What images does rain evoke for you? Write a poem or an essay that reveals how you feel when it rains.

331

What do earth science and poetry have in common? A lot, as you'll discover when you read the unit close to Unit 4. Each unit is closed with a reading from literature or an example of art that makes a connection with earth science.

1

UNIT

1

FOUNDATIONS OF EARTH SCIENCE

In Unit 1, students are introduced to the branches of science involved in earth science. Problem solving strategies and methods used in scientific measurement are described. The unit presents some of the basics used in the study of science.

CONTENTS

ADVANCE PREPARATION

Activities

▶ **Activity 1-2, page 22,** requires small rocks and shoe boxes. Have students bring rocks and shoe boxes from home.

▶ **Activity 2-1, page 39,** requires rock samples. Obtain them from around the school.

▶ **Activity 2-2, page 50,** requires pieces of quartz and clay, and small blocks of wood and metal.

Audiovisuals

▶ **Section 1-1, page 6:** Arrange to show the video, "Unseen Worlds," Infinite Voyage, Inovision.

▶ **Section 1-3, page 12:** Arrange to show the filmstrip/cassette, "Scientific Method and Discovery," National Geographic.

Field Trips and Speakers

▶ Arrange to take students to a local power plant to see science and technology in use.

▶ Ask an engineer from a local company to visit your class to explain the importance of science in our lives.

OPTIONS

Cross Curriculum

▶ Ask students to write down each time scientific or technological discoveries are discussed in their other classes.

▶ Have students write a report on the history of an invention that involves science and technology.

▶ Have students list items used to prepare food in domestic arts by name and state of matter.

Science at Home

▶ Have students choose an appliance used at home and describe the basic principles of technology that are employed in making it work. Have students report their findings to the class.

Cooperative Learning: Using the Paired Partner strategy, have students make flash cards of common items in the home. One side can be a picture of the object and on the reverse can be a measurement of one of its properties.

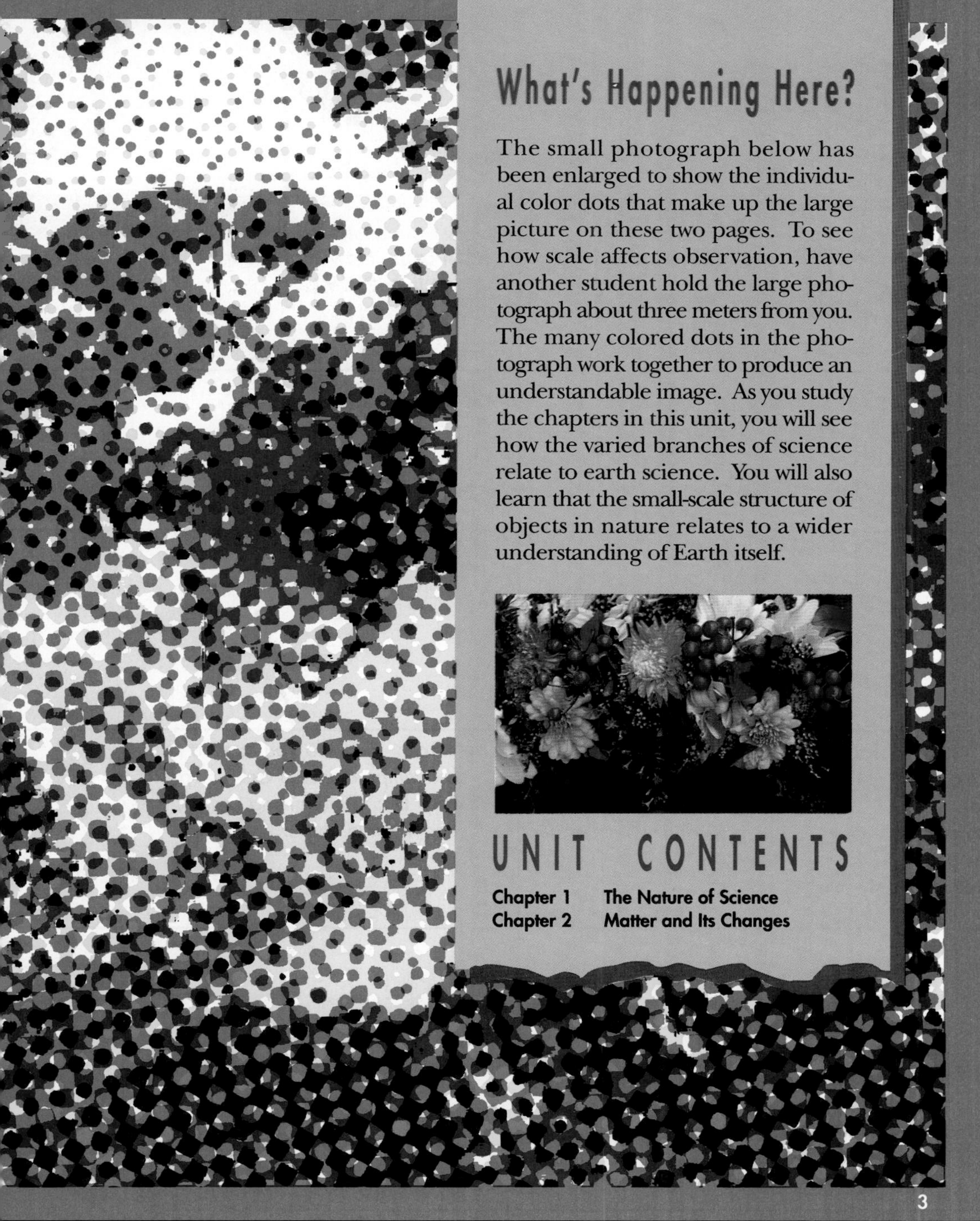

What's Happening Here?

The small photograph below has been enlarged to show the individual color dots that make up the large picture on these two pages. To see how scale affects observation, have another student hold the large photograph about three meters from you. The many colored dots in the photograph work together to produce an understandable image. As you study the chapters in this unit, you will see how the varied branches of science relate to earth science. You will also learn that the small-scale structure of objects in nature relates to a wider understanding of Earth itself.

UNIT CONTENTS

3

Multicultural Awareness

Have students research systems of measure used in various cultures around the world. Have them include the United States, Europe, and at least one non-industrialized culture. The English system is widely used in the United States. European countries use the International System of Units.

Inquiry Questions

Use the following questions to focus a discussion of how observed, large scale properties of matter are determined by small scale properties, such as composition and structure.

1. What causes your eyes to see different colors in commercial adds in the newspaper?
2. Why does the top of your desk feel solid to you?
3. What is true about the particles of a liquid that enable it to take the shape of its container?

INTRODUCING THE UNIT

What's Happening Here?

▶ Have students look at the photos and read the text. Ask them to tell you what's happening here. Point out to students that in this unit they will be studying how the four general areas of science are interrelated. They will learn how scientists use observations to solve problems. They will also study the structure of atoms of which all matter is composed.

▶ **Background:** The color image on a television screen is obtained by using red, blue, and green colored dots or rectangles. The combination of the intensity in each color dot is observed by the human eye as different colors. Similarly, photographs in this text are reproduced using red, blue, green, and black dots. Have students use a magnifying glass to examine the dot-pattern of a figure in this text.

Previewing the Chapters

▶ To help students understand how the main branches of science apply to a study of Earth and its place in space, have them study Table 1-1 on page 7.

▶ Encourage students to search through the unit for photographs of scientists who study Earth.

▶ Some students may not realize that matter is composed of tiny particles that make up its atomic structure. To help clear up misconceptions about the structure of matter, have students study the charts and tables located in Section 2-1.

▶ Have students compile a brief list of materials they use at home that would be classified as compounds or mixtures. Use misconceptions of the students to demonstrate the differences between compounds and mixtures.

Tying to Previous Knowledge

▶ Ask volunteers to describe the process they go through each morning when deciding what to wear to school. Relate this process to the scientific method used by scientists to solve problems.

▶ Have students brainstorm a list of items that would be classified as a gas, a liquid, or a solid.

▶ Use the **Inquiry Questions** in the OPTIONS box at the left to investigate properties of matter.

CHAPTER

The Nature of Science

CHAPTER SECTION	OBJECTIVES	ACTIVITIES
1-1 What Is Science? (1 day)	1. **Differentiate** among the following sciences: chemistry, physics, biology, and earth science. 2. **Identify** the topics you'll be studying this year in earth science.	**MINI-Lab:** *How many earth sciences are there?* p. 9
1-2 Science and Technology Science & Society (1 day)	1. **List** ways technology helps you. 2. **Discuss** ways that the use of technology can be harmful.	
1-3 Solving Problems (2 days)	1. **Describe** some problem-solving strategies. 2. **List** steps commonly used as scientific methods. 3. **Distinguish** among hypotheses, theories, and laws.	**Flex Your Brain,** p. 15
1-4 Measurements and Safety (2 days)	1. **List** the SI units for the following measurements: length, mass, weight, area, volume, density, and temperature. 2. **Differentiate** between the terms *mass* and *weight* and the terms *area* and *volume.* 3. **State** three lab safety rules.	**MINI-Lab:** *How do you convert Fahrenheit temperatures to Celsius?* p. 20 **Activity 1-1:** *Determining Length, Area, and Volume,* p. 22
Chapter Review		

ACTIVITY MATERIALS

FIND OUT	ACTIVITIES		MINI-LABS	
Page 5 notebook watch with second hand	**Flex Your Brain, p. 15** paper pencil	**1-2 Determining Length, Area, and Volume, p. 22** graph paper metric ruler string graduated cylinder (100 mL) small rock shoe box water	**How many earth sciences are there? p. 9** none	**How do you convert Fahrenheit temperatures to Celsius? p. 20** notebook paper pencil

CHAPTER FEATURES	TEACHER RESOURCE PACKAGE	OTHER RESOURCES
Skill Builder: *Concept Mapping,* p. 9	**Ability Level Worksheets** ◆ ***Study Guide,*** p. 5 ● ***Reinforcement,*** p. 5 ▲ ***Enrichment,*** p. 5 **MINI-Lab Worksheet,** p. 9	
You Decide! p. 11	**Ability Level Worksheets** ◆ ***Study Guide,*** p. 6 ● ***Reinforcement,*** p. 6 ▲ ***Enrichment,*** p. 6 **Science and Society,** p. 5 **Technology,** pp. 5-6	
Technology: *Building a Better Bicycle,* p. 13 **Problem Solving:** *New Uniforms for the Band,* p. 16 **Skill Builder:** *Comparing and Contrasting,* p. 17	**Ability Level Worksheets** ◆ ***Study Guide,*** p. 7 ● ***Reinforcement,*** p. 7 ▲ ***Enrichment,*** p. 7 **Critical Thinking/Problem Solving,** p. 7 **Concept Mapping,** pp. 7-8 **Transparency Masters,** pp. 3-4	**Color Transparency 2,** Flex Your Brain **Lab Manual:** *Problem Solving and the Scientific Method,* p. 1 **Lab Manual:** *The Law of Probability,* p. 3
Skill Builder: *Measuring in SI,* p. 21	**Ability Level Worksheets** ◆ ***Study Guide,*** p. 8 ● ***Reinforcement,*** p. 8 ▲ ***Enrichment,*** p. 8 **Cross-Curricular Connections,** p. 5 **Transparency Masters,** pp. 1-2 **Activity Worksheet,** pp. 6-7 **MINI-Lab Worksheet,** p. 10	**Color Transparency 1,** Metric/English Conversions **Lab Manual:** *Measuring Using SI Units,* p. 7 **Lab Manual:** *Mass and Weight,* p. 9
Summary Key Science Words Understanding Vocabulary Checking Concepts Understanding Concepts Think & Write Critically Apply More Skill Builders Projects	**Chapter Review,** pp. 5-6 **Chapter Test,** pp. 5-8	**Chapter Review Software** **Test Bank**

◆ **Basic** ● **Average** ▲ **Advanced**

ADDITIONAL MATERIALS

SOFTWARE	AUDIOVISUAL	BOOKS/MAGAZINES
Discovery Lab, MECC. *Modeling,* MECC.	*Nature of Science: Forming Hypotheses,* film, Coronet/MTI. *Nature of Science: Testing Hypotheses,* film, Coronet/MTI. *Observing and Describing,* film, CRM Films. *Conversations with Great Scientists Video Series—Steven Hawking: The Universe Within;—From Atoms to Asteroids: A Life of Philip Morrison,* video, Focus.	Bates, Robert L. *Geology of Industrial Rocks and Minerals.* NY: Dover Publishing Inc., 1969. Lisle, R.J. *Geological Structures and Maps: A Practical Guide.* Elmsford, NY: Pergamon Press, Inc., 1988. Tarbuck, Edward J. and Frederick K. Lutgens. *Earth Science* 4th ed. Columbus, OH: Merrill Publishing, 1984.

CHAPTER

1

THE NATURE OF SCIENCE

THEME DEVELOPMENT: Systems and interactions are the themes of this chapter. Science is a system of knowledge based on observations. Science is generally divided into four areas, but the topics overlap. The interaction of science and technology is the focus of Section 1-2.

CHAPTER OVERVIEW

- **Section 1-1:** This section defines *science* and differentiates among chemistry, physics, biology, and earth science.
- **Section 1-2: Science and Society:** The relationship between science and technology is discussed. The You Decide feature asks students to consider some of the effects of technology.
- **Section 1-3:** Problem-solving strategies, steps in the scientific method, and the evolution of theories from hypotheses are presented.
- **Section 1-4:** The International System of Units (SI) is introduced. Safety procedures to be used during activities are listed.

CHAPTER VOCABULARY

science	control
geology	theory
meteorology	law
astronomy	International System of Units (SI)
oceanography	mass
technology	weight
scientific methods	gravitational force
hypothesis	
variable	

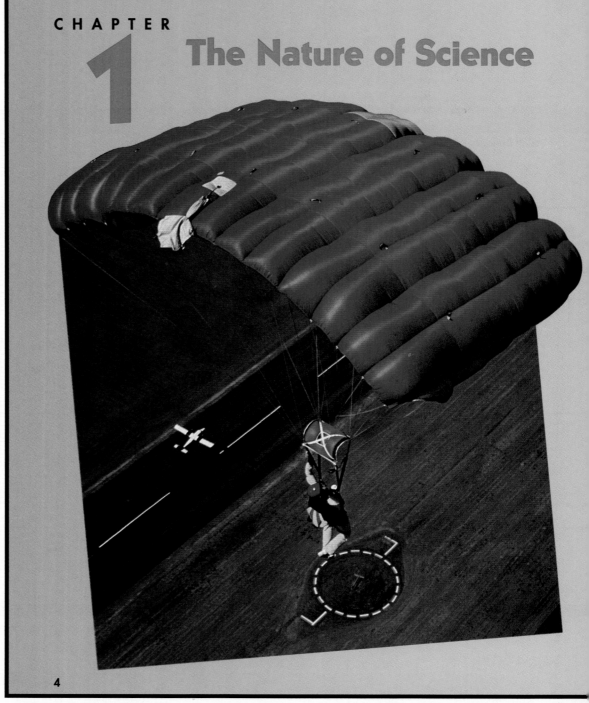

CHAPTER 1

The Nature of Science

4

OPTIONS

For Your Gifted Students

Ask students to make a time line of all the technological advances they can find that have occurred since 1940. Have students work in small groups to illustrate their work and show changes in the design, price, and so on of some inventions.

The parachutist in this photo is using the results of scientific experiments to enjoy skydiving. Previous experiments led to the modern design of the parachute.

FIND OUT!

Do this activity to find the best parachute design.

Fold a piece of notebook paper it in half, then in half again. You should have a piece of paper one-fourth as big as you started with. Have a friend hold the folded paper over his or her head. Using a watch with a second hand, record the time it takes for the paper to fall to the floor. Now unfold the paper so it is folded in half just once. Again, record the time it takes for this folded paper to fall to the floor. Now completely unfold the paper and flatten it out. Record the time it takes for the paper to fall to the floor. What is the best design for your parachute? How did you come to this conclusion?

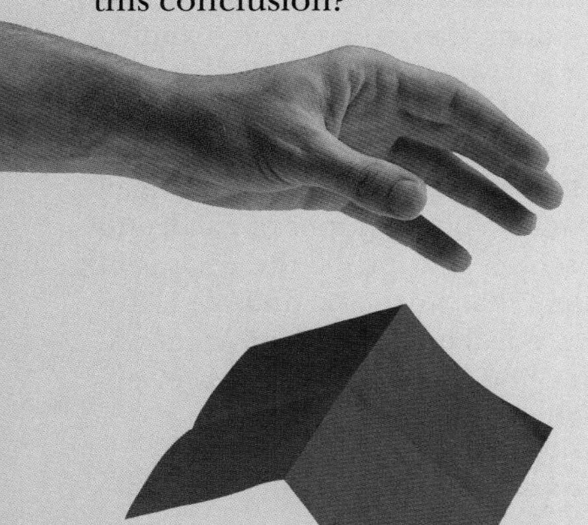

Gearing Up

Previewing the Chapter

Use this outline to help you focus on important ideas in this chapter.

Section 1-1 What Is Science?
- Science
- Earth Science

Section 1-2 Science and Society
Science and Technology
- Technology and You
- The Effects of Technology

Section 1-3 Solving Problems
- Problem-Solving Strategies
- Critical Thinking
- Using Scientific Methods
- Theories and Laws

Section 1-4 Measurement and Safety
- Measurement
- Safety

Previewing Science Skills

- In the **Skill Builders,** you will make a concept map, compare and contrast, and measure in SI.
- In the **Activities,** you will think critically and calculate and experiment.
- In the **MINI-Labs,** you will investigate specific areas of study in earth science, and learn about SI conversions.

What's next?

Now that you've seen how science can be used in solving the problem of parachute design, you're ready to explore earth science. In this chapter, you'll learn about other sciences related to earth science. You'll also become aware of the relationship between science and technology, and you'll study measurement and safety.

INTRODUCING THE CHAPTER

Use the Find Out activity to introduce students to problem-solving methods. Inform students that they will be learning more about science and problem solving as they read the chapter.

FIND OUT!

Materials: meterstick, watch with a second hand, piece of notebook paper

Cooperative Learning: Have Paired Partners perform this activity. One student should drop the paper while the other determines the exact time it takes the paper to drop.

Teaching Tips

- Results will be most accurate if the height from which the paper is dropped is exactly the same each time. Have students measure the dropping distance with the meterstick and carefully drop each paper from the same height.
- The best design for a parachute would be the unfolded paper. This was determined by measuring the time it took folded and unfolded paper to drop the same distance.

Gearing Up

Have students study the Gearing Up feature to familiarize themselves with the chapter. Discuss the relationships of the topics in the outline.

What's Next?

Before beginning the first section, make sure students understand the connection between the Find Out activity and the topics to follow.

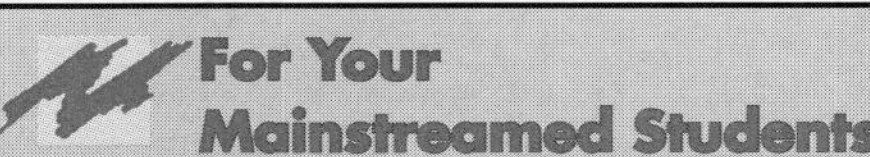

For Your Mainstreamed Students

Have students practice using the International System of Units (SI) by asking them to use it to measure items throughout the school. Their measurements should include those of volume, area, mass, distance, and density.

SECTION 1-1

PREPARATION

SECTION BACKGROUND

► A scientist's attitude about science is critical to his or her career. Scientists must be willing to allow others to question and challenge their ideas. Scientists must have a tolerance for the ideas and opinions of others.

► Discoveries are being made so rapidly today that some experts are calling this the "Information Age." When your students reach 50 years of age, more than 95 percent of all human knowledge will have been developed during their lifetimes.

1 MOTIVATE

► Invite a scientist to talk about his or her career.

► Ask students what they already know about science and in what ways it affects their lives.

► Prepare a bulletin board display of current topics in science. Discuss several of these with students.

1-1 What Is Science?

New Science Words

science
geology
meteorology
astronomy
oceanography

Objectives

- ► **Differentiate among the following sciences: chemistry, physics, biology, and earth science.**
- ► **Identify the topics you'll be studying this year in earth science.**

Figure 1-1. Science is used in many common objects such as radios.

Science

Science is all around you. It is such a common part of your life that you probably take it for granted. Have you ever wondered why a refrigerator keeps food cold or what makes a hair dryer blow hot air? Most everything you see has some connection to science. Think about the radio or stereo you listen to. It operates on scientific principles of electricity. The speakers change an electrical signal into a sound wave that you hear as your favorite song. The radio is constructed out of metal and plastic compounds. Determining the best compounds to use involves the science of chemistry. By simply turning on the radio, you are using science in many ways.

But where did all the scientific knowledge used in making radios and other appliances come from? This knowledge has accumulated since people first began observing the world around them.

At first, people had only their senses to rely on for their observations. Early astronomers studied the night sky with just their eyes because they didn't have telescopes yet. They acquired knowledge very slowly. Today, we have complex instruments such as microscopes that magnify small objects, satellites that take photographs of Earth and other planets, telescopes that probe the depths of space, and computers that store and analyze information. Today, we are learning more information, we are learning it faster, and there are more new inventions and discoveries than ever before.

OPTIONS

Meeting Different Ability Levels

For Section 1-1, use the following **Teacher Resource Masters** depending upon individual students' needs.

◆ **Study Guide Master** for all students.

● **Reinforcement Master** for students of average and above average ability levels.

▲ **Enrichment Master** for above average students.

Additional Teacher Resource Package masters are listed in the OPTIONS box throughout the section. The additional masters are appropriate for all students.

◆ STUDY GUIDE 5

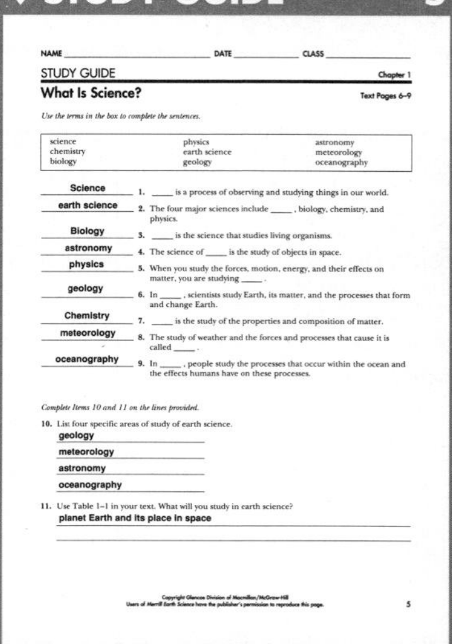

NAME ____________ DATE ________ CLASS ________

STUDY GUIDE — Chapter 1

What Is Science? — Text Pages 6–9

Use the terms in the box to complete the sentences.

science	physics	astronomy
chemistry	earth science	meteorology
biology	geology	oceanography

Science 1. _____ is a process of observing and studying things in our world.

earth science 2. The four major sciences include _____, biology, chemistry, and physics.

Biology 3. _____ is the science that studies living organisms.

astronomy 4. The science of _____ is the study of objects in space.

physics 5. When you study the forces, motion, energy, and their effects on matter, you are studying _____.

geology 6. In _____, scientists study Earth, its matter, and the processes that form and change Earth.

Chemistry 7. _____ is the study of the properties and composition of matter.

meteorology 8. The study of weather and the forces and processes that cause it is called _____.

oceanography 9. In _____, people study the processes that occur within the ocean and the effects humans have on these processes.

Complete Items 10 and 11 on the lines provided.

10. List four specific areas of study of earth science.
geology
meteorology
astronomy
oceanography

11. Use Table 1-1 in your text. What will you study in earth science?
planet Earth and its place in space

5

Science means "having knowledge." It's a process of observing and studying things in our world. Many of these observations can't be explained easily and therefore present a problem. Science involves trying to solve these problems. Science is a process that enables you to understand 1 your world. Every time you try to find out how and why things look and act the way they do, you are a scientist. For example, if you wonder and try to figure out why you keep getting a cold, you are doing science.

Science can be applied to just about anything, and hundreds of special subject areas fall within the broad scope of "science."

But basically, science can be divided into four general areas: chemistry, physics, biology, and earth science. These general topics do overlap. For example, in earth science, chemistry, physics, and biology are studied as they relate to Earth. In Table 1-1 you'll see what these different sciences are about and how they are connected to each other.

EcoTip

Find out how many trees are used for your junk mail in one year. Save your junk mail for one month. Then multiply the weight by 12 months. For every 907 kg of paper, 17 trees are used.

What are four general areas of science?

Table 1-1

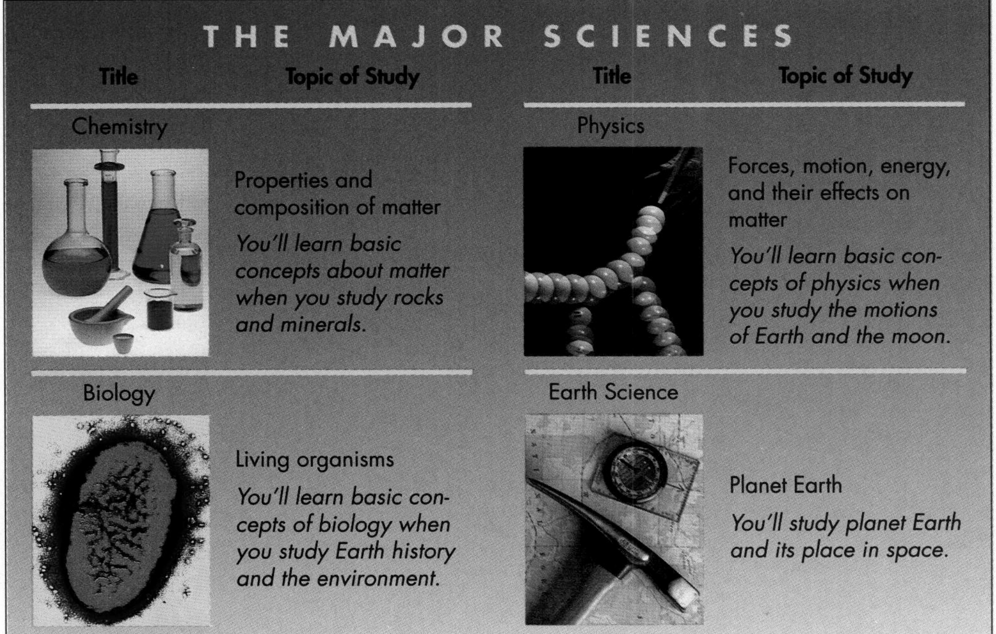

THE MAJOR SCIENCES

Title	Topic of Study	Title	Topic of Study
Chemistry	Properties and composition of matter *You'll learn basic concepts about matter when you study rocks and minerals.*	Physics	Forces, motion, energy, and their effects on matter *You'll learn basic concepts of physics when you study the motions of Earth and the moon.*
Biology	Living organisms *You'll learn basic concepts of biology when you study Earth history and the environment.*	Earth Science	Planet Earth *You'll study planet Earth and its place in space.*

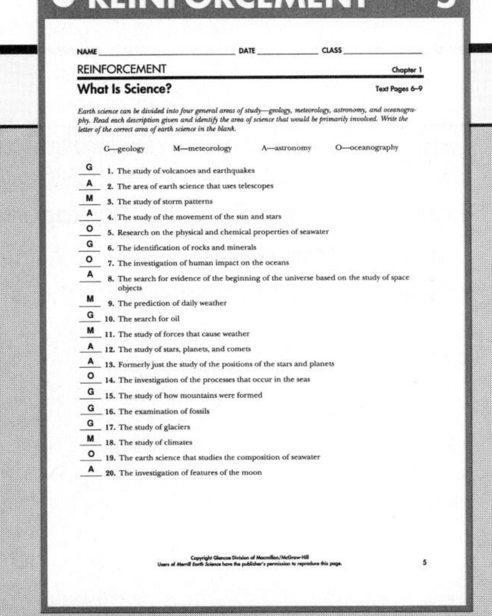

● REINFORCEMENT 5

NAME ____ DATE ____ CLASS ____

REINFORCEMENT Chapter 1

What Is Science? Text Pages 6–9

Earth science can be divided into four general areas of study—geology, meteorology, astronomy, and oceanography. Read each description given and identify the area of science that would be primarily involved. Write the letter of the correct area of earth science in the blank.

G—geology M—meteorology A—astronomy O—oceanography

G 1. The study of volcanoes and earthquakes
A 2. The area of earth science that uses telescopes
M 3. The study of storm patterns
A 4. The study of the movement of the sun and stars
O 5. Research on the physical and chemical properties of seawater
G 6. The identification of rocks and minerals
O 7. The investigation of human impact on the oceans
A 8. The search for evidence of the beginning of the universe based on the study of space objects
M 9. The prediction of daily weather
G 10. The search for oil
M 11. The study of forces that cause weather
A 12. The study of stars, planets, and comets
A 13. Formerly just the study of the positions of the stars and planets
O 14. The investigation of the processes that occur in the seas
G 15. The study of how mountains were formed
G 16. The examination of fossils
G 17. The study of glaciers
M 18. The study of climates
O 19. The earth science that studies the composition of seawater
A 20. The investigation of features of the moon

 5

▲ ENRICHMENT 5

NAME ____ DATE ____ CLASS ____

ENRICHMENT Chapter 1

What Is Science Text Pages 6–9

SCIENCE IN ANCIENT TIMES

Read the following information and answer the questions.

Native North and South Americans knew many things about Earth, the stars, and the planets. They observed the world and made discoveries that were steps in the development of modern science.

The Mayan Indians lived in a region that is now part of Mexico. Understanding planets and stars was important to the Mayas. They developed this knowledge so they could plant and hunt at the days and hours most pleasing to the gods. A fragment of a Mayan codex, a book made of bark-cloth paper, contains complicated calculations about the movements of the planet Venus.

In the region that is now Peru, the Inca Indians built the great Temple of the Sun in the 15th century. They decorated the rooms with beaten gold and golden fountains. The emperor had artisans make silver and gold figures of the birds and animals that lived in the region. He had these figures placed in his garden.

In Canada in the 16th century, Jacques Cartier and his sailors were victims of a terrible disease called scurvy. Twenty-five men died before Cartier asked the Huron Indians for help. The Hurons showed the Frenchmen how to make a tea from the bark and needles of a certain evergreen. Those who drank the tea recovered. The tea contained vitamin C, which is the only cure for scurvy, although no one knew about vitamins at the time.

1. The Mayas' study of planets was a part of what modern science? **astronomy**
2. What modern sciences use the information the early Hurons knew? **Biology deals with life, including human life. Medicine is a branch of biological science and scurvy is a disease.**
3. How would a modern cure for scurvy differ from that given to Cartier? **Doctors would probably prescribe vitamin C in natural foods, such as cranberries and citrus fruits, or in capsules, rather than in tea made from evergreen bark and needles.**
4. Which modern science includes knowledge used by the Incas to find gold and silver? Explain your answer. **Gold and silver are taken from rocks. Geology, an Earth science, is the study of rocks.**
5. The Incas had to remove gold and silver from Earth. This would involve work. What modern science explains work and the use of energy? **physics**
6. The emperor had a garden. What does this tell about the Incas' understanding of another kind of science? **They understood some things about biology since they knew about plants and plant growth.**

 5

TYING TO PREVIOUS KNOWLEDGE: Lead a discussion that will help students realize that they have been practicing science all their lives. Lead them to conclude that they were scientists when they made their first observations as infants.

OBJECTIVES AND SCIENCE WORDS: Have students review the objectives and science words to become familiar with this section.

2 TEACH

Key Concepts are highlighted.

CONCEPT DEVELOPMENT

▶ Using the four general categories of chemistry, physics, biology, and earth science, ask students to name as many different kinds of scientists as possible and identify what type of information each one attempts to acquire. Students should realize that many of the disciplines overlap.

▶ Ask the school librarian to arrange a session during which the use of science books, reference books, and magazines is explained.

▶ Ask the following questions. **What is science?** *Science is observing and studying things in our world. It involves trying to solve problems.* **Why would a person who is studying biology also need to know about chemistry?** *Living organisms are composed of matter.* **Oceanography is one of the topics studied in earth science. When you study oceanography, you will learn about the properties and composition of seawater, the plants and animals in the ocean, and the motion of waves. Besides earth science, which other major sciences will you be learning about?** *chemistry, biology, and physics*

Science and READING 

Information on earth science careers can be obtained from the American Geological Institute, the United States Geological Survey (USGS), or colleges and universities.

CONCEPT DEVELOPMENT

▶ Emphasize that although there are four areas of specialization in earth science, an earth scientist in any of these fields often will need to have an understanding of the other earth science areas in order to effectively analyze his or her data.

CROSS CURRICULUM

▶ **Social Studies:** Stress the effects that science events have on society by devoting part of one class period each week to discussing a current-events topic in earth science. Assign groups of three students to prepare the presentation for each week.

CHECK FOR UNDERSTANDING

Use the Mini Quiz to check for understanding.

MINI QUIZ

Use the Mini Quiz to check students' recall of chapter content.

1. **_____ is a process that enables you to understand your world.** *Science*
2. **_____ is the study of Earth.** *Geology*
3. **The study of weather and the forces and processes that cause it is _____ .** *meteorology*

RETEACH

Show students pictures of objects in nature, such as the sun, clouds, rocks, sea life, Saturn, fossils, and so on. Have students identify the earth science(s) associated with each.

EXTENSION

For students who have mastered this section, use the **Reinforcement** and **Enrichment** masters or other OPTIONS provided.

Figure 1-2. The study of volcanic lava is one area of earth science.

Science and READING 

Look at the table of contents in this book and try to name ten careers in earth science. Check the career resources in the library or guidance office for help.

Earth Science

Just as science can be divided into the four general areas of earth science, chemistry, physics, and biology, earth science in this book is divided into four specific areas of study.

❸ **Geology** is the study of Earth, its matter, and the processes that form and change Earth. Some of the things you'll look at are volcanoes, earthquakes, maps, fossils, mountains, and land use. Geologists search for oil, study volcanoes, identify rocks and minerals, study fossils and glaciers, and determine how mountains form.

❷ **Meteorology** is the study of weather and the forces and processes that cause it. You'll learn about storm patterns, climates, and what factors cause our daily weather. A mete-

Figure 1-3. Astronomers study objects in space using telescopes.

OPTIONS

ENRICHMENT

▶ Have students report on recent discoveries and new research methods in chemistry, astronomy, or geology that have contributed to our knowledge of Earth.

▶ Have students "shadow" scientists to find out more about their careers.

▶ Have students choose one of the four major areas of specialization in earth science to research. Have them list the tools, equipment, and/or instruments used by scientists in this field.

PROGRAM RESOURCES

From the **Teacher Resource Package** use:

Activity Worksheets, page 9, Mini-Lab: How many earth sciences are there?

orologist is a scientist who studies weather patterns in order to predict daily weather.

Astronomy is the study of objects in space, including stars, planets, and comets. Before telescopes were invented, this branch of earth science mainly dealt with descriptions of the positions of the stars and planets. Today, scientists who study space objects seek evidence about the beginning of the universe. The study of astronomy helps scientists understand Earth's origin.

Oceanography is the study of Earth's oceans. Scientists who study the oceans conduct research on the physical and chemical properties of ocean water. Oceanographers also study the processes that occur within oceans and the effects humans have on these processes.

As you study these topics, imagine how all this information was collected over the years. People just like you had questions about the universe, and they used science to find the answers. In Section 1-3, you'll learn ways that you too can find answers to questions and solutions to problems.

MINI-Lab

How many earth sciences are there?

Although the four major areas of earth science are geology, meteorology, astronomy, and oceanography, each of these are composed of subtopic areas of its own. Listed below are some very specific areas of study. In which of the four major areas of earth science do they belong? What would a scientist working in each of these fields study?

hydrology	seismology
volcanology	petrology
mineralogy	geomorphology
paleontology	geochemistry
stratigraphy	crystallography

SECTION REVIEW

1. What topics are studied in each of the following sciences: chemistry, physics, biology, and earth science?
2. How can chemistry and physics relate to earth science?
3. **Apply:** The following paragraph summarizes one idea of how the dinosaurs may have died. Explain how this paragraph relates to geology, oceanography, astronomy, and meteorology.

   Scientists think that in the past, large objects from outer space crashed onto Earth's crust. So much dust was created from these collisions that the sun's light was blocked out. Earth became colder, killing some plants and animals.

Concept Mapping — Skill Builder

Make a Network Tree concept map that shows which of the following topics are studied in a particular topic of earth science. Use the following words: *earth science, geology, waves, currents, astronomy, oceanography, stars, volcanoes, planets, meteorology, fossils, weather, climate.* If you need help, refer to Concept Mapping in the **Skill Handbook** on pages 688 and 689.

REVEALING MISCONCEPTIONS

▶Many people confuse the terms *astrology* and *astronomy*. Astronomy is a science, astrology is not. Astrology is the belief that people's lives are controlled by the stars. It is unsupported by any scientific evidence.

MINI-Lab

Answers: Hydrology is the study of fresh water; volcanology: volcanoes and igneous activity; mineralogy: minerals; paleontology: fossils; stratigraphy: sedimentary rocks; seismology: earthquakes and Earth movements; petrology: rocks; geomorphology: surface features; geochemistry: properties of Earth materials; crystallography: the atomic structure of minerals.

3 CLOSE

▶Ask questions 1-2 and the **Apply** Question in the Section Review.

▶Have students who have hobbies that involve earth sciences make presentations.

SECTION REVIEW ANSWERS

1. chemistry: properties and composition of matter; physics: forces, motion, and energy and their effects on matter; biology: living organisms; earth science: planet Earth and its place in space.

2. People need to know about the properties and composition of matter and how forces, motion, and energy affect matter.

3. Apply: Geology deals with changes that form and change Earth's crust. Plants and animals, including marine ones, were affected by the impacts. Astronomy is the study of space objects including the sun. Weather and climate are topics of meteorology.

Skill Builder

Possible Solution:

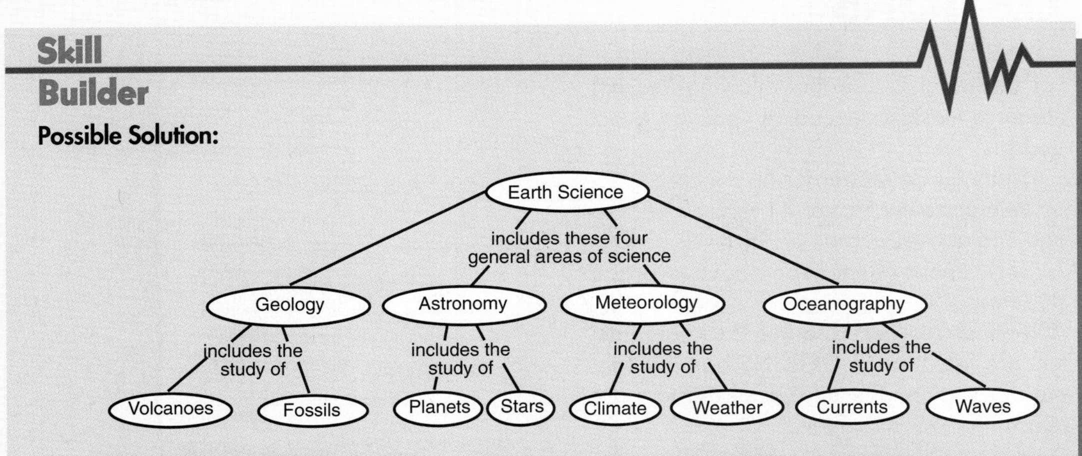

SECTION 1-2

PREPARATION

SECTION BACKGROUND

▶It is estimated that human knowledge doubles every few years due to technological breakthroughs.

1 MOTIVATE

▶Ask students to list ways they use electricity in their daily lives. They will quickly realize how much they depend on this scientific application.

▶Invite an inventor to discuss how science and technology are used in inventing new things.

TYING TO PREVIOUS KNOWLEDGE: Explain that without technology, we wouldn't have paper, pencils, clothing, and some types of food.

OBJECTIVES AND SCIENCE WORDS: Have students review the objectives and science words to become familiar with this section.

2 TEACH

Key Concepts are highlighted.

CONCEPT DEVELOPMENT

Cooperative Learning: Have Paired Partners make lists of technological inventions in categories such as space, medicine, food, communications, and transportation.

▶Have students give examples that show how science and technology are related. For example, by studying science, people have observed that cold air sinks and warm air is forced aloft. Hot air balloons and convection ovens were developed as a result of applying this knowledge.

SCIENCE & SOCIETY

1-2 Science and Technology

New Science Words

technology

Objectives

- ▶ List ways technology helps you.
- ▶ Discuss ways that the use of technology can be harmful.

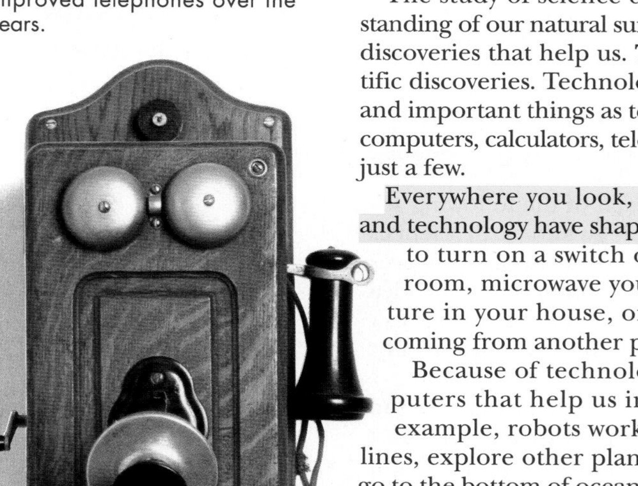

Figure 1-4. New technology has improved telephones over the years.

Technology and You

The study of science doesn't just add to our understanding of our natural surroundings, it allows us to make discoveries that help us. **Technology** is the use of scientific discoveries. Technology has produced such diverse and important things as televisions, artificial hearts, jets, computers, calculators, telephones, and satellites, to name just a few.

Everywhere you look, you can see ways that science and technology have shaped your world. You simply have to turn on a switch or a knob, and you light your room, microwave your food, control the temperature in your house, or watch a television program coming from another part of the world.

Because of technology we have robots and computers that help us in many ways. For example, robots work in assembly lines, explore other planets, and go to the bottom of oceans to perform work that would be dangerous

OPTIONS

Meeting Different Ability Levels

For Section 1-2, use the following **Teacher Resource Masters** depending upon individual students' needs.

◆ **Study Guide Master** for all students.

● **Reinforcement Master** for students of average and above average ability levels.

▲ **Enrichment Master** for above average students.

Additional Teacher Resource Package masters are listed in the OPTIONS box throughout the section. The additional masters are appropriate for all students.

◆ STUDY GUIDE 6

NAME ______ DATE ______ CLASS ______

STUDY GUIDE — Chapter 1

Science and Technology — Text Pages 10–11

Unscramble the scrambled words. Put your naswers in the blanks provided to complete the paragraph. Then answer the questions.

Technology is the use of **enifitsicc** scientific discoveries. Technology has enabled people to clear **sterofs** forests and build cities. It's led to the development of modern **camshine** machines such as cars and computers. Because of technology, work that is dangerous for people to do can now be done by **stoobr** robots. People can now live longer because **cloghoteny** technology has improved medicines, health care, and foods. Technology is responsible for many improvements, but it has also created **brompels** problems. Some uses of technology cause **loptulnoi** pollution. For example, air conditioners can keep rooms cool, but they also release a chemical that can harm the **montinvener** environment.

1. What is the topic of the paragraph? technology
2. What is technology? Technology is the use of scientific discoveries.
3. Name the machines identified in the paragraph. cars, computers, robots, and air conditioners
4. Why are robots useful to people? Robots can do work that is dangerous for people to do.
5. How has technology helped people live longer? Through technology, medicine, health care, and foods have been improved so that people now live longer than they used to live.
6. Does technology cause any problems? Explain. Yes, technology can cause such problems as pollution.
7. How are air conditioners helpful to people? Air conditioners can keep rooms cool.
8. How can air conditioners be harmful? Air conditioners can release a chemical harmful to the environment.

6

for people to do. Computers do everything from helping us predict weather to monitoring patients in hospitals. Advancements in robotics, computers, and medicine have enabled us to make artificial arms, legs, and other body parts to replace those that are diseased or injured. Technology has enabled us to live longer because we have improved medicines, health care, and foods.

We have the technology to clear forests, build cities, breed animals, and even create new types of organisms. Humans are unique because we're the only creatures on Earth that can change our surroundings to meet our needs.

Figure 1-5. Disposable items use resources and contribute to problems such as full landfills.

The Effects of Technology

Not all of the changes created by technology are good. Advances in medical technology have extended the time people live. But sometimes the quality of life for these people is very low. For example, people can be kept alive by machines, even though they are permanently unconscious—in a coma.

Technology has also led to the development of modern machines, such as cars. Cars allow us to be mobile and travel freely, but they also create pollution and contribute to congestion in cities. Another machine, the air conditioner, provides cool comfort but uses electricity; and the freon chemical released during its use harms the environment.

SECTION REVIEW

1. List ways technology helps you.
2. What problems can technology cause?

You Decide!

SCIENCE & SOCIETY

Many things, such as plastic razors and food wraps, are "disposable." Technology has made the cost of manufacturing these products so low that they can be thrown away. Even small appliances, such as blow dryers and curling irons, cost less to buy new than to repair. This use of technology has made us a "throwaway" society. Many people simply throw things away when they are broken and buy new ones. Is it better to have the convenience of disposable items, or does the excessive waste created by disposable items make them an unwise use of technology?

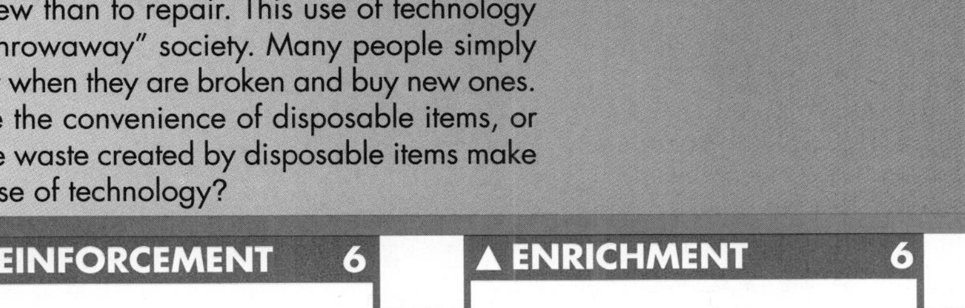

● REINFORCEMENT 6

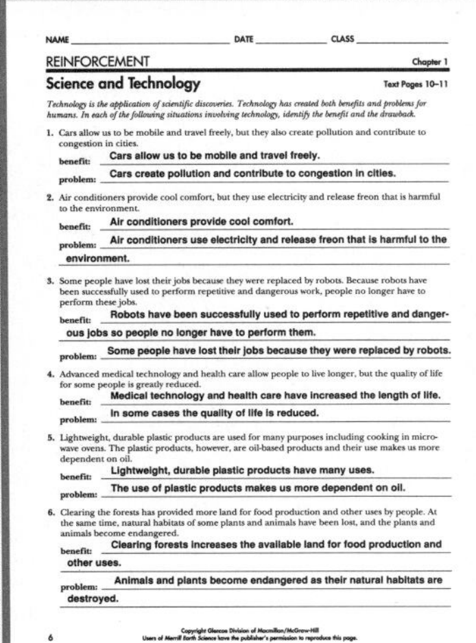

NAME ______ DATE ______ CLASS ______

REINFORCEMENT — Chapter 1

Science and Technology — Text Pages 10–11

Technology is the application of scientific discoveries. Technology has created both benefits and problems for humans. In each of the following situations involving technology, identify the benefit and the drawback.

1. Cars allow us to be mobile and travel freely, but they also create pollution and contribute to congestion in cities.
   benefit: **Cars allow us to be mobile and travel freely.**
   problem: **Cars create pollution and contribute to congestion in cities.**
2. Air conditioners provide cool comfort, but they use electricity and release freon that is harmful to the environment.
   benefit: **Air conditioners provide cool comfort.**
   problem: **Air conditioners use electricity and release freon that is harmful to the environment.**
3. Some people have lost their jobs because they were replaced by robots. Because robots have been successfully used to perform repetitive and dangerous work, people no longer have to perform these jobs.
   benefit: **Robots have been successfully used to perform repetitive and dangerous jobs so people no longer have to perform them.**
   problem: **Some people have lost their jobs because they were replaced by robots.**
4. Advanced medical technology and health care allow people to live longer, but the quality of life for some people is greatly reduced.
   benefit: **Medical technology and health care have increased the length of life.**
   problem: **In some cases the quality of life is reduced.**
5. Lightweight, durable plastic products are used for many purposes including cooking in microwave ovens. The plastic products, however, are oil-based products and their use makes us more dependent on oil.
   benefit: **Lightweight, durable plastic products have many uses.**
   problem: **The use of plastic products makes us more dependent on oil.**
6. Clearing the forests has provided more land for food production and other uses by people. At the same time, natural habitats of some plants and animals have been lost, and the plants and animals become endangered.
   benefit: **Clearing forests increases the available land for food production and other uses.**
   problem: **Animals and plants become endangered as their natural habitats are destroyed.**

6

▲ ENRICHMENT 6

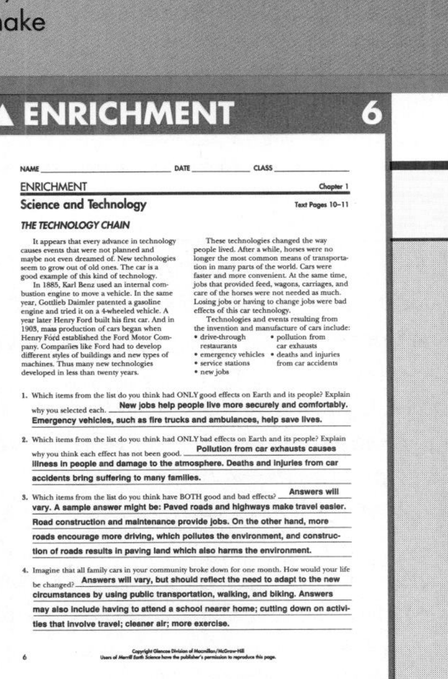

NAME ______ DATE ______ CLASS ______

ENRICHMENT — Chapter 1

Science and Technology — Text Pages 10–11

THE TECHNOLOGY CHAIN

It appears that every advance in technology causes events that were not planned and maybe not even dreamed of. New technologies seem to grow out of old ones. The car is a good example of this kind of technology.

In 1885, Karl Benz used an internal combustion engine to move a vehicle. In the same year, Gottlieb Daimler patented a gasoline engine and tried it on a 4-wheeled vehicle. A year later Henry Ford built his first car. And in 1903, mass production of cars began when Henry Ford established the Ford Motor Company. Companies like Ford had to develop different styles of buildings and new types of machines. Thus many new technologies developed in less than twenty years.

These technologies changed the way people lived. After a while, horses were no longer the most common means of transportation in many parts of the world. Cars were faster and more convenient. At the same time, jobs that provided feed, wagons, carriages, and care of the horses were not needed as much. Losing jobs or having to change jobs were bad effects of this car technology.

Technologies and events resulting from the invention and manufacture of cars include:

- drive-through restaurants
- emergency vehicles
- service stations
- new jobs
- pollution from car exhausts
- deaths and injuries from car accidents

1. Which items from the list do you think had ONLY good effects on Earth and its people? Explain why you selected each. **New jobs help people live more securely and comfortably. Emergency vehicles, such as fire trucks and ambulances, help save lives.**
2. Which items from the list do you think had ONLY bad effects on Earth and its people? Explain why you think each effect has not been good. **Pollution from car exhausts causes illness in people and damage to the atmosphere. Deaths and injuries from car accidents bring suffering to many families.**
3. Which items from the list do you think have BOTH good and bad effects? **Answers will vary. A sample answer might be: Paved roads and highways make travel easier. Road construction and maintenance provide jobs. On the other hand, more roads encourage more driving, which pollutes the environment, and construction of roads results in paving land which also harms the environment.**
4. Imagine that all family cars in your community broke down for one month. How would your life be changed? **Answers will vary, but should reflect the need to adapt to the new circumstances by using public transportation, walking, and biking. Answers may also include having to attend a school nearer home; cutting down on activities that involve travel; cleaner air; more exercise.**

6

CHECK FOR UNDERSTANDING

Have students describe what their world would be like if technology did not exist. Students will likely describe a world similar to that of the early humans.

RETEACH

Cooperative Learning: Have Study Buddies make two lists, one describing the benefits and the other the problems of technology.

EXTENSION

For students who have mastered this section, use the **Reinforcement** and **Enrichment** masters or other OPTIONS provided.

3 CLOSE

▶ Ask questions 1-2 in the Section Review.

▶ Inform students that each chapter has a Technology feature where students will learn how scientific discoveries are used.

▶ Have teams of students debate whether technology is good or bad.

SECTION REVIEW ANSWERS

1. It provides many conveniences and enables people to live longer.

2. Answers may include pollution and overpopulation.

YOU DECIDE!

Some students will feel that many disposables are real conveniences and save us money; therefore, the technology is good. Others may argue that most disposable items are an unwise use of technology because valuable resources are used to make them and landfill space is very limited.

PROGRAM RESOURCES

From the **Teacher Resource Package** use:

Science and Society, page 5, Dependence on Plastic.

Technology, page 5, Electron Microscope.

SECTION 1-3

PREPARATION

SECTION BACKGROUND

▶ Strategies are skills or procedures used in problem solving. Strategies can be used singly or in combination to solve a problem.

▶ Most scientists do not see themselves as following a stepwise procedure to solve a problem. Scientists may get new ideas, form new hypotheses, and think of new experiments before previous ones are finished and the data analyzed. However, upon analysis, the scientific process basically follows the course presented in this section.

▶ In a scientific experiment, factors that don't change are the constants. The factor being tested is the independent variable. The factor that changes as a result of changing the independent variable is called the dependent variable.

1 MOTIVATE

Cooperative Learning: Prior to beginning class, place the following objects into six different shoe boxes: a penny, a paper clip, a sponge, a spool, a roll of tape, and a shoe. Tape the boxes shut. During class, list the objects on the chalkboard. Have Paired Partners try to figure out which object is in each box. After all partners have observed all boxes, ask students to explain the problem-solving strategies they used during this activity.

▶ Have students list recently encountered problems on the chalkboard. Lead a discussion on how they solved or could solve these problems. This discussion will help students realize that problem-solving strategies are important not only in science but in everyday life.

1-3 Solving Problems

New Science Words

scientific methods
hypothesis
variable
control
theory
law

Objectives

- ▶ Describe some problem-solving strategies.
- ▶ List steps commonly used as scientific methods.
- ▶ Distinguish between hypotheses, theories, and laws.

Problem-Solving Strategies

Soccer practice, dinner, homework, chores, watching your favorite television program...how will you squeeze them all in tonight? This might be a problem you are facing. There are many methods you can use to find solutions to problems. These are called strategies. Let's look at a strategy you can use to solve the problem of how to squeeze so many activities into one evening.

To solve any problem, you need to have a strategy. Identifying the problem is the first step of any strategy. Next, you need to collect information about the problem. You need to know the basic facts of when soccer practice begins and ends, how much homework you have, what chores need to be done, and when the TV program

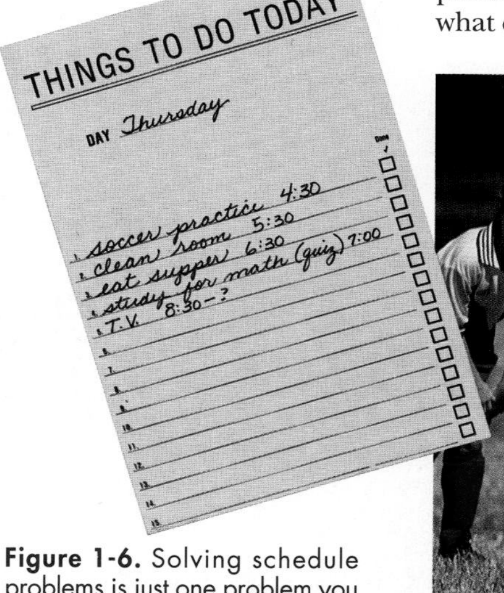

Figure 1-6. Solving schedule problems is just one problem you can learn to solve.

OPTIONS

Meeting Different Ability Levels

For Section 1-3, use the following **Teacher Resource Masters** depending upon individual students' needs.

◆ **Study Guide Master** for all students.

● **Reinforcement Master** for students of average and above average ability levels.

▲ **Enrichment Master** for above average students.

Additional Teacher Resource Package masters are listed in the OPTIONS box throughout the section. The additional masters are appropriate for all students.

◆ **STUDY GUIDE** 7

NAME ______ DATE ______ CLASS ______

STUDY GUIDE — Chapter 1

Solving Problems — Text Pages 12–17

In the blank, write the letter of the term or phrase that best completes each statement.

b 1. The first step in any problem-solving strategy is to ____.
a. collect information about the problem b. identify the problem

b 2. The methods used by scientists for solving problems are known as ____.
a. controls b. scientific methods

a 3. A proposed answer to a problem that can be tested is a ____.
a. hypothesis b. conclusion

b 4. A ____ is a standard for comparison in an experiment.
a. variable b. control

a 5. An explanation backed by results obtained from repeated tests or experiments is a ____.
a. theory b. variable

b 6. A process that uses certain skills to solve problems is called ____.
a. a theory b. critical thinking

a 7. A ____ is a changeable factor in an experiment.
a. variable b. control

a 8. The best experiments test only one ____ at a time.
a. variable b. control

b 9. If a conclusion does not support a hypothesis, the ____.
a. experiment did not work properly b. hypothesis should be revised

b 10. If a hypothesis is supported by new data gathered over a period of time, it may become a ____.
a. control b. theory

a 11. Making lists, drawing graphs, making a model, and eliminating possibilities are all ____ for solving problems.
a. strategies b. variables

b 12. If a hypothesis has been backed by results from repeated tests or experiments, it becomes a ____.
a. variable b. theory

 7

is on. After you have determined these things, you might try writing out a time schedule. First, write in the activities that have fixed times. Then, fill in each of the other activities. You may have to try different arrangements before you find the solution that you think is the best.

In solving this problem, making a list helped you organize the parts of your problem. There are other ways to solve problems. You might try the strategy of eliminating possibilities. You could do this by trying options until you find the one that works. This method is also known as trial and error. Sometimes it is easier to solve a problem by finding out what does *not* work. Another strategy is to solve a simpler, related problem, or to make a model, drawing, or graph to help you visualize the problem. If your first strategy does not work, keep trying different strategies.

Did You Know?

The average worldwide life expectancy has increased from 47.5 years in 1950 to about 65 years at the current time.

Name three problem-solving strategies.

TECHNOLOGY

Building a Better Bicycle

Would you be able to ride your bicycle if it didn't have any pedals? It would be difficult, but you probably could. In fact, that's how the first bicyclists rode their vehicles. People pushed their feet along the ground to propel a machine made of only two wheels and a seat.

In the early 1800s, bicycles were mostly wood, with two metal wheels that were the same size, a handlebar, and no pedals. Bicycle makers then worked on the problem of how to propel the bicycle. They used problem-solving strategies to add pedals and a gear. This allowed the bicycle to be propelled by the rider.

Today's bicycles are radically different from the first bicycles. Problem-solving strategies are used to make bikes lighter. Bicycle makers have experimented with aluminum, carbon fiber, molybdenum, and other very lightweight metals and alloys. Bicycles have been advanced and improved through the use of problem-solving skills.

Think Critically: How could you use problem-solving techniques to choose the most lightweight substance for a bike frame?

● REINFORCEMENT 7

NAME ______ DATE ______ CLASS ______

REINFORCEMENT — Chapter 1

Solving Problems — Text Pages 12–17

Write the terms that match the definitions on the lines provided.

hypothesis 1. A proposed answer to a problem that can be tested
control 2. A standard for comparison in an experiment
variable 3. A changeable factor in an experiment
critical thinking 4. Process that uses certain skills to solve problems
theory 5. An explanation backed by results from repeated tests or experiments
scientific methods 6. Problem-solving strategies used by scientists
strategy 7. Methods for finding solutions to problems

Number these scientific methods from 1 to 5, with 1 being the first step.

1 8. Determining the problem
4 9. Analyzing the results
2 10. Making a hypothesis
5 11. Drawing conclusions
3 12. Testing

Determine which step of these scientific methods corresponds to each of the following activities. Write the appropriate number of the step in the blank.

1 13. I realize the milk in the refrigerator is warm.
3 14. I turn down the setting on the refrigerator control and check the milk's temperature every fifteen minutes.
2 15. I think the refrigerator control may be set too high.
5 16. Based on the temperature of the milk, I conclude that my hypothesis was correct.
4 17. I examine my temperature readings to determine if the temperature has dropped.

 7

▲ ENRICHMENT 7

NAME ______ DATE ______ CLASS ______

ENRICHMENT — Chapter 1

Solving Problems — Text Pages 12–17

HOW CAN YOU DETERMINE VARIABLES AND CONTROLS?

Materials

- large beaker (1)
- small beakers (3)
- hot plate
- stirring rods (3)
- spoon
- paper
- water
- sugar
- pencil

Procedure

1. Work with a team of three.
2. Bring water to a gentle boil in the large beaker on the hot plate.
3. Half fill the first small beaker with this boiling water.
4. Half fill the second small beaker with warm tap water.
5. Half fill the third small beaker with cold water.
6. Have each team member put a spoonful of sugar into a different beaker. All should do this at the same time.
7. Stir contents of 3 beakers for the same length of time. Observe each beaker. Record your observations.

Analyze

1. What was the variable in the experiment? **the water temperature**
2. What was the control? **amount of sugar, amount of water, size of beakers, stirring time, sugar placed in water at the same time**

Conclude

3. How did the variables affect the experiment? **The hotter water dissolved the sugar faster.**

Apply

Suppose you want to know at which temperature a particular dishwashing liquid dissolves the most grease.

4. What would be your variable? **water temperature**
5. What would be the control? **using only one brand of dishwashing liquid, the same amount of liquid, the same size and number of dishes, the same time of soaking, the same type of towel**

 7

TYING TO PREVIOUS KNOWLEDGE: Students have had to solve a variety of problems throughout their lives. This section will help students see that many strategies are used to solve a variety of scientific and nonscientific problems.

OBJECTIVES AND SCIENCE WORDS: Have students review the objectives and science words to become familiar with this section.

2 TEACH

Key Concepts are highlighted.

CONCEPT DEVELOPMENT

▶ Emphasize that there is no set way to solve a problem. Any logical plan can be implemented. In fact, there are often several ways to solve the same problem.

TECHNOLOGY

▶ To have students get a feeling for the diversity of bicycles available today, refer them to a series of articles in *Bicycling,* March, 1990, pp. 150-169. Although the bikes discussed are those used by cycling professionals, students should be able to see how cycles have changed since their inception a few hundred years ago.

▶ Have interested students find drawings or photographs of the first bicycles. Display their findings and have students contrast these models with today's bikes.

Think Critically: Eliminating possibilities and making models are just two strategies that could be used to find the most lightweight substance for a bike frame.

CROSS CURRICULUM

▶ **Social Studies:** Have groups of students brainstorm to compile a list of social problems such as world hunger or war. Then have them suggest problem-solving strategies that might be used to solve each one.

CONCEPT DEVELOPMENT

▶ Discuss inductive and deductive reasoning aspects in determining why the chili discussed in the text tasted bland. In the process of inductive reasoning, one generalizes from many experiences. Having eaten many bowls of chili, one can generalize on the attributes of chili, such as a personal choice of color, texture, and taste. Having made many bowls of chili, one can generalize on the techniques of making it, such as cooking time and temperature. Having reached a general idea of what "good" chili is, *both* from making and eating a lot of it, one can evaluate a particular batch.

▶ From generalizing about the cooking times and temperatures of many batches of chili, one can eliminate these as factors in making this batch bland, unless it was uncooked or burned. This elimination is an example of deductive reasoning, or evaluating from a generalization.

Critical Thinking

Imagine yourself coming home from school on a cold, wintery Friday afternoon. It had begun to snow and the forecast for Saturday was one to three inches of snow. Saturday would be a great day for chili. You get out all of the ingredients and make the chili in a crock-pot so it will be ready for Saturday. After sledding on Saturday morning, you come home and get a bowl of chili.

What is critical thinking?

What went wrong with the chili? Even though you followed your usual recipe, it just seemed to taste bland. After thinking for a bit, you realized that you left out an essential ingredient—chili powder. How did you figure out that lack of chili powder was to blame? Without being aware of it, you probably used some aspect of critical thinking.

Critical thinking is a process that uses certain skills to solve problems. For example, you identified the problem by mentally comparing the bad batch of chili with other batches of chili you've eaten. You separated important information from unimportant information if you realized that the temperature of the chili had little to do with its flavor. You may have examined your assumption that you followed the recipe correctly. After looking at the recipe again, you concluded that chili powder had been left out.

You probably went one step further and analyzed your conclusion. Would leaving out the chili powder have made the chili taste bland? If your answer was "yes," then you may have solved the problem.

This book uses an activity called "Flex Your Brain" to help you think about and examine your thinking. "Flex Your Brain" is a way to keep your thinking on track when you are investigating a topic. It takes you through steps of exploration from what you already know and believe, to new conclusions and awareness. Then, it encourages you to review and talk about the steps you took.

"Flex Your Brain" and other features of this book will help you improve your critical thinking skills. You can get your first chance to "Flex Your Brain" on the next page. You'll become a better problem solver, and your next batch of chili will taste great.

OPTIONS

ENRICHMENT

▶ Have students interview their parents to see how they use problem solving in their lives.

FLEX Your Brain

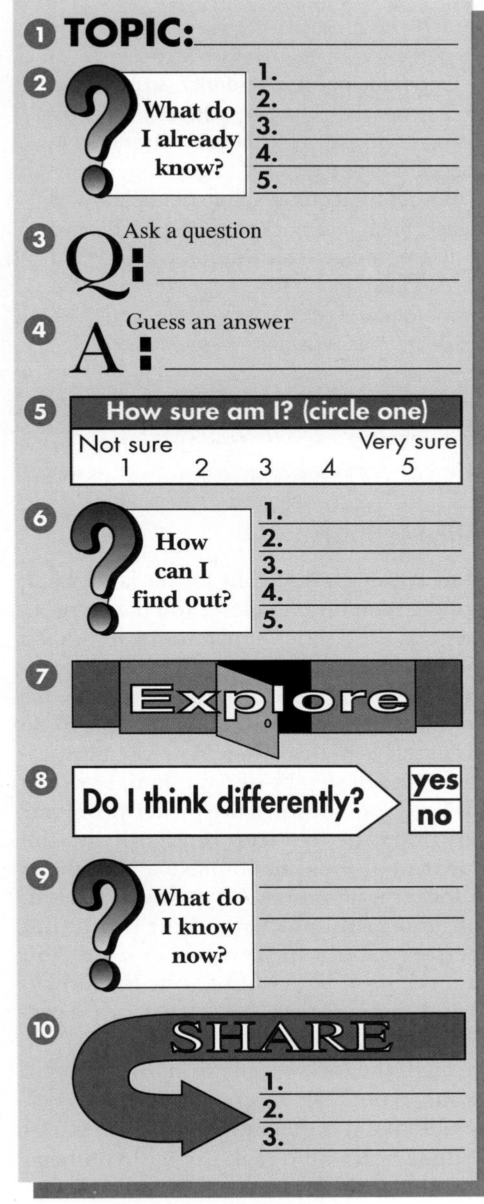

1. Fill in the topic your teacher gives you.
2. Jot down what you already know about the topic.
3. Using what you already know (Step 2), form a question about the topic. Are you unsure about one of the items you listed? Do you want to know more? Do you want to know what, how, or why? Write down your question.
4. Guess an answer to your question. In the next few steps, you will be exploring the reasonableness of your answer. Write down your guess.
5. Circle the number in the box that matches how sure you are of your answer in Step 4. This is your chance to rate your confidence in what you've done so far and, later, to see how your level of sureness affects your thinking.
6. How can you find out more about your topic? You might want to read a book, ask an expert, or do an experiment. Write down ways you can find out more.
7. Make a plan to explore your answer. Use the resources you listed in Step 6. Then, carry out your plan.
8. Now that you've explored, go back to your answer in Step 4. Would you answer differently? Mark one of the boxes.
9. Considering what you learned in your exploration, answer your question again, adding new things you've learned. You may completely change your answer.
10. It's important to be able to talk about thinking. Choose three people to tell about how you arrived at your response in every step. For example, don't just read what you wrote down in Step 2. Try to share how you thought of those things.

CONCEPT DEVELOPMENT

▶To acquaint students with this strategy, divide the class into small groups and have them explore a topic using the Flex Your Brain worksheet. Students should have some familiarity with the topic chosen. Possible topics might include cacti, volcanoes, and robots, or topics from a list the class brainstorms.

TEACHER F.Y.I.

▶ A reproducible version of the Flex Your Brain activity with space for students to write in their responses can be found in the Activity Worksheets booklet in the Teacher Resource Package. See Program Resources box below.

PROGRAM RESOURCES

From the **Teacher Resource Package** use:

Transparency Masters, pages 3-4, Flex Your Brain.

Activity Worksheets, page 5, Flex Your Brain.

Use **Color Transparency** number 2, Flex Your Brain.

PROBLEM SOLVING

Think Critically: Chris tested only one variable—the ability of a color to absorb heat. His constants included the size of the fabric samples, their shapes, and the amount of sun each sample received.

CONCEPT DEVELOPMENT

▶ Emphasize that the process known as the scientific method is not a set "recipe" for scientific research. Instead, it is a group of dynamic processes that each scientist adapts to his or her own needs.

▶ Explain that a hypothesis is an educated guess based on previous knowledge or experience.

▶ Using the background information given on page 12, explain the relationship between a dependent and independent variable.

CHECK FOR UNDERSTANDING

Use the Mini Quiz to check for understanding.

MINI QUIZ

Use the Mini Quiz to check students' recall of chapter content.

1. **In an experiment, the ____ is the proposed answer to the problem being tested.** *hypothesis*
2. **In an experiment, the ____ is the changeable factor.** *variable*
3. **In an experiment, the ____ is a standard of comparison.** *control*

RETEACH

Have students identify the hypothesis, variable, and control of an experiment titled "How does the volume of music affect the way plants grow?" One hypothesis might be that "Loud music stunts plant growth." The variable would be the volume of the music. Control plants would not be exposed to music.

EXTENSION

For students who have mastered this section, use the **Reinforcement** and **Enrichment** masters or other OPTIONS provided.

PROBLEM SOLVING

New Uniforms for the Band

The students in the band had worked hard to raise money to purchase new uniforms. The students were concerned about how hot they would get during football games and parades. Chris determined which color of uniform was the coolest.

Chris designed a scientific experiment to determine which color absorbed the least amount of heat. He obtained fabric samples of each color.

He cut the samples the same size and folded them into pockets. Then, he placed a thermometer inside each pocket and placed them in the sun. After recording the temperature of each sample after a set period of time, he was able to determine which color was the best.

Think Critically: How did Chris use scientific methods in his experiment?

Using Scientific Methods

What are scientific methods?

Suppose that nearly every day, your locker jams. First, you can't get it open, then it won't close. You have a problem to solve. Scientists use a series of planned steps, called **scientific methods,** to solve problems. The basic scientific methods are listed in Table 1-2 on the next page. It's portant to note that scientists don't always follow these exact steps or do the steps in this order. However, most scientists follow some type of step-by-step method. How can scientific methods be used to solve the locker problem?

You've already done the first step by identifying the problem. The next step would be to make a hypothesis about why your locker is jamming. (1) A **hypothesis** is a testable prediction of a problem. You might think that something is getting caught in your locker door. You hypothesize that taking things out of your locker will allow it to open and close properly. You have made a prediction. Now you're ready to test it.

If you remove all of the locker items and the door still doesn't work, your hypothesis was probably incorrect. You would conclude that it isn't jamming because things are stuck in the door. You would make a new hypothesis and start the problem-solving process over again.

EcoTip

Design an experiment to determine which things break down in the environment in one month's time. Use items such as an apple core, a foam cup, a plastic bag, and a carrot.

OPTIONS

INQUIRY QUESTIONS

▶ **Suppose you want to test which of three kinds of paper towels absorbs the most water. What might be your hypothesis?** *Possible hypotheses might be that the thickest towel will absorb the most water, the largest towel will absorb the most, or the most expensive towel will be the most absorbent.*

▶ **How could you test your hypothesis?** *Determine how much water one sheet of each of five different brands of paper towel absorbs by measuring the masses of the dry towels, allowing them to absorb water, and determining and comparing the new masses.*

Every experiment includes variables and controls. A **variable** is a changeable factor in an experiment. The 2
variables in you locker experiment would be the things in your locker, the hinges on the locker, the door, the latch, and the way you open and close your locker. Experiments should only test one variable at a time.

A **control** is a standard for comparison. In the experi- 3
ment with your jammed locker, a neighbor's locker that doesn't jam could be your control. By looking at it, you could tell how a locker should work.

Table 1-2

COMMONLY USED SCIENTIFIC METHODS
1. Determine the problem
2. Make a hypothesis
3. Test your hypothesis
4. Analyze the results
5. Draw conclusions

Theories and Laws

Many things we learn about in science, such as how animals evolve or how continents move, are called theories. Scientists are constantly testing hypotheses. When new data gathered over a long period of time support a hypothesis, scientists become convinced that the hypothesis is correct. They can use such hypotheses to form theories. An explanation backed by results obtained from repeated tests or experiments is a **theory.**

A scientific **law** is a "rule of nature" that describes the behavior of something in nature. Generally, laws predict or describe what will happen in a given situation, but don't explain why. An example of a law is Newton's first law of motion. It states that an object continues in motion, or at rest, until it's acted upon by an outside force.

In this section, you've learned a variety of problem-solving strategies. The "Flex Your Brain" activities will help you improve your critical thinking skills, and by understanding scientific methods, you'll better understand the activities in this book.

What's the difference between a theory and a law?

SECTION REVIEW

1. What are some strategies you can use to solve problems?
2. **Apply:** Imagine that your bike chain came off after riding over a stick, and you think the stick must have been the cause. Is that a hypothesis or a theory?

Comparing and Contrasting — Skill Builder

Compare and contrast a scientific variable with a control. If you need help, refer to Comparing and Contrasting in the **Skill Handbook** on page 683.

CONCEPT DEVELOPMENT

▶ **Why should you test only one variable at a time?** *If more than one variable is tested at a time, you really don't know what is causing the end result. By testing one variable at a time, you can better determine the cause-effect relationship.*

▶ **Suppose you wanted to test the effects of caffeine on mice. Why would you give a second group of mice a noncaffeine diet?** *They would be used as a standard for comparison, or control.*

3 CLOSE

▶ Ask question 1 and the **Apply** Question in the Section Review.

▶ Have students develop a plan or a strategy for solving current problems in science, for example, finding a cure for cancer or stopping global warming.

FLEX Your Brain

Use the Flex Your Brain activity to have students explore SCIENTIFIC METHODS.

SECTION REVIEW ANSWERS

1. Identify the problem; collect information; make lists to help organize information; use trial and error; solve a simpler problem; make a model or drawing or graph; separate important information from unimportant information; analyze your conclusion; use the scientific method.

2. Apply: It's a hypothesis because it's a testable prediction. A theory, on the other hand, is an explanation backed by results from repeated tests.

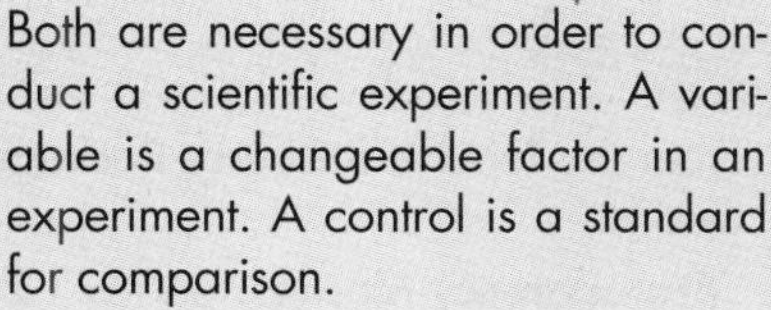

Skill Builder

Both are necessary in order to conduct a scientific experiment. A variable is a changeable factor in an experiment. A control is a standard for comparison.

OPTIONS

ENRICHMENT

▶ Have students research the discovery of some scientific laws, such as laws of planetary motion, Newton's laws, and the law of superposition.

▶ Have students use the scientific method to solve problems. Have them report back to the class on the steps they took to test their hypotheses and how they determined their results.

PROGRAM RESOURCES

From the **Teacher Resource Package** use:

Activity Worksheets, page 5, Flex Your Brain.

Critical Thinking/Problem Solving, page 7, Using Scientific Methods to Save Earth.

Concept Mapping, pages 7-8.

Use **Laboratory Manual** page 1, Problem Solving and Scientific Method; and page 3, The Law of Probability.

SECTION 1-4

PREPARATION

SECTION BACKGROUND

▶ Mass is a measure of the resistance of a body to change in motion.

▶ The density of water is 1 g/mL. The densities of other substances are sometimes compared to the density of water. This comparison is called specific gravity.

PREPLANNING

▶ To prepare for Activity 1-1, obtain graph paper, a metric ruler, string, a graduated cylinder, water, small rocks, and a shoe box for each group of students.

1 MOTIVATE

▶ Ask: **How big is big? How heavy is heavy? How hot is hot? How slow is slow?** *Students should realize that it is difficult to describe size, weight, temperature, and speed unless you can make comparisons. Students should realize that systems of units are needed.*

▶ Show students two identical jars. Fill one with jellybeans, the other with pennies. Ask: **Which jar has the greater volume?** *Some students may realize that both jars have the same volume. Prove this by emptying them and filling each with water. Both hold the same amount.* Refill the jars with the jellybeans and pennies, then ask: **Which jar has more mass? Which weighs more?** *Students will probably say that the jar of pennies has more mass and weighs more. Stress that mass and weight are not the same.*

PROGRAM RESOURCES

From the **Teacher Resource Package** use:

Transparency Masters, pages 1-2, Metric-English Conversions.

Use **Color Transparency** number 1, Metric-English Conversions.

Use **Laboratory Manual** page 7, Measuring Using SI Units; and page 9, Mass and Weight.

1-4 Measurement and Safety

New Science Words

International System of Units (SI)
mass
weight
gravitational force

Objectives

▶ List the SI units for the following measurements: length, mass, weight, area, volume, density, and temperature.

▶ Differentiate between the terms *mass* and *weight* and the terms *area* and *volume.*

▶ State three lab safety rules.

Figure 1-7. A guitar is about one meter long.

Measurement

How could you measure your classroom without a ruler or measuring tape? You might count your steps across the room. You could then say that the room is 25 steps by 30 steps. But this step measurement wouldn't mean the same thing to your friends because their steps would be different from yours. Because of this problem, there are standard units used for measurement.

Today, the measuring system used by most people around the world is the **International System of Units (SI).** SI is a modern version of the metric system, although some forms of the metric system are used in this book. SI is based on a decimal system which uses the number *10* as the base unit.

The standard unit in SI for length is the meter. It's about the length of a guitar. A decimeter is one-tenth of a meter. A centimeter is one one-hundredth of a meter. And a millimeter is one one-thousandth of a meter. Another common unit for longer distances is the kilo-
1 meter. A kilometer is 1000 times greater than a meter. Refer to Appendixes A and B for further explanation of SI and English/SI conversions.

Mass

2 **Mass** is a measure of the amount of matter in an object. Mass depends on the number and kinds of atoms that make up an object. It is measured using a balance. On a balance, it's determined by adding known masses to balance out the mass being studied.

OPTIONS

Meeting Different Ability Levels

For Section 1-4, use the following **Teacher Resource Masters** depending upon individual students' needs.

◆ **Study Guide Master** for all students.

● **Reinforcement Master** for students of average and above average ability levels.

▲ **Enrichment Master** for above average students.

Additional Teacher Resource Package masters are listed in the OPTIONS box throughout the section. The additional masters are appropriate for all students.

◆ STUDY GUIDE 8

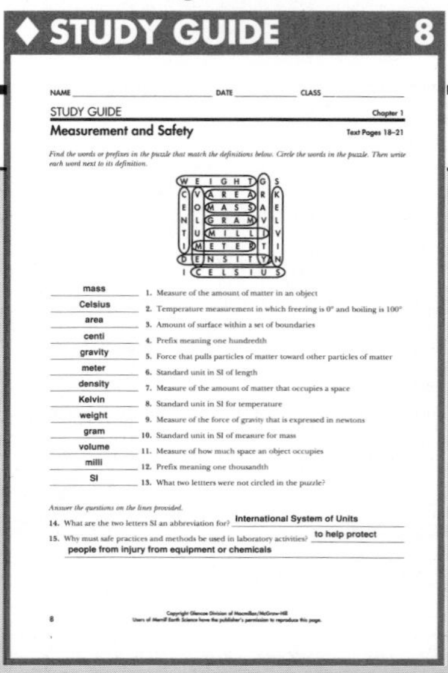

NAME ______ DATE ______ CLASS ______

STUDY GUIDE — Chapter 1

Measurement and Safety — Text Pages 18–21

Find the words or prefixes in the puzzle that match the definitions below. Circle the words in the puzzle. Then write each word next to its definition.

W E I G H T G S
C V A R E A R K
E O M A S S A E
N L G R A M V L
T U M I L L I V
I M E T E R T I
D E N S I T Y N
I C E L S I U S

mass — 1. Measure of the amount of matter in an object
Celsius — 2. Temperature measurement in which freezing is 0° and boiling is 100°
area — 3. Amount of surface within a set of boundaries
centi — 4. Prefix meaning one hundredth
gravity — 5. Force that pulls particles of matter toward other particles of matter
meter — 6. Standard unit in SI of length
density — 7. Measure of the amount of matter that occupies a space
Kelvin — 8. Standard unit in SI for temperature
weight — 9. Measure of the force of gravity that is expressed in newtons
gram — 10. Standard unit in SI of measure for mass
volume — 11. Measure of how much space an object occupies
milli — 12. Prefix meaning one thousandth
SI — 13. What two letters were not circled in the puzzle?

Answer the questions on the lines provided.

14. What are the two letters SI an abbreviation for? International System of Units

15. Why must safe practices and methods be used in laboratory activities? to help protect people from injury from equipment or chemicals

8

The standard unit of measure for mass is a gram. The mass of one bagel is about 57 grams. One gram equals 1000 milligrams, so what would be the mass of one bagel in milligrams? It would be 5700 milligrams.

3 **Weight** is a measure of gravitational force. **Gravitational force** is an attractive force that exists between all objects. A scale measures the force of Earth's gravitational pull on your mass. If you could weigh yourself on the moon, you would weigh one-sixth the amount you weigh on Earth. This is because the moon's gravitational force is one-sixth that of Earth's.

The standard unit for weight is a newton, named after Sir Isaac Newton, who was the first person to describe gravity. In SI, a can of soup weighs 0.4 newtons.

Figure 1-8. When you weigh yourself, you are measuring the force of gravity.

Area, Volume, and Density

Some measurements, such as area, volume, and density, require a combination of SI units. Area is the amount of surface included within a set of boundaries. Let's say you want to know the area of your desk top. First, you'd measure its length and width with a meterstick, and then you'd multiply these two measurements to find the area. In SI, area is expressed in units such as square centimeters (cm^2).

Density is a measure of the amount of matter that occupies a particular space. It's determined by dividing the mass of an object by its volume.

Liquid volume measurements are made using graduated cylinders and beakers. These volumes are usually expressed in milliliters (mL). Because one milliliter of a liquid will just fill a container with a 1 cm^3 volume, milliliters can be expressed as cubic centimeters. For example, a full can of soft drink is 355 mL or 355 cm^3.

Volume is a measure of how much space an object occupies, so if you wanted to know the volume of a solid object, like your book, you'd need to know its length, width, and height. Then you'd multiply these three measurements to find the volume. The cubic meter (m^3) is the basic unit of volume in SI, but liquid volumes are often measured in liters (L) and milliliters (mL).

How is volume calculated?

$$\text{density} = \frac{\text{mass}}{\text{volume}} \qquad D = \frac{m}{v}$$

An SI unit that is often used to express density is grams per cubic centimeter (g/cm^3). How might you express the density of a liquid? We often use grams per milliliter (g/mL).

● REINFORCEMENT 8

NAME ________ DATE ________ CLASS ________

REINFORCEMENT — Chapter 1

Meaurement and Safety — Text Pages 18–21

Match the descriptions in Column I with the terms in Column II. Write the letter of the appropriate term in the blank.

	Column I	Column II
a	1. Force that pulls particles of matter toward other particles of matter	a. gravity
c	2. International System of Units, a modern version of the metric system	b. density
i	3. Measure of the amount of matter in an object	c. SI
d	4. Measure of the force of gravity	d. weight
h	5. Measure of how much space an object occupies	e. Celsius
l	6. Standard unit in SI for length	f. area
f	7. Amount of surface included within a set of boundaries	g. Kelvin
j	8. The standard unit in SI of measure for mass	h. volume
b	9. Measure of the amount of matter that occupies a particular space	i. mass
g	10. SI unit for temperature	j. gram
k	11. Standard unit for weight	k. newton
e	12. Temperature scale in which 0 equals the freezing point and 100 equal the boiling point	l. meter

Use a metric ruler to measure the length and width of the figure below. Then find the area of the figure. Remember area equals length times width.

13. Length: 8 cm
14. Width: 4 cm
15. Area: 32 cm^2

Answer the question on the line provided.

16. Why must you wear goggles and a safety apron whenever an investigation requires heating, pouring, or using chemicals? **Many chemicals are harmful to the eyes and skin.**

8

▲ ENRICHMENT 8

NAME ________ DATE ________ CLASS ________

ENRICHMENT — Chapter 1

Measurement and Safety — Text Pages 18–21

MAKING ESTIMATES

To estimate size is to form a hypothesis. To measure for accurate size is to test your hypothesis. Use a metric ruler for the following steps and then answer the questions.

(1) Without using the ruler, look at your thumb. Estimate its length in centimeter (cm) units. Record your answer in the table in the "Estimate" column.
(2) Measure the length of your thumb. Use both centimeters and the smaller millimeter (mm) units. Since there are 10 mm in one cm, give the length of your thumb as a decimal number of centimeters. Record your answer in the "Measure" column.
(3) Look at your shortest finger and estimate its length. Record your answer.
(4) Measure the length of your shortest finger and record the answer as a decimal number of centimeters.
(5) Repeat the activity, using your index finger (forefinger), and record the estimate and measured length.

	Estimate	Measure
Thumb	**Answers will vary.**	
Shortest finger		
Index finger		

1. Was the estimate you made of your index finger length more accurate than the estimate of your thumb length? Did practice make an accurate estimate easier? **Answers will vary, but practice should enable students to estimate lengths with greater accuracy.**
2. In ancient times, measurements were often based on parts of the human body. A cubit, for example, was the length of an arm from elbow to fingertips. Estimate the length of your arm, then have a classmate measure it. Compare the measurement with those of at least three other classmates. Were all of the measurements the same? **no**
3. Why would a measurement like the cubit not be a satisfactory one today? **More exact measurement is needed.**
4. In what situation might an estimated measure be satisfactory? **Answers will vary but may include such things as distance between two locations or recipe ingredients.**
5. In what situation might an exact measure be needed? **Answers will vary but may include the following: building construction, laboratory work, tailoring, and manufacturing.**

8

TYING TO PREVIOUS KNOWLEDGE: Students are familiar with weighing themselves with scales. They will learn that their weights are measures of the force of gravity on their masses.

OBJECTIVES AND SCIENCE WORDS: Have students review the objectives and science words to become familiar with this section.

2 TEACH

Key Concepts are highlighted.

CONCEPT DEVELOPMENT

▶ Demonstrate how a balance, spring scale, and graduated cylinder are used. Make sure students understand that a balance measures mass, a spring scale measures weight, and a graduated cylinder measures liquid volume.

▶ Have students prepare a photo collage of items used daily that show different units of measurement, such as food labels, road signs, bathroom scales, and so on.

▶ Emphasize that for a measurement to be complete, a unit must follow the number.

▶ **Define the following words: milliliter, micrometer, kilogram.** *milliliter: one one-thousandth of a liter; micrometer: 0.000 001 of a meter; kilogram: 1000 times greater than a gram*

▶ **Convert these units: 1 km = ____ mm; 3 cm = ____ mm; 250 mm = ____ cm.** *1 000 000; 30; 25*

TEACHER F.Y.I.

▶ On Earth, acceleration due to gravity is 9.81 m/s^2. Every second, the speed of a falling body increases by 9.81 meters per second. On the moon, the acceleration due to gravity is one-sixth that of the acceleration on Earth.

CROSS CURRICULUM

▶ **Mathematics:** Have students write the formulas for and explain how to find the area, volume, and density of solid objects.

MINI-Lab

Materials: paper and pencil, Celsius and Fahrenheit thermometers (optional)

Teaching Tips

▶ **Answers:** 85°F = 29°C; −40°C = −40°F; 39°F = 4°C

CHECK FOR UNDERSTANDING

Use the Mini Quiz to check for understanding.

MINI QUIZ

Use the Mini Quiz to check students' recall of chapter content.

1. **One kilometer equals _____ meters.** *1000*
2. **_____ is a measure of the amount of matter in an object.** *Mass*
3. **The measure of the force of gravity on an object is the object's _____ .** *weight*
4. **What is the temperature scale used by many scientists?** *Celsius*

RETEACH

Have students take measurements from food labels and practice converting them to smaller and larger SI units.

EXTENSION

For students who have mastered this section, use the **Reinforcement** and **Enrichment** masters or other OPTIONS provided.

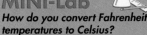

MINI-Lab

How do you convert Fahrenheit temperatures to Celsius?

Temperatures are often reported for public weather information in the non-SI units of the Fahrenheit scale, not the Celsius scale. You can change the temperature reading on one scale to the reading on the other scale by knowing how to convert. To convert from °F to °C, subtract 32 from the Fahrenheit temperature and divide by 1.8. To convert from °C to °F, multiply the Celsius temperature by 1.8 and add 32. Use this approach to convert the following temperatures.

85°F to °C
−40°C to °F
39°F to °C

Temperature

Temperature is a measure of how hot or cold something is. As you probably know, temperature is measured with a thermometer. What you probably didn't know is that the SI unit for temperature is a kelvin. On the Kelvin scale, absolute zero is 0, the coldest temperature. The symbol for kelvin is K. Instead of using kelvin thermometers, many scientists use Celsius thermometers. 4 The symbol for a Celsius degree is °C. The Celsius temperature scale is based on the freezing and boiling points of water. The freezing point of pure water is 0°C, and the boiling point is 100°C. A comfortable room temperature is 21°C, and the average human body temperature is about 37°C. You can use these temperatures as reference points when you measure other Celsius temperatures. Now, suppose you wanted to change Celsius temperatures to SI. You'd simply add 273.16 to the degrees Celsius to find the number of kelvins.

$$\text{degrees Celsius} + 273.16 = \text{kelvin}$$

Making accurate measurements in SI is an important part of any experiment. If you don't make accurate measurements, your results and conclusions are invalid.

Safety

The laboratory activities you'll complete in this book will require you to handle potentially hazardous materials. When performing these activities, safe practices and methods must be used. Scientific equipment and chem-

Figure 1-9. Temperature is a measurement we use almost daily.

OPTIONS

INQUIRY QUESTIONS

▶ **Why should you never use laboratory glassware as food or drink containers?** *They are not sanitary and may even contain poisonous substances.*

▶ **Why should you always wash your hands thoroughly after working in the lab?** *Washing removes any substances that might cause harm.*

PROGRAM RESOURCES

From the **Teacher Resource Package** use:

Activity Worksheets, page 10, Mini-Lab: How do you convert Fahrenheit temperatures to Celsius?

Cross-Curricular Connections, page 5, First Aid in the Laboratory.

icals need to be handled safely and properly. The safety rules that follow will help you protect yourself and others from injury and will make you aware of possible hazards.

1. Before beginning any lab, understand the safety symbols shown in Appendix D, on page 665.
2. Wear goggles and a safety apron whenever an investigation involves heating, pouring, or using chemicals.
3. Always slant test tubes away from yourself and others when heating them. Keep all materials away from open flames. Tie back long hair and loose clothing.
4. Never eat or drink in the lab, and never use laboratory glassware as food or drink containers. Never inhale chemicals, and don't taste any substance or draw any material into a tube with your mouth.
5. Know what to do in case of fire. Also, know the location and proper use of the fire extinguisher, safety shower, fire blanket, first aid kit, and fire alarm.
6. Report any accident or injury to your teacher.
7. When cleaning up, dispose of chemicals and other materials as directed by your teacher, and always wash your hands thoroughly after working in the lab.

Figure 1-10. Several safety rules are being followed by this student.

SECTION REVIEW

1. List the SI units for the following measurements: length, mass, weight, area, volume, density, and temperature.
2. Explain the differences between mass and weight and between area and volume.
3. When should you use safety goggles? Refer to Appendix D on page 665.
4. **Apply:** Why do you suppose you should always slant test tubes away from yourself and others when heating them? Why should you tie back long hair and loose clothing?

Measuring in SI — Skill Builder

Use your knowledge of SI units to answer the following questions. If you need help, refer to Measuring in SI in the **Skill Handbook** on page 684.

1. Which SI unit would you use to measure the amount of orange juice in a glass?
2. How many meters are in a kilometer?
3. Which unit would you use to measure the amount of carpet needed to cover the floor of your bedroom?

CONCEPT DEVELOPMENT

▶ Show students the location of the fire extinguisher, safety shower, fire blanket, first aid kit, and fire alarm. Remind students that they are to use this equipment **only** when an emergency arises.

▶ Show students the designated containers for broken glass and solid substances.

3 CLOSE

▶ Ask questions 1-3 and the **Apply** Question in the Section Review.

▶ Have students do Activity 1-1.

SECTION REVIEW ANSWERS

1. Length is measured in meters; mass in grams; weight in newtons; area in square meters or square centimeters; volume in cubic meters; density in grams per cubic centimeter; and temperature in degrees Kelvin.

2. Mass is the amount of matter in an object. Weight is a measure of the force of gravity on an object's mass. Area is the amount of surface included within a set of boundaries, and volume is a measure of how much space an object occupies.

3. Safety goggles should be worn when heating, pouring, or using chemicals, or whenever danger to the eyes exists.

4. Apply: By slanting test tubes away from yourself and others, you prevent boiling liquids from splattering anyone. Tying back long hair and loose clothing avoids their catching on fire or accidentally getting into chemicals.

Skill Builder

1. milliliters
2. 1000 m = 1 km
3. cm^2 or m^2

ENRICHMENT

▶ Have students research several systems of units, including SI, Native American, Chinese, and Greek. Have them compare and contrast the different systems.

▶ Have interested students research the history of the metric system and how it evolved into SI.

▶ Have each student list at least ten careers related to safety.

ACTIVITY 1-1
30 minutes

OBJECTIVE: Calculate and **determine** length, area, and volume.

PROCESS SKILLS applied in this activity:
▶ **Measuring** in Procedure Steps 1, 4, 5, and 6.
▶ **Using Numbers** in Procedure Steps 2-6 and 8 and Conclude and Apply Question 5.
▶ **Interpreting Data** in Analyze Questions 1 and 3.
▶ **Communicating** in Analyze Question 2.
▶ **Hypothesizing** in Conclude and **Apply** Question 4.

COOPERATIVE LEARNING Have students work as Science Investigation teams of three students each.

TEACHING THE ACTIVITY

▶ Start to collect shoe boxes at least a week before you intend to do this activity.
▶ Remind students that surface area is determined by counting the number of squares on the graph paper.
Troubleshooting: Avoid using porous sandstones in this activity. Best results are obtained using rocks such as quartzite, granite, or marble.
▶ It is important that the rock fit comfortably inside the graduated cylinder.
▶ Procedure Steps 5-8 demonstrate how volume can be measured using the displacement method. Show students how to read the water level in the graduated cylinder. Discuss the term *meniscus* with students.

PROGRAM RESOURCES

From the **Teacher Resource Package** use:

Activity Worksheets, page 6-7, Activity 1-1: Determining Length, Area, and Volume.

ACTIVITY 1-1
Determining Length, Area, and Volume

Problem: *How are length, area, and volume determined?*

Materials 

- graph paper
- metric ruler
- string
- graduated cylinder (100 mL)
- small rock
- shoe box
- water

Procedure

1. Measure and record the length, width, and height of the shoe box using the metric ruler.
2. Calculate and record the area of the top, side, and end of the shoe box using the equation: area = length × width.
3. Calculate and record the volume of the shoe box using the equation: volume = length × width × height.
4. Trace the outline of the rock on a piece of graph paper. Determine the surface area of the rock. Explain your answer.
5. Fill the graduated cylinder half full of water and record the volume in mL.
6. Tie a piece of string around the rock and lower it into the cylinder. Record the volume reading. Remember to express each volume measurement in cm^3 or mL.
7. Remove the rock. Check to make sure that the cylinder has the same volume of water in it as when you started.
8. Subtract the volume of the cylinder with water from the volume of the cylinder with the water and the rock. Record the volume of the rock.

Analyze

1. How did you determine the volume of the box?
2. Which was easier to measure, the area or the volume of the rock?
3. Why did you need to know the volume of water in the cylinder before you added the rock?

Conclude and Apply

4. How could you determine the volume of an oddly shaped object that floats in water?
5. What area does a house 10 m wide, 15 m long and 18 meters high cover?

Data and Observations

Object	Length	Width	Height	Area	Volume
Shoe box					
Coffee can					
Rock					
Graduated cylinder					

ANSWERS TO QUESTIONS

1. by multiplying the length times the width times the height in millimeters or centimeters
2. the volume
3. The volume of the rock is determined by the water level change. The volume of the water must be measured before the rock is immersed in order to determine the change in water level.
4. Answers will vary. Students may say to force the object under the water surface. A second method is to attach the object to a heavy sinker and subtract the volume of the sinker from the combined volume.
5. Only the dimensions of width and length are used to determine area; thus, the area is 150 m^2.

CHAPTER REVIEW

SUMMARY

1-1: What Is Science?

1. Chemistry is the study of properties and composition of matter. Physics is the study of forces, energy, motion, and their effects on matter. Biology is the study of living organisms. The study of Earth is earth science.

2. Some topics studied in earth science are volcanoes, earthquakes, fossils, weather, climate, mountains, land use, planets, stars, and oceans.

1-2: Science and Technology

1. Technology has made possible various appliances you use every day, such as calculators and TVs. Technology also has allowed people to explore space and make advances in medicine.

2. Technology allows some people to live longer, but sometimes with a poor quality of life. Technology also contributes to pollution.

1-3: Solving Problems

1. Problem-solving strategies include identifying the problem; collecting data about the problem; eliminating possibilities; using trial and error; solving a simpler, related problem; and making a model or drawing.

2. Commonly used scientific methods include determining the problem, making a hypothesis, testing, analyzing results, drawing conclusions.

3. A hypothesis is a testable prediction for a problem. Hypotheses may be used to form theories, which are explanations backed by results obtained from repeated tests or experiments. A law is a "rule of nature" that generally describes what will happen in a given situation, but not why it happens.

1-4: Measurement and Safety

1. In SI, the unit for length is the meter; mass, the gram; weight, the newton; area, square centimeters; volume, cubic meters; and density, grams per cubic centimeter.

2. Mass is the amount of matter in an object. Weight is a measure of the force of gravity. Area is the amount of surface in a set of boundaries.

3. Lab safety includes: understanding how to do the activity, using caution while working with flames, never eating or drinking in the lab, using care with all substances, and reporting any accident to your teacher.

KEY SCIENCE WORDS

a. **astronomy**
b. **control**
c. **geology**
d. **gravitational force**
e. **hypothesis**
f. **International System of Units (SI)**
g. **law**
h. **mass**
i. **meteorology**
j. **oceanography**
k. **science**
l. **scientific methods**
m. **technology**
n. **theory**
o. **variable**
p. **weight**

UNDERSTANDING VOCABULARY

Match each phrase with the correct term from the list of Key Science Words.

1. having knowledge by observing and studying things around you
2. the study of objects in space
3. the use of scientific discoveries
4. a testable prediction
5. a factor in an experiment that changes
6. a scientific "rule of nature"
7. a modern version of the metric system
8. the amount of matter in an object
9. a measure of gravitational force
10. the study of weather conditions

OPTIONS

ASSESSMENT

To assess student understanding of material in this chapter, use the resources listed.

COOPERATIVE LEARNING

Consider using cooperative learning in the THINK AND WRITE CRITICALLY, APPLY, and MORE SKILL BUILDERS sections of the Chapter Review.

PROGRAM RESOURCES

From the **Teacher Resource Package** use:

Chapter Review, pages 5-6.

Chapter and Unit Tests, pages 5-8, Chapter Test.

CHAPTER REVIEW

SUMMARY

Have students read the summary statements to review the major concepts of the chapter.

UNDERSTANDING VOCABULARY

1. k
2. a
3. m
4. e
5. o
6. g
7. f
8. h
9. p
10. i

CHAPTER REVIEW

CHECKING CONCEPTS

1. d
2. b
3. b
4. c
5. d
6. c
7. b
8. a
9. c
10. d

UNDERSTANDING CONCEPTS

11. oceanography or biology
12. geology
13. Scientific methods
14. weight
15. Volume

THINK AND WRITE CRITICALLY

16. A volcano like Mount St. Helens erupts with much force, throwing material into the air. Thus, a knowledge of forces, motion, and energy is needed to study volcanoes. Knowing the composition of the material ejected might also help the scientist with her study of volcanoes.

17. Advances in medicine have enabled humans to live longer. The prolonged life span has led to overpopulation. The increased number of people has lead to over-usage of many of Earth's resources.

18. A hypothesis is an educated guess as to what the answer is to a problem. A theory is an explanation of a problem that is backed by results obtained from repeated testing.

19. Both are measures. Mass is a measure of the amount of matter in an object. It is measured using a balance. Weight is a measure of the force of gravity and is determined using a spring scale.

20. Volume of a solid is the length times the width times the height. Area is length times width. By measuring the third dimension, height, the volume of the box could be calculated.

CHAPTER REVIEW

CHECKING CONCEPTS

Choose the word or phrase that completes the sentence or answers the question.

1. The word *science* means to ______.
   - **a.** have knowledge
   - **b.** solve problems
   - **c.** observe things
   - **d.** all of these
2. ______ is the study of organisms.
   - **a.** Chemistry
   - **b.** Biology
   - **c.** Geology
   - **d.** Physics
3. Oceanographers study Earth's ______
   - **a.** place in space
   - **b.** oceans
   - **c.** weather
   - **d.** glaciers
4. ______ involves the study of stars.
   - **a.** Chemistry
   - **b.** Physics
   - **c.** Astronomy
   - **d.** None of these
5. Technology has resulted in ______.
   - **a.** advances in medicine
   - **b.** air pollution
   - **c.** computers
   - **d.** all of these
6. A ______ is a standard used for comparison in an experiment.
   - **a.** variable
   - **b.** theory
   - **c.** control
   - **d.** law
7. The length of your toe is best measured in ______.
   - **a.** meters
   - **b.** centimeters
   - **c.** cubic centimeters
   - **d.** degrees Celsius
8. A balance is used to measure ______.
   - **a.** mass
   - **b.** weight
   - **c.** volume
   - **d.** density
9. ______ is measured with a thermometer.
   - **a.** Length
   - **b.** Area
   - **c.** Temperature
   - **d.** Volume
10. Which of these is *not* a lab safety rule?
    - **a.** Slant tests tubes away from people when heating them.
    - **b.** Know where the fire extinguisher is.
    - **c.** Wash your hands after working in the lab.
    - **d.** Taste substances to find out what they are.

UNDERSTANDING CONCEPTS

Complete each sentence.

11. Finding out how sea lillies feed would be studied in ______.
12. Soils are studied in the field of ______.
13. ______ could be used to find out how light affects plants.
14. The SI unit of ______ is the newton.
15. ______ is a measure of how much space an object occupies.

THINK AND WRITE CRITICALLY

16. Why would a scientist studying a volcano like Mount Saint Helens also need some knowledge of physics and chemistry?
17. How have advances in technology been harmful to our planet?
18. How does a theory differ from a hypothesis?
19. Compare and contrast mass and weight.
20. How could you determine the volume of a cardboard box given that its area is 100 m^2?

APPLY

21. Brent had decided to go to college to become a sports trainer. In addition to human biology courses, she was required to take a physics course. Explain
22. Describe how you use technology to do your homework.
23. Suppose you had two plants—a cactus and a palm. You planted them both in potting soil and watered them daily. After a week, the cactus was dead. What problem-solving strategies could you use to find out why the cactus died?
24. Are the steps of the scientific method always followed in the order given on page 17? Explain.

25. The moon's gravitational force is one-sixth hat of our planet. How would your mass differ on the moon?

MORE SKILL BUILDERS

If you need help, refer to the Skill Handbook.

1. **Concept Mapping:** Make a concept map using the following terms and phrases: *centimeters; kilometer; deciliter; liquid medicine for a baby; distance from Houston, TX, to Columbus, OH; and area of a postage stamp, the appropriate use.*

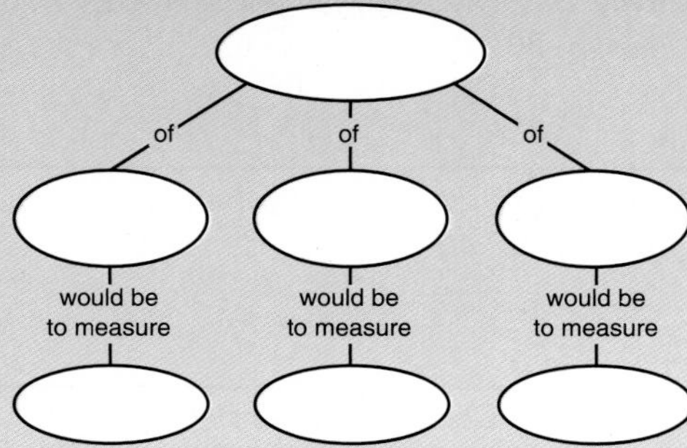

2. **Using Variables, Constants, and Controls:** Suppose you wanted to know whether cold water causes fish to breathe slower than they do in warm water. How would you set up a simple experiment to test this?
3. **Comparing and Contrasting:** Contrast science and technology.
4. **Sequencing:** Ann wants to see how much rain falls in her city during March. Sequence the following steps in the most logical order that she needs to follow to solve her problem.
   a. Collect rain.
   b. Make a rain gauge.
   c. Measure the amount of rainfall each day.
   d. Research how much rain usually falls during March in her city.
   e. Hypothesize how much rain will fall.
   f. Graph her results.
5. **Measuring in SI:** Describe how you would calculate the volume of a coffee can.

PROJECTS

1. Perform an activity to study what happens to air as it is heated. Partially fill a balloon with air. Tape two wooden sticks parallel to the sides of the balloon. Then tape the balloon to a ring stand with a heating lamp above it. Record the temperature near the balloon, the size of the balloon, and the time at set intervals. Use SI units. Record your data in a table.
2. Design an experiment to determine the effects of water on small plants. Use three identical plants and give each a different amount of water every other day. Record the amount of water used and plant growth using SI units.

APPLY

21. Knowing the parts of the body and the forces and motions that affect these parts, as well as their effects on athletes, is important to a sports trainer.
22. Answers will vary but students might list writing implements, calculators, electricity, and computers.
23. Answers will vary but may include collecting information about the requirements needed by both plants to survive and then eliminating possibilities.
24. Although this sequence is probably the most logical, often experiments lead to the formulation of new hypotheses or data, which require that further testing be done on the same problem. The steps are not always followed in that order.
25. It wouldn't. Mass is a measure of the amount of matter in an object. You would have the same mass no matter where you were.

MORE SKILL BUILDERS

1. Concept Mapping: See below left.
2. Using Variables, Controls, and Constants: One possible solution is to have three bowls containing the same number, age, and size of goldfish. The bowls would be identical in every way, except that one bowl would be slightly heated, one would be slightly cooled, and one would remain at room temperature as the control. Fish could be observed for one hour. The variable of the activity is temperature.
3. Comparing and Contrasting: Science is a process of observing and studying things in order to understand the world. Technology applies what is learned through science to improve our style of life.
4. Sequencing: Answers may vary slightly, but the most logical sequence is probably d, e, b, a, c, and f.
5. Measuring in SI: First, the diameter of the top of the can should be measured. The radius of a circle is one-half the diameter. Then by measuring the height of the cylinder, the formula $1/2\pi r^2 \times$ *height* could be used to calculate the volume of the can.

Possible Solution:

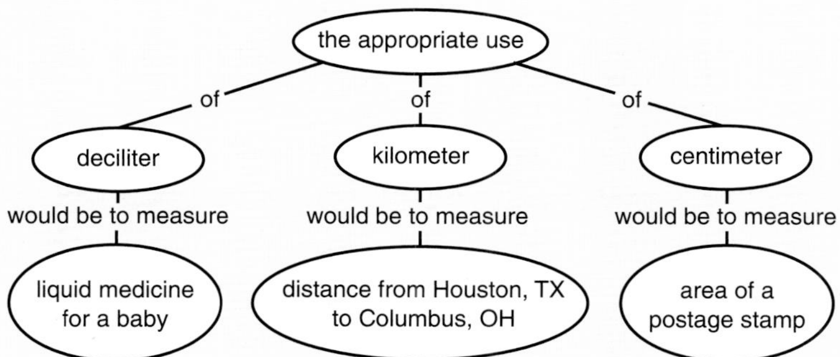

CHAPTER

2 Matter and Its Changes

CHAPTER SECTION	OBJECTIVES	ACTIVITIES
2-1 Atoms (1 day)	1. **Identify** matter as anything that has mass and takes up space. 2. **Describe** the internal structure of an atom. 3. **Relate** that isotopes of the same element have the same atomic number but different mass numbers.	
2-2 Combinations of Atoms (2 days)	1. **Discuss** several ways atoms combine to form compounds. 2. **Compare** and **contrast** compounds and mixtures.	**MINI-Lab:** *What are some different forms of matter?* p. 36 **Activity 2-1:** *Measuring Physical Properties,* p. 39
2-3 Matter (2 days)	1. **Distinguish** between chemical and physical properties. 2. **Contrast** the four states of matter.	**MINI-Lab:** *What happens when water freezes?* p. 46
2-4 Superconductors Science & Society (2 days)	1. **Compare** and **contrast** superconductors with other conductors. 2. **Discuss** one possible use of superconducting materials.	**Activity 2-2:** *Determining Density,* p. 50
Chapter Review		

ACTIVITY MATERIALS

FIND OUT	ACTIVITIES		MINI-LABS	
Page 27 clear plastic cup tea bag ten sugar cubes	**2-1 Measuring Physical Properties, p. 39** balance graduated cylinder (100 mL or larger) 2 metersticks 3 thermometers stick rock sample string globe water	**2-2 Determining Density, p. 50** pan balance beaker (100 mL) piece of quartz graduated cylinder (250 mL) water piece of clay small wood block small metal block	**What are some different forms of matter? p. 36** paper pencil beakers water sand, sugar, or salt	**What happens when water freezes? p. 46** water graduated cylinder masking tape freezer

CHAPTER FEATURES	TEACHER RESOURCE PACKAGE	OTHER RESOURCES
Skill Builder: *Outlining,* p. 33	**Ability Level Worksheets** ◆ ***Study Guide,*** p. 9 ● ***Reinforcement,*** p. 9 ▲ ***Enrichment,*** p. 9 **Critical Thinking/Problem Solving,** p. 8 **Cross-Curricular Connections,** p. 6 **Transparency Masters,** pp. 5-6	**Color Transparency 3,** Periodic Table
Technology: *One at a Time!* p. 35 **Problem Solving:** *Filled to the Rim?* p. 37 **Skill Builder:** *Concept Mapping,* p. 38	**Ability Level Worksheets** ◆ ***Study Guide,*** p. 10 ● ***Reinforcement,*** p. 10 ▲ ***Enrichment,*** p. 10 **Concept Mapping,** pp. 9-10 **Activity Worksheet,** pp. 12-13 **MINI-Lab Worksheet,** p. 18	**Lab Manual:** *Mixtures and Compounds,* pp. 11-12 **Lab Manual:** *Ions,* pp. 13-14 **Lab Manual:** *Electrical Charges,* pp. 15-16
Skill Builder: *Making and Using Tables,* p. 47	**Ability Level Worksheets** ◆ ***Study Guide,*** p. 11 ● ***Reinforcement,*** p. 11 ▲ ***Enrichment,*** p. 11 **MINI-Lab Worksheet,** p. 19	**Lab Manual:** *Density and Buoyancy,* pp. 17-18 **Lab Manual:** *States of Matter,* pp. 19-20
You Decide! p. 49	**Ability Level Worksheets** ◆ ***Study Guide,*** p. 12 ● ***Reinforcement,*** p. 12 ▲ ***Enrichment,*** p. 12 **Science and Society,** p. 6 **Activity Worksheet,** pp. 14-15	
Summary Key Science Words Understanding Vocabulary Checking Concepts Understanding Concepts Think & Write Critically Apply More Skill Builders Projects	**Chapter Review,** pp. 7-8 **Chapter Test,** pp. 9-12 **Unit Test,** pp. 13-14	**Chapter Review Software** **Test Bank**

◆ **Basic** ● **Average** ▲ **Advanced**

ADDITIONAL MATERIALS

SOFTWARE	AUDIOVISUAL	BOOKS/MAGAZINES
Structure of Matter, Classroom Consortia Media. *Physical or Chemical,* EME. *Earth Chemistry,* Queue.	*Explaining Matter: Molecules in Motion,* film, EBEC. *What Are Things Made Of?,* film, Coronet/MTI. *Mixtures, Solutions, and Compounds,* filmloop, Science Software. *The Nature of Matter,* video, CRM.	Hamblin, Kenneth W. *The Earth's Dynamic Systems: A Textbook of Physical Geology.* Edina, Mn: Burgess International Group, Inc., 1985 Matsubara, T. *The Structure and Properties of Matter.* NY: Springer-Verlag New York Inc., 1982. Zuborwski, Bernie. *Messing Around with Baking Chemistry: A Children's Museum Activity Book.* Boston, MA: Little, Brown. & Co., 1981.

CHAPTER

2

MATTER AND ITS CHANGES

THEME DEVELOPMENT: Structure is the main theme covered in Chapter 2. The properties of matter are determined by the structure of the molecules or atoms that compose the matter. Models are used to show atomic structures.

CHAPTER OVERVIEW

- **Section 2-1:** Atoms, the building blocks of matter, and their internal structures are described in this section. Mass number and atomic number are defined. The structural relationship between atoms and elements is explored, and some common uses of elements are discussed.
- **Section 2-2:** This section describes how atoms combine to form molecules and compounds. Compounds and mixtures are discussed in terms of physical and chemical changes.
- **Section 2-3:** Physical properties of matter, with an emphasis on density, are presented in this section. The four states of matter are compared and contrasted. Students also discover that when matter changes from one state to another, energy is gained or lost by atoms or molecules.
- **Section 2-4: Science and Society:** The possibilities and problems associated with using superconductors to store electricity are explored.

CHAPTER VOCABULARY

matter
atoms
elements
protons
neutrons
electrons
isotopes
molecule
compound
chemical properties
ions
mixture
physical properties
density
superconductors

CHAPTER

2 Matter and Its Changes

26

OPTIONS

For Your Gifted Students

- Have students gather small, disposable objects from home and school such as foil, spools, candles, rubber bands, paper clips, buttons, and so on. Artistically talented students can take these objects with different physical characteristics and form a sculpture (mixture).
- Have students brainstorm to compile a list of the many mixtures of people and their diverse characteristics. Responses might include musical groups, people in a classroom, other school groups, city residents, people in the workplace, club members, and so on. Ask each student to pick one of these mixtures and write a story using these people as the characters.

You've probably combined ingredients to form a mixture called a pizza. You may have made ice tea to drink with your pizza. If you added sugar to your tea, you created another mixture called a solution. In fact, you make and use many mixtures each day. But do you know what mixtures are? Why is sweetened tea a special type of mixture called a solution?

FIND OUT!

Do this activity to find out how much sugar can be dissolved in tea.

Make yourself a cup of warm tea in a cup that allows you to see the bottom. Place a sugar cube in the tea and stir until all of the sugar dissolves. Continue adding sugar cubes, one at a time, until no more sugar can be dissolved. How many sugar cubes dissolved in the tea before sugar started collecting on the bottom of the cup? Try the activity again using cold tea. Does temperature affect the amount of sugar that can dissolve?

Gearing Up

Previewing the Chapter

Use this outline to help you focus on important ideas in this chapter.

Section 2-1 Atoms
- The Building Blocks of Matter
- The Structure of Atoms
- Mass Numbers and Atomic Numbers

Section 2-2 Combinations of Atoms
- How Atoms Combine
- Ions
- Mixtures

Section 2-3 Matter
- Physical Properties of Matter
- Density
- States of Matter
- Changing the State of Matter
- Changes in Physical Properties

Section 2-4 Science and Society Superconductors
- How Can Superconductors Store Energy?

Previewing Science Skills

- In the **Skill Builders**, you will outline, make concept maps, and make and use tables.
- In the **Activities**, you will observe, collect and organize data.
- In the **MINI-Labs**, you will classify, observe, and infer.

What's next?

Now that you've discovered how much sugar dissolves in a cup of tea, learn why this happens. In this chapter, you'll investigate the basic building blocks of matter — atoms and molecules. And you'll learn that the structure of atoms and molecules in a substance affects how it behaves in the presence of other substances.

27

For Your Mainstreamed Students

In one area of the classroom, open a bottle of perfume, clove oil, or oil of peppermint without identifying the substance to the students. Have students throughout the room raise their hands when they detect the new odor. You may want to have students determine the time it takes the different substances to travel laterally, or place students at varying heights in the room. Students should be able to describe the direction of the flow of molecules of the gas fumes from the bottle through the air.

INTRODUCING THE CHAPTER

Use the Find Out activity to introduce students to mixtures. Inform students that they will learn more about how substances combine as they read the chapter.

FIND OUT!

Preparation: Several days before beginning this chapter, obtain clear plastic cups, tea bags, and a box of sugar cubes.

Materials: Provide one clear plastic cup, one tea bag, and ten sugar cubes for each group of three to four students.

Cooperative Learning: Form Science Investigation groups of three students per group. As one student stirs the tea, another can be placing sugar cubes into it. The third student should record all observations. Have students change roles for the second part of the activity.

Teaching Tips

- Test the water to be used for the tea to make sure it is warm but not hot enough to cause burns.
- Make sure that the student stirring stirs the tea after each sugar cube is placed into the cup until all of the cube dissolves.
- The student who is assigned to observe the mixture must make sure that the whole cube has dissolved before a new cube is added.
- Have the recorder count the number of sugar cubes that completely dissolved in the tea.
- Remind students of safety procedures to be followed when using liquids in any activity.

Gearing Up

Have students study the Gearing Up feature to familiarize themselves with the chapter. Discuss the relationships of the topics in the outline.

What's Next?

Before beginning the first section, make sure students understand the connection between the Find Out activity and the topics to follow.

SECTION 2-1

PREPARATION

SECTION BACKGROUND

▶ Of the 109 known elements, only 90 occur in nature. Elements that do not occur in nature are those with atomic numbers from 93 to 109, as well as technetium, atomic number 43, and promethium, atomic number 61.

▶ Present-day physicists believe an atom has no definite shape and that electrons can be anywhere in an atom's electron cloud.

▶ The maximum number of electrons in an energy level within the electron cloud at any given time can be determined using the formula $2n^2$, where n represents the number of the energy level. For example, the first energy level can hold $(2)(1^2)$, or 2 electrons. The fourth energy level can hold $(2)(4^2)$, or 32 electrons.

▶ Each energy level is divided into orbitals. Each orbital can hold up to two electrons of opposite spin.

▶ Appendix E shows the periodic table. Vertical columns of elements in the periodic table are families or groups. Elements within a family or group have similar properties, the same number of electrons in the outermost orbital, and can replace one another in a compound. Horizontal rows of elements are called periods.

PREPLANNING

▶ Obtain small rock samples to be used in Activity 2-1.

▶ If possible, obtain a large periodic table and display it on the wall in the room.

▶ Obtain a set of colorful, interlocking, plastic building blocks.

▶ Polystyrene balls of various sizes and colors and toothpicks are needed to make models of different atoms.

2-1 Atoms

New Science Words

matter
atoms
elements
protons
neutrons
electrons
isotopes

Objectives

- ▶ **Identify matter as anything that has mass and takes up space.**
- ▶ **Describe the internal structure of an atom.**
- ▶ **Relate that isotopes of the same element have the same atomic number but different mass numbers.**

The Building Blocks of Matter

What do this book, the air you breathe, and the food you eat all have in common? The book, the air, and the food are all matter. **Matter** is anything that takes up space and has mass. You can't always see matter; for example, you can't see air. On the other hand, not everything you see is matter. You can see light reflecting off surfaces, but light doesn't take up space or have mass. Light, despite being visible, isn't matter.

Matter is all around you, yet various forms can be very different. Air is a colorless gas, water is a transparent liquid, and rocks are colorful solids. Why do the characteristics of one form of matter differ from the characteristics of another? This chapter will help you answer that question.

Figure 2-1. More than 99 percent of the matter in our solar system is contained in the sun.

OPTIONS

Meeting Different Ability Levels

For Section 2-1, use the following **Teacher Resource Masters** depending upon individual students' needs.

◆ **Study Guide Master** for all students.

● **Reinforcement Master** for students of average and above average ability levels.

▲ **Enrichment Master** for above average students.

Additional Teacher Resource Package masters are listed in the OPTIONS box throughout the section. The additional masters are appropriate for all students.

◆ STUDY GUIDE 9

NAME ______________ DATE ________ CLASS ________

STUDY GUIDE — Chapter 2

Atoms — Text Pages 28–33

Circle the term in parentheses that makes each statement correct.

1. Protons are particles (outside, in) the nucleus of an atom.
2. Electrons are atomic particles with a (positive, negative) charge.
3. An example of matter is (air, light).
4. The building blocks of matter are (atoms, compounds).
5. (Neutrons, Protons) are particles in the atom's nucleus that have no electric charge.
6. The atomic particles outside of the atom's nucleus are (electrons, protons).
7. Substances made up of only one kind of atom are called (isotopes, elements).
8. Isotopes are atoms of the same element that have different numbers of (neutrons, protons).
9. Negatively charged particles that circle the atom's nucleus are (neutrons, electrons).
10. Two atoms of the same element that have different (mass numbers, atomic numbers) are isotopes of the element.
11. A difference in the (mass number, atomic number) of atoms means the atoms are of different elements.
12. The nucleus of an atom has a (positive, negative) charge.
13. Carbon-14 is an (isotope, element) of carbon.
14. The mass number of an atom with 12 protons and 12 neutrons is (12, 24).
15. The atomic number of an atom is equal to the number of (protons, neutrons) in its nucleus.
16. In atoms with equal numbers of electrons and protons, there is (a positive, no) electric charge.
17. Anything that takes up space and has mass is (matter, an element).
18. A model of an atom is (larger, smaller) than the actual atom.
19. The nucleus of an atom is made up of neutrons and (electrons, protons).
20. Isotopes enable scientists to determine the (age, size) of ancient objects.

All matter is composed of "building blocks." The structure of these building blocks determines the structure of the matter you observe. Think about when you were younger and played with snap-together blocks. You could snap the blocks together in many ways to build cars, ships, or buildings. Matter is put together in a similar way. The building blocks of matter are **atoms.** The arrangement and types of atoms give matter its properties.

Atoms combine, like the blocks snapping together, to form many different types of matter. Your body has only a few of these atoms in it, but they have combined in many different ways to form the matter that composes your body. Other forms of matter contain only one type
1 of atom. Such substances are **elements.** Let's take a look at the structure of an element.

Suppose you have a copper wire. What kind of atoms are in the wire? Because copper is an element, it's made up of only copper atoms. Look at Table 2-1. It shows copper and some other common elements and their uses. Appendix E of your book is a table of the known elements called the periodic table.

Figure 2-2. Like atoms, the same few blocks can combine in many different ways.

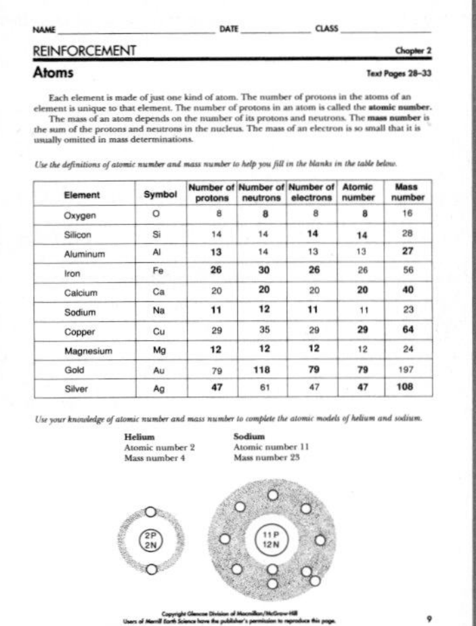

● REINFORCEMENT 9

NAME ____________ DATE ________ CLASS ________

REINFORCEMENT — Chapter 2

Atoms — Text Pages 28–33

Each element is made of just one kind of atom. The number of protons in the atoms of an element is unique to that element. The number of protons in an atom is called the **atomic number.**

The mass of an atom depends on the number of its protons and neutrons. The **mass number** is the sum of the protons and neutrons in the nucleus. The mass of an electron is so small that it is usually omitted in mass determinations.

Use the definitions of atomic number and mass number to help you fill in the blanks in the table below.

Element	Symbol	Number of protons	Number of neutrons	Number of electrons	Atomic number	Mass number
Oxygen	O	8	**8**	8	**8**	16
Silicon	Si	14	14	**14**	**14**	28
Aluminum	Al	**13**	14	13	13	**27**
Iron	Fe	**26**	**30**	**26**	26	56
Calcium	Ca	20	**20**	20	**20**	**40**
Sodium	Na	**11**	**12**	**11**	11	23
Copper	Cu	29	35	29	**29**	**64**
Magnesium	Mg	**12**	**12**	**12**	12	24
Gold	Au	79	**118**	**79**	**79**	197
Silver	Ag	**47**	61	47	**47**	**108**

Use your knowledge of atomic number and mass number to complete the atomic models of helium and sodium.

Helium
Atomic number 2
Mass number 4

Sodium
Atomic number 11
Mass number 23

2P 2N

11 P 12 N

9

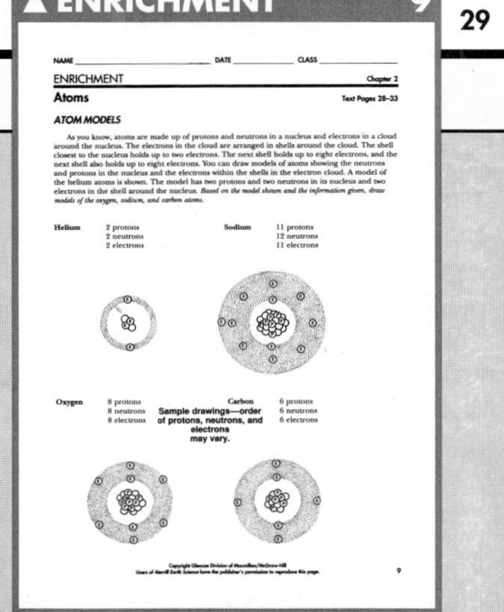

▲ ENRICHMENT 9

NAME ____________ DATE ________ CLASS ________

ENRICHMENT — Chapter 2

Atoms — Text Pages 28–33

ATOM MODELS

As you know, atoms are made up of protons and neutrons in a nucleus and electrons in a cloud around the nucleus. The electrons in the cloud are arranged in shells around the cloud. The shell closest to the nucleus holds up to two electrons. The next shell holds up to eight electrons, and the next shell also holds up to eight electrons. You can draw models of atoms showing the neutrons and protons in the nucleus and the electrons within the shells in the electron cloud. A model of the helium atoms is shown. The model has two protons and two neutrons in its nucleus and two electrons in the shell around the nucleus. *Based on the model shown and the information given, draw models of the oxygen, sodium, and carbon atoms.*

Helium 2 protons, 2 neutrons, 2 electrons

Sodium 11 protons, 12 neutrons, 11 electrons

Oxygen 8 protons, 8 neutrons, 8 electrons

Carbon 6 protons, 6 neutrons, 6 electrons

Sample drawings—order of protons, neutrons, and electrons may vary.

9

29

1 MOTIVATE

▶Show students a glass of water. Ask how many times they think the water can be divided and still be water. Some students will think there is a physical limit to the number of divisions that can be made. Other students will realize that theoretically the water can be separated until the separation yields one molecule. Separating a single molecule of water would yield hydrogen and oxygen.

FLEX Your Brain

Use the Flex Your Brain activity to have students explore THE STRUCTURE OF ATOMS.

REVEALING MISCONCEPTIONS

▶Some students may not realize that substances they cannot see are also matter. Show that air is matter by blowing up a balloon. Then, have students use a balance to demonstrate that the balloon filled with air has more mass than the empty balloon.

TEACHER F.Y.I.

▶Protons and neutrons are made up of subatomic particles called quarks. Scientists have identified six different types of quarks.

TYING TO PREVIOUS KNOWLEDGE: Students should recall that most soft drink cans and aluminum foil are made from the lightweight element aluminum.

OBJECTIVES AND SCIENCE WORDS: Have students review the objectives and science words to become familiar with this section.

2 TEACH

Key Concepts are highlighted.

CONCEPT DEVELOPMENT

▶Use interlocking plastic blocks to demonstrate how atoms are the building blocks of matter.

Cooperative Learning: Form Numbered Heads Together groups of three students per group. Have them use the periodic table in Appendix E to come up with a list of about ten elements they think would be found in Earth's rocks. Then, tell students that oxygen is the most common element found in Earth's rocks. Have the groups write brief paragraphs explaining how oxygen, a gas, can be a major component of a solid. Students' answers can be used to discuss how the properties of elements change when they become part of a compound, which will be covered in the next section.

▶Refer students to Table 2-1. Discuss the terms "copper ore" and "aluminum ore." Make sure students realize that most minerals have to be extracted from the rock deposits in which they occur. An ore is the deposit in which a mineral exists in a large enough amount that it can be mined at a profit. The term *ore* is usually used to refer to metallic minerals and the deposits containing them. For example, "iron ore" is a common term whereas "fluorite ore" is not.

Table 2-1

COMMON ELEMENTS AND THEIR USES

Copper ore	Aluminum ore	Silicon (quartz)	Fluorine
Electrical wire	Soft drink cans	Computer chip	Toothpaste

The Structure of Atoms

Why are models useful?

You already know that atoms are very small. Atoms are far too small to be seen, even with a microscope. How can you study something this small? How can you determine the internal structure of an atom?

When substances are too large or too small to handle or directly observe, models are often used to take their place. Have you ever worked with model cars, trains, or houses? If so, your model was a small version of a large object. In the case of atoms, the opposite is true. A large model is made of a very small object. We construct drawings, sculptures, and mental pictures of the internal structure of atoms. These models are based on information we've gathered by observing the ways atoms of elements react when in contact with other atoms or with light.

OPTIONS

INQUIRY QUESTIONS

▶**What advantage do aluminum soft drink cans have over cans made of steel?** *Aluminum is lightweight and does not rust like the iron in steel.*

▶**What is the electric charge of the helium atom shown in Figure 2-4?** *It is neutral because the number of positive protons equals the number of negative electrons.*

▶**In Table 2-1, fluorine is shown as a gas. Why doesn't it escape from the toothpaste?** *When fluorine atoms combine with the other atoms in the compounds used in toothpaste, the physical properties of fluorine are changed. It is no longer a gas.*

Let's construct a mental model of the internal structure of an atom. Three basic particles make up an atom—protons, neutrons, and electrons. Protons and neutrons are located in the center of an atom and make
(2) up its nucleus. **Protons** are particles that have a positive electric charge. **Neutrons** are particles that have no electric charge. The nucleus, therefore, has a positive charge because of the positively charged protons in it. This positive electric charge of the nucleus is balanced by the electrons of the atom.

Electrons are negatively charged particles that circle the nucleus. There is one electron for each proton. Our
(3) model in Figure 2-4 shows electrons existing as a negatively charged electron cloud. This cloud completely surrounds the nucleus of the atom. Electrons can be anywhere within the cloud, but evidence suggests that they are located near the nucleus most of the time. A swarm of bees flying around its hive can be a model of an atom. The hive represents the nucleus of the atom. The bees flying around the hive in all directions are like the electrons circling the nucleus. You can't determine exactly where each bee is, but each is usually close to the hive.

Figure 2-3. Bees model electrons as they swarm around their hive —the nucleus.

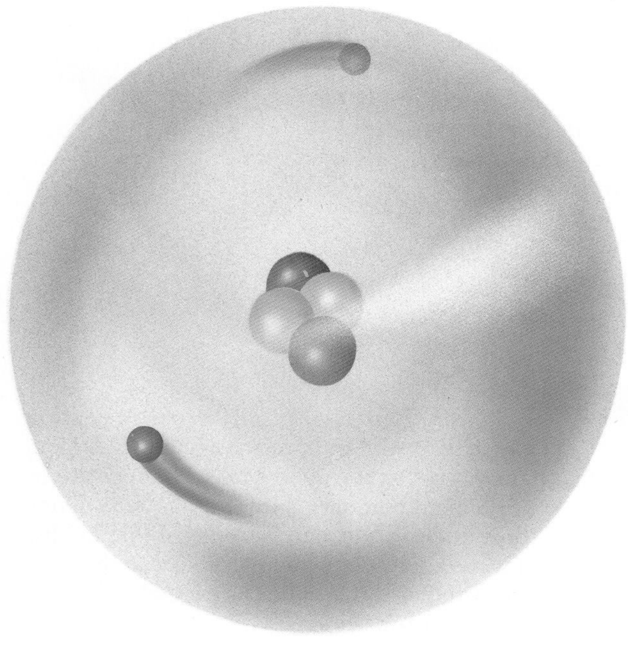

Figure 2-4. This model of a helium atom shows two protons and two neutrons in the nucleus and two electrons in the electron cloud.

CONCEPT DEVELOPMENT

▶ **Demonstration:** Use different colored polystyrene balls and toothpicks to demonstrate the structures of hydrogen, helium, and oxygen nuclei. Use one color of balls for protons and another for neutrons. Then ask: **Where are the electrons of each atom?** *orbiting the nucleus much like bees buzz around a hive*

MINI QUIZ

Use the Mini Quiz to check students' recall of chapter content.

1. **What form of matter contains only one type of atom?** *elements*
2. **Which particle in the nucleus of an atom is positively charged?** *proton*
3. **Where are electrons found?** *in the electron cloud*
4. **Atoms of the same element that have different numbers of neutrons are _____.** *isotopes*

INQUIRY QUESTIONS

▶ **Why are electrons usually near the nucleus?** *The nucleus has a positive charge because of the protons within it. Because electrons are negatively charged, they are attracted to the nucleus. Opposite electrical charges attract.*

PROGRAM RESOURCES

From the **Teacher Resource Package** use:

Activity Worksheets, page 5, Flex Your Brain.

Transparency Masters, pages 5-6, Periodic Table.

Use **Color Transparency** number 3, Periodic Table.

CONCEPT DEVELOPMENT

▶After students have read pages 32 and 33, ask the following questions. **If a uranium atom contains 92 protons and 142 neutrons, what is the atomic mass?** *92 + 142 = 234* **A neutral atom of oxygen-17 has eight protons and nine neutrons. How many electrons does the atom have?** *eight*

CHECK FOR UNDERSTANDING

Have students draw a model of a nitrogen atom showing the positions and charges of the protons, neutrons, and electrons.

RETEACH

Cooperative Learning: Using the Paired Partner strategy, have students use different colored polystyrene balls to construct the hydrogen-1 and hydrogen-2 isotopes.

EXTENSION

For students who have mastered this section, use the **Reinforcement** and **Enrichment** masters or other OPTIONS provided.

CROSS CURRICULUM

▶ **Archaeology:** Have students research how archaeologists use isotopes with short half-lives to determine the ages of artifacts such as clothing, wood, bones, and structures. Refer students to Chapter 16 for a discussion of half-lives and absolute dating methods.

STUDENT TEXT QUESTIONS

▶ Page 32, paragraph 1: **How many protons and neutrons does carbon have?** *six protons and six neutrons*

Mass Numbers and Atomic Numbers

Just as an atom has a characteristic number of protons, neutrons, and electrons, it also has a characteristic mass. The mass number of an atom is equal to the number of protons and neutrons making up its nucleus. Just as you have more mass when you are carrying many books, an atom has more mass if it contains more particles. So oxygen, which contains eight protons and eight neutrons, has a mass number of 16. Carbon has a mass number of 12. How many protons and neutrons does carbon have?

You've probably noticed that electrons aren't counted when we compute an atom's mass number. This is because electrons aren't massive enough to add much to the atom's mass. They have much less mass than protons and neutrons.

Another property of an atom that's convenient to know is its atomic number. An atom's atomic number equals the number of protons in its nucleus. This number also equals the number of electrons contained in its electron cloud. All atoms of a specific element have the same atomic number. For example, all atoms of iron have an atomic number of 26. How many protons does an atom of iron contain? Whether it's in the metal of a car fender or in the nails in a bookcase, an iron atom has 26 protons.

If the number of protons in an atom is changed, a new element is formed.

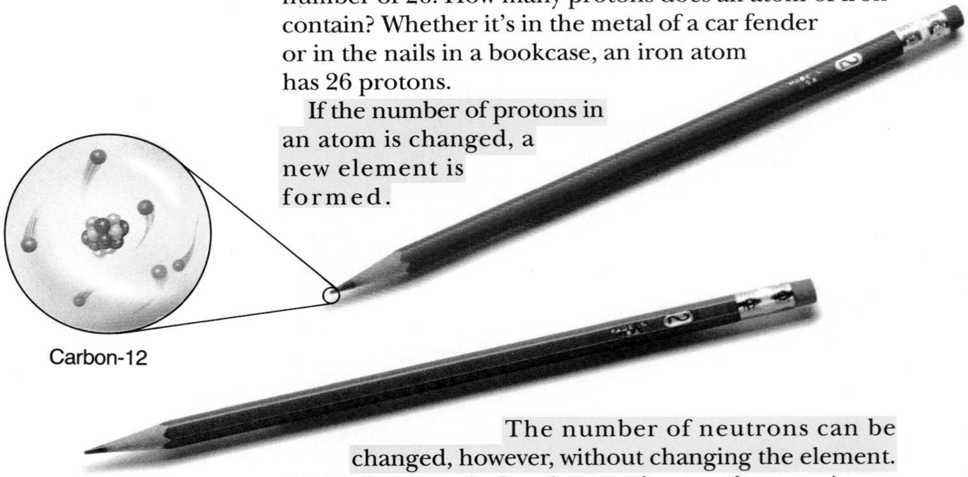

Carbon-12

Figure 2-5. The carbon in your pencil lead is mostly carbon-12. Its atomic mass is 12 and its atomic number is 6.

The number of neutrons can be changed, however, without changing the element. All that happens is that the atom's mass changes. Atoms of the same element that have different numbers of neutrons in their nuclei are called **isotopes.** Table 2-2 lists isotopes of some common elements. Note that the number of protons remains the same for each element, but the number of neutrons changes. 4

OPTIONS

ENRICHMENT

▶Have students construct models of carbon atoms. A carbon atom has six protons, six neutrons, and six electrons. Students may find their models useful as you discuss the concepts of atomic mass and atomic number.

PROGRAM RESOURCES

From the **Teacher Resource Package** use:
Cross-Curricular Connections, page 6, Using Math Operations.
Critical Thinking/Problem Solving, page 8, Atomic Energy.

Table 2-2

ISOTOPES			
Isotope	Number of Protons	Number of Neutrons	Number of Electrons
Hydrogen-1	1	0	1
Hydrogen-2	1	1	1
Hydrogen-3	1	2	1
Carbon-12	6	6	6
Carbon-14	6	8	6
Uranium-234	92	142	92
Uranium-235	92	143	92
Uranium-238	92	146	92

Isotopes provide us with a way to determine the age of ancient objects. Geologists use isotopes to date fossils and layers of rock. Archeologists use them to determine the age of artifacts such as clothing, wood, bones, and structures. You will be learning more about isotopes and some of their uses in Chapter 16.

Our model of an atom allows us to predict how a particular element will react when it's in contact with another element. As you continue to investigate matter in this chapter, you will explore how atoms of different elements combine to form the matter around you.

Figure 2-6. Isotopes have helped geologists verify the dates of rock layers and fossils.

SECTION REVIEW

1. List two facts that are true of all matter.
2. What is the electric charge of each of the particles of an atom?
3. **Apply:** Oxygen-16 and oxygen-17 are two different isotopes of oxygen. The numbers 16 and 17 represent their mass numbers. How many protons and neutrons are in each isotope?

☑ Outlining

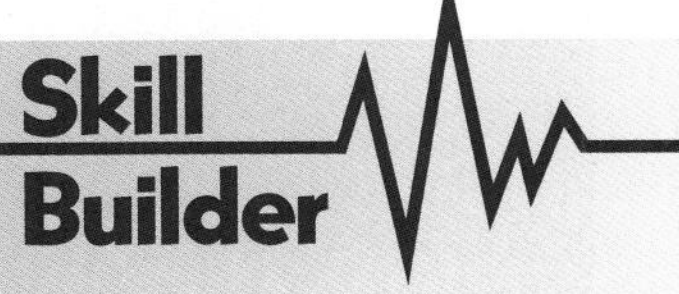

Outline the material in Section 2-1. What is the main topic of this section? How do atoms and elements differ? If you need help, refer to Outlining in the **Skill Handbook** on page 681.

3 CLOSE

▶Ask questions 1-2 and the **Apply** Question in the Section Review.

▶Ask for a volunteer to present a summary of the section as if he or she were informing a classmate who had been absent from class when the topics were discussed.

▶Ask a high school chemistry student to present a general talk on the structure of atoms.

▶State each objective and ask a student if he or she thinks the objective was attained. Then ask another student to briefly state how the objective was accomplished.

SECTION REVIEW ANSWERS

1. Matter has mass and takes up space.

2. A proton is positive; an electron is negative; and a neutron is neutral.

3. Apply: Oxygen-16 has eight protons and eight neutrons; oxygen-17 has eight protons and nine neutrons.

Skill Builder

Answers will vary slightly but students should indicate that the main topic of the section is that atoms, the building blocks of all matter, are composed of three kinds of particles. Atoms are the basic units that compose all matter. An element is matter made of only one type of atom.

ENRICHMENT

▶Have students research to find out about the Stanford Linear Collider and Europe's Large Electron-Positron Collider.

▶Have students research uses of isotopes in medical research or in generating nuclear energy.

▶ Have students hypothesize how the properties of water might be different if it contained the hydrogen-2 isotope. Water composed of hydrogen-2 is known as heavy water.

SECTION 2-2

PREPARATION

SECTION BACKGROUND

▶ Unlike mixtures, compounds form when one substance chemically reacts with another.
▶ Atoms tend to be stable when they have eight electrons in the outer shell of the electron cloud.
▶ Solid solutions are called alloys.

PREPLANNING

▶ Obtain some steel wool and vinegar and some carbonated drinks in bottles for the Demonstrations on page 35.

1 MOTIVATE

Cooperative Learning: Form Problem Solving groups of four students per group. Give each group a bowl of small and large paper clips and a single large paper clip. Have them brainstorm to come up with a list of similarities and differences between the two mixtures.
▶ Have students describe the properties of milk. Ask them to classify milk as a compound or a mixture.

TYING TO PREVIOUS KNOWLEDGE: Remind students that electrons are located outside the nucleus in the electron cloud. Ask students which electrons, those closer to the nucleus or those farther from the nucleus, would most likely react to form compounds.

OBJECTIVES AND SCIENCE WORDS: Have students review the objectives and science words to become familiar with this section.

2-2 Combinations of Atoms

New Science Words

molecule
compound
chemical properties
ions
mixture

Objectives

▶ Discuss several ways atoms combine to form compounds.
▶ Compare and contrast compounds and mixtures.

Figure 2-7. Carbonated drinks are a mixture of carbon dioxide and other compounds.

How Atoms Combine

Suppose you've just eaten a snack such as an apple or an orange. It's unlikely that you were concerned about the elements that were in the snack. Yet anything you have ever eaten and anything you've ever touched has had the same few elements in it. The sugar in the apple or orange contains the elements carbon, oxygen, and hydrogen. The air you're breathing contains nitrogen, oxygen, argon, and other elements.

Notice that both the apple and the air contain the element oxygen. Yet in one case oxygen is in a colorless gaseous form. In the other case it's part of a structure that's hard and colorful. How can the same element, made from the same type of atom, help make up two objects that are so different? The atoms of elements combine to form new substances called compounds. When they do, the properties of the individual elements change. Let's see how this happens.

1 One way that atoms combine is by sharing the electrons in the outermost portion of their electron clouds. The combined atoms form a **molecule**. For example, two atoms of hydrogen can share electrons with one atom of oxygen to form one molecule of water. Water is a compound. A **compound** is a type of matter that has properties different from the properties of each of the elements in it.

The properties of hydrogen and oxygen are changed when they combine to form water. Under normal conditions on Earth, you will find the elements oxygen and hydrogen only as gases. Yet water can be a liquid or a solid as well as a gas. When hydrogen and oxygen com-

OPTIONS

Meeting Different Ability Levels

For Section 2-2, use the following **Teacher Resource Masters** depending upon individual students' needs.
◆ **Study Guide Master** for all students.
● **Reinforcement Master** for students of average and above average ability levels.
▲ **Enrichment Master** for above average students.
Additional Teacher Resource Package masters are listed in the OPTIONS box throughout the section. The additional masters are appropriate for all students.

◆ STUDY GUIDE 10

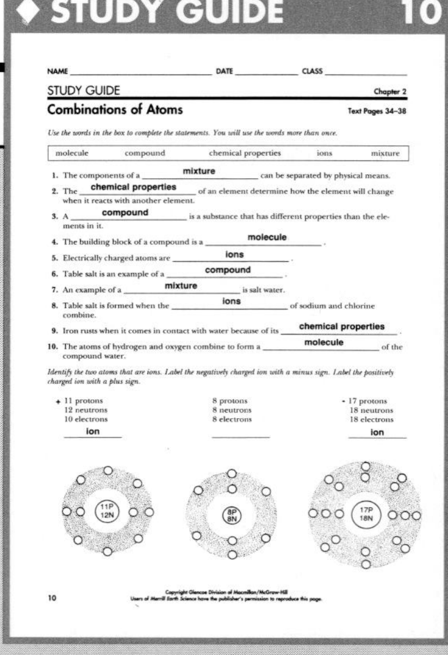

NAME ______ DATE ______ CLASS ______

STUDY GUIDE Chapter 2

Combinations of Atoms Text Pages 34–38

Use the words in the box to complete the statements. You will use the words more than once.

molecule	compound	chemical properties	ions	mixture

1. The components of a **mixture** can be separated by physical means.
2. The **chemical properties** of an element determine how the element will change when it reacts with another element.
3. A **compound** is a substance that has different properties than the elements in it.
4. The building block of a compound is a **molecule**.
5. Electrically charged atoms are **ions**.
6. Table salt is an example of a **compound**.
7. An example of a **mixture** is salt water.
8. Table salt is formed when the **ions** of sodium and chlorine combine.
9. Iron rusts when it comes in contact with water because of its **chemical properties**.
10. The atoms of hydrogen and oxygen combine to form a **molecule** of the compound water.

Identify the two atoms that are ions. Label the negatively charged ion with a minus sign. Label the positively charged ion with a plus sign.

+ 11 protons 12 neutrons 10 electrons	8 protons 8 neutrons 8 electrons	- 17 protons 18 neutrons 18 electrons
ion	______	ion

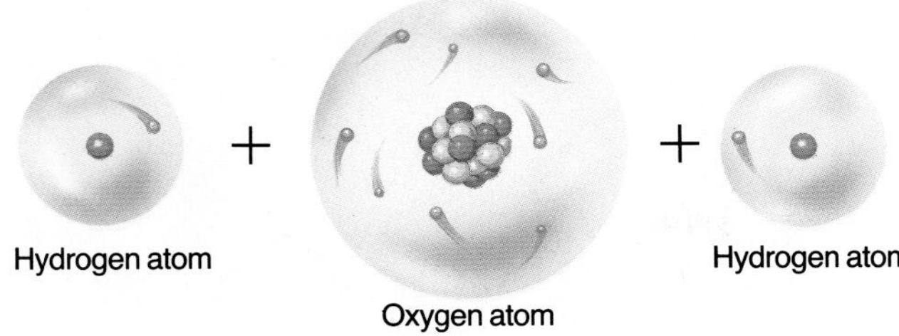

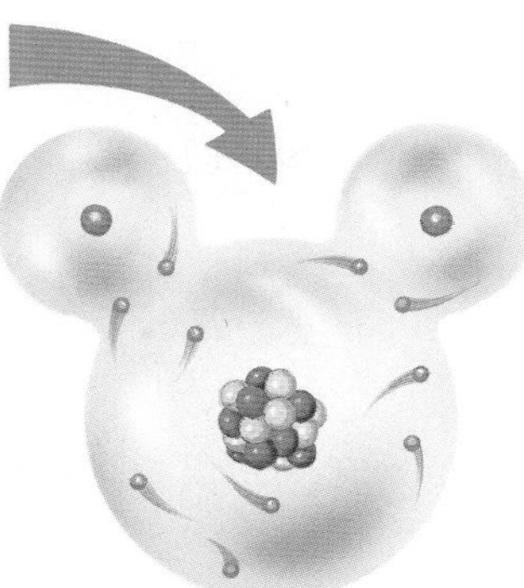

bine, a chemical change occurs. A new substance forms with chemical properties that are different from those of the elements in it.

The properties of hydrogen that determine how it will react with oxygen are chemical properties. **Chemical properties** describe how one substance changes when it reacts with other substances. For example, the chemical properties of iron cause it to change to rust when it reacts with water and oxygen.

Figure 2-8. A molecule of water has chemical properties that are different than those of hydrogen and oxygen atoms.

TECHNOLOGY

One at a Time!

Atoms are extremely small. Many are hundreds of billionths of centimeters in diameter. Yet, scientists have discovered how to move individual atoms in much the same way you may have used a magnet to move small game pieces around a plastic covered board. Using a scanning tunnel microscope (STM), physicists drag a fine-tipped needle over the material's surface. When the desired position is reached, the needle is raised and the atom "drops" into this new position.

This discovery may lead to the building of molecules one atom at a time. Even smaller electrical circuits could be made for everything from watches to computers. New drugs that would cure or eliminate certain illnesses could be constructed using this method. The illustration shows xenon atoms arranged to spell out "IBM."

Think Critically: How could STMs be used to permanently store information?

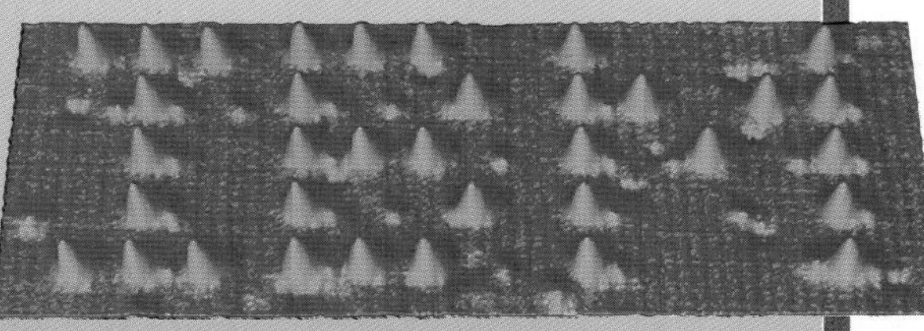

2 TEACH

Key Concepts are highlighted.

CONCEPT DEVELOPMENT

▶ **Demonstration:** Soak some steel wool in vinegar to remove the soap or any other coating on the wool. Thoroughly rinse the steel wool and place it in a shallow open dish. Place the dish on the windowsill and have students observe what happens to it over the next few days.

▶ **Demonstration:** Demonstrate the presence of carbon dioxide in a carbonated drink by opening the bottle. The mixture is under pressure, and some carbon dioxide is released when the bottle is opened.

TEACHER F.Y.I.

▶ The two most common types of bonds in compounds are covalent bonds and ionic bonds. In covalent bonds, the outermost electrons are shared by the atoms in the compound. In compounds with ionic bonds, ions are held together by the strong attraction of their opposite charges.

TECHNOLOGY

For more information, see "Manipulating Atoms," *Popular Science,* July 1990, p. 30.

Think Critically: The atoms can be arranged into almost any pattern. For example, the illustration demonstrates how atoms have been manually placed to spell out, "IBM." The illustration has been magnified more than 2 million times. The atoms are about 8 billionths of a centimeter apart. Data could be stored at densities more than one million times greater than can be stored today using conventional data-storage methods.

● REINFORCEMENT 10

NAME ______ DATE ______ CLASS ______

REINFORCEMENT — Chapter 2

Combinations of Atoms — Text Pages 34–38

Define the following terms.

1. compound **a substance made up of two or more combined elements that have different chemical properties from each of the elements in it**
2. mixture **a substance made up of components that retain their chemical properties**

Identify each of the following as a mixture or a compound.

3. H_2O **compound**
4. solution **mixture**
5. NaCl **compound**
6. salt water **mixture**
7. salt **compound**
8. water **compound**
9. NaCl + H_2O **mixture**
10. air **mixture**
11. vinegar and oil **mixture**

Complete the following sentences.

12. A water molecule is made up of two atoms of **hydrogen** and one atom of **oxygen**.
13. Table salt is made up of one ion of **sodium** and one ion of **chlorine**.
14. The substances in a(n) **mixture** can be physically separated from one another.
15. Sweetened tea is a type of mixture called a(n) **solution**.
16. A(n) **compound** cannot be separated into its individual elements by physical means.

10

▲ ENRICHMENT 10

NAME ______ DATE ______ CLASS ______

ENRICHMENT — Chapter 2

Combination of Atoms — Text Pages 34–38

SEPARATING ELEMENTS IN A COMPOUND

Remember that water is a compound made up of two atoms of hydrogen and one atom of oxygen. Sugar is a compound too. It is composed of 22 atoms of hydrogen, 11 atoms of oxygen, and 12 atoms of carbon. You can separate the carbon from the hydrogen and oxygen by applying heat to the sugar.

Do the following experiment and answer the questions that follow.

Materials

- sugar (1 tablespoonful)
- shallow cooking pan
- drinking glass or glass jar
- stove or hot plate
- pot holder

Procedure

1. Place a tablespoon of sugar in a shallow pan.
2. Cover the sugar with a drinking glass (or glass jar).
3. Heat the sugar slowly over a burner.
4. After a few minutes, you will notice a liquid forming on the sides of the glass. Using a pot holder to protect your hands, remove the glass from the pan. Allow the glass to cool.
5. Continue heating the sugar until it is completely dry.
6. Using a pot holder remove the pan from the heat and allow it to cool.

Observations

The remaining substance in the pan is carbon. What color is it? **The carbon is black.**

Conclude and Apply

1. What do you think the liquid that formed on the glass is? Explain why the liquid formed. **The liquid is water. The hydrogen and oxygen in the sugar escape the compound as water molecules when heated.**
2. Do you think the liquid and carbon would taste like sugar? Why? **No, the liquid and the carbon aren't sweet like sugar. Sugar is a compound that has properties different from its elements. Sweetness is a property of the sugar that is not a property of its individual elements.**

10

CHECK FOR UNDERSTANDING

Have each student write a short paragraph describing the difference between compounds and mixtures and give an original example of each.

RETEACH

Demonstrate how the properties of substances change when they combine to form a compound. Do the same to show how the components of a mixture retain their properties. Readily available examples are water (a compound of oxygen and hydrogen) and a mixture of salt and pepper.

EXTENSION

For students who have mastered this section, use the **Reinforcement** and **Enrichment** masters or other OPTIONS provided.

MINI-Lab

Materials: paper; pencil; beakers; water; and sand, sugar, or salt

Teaching Tips

Cooperative Learning: Form Problem Solving teams of three to four students per team.

►Once students have completed the list, have them make a solution from two or more of the items on their list. This can most easily be done by mixing small amounts of sand, salt, or sugar into a beaker of water. Ask them how they could separate the materials in solution.

Mixtures	Compounds	Elements
air	water	gold
muddy water	ice	oxygen
salt water	sugar	hydrogen
sand	salt	copper

►A solution can be made when one of the items on the list is dissolved in any one of the others.

►A solution is a homogeneous mixture of two or more substances.

►Compounds are chemical combinations of two or more elements that cannot be separated physically.

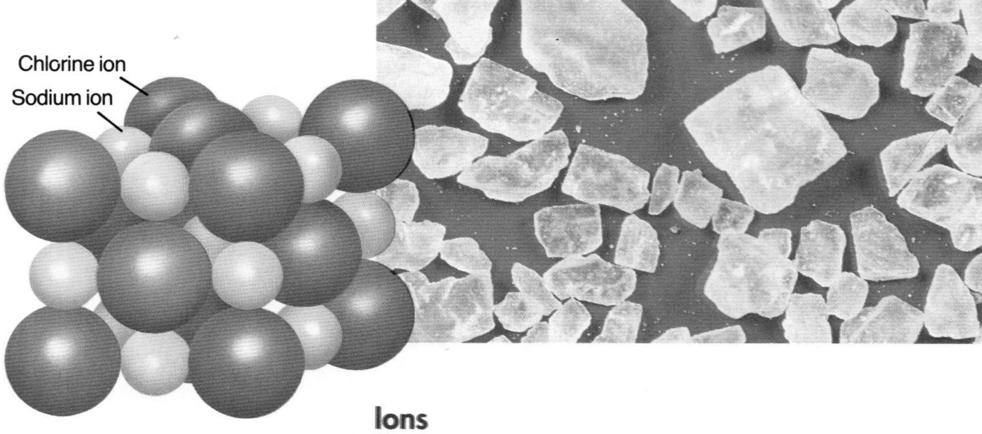

Figure 2-9. The cubic arrangement of sodium and chlorine ions gives salt crystals their cubic shape.

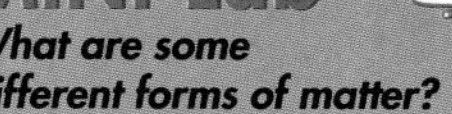

MINI-Lab

What are some different forms of matter?

Make a chart with columns titled "Mixtures," "Compounds," and "Elements." Classify each of the items listed below and list each in the proper column. Describe how you could make a solution using two or more of the items. How does a solution differ from other mixtures? How does an element differ from a compound?

air	sand
gold	hydrogen
muddy water	sugar
ice	salt water
water	salt
oxygen	copper

Ions

You know that atoms combine by sharing electrons of the outer portion of their electron cloud. But atoms also combine because they've become positively or negatively charged.

As you discovered earlier, atoms are usually neutral—they have no overall electric charge. Under certain conditions, however, atoms can lose or gain electrons. When an atom loses electrons, it has more protons than electrons so the atom is positively charged. When an atom gains electrons, it has more electrons than protons so the
atom is negatively charged. Electrically charged atoms 2
are called **ions.**

Ions are attracted to each other when they have opposite charges. Oppositely charged ions join to form electrically neutral compounds. Table salt forms in this way. A sodium (Na) atom loses an electron and becomes a positively charged ion. Then it comes close to a negatively charged chlorine (Cl) ion. They are attracted to each other and form the compound NaCl. This is the compound that you use on your french fries or popcorn.

Mixtures

If you look into your book bag, you will see an example of a **mixture.** Many different objects are mixed 3
together, but each retains its own properties. Your math book isn't any different whether it's beside your comb or beside your history book.

OPTIONS

INQUIRY QUESTIONS

►**What determines how one element reacts in the presence of another to form a compound?** *The electrons located in the outermost part of the electron cloud determine how one element will react with another.*

►**What might happen when a negatively charged ion comes in contact with a positively charged ion?** *The two ions may combine to form an electrically neutral compound.*

PROGRAM RESOURCES

From the **Teacher Resource Package** use:
Activity Worksheets, page 18, Mini-Lab: What are some different forms of matter?

Another example of a mixture is a cup of tea with sugar dissolved in it. The sweetness of the sugar can be tasted whether it's in the tea or not. So, the properties of the sugar molecules aren't changed just because they're mixed in with the tea.

Sweetened tea is an example of a kind of mixture called a solution. When one substance of a mixture is dissolved in another substance, a solution is formed. In the case of our sweetened tea, the sugar molecules are separated from each other by other molecules within the tea. Therefore, the sugar has dissolved in the tea. Another property of a solution is that it is the same throughout. One part of a solution is the same as all other parts. To make the sweetened tea a solution, we had to stir it. If we've stirred the tea enough, the sugar molecules are spread evenly throughout. Our first drink of tea will taste as sweet as our last.

Define solution.

The components of a mixture can be separated by physical means. You can sit at your desk and pick out the separate items in your book bag. You can let the tea evaporate and the sugar will remain in the cup. But is it possible to separate the components of a compound in a similar way?

PROBLEM SOLVING

Filled to the Rim?

Janice went to her favorite delicatessen on a bitter cold day in January. After carefully studying the menu, she ordered a cheese sandwich on rye bread and a cup of hot tea. Her waiter brought the food to her table, but much to Janice's dismay, he filled her teacup to the rim. Janice wondered how she was going to put her usual two teaspoons of sugar into the tea. Rather than risk burning her fingers by trying to pour some of the tea onto the saucer, Janice put a heaping spoonful of sugar into the tea. It didn't overflow. Janice was surprised. She then added another spoonful of sugar. Intrigued, she added still another spoonful of sugar. As she ate her sandwich, Janice thought about the seemingly full cup of tea.

Think Critically: Why didn't the tea spill from the cup when the sugar was added? If Janice had ordered ice tea, would she have been able to add as much sugar?

CROSS CURRICULUM

▶ **Environmental Science:** Have students research to find out about the damage done to the environment by certain common compounds such as chlorofluorocarbons (CFCs), which are used as refrigerants. CFCs are responsible for damaging Earth's ozone layer.

MINI QUIZ

Use the Mini Quiz to check students' recall of chapter content.

1. **What are the building blocks of compounds?** *molecules*
2. **Electrically charged atoms are _____ .** *ions*
3. **A(n) _____ forms when different substances combine while retaining their own properties.** *mixture*
4. **What type of change converts one substance into one or more new substances?** *chemical change*

PROBLEM SOLVING

Think Critically: Sugar enters the spaces between the water molecules. Cold tea won't hold as much sugar as warm tea. Temperature affects solubility.

INQUIRY QUESTIONS

▶ **How could you separate the different materials contained in a mixture of rocks and soil?** *You could remove the rocks by picking them out of the mixture. Sifting will also separate the mixture into its components.*

▶ **If you were brewing a cup of tea, and some of the tea leaves broke through the tea bag, how could you remove them from the tea?** *Small tea leaves could be removed by pouring the tea through a filter like those used in coffee makers.*

▶ **A solution is a mixture in which two or more substances are spread evenly throughout. Why would two sugar cubes sitting in a glass of tea be a mixture but not a solution?** *The sugar molecules are not spread evenly throughout the tea. The mixture is not homogeneous.*

3 CLOSE

▶ Ask questions 1-2 and the **Apply** Question in the Section Review.

FLEX Your Brain

Use the Flex Your Brain activity to have students explore OCEAN WATER AS A MIXTURE. Students should discover that salts and other minerals and substances are dissolved in ocean water. There are also many solids and gases that are mixed with, but not dissolved in, ocean water.

▶ List the objectives of the section on the chalkboard. Have students determine whether or not the objectives were met. Assign two students to tally responses.

SECTION REVIEW ANSWERS

1. Atoms can share electrons to form molecules. They can also lose or gain electrons to form ions. Ions in turn combine to form molecules.

2. molecule, H_2O

3. **Apply:** Boiling salt water or allowing it to evaporate, both of which are physical processes, will separate the salt and water.

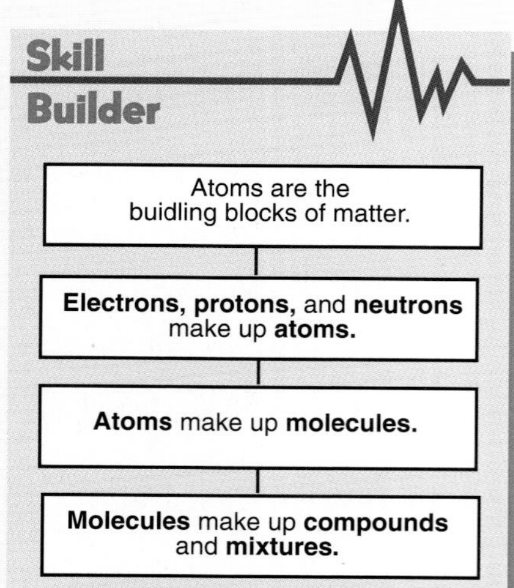

Skill Builder
Atoms are the buidling blocks of matter.
Electrons, protons, and neutrons make up atoms.
Atoms make up molecules.
Molecules make up compounds and mixtures.

Figure 2-10. Water can be easily separated from the spaghetti mixture. However, it is more difficult to separate the compound water into its component parts.

Suppose you take the sugar in the cup and try to separate its carbon atoms from its hydrogen and oxygen atoms. How can you do it? It's much more difficult than separating the components of a mixture. The only way is to separate the carbon, hydrogen, and oxygen atoms of each sugar molecule. This is an example of a chemical
4 change. A chemical change converts one substance into one or more new substances.

Sweetened tea, air, ocean water, and the contents of your book bag are all examples of mixtures. These mixtures are made from materials that have mixed together but still retain their individual properties. The materials themselves are made of compounds. The atoms of these compounds lost their individual chemical properties when they combined. As you continue to explore matter, use the mental models you've developed for atoms, elements, molecules, compounds, and mixtures.

EcoTip

When making homemade cleaners, never combine chlorine products with ammonia products. A dangerous gas is produced.

SECTION REVIEW

1. How do atoms or ions combine to form molecules?
2. Is the basic unit of water an atom, a molecule, or an element? Write water's molecular formula.
3. **Apply:** How can you determine if salt water is a solution or a compound?

Skill Builder

Concept Mapping

Make an events chain map using the terms *mixtures, atoms, molecules, compounds, electrons, protons,* and *neutrons.* If you need help, refer to Concept Mapping in the **Skill Handbook** on pages 688 and 689.

OPTIONS

PROGRAM RESOURCES

From the **Teacher Resource Package** use:
Concept Mapping, pages 9-10.
Activity Worksheets, page 5, Flex Your Brain.

ACTIVITY 2-1
Measuring Physical Properties

Problem: *How can you use laboratory equipment to make observations about physical properties of objects?*

Materials

- balance (beam)
- graduated cylinder (100 mL or larger)
- metersticks (2)
- thermometers (3)
- stick or dowel
- rock sample
- string
- globe
- water

Procedure

1. Begin at any station and determine the measurement requested. Record the data and list sources of error.
   a. Use a balance to determine the mass, to the nearest 0.1 g, of a rock sample.
   b. Use a graduated cylinder to determine the volume, to the nearest 0.5 mL, of the water.
   c. Use 3 thermometers to measure the average temperature, to the nearest 0.5°C, at a certain location in the room.
   d. Use a meterstick to measure the length, to the nearest 0.1 cm, of a stick or dowel.
   e. Use a meterstick and string to measure the circumference of a globe. Be accurate to the nearest 0.1 cm.
2. Proceed to the other four stations as directed by your teacher. Complete the procedure, as in Step 1, at each station.

Analyze

1. Compare your measurements with those who used the same objects. Review the values provided by your teacher. How do the values you obtained compare to those provided by your teacher and those of other students?
2. Determine your percentage of error in each case. Use this formula.

$$\frac{\text{your value} - \text{teacher's value}}{\text{teacher's value}} \times 100 = \%\text{ of error}$$

Conclude and Apply

3. Decide what percentage error will be acceptable. Generally, being within 5% to 7% of the correct value is considered good. If your values exceed 10% error, try the measurement again to see where the error occurred. What was the most common source of error?

Data and Observations

Station	Sample #	Value of Measurement	Causes of Error
a	____	Mass = ____ g	
b	____	Volume = ____ mL	
c	____ (location)	Average temp. = ____ °C	
d	____	Length = ____ cm	
e	____ (globe)	Circumference = ____ cm	

ACTIVITY 2-1
40 minutes

OBJECTIVE: Demonstrate safety, accuracy, and precision in utilizing simple laboratory equipment for **determining** some of the physical properties of sample objects.

PROCESS SKILLS applied in this activity:
▶ **Measuring** in Procedure Steps 1 and 2.
▶ **Communicating** in Analyze Question 1.
▶ **Using Numbers** in Analyze Question 2.
▶ **Interpreting Data** in Analyze Question 1 and Conclude and Apply Question 3.

TEACHING THE ACTIVITY

▶ Set up stations in advance for each of the five tasks.
▶ Obtain rock samples ranging in mass from 110 to 399 grams.
▶ Half-fill the graduated cylinder with water. Remind students how to read a meniscus.
Troubleshooting: Each sample should be identified with a letter or number to avoid later confusion.
▶ Before providing students with the correct values, show them how to determine percentage of error.
▶ Review with students the various sources of error that contributed to the determination of incorrect values in each task. Allow the students to provide suggestions as to how these errors can be avoided.

PROGRAM RESOURCES

From the **Teacher Resource Package** use:
Activity Worksheet, pages 12-13, Activity 2-1: Measuring Physical Properties.

ANSWERS TO QUESTIONS

1. and 2. Answers will vary depending on the samples used and students' results.
3. Any value under 10% error should be accepted. A seamstress, chef, surgeon, undersea diver, oil well driller, or navigator would probably not find a 10% error acceptable. Common errors include: **balance:** not preset at 0 g, pan not clear of other materials, sliding value indicator not set in slot, balance not level, incorrect reading of scale; **graduated cylinder:** incorrect reading of water level; **thermometers**: inaccurate or broken, misreading of temperature scale; **meterstick:** not starting measurement at 0 cm, inordinate stretching of string, string not exactly placed around circumference, misreading of scale. Depending upon the actual errors, a discussion of this question should lead to an understanding of the pitfalls to avoid in order to increase the accuracy of values.

SECTION 2-3

PREPARATION

SECTION BACKGROUND

▶ The major difference between molecules of substances in each state of matter involves the amount of energy contained in the molecules. As energy is added to a solid, it will change to a liquid. More energy will cause the liquid to change to a gas. If enough energy is added, the gas can be changed to a plasma. Changing a gas to a plasma, however, takes a great deal of energy.

▶ As a substance changes to a state of matter with a higher energy level, energy is absorbed and stored. As a substance changes to a state of matter with a lower energy level, the stored energy is released.

1 MOTIVATE

Cooperative Learning: Place several items on a table in the front of the classroom. Use items with a wide variety of physical properties. Using the Paired Partner strategy, have students discuss and list as many physical properties of the items as possible.

FLEX Your Brain

Use the Flex Your Brain activity to have students explore DIFFERENT STATES OF MATTER.

TYING TO PREVIOUS KNOWLEDGE: Ask students to list characteristics of clothes that are important to them. Responses might include style, color, and size as being important characteristics. Lead them to conclude that they were listing physical properties and that all matter has physical properties that can be observed.

2-3 Matter

New Science Words

physical properties
density

Objectives

▶ Distinguish between chemical and physical properties.
▶ Contrast the four states of matter.

Physical Properties of Matter

So far in this chapter, you've been investigating chemical properties of matter—the properties that describe how one substance changes into another substance. But you can observe other properties of matter. The properties that you can observe without changing a substance
1 into a new substance are **physical properties.**

What are some physical properties of your clothing? If you say your jeans are blue, soft, and about 80 cm long, you've described some of their physical properties. You can observe these without changing the material in your jeans into new substances.

Figure 2-11. A chemical property of iron causes the chain to react with oxygen and to rust. Some physical properties of the chain, such as length and hardness, make it useful.

OPTIONS

Meeting Different Ability Levels

For Section 2-3, use the following **Teacher Resource Masters** depending upon individual students' needs.

◆ **Study Guide Master** for all students.

● **Reinforcement Master** for students of average and above average ability levels.

▲ **Enrichment Master** for above average students.

Additional Teacher Resource Package masters are listed in the OPTIONS box throughout the section. The additional masters are appropriate for all students.

◆ STUDY GUIDE 11

NAME ______ DATE ______ CLASS ______

STUDY GUIDE — Chapter 2

Matter — Text Pages 40–47

Change the italicized word in each statement to make the statement correct.

1. The *size* of an object determines whether it will float in water. **The density of an object determines whether it will float in water.**
2. Orange juice and milk are both *solids.* **Orange juice and milk are both liquids.**
3. Stars are made up of matter in the *gaseous* state. **Stars are made up of matter in the plasma state.**
4. An object's density is equal to its mass divided by its *length.* **An object's density is equal to its mass divided by its volume.**
5. Matter with atoms in a fixed position in relation to one another is in the *liquid* state. **Matter with atoms in a fixed position in relation to one another is in the solid state.**
6. Density and state of matter are *chemical properties.* **Density and state of matter are physical properties.**
7. *Hydrogen* is the only substance that occurs naturally on Earth as a gas, a liquid, and a solid. **Water is the only substance that occurs naturally on Earth as a gas, and a solid.**
8. The *physical properties* of a liquid do not change when it becomes a gas. **The chemical properties of a liquid do not change when it becomes a gas.**
9. *Liquids* fill their entire container regardless of the container's size or shape. **Gases fill their entire container regardless of the container's size or shape.**
10. On Earth the *solid* state of matter is least common. **On Earth the plasma state of matter is least common.**

 11

Figure 2-12. One physical property of oil is its density. How does the density of oil compare with the density of water?

Density

One physical property that you will use to describe matter is density. **Density** is a measure of the mass of an object divided by its volume. Generally, this measurement is given in grams per cubic centimeter (g/cm^3). For example, the average density of liquid water is 1 g/cm^3. So 1 cm^3 of water has a mass of 1 g.

Suppose you have a small pebble and need to find its density. First measure its mass and volume. If its volume is 2 cm^3 and its mass is 8 g, its density is:

$$\text{Density} = \frac{\text{mass}}{\text{volume}}$$

$$D = \frac{8\ g}{2\ cm^3}$$

$$D = \frac{4\ g}{cm^3} \quad \text{or} \quad 4\ g/cm^3$$

An object that's denser than water will sink, whereas one that's less dense will float. You've heard about the oil spills off the coast of the United States. Why does this oil float on the surface of the water and wash up on the beaches?

Suppose you have a small object with a volume of 7 cm^3 and a mass of 4.2 g. What is the density? Will the object float in water?

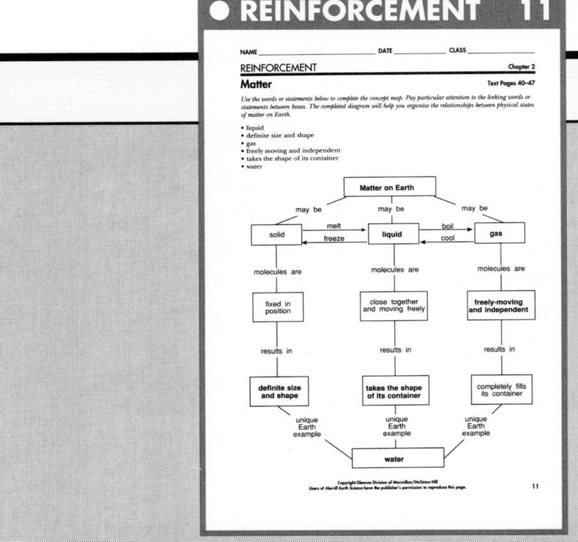

● REINFORCEMENT 11

NAME ______ DATE ______ CLASS ______

REINFORCEMENT — Chapter 2

Matter — Text Pages 40–47

Use the words or statements below to complete the concept map. Pay particular attention to the linking words or statements between boxes. The completed diagram will help you organize the relationships between physical states of matter on Earth.

- liquid
- definite size and shape
- gas
- freely moving and independent
- takes the shape of its container
- water

 11

▲ ENRICHMENT 11

NAME ______ DATE ______ CLASS ______

ENRICHMENT — Chapter 2

Matter — Text Pages 40–47

FREEZING AND BOILING POINTS

Different substances have different freezing and boiling points. At its freezing point, a substance becomes a solid. At temperatures over its freezing point, the substance melts into a liquid. Ice forms from water when the temperature reaches 0°C. At temperatures above 0°C, the ice melts and the water becomes a liquid. Paraffin wax is a substance that is solid at room temperatures. At what temperature does this wax melt? At what temperature will the melted wax become a solid again?

Devise an experiment that could help you answer the questions about the temperatures at which paraffin wax will melt and solidify.

Identify the materials you will need and tell why you need them. **a metal container in which to melt the wax, a pot holder for touching the heated container, a thermometer for measuring the temperatures, a source of heat to melt the wax, paraffin wax, paper and pencil to record the measurements**

Describe the procedures you would follow in your experiment. **Step 1: Gather the needed materials. Step 2: Put the paraffin wax in the container. Step 3: Put the container over the heat source and turn the heat source on. Step 4: Hold the thermometer in the wax and measure the temperature at which the wax melts. Step 5: Record the temperature. Step 6: Remove the container from the heat source. Step 7: Measure the temperature at which the wax becomes a solid. Step 8: Record the temperature at which the wax solidifies. Step 9: Clean up.**

If possible, perform your experiment. Then answer these questions. If you are unable to perform the experiment, use reasoning and information from the chapter to help you answer the questions.

1. Why is a heat source needed for the experiment? **A heat source is needed because the wax remains a solid at room temperatures.**

2. Is the freezing point of the wax higher or lower than the freezing point of water? Explain your answer. **The freezing point of the wax is higher than water because the wax remains a solid at temperatures that would cause ice to melt.**

 11

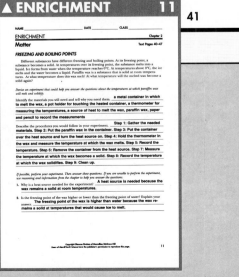

OBJECTIVES AND SCIENCE WORDS: Have students review the objectives and science words to become familiar with this section.

STUDENT TEXT QUESTION

▶ Page 41, paragraph 3: **Why does this oil float on the surface of the water and wash up on the beaches?** *Oil floats on water because it is less dense than water.*

Science and MATH

4.2 g/7 cm^3 = 0.6 g/cm^3; the object will float on water because its density is less than the density of water

2 TEACH

Key Concepts are highlighted.

CONCEPT DEVELOPMENT

▶ If necessary, review with students the meanings of the following terms: *melting, freezing, evaporation,* and *condensation.*

▶ Ask students to compare and contrast the processes of evaporation and boiling. Both involve a change of state from a liquid to a gas. Evaporation occurs at the liquid's surface; boiling occurs throughout the liquid.

▶ **Demonstration:** Have students observe as you pour syrup and milk into two separate containers. Ask students to contrast the rates at which the two liquids flow. Lead a discussion as to why the two liquids flow so differently. Help students conclude that one of the reasons the rates of flow differ is that the attraction among the molecules of the syrup is greater than that among the milk molecules.

TEACHER F.Y.I.

▶ Solids can be classified as either crystalline or amorphous. Crystalline solids have regular shapes and may cleave along well-defined faces. This is due to the regularity of the crystal lattice. Amorphous solids do not break along defined surfaces. Instead, they shatter into irregular, curved pieces. Unlike crystalline solids, amorphous solids are composed of randomly arranged structural units.

▶ Amorphous solids are often classified as liquids. For example, glass is actually an amorphous solid, or a very viscous liquid.

▶ The extrusive igneous rock obsidian is a type of natural glass. The lava which forms it cools too rapidly for crystal to form. Thus, obsidian is an amorphous solid.

Did You Know?

Glass is actually a liquid. Molecules in glass slowly move over and around one another. Panes of window glass in old houses are thicker at the bottom than at the top because the glass "runs" down over the years.

States of Matter

Think back to breakfast this morning. You may have had solid toast, liquid milk or juice, and of course you breathed air, which is a gas. If you happen to have a fluorescent light in your home, you also used matter in its plasma state. On Earth matter occurs in four physical
states. These four states are solid, liquid, gas, and plas- 3
ma. What causes the differences among these four states of matter?

Solids

The reason some matter is solid is that its atoms or molecules are in a fixed position relative to each other. The individual atoms may vibrate but they don't switch positions with each other. You can make a mental model of this.

Suppose you have a puzzle with its many pieces in place. The pieces are packed so tightly that no one piece can switch positions with another piece. But the pieces can move a little. For example, you can twist the whole puzzle a few millimeters without breaking it apart. If it's on a table, you can shake the table and the puzzle's individual pieces will vibrate. But the pieces of the puzzle are held together even though they do move some.

The puzzle pieces in our model represent atoms or molecules of a substance in a solid state. Such atoms or molecules are strongly attracted to each other and resist being separated.

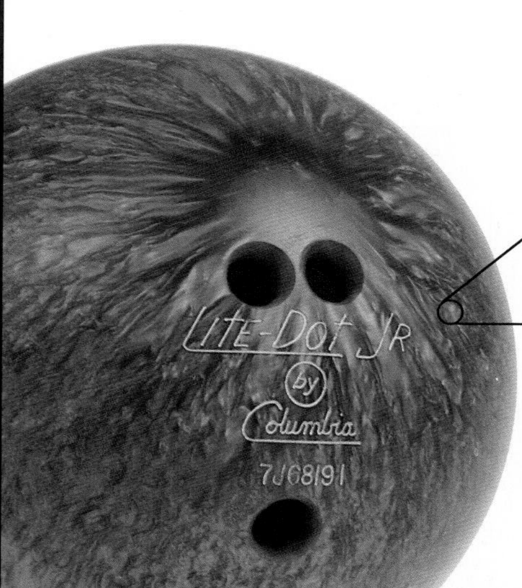

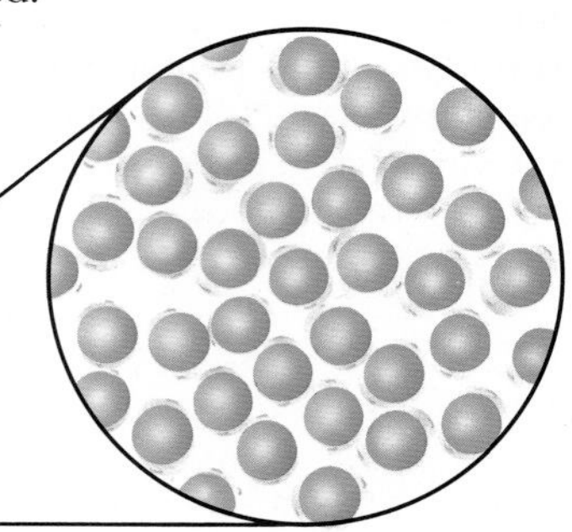

Figure 2-13. The atoms or molecules in a solid are strongly attracted to one another and tightly packed. However, they do vibrate.

OPTIONS

INQUIRY QUESTIONS

▶ **What happens to atoms and molecules that enables matter to change from the solid state to the liquid state?** *Atoms and molecules in the solid state gain energy and move more freely as the solid changes to a liquid.*

▶ **Although glass is hard to the touch, it is not considered a solid. Can you explain why?** *Atoms and molecules in solids vibrate but do not move around. The molecules that compose glass are able to move around.*

▶ **What happens to water molecules in a swimming pool when you jump in?** *Molecules that make up liquids, such as water, are free to change positions. As you jump in, the water molecules move aside to make room for you.*

PROGRAM RESOURCES

From the **Teacher Resource Package** use:

Activity Worksheets, page 5, Flex Your Brain.

Figure 2-14. The atoms or molecules in a liquid are not as strongly attracted to each other as those of a solid. They are free to move over and around each other.

Liquids

Atoms or molecules in a liquid are also strongly attracted to each other, but they aren't as strongly attracted as they are in a solid. Atoms or molecules remain close to one another in a liquid but are free to change positions with each other. This allows liquids to flow.

When you sit down to breakfast, you may have several liquids at the table. You may have milk in a glass and syrup on your pancakes. Both are substances in the liquid state, even though one flows more freely than the other.

A liquid flows as it takes the shape of the container it's placed in, but it resists changes in volume. You can pour orange juice into a short, wide glass and it will match the shape of the glass. You can then pour the same juice into a tall, skinny glass and it will flow until it matches the shape of its new container. It does so because its molecules move over and around each other.

REVEALING MISCONCEPTIONS

▶ Some students may not realize that matter can change from a solid to a gas without going through the liquid phase. This process is called sublimation.

▶ **Demonstration:** Obtain a piece of dry ice (carbon dioxide in a frozen, solid state). Place the dry ice on a plate in view of students. The dry ice will quickly change into carbon dioxide gas via sublimation. Students should note that it doesn't pass through a liquid state. **CAUTION:** *Do not touch the dry ice. Always use a thermal mitt and tongs to manipulate the ice.*

CONCEPT DEVELOPMENT

▶ Discuss the fact that energy is needed to change the state of a material. The amount of energy needed to change a solid to a liquid is the heat of fusion for that material. For example, the heat of fusion for water is 334 kJ/kg. It takes 334 kJ (kilojoules) of energy to melt 1 kg of ice.

▶ Ask students to explain why boiling water can't be heated over 100°C. Water particles are absorbing energy, which enables them to overcome attractive forces holding them in a liquid state. The absorbed energy allows them to separate from each other. They become particles of gaseous water, or steam. The amount of energy needed to change a material from a liquid to a gas is the heat of vaporization of that material. For water, the heat of vaporization is 2260 kJ/kg. The energy added by a burner or flame to a boiling pot of water is absorbed by the water particles and used to overcome attractive forces. Thus the temperature doesn't rise.

ENRICHMENT

▶ Have students perform the following activity to explore energy absorption as water changes state. Put 100 mL of water and 5 ice cubes in a 600-mL beaker. Record the temperature of the water. Then, slowly heat the beaker and water, recording the temperature at one-minute intervals. Note when the ice melts and when the water begins to boil. Measure and record the temperature as the water boils for 5 minutes. Graph the temperature of the water versus time. **What was the maximum temperature reached when ice was still in the water?** *0° C* **What was the maximum temperature reached?** *100°C* **What do the horizontal portions of your graph represent?** *changes of state*

CHECK FOR UNDERSTANDING

Ask the class what they think could cause the attraction among atoms and molecules and changes in their rates of movement. Discuss all responses and help students to conclude that changes in temperature and pressure can cause changes in atomic and molecular attraction and movement.

RETEACH

Demonstrate how water changes state when heat is added or when pressure is applied. Place an ice cube in a pan on your desk. As the ice cube warms, it will change to liquid water. Then show students how ice will change to a liquid when pressure is applied by pressing down on the ice with a massive object.

EXTENSION

For students who have mastered this section, use the **Reinforcement** and **Enrichment** masters or other OPTIONS provided.

CROSS CURRICULUM

► **Chemistry:** Have students research the formation of plasma. Students will find out that plasma forms at very high temperatures when electrons are stripped from atoms to form a mixture of positive ions and electrons.

TEACHER F.Y.I.

► Over 99 percent of the matter in the universe occurs as plasma.

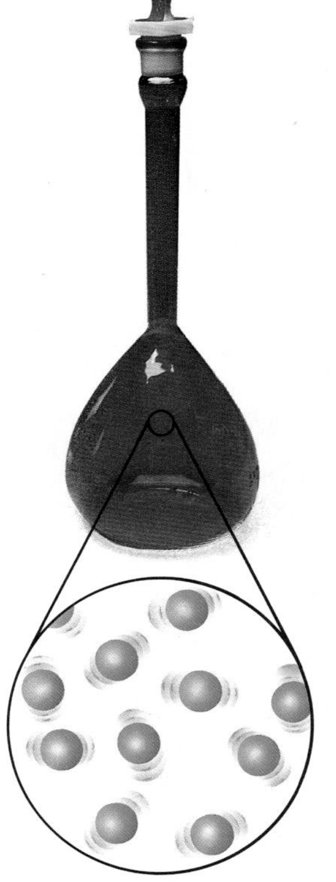

Figure 2-15. Molecules in a gas are not strongly attracted to each other.

Gases

4 Gases behave the way they do because their atoms or molecules have very little attractive force on each other. This causes them to move freely and independently. Air fresheners work because of this property. If an air freshener is placed in a corner, it isn't long before molecules from the air freshener have spread throughout the room. Gases fill the entire container they are placed in no matter what size or shape it is. The atoms or molecules move apart until they're evenly spaced throughout the container.

Plasma

What's the most common state of matter? So far we've investigated matter in the solid, liquid, and gaseous states. But most of the matter in the universe is in the plasma state. Matter in this state is composed of ions and electrons. Many of the electrons normally in the electron cloud have escaped and are outside of the ion's electron cloud.

Stars are composed of matter in the plasma state. And plasma exists in the space between the stars. On Earth, plasma is found in fluorescent lights and lightning bolts.

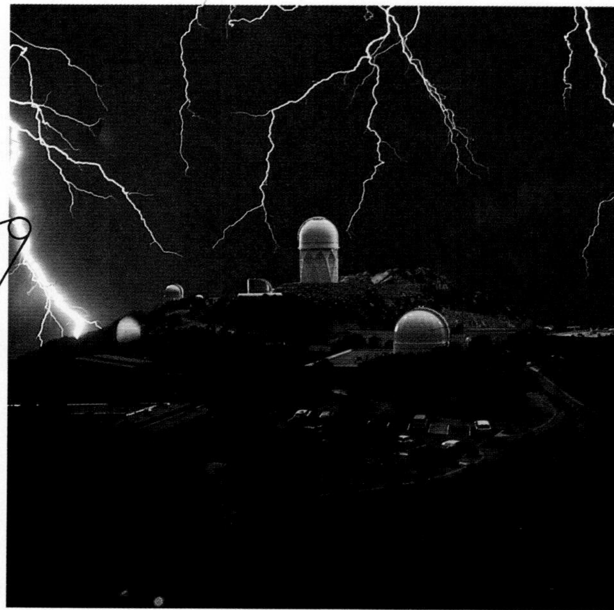

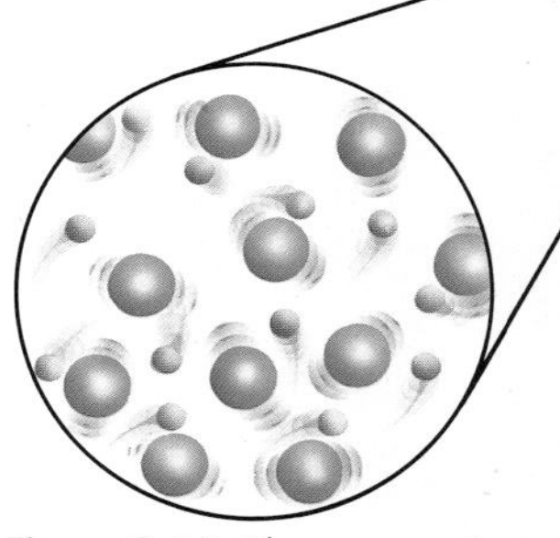

Figure 2-16. Plasma consists of ions and electrons moving freely.

OPTIONS

INQUIRY QUESTIONS

► **What general statement can be made about the attractive forces among atoms and molecules in solids, liquids, and gases?** *Attractive forces among atoms and molecules in a solid are strong; they are weaker in liquids, and relatively very weak in gases.*

► **Do changes in state cause changes in either physical or chemical properties of matter?** *When matter changes state, it retains its chemical properties, but some of its physical properties will change.*

► **Why is matter in the plasma state harmful to life-forms?** *Plasma contains vast amounts of energy, which would be harmful to life-forms.*

Figure 2-17. A solid metal can be converted into liquid by adding thermal energy to its molecules.

Changing the State of Matter

Matter is changed from a liquid to a solid at its freezing point and from a liquid to a gas at its boiling point. You're probably familiar with the freezing and boiling points of water. Water changes from a liquid to a solid at its freezing point of 0°C. It boils at 100°C. Water is the only substance that occurs naturally on Earth as a solid, liquid, and gas.

Most substances don't naturally exist in these three states on Earth. Their boiling and freezing points are above or below the temperatures we experience. Temperatures and conditions needed for matter to exist as plasma are even less common on Earth.

The attraction between atoms or molecules and their rate of movement are two factors that determine the state of matter. When you melt ice you increase the rate of movement of its molecules. They are then able to move apart. Adding thermal energy to the ice causes this change.

What are two factors that determine matter's state?

Changes in state can also occur because of increases or decreases in pressure. You can demonstrate this by applying pressure to an ice cube. It will change to liquid water even though its temperature stays the same.

EcoTip

Cover water when you heat it, and you'll use less energy. Covered water boils faster than uncovered water.

MINI QUIZ

Use the Mini Quiz to check students' recall of chapter content.

1. **A property you can observe without changing a substance into a new substance is a(n) ____ property.** *physical*
2. **The relationship between the mass of an object and its volume is ____.** *density*
3. **The four states of matter are ____.** *solid, liquid, gas, and plasma*
4. **In which state of matter do atoms or molecules have very little attractive force on one another?** *in a gas*

TEACHER F.Y.I.

▶ The pressure exerted by ice skates on the ice melts a small amount of it, allowing a skater to move on a thin film of water. After the skater has passed over an area, the water freezes.

ENRICHMENT

▶ Have students explain why the boiling point of water differs from one location to another. The temperature at which a liquid boils depends on atmospheric pressure. Because atmospheric pressure differs with elevation, boiling points of a liquid also vary with elevation. For example, the boiling point of water at sea level is 100°C. Its boiling point in Denver, CO, at 1600 m above sea level, is 95°C.

MINI-Lab

Materials: graduated cylinders or small beakers, water, freezer, masking tape

Teaching Tips

▶ Have students predict what changes, if any, they think will occur in the volume of the water when it changes to ice.

▶ Make sure they record the level of the water before freezing.

▶ As long as the container is uncovered, it will not break when the water expands as it freezes.

▶ The level of the ice is higher than the level of the liquid water.

▶ **Answer:** Water expands as it freezes but does not change mass. Also, ice is less dense than liquid.

CONCEPT DEVELOPMENT

▶ Discuss the significance of water's unusual property of being less dense when frozen. Most materials increase in density when they change state from a liquid to a solid.

▶ When ice forms on the surface of a body of water, it insulates the water below from the cold air. As a result, the underlying water doesn't freeze.

STUDENT TEXT QUESTION

▶ Page 46, Figure caption: **What would happen to the life in a pond if this were true?** *Fish and other organisms would die. Organisms would be encased in ice.*

MINI-Lab

What happens when water freezes?

Pour water into a graduated cylinder or small beaker so that it is about half filled. Mark the level of the water with a small piece of masking tape. Then place the uncovered container of water into a freezer until all of the water turns to ice. How does the level of the ice in the container compare to the original level of the water? Describe some of the changes in the physical properties of water when it changes to ice.

Changes in Physical Properties

Chemical properties of matter don't change when the matter changes state. But some of its physical properties change. For example, the density of water changes as it changes state. In which state is water the most dense? You may be tempted to say when it's a solid, but think critically about this. Ice will float in liquid water, therefore ice is less dense than liquid water. This is because water molecules move farther apart and the water expands as it freezes.

Some physical properties of substances don't change when they change state. For example, water is colorless and transparent in each of its states.

Chemical and physical properties allow us to identify and classify matter. One way to classify matter is by its state. Matter in one state can often be changed to another state by adding or removing heat. When matter changes state in this way, it retains its chemical properties while some of its physical properties change.

Figure 2-18. If ice was more dense than water, lakes would freeze solid from the bottom up. What would happen to the life in a pond if this were true?

OPTIONS

PROGRAM RESOURCES

From the **Teacher Resource Package** use:
Activity Worksheets, page 19, Mini-Lab: What happens when water freezes?

Figure 2-19. Water-carved valley on the Planet Mars

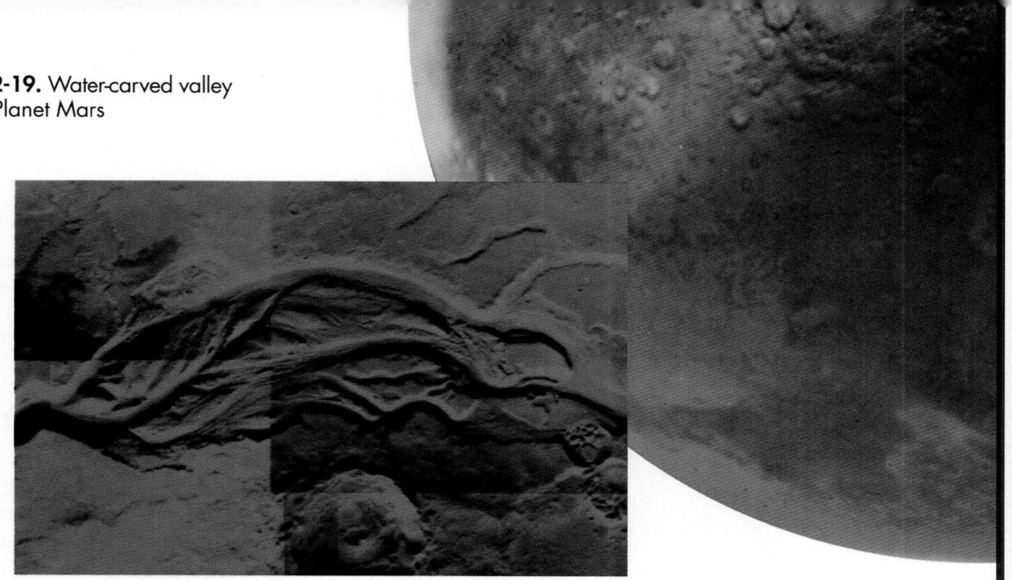

SECTION REVIEW

1. What property of a substance is calculated by dividing its mass by its volume? Is it a chemical or physical property?
2. In which state are the molecules of water prevented from moving over and around each other? In which state can water molecules spread the farthest apart?
3. Suppose you blow up a balloon and then place it in a freezer. Later, you find the balloon has shrunk and it contains liquid in it. Explain what has happened.
4. **Apply:** The planet Mars has what appears to be ancient stream beds, yet there's no liquid water on Mars. Explain what may have happened to Mars' liquid water.

Making and Using Tables

Skill Builder

Jonathon had a glass of milk, an orange, celery sticks, and a peanut butter and jelly sandwich for lunch. Make a table listing the state of matter of each item of his lunch. Also list at least one physical property of each item. If you need help, refer to Making and Using Tables in the **Skill Handbook** on page 690.

3 CLOSE

►Ask questions 1-3 and the **Apply** Question in the Section Review.

Cooperative Learning: Form Science Investigation groups with three students per group. Assign one student to measure the volume of a block of wood. Another student is to measure its mass using a balance. Once these data are collected, the third student in the group should calculate the density of the block, using the equation on page 41.

SECTION REVIEW ANSWERS

1. density; physical property
2. solid; gas
3. The temperature of the air was lowered. The molecules of air moved closer together, reducing the size of the balloon. Molecules of water vapor in the air condensed to form liquid water.
4. Apply: The low atmospheric pressure on Mars may have caused some of the liquid water to evaporate. Some of the liquid water froze to form polar ice caps. Some water may have soaked into the ground and frozen.

Skill Builder

Students' tables will vary. One possible solution is shown.

Item	State	Physical Properties
milk	liquid	white, cold
sandwich	solid	made of bread, peanut butter, and jelly
orange	solid, liquid	orange, round
celery	solid	green, stringy

SECTION 2-4

PREPARATION

SECTION BACKGROUND

▶ The resistivity of a conductor is a function of its temperature. As temperature decreases, electrons in a conductor are able to move more freely. At one point, called the transition temperature, all resistance to electron flow stops. This condition is called superconductivity.

▶ Recently discovered ceramic superconductors are copper oxides consisting of electronically active planes of copper and oxygen atoms. The amount of charge on the planes of copper and oxygen atoms determines the temperature at which superconductivity may occur.

PREPLANNING

▶ Obtain the materials listed on page 50, which are needed for Activity 2-2.

1 MOTIVATE

TYING TO PREVIOUS KNOWLEDGE: Have students list as many household objects as they can that are powered by electricity. Ask if any of the objects become warm when electricity flows through them. Relate this to the resistance to electron flow, which causes materials to get warmer due to friction.

OBJECTIVES AND SCIENCE WORDS: Have students review the objectives and science words to become familiar with this section.

PROGRAM RESOURCES

From the **Teacher Resource Package** use:

Science and Society, page 6, The Question of Superconductors.

Activity Worksheets, page 5, Flex Your Brain.

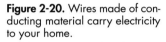

2-4 Superconductors

New Science Words

superconductors

Objectives

- ▶ Compare and contrast superconductors with other conductors.
- ▶ Discuss one possible use of superconducting materials.

How Can Superconductors Store Energy?

It's 8:00 PM and the electricity in your home suddenly goes out. You have no lights, no radio, no refrigeration, and no television. Your local power company didn't produce enough electricity to power all the homes and businesses in your neighborhood. How can this be? Isn't there a way to prevent this from happening?

When coal-burning and nuclear power plants produce electricity, they send it out over utility lines and it eventually reaches your house. But if the power company produces more energy than is needed, the electricity can't be stored; it goes to waste. If they don't produce enough, you and your neighbors lose power. If there were a way for power companies to store electricity, they could produce more than was needed at one time, store it, and tap into it when energy demands are high. Superconductors may make this possible.

Figure 2-20. Wires made of conducting material carry electricity to your home.

Any material that allows electrons to pass through it is called a conductor. Electrons flowing through a conductor produce the electricity you use in your home.

As electrons pass through a wire they collide with atoms in the wire. This resistance to the flow of electricity causes the material to heat up. Part of the electric energy is wasted as it's converted to thermal energy. But in **superconductors,** no electricity is wasted because there's no resistance to the flow of electrons.

Materials such as titanium, zinc, lead, and mercury conduct electricity with no resistance when they are cooled to extremely low temperatures. Planes of atoms provide highways for electrons to flow without collisions with atoms.

Because there's no resistance in a superconductor, elec-
1 tric current continues once it's started. Electric currents

OPTIONS

Meeting Different Ability Levels

For Section 2-4, use the following **Teacher Resource Masters** depending upon individual students' needs.

◆ **Study Guide Master** for all students.

● **Reinforcement Master** for students of average and above average ability levels.

▲ **Enrichment Master** for above average students.

Additional Teacher Resource Package masters are listed in the OPTIONS box throughout the section. The additional masters are appropriate for all students.

◆ STUDY GUIDE 12

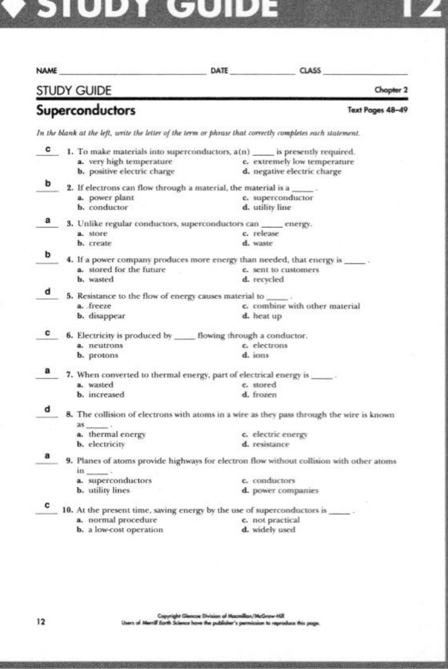

NAME ______ DATE ______ CLASS ______

STUDY GUIDE — Chapter 2

Superconductors — Text Pages 48–49

In the blank at the left, write the letter of the term or phrase that correctly completes each statement.

c 1. To make materials into superconductors, a(n) ____ is presently required.
a. very high temperature c. extremely low temperature
b. positive electric charge d. negative electric charge

b 2. If electrons can flow through a material, the material is a ____.
a. power plant c. superconductor
b. conductor d. utility line

a 3. Unlike regular conductors, superconductors can ____ energy.
a. store c. release
b. create d. waste

b 4. If a power company produces more energy than needed, that energy is ____.
a. stored for the future c. sent to customers
b. wasted d. recycled

d 5. Resistance to the flow of energy causes material to ____.
a. freeze c. combine with other material
b. disappear d. heat up

c 6. Electricity is produced by ____ flowing through a conductor.
a. neutrons c. electrons
b. protons d. ions

a 7. When converted to thermal energy, part of electrical energy is ____.
a. wasted c. stored
b. increased d. frozen

d 8. The collision of electrons with atoms in a wire as they pass through the wire is known as ____.
a. thermal energy c. electric energy
b. electricity d. resistance

a 9. Planes of atoms provide highways for electron flow without collision with other atoms in ____.
a. superconductors c. conductors
b. utility lines d. power companies

c 10. At the present time, saving energy by the use of superconductors is ____.
a. normal procedure c. not practical
b. a low-cost operation d. widely used

12

can even be stored in a superconducting ring. The current continually flows around the ring and can be tapped when the electricity is needed in another circuit. Power plants could have a way to store excess electricity that would otherwise be wasted.

The biggest problem with superconductors is that extremely low temperatures are needed to make materials into superconductors. So far the highest temperature superconductor must be cooled to about –150°C. In fact, much of the energy saved by using superconductors must then be used to keep them cool. ②

Figure 2-21. Superconductors generate powerful magnetic fields as they conduct electricity. This magnet is suspended in a magnetic field over a superconductor.

SECTION REVIEW

1. Why is some of the energy flowing through conductors wasted? How are superconductors different?
2. Why can't superconductors be used to replace the wires in utility lines so that no electricity would be wasted as it passes through them?
3. How might power companies use superconductors ?

You Decide!

It's unlikely that materials will ever be developed that can superconduct at room temperature. Is the possibility of reduced cost and reduced waste of electric energy worth the expense in an attempt to find higher temperature superconductors? Or would it be better to spend the money on educating people on how to conserve energy?

● REINFORCEMENT 12

NAME ______ DATE ______ CLASS ______

REINFORCEMENT — Chapter 2

Superconductors — Text Pages 48–49

Answer the following questions on the lines provided.

1. It is the hottest day of the year. Most of the homes in your area including your home have air conditioning. The demand for electricity is very high. At three o'clock in the afternoon, your lights flicker and then go out. You notice that none of your electrical appliances are working. You call your neighbors and they do not have electricity either. What might have happened? **The power company may not have been able to generate enough electricity to meet the demand. Some areas lost power as a result.**
2. Suppose electric companies had developed technology that enabled them to use superconductors. How might the situation given in Question 1 have differed? **Most likely there would not have been a shortage of electric power because the electric company would have released the energy that the superconductors had stored. As a result, you would not have experienced a power outage.**
3. Compare and contrast superconductors and conductors. **Both superconductors and conductors allow the flow of electrons to provide a source of energy. Superconductors can store energy and do not lose energy through resistance. Conductors can't store energy, and they lose energy through resistance. At present, superconductors require very low temperatures to operate. Conductors can transport energy within a greater range of temperatures.**
4. Why aren't superconductors used by electric companies at the present time? **Superconductors require very low temperatures to operate. Methods of cooling the superconductors require the use of energy. Power companies would have to use most of the energy saved by using superconductors to cool them. As a result, power companies wouldn't save money or energy.**
5. If superconductors could operate at room temperatures, would they be more practical? **Yes, they would be more practical because energy would not be needed to keep the superconductors cool.**

12

▲ ENRICHMENT 12

NAME ______ DATE ______ CLASS ______

ENRICHMENT — Chapter 2

Superconductors — Text Pages 48–49

MAGNETIC RESONANCE IMAGING SCANNERS

Unlike most conductors, superconductors can operate in a high magnetic field while carrying an electric current. As a result, superconductors are used to power electromagnets. These magnets have led to the development of magnetic resonance imaging scanners (MRIs). These machines are an important development in the medical field. They enable doctors to more easily make medical diagnoses of soft tissues in the body.

Use encyclopedias or other reference books or go to the library to research information about magnetic resonance imaging scanners. Then answer these questions.

1. What do magnetic resonance imaging scanners provide images of? **The scanners provide images of soft tissues including organs, veins, and arteries.**
2. How do the MRIs differ from X rays? **X rays expose patients to radiation and require the use of special dyes or other agents to show soft tissues. MRIs do not expose patients to radiation and can show soft tissues without the use of dyes.**
3. Why is using the magnetic resonance imaging scanners beneficial to patients? **The scanners provide clear images of tissues that cannot be seen with X rays without the use of potentially harmful dyes or other agents. The patient is not exposed to harmful radiation, but only a harmless magnetic field. The images provided can also sometimes eliminate the need for exploratory surgery.**
4. Why should some patients not be tested using the MRIs? **Patients with pacemakers or artificial metal implants should not be exposed to the magnetic field of the MRIs, because the magnetic exposure would interfere with the operation of these devices.**
5. MRIs are very expensive equipment to buy, operate, and maintain. As a result, using them for physical examinations is a very costly procedure. Do you think the benefits provided by the MRIs justify the costs? **Students' opinions will vary, but they should consider the benefits to the patient and the doctor in stating their opinions. The reduced risk to patients because of the lack of exposure to radiation, chemicals, and surgery as well as the assistance to the doctor in making medical diagnoses may well justify the cost of an MRI examination.**

12

2 TEACH

Key Concepts are highlighted.

CHECK FOR UNDERSTANDING

Use the Mini Quiz to check for understanding.

MINI QUIZ

Use the Mini Quiz to check students' recall of chapter content.

① **Why does electric current continue to flow in a superconductor once it is started?** *There is no resistance to the flow of electrons.*

② **What is presently the biggest problem with superconductors?** *Extremely low temperatures are needed to make them work.*

RETEACH

FLEX Your Brain

Use the Flex Your Brain activity to have students explore SUPERCONDUCTORS.

EXTENSION

For students who have mastered this section, use the **Reinforcement** and **Enrichment** masters or other OPTIONS provided.

3 CLOSE

► Ask questions 1-3 in the Section Review.

SECTION REVIEW ANSWERS

1. It's converted to thermal energy. No energy is wasted in superconductors because there's no resistance to the flow of electrons.

2. Currently, there is no way to cool the utility lines to such low temperatures.

3. to store electricity

YOU DECIDE!

Cooperative Learning: Divide the class into Numbered Heads Together groups of three students per group. Have the members of each group discuss the questions in the You Decide feature.

ACTIVITY 2-2
50 minutes

OBJECTIVE: Measure the mass and volume and **determine** the densities of various objects and materials.

PROCESS SKILLS applied in this activity:
▶ **Measuring** in Procedure Steps 1-3, 5, and 6.
▶ **Using Numbers** in Procedure Steps 3, 4, and 7.
▶ **Predicting** in Procedure Steps 4 and 6 and Analyze Question 2.
▶ **Interpreting Data** in Conclude and Apply Questions 3 and 5.
▶ **Inferring** in Conclude and Apply Question 4.

TEACHING THE ACTIVITY

▶ Before starting this activity, have students review Section 2-3 as well as the procedures that were followed in Activity 2-1.

▶ Discuss and demonstrate how to determine the volume of a solid by water displacement in a graduated cylinder. Remind students that sources of error may include water splashed from the graduated cylinder.

▶ After all calculations have been completed and all questions answered, provide students with the accepted density values and have them calculate their percentage of error for each object. Answers with less than 10% error are acceptable.

Alternate Materials: Density kits containing many of these samples are available from a number of science supply distributors. A sample of any nonsoluble mineral may be substituted for the quartz.

Troubleshooting: The clay must be oil-based and not water-soluble. Since the wood block may absorb water, it should not be left in water for any extended length of time.

PROGRAM RESOURCES

From the **Teacher Resource Package** use:
Activity Worksheets, pages 14-15, Activity 2-2: Determining Density.

ACTIVITY 2-2
Determining Density

Problem: *How are the densities of substances determined?*

Materials

- pan balance
- beaker (100 mL)
- piece of quartz
- graduated cylinder (250 mL)
- water
- piece of clay
- small wood block
- small metal block

Procedure

1. Using the pan balance, measure the mass of the wood block, metal block, clay, and quartz. Record these values.
2. Use the graduated cylinder to determine the volume of each sample. Record these values.
3. Calculate the density of each sample by using this equation:
   density = mass/volume
4. After completing these calculations, split the piece of clay into two pieces. Predict what the density of each of the two smaller pieces of clay will be. Determine the density of each piece using the procedure outlined above.
5. Empty the graduated cylinder and determine its mass.
6. Put 100 mL of water in the graduated cylinder and determine the mass of the cylinder and water. Calculate the mass of the water using this equation:

$$\text{mass of water} = \text{mass of cylinder and water} - \text{mass of empty cylinder}$$

7. Calculate the density of water.

Analyze

1. How does the density of each of the smaller pieces of clay compare to the original larger piece?
2. If you broke the quartz into many small pieces, would one of these pieces be more dense, less dense, or equally dense as the one large original piece?

Conclude and Apply

3. What effect does the size or amount of a substance have on its density?
4. Isopropyl alcohol is less dense than liquid water and ice. How could you use isopropyl alcohol to determine the density of an ice cube?
5. How are the densities of various substances determined?

Data and Observations

Sample Data

Object	Mass	Volume	Density
Wood	28.7 g	43.0 cm^3	0.6 g/cm^3
Metal	112.4 g	32.7 cm^3	3.43 g/cm^3
Clay (lg. piece)	57.5 g	21.3 cm^3	2.7 g/cm^3
Quartz	157.3 g	59.3 cm^3	2.65 g/cm^3
Clay (sm. piece)	28.8 g	10.7 cm^3	2.7 g/cm^3
Water	100.0 g	100.0 cm^3	1.0 g/cm^3

ANSWERS TO QUESTIONS

1. The density is the same.
2. Equally dense; the density of a substance is not related to size.
3. The size or amount of a substance has no effect on its density.
4. Answers will vary. Any method that proposes that the ice cube be submerged to determine its volume while simultaneously determining its mass, should be accepted. One method involves adding isopropyl alcohol to water with an ice cube until the cube remains suspended below the liquid's surface, but above the bottom of the container. The density of the liquid will then be identical to that of the ice cube.
5. The density of any substance is the amount of mass *compared* to its volume. Density is a ratio; it cannot be measured directly. It must be calculated.

CHAPTER

REVIEW

SUMMARY

2-1: Atoms

1. Matter is everything that has mass and takes up space. Atoms are the building blocks of matter.
2. Protons and neutrons make up the nucleus of an atom. Protons have a positive charge whereas neutrons have no charge. Electrons circle the nucleus, forming an electron cloud. Electrons are negatively charged.
3. Isotopes are atoms of the same element. Isotopes have the same atomic number, but differ in the number of neutrons.

2-2: Combinations of Atoms

1. A compound is a substance made of two or more elements. The properties of a compound differ from the chemical and physical properties of the elements of which it is composed.
2. Atoms join to form molecules — the building blocks of compounds. A mixture is a substance in which each of the components retains its own properties.

2-3: Matter

1. Physical properties can be observed and measured without causing a chemical change in a substance. Chemical properties can only be observed when one substance reacts with another substance.
2. Atoms or molecules in a solid are in fixed positions relative to one another. In a liquid, the atoms or molecules are close together but are freer to change positions. Atoms or molecules in a gas have very little attractive force on one another. Plasma is composed of ions and electrons.

2-4: Science and Society: Superconductors

1. Electrons flow through superconductors with no resistance.
2. Superconducting rings may be used to store electricity.

KEY SCIENCE WORDS

a. **atoms**
b. **chemical properties**
c. **compound**
d. **density**
e. **electrons**
f. **elements**
g. **ions**
h. **isotopes**
i. **matter**
j. **mixture**
k. **molecule**
l. **neutrons**
m. **physical properties**
n. **protons**
o. **superconductors**

UNDERSTANDING VOCABULARY

Match each phrase with the correct term from the list of Key Science Words.

1. building blocks of matter
2. particles with no electric charge
3. allow electrons to flow with no resistance
4. anything that takes up space and has mass
5. a solution is one type
6. circle the nucleus of an atom
7. composed of only one type of atom
8. mass divided by volume
9. two or more atoms combine to form this building block of compounds
10. atoms of the same element but with different numbers of neutrons

OPTIONS

ASSESSMENT

To assess student understanding of material in this chapter, use the resources listed.

COOPERATIVE LEARNING

Consider using cooperative learning in the THINK AND WRITE CRITICALLY, APPLY, and MORE SKILL BUILDERS sections of the Chapter Review.

PROGRAM RESOURCES

From the **Teacher Resource Package** use:
Chapter Review, pages 7-8.
Chapter and Unit Tests, pages 9-12, Chapter Test.
Chapter and Unit Tests, pages 13-14, Unit Test.

CHAPTER

REVIEW

SUMMARY

Have students read the summary statements to review the major concepts of the chapter.

UNDERSTANDING VOCABULARY

1. a
2. l
3. o
4. i
5. j
6. e
7. f
8. d
9. k
10. h

CHAPTER

REVIEW

CHECKING CONCEPTS

1. c
2. b
3. a
4. a
5. b
6. c
7. d
8. b
9. c
10. a

UNDERSTANDING CONCEPTS

11. protons
12. 23
13. 11
14. mixture
15. freezing point

THINK AND WRITE CRITICALLY

16. All are atomic particles. Protons have a positive charge; electrons a negative charge; and neutrons have no charge. Protons and neutrons make up the nucleus of an atom, whereas electrons circle the nucleus in an electron cloud.

17. proton, atomic nucleus, atom, element, molecule, compound

18. The mass number is 39.

19. density = mass ÷ volume
$23\text{ g} \div 25\text{ cm}^3 = 0.92\text{ g/cm}^3$

20. Conductors resist the flow of electrons whereas superconductors do not.

CHAPTER

REVIEW

CHECKING CONCEPTS

Choose the word or phrase that completes the sentence.

1. ______ contain only one type of atom.
   - **a.** Plasmas
   - **b.** Mixtures
   - **c.** Elements
   - **d.** Solids
2. A(n) ______ has a positive charge.
   - **a.** electron
   - **b.** proton
   - **c.** neutron
   - **d.** plasma
3. In an atom, the ______ form a cloud around the nucleus..
   - **a.** electrons
   - **b.** protons
   - **c.** neutrons
   - **d.** all of these
4. Carbon has a mass number of 12. Thus, it has ______ protons and ______ neutrons.
   - **a.** 6, 6
   - **b.** 12, 12
   - **c.** 6, 12
   - **d.** 12, 6
5. On Earth, oxygen is usually a ______.
   - **a.** solid
   - **b.** gas
   - **c.** liquid
   - **d.** plasma
6. An isotope of carbon is ______.
   - **a.** boron-12
   - **b.** nitrogen-12
   - **c.** carbon-14
   - **d.** hydrogen-2
7. Electrically charged atoms are ______.
   - **a.** molecules
   - **b.** solutions
   - **c.** isotopes
   - **d.** ions
8. The color of your clothes is a(n) ______.
   - **a.** chemical property
   - **b.** physical property
   - **c.** isotope property
   - **d.** all of these
9. A rock with a volume of 4.0 cm^3 and a density of 3.0 g/cm^3 has a mass of ______.
   - **a.** 0.75 g
   - **b.** 3.0 g
   - **c.** 12.0 g
   - **d.** 4.0 g
10. Water changes state at ______.
    - **a.** 0°C and 100°C
    - **b.** 32°C and 100°C
    - **c.** 0°C and 32°C
    - **d.** none of these

UNDERSTANDING CONCEPTS

Complete each sentence.

11. Carbon-12 and carbon-14 have the same number of ______.
12. Sodium has 11 protons and 12 neutrons. Its mass number is ______.
13. The atomic number of sodium is ______.
14. A bowl of fruit salad can best be classified as a(n) ______.
15. Liquid water changes to ice at its ______.

THINK AND WRITE CRITICALLY

16. Compare and contrast protons, electrons, and neutrons.
17. Arrange the following terms in order of size, from smallest to largest: *atomic nucleus, proton, molecule, atom, compound, element.*
18. One isotope of argon is argon-39. What is the mass number of this element?
19. What is the density of 25 cm^3 of salad oil if its mass is 23 grams?
20. How do conductors and superconductors differ?

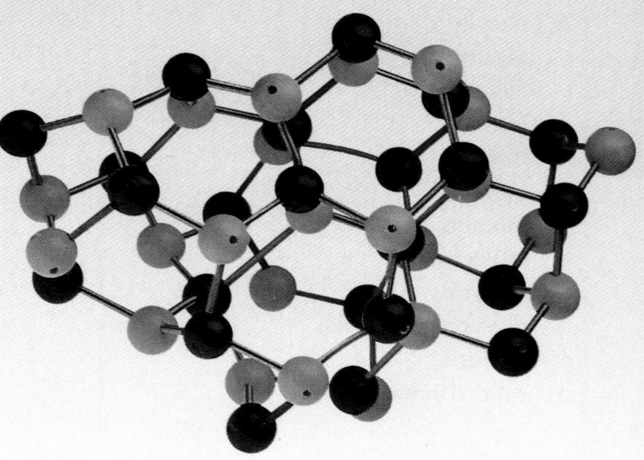

APPLY

21. Would isotopes of the same element have the same number of electrons? Explain.
22. Two chlorine ions are both negatively charged. Will they combine to form a compound? Why or why not?
23. You pour salad oil into a glass of water. After several minutes, you observe that the water is at the bottom of the glass and all of the oil is floating on top of the water. Does your glass contain a mixture? Does it contain a solution?
24. When oxygen combines with iron, rust is formed. Is this a chemical or physical property of iron?
25. Would rubber or copper make a better superconductor? Explain.

MORE SKILL BUILDERS

If you need help, refer to the Skill Handbook.

1. **Classifying:** Use Appendix E to classify the following substances as elements or compounds: *iron, aluminum, carbon dioxide, gold, water,* and *sugar.*
2. **Concept Mapping:** Make a network tree to illustrate the three main parts of an atom.
3. **Hypothesizing:** You put a bottle full of water in the freezer to cool it quickly. You forgot about it, though, and found a broken glass when you went to get it. What hypothesis can you make about water as it changes from a liquid to a solid?
4. **Observing and Inferring:** Your brother is drinking a dark-colored liquid from a clear glass. As you watch from across the room, you think to yourself that the cola is probably refreshing. Is thinking that the liquid is cola an observation or an inference?

Element	Atomic No.	Mass No.
Fluorine	9	19
Lithium	3	7
Carbon	6	12
Nitrogen	7	14
Beryllium	4	9
Boron	5	11
Oxygen	8	16
Neon	10	20

5. **Making and Using Graphs:** Use the data above to make a line graph of increasing mass number and atomic number of each element. What is the relationship between mass number and atomic number?

PROJECTS

1. Use different-sized foam balls and wooden sticks to make scale models of the atomic structure of the first ten elements in the periodic table.
2. Classify all the items in your family's refrigerator according to physical state. Then list at least two chemical and two physical properties of each item.
3. Research how the model of an atom has evolved with time. Include sketches that compare and contrast the different models.

APPLY

21. Yes, isotopes differ in the number of neutrons.
22. They will not combine. Like charges repel.
23. Yes, the oil and water is a mixture. It is not a solution, however, because neither the water nor the oil is evenly spread throughout the other.
24. chemical
25. Metals, such as copper, are better conductors than materials like glass and rubber. Rubber and glass are insulators.

MORE SKILL BUILDERS

1. Classifying: Iron, aluminum, and gold are elements; carbon dioxide, water, and sugar are compounds.
2. Concept Mapping: See the concept map shown below for one possible solution.
3. Hypothesizing: It expands as it freezes.
4. Observing and Inferring: It is an inference because the liquid might be tea or perhaps grape juice.
5. Making and Using Graphs:

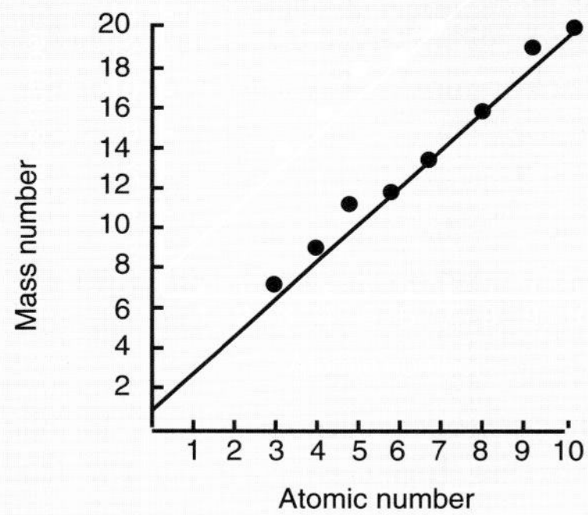

The mass number increases as the atomic number increases.

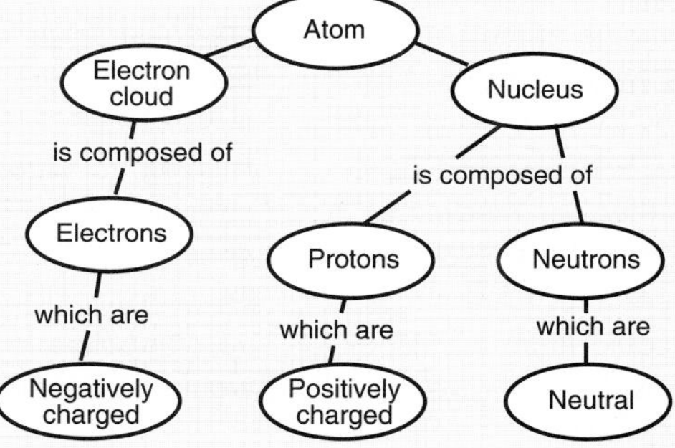

UNIT 1
GLOBAL CONNECTIONS

Objective

In this unit ending feature, the unit topic, "Earth Science Foundations," is extended into other disciplines. Students will see how the study of atoms and other fundamental concepts relates to other disciplines.

Motivate

Cooperative Learning: Assign one Connection to each group of students. Using the Expert Teams strategy, have each group research to find out more about the geographic location of the Connection—its climate, culture, plants, animals, and ecological issues.

Wrap-Up

After students have reviewed all the boxes on these pages, ask them to form a hypothesis about whether electrons are basic units of matter or whether they, like protons and neutrons, consist of smaller units of matter.

ASTRONOMY

Background: The discovery of the "Great Wall" has created a problem for scientists. The models of how matter became organized in the universe allow only for a nearly homogenous universe with matter evenly distributed.
Discussion: Discuss with students that the big bang theory for the beginning of the universe calls for a universe that is extremely smooth with matter evenly distributed. The big bang theory is constantly being modified as new observations are made.
Answer to Question: Astronomers used to think that the matter of the universe was evenly distributed. Recent discovery of a place in the universe where there are five times the average number of galaxies has changed this idea.
Extension: Have students draw a chart of uniform galaxy concentrations and one showing areas of greater concentration.

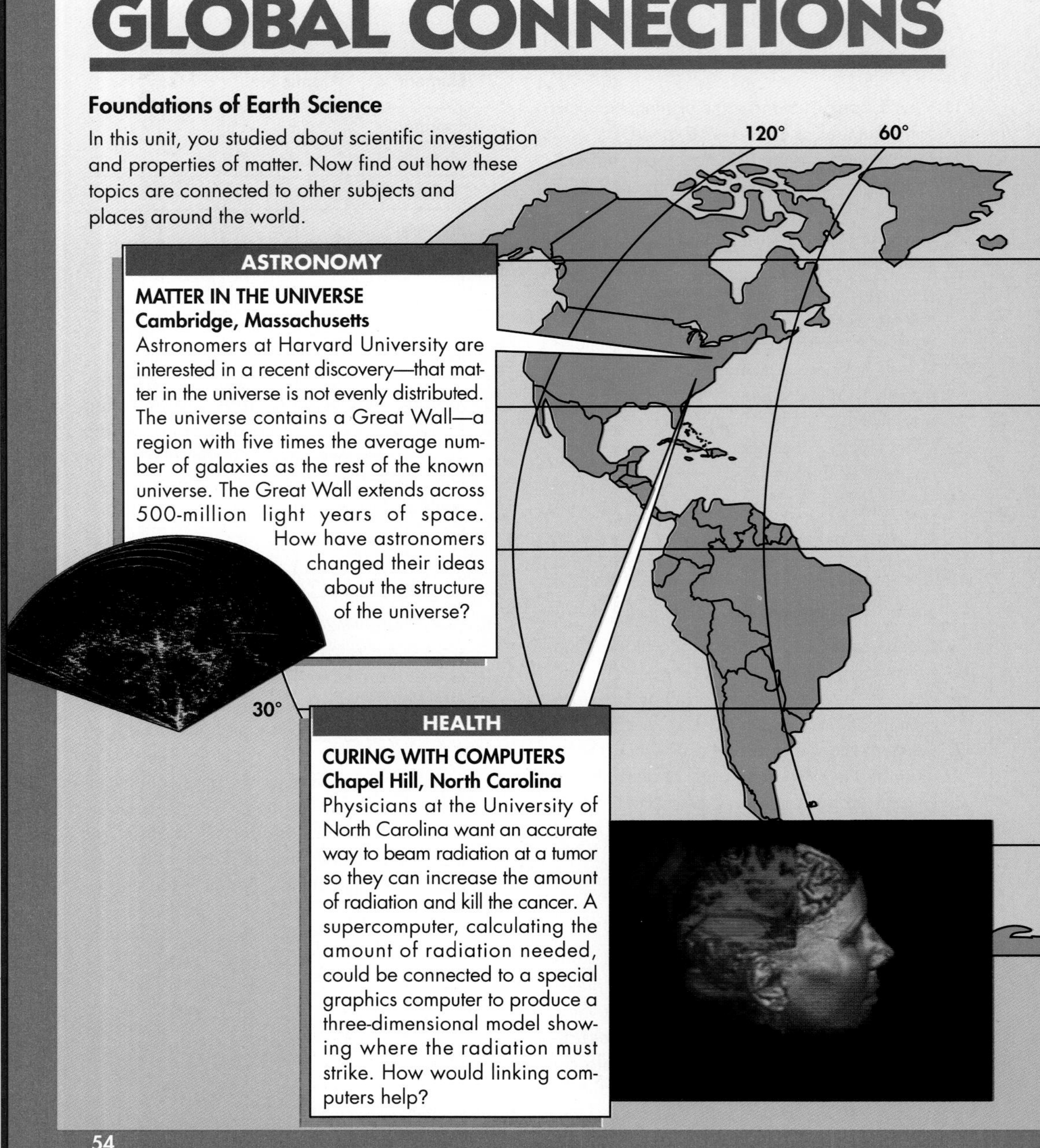

UNIT 1

GLOBAL CONNECTIONS

Foundations of Earth Science

In this unit, you studied about scientific investigation and properties of matter. Now find out how these topics are connected to other subjects and places around the world.

ASTRONOMY

MATTER IN THE UNIVERSE
Cambridge, Massachusetts
Astronomers at Harvard University are interested in a recent discovery—that matter in the universe is not evenly distributed. The universe contains a Great Wall—a region with five times the average number of galaxies as the rest of the known universe. The Great Wall extends across 500-million light years of space. How have astronomers changed their ideas about the structure of the universe?

HEALTH

CURING WITH COMPUTERS
Chapel Hill, North Carolina
Physicians at the University of North Carolina want an accurate way to beam radiation at a tumor so they can increase the amount of radiation and kill the cancer. A supercomputer, calculating the amount of radiation needed, could be connected to a special graphics computer to produce a three-dimensional model showing where the radiation must strike. How would linking computers help?

54

HEALTH

Background: The network envisioned by the staff at the School of Medicine at the University of North Carolina has many applications. Researchers in many parts of the country could work on the same project, whether it be astronomy, mathematics, weather, or medicine. A Cray supercomputer would share processing duties with parallel processors. One surgeon with a special expertise could team with another surgeon at a distant hospital with a different expertise to operate on a patient.
Discussion: Discuss with students how computers could solve intricate health-related problems and help physicians serve more people more efficiently.
Answer to Question: Because one computer cannot perform all the needed functions quickly enough.
Extension: Have students list ways that linking up computers in hospitals all across the nation would be beneficial to doctors.

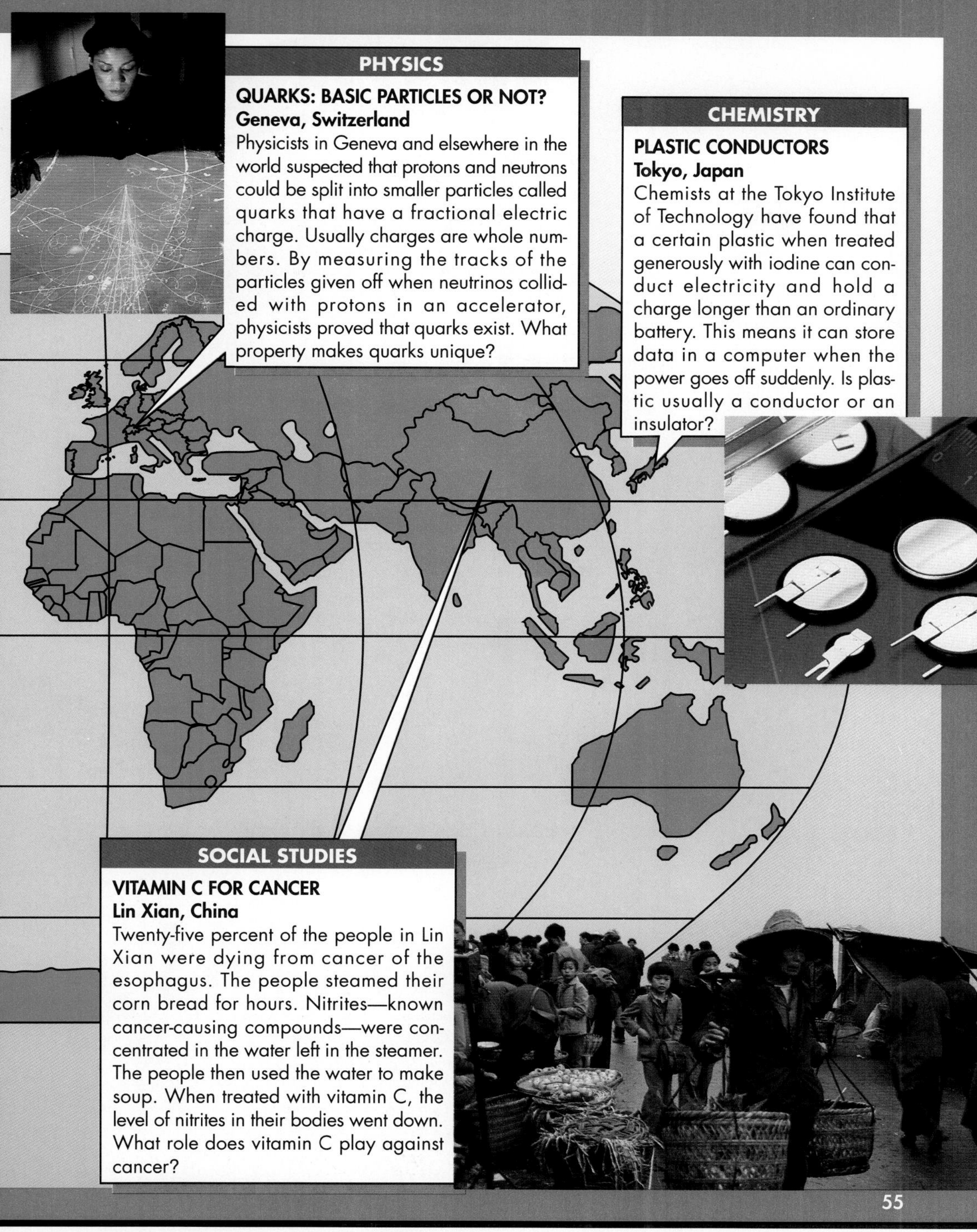

PHYSICS
QUARKS: BASIC PARTICLES OR NOT?
Geneva, Switzerland
Physicists in Geneva and elsewhere in the world suspected that protons and neutrons could be split into smaller particles called quarks that have a fractional electric charge. Usually charges are whole numbers. By measuring the tracks of the particles given off when neutrinos collided with protons in an accelerator, physicists proved that quarks exist. What property makes quarks unique?
CHEMISTRY
PLASTIC CONDUCTORS
Tokyo, Japan
Chemists at the Tokyo Institute of Technology have found that a certain plastic when treated generously with iodine can conduct electricity and hold a charge longer than an ordinary battery. This means it can store data in a computer when the power goes off suddenly. Is plastic usually a conductor or an insulator?
SOCIAL STUDIES
VITAMIN C FOR CANCER
Lin Xian, China
Twenty-five percent of the people in Lin Xian were dying from cancer of the esophagus. The people steamed their corn bread for hours. Nitrites—known cancer-causing compounds—were concentrated in the water left in the steamer. The people then used the water to make soup. When treated with vitamin C, the level of nitrites in their bodies went down. What role does vitamin C play against cancer?
55

SOCIAL STUDIES

Background: Several practices of the residents of Lin Xian produced harmful carcinogens. In one practice, they steamed their corn bread for hours. The moist bread developed mold in a few days, which was exactly what the people had a taste for, much as Western people consider Bleu cheese a delicacy. Unfortunately, the fungus has high levels of nitrosamines, a known carcinogen. Even the tumors people developed had the fungus growing on them. However, when the people took vitamin C, they were able to destroy the nitrosamines in their body.
Discussion: Discuss that nitrites and nitrosamines are used to cure meats and give them flavor, particularly bacon, ham, and lunchmeat. Taken in small amounts, these chemicals may not cause any harm. Stress that the people in Lin Xian consumed large amounts of these carcinogens and they lacked vitamin C, which was needed to destroy the harmful substances in the body.
Answer to Question: Vitamin C helps control the level of nitrites in the body.
Extension: Have students list some cancer-causing compounds that are a part of our everyday life.

PHYSICS

Background: Before quarks were discovered, no one thought an electric charge could be split into fractional parts. Scientists now believe there are six kinds of quarks, to which they have assigned the names: *up, down, strange, charm, bottom,* and *top*.
Discussion: Discuss with students the task of theoretical physicists, who must often study particles too small for observation. Mention that Nobel prize laureate Murray Gell-Mann described the properties of quarks long before the information was verified by experiments.
Answer to Question: Quarks are unlike protons and electrons because they have a fractional charge.
Extension: Have students research the Nobel prize in physics awarded to Murray Gell-Mann in 1969 for work on subatomic particles.

CHEMISTRY

Background: Metals conduct electricity because their electrons are free to move about. When its outer electron band is empty, a material cannot conduct electricity. The plastics called polymers have to be treated, or "doped," with an element such as iodine in order to become a conductor. The iodine provides electrons, which go to the empty band and form islands of electrons. When the polymer is treated with much iodine, the electron islands overlap, allowing the electric charge to flow.
Discussion: Discuss with students that the electrons in plastics usually are not available to flow as electricity. Explain how some plastics can become conductors.
Answer to Question: Plastic is usually an insulator.
Extension: Have students hypothesize whether plastic coatings of electrical cords conduct electricity or act as insulators.

RESEARCH CHEMIST

Background: Research chemists may work for industries, for government agencies, or for universities. Several research chemists have won the Nobel prize for chemistry.

Related Career	Education
Chemistry Teacher	college
Chemical Sales Person	college
Laboratory Technician	two-year college
Factory Inspector	high school

Career Issue: Some products produced by chemists may be controversial because they have been found to cause cancer and because they can easily enter the groundwater system.

What do you think? Lead students in a discussion about the harmful effects of some products produced by research chemists.

CHEMICAL TECHNICIAN

Background: Chemical technicians may work wherever a chemist works. The technicians help the chemists in their work of setting up experiments and collecting data. They use many kinds of instruments and equipment.

Related Career	Education
Chemical Librarian	college
Technical Writer	college
Pharmacist	college
Quality-Control Worker	high school

Career Issue: This is an interesting career if you enjoy working with instruments and keeping accurate records. This career requires that a person be careful, patient, and responsible.

What do you think? Have students discuss why technicians must be very careful, patient, and responsible when helping chemists.

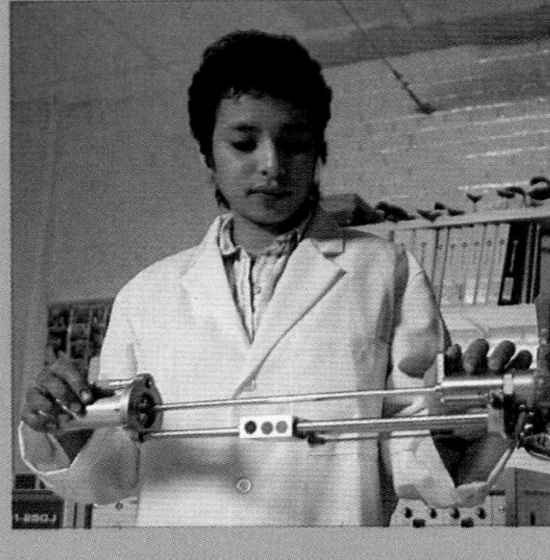

CAREERS

RESEARCH CHEMIST

A *research chemist* may do basic research to learn how chemical substances react. Some research chemists try to develop new products. One new product chemists are working on is polymers, or plastics, that can conduct electricity.

A research chemist needs a college degree in chemistry. Many earn doctorates. A student interested in becoming a research chemist should take courses in chemistry, physics, and mathematics.

For Additional Information

Contact the American Chemical Society, 1155 16th Street NW, Washington, DC 20036.

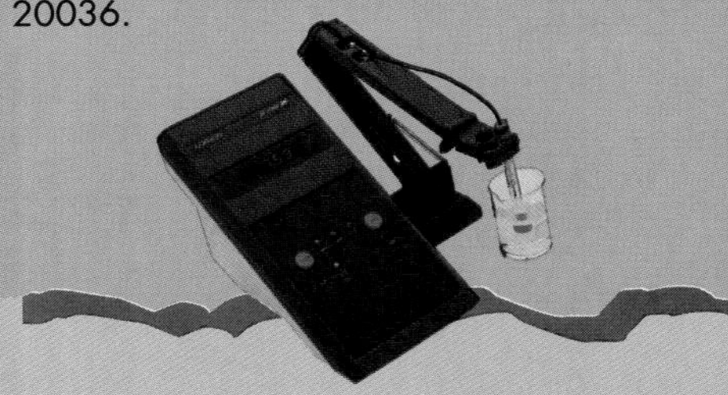

CHEMICAL TECHNICIAN

A *chemical technician* has an opportunity to work on projects in which new materials are developed by a chemical company. A technician's work consists of routine analyses of materials. They also help research chemists perform experiments and record accurate data. They may also test new products.

A chemical technician requires a degree in laboratory techniques from a two-year college. A student interested in becoming a chemical technician should study chemistry and mathematics in high school.

For Additional Information

Contact the American Chemical Society, 1155 16th Street NW, Washington, DC 20036.

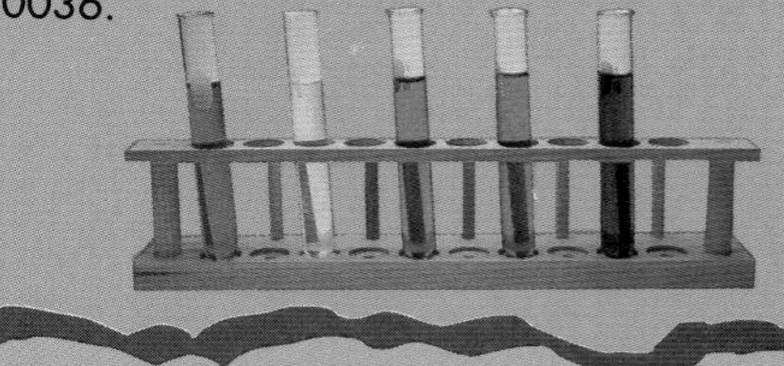

UNIT READINGS

- ▶ Ballard, Robert. *Exploring Our Living Planet.* Washington, DC: National Geographic Society, 1983.
- ▶ Edelson, Edward. "The Strangest Plastics." *Popular Science,* June, 1990, pp. 90-93.
- ▶ Zewail, Ahmed. "The Birth of Molecules." *Scientific American,* December, 1990, pp. 76-82.

56

UNIT READINGS

Background

▶ *Exploring Our Planet* provides a well illustrated, informative explanation of how Earth has evolved.

▶ "The Strangest Plastics" is the story of how plastics that can conduct electricity have come out of the laboratory and into batteries.

▶ "The Birth of Molecules" reveals how a scientist discovered a way to follow chemical reactions in molecules that occur faster than one-trillionth of a second.

More Readings

1. Hawkings, Stephen. *A Brief History of Time.* New York: Bantam Books, 1988, pp. 63-79. In one chapter of this book, the author explains the elementary particles of matter in a clear and amusing way.
2. *NOVA: Adventures in Science.* Boston: Addison-Wesley Publishing Company, 1983. This book includes an excellent history of the search for the elusive quarks.

Computer Impressionist

How has science and technology led to a new generation of art? Read the following paragraphs to find out.

If you've watched television documentaries you've probably been amazed by the beauty of many of the computer-drawn scenes. Computer animations can even make it possible to travel back in time and envision what occurred before people inhabited Earth.

Many artists have begun to use computers, lasers, and holograms to express their creative talents. You may wonder if artists will someday turn in their paint brushes altogether and let computers do their work. But artists that work with computers must make the computer do what they want it to do. As long as the artists feel that they are creating something beautiful and others are pleased with the results, computer art will thrive.

David Em, who produced the art on this page, is one of the new kind of artists. He uses high-tech computer programs produced by James Blinn at the Jet Propulsion Laboratory in Pasadena. Blinn didn't plan his programs in order to produce purely creative images. His purpose was to produce scientifically accurate images of the surfaces of planets. Em uses the textures and twists that are made possible by Blinn's programs to create graphically unique impressions.

Many artists wouldn't find inspiration in staring at a blank computer screen. David Em does. He uses a metal-tipped stylus to draw lightly across a pad. The pad transmits the corresponding lines to the screen. The artist claims that the computer expands his artistic abilities. He can choose from an almost infinite choice of colors and dimensions and can manipulate them in many ways.

In Your Own Words

▶ Do you think someone needs artistic ability to create computer art? Support your opinions in an essay.

Source: *NOVA: Adventure in Science.* Boston: Addison Wesley Publishing Company, 1983, pp. 226-231; and "An Impressionist with a Computer." *Smithsonian,* March, 1988, pp. 138-142.

Biography: David Em (1952-) is an impressionist artist who has chosen electronics as his tools for painting. He has been fortunate to have at his disposal James Blinn's masterful computer graphics programs. These were designed to plot the planetary explorations of the *Voyager* space probes and are the most advanced computer graphics technology. Em's traditional art school background was followed by sculpturing with industrial plastics.

TEACHING STRATEGY

▶ Ask students to discuss their opinions of whether or not artistic ability is required to create computer art like that of David Em's.

Cooperative Learning: Using the Paired Partner strategy, have students work together to decide if impressionism as expressed by a computer differs from impressionism conveyed by a painting. Ask students if a realistic work of art could be expressed as well on a computer as in a painting.

▶ Possible essay topics could include descriptions of other works by David Em. See the *Smithsonian,* March 1988.

▶ Discuss with students whether or not work done with a graphics program qualifies as true art. Also discuss if the kind of graphics software is important in the actual creation of the art work.

Other Works

▶ Other works by David Em include: *Persepol* (1980), *The Five of Us* (1983), *Nubes* (1985), *Zwirlz* (1986), *Spark* (1986).

Classics

▶ Asimov, Isaac. *Building Blocks of the Universe.* Rev. ed. New York: Harper, 1974. This book provides information about the elements and their uses.

▶ Gallant, Roy A. *Explorers of the Atom.* Garden City, New York: Doubleday and Company, 1974. This book tells the story of the atom, its parts, and those who discovered them.

2

ROCKS AND MINERALS

In Unit 2, students are introduced to Earth materials. The unit is organized to show the structure, formation, identification, and uses of minerals. Mixtures of minerals are identified as rocks. The rock cycle and the three major classifications of rocks are described.

CONTENTS

ADVANCE PREPARATION

Activities

▶ **Activity 3-1, page 65,** requires table salt and granulated sugar for solutions.
▶ **Activity 3-2, page 73,** requires boxed and labeled mineral samples.
▶ **Activity 4-1, page 89,** requires boxed and labeled igneous rock specimens.
▶ **Activity 4-2, page 99,** requires boxed and labeled sedimentary rock specimens.

Audiovisuals

▶ **Section 3-3, page 74:** Arrange to show the video "Planet Earth—Gifts from the Earth," The Annenberg/CPB Project.
▶ **Section 4-1, page 86:** Arrange to show the filmstrip/cassette "Rocks and Minerals," National Geographic.

Field Trips and Speakers

▶ Arrange to take your class to a museum to see a mineral and gem collection.
▶ Invite a lapidary in to talk to the class about collecting, cutting, and polishing gems and other stones.

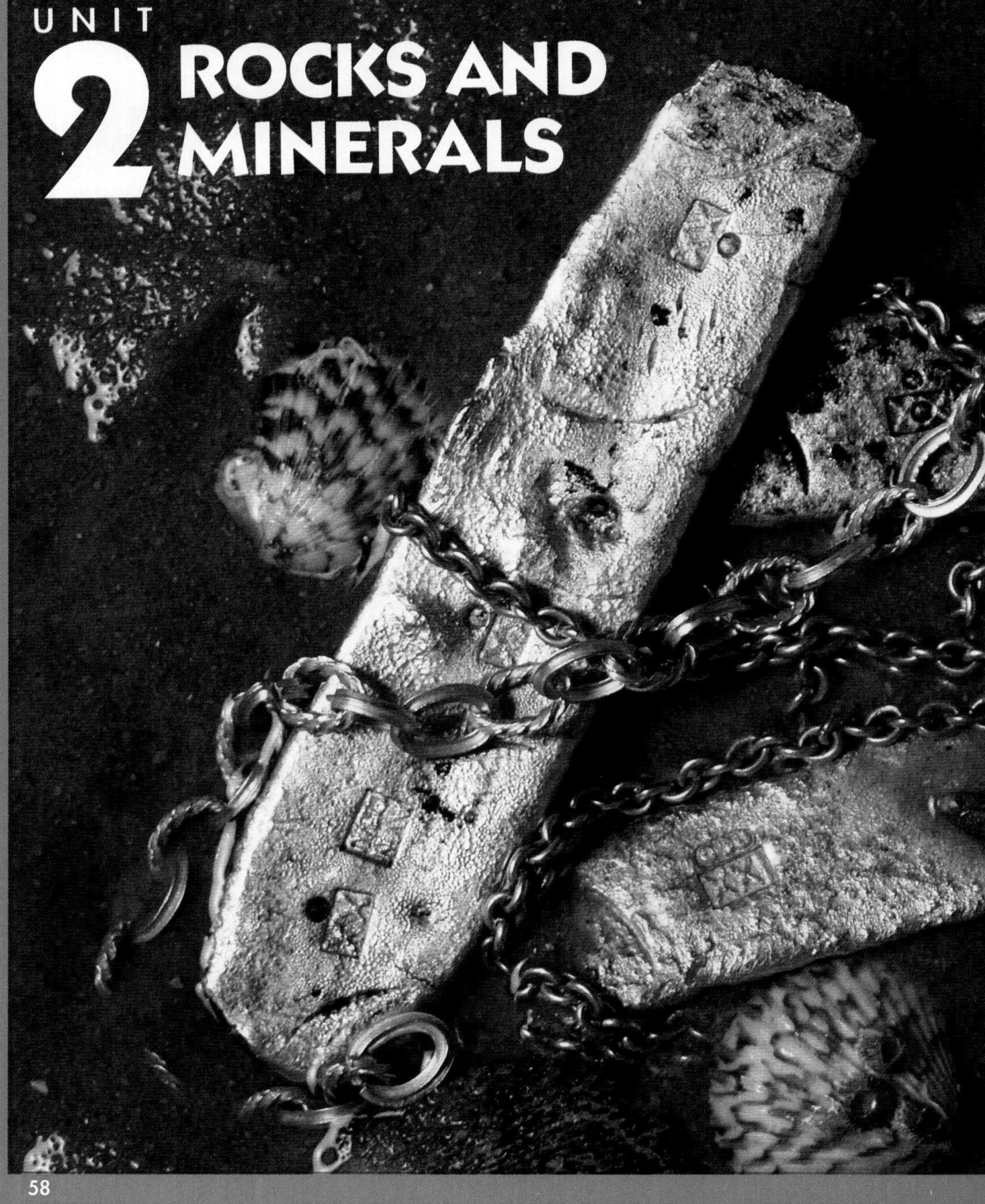

OPTIONS

Cross Curriculum

▶ Ask students to discuss how international boundaries between countries may be related to deposits of mineral resources.
▶ Ask students to check with their art teacher to see what minerals are used in making plaster of paris.
▶ Have students determine the geographic location of coal beds in the United States.
▶ Have students write a brief report on how their lives might change if the supply of coal were to run out.

Science at Home

▶ Have students hypothesize why granite and marble are used as building stones for homes and large office buildings.

Cooperative Learning: Using the Numbered Heads Together strategy, have students brainstorm and compile a list of objects in the home that are made of common minerals. Have them list the mineral from which each object is made.

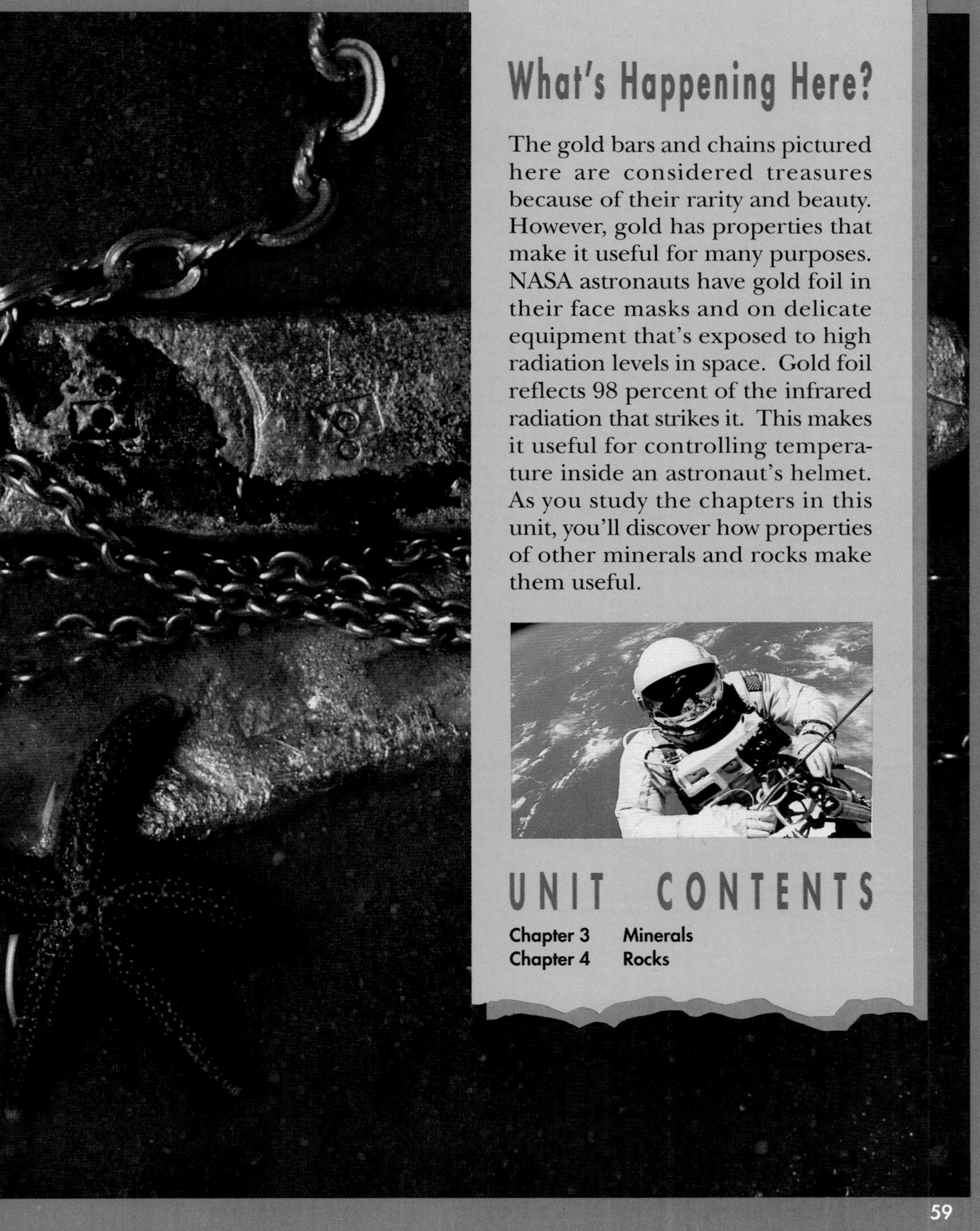

What's Happening Here?

The gold bars and chains pictured here are considered treasures because of their rarity and beauty. However, gold has properties that make it useful for many purposes. NASA astronauts have gold foil in their face masks and on delicate equipment that's exposed to high radiation levels in space. Gold foil reflects 98 percent of the infrared radiation that strikes it. This makes it useful for controlling temperature inside an astronaut's helmet. As you study the chapters in this unit, you'll discover how properties of other minerals and rocks make them useful.

UNIT CONTENTS

INTRODUCING THE UNIT

What's Happening Here?

▶ Have students look at the photos and read the text. Ask them to tell you what's happening here. Point out to students that in this unit they will be studying how certain properties of minerals and rocks determine how they are used, as well as help in their identification.

▶ **Background:** The first true coins, made of gold and silver, were produced around 550 B.C. by the Lydian empire. The area of this empire is now part of Turkey. The rarity, beauty, and luster of gold and silver have caused them to be used as currency for over 2500 years.

Previewing the Chapters

▶ Students should be encouraged to search through Chapter 3 for photographs that demonstrate important identifying characteristics.

▶ Some students may be surprised that a rock is a mixture of minerals. To preview Chapter 4 and clear up misconceptions, have students look at Figure 4-1, page 86, that shows the mixture of minerals in granite.

▶ Encourage students to study key tables and figures in the unit. Minerals are shown on pages 63, 64, 67, 69, 70, 71, and 72. Rocks are shown on pages 86, 90, 91, 92, 94, 95, 97, 100, 103, and 104.

Tying to Previous Knowledge

▶ Ask students to bring in and share with the class any rock or mineral collections they might have. After studying the minerals and rocks collected by students, ask the class why they think the specific samples were collected.

▶ Use the **Inquiry Questions** in the OPTIONS box below to investigate properties of minerals and rocks that make them valuable.

Multicultural Awareness

Have students research the importance of gems and gemstones to several cultures around the world. Have them include monarchies as well as elected governments. They may also research how ancient cultures in a particular location regarded gems and gemstones and compare that to the present-day culture of the same area.

Inquiry Questions

Use the following questions to focus a discussion of how properties of certain minerals and rocks make them more valuable than others.

1. Why are diamonds considered valuable?
2. What property of gold makes it valuable as a coating on visors worn by astronauts in space or on the moon?
3. What would happen to the value of gold if large, easily minable reserves were found?

CHAPTER

3 Minerals

CHAPTER SECTION	OBJECTIVES	ACTIVITIES
3-1 Minerals (3 days)	1. **List** five characteristics all minerals share. 2. **Describe** the structure of minerals. 3. **Give** examples of two ways that minerals form.	**MINI-Lab:** *What do salt crystals look like up close?* p. 64 **Activity 3-1:** *Crystal Formation,* p. 65
3-2 Mineral Identification (3 days)	1. **List** the physical characteristics used to identify minerals. 2. **Describe** how physical characteristics such as hardness and streak are used to identify minerals.	**MINI-Lab:** *How do clear minerals compare?* p. 72 **Activity 3-2:** *Mineral Identification,* p. 73
3-3 Uses of Minerals (1 day)	1. **Discuss** characteristics gems have that make them different from and more valuable than other minerals. 2. **List** the conditions necessary for a mineral to be classified as an ore.	
3-4 Asbestos Removal Science & Society (1 day)	1. **List** the properties of asbestos that make it useful as a flame retardant and an insulator. 2. **State** why people are so concerned about the asbestos used in buildings. 3. **Compare** the pros and cons of asbestos removal.	
Chapter Review		

ACTIVITY MATERIALS

FIND OUT	ACTIVITIES		MINI-LABS	
Page 61 cup (1) flat pan(1) two teaspoons of salt	**3-1 Crystal Formation, p. 65** salt solution sugar solution large test tube toothpick cotton string hand lens shallow pan (2) thermal mitt test-tube rack cardboard table salt granulated sugar hot plate	**3-2 Mineral Identification, p. 73** mineral samples hand lens pan balance graduated cylinder copper penny glass slide steel file streak plate 5% hydrochloric acid w/dropper goggles	**What do salt crystals look like up close? p. 64** microscope or magnifying glass	**How do clear minerals compare? p. 72** transparent samples of calcite, muscovite, gypsum, halite or quartz magnifying glass

CHAPTER FEATURES	TEACHER RESOURCE PACKAGE	OTHER RESOURCES
Skill Builder: *Classifying,* p. 67	**Ability Level Worksheets** ◆ ***Study Guide,*** p. 13 ● ***Reinforcement,*** p. 13 ▲ ***Enrichment,*** p. 13 **Critical Thinking/Problem Solving,** p. 9 **Transparency Masters,** pp. 7-8 **MINI-Lab Worksheet,** p. 27 **Activity Worksheet,** pp. 21-22	**Lab Manual:** *Crystal Formations,* pp. 21-24 **Color Transparency 4,** Crystal Systems
Problem Solving: *Is it Real?* p. 71 **Skill Builder:** *Making and Using Graphs,* p. 72	**Ability Level Worksheets** ◆ ***Study Guide,*** p. 14 ● ***Reinforcement,*** p. 14 ▲ ***Enrichment,*** p. 14 **Cross-Curricular Connections,** p. 7 **Transparency Masters,** pp. 9-10 **MINI-Lab Worksheet,** p. 28 **Activity Worksheet,** pp. 23-24	**Lab Manual:** *Minerals and Optical Crystallography,* pp. 25-26 **Color Transparency 5,** Moh's Scale of Hardness
Technology: *Diamonds Are Forever?* p. 76 **Skill Builder:** *Concept Mapping,* p. 77	**Ability Level Worksheets** ◆ ***Study Guide,*** p. 15 ● ***Reinforcement,*** p. 15 ▲ ***Enrichment,*** p. 15 **Concept Mapping,** pp. 11-12	**Lab Manual:** *Mineral Resources,* pp. 27-28 **Lab Manual:** *Removal of Waste Rock,* pp. 29-30
You Decide! p. 80	**Ability Level Worksheets** ◆ ***Study Guide,*** p. 16 ● ***Reinforcement,*** p. 16 ▲ ***Enrichment,*** p. 16 **Science and Society,** p. 7	
Summary Key Science Words Understanding Vocabulary Checking Concepts Understanding Concepts Think & Write Critically Apply More Skill Builders Projects	**Chapter Review,** pp. 9-10 **Chapter Test,** pp. 20-23	**Chapter Review Software** **Test Bank**

◆ **Basic** ● **Average** ▲ **Advanced**

ADDITIONAL MATERIALS

SOFTWARE	AUDIOVISUAL	BOOKS/MAGAZINES
Identifying Minerals, Focus. *Minerals,* MECC. *Minerals,* Queue. *Mineral Tests,* Focus. *Rocks and Minerals Identification,* Focus.	*Minerals and Rocks,* film, Indiana University. *Recognizing Rock Making Minerals,* film, EBEC. *Rocks and Minerals: How We Identify Them,* film, Coronet/MTI. *Identifying Minerals: Searching for Clues,* video, Focus. *Gems and Minerals: The Ultimate Rock, video,* laserdisc, Lumivision.	Crowson, Phillip. *Minerals Handbook.* NY: Groves Dictionaries of Music, Inc., 1988. Foster, Robert J. *Physical Geology.* Westerville, OH: Merrill Publishing Co., 1983.

CHAPTER

3

MINERALS

THEME DEVELOPMENT: The structure of minerals is the major theme of this chapter. The atomic arrangement and the other characteristics that define minerals should be emphasized in all lessons. Emphasizing the relationship between the internal structure of a mineral and its properties and uses will help to clarify the uniqueness of these solids that make up Earth's rocks.

CHAPTER OVERVIEW

- **Section 3-1:** This section explains the five characteristics shared by all minerals. Classification of minerals into six crystal systems based on the internal structure of minerals is explained. The ways in which minerals form and how they can be grouped are also described.

- **Section 3-2:** This section describes how physical properties of a mineral are used to identify it. Common properties and how to test them are explained.

- **Section 3-3:** The characteristics that make a mineral a gem are explained. Conditions needed in order for minerals to be classified as ores also are presented.

- **Section 3-4: Science and Society:** The dangers of using asbestos as an insulator as well as the dangers involved with removing it are discussed. The You Decide feature asks students to consider whether all asbestos should be removed.

CHAPTER VOCABULARY

mineral	streak
crystal	cleavage
magma	fracture
silicates	gems
hardness	ore
luster	asbestos

CHAPTER 3

Minerals

60

OPTIONS

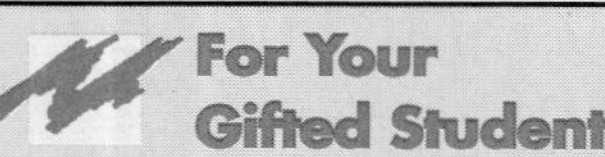

For Your Gifted Students

After students complete Section 3-2 and Activity 3-2, have them play a game based on "20 Questions." One student can think of a mineral while others try to narrow the choice by asking five yes or no questions related to luster, hardness, cleavage or fracture, and so on. This activity encourages the students to use good questioning strategies, classification, and memory skills.

Minerals are used for many things. They are used in jewelry, pencil lead, powders, and in the metal used in bicycles. Table salt, for example, is the mineral halite. The huge cavern shown at the left is the interior of a salt mine. How does this mineral form?

FIND OUT!

Do this simple activity to see how halite forms.

Fill a cup about half full of warm tap water. Place two teaspoons of salt in the water. Stir the water until all of the salt has dissolved. Pour the water into a pan. Place the pan somewhere where it won't be disturbed. Check on the pan each day for two or three days. Has the water level gone down? What happened to the water? Is anything forming in the pan? Try to describe the cause of what you have observed. How does this relate to the formation of the mineral halite?

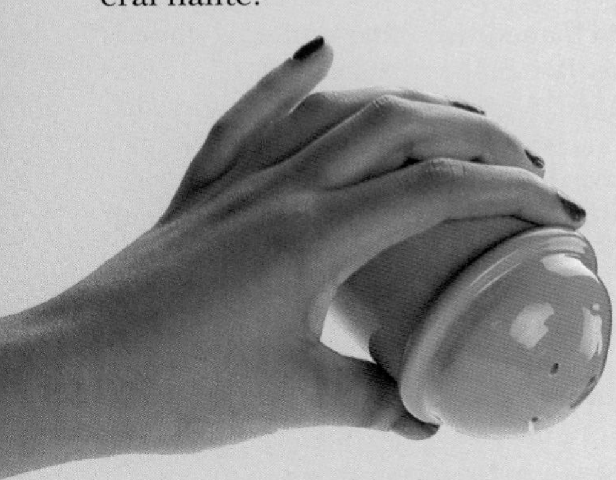

Gearing Up

Previewing the Chapter

Use this outline to help you focus on important ideas in this chapter.

Section 3-1 Minerals
- What Is a Mineral?
- The Structure of Minerals
- How Minerals Form
- Mineral Compositions and Groups

Section 3-2 Mineral Identification
- Physical Properties

Section 3-3 Uses of Minerals
- Gems
- Ores

Section 3-4 Science and Society Asbestos Removal
- Should All Asbestos Be Removed?

Previewing Science Skills

- In the **Skill Builders**, you will classify, graph, and make a concept map.
- In the **Activities**, you will observe, collect, and organize data.
- In the **MINI-Labs**, you will experiment and compare.

What's next?

Now that you've seen how a mineral can form, read to find out more about what minerals are, their properties, and their uses. You'll also find out about a mineral that can be harmful.

For Your Mainstreamed Students

Have students glue several sugar cubes together to form a large cube. Explain that they must be sure to spread the glue evenly on the joining faces of the cube. After the glue has dried, instruct students to place the cube into a glass of water. When the sugar has dissolved, have students remove the glue skeleton and let it dry. Have them experiment with other glues to make other geometric designs. Have the students predict the shape of the glue skeletons. If possible, allow students to view the "crystals" under a microscope.

INTRODUCING THE CHAPTER

Use the Find Out activity to introduce students to one method of mineral formation. Inform students that they will be learning more about minerals as they read the chapter.

FIND OUT!

Preparation: Several days before you begin this chapter, have students bring in cups and flat pans. Obtain several packages of table salt, NaCl.

Materials: one cup, one flat pan, and two teaspoons of salt for every two students

Cooperative Learning: Form Science Investigation groups of two students per group. As one student pours salt into the water, the other should stir the solution. When the salt is completely dissolved, one student should pour the solution into a flat pan, while the other makes a label for the pan with the students' names on it and prepares a place to put the pan. The two students should check the pan each day and record their observations.

Teaching Tips

- Test the water to be used in the activity to be sure it is warm, but not hot enough to cause burns. Explain that warm water rather than cold water is used to speed up the rate at which the salt dissolves. Have students hypothesize how their stirring affects the dissolving process.
- Have students recall from Chapter 2 that mixing the salt with the water forms a mixture called a solution.
- Have each pair of students keep a written log of their observations. The log should also be used to write down the answers to the questions in the activity.

Gearing Up

Have students study the Gearing Up feature to familiarize themselves with the chapter. Discuss the relationships of the topics in the outline.

What's Next?

Before beginning the first section, make sure students understand the connection between the Find Out activity and the topics to follow.

SECTION 3-1

PREPARATION

SECTION BACKGROUND

▶The chemical composition of a specific mineral is not always exactly the same. In some minerals, an atom with a similar size and the same charge can substitute for other atoms. In olivine, $(Mg,Fe)_2SiO_4$, for example, iron can be totally replaced by magnesium without changing the mineral. Some forms of olivine contain iron and magnesium.

▶The internal structure of all silicate minerals is basically the same. The silicon-oxygen tetrahedron is a molecule containing four oxygen atoms, which surround a much smaller silicon atom. The characteristics of different silicate minerals are a function of how the individual tetrahedra bond. Silicon-oxygen tetrahedra can bond to form pairs, chains, rings, sheets, or frameworks.

PREPLANNING

▶Obtain table salt for the Mini-Lab.

▶To prepare for Activity 3-1, obtain the materials listed on page 65.

▶Obtain a piece of granite from a scientific supply company or a local tombstone maker.

1 MOTIVATE

FLEX Your Brain

Use the Flex Your Brain activity to have students explore CHARACTERISTICS SHARED BY ALL MINERALS.

Cooperative Learning: After students have read page 62, have them compile lists of ten common items found around their homes. Use the Numbered Heads Together strategy to have students determine whether or not the items listed are minerals.

▶**Demonstration:** Obtain a piece of coarse-grained granite from a scientific supply company or a local tombstone maker. Have students identify two or three components (minerals) that make up the rock.

3-1 Minerals

New Science Words

mineral
crystal
magma
silicates

Objectives

- ▶ List five characteristics all minerals share.
- ▶ Describe the structure of minerals.
- ▶ Give examples of two ways that minerals form.

What Is a Mineral?

Have you ever used minerals? You may not realize it, but you use them all of the time. Rock salt, a diamond, and the graphite in a pencil are all minerals. (1) A **mineral** is a naturally occurring, nonliving solid, with a definite structure and composition. Although more than 4000 different minerals are found on Earth, they all share five characteristics. Let's look at rock salt, diamonds, and graphite, and the characteristics they share.

First, all minerals are formed by natural processes. Rock salt, diamonds, and graphite are minerals because they formed naturally. You'll investigate more about these processes later in this lesson.

Second, minerals are nonliving. They aren't alive and never were alive. Diamonds and coal are both made from the element carbon, but they are not both minerals. Diamonds form from nonliving carbon inside Earth, whereas coal is made of carbon from living things. Which one would you classify as a mineral?

The third characteristic that minerals share is that they are all solids. Remember that all solids have a definite volume and shape. A gas such as air or a liquid such as water isn't a mineral because its shape changes. Neither a gas nor a liquid have definite shape.

Fourth, every mineral is an element or compound with a chemical composition unique to that mineral. Rock salt's composition gives it a distinctive flavor. Graphite's arrangement of atoms makes it feel soft and slippery.

Finally, the atoms in a mineral are arranged in a pattern, repeated over and over again. Read on to find out more about the structure of minerals.

Figure 3-1. Shown here are just a few examples of how we use minerals.

OPTIONS

Meeting Different Ability Levels

For Section 3-1, use the following **Teacher Resource Masters** depending upon individual students' needs.

◆ **Study Guide Master** for all students.

● **Reinforcement Master** for students of average and above average ability levels.

▲ **Enrichment Master** for above average students.

Additional Teacher Resource Package masters are listed in the OPTIONS box throughout the section. The additional masters are appropriate for all students.

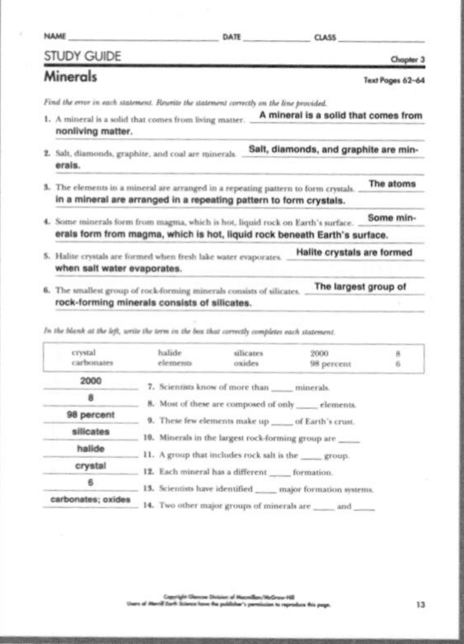

◆ STUDY GUIDE 13

NAME ____ DATE ____ CLASS ____

STUDY GUIDE — Chapter 3

Minerals — Text Pages 62–64

Find the error in each statement. Rewrite the statement correctly on the line provided.

1. A mineral is a solid that comes from living matter. **A mineral is a solid that comes from nonliving matter.**
2. Salt, diamonds, graphite, and coal are minerals. **Salt, diamonds, and graphite are minerals.**
3. The elements in a mineral are arranged in a repeating pattern to form crystals. **The atoms in a mineral are arranged in a repeating pattern to form crystals.**
4. Some minerals form from magma, which is hot, liquid rock on Earth's surface. **Some minerals form from magma, which is hot, liquid rock beneath Earth's surface.**
5. Halite crystals are formed when fresh lake water evaporates. **Halite crystals are formed when salt water evaporates.**
6. The smallest group of rock-forming minerals consists of silicates. **The largest group of rock-forming minerals consists of silicates.**

In the blank at the left, write the term in the box that correctly completes each statement.

crystal	halide	silicates	2000	8
carbonates	elements	oxides	98 percent	6

2000 7. Scientists know of more than ____ minerals.
8 8. Most of these are composed of only ____ elements.
98 percent 9. These few elements make up ____ of Earth's crust.
silicates 10. Minerals in the largest rock-forming group are ____
halide 11. A group that includes rock salt is the ____ group.
crystal 12. Each mineral has a different ____ formation.
6 13. Scientists have identified ____ major formation systems.
carbonates; oxides 14. Two other major groups of minerals are ____ and ____

13

Figure 3-2. Some mineral specimens have flat surfaces and sharp edges, showing crystal structure on the outside (a). Even if a mineral doesn't show its crystal structure on the outside, its atoms are still arranged in a crystal structure (b).

The Structure of Minerals

Did you know that each little grain of salt in a salt shaker is a cube? The atoms contained in each grain of salt are grouped in such a way that they form a cube. These cubes are crystals. A **crystal** is a solid in which the atoms are arranged in repeating patterns.

Even though all minerals are crystals, they don't all have smooth surfaces and sharp edges like the quartz crystal in Figure 3-2a. The quartz in Figure 3-2b has atoms arranged in repeating patterns, but you can't see the crystal structure on the outside of the mineral. This is because quartz 3-2b developed in a tight space. Quartz 3-2a, on the other hand, developed freely in an open space. Quartz has a hexagonal crystal shape.

Science and READING

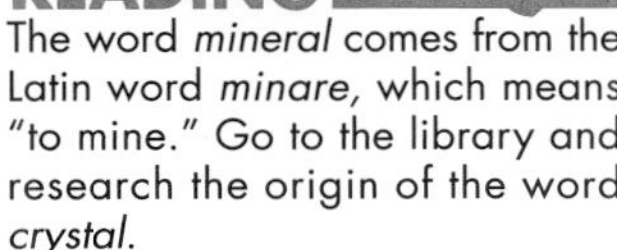

The word *mineral* comes from the Latin word *minare,* which means "to mine." Go to the library and research the origin of the word *crystal.*

Table 3-1

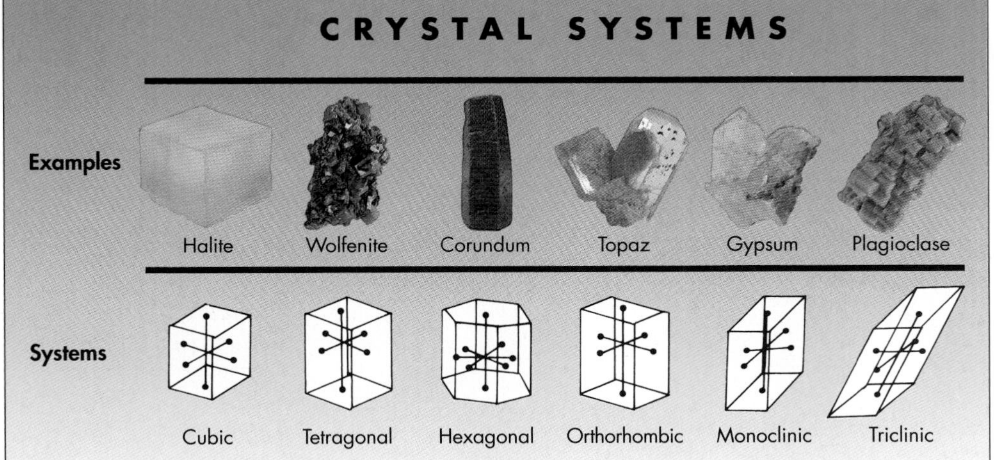

● REINFORCEMENT 13

NAME ______ DATE ______ CLASS ______

REINFORCEMENT — Chapter 3

Minerals — Text Pages 62–64

Use the table below and your text to answer Questions 1–10.

Rock-forming minerals

Chemical classification	Mineral	Elements
Silicates	orthoclase plagioclase amphiboles pyroxenes olivine micas clay minerals quartz	K, Al, Si, O Al, Si, O, Ca, Na Mg, Fe, Ca, Na, Al, Si, O Al, Si, O, F, Mg, Ca, Na Mg, Fe, Si, O K, Al, Si, O, (OH), Mg, Fe Al, Si, O, (OH) Si, O
Carbonates	calcite dolomite	Ca, (CO_3) Ca, Mg, (CO_3)
Oxides	hematite	Fe, O
Sulfates	gypsum anhydrite	Ca, (SO_4), H_2O
Halides	rock salt	Na, Cl

1. Draw a circle around each of the minerals listed below that do not belong to the silicate family.
   plagioclase (gypsum) mica pyroxene (calcite) quartz
2. Write the names and symbols of the two elements found in all silicate minerals.
   silicon, Si and **oxygen, O**
3. To which chemical classification group does dolomite belong? **carbonates**
4. Give an example of a mineral that contains the (CO_3) group. **calcite, dolomite**
5. From what element do the sulfates get their names? **sulfur**
6. Give an example of an oxide. **hematite**
7. Which of the rock-forming mineral groups makes up the largest group of minerals in Earth's crust? **silicates**
8. Which group of rock-forming minerals contains the mineral gypsum? **sulfates**
9. What commonly used metal is extracted from hematite? **iron, Fe**
10. To which chemical classification group does rock salt belong? **halide group**

13

▲ ENRICHMENT 13

NAME ______ DATE ______ CLASS ______

ENRICHMENT — Chapter 3

Minerals — Text Pages 62–64

MINERALS COMMONLY FOUND IN THE HOME

Materials
- five ordinary objects made from minerals
- pen or pencil

Procedure
1. Collect five examples of items commonly found in the home that are made from minerals. The following list will provide you with some examples: salt, pencil, sandpaper, talcum powder, jewelry, plaster.
2. List the five items in the table below.
3. Write the name(s) of the minerals each item contains.
4. If you have difficulty finding five items, study the "Uses" column of Appendices L and M of your textbook.

Analyze

Item	Minerals
1.	
2.	
3.	
4.	
5.	

Conclude and Apply
Use your textbook to help answer these questions.
1. What is the name of the most common group of minerals? **silicates**
   Do you have any examples of this group? What are they? **Answers will vary.**
2. What mineral group contains limestone, dolomite, and marble? **carbonates**
   Do you have any examples of this group? What are they? **Answers will vary.**
3. What is the most common carbonate mineral? **calcite**
   Do you have an example of this mineral? What is it? **Answers will vary.**

13

TYING TO PREVIOUS KNOWLEDGE: Have students recall from Chapter 2 that atoms are the building blocks of matter and that atoms combine to form molecules and compounds. The structure of a mineral is determined by the repeating pattern of atoms and molecules in the mineral.

OBJECTIVES AND SCIENCE WORDS: Have students review the objectives and science words to become familiar with this section.

REVEALING MISCONCEPTIONS

▶Students may think that all minerals are beautiful like cut diamonds and other gems. Show students a piece of jewelry containing a gemstone. Also obtain some sheets of mica. Have students contrast the minerals.

2 TEACH

Key Concepts are highlighted.

CONCEPT DEVELOPMENT

▶**What is a mineral?** *a naturally occurring, nonliving solid, with a definite structure and composition*

▶**What is a crystal?** *a solid in which the atoms are arranged in repeating patterns*

▶**Sugar is a solid substance that forms in nature and has a definite structure and composition. Is sugar a mineral?** *No, sugar is an organic compound and thus isn't a mineral.*

STUDENT TEXT QUESTION

▶Page 62, paragraph 3: **Which one would you classify as a mineral?** *diamond*

Science and READING

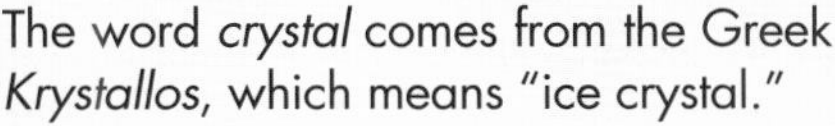

The word *crystal* comes from the Greek *Krystallos,* which means "ice crystal."

MINI-Lab
Materials: microscope or magnifying glass, table salt
Teaching Tips
▶ Inform students that table salt is the mineral halite, NaCl.
▶ Ask students to list those physical properties that can be observed without magnification and compare that list to those properties that become evident with magnification.
▶ All the salt grains are cubes.
▶ Halite belongs to the isometric crystal system.
▶ Other common minerals of the isometric system are chromite, copper, diamond, fluorite, galena, gold, magnetite, pyrite, and silver.

TEACHER F.Y.I.
▶The six crystal systems are defined by three or four imaginary axes that intersect at the center of a perfect crystal. The lengths of the axes and the angles between them determine the shape of the crystal.

CHECK FOR UNDERSTANDING
Use the Mini Quiz to check for understanding.

MINI QUIZ
Use the Mini Quiz to check students' recall of chapter content.
1. **What is a mineral?** *a naturally occurring, nonliving solid, with a definite structure and composition.*
2. **A _____ is a solid in which the atoms are arranged in repeating patterns.** *crystal*
3. **Minerals can form when hot, melted material, called _____ , cools.** *magma*
4. **The largest group of minerals is the _____ .** *silicates*

RETEACH
Cooperative Learning: Using the Paired Partner strategy, have students make flash cards of the mineral groups shown in Table 3-2. On the reverse side of each card, the compositional unit of that group and an example can be listed. Partners can then test each other with the cards.

MINI-Lab
What do salt crystals look like up close?
Use a microscope or a magnifying glass to make a close-up observation of common grains of table salt. What characteristics do all of the grains have in common? Can you name another mineral with the same crystal system as salt? What is the name of this crystal system?

There are six major crystal systems, as shown in Table 3-1. These crystal systems refer to the set patterns that atoms form in a crystal. The simplest crystal system is cubic. Salt and pyrite are minerals whose crystals form cubes. Quartz belongs to the hexagonal crystal system.

How Minerals Form

There are two main ways that minerals can form. One way is from the cooling of hot melted rock, called **magma**, 3
inside Earth. As magma cools, its atoms form a crystal structure and it becomes a mineral. The atoms will continue to line up in repeated patterns until there are no more atoms of the mineral available. The type of mineral that is formed depends on the type of elements present in the magma.

Crystals may also form from minerals dissolved in liquids. When the liquid evaporates, the atoms in the minerals stay behind and form crystals. Perfectly shaped crystals of a mineral can form when they have an open space to grow. Without space to grow, a mineral still has crystal form, but you can't see the crystal shape on the outside. When salt water evaporates, perfectly shaped crystals of halite—rock salt—are left behind.

Figure 3-3. Atoms of the mineral galena arrange themselves in a cubic crystal system.

OPTIONS

INQUIRY QUESTIONS
▶**In a cubic crystal, three imaginary axes intersect at right angles in the center of the crystal. What can be said about the lengths of these three axes?** *The three axes are equal in length.*
▶**If you found a nearly perfect hexagonal crystal of quartz, what could you conclude about its formation?** *The crystal formed in an open space. No other crystals interfered with its growth.*

PROGRAM RESOURCES
From the **Teacher Resource Package** use:
Activity Worksheet, page 27, Mini-Lab: What do salt crystals look like up close?
Transparency Master, pages 7-8, Crystal Systems.
Use **Color Transparency** number 4, Crystal Systems.
Use **Laboratory Manual,** page 21, Crystal Formation.

ACTIVITY 3-1
Crystal Formation

Problem: *In what two ways can crystals form?*

Materials

- salt solution
- sugar solution
- large test tube
- toothpick
- cotton string
- hand lens
- shallow pan (2)
- thermal mitt
- test-tube rack
- cardboard
- table salt
- granulated sugar
- hot plate

Procedure
1. Pour the sugar solution into one of the shallow pans. Use the hot plate to gently heat the solution.
2. Place the test tube in the test-tube rack. Using a thermal mitt to protect your hand, pour some of the hot sugar solution into the test tube. **CAUTION:** *The liquid is hot. Do not touch the test tube without protecting your hands.*
3. Tie the thread to one end of the toothpick. Place the thread in the test tube. Be sure that it does not touch the sides or bottom of the tube.
4. Cover the test tube with a piece of cardboard and place the rack containing the test tube in a location where it will not be disturbed.
5. Pour a thin layer of the salt solution into the second shallow pan.
6. Place the pan in a warm area in the room.
7. Leave both the test tube and the shallow pan undisturbed for at least one week.
8. Examine sample grains of table salt and sugar with the hand lens. Note any similarities or differences.
9. At the end of one week, examine each solution and see if crystals have formed. Use a hand lens to observe the crystals.

Analyze
1. Describe the crystals that formed from the salt and sugar solutions. Include a sketch of each crystal.
2. What happened to the salt water in the shallow pan?
3. Did this same process occur in the test tube? Explain.

Conclude and Apply
4. What caused the formation of crystals in the test tube? What caused the formation of crystals in the shallow pan?
5. Are salt and sugar both minerals? Explain your answer.
6. In what two ways can crystals form?

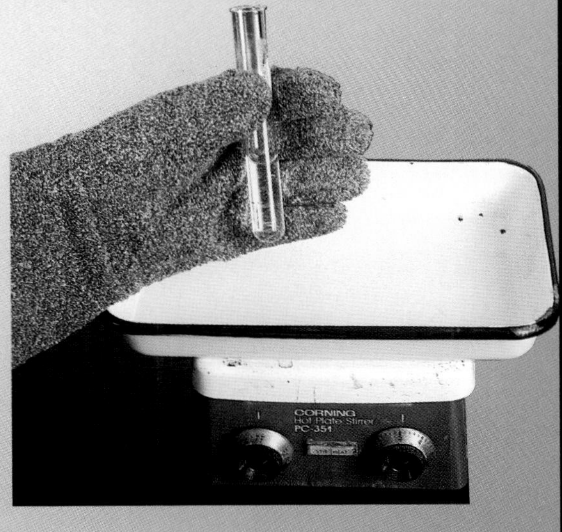

ACTIVITY 3-1
20 minutes; two different days

OBJECTIVE: **Demonstrate** and **describe** two methods of growing crystals.

PROCESS SKILLS applied in this activity:
▶ **Observing** in Procedure Steps 8 and 9.
▶ **Inferring** in Analyze Questions 2 and 3.
▶ **Communicating** in Analyze Question 1 and Conclude and Apply Question 6.
▶ **Interpreting Data** in Conclude and Apply Questions 4 and 5.
▶ **Experimenting** in Procedure Steps 1-9.

TEACHING THE ACTIVITY
Troubleshooting: The beakers need to remain undisturbed for at least a week if you wish to have large crystals grow. When solutions are cooled suddenly, only small crystals will form. The more gradually the solution is cooled, the larger the crystals tend to grow.
▶ Stereo or binocular microscopes are excellent to use for the observation of the crystals in Steps 8 and 9 of the procedure.

PROGRAM RESOURCES

From the **Teacher Resource Package** use:
Activity Worksheets, pages 21-22, Activity 3-1: Crystal Formation.

ANSWERS TO QUESTIONS
1. Crystals of salt will be cubic, sugar crystals will be orthorhombic.
2. The water evaporated.
3. No, the liquid in the test tube cooled, and sugar crystals precipitated from a saturated solution.
4. As the sugar solution cooled, the water was not able to hold all the sugar, and crystals formed. As the water evaporated from the salt solution, the water became saturated and crystals formed.
5. No, sugar is an organic compound and is not a mineral.
6. Crystals can form from a hot solution that cools slowly or by evaporation of a liquid.

TEACHER F.Y.I.

►The presence of trace elements can change the appearance of a mineral. The mineral corundum, which is often used as an abrasive, also can be found as rubies and sapphires. Rubies contain trace amounts of chromium, and sapphires contain trace amounts of iron or titanium.

CROSS CURRICULUM

►**Chemistry:** Have students use chemistry books, geology books, or an encyclopedia to find out the chemical formulas of several minerals. Require that they find at least one example of a silicate, a carbonate, an oxide, a sulfide, a sulfate, a halide, and a native element. You may wish to help students begin this assignment by giving them the formula for quartz, SiO_2.

3 CLOSE

►Ask questions 1-4 and the **Apply** Question in the Section Review.

►Hold up several items in front of the class. Ask students whether or not each item is a mineral by reviewing the characteristics of a mineral.

FLEX Your Brain

Use the Flex Your Brain activity to have students explore HOW MINERALS ARE GROUPED.

Mineral Compositions and Groups

With over 4000 known minerals, studying all of their compositions might seem very hard. This isn't the case, though, because most of the known minerals are made of only eight elements. In fact, these eight elements make up 98 percent of Earth's crust, as shown in Figure 3-4.

How are minerals classified?

There are twelve common rock-forming minerals that are composed almost entirely of these eight elements. Most of the rock-forming minerals are silicates. Feldspar, quartz, and calcite are examples of rock-forming minerals. All minerals are classified according to their compositions.

4 The largest group of minerals is the silicates. **Silicates** are minerals that contain silicon and oxygen and one or more other elements. Silicon and oxygen are the two most abundant elements in Earth's crust. Because of this, silicates are the most common group of minerals.

Other major groups of minerals are carbonates, oxides, sulfides, sulfates, halides, and native elements. Table 3-2 lists these groups, what each is made of, and an example of each.

You now know a lot more about common rock salt than you did before reading this section. You know that its real name is halite and that it is a mineral. You also know that halite has a cubic crystal shape that is formed when salt water evaporates. And remember, halite is just one of over 4000 minerals on Earth.

EcoTip

The glass in bottles is made from the mineral resource quartz. The aluminum in cans comes from mineral resources in Earth also. Help conserve energy and resources by recycling glass bottles and aluminum cans.

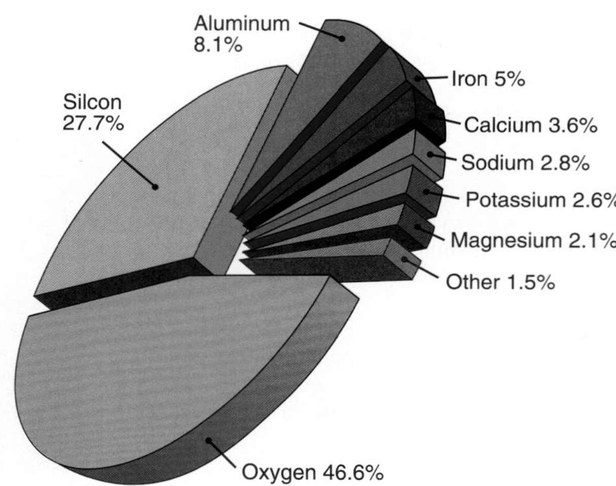

Figure 3-4. Most of Earth's crust is composed of these elements.

OPTIONS

INQUIRY QUESTIONS

►**Why are most minerals made of only eight elements?** *These eight elements make up 98 percent of Earth's crust.*

►**What is true of all carbonate minerals?** *All carbonate minerals contain the carbonate group, CO_3^{-2}.*

PROGRAM RESOURCES

From the **Teacher Resource Package** use: **Activity Worksheets,** page 5, Flex Your Brain.

Table 3-2

NONSILICATE MINERAL GROUPS

Carbonates	Sulfates	Halides
Compounds of certain elements and a carbon atom with three oxygen atoms.	Compounds of certain elements and a sulfur atom with four oxygen atoms.	Compounds of certain elements and chlorine, fluorine, iodine, or bromine.
Example: Malachite	Example: Gypsum	Example: Fluorite
Oxides	**Sulfides**	**Native Elements**
Compounds of elements and oxygen.	Compounds of elements and sulfur.	Elements found uncombined with other elements.
Example: Hematite	Example: Chalcopyrite	Example: Native Copper

SECTION REVIEW

1. List briefly the five conditions a substance must meet to be a mineral.
2. To what crystal system does halite belong?
3. What are the silicate minerals made of?
4. What are two ways that minerals can form?
5. **Apply:** Is ice a mineral? Explain.

Classifying

Skill Builder

Classify each of these minerals into the correct mineral group. Evaluate their chemical formulas using Appendix E on page 666 and Table 3-2. If you need help, refer to Classifying in the **Skill Handbook** on page 680.

siderite ($FeCO_3$)	barite ($BaSO_4$)
talc ($Mg_3Si_4O_{10}(OH)_2$)	enstatite ($MgSiO_3$)
cinnabar (HgS)	malachite($Cu_2CO_3(OH)_2$)
silver (Ag)	sylvite (KCl)

▶Ask a volunteer to read each lesson objective aloud. Ask another student to summarize how each objective was covered. Ask one or two other students to state whether or not the objective was attained.

SECTION REVIEW ANSWERS

1. naturally occurring, nonliving, must be a solid, and have a definite structure and composition
2. cubic
3. silicon, oxygen, and, in most cases, other elements
4. Certain minerals form when magma cools. Other minerals form when water containing dissolved minerals evaporates.
5. Apply: Ice can be classified as a mineral if it forms naturally as it does in the high latitudes. Ice in a freezer is human-made and therefore not a mineral.

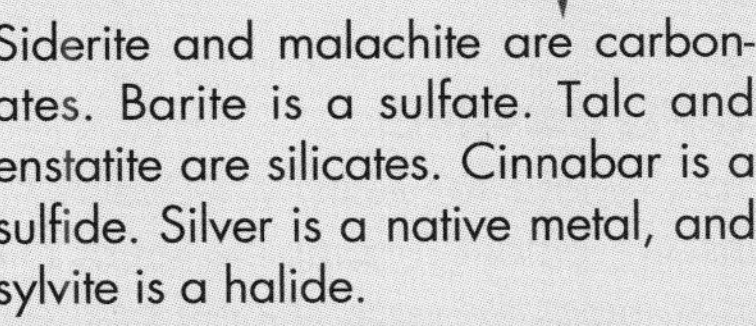

Siderite and malachite are carbonates. Barite is a sulfate. Talc and enstatite are silicates. Cinnabar is a sulfide. Silver is a native metal, and sylvite is a halide.

INQUIRY QUESTIONS

▶**What's the difference between a sulfide and a sulfate?** *Sulfates are combinations of elements with sulfur and oxygen. Sulfides are combinations of elements and sulfur.*

▶**What makes native elements different from other mineral groups?** *They are simply uncombined elements.*

PROGRAM RESOURCES

From the **Teacher Resource Package** use: **Critical Thinking/Problem Solving,** page 9, Phosphates — Help or Hazard?

SECTION 3-2

PREPARATION

SECTION BACKGROUND

▶Minerals softer than unglazed porcelain tile will leave a streak on the tile, whereas minerals harder than the tile will scratch it.

▶Relatively large samples of muscovite or biotite are called "books" because the individual sheets of mica can be separated along one cleavage plane, similar to the pages in a book.

▶The hardness of a mineral is related to crystal structure and to the type of atomic bond in the mineral.

▶Calcite can be identified by its hardness, cleavage, crystal shape, and two other properties. When HCl acid is placed on calcite, it "fizzes." A variety of calcite called Iceland Spar will refract light in two directions to produce a double image.

PREPLANNING

▶To prepare for Activity 3-2 and the Mini-Lab, obtain a complete set of mineral samples for each student or group of students.

▶Collect the other materials needed for Activity 3-2 and put them into "kits" for each student or group of students.

1 MOTIVATE

▶Allow students to examine several varieties of quartz. Ask students if they can identify any of the specimens and what enabled them to do so. Make sure students discover that all the samples are the same mineral.

▶Have volunteers bring in their mineral collections to share with the class.

TYING TO PREVIOUS KNOWLEDGE: Have students recall from Chapter 2 what physical properties are. Remind students that physical properties can be observed without changing a substance into a new substance. Show students two or three different minerals and have them list several physical properties of each.

3-2 Mineral Identification

New Science Words

- hardness
- luster
- streak
- cleavage
- fracture

Objectives

- ▶ List the physical characteristics used to identify minerals.
- ▶ Describe how physical characteristics such as hardness and streak are used to identify minerals.

Physical Properties

How can you tell the difference between one of your classmates and another? You can tell the difference between them without even thinking about it because you observe things about them that make them different. The color of a classmate's hair or the type of shoe he or she wears helps you tell him or her from the rest of your class. Hair color and shoe type are two properties unique to that individual.

Individual minerals also have unique properties. These properties help us tell the difference between minerals. Color and appearance are just two of the clues that are used to identify minerals.

But color and appearance alone aren't enough to tell most minerals apart. The minerals pyrite and gold are both gold in color and can appear to be the same. But we all know they are very different. Gold is worth a lot of money, whereas pyrite has little value. You need to look at other properties of minerals such as hardness to tell them apart.

Figure 3-5. Minerals have many different characteristics.

OPTIONS

Meeting Different Ability Levels

For Section 3-2, use the following **Teacher Resource Masters** depending upon individual students' needs.

◆ **Study Guide Master** for all students.

● **Reinforcement Master** for students of average and above average ability levels.

▲ **Enrichment Master** for above average students.

Additional Teacher Resource Package masters are listed in the OPTIONS box throughout the section. The additional masters are appropriate for all students.

◆ STUDY GUIDE 14

NAME ______ DATE ______ CLASS ______

STUDY GUIDE — Chapter 3

Mineral Identification — Text Pages 68–72

Match the terms in Column I with the phrases in Column II. Write the letter of the correct phrase in the blank on the left.

	Column I	Column II
g	1. cleavage	a. The measure of how easily a mineral can be scratched
d	2. diamond	b. Name given to the Scale of Hardness
i	3. fracture	c. One of the softest known minerals
a	4. hardness	d. The hardest known mineral
h	5. mica	e. Reflection of light from a mineral's surface
e	6. luster	f. Color left by powdered mineral on unglazed porcelain
b	7. Mohs	g. Tendency to break along smooth, flat surfaces
j	8. quartz	h. A common mineral that breaks along smooth, flat surfaces
f	9. streak	i. Tendency to break with rough or jagged edges
c	10. talc	j. A common mineral that breaks with rough or jagged edges

Answer the following question on the lines provided.

11. What three tests would you perform to help you identify an unknown mineral?
1. Use the Mohs scale to measure hardness. Experiment to see which minerals the sample will scratch and which will scratch the sample. 2. Examine the mineral's streak on unglazed porcelain. 3. Identify the luster of the unknown mineral as metallic or nonmetallic and describe it. Other correct answers include: Examine its color. See if the sample shows cleavage or fracture.

In the blanks at the left, write the terms that correctly complete each statement.

pyrite; gold 12. The mineral ____ is sometimes confused with gold because both minerals are the color of ____ .

graphite; pencils 13. The mineral ____ is soft enough to leave a streak on paper and is commonly used in ____ .

14

Hardness

A measure of how easily a mineral can be scratched is its **hardness.** The mineral talc is so soft, you can scratch it loose with your fingernail. You might be familiar with talcum powder made from this mineral. Diamonds, on the other hand, are the hardest mineral. Some diamonds 1 are used as cutting tools. A diamond can be scratched only by another diamond.

In order to compare the hardnesses of minerals, a list of common minerals and their hardnesses was developed. The German scientist Friedrich Mohs developed Mohs' Scale of Hardness, as seen in Table 3-3. The scale lists the hardnesses of ten minerals, with 1 being the softest and 10 the hardest.

Here's how the scale works. Let's say you have a clear or whitish colored mineral that you know is either calcite or quartz. You scratch it on your fingernail and then on a copper penny. You find that the mineral scratches your fingernail but doesn't scratch the penny. Because the hardness of your fingernail is 2.5 and that of a copper penny is 3.5, you can determine the unknown mineral's hardness to be about 3. Now you know it's not quartz because quartz has a hardness of 7. Your mystery mineral must be calcite.

Figure 3-6. Talc can be scratched with your fingernail.

Table 3-3

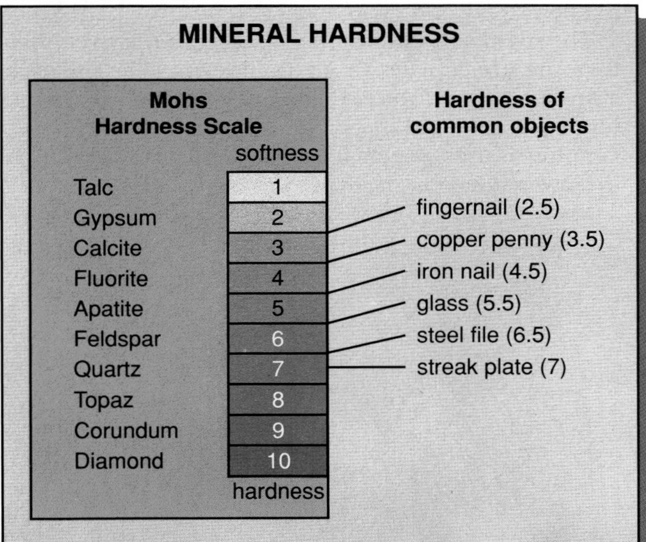

MINERAL HARDNESS

Mohs Hardness Scale	softness → hardness
Talc	1
Gypsum	2
Calcite	3
Fluorite	4
Apatite	5
Feldspar	6
Quartz	7
Topaz	8
Corundum	9
Diamond	10

Hardness of common objects:
- fingernail (2.5)
- copper penny (3.5)
- iron nail (4.5)
- glass (5.5)
- steel file (6.5)
- streak plate (7)

● REINFORCEMENT 14

NAME ______ DATE ______ CLASS ______

REINFORCEMENT — Chapter 3

Mineral Identification — Text Pages 68–72

In the blank at the left, put a check mark next to each statement that agrees with the textbook.

✓ 1. The physical properties of a mineral can be seen or measured in some way.
✓ 2. The physical properties of a mineral make it possible to identify the mineral.
___ 3. Any mineral can be identified by a careful check of one physical characteristic.
___ 4. Hardness is a measure of how easily a mineral can be located.
✓ 5. Friedrich Mohs developed a scale which lists minerals according to their hardness.
✓ 6. Quartz will scratch a copper penny, so quartz is harder than the penny.
✓ 7. The luster of a mineral is described as metallic or nonmetallic.
___ 8. The luster of chrome would be described as nonmetallic.
✓ 9. Color alone is not usually enough to identify a mineral.
✓ 10. When some minerals are rubbed across unglazed porcelain, they leave a streak of powdered material.
___ 11. Graphite is a mineral that does not leave a clear streak.
✓ 12. Topaz is a mineral that does not leave a clear streak.
___ 13. Most minerals cannot be broken.
✓ 14. Mica shows clear cleavage.
✓ 15. Quartz is a mineral with fracture.

Match the mineral names in Column I with the descriptions in Column II. Write the letter of the correct description in the blank on the left.

Column I	Column II
c 16. magnetite	a. Light yellow color; metallic luster; hardness of 6; greenish-black streak
a 17. pyrite	b. Light color; fingernail will scratch it out of the rock; leaves thick, powdery streak
b 18. talc	c. Black color; black streak; dull metallic luster; attracts small iron objects
e 19. calcite	d. Yellow color; scratched by copper penny; often found in flakes
d 20. gold	e. White color; irregular shape; dull luster; hardness of 3; fizzes in hydrochloric acid

14

▲ ENRICHMENT 14

NAME ______ DATE ______ CLASS ______

ENRICHMENT — Chapter 3

Mineral Identification — Text Pages 68–72

HALIDES

Use the table below to help answer Questions 1–4.

The **halides** form a small group of minerals. Minerals in this group differ in many ways from each other, but are similar in composition. Halides are soft minerals, and most are water-soluble. The chart shows some characteristics of the two most common halides.

Characteristic	Halite	Fluorite	Any other halide
Composition	sodium and chlorine	calcium and fluorine	**Answers**
Location	dried lakes, rock beds	rock beds	**will vary.**
Occurrence	worldwide in dry areas	common vein mineral	
Crystal	cubic	cubic	
Color	colorless or light	all colors	
Hardness	2.5	4.0	
Luster	glassy	glassy	
Other characteristics	brittle, transparent, sometimes fluorescent, water soluble	brittle, transparent, often fluorescent	

Less common halides and their composition include:
sylvite (potassium and chlorine)
sal ammoniac (aluminum and chlorine)
cerargyrite (silver and chlorine)
bromyrite (silver and bromine)
calomel (mercury and chlorine)
atacamite (copper and chlorine)
cryolite (sodium, aluminum, and fluorine)

1. Describe similarities in the physical characteristics of halite and fluorite. **Their crystals are cubic. Both are soft, their luster is glassy, and they are brittle, transparent, sometimes fluorescent.**
2. Most halides are water-soluble. Why do you think minerals that are highly water-soluble are difficult to find in large deposits or are found only in dry regions? **Water in the ground will carry soluble minerals with it.**
3. The halides listed include sodium, calcium, potassium, aluminum, mercury, silver, or copper in their composition. Tell how these elements are alike. Then write a definition of halides based on composition. **Sodium, calcium, potassium, aluminum, mercury, silver, and copper are metals. Halides are compounds of a metal and fluorine, chlorine, or bromine. (Some unlisted halides include iodine.)**
4. Research a third halide. Add its characteristics to the chart.

14

69

OBJECTIVES AND SCIENCE WORDS: Have students review the objectives and science words to become familiar with this section.

2 TEACH

Key Concepts are highlighted.

CONCEPT DEVELOPMENT

▶Explain that certain minerals have unique physical properties. Obtain some sulfur and explain that its bright yellow color is unique. Drop dilute hydrochloric acid on calcite to show the "fizzing" reaction. **CAUTION:** *Be sure you and all students wear goggles.* Demonstrate the magnetic property of magnetite.

Cooperative Learning: Form Science Investigation groups to have students test the properties of hardness and streak of five mineral samples, including quartz, talc, calcite, galena, and pyrite. One student in each group should determine the streak of each sample. Another student should determine which minerals are harder than glass and which are softer than a fingernail. The third student in the group should make a table to record the data gathered by the group.

CROSS CURRICULUM

▶**Automechanics:** Have students find out why graphite is added to motor oil. Because of its softness, graphite can be used to lubricate the moving parts of a motor.

CONCEPT DEVELOPMENT

▶Place samples of the following minerals on the desk in front of the room: quartz, pyrite, galena, talc, sulfur, and corundum. Ask students the following questions about the minerals. **How can you use a glass plate to separate the minerals into two groups?** *Scratch the minerals against the glass to see which ones are harder than 5.5 and which are softer than the glass.* Have students quickly determine the hardness of each mineral, and then ask: **Of the minerals harder than glass, what property could be used to determine which one is quartz?** *The luster of quartz is glassy.* Have students separate the minerals on the table according to luster, then ask: **How many have metallic lusters? How many are nonmetallic?** *Two minerals have metallic lusters and four minerals have nonmetallic lusters.*

MINI QUIZ

Use the Mini Quiz to check students' recall of chapter content.

1. **What is the hardest known mineral?** *diamond*
2. **The way light is reflected from a mineral is called _____ .** *luster*
3. **The color of a powdered mineral is the mineral's _____ .** *streak*
4. **When a mineral breaks along smooth, flat planes, the mineral is said to have _____ .** *cleavage*

a

b

Figure 3-7. A mineral may have a metallic (a) or a dull (b) luster.

Luster

2 **Luster** describes how light is reflected from a mineral's surface. Luster is defined as either metallic or nonmetallic. Minerals with a metallic luster always shine like metal. Metallic luster can be compared to the shine of a fancy metal belt buckle or the shiny chrome trim on some cars.

When a mineral does not shine like metal, its luster is nonmetallic. Examples of names for nonmetallic luster include dull, pearly, silky, glassy, and brilliant. Examples of minerals with metallic and nonmetallic lusters can be seen in Figure 3-7.

Color

The color of a mineral can also be a clue to its identity. An example of a mineral whose color helps in identification is sulfur. Sulfur has a very distinctive yellow color. Just remember that, as you learned with gold and pyrite, color alone usually isn't enough to identify a mineral.

Streak

3 **Streak** is the color of the mineral when it is broken up and powdered. When a mineral is rubbed across a piece of unglazed porcelain tile such as in Figure 3-8, a streak is left behind. This streak is the powdered mineral. Gold and pyrite can be identified with the streak test. Gold has a yellow streak and pyrite has a greenish-black streak.

The streak test works only for minerals that are softer than the streak plate. Very soft minerals will even leave a streak on paper. The last time you used a pencil to write on paper, you used the streak of the mineral graphite. Graphite is used in pencil lead because it is soft enough to leave a streak on paper.

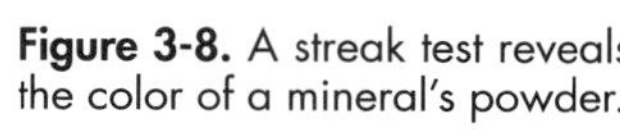

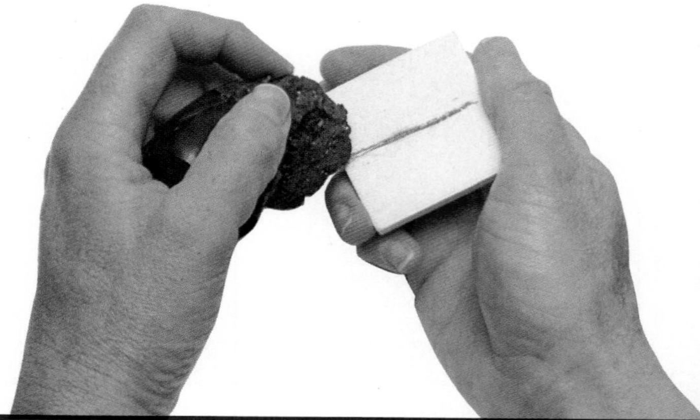

Figure 3-8. A streak test reveals the color of a mineral's powder.

OPTIONS

INQUIRY QUESTIONS

▶**Streak is a good property to test when identifying minerals. Instead of using an unglazed porcelain tile, how else could a mineral's streak be studied?** *The mineral could be crushed into a fine powder.*

▶**Describe what a brilliant luster might be like and name a mineral you think might have a brilliant luster.** *A mineral with a brilliant luster would sparkle and shine under light. Diamond has a brilliant luster.*

▶**Quartz has a glassy luster. What common substance does quartz resemble?** *glass*

▶**What determines whether a mineral cleaves or fractures?** *Cleavage or fracture is determined by the type and strength of the bonds among atoms within a mineral.*

▶**Calcite cleaves to produce six smooth sides, yet it is considered to have only three directions of cleavage. Explain.** *Each set of parallel surfaces is the same cleavage plane.*

PROBLEM SOLVING

Is It Real?

Hazel has visited several areas of California. At one stop, a place called Sutter's Mill, where gold was discovered in 1849, Hazel saw some bright yellow metallic objects glistening in the clear water of a fast moving stream. Reaching into the stream, she found what appeared to be four or five nuggets of gold.

Excitedly, Hazel, who had been working in a jewelry store, tested the nuggets. She found that the gold nuggets left a greenish-black powder when rubbed across a piece of white porcelain. The nuggets scratched a copper penny she had with her.

Think Critically: Did Hazel hit pay dirt?

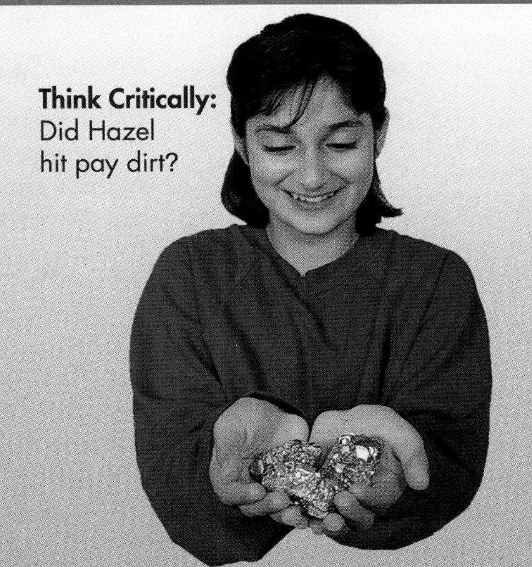

Cleavage and Fracture

The way a mineral breaks is also a clue to its identity.  Minerals that break along smooth, flat surfaces have **cleavage.** Mica is a mineral that has perfect cleavage. You can see in Figure 3-9 how it breaks along smooth, flat surfaces. If you were to take a layer cake and separate its layers, you would show that the cake has cleavage. But not all minerals have cleavage. Minerals that break with rough or jagged edges have **fracture.** Quartz is a mineral with fracture. If you were to grab a chunk out of the side of that cake, it would be like breaking a mineral with fracture.

Why is mica said to have perfect cleavage?

Figure 3-9. Mica's perfect cleavage allows it to be broken along smooth, flat surfaces.

PROBLEM SOLVING

Think Critically: No, the "nuggets" Hazel found were pyrite. Pyrite has a greenish-black streak; gold has a yellow streak. The nuggets scratched the penny, which has a hardness of 3. The hardness of gold is between 2.5 and 3. The hardness of pyrite is 6.5.

CONCEPT DEVELOPMENT

▶**Demonstration:** Demonstrate the property of cleavage by separating a layer cake between layers. Then explain how a mineral fractures by grabbing a chunk out of the side of the cake.

CHECK FOR UNDERSTANDING

Have students write a brief paragraph describing the tests they would employ to identify an unknown mineral.

RETEACH

Review with students each property used to identify minerals. Obtain a sample of magnetite. Have students determine that magnetite has a metallic luster, a hardness greater than glass, a black color, a black streak, fracture, and is magnetic. Allow them ample time to examine the mineral and its properties.

EXTENSION

For students who have mastered this section, use the **Reinforcement** and **Enrichment** masters or other OPTIONS provided.

ENRICHMENT

▶Specific gravity can be used to identify minerals. Have students determine the specific gravity of quartz by first determining its mass and volume using a balance and a graduated cylinder and water, respectively. Students should calculate the density of quartz by dividing its mass by its volume. The specific gravity of quartz can be computed using the following equation:

$$S.G. = \frac{\text{density of quartz}}{\text{density of water at 4°C}}$$

The density of water at 4°C is 1.0 g/mL.

PROGRAM RESOURCES

From the **Teacher Resource Package** use:
- **Transparency Master,** pages 9-10, Mohs' Scale of Hardness.
- **Cross-Curricular Connections,** page 7, Minerals.

Use Color Transparency number 5, Mohs' Scale of Hardness.

Use Laboratory Manual, page 25, Minerals and Optical Crystallography.

MINI-Lab

Materials: transparent samples of calcite, muscovite, gypsum, halite, or quartz; magnifying glass

Teaching Tips

► Students should observe that the calcite causes a double image to appear. The other minerals do not demonstrate this effect.

REVEALING MISCONCEPTIONS

► Ask students how they might test for metallic minerals. Many students will think that all metallic minerals are magnetic. Explain that certain iron-rich minerals, such as magnetite, are magnetic. Other metallic minerals can often be identified by their luster or specific gravity.

3 CLOSE

► Ask questions 1-4 and the **Apply** Question in the Section Review.

FLEX Your Brain

Use the Flex Your Brain activity to have students explore HOW PHYSICAL PROPERTIES ARE USED TO IDENTIFY UNKNOWN MINERALS.

► Ask volunteers to explain how the lesson objectives were attained. If students are unsure as to whether or not objectives were attained, list the physical properties of minerals on the board.

SECTION REVIEW ANSWERS

1. A mineral with cleavage breaks along smooth, flat planes. A mineral that fractures breaks with rough or jagged edges.

2. luster

3. A mineral softer than an unglazed porcelain tile will leave a powdered streak on the tile. The streak color can identify the mineral.

4. A chemical reaction occurs and the mineral "fizzes."

5. Apply: between 4.5 and 5.5

Figure 3-10. A clear specimen of calcite can be identified by its unique ability to bend light, causing a double image.

MINI-Lab

How do clear minerals compare?

Obtain samples of clear minerals such as gypsum, muscovite mica, halite, or quartz. Place each over the print on this page or over letters you have printed on a white sheet of paper. Now do the same with a clear piece of calcite. Describe any differences that you observe. What happens to light as it passes through these minerals?

Other Properties

Here are some less common properties of minerals. Some mineral specimens are in the form of perfect crystals and are easy to recognize by their crystal system. The crystal form of quartz has six sides. Halite and pyrite have cubic crystals.

Other minerals have unique properties. Magnetite, as you can guess by its name, attracts metal objects like a magnet. Light bends when it passes through some calcite specimens, causing you to see a double image, as in Figure 3-10. Calcite can also be identified because it fizzes when hydrochloric acid is put on it.

You can see that you sometimes need more information than just color and appearance to identify most minerals. You might also need to test its streak, its hardness, its luster, and its cleavage or fracture. You can be just as good at identifying minerals as you are recognizing your friends in class.

SECTION REVIEW

1. What's the difference between a mineral that has cleavage and one that has fracture?
2. Which property of a mineral refers to how light reflects from its surface?
3. How can an unglazed porcelain tile be used to identify a mineral?
4. What happens to calcite when hydrochloric acid is placed on it?
5. **Apply:** What hardness does a mineral have if it is scratched by glass but scratches an iron nail?

Skill Builder

Making and Using Graphs

Make a bar graph of the hardnesses of the common objects used for comparison to the minerals in Mohs' Scale of Hardness. If you need help, refer to Making and Using Graphs in the **Skill Handbook** on page 691.

Skill Builder

Hardness (1–10): Finger-nail, Copper penny, Iron nail, Glass, Steel file, Streak plate

ACTIVITY 3-2
Mineral Identification

Problem: *How are minerals identified?*

Materials    

- mineral samples
- hand lens
- pan balance
- graduated cylinder
- water
- copper penny
- glass slide
- steel file
- streak plate
- 5% hydrochloric acid with dropper
- goggles
- Mohs' Scale of Hardness
- Appendices L and M

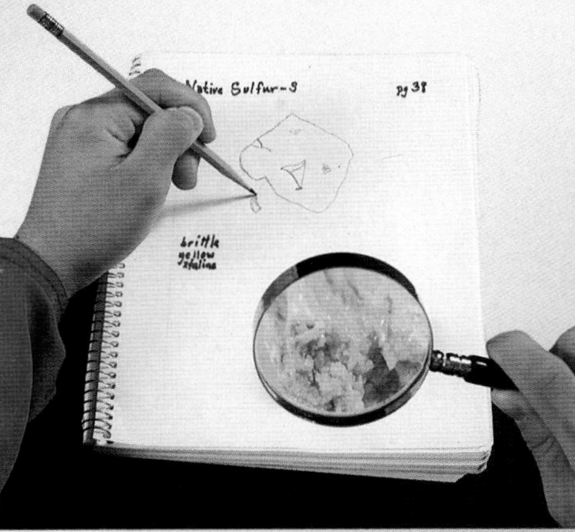

Procedure

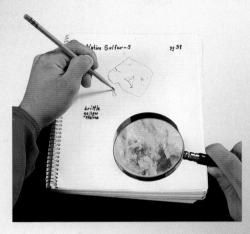

1. Use the hand lens to examine the mineral samples. Determine and record the luster, hardness, streak, cleavage or fracture, and color of each sample.
2. Test the samples for special properties such as reaction to hydrochloric acid. **CAUTION:** *HCl may cause burns. If spillage occurs, rinse with water. Wear your goggles.*
3. Record all observable characteristics in a table like the one shown.

Analyze

1. What property was most useful to you in mineral identification?
2. Which test was most difficult to perform?

Conclude and Apply

3. What property was least helpful in identifying minerals? Why?
4. How are minerals identified?

Data and Observations

Sample Data

Mineral	Luster	Hardness	Streak	Cleavage/ fracture	Color	Other properties
quartz	non-metallic, glassy	7	none	fracture	white/clear	none

ACTIVITY 3-2
50-60 minutes

OBJECTIVE: Identify unknown minerals by **comparing** them against known minerals.

PROCESS SKILLS applied in this activity:
▶**Observing** in Procedure Steps 1 and 2.
▶**Communicating** in Procedure Step 3, Analyze Questions 1 and 2, and Conclude and Apply Question 3.
▶**Separating and Controlling Variables** in Procedure Steps 1 and 3 and Conclude and Apply Question 4.
▶**Experimenting** in Procedure Steps 1, 2, and 3.

TEACHING THE ACTIVITY

▶Have students compare their data with the description of physical properties given in Appendices L and M.

Troubleshooting: If more than one class will be doing this activity, or if more than one class period will be involved, double check to see that students are still working with the original samples and that each is appropriately labeled. Occasionally samples will be misplaced from one student group to another.

▶Remind students about the safe use of acids. Students should wear goggles and aprons while conducting this activity.

PROGRAM RESOURCES

From the **Teacher Resource Package** use:
Activity Worksheets, pages 23-24, Activity 3-2: Mineral Identification.
Activity Worksheets, page 28, Mini-Lab: How do clear minerals compare?

ANSWERS TO QUESTIONS

1. Although answers will vary, streak and hardness will generally be the most common answers.
2. Answers will vary, but many students will have difficulty describing cleavage and fracture. Crystal faces are often confused with cleavage surfaces.
3. Color is generally the least helpful property.
4. Minerals are identified by their physical and chemical properties.

SECTION 3-3

PREPARATION

SECTION BACKGROUND

▶The value of diamonds varies depending on whether or not they are tinted. The most common diamonds of gem quality have yellow or brown tints and are less valuable than diamonds with no tints. Diamonds with blue or pink tints are more valuable than those with no tints.

▶Diamonds are cut using a bronze saw coated with diamond dust. Tiny flat surfaces called facets are cut into the diamond at angles that will best enhance refracted light. Most diamonds used for gems have 58 facets.

▶Ores located deep in Earth's crust are removed by underground mining. Ores near Earth's surface are removed by open-pit mining.

▶Unwanted elements are removed from a metallic ore by a chemical process called smelting. One type of smelting involves mixing iron ore with charcoal. The mixture is heated, and carbon atoms from the charcoal replace the iron atoms in the ore. This process releases iron.

1 MOTIVATE

▶Amethyst is a variety of quartz often used as a gemstone. Have a jeweler display some amethyst jewelry for the class.

▶Ask students what they think is the most precious gem. Many students will be surprised to learn that rubies and emeralds are considered more valuable than diamonds because of their relative rareness.

FLEX Your Brain

Use the Flex Your Brain activity to have students explore USES FOR GEMS.

3-3 Uses of Minerals

New Science Words

gems
ore

Objectives

- ▶ Discuss characteristics gems have that make them different from and more valuable than other minerals.
- ▶ List the conditions necessary for a mineral to be classified as an ore.

Gems

What makes one mineral more useful or valuable to us than another? Why are diamonds and rubies so valuable? The next time you go shopping, look in the window of a jewelry store. Chances are you will see rings, bracelets, and maybe even a watch with diamonds or other gems on them. What properties do gems possess that make them valuable?

What makes a gem different from other minerals?

1 **Gems** or gemstones are highly prized minerals because they are rare and beautiful. Many gems are cut and polished and used for jewelry. They are more bright and colorful than common samples of the same mineral.

The difference between a gem and the common form of the same mineral can be very slight. Amethyst, a gem form of quartz, contains just traces of iron in its structure. This iron gives amethyst a desirable purple color. And sometimes a gem has a crystal structure that allows it to be cut and polished to a higher quality than a nongem mineral.

Figure 3-11. It is easy to see why gems are prized—for their beauty and rarity.

OPTIONS

Meeting Different Ability Levels

For Section 3-3, use the following **Teacher Resource Masters** depending upon individual students' needs.

◆ **Study Guide Master** for all students.

● **Reinforcement Master** for students of average and above average ability levels.

▲ **Enrichment Master** for above average students.

Additional Teacher Resource Package masters are listed in the OPTIONS box throughout the section. The additional masters are appropriate for all students.

◆ STUDY GUIDE 15

NAME ____ DATE ____ CLASS ____

STUDY GUIDE — Chapter 3

Uses of Minerals — Text Pages 74–76

Use the words in the box to fill in the blanks.

aluminum	amethyst	crystal	demand
expense	gems	ores	polished
profit	rare	supply	
traces	useful	value	

Stones called **gems** are highly prized minerals because they are beautiful and often **rare**. Many gemstones have a **crystal** structure that allows them to be cut and **polished** to the high quality needed for jewelry. The difference between a gemstone and the common form of the same mineral is sometimes slight. The purple stone **amethyst**, for example, is quartz with just **traces** of iron in its structure.

Some minerals contain a **useful** substance that can be mined at a **profit**. Such minerals are called **ores**. Bauxite is this kind of mineral because **aluminum** can be taken from it and made into useful products. In most cases, waste rock or material must be removed before a mineral can be used. If the **expense** of mining gets higher than the **value** of the material, the mineral is no longer considered to be an ore. The value of the material can also change if the **supply** or the **demand** increases or decreases.

Use words in the box at the top of the page that fit to complete the puzzle.

G E M S
P R O F I T
A L U M I N U M
A M E T H Y S T
O R E S
T R A C E S
C R Y S T A L

15

Figure 3-12. Ores must be processed and refined into more useful materials.

Ores

If you look around your room at home, you will find many things made from mineral resources. See how many you can name. Is there anything in your room with iron in it? If so, the iron may have come from the mineral hematite. The aluminum in soft drink cans comes from the mineral bauxite.

Bauxite and hematite are minerals that can also be called ores. A mineral is an **ore** if it contains a useful substance that can be mined at a profit. ❷ Aluminum can be taken from bauxite and made into useful and valuable products. These products are worth more money than the cost of the mining, so bauxite is an ore.

Science and READING

Find some jewelry advertisements in your local paper. Read them to find out some of the gems that are commonly used in jewelry. Also, find out what kinds of minerals the gems are set in.

a

b

Figure 3-13. Bauxite ore (a) is used to make aluminum products (b).

● REINFORCEMENT 15

NAME ________ DATE ________ CLASS ________

REINFORCEMENT — Chapter 3

Uses of Minerals — Text Pages 74–76

Answer the following questions on the lines provided.

1. Why are diamonds and rubies valuable? What are minerals like these called? **Such stones are beautiful and rare. They are called gems.**
2. What characteristics make gemstones beautiful? **Gemstones may have unusual luster and beautiful color. Their crystal formation makes good cutting possible.**
3. What processes must a stone undergo if it is to be made ready for use in jewelry? **It must be separated from rock in which it is found. It must be cut properly and polished.**
4. What useful material may be obtained from bauxite? What useful material may be obtained from hematite? What are bauxite and hematite called, since they produce useful materials? **Aluminum is from bauxite, iron from hematite. Bauxite and hematite are ores.**
5. Explain why the cost of obtaining some minerals is very high. **Many minerals are rare or difficult to obtain because of their location. In some cases, enormous amounts of ore must be crushed in order to obtain a valuable mineral.**
6. State two reasons why recycling some products made from minerals is helpful. **In many cases, recycling costs less than mining new ores. This will keep the price down. Recycling can also protect the environment by making less mining necessary and by reducing the need for landfills.**

15

▲ ENRICHMENT 15

NAME ________ DATE ________ CLASS ________

ENRICHMENT — Chapter 3

Uses of Minerals — Text Pages 74–76

GOLD!

Use information from the paragraphs below and from library references to answer Questions 1–4.

Gold was among the earliest metals discovered. It occurs in octahedral crystals, but is also found as flakes, thin wires, and plates. From the beginning, it was prized for its beauty and its rarity and came to be a sign of wealth. It was used to make coins and bars which, like money today, could be used to buy things.

The ancient Egyptians were among the earliest peoples to develop goldsmithing as an art, making jewelry and other beautiful objects from the metal. They used solid gold, beating and pounding it to the shape they wanted. Gold is easily worked, since it has a hardness of only 2.5.

Early in America, gold was mined for decorative uses. The Inca writer Garcilaso de la Vega, writing in the early 17th century, described the Temple of the Sun at Cusco: "The four walls were hung with plaques of gold, from top to bottom, and a likeness of the Sun topped the high altar. This likeness was made of a gold plaque twice as thick as those that paneled the walls . . . the whole thing was so immense that it occupied the entire back of the temple. . . ."

Gold can be found in most parts of the world, but it is often difficult to separate it from the other minerals, usually quartz, where it is found. Frequently a ton or more of rock will yield only a few dollars' worth of pure gold. When gold is found on the surface of the ground, it is usually in slow-flowing parts of rivers, dropped because of its weight after being uncovered by erosion and washed downhill by rapidly moving water. These are called placer deposits. It was this visible gold that began the famous gold rushes in the western United States and in Australia. When gold is found in quartz veins, it is separated by crushing ore and obtaining a concentrate to be smelted (heated and melted).

Gold is still used for jewelry and other art objects. Today, however, other metals, such as copper or silver, are usually added to gold to make it harder and more durable. More recent markets for gold include dentistry and electronics. Strangely, most of the gold that is dug out of the rocks with such hard work ends up underground again—in bank vaults where it is stored by governments and investors!

1. How have its hardness and luster made gold an important metal? **Its luster makes it desirable for ornament; its softness makes it easy to work with.**
2. Explain how the weight of gold affected the history of some western states. **The weight of gold caused it to sink in slow-running water. These placer deposits were easily seen and began several gold rushes, settling parts of the west.**
3. Why is gold expensive? **Gold is difficult to find and very much in demand.**
4. The Spanish came to America from Europe in the 16th century. Use a history of Mexico or Peru to find how the presence of gold affected the lives of the Native Americans who lived in those places during the 16th and 17th centuries. **Answers should include the fact that Europeans conquered many peoples in order to take their gold.**

15

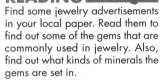

▶Have students look around the room for items made at least partially of metal. Have one student list each item on the board. Help students to determine the type of metal found in each item. Then have students hypothesize where the metals came from. Explain that many metals are found as ores. Iron used in steel comes from hematite. Aluminum is derived from bauxite. Copper occurs as native copper ore, or it is processed from the ore malachite.

TYING TO PREVIOUS KNOWLEDGE: Have students recall the last time they saw jewelry in the window of a jewelry store or at a department store. Have students describe the jewelry. Most will say it was shiny, or colorful, or looked brilliant under the lights of the store.

OBJECTIVES AND SCIENCE WORDS: Have students review the objectives and science words with this section.

2 TEACH

Key Concepts are highlighted.

CONCEPT DEVELOPMENT

▶**Demonstration:** Demonstrate a smelting process used for separating metals from an ore by mixing some black copper oxide and some powdered charcoal in the bottom of a test tube. A tablespoon of each will be enough. Carefully heat the mixture for a few minutes. Pour the hot mixture into a beaker of water. The copper will settle to the bottom, and the waste will float on the water.

▶Briefly explain the 1849 California Gold Rush to students. Then ask: **Why were the miners able to pan the water to recover the gold?** *Because of its high specific gravity, gold will sink to the bottom of the pan.*

Science and READING

Students should discover that diamonds and "birthstones" are commonly used in jewelry. Most gems are set in the mineral gold, although silver and platinum are sometimes used as settings.

CROSS CURRICULUM

▶**Geography and World Cultures:** Have students research and record areas of the world that supply large amounts of the world's diamonds, gold, rock salt, bauxite, iron, and other mineral resources. Have students write a brief paragraph explaining the importance of these mineral resources to each area's economy.

CHECK FOR UNDERSTANDING

Have students compare and contrast gems and ores.

RETEACH

Cooperative Learning: Using the Paired Partners strategy, have students make flash cards with names of common metals. On the reverse side of each card, have them identify the ore from which each metal is obtained. Students could also include a location where each ore is presently mined. Partners can test each other using the flash cards.

EXTENSION

For students who have mastered this section, use the **Reinforcement** and **Enrichment** masters or other OPTIONS provided.

MINI QUIZ

Use the Mini Quiz to check students' recall of chapter content.

1. **Minerals that are highly prized because of their rareness and beauty are called _____ .** *gems*
2. **Minerals that contain useful substances that can be mined at a profit are _____ .** *ores*
3. **Ores containing sulfur are used to make _____ .** *fertilizers*

TECHNOLOGY

Think Critically: These diamonds aren't minerals because they are made by people.

Did You Know?

The state of Colorado is famous for its mineral resources. In 1894, the largest silver nugget ever found in North America was discovered there. The nugget had a mass of 835 kg. That's about 15 times the mass of the average person in your class.

Most ore contains unwanted material along with the valuable material. The waste rock or material must be removed before a mineral can be used. Removing the waste rock can be very expensive. If the cost of removing the waste rock gets higher than the value of the desired material, the mineral will no longer be classified as an ore.

Think back to the last soft drink you had in an aluminum can. What do you think would happen if people stopped using aluminum cans? This would cause the demand for aluminum to go down. Some bauxite mines would close down because they would no longer be able to make money. The bauxite mined at these locations would no longer be an ore. The value of a mineral can change if the supply of or the demand for that mineral changes.

TECHNOLOGY

Diamonds Are Forever?

You probably knew that diamonds were used in jewelry, but did you know that diamonds are used on drill bits and other instruments? Diamond-tipped drill bits can cut through very hard substances such as steel and rock. Diamonds are used on the bits because they are the hardest mineral.

Recently, scientists developed a way to put a thin coating of diamonds on objects, as shown in this photo. They use a gas called methane and microwaves to make the diamonds. A methane molecule consists of a carbon atom surrounded by four hydrogen atoms. Microwaves are used to strip the hydrogen atoms away from the molecule. Then the carbon atoms link together on the surface of the object being coated, forming tiny rows of diamonds. This process can be used to make diamond-edged surgical scalpels, razor blades, diamond surfaces that can't be scratched, and diamond coated computer parts.

Think Critically: These diamonds aren't true minerals. Why not?

OPTIONS

INQUIRY QUESTIONS

▶**Sometimes waste rock, called gangue, left in piles at a mine is later processed to remove mineral resources. Why were the minerals not removed earlier?** *It was initially too expensive to remove the minerals from the waste rock. As the selling price of the mineral increased, it became profitable to remove it from the waste rock.*

▶**Diamonds are used to cut most other materials. What can be used to cut a diamond?** *A diamond can be cut by another diamond.*

ENRICHMENT

▶Have students find pictures of gems such as sapphires, rubies, jade, opals, topaz, garnets, and diamonds. Have them write a short report on the processes involved in changing the raw minerals into gems.

▶Have students research to find out whether or not any gems or ores are mined in your area of the country.

Figure 3-14. Many ores are obtained from large open pit mines.

You'd be surprised to find out all of the things that come from ores. Magnetite is used to make iron used in everything from buildings to ships. Sulfur is used to make fertilizers, and clay is used in bricks and pottery. Garnet and corundum are used to make abrasives such as sandpaper. There's probably even an ore in the walls where you live. Gypsum is used to make plaster. Gems and ores are important mineral resources. 3

REVIEW

1. List some physical properties that are used to classify a mineral as a gem.
2. When is a mineral deposit classified as an ore?
3. **Apply:** Why couldn't a company stay in business if the mineral it was mining was no longer an ore?

Concept Mapping — Skill Builder

Make an events chain showing why bauxite can be an ore. Use the following terms: *gives aluminum, ore, mined at profit, bauxite.* If you need help, refer to Concept Mapping in the **Skill Handbook** on page 688.

CONCEPT DEVELOPMENT

►**Give one reason the demand for unprocessed bauxite might decrease.** *If aluminum products such as cans were recycled, the amount of new aluminum needed would decrease.*

►**Why do you think the mine shown in Figure 3-14 is called an open-pit mine?** *The overlying waste rock was removed to expose an open pit from which the ore was removed.*

3 CLOSE

►Ask questions 1-2 and the **Apply** Question in the Section Review.

►Have a lapidary, a person who cuts and polishes minerals, come to class to discuss methods used to bring out the beauty of gems.

FLEX Your Brain

Use the Flex Your Brain activity to have students explore ORES.

►Call on one student in the class to review the main concepts of the lesson as if he or she were discussing the lesson with a friend who had missed class.

SECTION REVIEW ANSWERS

1. color, luster, rarity, crystal structure
2. when there is enough of the mineral present for it to be mined at a profit
3. Apply: If the mineral could not be mined at a profit, it would no longer be an ore. A small company would sustain losses.

PROGRAM RESOURCES

From the **Teacher Resource Package** use:
Concept Mapping, pages 11-12, Minerals.
Activity Worksheets, page 5, Flex Your Brain.
Use Laboratory Manual, page 27, Mineral Resources.
Use Laboratory Manual, page 29, Removal of Waste Rock.

INQUIRY QUESTIONS

►**Why are garnet and corundum used as abrasives on sand paper?** *Both minerals are very hard.*

Skill

Possible Solution:

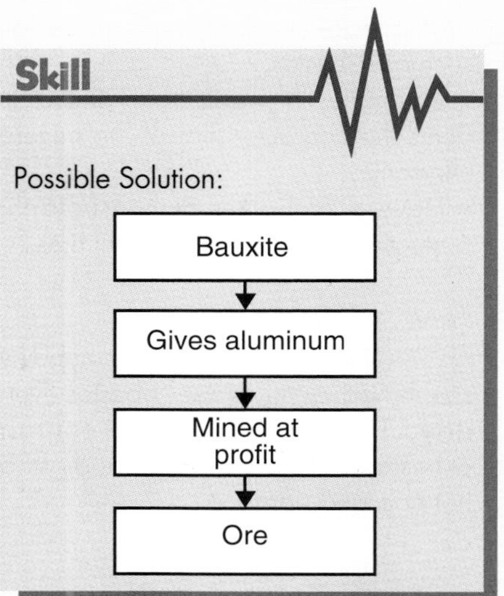

SECTION 3-4

PREPARATION

SECTION BACKGROUND

▶ Asbestos is a carcinogen, a substance that causes cancer.

▶ Two forms of asbestos that have been used for insulation and fire protection are chrysotile and crocidolite.

▶ Chrysotile belongs to the serpentine group of minerals. It is the type most often used for insulation and fire protection. Chrysotile is fibrous and soluble. Its soluble nature tends to make it disappear from human tissue over time.

▶ Crocidolite belongs to a group of minerals called amphiboles. Its fibers are long, thin, straight, and very penetrating. This form of asbestos is insoluble and tends to remain imbedded in human tissue.

▶ The Environmental Protection Agency (EPA) estimates that up to 45 000 of the 100 000 schools nationwide contain potentially dangerous asbestos.

▶ Almost all diseases that have been caused by asbestos have occurred in people who mine it, manufacture it, or install it.

1 MOTIVATE

▶ Ask students if they have seen or heard any news reports dealing with the removal of asbestos from buildings in your community. Have them discuss who is responsible for protecting the public against dangerous materials such as asbestos.

▶ If samples are available, show students the characteristics of the mineral chrysotile.

▶ Have a firefighter demonstrate the protective clothing used to fight fires.

TYING TO PREVIOUS KNOWLEDGE: Have students hypothesize how they might use asbestos every day. Thermal oven mitts contain asbestos, which protects hands from hot pots and pans.

3-4 Asbestos Removal

New Science Words

asbestos

Objectives

- ▶ List the properties of asbestos that make it useful as a flame retardant and an insulator.
- ▶ State why people are so concerned about the asbestos used in buildings.
- ▶ Compare the pros and cons of asbestos removal.

a

Figure 3-15. The mineral asbestos is made of threadlike fibers (a). Asbestos is being removed from many buildings (b).

Should All Asbestos Be Removed?

Do you know of a building where asbestos has been removed? Perhaps your school has had asbestos removed. The Environmental Protection Agency (EPA) requires school officials to inspect buildings every six months. If flaking asbestos is found, it must be removed or contained. Some people want all asbestos removed from schools and other public buildings. Why is the public so concerned about asbestos?

Asbestos is a mineral with threadlike, flexible fibers. Different forms of the mineral are used as insulation and as fire protection. Asbestos fibers have been shown to cause cancer.

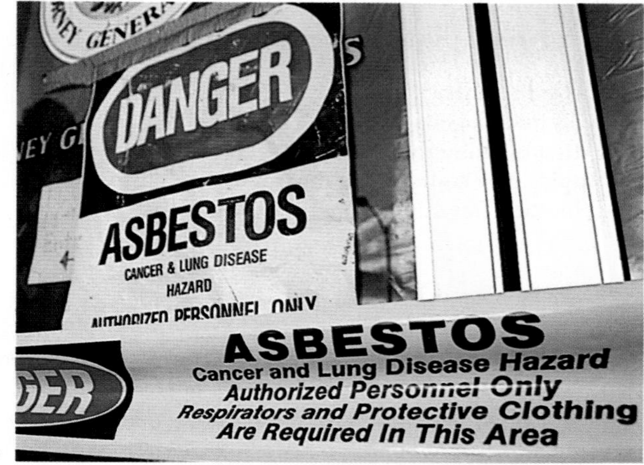

b

OPTIONS

Meeting Different Ability Levels

For Section 3-4, use the following **Teacher Resource Masters** depending upon individual students' needs.

◆ **Study Guide Master** for all students.

● **Reinforcement Master** for students of average and above average ability levels.

▲ **Enrichment Master** for above average students.

Additional Teacher Resource Package masters are listed in the OPTIONS box throughout the section. The additional masters are appropriate for all students.

◆ **STUDY GUIDE 16**

NAME ________ DATE ________ CLASS ________

STUDY GUIDE — Chapter 3

Asbestos Removal — Text Pages 78–80

In the blank at the left, write the letter of the term or phrase that matches each definition.

a 1. A government office that investigates pollution problems
a. Environmental Protection Agency b. Federal Reserve System c. Federal Bureau of Investigation d. Congress

c 2. A mineral with threadlike, flexible fibers
a. insulation b. flame retardant c. asbestos d. quartz

d 3. A term that means "resists burning"
a. insulation b. construction c. asbestos d. flame retardant

c 4. Process by which fibers may enter the lungs
a. touching insulation containing asbestos b. living near asbestos c. inhaling asbestos fibers d. burning fibers

b 5. A disease that may be caused by inhaling fibers
a. irritated skin b. lung cancer c. bone weakness d. flu

b 6. Common use of asbestos
a. to make materials stronger b. to make materials flame-resistant c. to make materials water-resistant d. to make materials lighter

a 7. Situation in which asbestos is a hazard
a. when fibers break loose b. when wet c. when used in ceilings d. when woven into clothing

d 8. Object for which asbestos would not be useful
a. hot pad b. cover for hot water pipes c. building insulation d. pots and pans for cooking

Answer the following questions on the lines provided.

9. Why is asbestos used in buildings? Asbestos is a flame retardant.

10. Why do some people want to remove all asbestos from buildings? Asbestos can cause lung disease.

11. Why do some people think that only damaged asbestos should be removed? Undamaged asbestos is not harmful. It provides fire protection. Removal of asbestos is very costly.

16

Figure 3-16. Asbestos is used to make fireproof clothing because it resists burning.

The threadlike structure and flexibility of asbestos allow it to be woven into cloth or pressed into sheets. Asbestos materials don't burn easily and don't conduct heat or electricity very well. When you pick up something hot from the stove, you use a hot pad to insulate your hand against the heat. Asbestos is used in the same way. Asbestos is also used to make flame retardant material because it resists burning. Asbestos is often found in the insulation around hot water pipes and electrical wires and motors.

How can asbestos be harmful?

The properties that make asbestos useful, also make it dangerous. If fibers break loose, they can float around in the air. Breathing in some types of asbestos fibers can cause several diseases, including lung cancer. The fibers get into the lungs where they can cause healthy cells to change into cancer cells. This is the reason that asbestos is removed.

Some people think that removing all asbestos from buildings is an overreaction. It has been shown that the amount of asbestos fibers contained in the air of buildings with asbestos is not much more than the amount in air outside the building. The only time asbestos in a building sheds fibers into the air is when it is damaged. In fact, the removal process releases fibers into the air that are a hazard to the people removing the asbestos.

OBJECTIVES AND SCIENCE WORDS: Have students review the objectives and science words to become familiar with this section.

2 TEACH

Key Concepts are highlighted.

CONCEPT DEVELOPMENT

▶**Demonstration:** Use the following analogy to demonstrate the dangers of asbestos removal. Coat a flat board with a layer of flour to represent asbestos. Allow the board with flour to sit on a table at the front of the class for several minutes while you begin class. Partially clean the board by scraping, the flour into a previously prepared can. Explain that when the flour was left alone, it did not enter the air. When it was disturbed during scraping most went into the disposal can but some of the powder formed a cloud in the air near the can.

Cooperative Learning: Using the Problem Solving Team strategy, have students suggest solutions to the asbestos removal problem. Questions they should try to answer include the following: **Who should decide if removal is necessary? Who should pay for the removal?**

▶Relate that airborne asbestos particles entering the lungs are dangerous and can cause cancer.

▶Have students list other harmful air pollutants.

● REINFORCEMENT 16

NAME ____ DATE ____ CLASS ____

REINFORCEMENT — Chapter 3

Asbestos Removal — Text Pages 78–80

Answer the following questions on the lines provided.

1. What two properties of the mineral asbestos made it useful in building construction? **Asbestos is flame-resistant and its flexible, thread-like form makes it adaptable for use with other materials.**
2. What information was made public in the 1970s that brought an end to the use of asbestos in most construction? **Asbestos often flakes. When inhaled, asbestos fibers may cause lung disease.**
3. What properties of the mineral asbestos make it dangerous? **Its light, thread-like fibers float in air.**
4. What government agency requires inspection of school buildings to check asbestos? **The Environmental Protection Agency**
5. When must asbestos be removed from school buildings? **Asbestos must be removed when it is exposed and flaking.**
6. Give an argument that might be used by persons who want all asbestos removed. **Small particles may escape into the air. Such particles can cause disease.**
7. Give an argument that might be used by persons who do not want asbestos removed unless it is damaged. **Undamaged asbestos can save lives by preventing the spread of fire.**

16

▲ ENRICHMENT 16

NAME ____ DATE ____ CLASS ____

ENRICHMENT — Chapter 3

Asbestos Removal — Text Pages 78–80

BREATHING AND AIR POLLUTANTS

Use the information below to help you start the project described at the bottom of the page.

You have been reading about the dangers of asbestos. People who work with asbestos, as well as those who live in buildings that contain asbestos, have sometimes become ill from inhaling asbestos fibers that, when broken, are light enough to float in the air.

Your lungs are spongelike organs that consist of three lobes, or sections, on the right and two lobes on the left. When you inhale, air enters through your mouth or nose and is sucked into your lungs and then into thousands of small tubes. These tubes divide into millions of bronchioles. At the end of each bronchiole are alveoli, tiny air sacs through which blood and oxygen are diffused.

In about one minute, your heart pumps your body's entire blood supply through your lungs. The alveoli soak up the oxygen-starved blood and remove the carbon dioxide that has accumulated. When you exhale, the carbon dioxide leaves your body. Your blood is then given fresh oxygen and is pumped back into the body to feed hungry tissues.

Consider the importance of keeping healthy lungs. Your body needs a great amount of air every minute. Even when you are lying down, you need to inhale about 7.6 liters of air; and when you are running, you use about 47 liters a minute! Throughout your whole life, you will probably breathe about 284 billion liters of air.

Of course, along with the air, you breathe in millions of particles of foreign matter. It is this air pollution, taken into your body, that may cause breathing problems or even serious illness.

Pollution Project: Think about how important healthy lungs are to the rest of the body. List at least four questions you have about asbestos and other indoor pollutants that may affect the health of the lungs. Compare your questions and concerns with those of your classmates. Plan a library research project to find answers. Note that you may not find all the answers since there are still some things scientists don't know. Discuss unanswered questions and share information you have on

Answers will vary. They might include: Are there filters or air cleaners that will screen out pollutants? Are there air monitors to determine what kind of and how much of the pollutants are in the air? What is the worst kind of air pollutant? Is there some way to treat asbestos so it won't flake?

16

RETEACH

Have students hypothesize as to why people who work with asbestos removal wear protective masks over their mouths and noses. Show pictures of other people who wear protective masks, such as sand blasters and incinerator workers.

EXTENSION

For students who have mastered this section, use the **Reinforcement** and **Enrichment** masters or other OPTIONS provided.

3 CLOSE

▶Ask questions 1-2 in the Section Review.

FLEX Your Brain

Use the Flex Your Brain activity to have students explore ASBESTOS REMOVAL.

▶Invite an agent from the EPA to visit class and explain the dangers of asbestos materials and what needs to be done to buildings containing asbestos to protect people from the dangers.

▶Have a person who removes asbestos come to class to review the methods used to remove asbestos as well as the safety procedures used to protect the workers.

SECTION REVIEW ANSWERS

1. It is used as an insulator because it is a poor conductor of heat.

2. People are concerned that asbestos fibers might get into the air where they can be inhaled by people and possibly cause cancer.

YOU DECIDE!

Some students will argue to "leave well enough alone" when it comes to the topic of asbestos removal. Others will feel that the potential risks warrant immediate removal.

Figure 3-17. Removing asbestos is hazardous.

As stated earlier, there are different forms of asbestos used in buildings. The type that is used most often has been shown to be much less dangerous than some less common types of asbestos. The curly nature of the fibers in this common asbestos keeps it from being imbedded in the outer portion of the lungs. It also disappears from tissue over time. Removing this type of asbestos may be unnecessary.

Another type of asbestos has been shown to cause other diseases. This form of asbestos has long, thin, straight fibers. The fibers penetrate into the lungs, causing cancer. This asbestos has not been used very often.

SECTION REVIEW

1. Why is asbestos used in buildings?
2. Why is asbestos being removed from buildings?

You Decide!

Some people feel all asbestos shouldn't be removed because removal is very expensive and not all asbestos is harmful. They feel that removing all asbestos even if it isn't shedding fibers is a waste of money. On the other hand, some asbestos has been linked to cancer. What do you think? Should all asbestos be removed?

OPTIONS

PROGRAM RESOURCES

From the **Teacher Resource Package** use:
Science & Society, page 7, Asbestos and the Workplace.
Activity Worksheets, page 5, Flex Your Brain.

CHAPTER

REVIEW

SUMMARY

3-1: Minerals

1. All minerals are formed by natural processes, are nonliving solids, with unique compositions and distinct internal structures.
2. Minerals have crystal structures in one of six major crystal systems.
3. Minerals can form when magma cools or when liquids containing dissolved minerals evaporate.

3-2: Mineral Identification

1. Hardness is a measure of how easily a mineral can be scratched. Luster describes how light is reflected from a mineral's surface. Color is sometimes a property that can be used to identify a mineral.
2. Streak is the color left by a mineral on an unglazed porcelain tile. Minerals that break along smooth, flat surfaces have cleavage. Minerals that break with rough or jagged surfaces have fracture.

3-3: Uses of Minerals

1. Gems are minerals that are more rare and beautiful than common minerals.
2. An ore is a mineral or group of minerals that can be mined at a profit.

3-4: Science and Society: Asbestos Removal

1. Asbestos is used as a flame retardant and an insulator because it is a poor conductor of heat and electricity.
2. Some kinds of asbestos used in building construction have been shown to cause cancer.
3. Removing asbestos can reduce the threat of cancer caused by asbestos. On the other hand, not all asbestos causes cancer.

KEY SCIENCE WORDS

a. **asbestos**
b. **cleavage**
c. **crystal**
d. **fracture**
e. **gems**
f. **hardness**
g. **luster**
h. **magma**
i. **mineral**
j. **ore**
k. **silicates**
l. **streak**

UNDERSTANDING VOCABULARY

Match each phrase with the correct term from the list of Key Science Words.

1. naturally occurring solid
2. hot, melted rock
3. minerals containing silicon, oxygen, and one or more other elements
4. how light is reflected from a mineral
5. fiber mineral used as insulation
6. valuable, rare minerals
7. a mineral mined at a profit
8. breakage along smooth, flat planes
9. solid with a repeating arrangement of atoms
10. the color of a mineral's powder

CHAPTER

REVIEW

SUMMARY

Have students read the summary statements to review the major concepts of the chapter.

UNDERSTANDING VOCABULARY

1. i
2. h
3. k
4. g
5. a
6. e
7. j
8. b
9. c
10. l

ASSESSMENT

To assess student understanding of material in this chapter, use the resources listed.

COOPERATIVE LEARNING

Consider using cooperative learning in the THINK AND WRITE CRITICALLY, APPLY, and MORE SKILL BUILDERS sections of the Chapter Review.

PROGRAM RESOURCES

From the **Teacher Resource Package** use:
Chapter Review, pages 9-10.
Chapter and Unit Tests, pages 20-23, Chapter Test.

CHAPTER
REVIEW

CHECKING CONCEPTS

1. d	**6.** d
2. c	**7.** b
3. a	**8.** c
4. d	**9.** c
5. b	**10.** d

UNDERSTANDING CONCEPTS

11. cubic
12. Silicates
13. Feldspar
14. carbon
15. minerals

THINK AND WRITE CRITICALLY

16. A gem is a mineral that is highly prized because it is rare and beautiful. An ore is a substance that contains one or more useful minerals which are mined at a profit.
17. Certain asbestos fibers can cause cancer and other diseases if inhaled.
18. Air isn't a mineral because it isn't a solid and its components aren't arranged in a repeating pattern.
19. Both are terms used to describe how a mineral breaks. Cleavage refers to breakage along smooth, flat surfaces. Mica cleaves. Fracture describes minerals that break with rough or jagged edges, such as quartz.
20. Not all asbestos causes cancer. Also, the removal process causes fibers to enter the air, where they can be inhaled.

CHAPTER
REVIEW

CHECKING CONCEPTS

Choose the word or phrase that completes the sentence.

1. Minerals ______ .
a. are solids **c.** are not alive
b. have crystal structure **d.** all of these

2. All silicates contain ______ .
a. magnesium
b. silicon and aluminum
c. silicon and oxygen
d. oxygen and carbon

3. ______ is hot, melted material.
a. Magma **c.** Salt water
b. Quartz **d.** None of these

4. Graphite is a(n) ______ .
a. oxide **c.** silicate
b. carbonate **d.** none of these

5. ______ is a measure of how easily a mineral can be scratched.
a. Luster **c.** Cleavage
b. Hardness **d.** Fracture

6. The color of a powdered mineral on an unglazed porcelain tile is its ______ .
a. luster **c.** hardness
b. density **d.** streak

7. Quartz breaks with ______ .
a. cleavage **c.** luster
b. fracture **d.** all of these

8. ______ can cause cancer.
a. Aluminum **c.** Asbestos
b. Hematite **d.** Quartz

9. The largest group of rock-forming minerals is the ______ .
a. oxides **c.** silicates
b. halides **d.** sulfides

10. Halite is ______ .
a. cubic **c.** formed by evaporation
b. rock salt **d.** all of these

UNDERSTANDING CONCEPTS

Complete each sentence.

11. Halite forms ______ crystals.
12. ______ contain the two most abundant elements in Earth's crust.
13. The mineral ______ is harder than apatite and softer than quartz.
14. Diamonds and coal are both made of ______ .
15. ______ have a definite volume and shape.

THINK AND WRITE CRITICALLY

16. What's the difference between an ore and a gem?
17. Describe the dangers of asbestos fibers.
18. Explain why air is not a mineral.
19. Compare and contrast the properties of cleavage and fracture. List an example of a mineral that cleaves and one that fractures.
20. Why is asbestos removal a controversy?

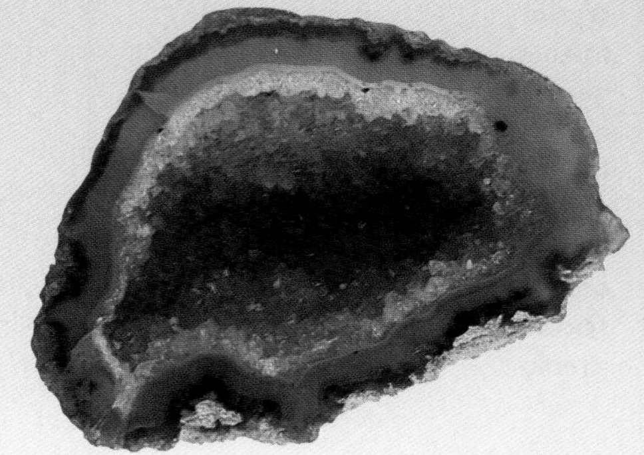

APPLY

21. Water is a nonliving substance formed by natural processes on Earth. It has a unique composition. Sometimes water is a mineral and other times it is not. Explain.

22. How many sides are there to a perfect salt crystal?

23. Suppose you let a sugar solution evaporate, leaving sugar crystals behind. Are these crystals minerals? Explain.

24. Will diamond leave a streak on a streak plate? Explain.

25. Explain how you would use Table 3-3 to determine the hardness of any mineral.

MORE SKILL BUILDERS

If you need help, refer to the Skill Handbook.

1. **Observing and Inferring:** Suppose you found a white, nonmetallic mineral that was harder than calcite. You identify the sample as quartz. What are your observations? What is your inference?
2. **Interpreting Data:** Suppose you were given these properties of a mineral: pink color; nonmetallic; softer than topaz and quartz; scratches apatite; harder than fluorite; has cleavage; and is scratched by a steel file. What is it?
3. **Outlining:** Make an outline of how at least seven physical properties can be used to identify unknown materials.
4. **Measuring in SI:** The volume of water in a graduated cylinder is 107.5 mL. A specimen of quartz, tied to a piece of string, is immersed into the water. The new water level reads 186 mL. What is the volume of the piece of quartz?
5. **Concept Mapping:** Make a network tree concept map showing the six nonsilicate mineral groups and examples from that group. Use the following words and phrases: *nonsilicate groups, carbonates, oxides, sulfides, sulfates, halides, native elements, corundum, galena, halite, azurite, gypsum, gold, hematite, pyrite, fluorite, malachite, barite, copper.*

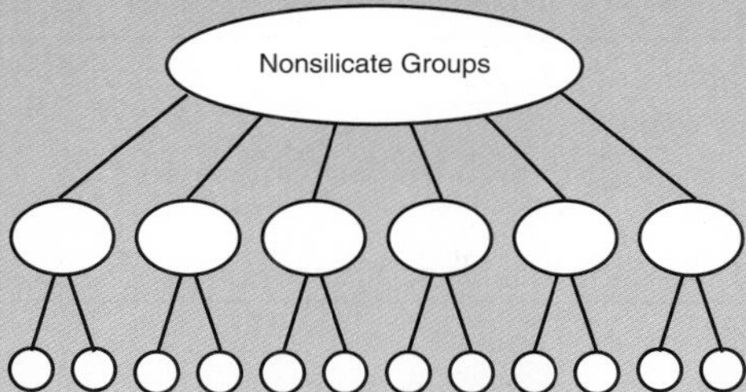

PROJECTS

1. Do research to find out about the six major crystal systems. Use cardboard to make models of each major crystal shape for each system.
2. Go to the library or bookstore to find books that explain how to grow crystals. Follow the instructions given to grow your own crystals.
3. Collect samples of objects that you think are minerals. Then use a mineral identification book to find out which specimens actually are minerals. Identify each mineral and list some of its uses.

APPLY

21. On Earth, water can exist as a solid, a liquid, and/or a gas. Water is a mineral only when it is a solid that has formed naturally.

22. There are six sides to each cubic crystal.

23. No, sugar, although it is a solid formed in nature with a definite composition and internal structure, is not a mineral because it is an organic compound.

24. No, a diamond is harder than a streak plate and will scratch the plate.

25. Using common objects and the minerals on the Mohs' Scale of hardness allows you to determine the relative hardness of any mineral.

MORE SKILL BUILDERS

1. Observing and Inferring: The observations include the color, luster, and hardness of the mineral. The inference is that the mineral is quartz.

2. Interpreting Data: feldspar

3. Outlining: Answers will vary but should include at least the boldfaced terms in Section 3-2.

4. Measuring in SI: 186 mL − 107.5 mL = 78.5 mL

5. Concept Mapping Students should use the chemical formulas for these minerals found in Appendices L and M in order to classify them with the proper group. They will also need to use Table 3-2. The following minerals' formulas are not in the Appendices: Azurite—$Cu_3(CO_3)_2(OH)_2$, Malachite—$Cu_2CO_3(OH_2)$, and Barite—$BaSO_4$. Answer at the bottom of this page.

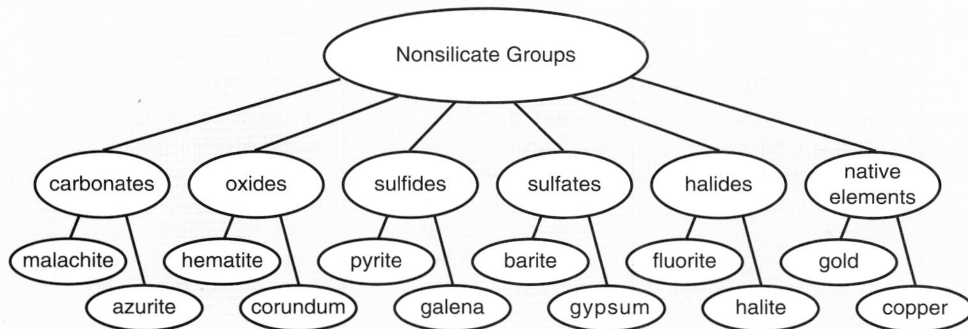

CHAPTER 4 Rocks

CHAPTER SECTION	OBJECTIVES	ACTIVITIES
4-1 The Rock Cycle (2 days)	1. **Differentiate** between a rock and a mineral. 2. **Describe** the rock cycle and the changes that a rock may undergo.	**Activity 4-1:** *Igneous Rocks,* p. 89
4-2 Igneous Rocks (1 day)	1. **Recognize** magma and lava as the materials that cool to form igneous rocks. 2. **Contrast** the formation of intrusive and extrusive igneous rocks. 3. **Contrast** granitic and basaltic igneous rocks.	
4-3 Metamorphic Rocks (2 days)	1. **Describe** conditions that cause metamorphic rocks to form. 2. **Classify** metamorphic rocks as foliated or nonfoliated.	**MINI-Lab:** *What do metamorphic rocks form from?* p. 97 **Activity 4-2:** *Sedimentary Rocks,* p. 99
4-4 Sedimentary Rocks (2 days)	1. **Explain** how sedimentary rocks form from sediments. 2. **Classify** sedimentary rocks as clastic, chemical, or organic in origin.	**MINI-Lab:** *What are rocks made of?* p. 101
4-5 Environmental Effects of Coal Mines Science & Society (1 day)	1. **Contrast** strip mines and underground coal mines. 2. **List** several environmental effects associated with coal mining.	
Chapter Review		

ACTIVITY MATERIALS

FIND OUT	ACTIVITIES		MINI-LABS	
Page 85 magnifying glass rocks brought in by students	**4-1 Igneous Rocks, p. 89** igneous rock specimens, A-F hand lens Table 4-1	**4-2 Sedimentary Rocks, p. 99** unknown sedimentary rock samples marking pen 5% HCL dropper goggles paper towels water	**What do metamorphic rocks form from? p. 97** samples of: gneiss, granite, marble, limestone, quartzite, sandstone, slate, and shale hand lens	**What are rocks made of? p. 101** mixtures of different sized and shaped sediments: sandgrains, pebbles, silt, clay-sized grains tweezers or dissecting probe

CHAPTER FEATURES	TEACHER RESOURCE PACKAGE	OTHER RESOURCES
Skill Builder: *Concept Mapping,* p. 88	**Ability Level Worksheets** ◆ ***Study Guide,*** p. 17 ● ***Reinforcement,*** p. 17 ▲ ***Enrichment,*** p. 17 **Activity Worksheet,** pp. 30-31 **Transparency Masters,** pp. 11-12	**Color Transparency 6,** Rock Cycle
Skill Builder: *Interpreting Scientific Illustrations,* p. 94	**Ability Level Worksheets** ◆ ***Study Guide,*** p. 18 ● ***Reinforcement,*** p. 18 ▲ ***Enrichment,*** p. 18 **Concept Mapping,** pp. 13-14	**Lab Manual:** *Gas Production in Magma,* pp. 31-32
Technology: *Solid As a Rock?* p. 96 **Skill Builder:** *Sequencing,* p. 98	**Ability Level Worksheets** ◆ ***Study Guide,*** p. 19 ● ***Reinforcement,*** p. 19 ▲ ***Enrichment,*** p. 19 **Activity Worksheet,** pp. 32-33 **MINI-Lab Worksheet,** p. 36	**Lab Manual:** *Metamorphic Processes,* pp. 33-34
Problem Solving: *A Geology Trip in the City,* p. 105 **Skill Builder:** *Interpreting Data,* p. 107	**Ability Level Worksheets** ◆ ***Study Guide,*** p. 20 ● ***Reinforcement,*** p. 20 ▲ ***Enrichment,*** p. 20 **Critical Thinking/Problem Solving,** p. 10 **Cross-Curricular Connections,** p. 8 **Technology,** pp. 7-8 **MINI-Lab Worksheet,** p. 37	**Lab Manual:** *Concretions,* pp. 35-36
You Decide! p. 110	**Ability Level Worksheets** ◆ ***Study Guide,*** p. 21 ● ***Reinforcement,*** p. 21 ▲ ***Enrichment,*** p. 21 **Science and Society,** p. 8	
Summary Key Science Words Understanding Vocabulary Checking Concepts Understanding Concepts Think & Write Critically Apply More Skill Builders Projects	**Chapter Review,** pp. 11-12 **Chapter Test,** pp. 24-27 **Unit Test,** pp. 28-29	**Chapter Review Software** **Test Bank**

◆ **Basic** ● **Average** ▲ **Advanced**

ADDITIONAL MATERIALS

SOFTWARE	AUDIOVISUAL	BOOKS/MAGAZINES
Rocks and Minerals Identification, Focus. *Rocks,* CDL. *Rocks,* Queue. *Earth and Environment Investigations: Rock Search,* Focus.	*Rocks That Originate Underground,* film, EBEC. *Igneous Rocks,* slide set, NESTA. *Sedimentary Rocks,* slide set, NESTA. *Limestone,* film, Indiana University. *Comparing Rocks,* film, EBEC. *Minerals and Rocks,* film, EBEC. *Earth Science: The Rock Cycle,* filmstrip/cassette, SVE. *Rocks and Minerals: The Hard Facts,* video, Focus.	Barker, Daniel. *Igneous Rocks.* Englewood Cliffs, NJ: Prentice-Hall, 1983. Ehlers, Ernest G. and Harvey Blatt. *Petrology: Igneous, Sedimentary, and Metamorphic.* NY: Freeman, W.H. and Company, 1982.

CHAPTER

4

ROCKS

THEME DEVELOPMENT: Rocks undergo constant changes through a cycle known as the rock cycle. The interaction of processes that cause the changes is the major theme of this chapter.

CHAPTER OVERVIEW

- **Section 4-1:** Rocks and the processes they undergo are described in this section.
- **Section 4-2**: This section explains how igneous rocks form and contrasts igneous rocks that form from magma with those that form from lava. The classification of igneous rocks based on composition is also described.
- **Section 4-3**: This section explains how metamorphic rocks form and how they are classified.
- **Section 4-4:** How sedimentary rocks form is the emphasis of this section. The processes of compaction and cementation are described. Students also learn that sedimentary rocks are classified according to composition and the processes that formed them.
- **Section 4-5: Science and Society:** This section describes the harmful effects coal mines have on the environment.

CHAPTER VOCABULARY

rock
rock cycle
igneous rocks
lava
intrusive
extrusive
basaltic
granitic
metamorphic rocks
foliated
nonfoliated
sedimentary rocks
sediments
compaction
cementation
strip mine

CHAPTER 4

Rocks

84

OPTIONS

For Your Gifted Students

Have students contact the United States Government Department of the Interior's Office of Surface Mining in Washington, DC, for information and written material on mining and reclamation on a state or national level. Field offices are located in the capital city of most states and may be able to provide speakers on the subject.

The Great Wall of China was constructed more than 2000 years ago. The wall is a collection of rocks, 6400 kilometers long. Today, we use rocks to construct our buildings, roads, and monuments. Minerals from rocks are even in the foods you eat. Rocks are all around you. Can you describe what rocks are made of?

FIND OUT!

Do this simple activity to find out what rocks are made of.

Collect three or four rocks from around your home. Look at each rock carefully. Use a magnifying glass so you can see each rock more clearly. What do you notice? Try drawing a picture of the details in each rock. Can you see different types of material within the same rock? Think of the terms used in Chapter 2. Would you classify rocks as mixtures? If so, what are they mixtures of?

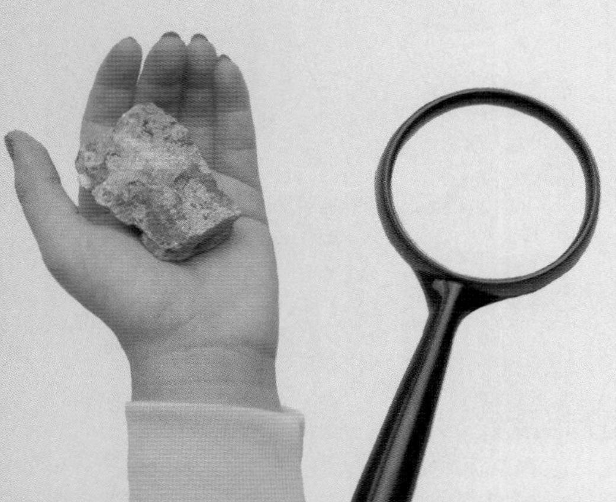

Gearing Up

Previewing the Chapter

Use this outline to help you focus on important ideas in this chapter.

Previewing Science Skills

- In the **Skill Builders,** you will make concept maps, interpret scientific illustrations, sequence events, and interpret data.
- In the **Activities,** you will classify, analyze, and draw conclusions.
- In the **MINI-Labs,** you will classify, observe, and infer.

What's next?

Now you can investigate what kinds of materials make up rocks. As you read this chapter, you will explore how rocks are formed and how they change from one form to another.

For Your Mainstreamed Students

Students can simulate the formation of a sedimentary rock by doing the following activity. Have students cut two cardboard milk cartons to a height of 10 cm each. Instruct them to punch several holes in the sides and bottom of one carton, then fill this carton one-third full of small, washed pebbles. Prepare a mixture of two parts white glue to one part water. Have students hold the perforated carton a few centimeters above the other carton and pour the mixture over the pebbles, collecting the liquid that runs through for reuse. Instruct students to pour the mixture several more times to cover all pebbles. Let cartons stand in a warm place for 24 hours. Have students strip away the carton and describe their "rocks."

INTRODUCING THE CHAPTER

Use the Find Out activity to introduce students to the compositions of different rocks. Inform students that they will be learning more about rocks as they read the chapter.

FIND OUT!

Preparation: Several days before you begin this chapter, have each student bring in three or four rocks from around his or her home.

Materials: one magnifying glass for each group of students, rocks brought in by students

Cooperative Learning: Using the Science Investigation strategy, have students work in groups of four. Individual student roles should include a reader, a materials handler, a recorder, and a reporter. All students within each group should observe the rocks using a magnifying glass.

Teaching Tips

- Not all students will remember to bring in rocks from home, so you might want to have 10-15 rocks available for this activity.
- Have students identify different minerals in each rock.
- Allow students time to discuss the size and shape of the components of each rock.
- Call on the reporters of each group to answer the in-text questions.

Answers: Rocks are classified as mixtures. They are mixtures of minerals.

Gearing Up

Have students study the Gearing Up feature to familiarize themselves with the chapter. Discuss the relationships of the topics in the outline.

What's Next?

Before beginning the first section, make sure students understand the connection between the Find Out activity and the topics to follow.

SECTION 4-1

PREPARATION

SECTION BACKGROUND

▶There is no set path that a rock undergoes to become another rock. A rock from any of the three groups of rocks can be changed into a rock belonging to another group or can evolve into a rock belonging to its original group.

▶Rocks are classified into three groups based on the processes that form them.

PREPLANNING

▶To prepare for Activity 4-1, obtain small igneous rock samples and hand lenses. Samples should be boxed and labeled.

▶If possible, obtain and display a large drawing of the rock cycle for students to refer to as you discuss this section.

1 MOTIVATE

▶**Demonstration:** Place large samples of basalt, granite, gneiss, slate, shale, sandstone, and limestone on a table in front of the class. Ask students to describe each sample. Have students determine whether or not the samples they brought from home for the Find Out activity are similar to the rocks on display.

Cooperative Learning: Using the Paired Partner strategy, ask students to compile a list of ten items they are familiar with that are made of rocks. Have partners compare lists with other groups.

PROGRAM RESOURCES

From the **Teacher Resource Package** use:

Transparency Masters, pages 11-12, Rock Cycle.

Use **Color Transparency** number 6, Rock Cycle.

4-1 The Rock Cycle

New Science Words

rock
rock cycle

Objectives

▶ Differentiate between a rock and a mineral.

▶ Describe the rock cycle and the changes that a rock may undergo.

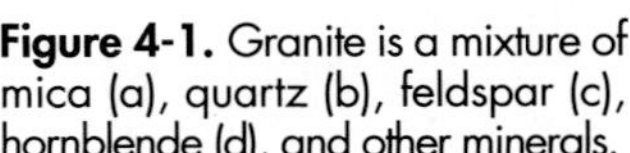

Figure 4-1. Granite is a mixture of mica (a), quartz (b), feldspar (c), hornblende (d), and other minerals.

What Is a Rock?

Imagine that you're on your way home from a friend's house when you notice an unusual rock in a driveway. You pick it up, wondering why it looks different from most of the other rocks in the driveway. Most of the other rocks are flat and dull, but this one is rounded and has shiny crystals in it. You decide to stick the interesting rock in your pocket and ask your earth science teacher about it tomorrow.

What exactly should you ask your teacher? You might begin by asking, "What is a rock?" and "Why are rocks so different from one another?"

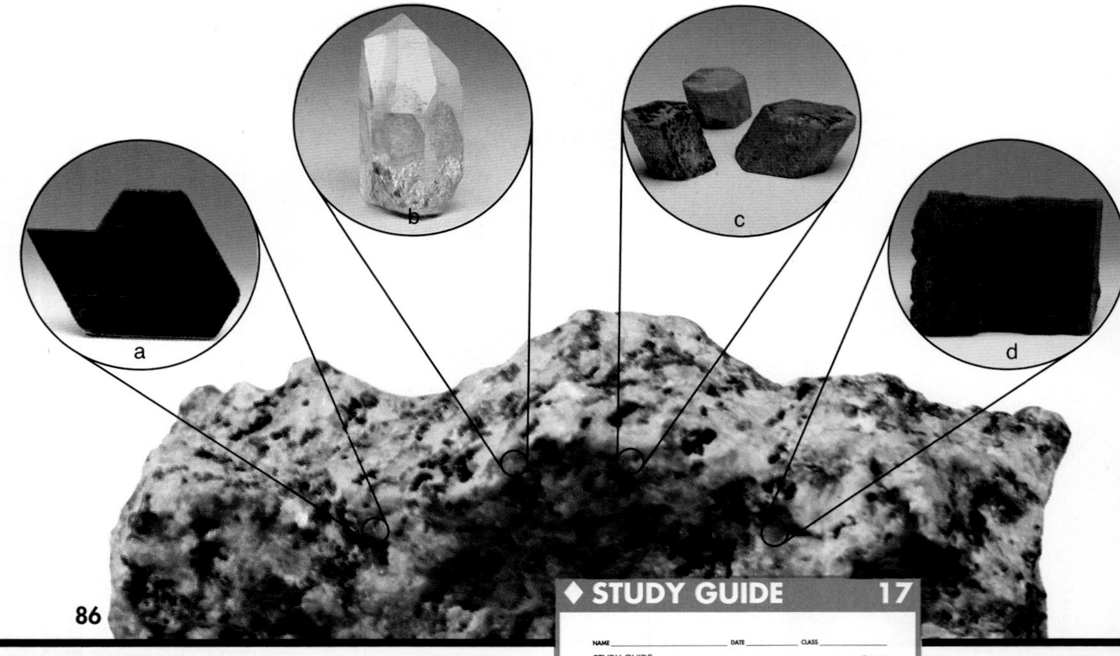

86

OPTIONS

Meeting Different Ability Levels

For Section 4-1, use the following **Teacher Resource Masters** depending upon individual students' needs.

◆ **Study Guide Master** for all students.

● **Reinforcement Master** for students of average and above average ability levels.

▲ **Enrichment Master** for above average students.

Additional Teacher Resource Package masters are listed in the OPTIONS box throughout the section. The additional masters are appropriate for all students.

◆ STUDY GUIDE 17

NAME ________ DATE ________ CLASS ________

STUDY GUIDE — Chapter 4

The Rock Cycle — Text Pages 86–88

Match the items in Column I with the terms in Column II. Write the letter of the correct term in the blank at the left.

Column I

b 1. A naturally occurring, nonliving solid, with a definite structure and composition

a 2. A mixture of minerals

e 3. Processes by which rocks form and change

c 4. A hard silicate mineral

d 5. An igneous rock made up of mica, feldspar, quartz, and hornblende

Column II

a. rock
b. mineral
c. quartz
d. granite
e. rock cycle

In the blank, write the term that correctly completes each sentence. Use the information in the textbook.

6. If the minerals in a sedimentary rock melt and then cool, they can form a(n) **igneous** rock.
7. Quartz is a common **mineral** found in rocks.
8. Sedimentary and igneous rocks can be changed into metamorphic rocks by **heat** and **pressure**.
9. If an igneous rock weathers and erodes into fragments, the fragments can form a(n) **sedimentary** rock.
10. Weathering and erosion are two of the **processes** that change rocks.

Write each word in the box under the correct heading.

weathering	igneous	melting	cooling
erosion	sedimentary	compaction	cementation
deposition	heating	metamorphic	

Processes in the rock cycle		Kinds of rocks
weathering	heating	sedimentary
deposition	compaction	igneous
melting	cooling	metamorphic
erosion	cementation	

17

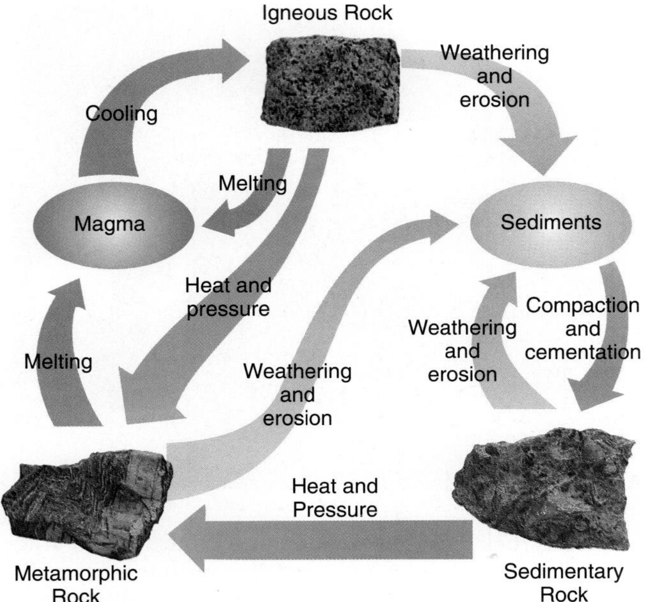

Figure 4-2. This model of the rock cycle shows how rocks are constantly changed from one form to another.

A **rock** is a mixture of minerals. You learned about the mineral quartz in the last chapter. You know that it's a common mineral found in rocks. Other common minerals include feldspar, hornblende, and mica. Look at Figure 4-1. It shows that all of these minerals mix together to form the rock granite. ❶ ❷

What is a rock?

But how do these minerals mix together? And once they've formed a rock, do they stay in that same rock forever? You can answer these questions by studying the rock cycle.

The Rock Cycle

Figure 4-2 is a model of the **rock cycle.** It shows how one rock changes into another. Notice that rocks are classified as igneous, metamorphic, or sedimentary. You will learn more about each of these groups of rocks in this chapter. ❸

Rocks are changed by processes such as weathering, erosion, compaction, cementation, melting, and cooling. For example, the minerals of a sedimentary rock can melt and later cool to form an igneous rock. The

TYING TO PREVIOUS KNOWLEDGE: Have students recall from Chapter 3 the physical properties used to identify minerals. Explain that rocks are grouped and named according to the processes that form them and the minerals they contain.

OBJECTIVES AND SCIENCE WORDS: Have students review the objectives and science words to become familiar with this section.

2 TEACH

Key Concepts are highlighted.

CONCEPT DEVELOPMENT

Cooperative Learning: Using the Numbered Heads Together strategy, have students answer the following questions. **If a geologist finds a sedimentary rock composed of pieces of igneous rock, what conclusion might he or she draw?** *Weathering has broken the igneous rock into pieces, which became cemented to form a sedimentary rock.* **Where do the different processes of the rock cycle occur?** *Melting occurs deep within Earth. Metamorphic changes can occur in the crust or deep within the mantle. Weathering and erosion occur at Earth's surface.*

CHECK FOR UNDERSTANDING

Use the Mini Quiz to check for understanding.

MINI QUIZ

Use the Mini Quiz to check students' recall of chapter content.

❶ **A mixture of one or more minerals is a (n) _____ .** *rock*
❷ **Granite is a mixture of which minerals?** *quartz, feldspar, hornblende, and mica*
❸ **The processes that a rock undergoes to change into another rock is the _____ .** *rock cycle*

● REINFORCEMENT 17

NAME ____ DATE ____ CLASS ____

REINFORCEMENT — Chapter 4

The Rock Cycle — Text Pages 86–88

Study the diagram of the rock cycle. Explain how minerals originally in magma could travel through the cycle and eventually end up in each of the three main classifications of rocks. Tell what must happen for each rock type to change into an other.

IGNEOUS ROCK · Cooling · Melting · Weathering and erosion · MAGMA · Heat and pressure · SEDIMENTS · Melting · Weathering and erosion · Weathering and erosion · Compaction and cementation · METAMORPHIC ROCK · Heat and pressure · SEDIMENTARY ROCK

Answers will vary but should include the following information. Magma cools and crystallizes to form igneous rock. Igneous rock erodes and is deposited as sediments, which are compacted and cemented to form sedimentary rock. Sedimentary rock can become metamorphic rock from increases in heat and pressure. Metamorphic rock can melt into magma. Additional cycles include: Igneous rock can be affected by increases in heat and pressure and become metamorphic rock. Metamorphic rock can erode and be deposited as sediments which become sedimentary rock. Sedimentary rock can also erode and be deposited as sediments which form sedimentary rock.

17

▲ ENRICHMENT 17

NAME ____ DATE ____ CLASS ____

ENRICHMENT — Chapter 4

The Rock Cycle — Text Pages 86–88

ANALYZING ROCKS

Materials
- paper and pencil
- goggles
- metric ruler
- rock hammer
- streak plate
- rock samples
- hand lens
- glass slide
- steel file
- towel

Procedure
1. On a separate piece of paper, copy the table headings shown in "Data and Observations." Make your table 10 rows long to provide space for recording information about the 10 rock samples.
2. Examine the rock samples. Observe characteristics such as minerals present, the size and shape of mineral grains, and the arrangement of grains. Record your observations in the table you made. An example of what you might observe has been done for you in "Data and Observations."
3. Group all the rocks that have a common characteristic. Make at least three categories. In the last column of the table, record the common characteristics on which you based your groupings.
4. Compare your system of classification with those devised by your classmates.
5. Crush bits of the rocks. **CAUTION:** *Wrap rock samples in a towel before hitting them with the hammer. Always wear goggles when using a rock hammer.*
6. Examine the crushed samples with the hand lens. Record any observable characteristics not seen in the larger specimens.

Data and Observations

Sample	Minerals present	Size/Shape of minerals	Arrangement of grains	Other information	Common characteristic
1	Quartz Feldspar Diotite	0.5 cm, rectangular			grain size similar to samples 3 and 7

Analyze and Conclude
1. Was there any characteristic common to all the rock samples? **Students may say that all the rocks were hard, or that they all contained minerals.**
2. What feature was most useful in grouping the rocks? **texture**
3. What feature was least helpful in grouping the rocks? **color or size**
4. Was there a characteristic observed in the crushed rocks that aided or changed your system of grouping? Explain. **mineral composition**
5. Was your system of grouping different from those of your classmates? Why might different classification systems be devised? **Answers will vary. Some people observe different characteristics than others. A special-purpose system might be devised, such as one in which texture is more important than mineral in a composition.**

17

RETEACH

Demonstration: Demonstrate that rocks are mixtures of minerals by showing a sample of granite to the students. Have volunteers point out the various minerals. Wearing safety goggles, crush the granite. Have students observe the small pieces of rock.

EXTENSION

For students who have mastered this section, use the **Reinforcement** and **Enrichment** masters or other OPTIONS provided.

CROSS CURRICULUM

▶ **Vocational-Technical:** Have students use the processes listed on Figure 4-2 to describe the process of making bricks from clay. They might want to interview a brick layer for background information.

3 CLOSE

▶ Ask questions 1-2 and the **Apply** Question in the Section Review.

▶ Call on one student to pick a group of rocks. Call on another to explain which processes might act on rocks of that group and cause them to change into other rocks. Call on a third student to explain what might happen to these new rocks. Continue with this exercise until all students understand that Earth's rocks undergo continuous changes via the rock cycle.

SECTION REVIEW ANSWERS

1. one or more minerals

2. The rock cycle shows how rocks continually change to become other rocks due to certain Earth processes.

3. Apply: Magma is melted material. Sediments are broken rock fragments that have been eroded (transported). Sedimentary rock is rock formed from fragments of other rocks.

Figure 4-3. By studying rocks and the changes they undergo, geologists have helped explain how our world formed and how it is changing.

What are the three major classifications of rocks?

igneous rock may then weather and erode and the fragments from it might form another sedimentary rock. Heat and pressure can change both sedimentary and igneous rocks into metamorphic rocks.

In Chapters 5 and 6, you will explore weathering, erosion, deposition, and other processes involved in the rock cycle. And you already know something about minerals. The rock cycle shows how all of these things interact to form and change the rocks around you. Let's now investigate how igneous, metamorphic, and sedimentary rocks fit into the rock cycle.

SECTION REVIEW

1. What materials mix together to form a rock?
2. What is the rock cycle?
3. **Apply:** Look at the model of the rock cycle. How would you define *magma* based on Figure 4-2? How would you define *sediments* and *sedimentary rock*?

Skill Builder

Concept Mapping

Make a concept map that explains how igneous rocks can become sedimentary, then metamorphic, and finally other igneous rocks. If you need help, refer to Concept Mapping in the **Skill Handbook** on pages 688 and 689.

Skill Builder

One possible solution is shown:

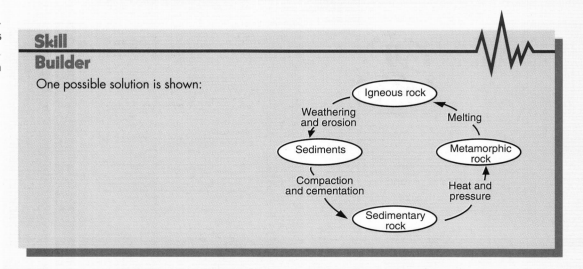

Igneous rock → Weathering and erosion → Sediments → Compaction and cementation → Sedimentary rock → Heat and pressure → Metamorphic rock → Melting → Igneous rock

ACTIVITY 4-1
Igneous Rocks

Problem: *How are igneous rocks classified?*

Materials

- igneous rock specimens, A-F
- hand lens
- Table 4-1

Procedure

1. Examine each rock specimen with a hand lens. Determine the texture of each rock sample. If the grains or crystals are large and easily seen, the texture is coarse. If the grains are so small that they are not easily distinguished, the texture is described as fine. Separate the rocks into groups based on the texture.
2. Answer Analyze 1 and 2.
3. Determine the color of each rock. Is the rock light-colored, dark-colored, or intermediate? Regroup your samples based on color.
4. Answer Analyze 3 and 4.
5. Examine the coarse-grained rocks to determine the minerals present.
6. Refer to Table 4-1 and give each sample a name according to its composition and grain size.

Analyze

1. What's the difference between the size of the grains in intrusive and extrusive igneous rocks?
2. If grain sizes within one sample are noticeably different, what type of rock is it?
3. What minerals must be responsible for the color of sample B?
4. Name at least two other igneous rocks that owe their colors to the presence of these minerals.

Conclude and Apply

5. Why do igneous rocks of the same composition sometimes have different sizes of grains?
6. What two characteristics determine the identity of an igneous rock?
7. How does obsidian differ from most other igneous rocks?

Data and Observations

Sample Data

Rock Sample	Texture	Color	Minerals present	Rock name
A	glassy	black	quartz, feldspar	obsidian
B	fine	black	feldspar, pyroxene	basalt
C	coarse	varies	quartz, feldspar, micas, hornblende	granite
D	glassy, porous	usually gray	quartz, feldspar, micas, hornblende	pumice
E	fine	gray, yellow, red	quartz, feldspar, micas, hornblende	rhyolite
F	coarse	dark gray, greenish black	feldspar, pyroxene, hornblende, olivine	gabbro

ACTIVITY 4-1
50 minutes

OBJECTIVE: Classify igneous rocks by texture and composition.

PROCESS SKILLS applied in this activity:
►**Observing** in Procedure Steps 1, 3, and 5.
►**Separating** and **Controlling Variables** in Procedure Steps 1, 3, and 5.
►**Classifying** in Procedure Step 6.
►**Interpreting Data** in Analyze Questions 1 and 3.
►**Communicating** in Conclude and Apply Questions 6 and 7.

COOPERATIVE LEARNING Use the Science Investigation strategy for this activity.

TEACHING THE ACTIVITY

►Rock samples should be identified either by a letter taped onto the rock or by being placed in a box. Label them as follows: A—obsidian; B—basalt; C—granite or diorite; D—pumice; E—rhyolite or andesite; F—gabbro or peridotite.

►Refer students to Appendix M on pages 678 and 679 for assistance with this activity.

Troubleshooting: Students may have difficulty describing the texture of sample D since it appears pervious and filled with small pores. The term applied to this type of texture is vesicular. Both the glassy-textured obsidian and pumice are described in Section 4-2.

ANSWERS TO QUESTIONS

1. The grains of intrusive igneous rocks are generally coarse and easily seen while the grains of extrusive igneous rocks are generally so small that they are often indistinguishable without the aid of a magnifying glass or microscope.
2. a porphyry
3. olivine, pyroxene, and biotite
4. gabbro, peridotite, and basalt
5. Different grain sizes indicate different rates of cooling.
6. texture and composition
7. Obsidian cools so quickly that it has a glassy texture. It doesn't contain mineral crystals.

PROGRAM RESOURCES

From the **Teacher Resource Package** use:
Activity Worksheets, pages 30-31, Activity 4-1: Igneous Rocks.

SECTION 4-2

PREPARATION

SECTION BACKGROUND

▶ The size and arrangement of mineral grains are used to determine igneous rock textures. Rocks with phaneritic textures are coarse-grained and individual grains can be seen with the unaided eye. Rocks with aphanitic textures are fine-grained and individual minerals are not visible with the unaided eye. Rocks with porphyritic textures contain large minerals surrounded by smaller minerals. In rocks with glassy textures, no minerals are visible.

▶ Magma whose composition lies between basaltic magma and granitic magma is andesitic magma. The igneous rocks diorite and andesite are andesitic.

▶ As magma cools, different minerals will crystallize at different temperatures. This relationship is known as Bowen's reaction series.

PREPLANNING

▶ Obtain small samples of various intrusive and extrusive rocks and the common minerals found in most igneous rocks. Samples should be boxed and labeled.

1 MOTIVATE

Cooperative Learning: Using the Numbered Heads Together strategy, have students explain why igneous rocks are considered the "parents" of all rocks. Students should conclude that igneous rocks were the first to form as Earth cooled early in its history billions of years ago.

▶ Obtain samples of obsidian, pumice, granite, scoria, basalt, and gabbro. Challenge students to divide the rocks into two groups based on similarities and differences. Then have students form two new rock groups. Discuss how rocks can be grouped by color and texture or grain size. Help students conclude that rocks can be grouped in different ways.

4-2 Igneous Rocks

New Science Words

igneous rocks
lava
intrusive
extrusive
basaltic
granitic

Objectives

- ▶ Recognize magma and lava as the materials that cool to form igneous rocks.
- ▶ Contrast the formation of intrusive and extrusive igneous rocks.
- ▶ Contrast granitic and basaltic igneous rocks.

Origin of Igneous Rocks

In December of 1989, Mount Redoubt in Alaska began to erupt. Perhaps you've heard of other recent volcanic eruptions. When most volcanoes erupt, they eject a thick, gooey flow of molten material. This material is similar to fudge candy before it has cooled. You know that if you allow the fudge to cool, it becomes hard and you have to cut it with a knife. 1 When molten material from a volcano or from deep inside Earth cools, it forms **igneous rocks.** But why do volcanoes erupt and where does the molten material come from?

Figure 4-4. Intrusive rocks such as gabbro (a) and diorite (b) form when magma cools slowly.

Intrusive igneous rocks

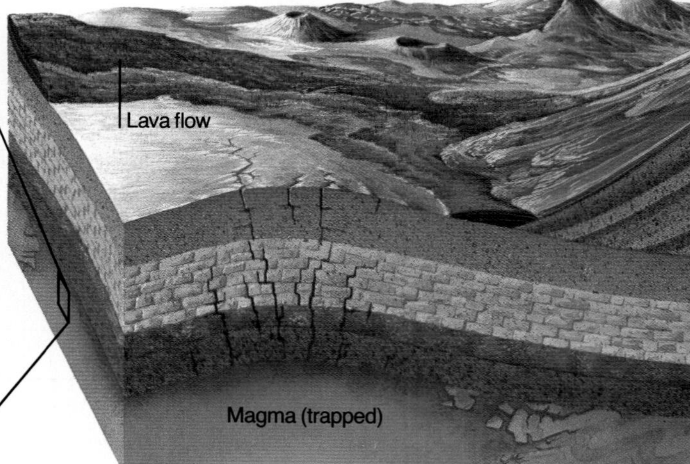

OPTIONS

Meeting Different Ability Levels

For Section 4-2, use the following **Teacher Resource Masters** depending upon individual students' needs.

◆ **Study Guide Master** for all students.

● **Reinforcement Master** for students of average and above average ability levels.

▲ **Enrichment Master** for above average students.

Additional Teacher Resource Package masters are listed in the OPTIONS box throughout the section. The additional masters are appropriate for all students.

◆ STUDY GUIDE 18

NAME ______ DATE ______ CLASS ______

STUDY GUIDE Chapter 4

Igneous Rocks Text Pages 90–94

Use the words in the box to fill in the blanks.

200	iron	slow	lava
fine	1400	lighter	dense
magma	large	silicon	abundant
formation	surface	igneous	granitic
basaltic	radioactive	crystals	pressure
intrusive	extrusive	minerals	magnification

Rocks formed from molten Earth materials are **igneous** rocks. There are two kinds of molten materials: magma and **lava**. Most **magma** originates 60 to **200** km below Earth's surface. Temperatures reach about **1400** °C at these depths. **Pressure** and heat caused by overlying rocks and **radioactive** elements produce magma. When magma cools below Earth's surface, it forms **large**-grained, **intrusive** igneous rocks. The **crystals** of these common rocks grow large because of the **slow** rate of cooling. When magma moves to Earth's **surface**, it is called lava. When lava cools on Earth's surface, it forms **fine**-grained, **extrusive** igneous rocks. Minerals of extrusive rocks are so small that **magnification** is needed for identification. Igneous rocks can be classified by their **formation**. They can also be classified by the types of **minerals** in them. **Basaltic** igneous rocks are dark-colored, heavy, and **dense**. They contain **iron** and magnesium. **Granitic** igneous rocks are **lighter**-colored and less dense. They contain a lot of oxygen and **silicon**. Igneous rocks are the most **abundant** on Earth.

18

Temperatures reach about 1400°C at depths ranging from 60 to 200 km below Earth's surface. The rocks at this depth are under great pressure from overlying rocks. Radioactive elements in the rocks generate thermal energy, heating the rocks. In certain locations on Earth, the temperature and pressure are just right to melt the minerals and form magma.

The magma is less dense than the surrounding solid rock, so it tends to rise toward Earth's surface. Magma that eventually reaches Earth's surface flows from volcanoes as **lava.**

Compare and contrast lava and magma.

Magma that's trapped below Earth's surface is insulated by the rocks surrounding it. This holds in the heat and causes the magma to cool very slowly. Remember, magma is made up of atoms of melted minerals. When it cools, these atoms rearrange themselves into new mineral crystals. If the magma cools slowly, the atoms have time to arrange into large crystals. These crystals are called mineral grains.

Figure 4-5. Extrusive rocks such as rhyolite (a) and andesite (b) form from fast-cooling lava.

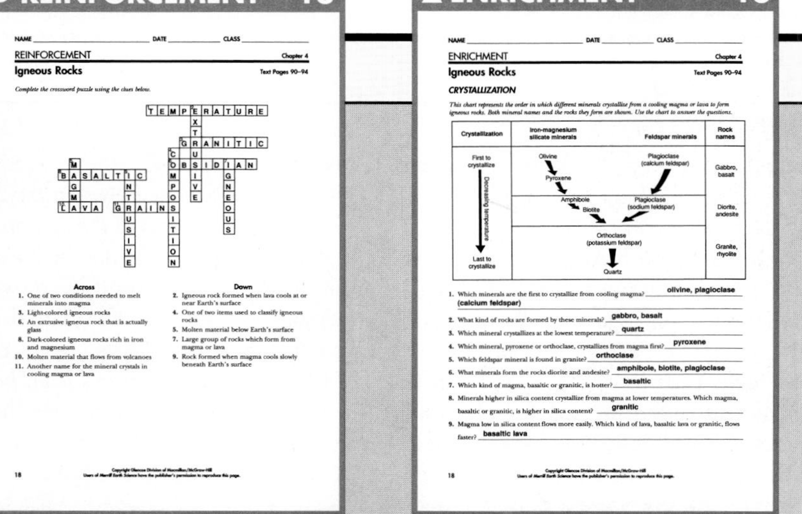

● REINFORCEMENT 18

NAME ____ DATE ____ CLASS ____

REINFORCEMENT — Chapter 4

Igneous Rocks — Text Pages 90–94

Complete the crossword puzzle using the clues below.

Across

1. One of two conditions needed to melt minerals into magma — TEMPERATURE
3. Light-colored igneous rocks — GRANITIC
6. An extrusive igneous rock that is actually glass — OBSIDIAN
8. Dark-colored igneous rocks rich in iron and magnesium — BASALTIC
10. Molten material that flows from volcanoes — LAVA
11. Another name for the mineral crystals in cooling magma or lava — GRAINS

Down

2. Igneous rock formed when lava cools at or near Earth's surface — EXTRUSIVE
4. One of two items used to classify igneous rocks — COMPOSITION
5. Molten material below Earth's surface — MAGMA
7. Large group of rocks which form from magma or lava — IGNEOUS
9. Rock formed when magma cools slowly beneath Earth's surface — INTRUSIVE

18

▲ ENRICHMENT 18

NAME ____ DATE ____ CLASS ____

ENRICHMENT — Chapter 4

Igneous Rocks — Text Pages 90–94

CRYSTALLIZATION

This chart represents the order in which different minerals crystallize from a cooling magma or lava to form igneous rocks. Both mineral names and the rocks they form are shown. Use the chart to answer the questions.

Crystallization	Iron-magnesium silicate minerals	Feldspar minerals	Rock names
First to crystallize	Olivine → Pyroxene	Plagioclase (calcium feldspar)	Gabbro, basalt
↓ Decreasing temperature	Amphibole → Biotite	Plagioclase (sodium feldspar)	Diorite, andesite
Last to crystallize	Orthoclase (potassium feldspar) → Quartz		Granite, rhyolite

1. Which minerals are the first to crystallize from cooling magma? olivine, plagioclase (calcium feldspar)
2. What kind of rocks are formed by these minerals? gabbro, basalt
3. Which mineral crystallizes at the lowest temperature? quartz
4. Which mineral, pyroxene or orthoclase, crystallizes from magma first? pyroxene
5. Which feldspar mineral is found in granite? orthoclase
6. What minerals form the rocks diorite and andesite? amphibole, biotite, plagioclase
7. Which kind of magma, basaltic or granitic, is hotter? basaltic
8. Minerals higher in silica content crystallize from magma at lower temperatures. Which magma, basaltic or granitic, is higher in silica content? granitic
9. Magma low in silica content flows more easily. Which kind of lava, basaltic lava or granitic, flows faster? basaltic lava

18

CROSS CURRICULUM

▶**Language Arts:** Have students use dictionaries to compare the origins of the words *intrusive* and *extrusive* with the origins of *interior, inside, exterior,* and *exit.*

TYING TO PREVIOUS KNOWLEDGE: Have students recall from Chapter 3 that one way minerals form is from the cooling of hot melted material. Rocks formed in this way are called igneous rocks.

OBJECTIVES AND SCIENCE WORDS: Have students review the objectives and science words to become familiar with this section.

2 TEACH

Key Concepts are highlighted.

CONCEPT DEVELOPMENT

▶Show students a piece of granite. Ask whether they think granite formed from magma or lava. Most students will infer that because of the size of the mineral grains, granite is an intrusive rock that formed from magma.

▶While displaying large samples of granite and basalt, ask the following questions. **Which of these two rocks contains large mineral grains?** *granite* **Based on the size of the mineral grains in the basalt, did it form deep inside Earth or near Earth's surface?** *near Earth's surface* **Would you classify basalt as an intrusive or extrusive rock?** *extrusive* **Based on color, what can you say about granitic and basaltic rocks in general?** *Granitic rocks are light in color; basaltic rocks are dark in color.*

CONCEPT DEVELOPMENT

▶Help students comprehend the relative rates of cooling of intrusive and extrusive molten material. Lava may cool almost instantly, especially if it comes into contact with cool ocean water. Magma deep in Earth's crust may take millions of years to solidify.

▶Show students a rock with a porphyritic texture. Such rocks have a groundmass of relatively small crystals in which large crystals are embedded. Ask them to hypothesize how such a rock might form. Since minerals within a body of magma don't all crystallize at the same time (or temperature), some mineral crystals become fairly large before others even begin to form. If the magma is suddenly erupted to the surface where it rapidly cools, other small crystals will solidify. The result is a rock of porphyritic texture.

a

b

c

Figure 4-6. Pumice (a), Obsidian (b), and Scoria (c)

Did You Know?

Pumice will float in water. Its density is less than water because of the gases trapped in its many holes, or vesicles.

Figure 4-7. Processes bring magma to Earth's surface where it cools to form extrusive igneous rocks.

Rock forms as these mineral grains grow together. ❷ Rocks that form below Earth's surface are **intrusive** igneous rocks. Generally, intrusive igneous rocks have large mineral grains. Look at Figure 4-4. It shows coarse-grained, intrusive igneous rocks. Intrusive rocks are found at Earth's surface when the kilometers of rock and soil that once covered them have been removed, or when forces in Earth have pushed them up. You will be investigating these forces in later chapters.

Extrusive igneous rocks are formed when lava cools on Earth's surface. When lava flows on Earth's surface, it is exposed to air and moisture. Lava cools quickly under these conditions. The quick rate of cooling keeps large mineral grains from growing. The atoms don't have time to arrange into large crystals. Extrusive igneous rocks have a fine-grained texture. Often, the individual grains are too small to be seen without a magnifying glass. Figure 4-5 shows some extrusive igneous rocks.

OPTIONS

INQUIRY QUESTIONS

▶**Why does lava cool more quickly than magma?** *The lava is exposed to cooler temperatures than the magma.*

▶**Why are extrusive igneous rocks fine-grained?** *The rapid cooling of the lava does not allow time for atoms to form large mineral grains.*

▶**Igneous rocks such as andesite and diorite contain minerals found in both basaltic and granitic rocks. What does this tell you about the melted material from which the andesite and diorite formed?** *The composition of the melted material lies between the basaltic end and the granitic end of the spectrum.*

▶**Pumice floats on water because of its low density, which is caused by gases that were trapped in the lava as it cooled. Scoria also has this type of texture, but scoria doesn't float. Why?** *Scoria forms from basaltic lava, which contains heavier atoms than the lava from which pumice forms. Thus, the density of scoria is greater than that of water.*

Table 4-1

COMMON IGNEOUS ROCKS		
Type of Magma or Lava	Intrusive	Extrusive
Basaltic	Gabbro	Basalt
		Scoria
Andesitic	Diorite	Andesite
Granitic	Granite	Rhyolite
		Pumice
		Obsidian

Figure 4-6 shows pumice, obsidian, and scoria. These objects cooled so quickly that no mineral grains formed at all. The atoms in these objects are not arranged into neat crystal patterns. Obsidian, scoria, and pumice are actually glass, and not a mixture of minerals. However, they are classified as extrusive igneous rocks.

In the case of pumice and scoria, air and other gases are trapped in the gooey molten material as it cools. Many of these gases eventually escape, but holes are left behind where the rock formed around the pockets of gas.

Classification of Igneous Rocks

You've learned to classify igneous rocks as either intrusive or extrusive depending on where they formed. A way to further classify these rocks is by the types of minerals in them. An igneous rock can be either basaltic, granitic, or andesitic.

Basaltic igneous rocks are dense, heavy, dark-colored rocks that form from basaltic magma or lava. Basaltic magma and lava are rich in iron and magnesium. These elements make the molten materials dense and dark colored. Basaltic lava flows from the volcanoes in Hawaii.

Granitic igneous rocks are light-colored rocks of a lower density than basaltic rocks. Granitic magma and lava are thick and stiff and contain a lot of silicon and oxygen. Granitic magma can build up a great deal of pressure, which is released during violent volcanic eruptions. 3

Andesitic rocks have mineral compositions between those of granitic and basaltic rocks. Many volcanoes in the Pacific Ocean are andesitic.

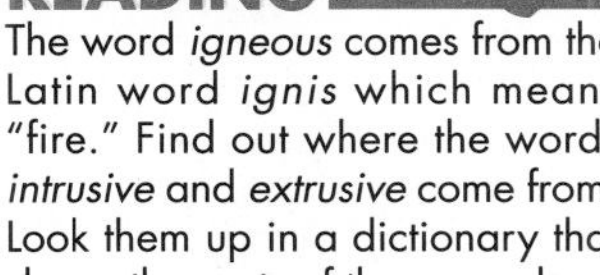

The word *igneous* comes from the Latin word *ignis* which means "fire." Find out where the words *intrusive* and *extrusive* come from. Look them up in a dictionary that shows the roots of these words.

ENRICHMENT

▶Have students research and write a report on the uses of granite, scoria, and pumice.

▶Have students research Bowen's reaction series, which illustrates that different minerals form at different temperatures. Have a volunteer make a poster of the series and explain it to the class.

PROGRAM RESOURCES

From the **Teacher Resource Package** use:
Concept Mapping, pages 13-14.
Use **Laboratory Manual,** page 31, Gas Production in Magma.

TEACHER F.Y.I.

▶Some igneous rocks are formed when particles ejected by volcanic eruptions become consolidated. Rocks with this type of texture are called pyroclastic rocks. Volcanic tuff is an igneous rock with pyroclastic texture.

Science and READING

If necessary, review the meaning of the term *root word.*

MINI QUIZ

Use the Mini Quiz to check students' recall of chapter content.

1. **When melted material from a volcano or deep inside Earth cools and hardens, it forms ____ .** *igneous rocks*
2. **____ igneous rocks form deep inside Earth and contain large mineral grains.** *Intrusive*
3. **Light-colored igneous rocks are classified as ____ .** *granitic rocks*

CHECK FOR UNDERSTANDING

Pose the following questions to students. **If you had samples of granite and gabbro that were exactly the same size, which of the two would feel heavier to you?** *gabbro* **Why?** *Gabbro is rich in iron and magnesium minerals. The iron and magnesium have more mass than most of the elements found in granitic magmas.*

RETEACH

Cooperative Learning: Using the Paired Partner strategy, have students compare the masses of similarly sized samples of granitic and basaltic rocks. While one student closes his or her eyes, have the second student place the appropriate rocks in the first student's hands. Encourage students to hypothesize which rocks are basaltic and which are granitic based on the heft of the rock.

EXTENSION

For students who have mastered this section, use the **Reinforcement** and **Enrichment** masters or other OPTIONS provided.

TEACHER F.Y.I.

▶Intrusive igneous rocks, the most common of all rocks, make up approximately 95 percent of Earth's crust to a depth of 10 km.

REVEALING MISCONCEPTIONS

▶Students may think that sedimentary rocks are the most common kind of rocks that make up Earth's crust because many of the rocks they have observed were probably sedimentary. Explain that igneous rocks make up about 95 percent of Earth's crust, but they are covered by sediment and sedimentary rocks in most places.

3 CLOSE

▶Ask questions 1-3 and the **Apply** Question in the Section Review.

▶Invite a local rock collector to share his or her collection with the class and to explain how students might begin their own collections.

▶Have students write a paragraph or two describing the general characteristics of intrusive and extrusive rocks.

SECTION REVIEW ANSWERS

1. Igneous rocks form when magma or lava cools and hardens.

2. basaltic

3. Intrusive rocks contain large mineral grains and are said to be coarse-grained. Extrusive rocks are made of small grains and thus are fine-grained.

4. Apply: Granite and rhyolite are both igneous rocks composed of the same minerals. Both are classified as light-colored, granitic rocks. They differ in that granite has larger mineral grains than rhyolite because it forms deep underground.

Figure 4-8. Basalt is the most common extrusive rock. Sediments from weathered and eroded basalt form the black-sand beaches of the Hawaiian Islands.

The classification of an igneous rock tells you quite a bit about its formation and composition. Granite, for example, is an intrusive, granitic igneous rock. This means that it formed deep in Earth, where cooling was very slow and large mineral grains had a chance to grow. The rock has a high concentration of silicon and oxygen because it formed from granitic magma.

Igneous rocks are the most abundant type of rock on Earth. They've been classified to make them easier to study. By studying all rocks, geologists and other scientists have been able to hypothesize how Earth formed.

SECTION REVIEW

1. How do igneous rocks form?
2. Which type of magma and lava form igneous rocks that are dark-colored and dense?
3. How do intrusive and extrusive igneous rocks differ?
4. **Apply:** How are granite and rhyolite similar? How are they different?

Skill Builder

Interpreting Scientific Illustrations

Suppose you are given a photograph of two igneous rocks. You are told one is an intrusive rock and one is extrusive. By looking only at the photographs, how could you know which is which? If you need help, refer to Interpreting Scientific Illustrations in the **Skill Handbook** on page 693.

Skill Builder

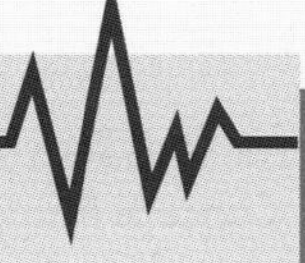

Texture is used to differentiate igneous rocks. Intrusive rocks are made of relatively large mineral grains, whereas extrusive rocks are fine-grained.

Metamorphic Rocks 4-3

Objectives

- ▶ Describe conditions that cause metamorphic rocks to form.
- ▶ Classify metamorphic rocks as foliated or nonfoliated.

New Science Words

metamorphic rocks
foliated
nonfoliated

Origin of Metamorphic Rocks

You wake up, go into the kitchen, and pack a lunch for school. You place a sandwich and a cream-filled cake in the bag. As you leave for school, you decide to throw in an apple. At lunch-time, you open your lunch bag and notice things have changed. Your cream-filled cake doesn't look too good anymore. The apple was resting on your cake all morning. The heat in your locker and the pressure from the apple have changed the form of your lunch. Rocks can also be affected by temperature changes and pressure.

Rocks that have changed due to temperature and pressure increases are **metamorphic rocks.** Metamorphic rocks can be formed from changes in igneous, sedimentary, or other metamorphic rocks. What occurs in Earth to change these rocks? 1

Figure 4-9. The mineral grains in granite (a) are flattened and aligned when pressure is applied to them. Gneiss (b) is formed.

OPTIONS

INQUIRY QUESTIONS

Ask these questions after students have read pages 95, 96, and 97.

▶ **What causes the heat and pressure that changes rocks into metamorphic rocks?** *Pressure is due to overlying rocks. Heat is generated by radioactive elements.*

▶ **What type of changes do rocks undergo as they change into metamorphic rocks?** *Mineral grains may align into bands. Minerals may also change size and shape. New minerals can also form.*

PROGRAM RESOURCES

From the **Teacher Resource Package** use:
Activity Worksheets, page 5, Flex Your Brain.
Activity Worksheets, page 36, Mini-Lab: What do metamorphic rocks form from?
Use **Laboratory Manual,** page 33, Metamorphic Processes.

SECTION 4-3

PREPARATION

SECTION BACKGROUND

▶ There are several types of metamorphism. Metamorphism that occurs during mountain building is very widespread, and massive rock bodies are subjected to extreme temperatures and pressures. Metamorphic changes can also occur in rocks that are in contact with magma bodies. Burial metamorphism occurs when rocks are changed because of the mass of overlying rocks.

▶ Generally, the compositions of metamorphic rocks are very similar to the compositions of the rocks from which they formed. New minerals form only when pressures and temperatures are extreme.

PREPLANNING

▶ To prepare for the Mini-Lab and Activity 4-2, obtain boxed sets of minerals and rocks. The common rock-forming minerals and samples from each of the three types of rocks should be included. The samples should be labeled.

1 MOTIVATE

▶ **Demonstration:** Use a toaster set on medium to demonstrate how metamorphic changes can be caused by heat generated from nearby magma bodies. Have a volunteer slice the toast and compare the color and texture of the outer surface of bread with the untoasted center.

TYING TO PREVIOUS KNOWLEDGE: Have students recall from Chapter 3 the physical properties of quartz and calcite. Show students pieces of pink quartzite and pink marble. Have students test the physical properties of quartz and calcite to determine which specimen is quartzite and which is marble.

TECHNOLOGY

▶ Inform students that Granitech is available as a flexible veneer that can be heated and bent, making it a very versatile building material.

▶ For more information, see "Taken for Granite," *Popular Science*, Aug. 1990, p. 44.

Think Critically: Granitech is made from crushed granite that is glued together. The mineral grains aren't interconnected in this human-made material.

OBJECTIVES AND SCIENCE WORDS: Have students review the objectives and science words to become familiar with this section.

2 TEACH

Key Concepts are highlighted.

CONCEPT DEVELOPMENT

▶ Pose the following questions to students after they have read pages 95 and 96. **An increase in temperature and pressure can cause rocks to become metamorphic rocks. What happens if the temperatures are high enough to cause rocks to melt?** *Metamorphic rocks will not form; rather, when the melted material cools, igneous rocks will form.* **Why does the metamorphic rock gneiss resemble the igneous rock granite?** *Both rocks are composed of the same minerals. High temperatures and pressures can change granite into gneiss.*

CROSS CURRICULUM

▶ **Economics:** Have students find out if their state quarries metamorphic rocks. If so, have students find out for what the rocks are used. If there are no quarries in your state, have students research some of the larger quarries in the United States.

TECHNOLOGY

Solid As a Rock?

Rocks are used as building materials because of their durability and appearance. Large slabs of rock, however, are expensive and difficult to work with.

A company in Iowa has made a material that looks like granite, wears like granite, and in fact, is about 90 percent granite. Granitech is a humanmade material made of crushed granite that's glued together. This material weighs less than natural granite and ranges in thickness from less than 0.5 cm to almost 1 cm. Granitech can be used on countertops, as floors, to make furniture, and to cover walls.

Think Critically: Granite is made of interlocking mineral crystals that have grown together. How does Granitech differ from this?

Rocks beneath Earth's surface are under great pressure from overlying rock layers. They also experience heat generated by the radioactive elements in them. If the heat and pressure are great enough, the rocks melt and magma forms. But what happens if the heat and pressure are not great enough to melt the rocks?

In areas where melting doesn't occur, mineral grains in the rock change in size or shape. Some are flattened like the cake in your lunch bag. Sometimes minerals exchange atoms with surrounding minerals and new or bigger minerals form.

Look at the model of the rock cycle in Section 4-1. You see that a rock that is classified as igneous can be transformed into a rock classified as metamorphic. For
2 example, the igneous rock granite can be changed into the metamorphic rock gneiss (NISE).

What type of rocks does schist form from?

One type of metamorphic rock can form from different types of existing rock. For example, the metamorphic rock schist (SHIHST) can form from igneous rock, basalt; from sedimentary rock, shale; or it can form from metamorphic rock, slate.

96 ROCKS

OPTIONS

Meeting Different Ability Levels

For Section 4-3, use the following **Teacher Resource Masters** depending upon individual students' needs.

◆ **Study Guide Master** for all students.

● **Reinforcement Master** for students of average and above average ability levels.

▲ **Enrichment Master** for above average students.

Additional Teacher Resource Package masters are listed in the OPTIONS box throughout the section. The additional masters are appropriate for all students.

◆ STUDY GUIDE 19

NAME ____ DATE ____ CLASS ____

STUDY GUIDE Chapter 4

Metamorphic Rocks Text Pages 96–98

Determine whether each of the following statements is true or false. Write the word "true" or "false" in the blank. If the sentence is false, rewrite it so that it is true.

true 1. Metamorphic rocks are rocks that have been changed by temperature and pressure.

false 2. Nonfoliated rock will separate easily into layers.
Foliated rock will separate easily into layers.

false 3. Pressure does not play a role in the formation of metamorphic rocks.
Pressure does play a role in forming metamorphic rocks.

true 4. A metamorphic rock with a foliated texture has bands of minerals.

true 5. Metamorphic rocks can be formed from changes in igneous, sedimentary, or other metamorphic rocks.

false 6. Sandstone is a metamorphic rock.
Sandstone is a sedimentary rock.

true 7. A metamorphic rock with no banding is nonfoliated.

true 8. The mineral grains in metamorphic rocks may be flattened.

Complete the chart using information in your textbook.

Type of rock	Can change into	Metamorphic rock
Sedimentary		
Shale	→	schist
Sandstone	→	quartzite
Igneous		
Basalt	→	schist
Granite	→	gneiss
Metamorphic		
Slate	→	schist

 19

Classification of Metamorphic Rocks

When mineral grains flatten and line up in parallel bands, the metamorphic rock has a **foliated** texture. Foliated rocks form when minerals in the original rock flatten under pressure.

Two examples of foliated rocks are slate and gneiss. Slate forms from the sedimentary rock shale. The minerals in shale are arranged into layers when they're exposed to heat and pressure. Slate is easily separated along these foliation layers. The minerals in slate are so tightly compacted that water can't pass between them.

Gneiss, another foliated rock, forms when granite and other rocks are changed. Quartz, feldspar, mica, and other minerals in granite aren't changed much, but they are rearranged into alternating bands.

In some metamorphic rocks, no banding occurs. The mineral grains change, grow, and rearrange but they don't form bands. This process produces a **nonfoliated** (3) texture. Such rocks don't separate into layers. Instead they fracture into pieces of random size and shape.

Sandstone is a sedimentary rock that's often composed mostly of quartz minerals. When its mineral grains are changed by heat and pressure, the nonfoliated rock quartzite is formed. The only change that occurs is in the size of the mineral grains.

What do metamorphic rocks form from?

Your teacher will provide you with samples of four metamorphic rocks and four nonmetamorphic rocks. Each of the metamorphic rocks formed from one of the nonmetamorphic rocks. For each metamorphic rock, determine which nonmetamorphic rock was its "parent."

Figure 4-10. The varying abundances of minerals in shale result in the many different colors of slate. The properties of slate make it useful as patio and stepping stones and roofing shingles.

97

● REINFORCEMENT 19

NAME ______ DATE ______ CLASS ______

REINFORCEMENT — Chapter 4

Metamorphic Rocks — Text Pages 96–98

In the spaces, write the word that matches each description below.

1. M I N E R A L S
2. I G N E O U S
3. S L A T E
4. B A S A L T
5. M A G M A
6. N O N F O L I A T E D
7. Q U A R T Z I T E
8. P R E S S U R E
9. S H A L E
10. F O L I A T E D
11. S C H I S T

1. Components that change in size or shape when metamorphic rocks are formed
2. Term for rocks formed from magma or lava
3. Metamorphic rock formed from shale
4. Igneous rock that can be changed into schist
5. Rocks melted by heat and pressure
6. Texture term for metamorphic rocks which lack banding
7. Metamorphic rock formed from sandstone
8. Force that flattens mineral grains into layers
9. Sedimentary rock that can be changed into schist
10. Texture term for banded, metamorphic rocks
11. A common metamorphic rock

19

▲ ENRICHMENT 19

NAME ______ DATE ______ CLASS ______

ENRICHMENT — Chapter 4

Metamorphic Rocks — Text Pages 95–98

METAMORPHIC PROCESS

Use the graph to answer questions about the formation of metamorphic rocks.

Temperature (°C): 100, 200, 300, 400, 500, 600, 700, 800
Depth (kms): 0, 5, 10, 15, 20, 25
Sediments
Shale → Slate → Schist → Gneiss
Melting

1. What is the relationship between rock temperature and depth beneath the surface? **Temperature increases with depth.**
2. At a depth of 10 kilometers, what would the temperature be? **250°C**
3. Between 0 and 10 kilometers, how many degrees per kilometer does the temperature increase? **10 km)250°C = 25°C/km or $\frac{250°C}{10 km}$ = 25°C/km**
4. Which metamorphic rock shown forms at the highest temperature? **gneiss**
5. Through what general temperature range would you expect schist to form? **300°–400°C**
6. How many kilometers beneath the surface does gneiss occur? **17–22 km**
7. As depth increases, what happens to the temperature at which rock melts? **Melting temperatures decrease.**
8. Suppose you knew that a certain metamorphic rock begins to form at about 300°C. How many kilometers beneath the surface might this rock temperature occur? **12 km**
9. How far beneath the surface does shale metamorphose to slate? **6–8 km**
10. Metasomatism is described as a process by which metamorphic rocks may gradually change into granite (an igneous rock). At which temperature does metasomatism begin? **500°C–600°C**

19

MINI QUIZ

Use the Mini Quiz to check students' recall of chapter content.

1. **Rocks that have been changed by temperature and pressure are _____ rocks.** *metamorphic*
2. **Granite can be changed into the metamorphic rock _____ .** *gneiss*
3. **Metamorphic rocks that show no banding are classified as _____ .** *nonfoliated rocks*

MINI-Lab

Materials: samples of each of the following: gneiss, granite, marble, limestone, quartzite, sandstone, slate, and shale; and hand lenses

Teaching Tips

► Provide the rocks listed above arranged into two groups: the metamorphic rocks, which include gneiss, marble, quartzite, and slate; and the nonmetamorphic rocks: granite, limestone, sandstone, and shale.

► **Answer:** Granite is the parent rock of gneiss; limestone of marble; sandstone of quartzite; and shale of slate.

CONCEPT DEVELOPMENT

Cooperative Learning: Use the Paired Partner strategy to have students classify metamorphic rocks. Have one student query the partner as to whether each specimen is foliated or nonfoliated. Have the students reverse roles with a second set of rocks.

FLEX Your Brain

Use the Flex Your Brain activity to have students explore THE FORMATION OF ZIRCON. Zircon is a mineral often used as a gemstone. It develops in igneous and metamorphic rocks. Gem-quality zircon is produced by heat-treating naturally occurring zircon. Colors are often produced by heat treatments. Yellow, orange, and red zircon gems are called *hyacinth*. Colorless or gray gems are called *jargoon*. Zircon is a source of zirconium. Others of metamorphic origin to explore include sapphire (corundum), ruby (corundum), jade (tremolite).

CHECK FOR UNDERSTANDING

Have volunteers compare and contrast the textures of metamorphic rocks.

RETEACH

Have students sketch foliated and nonfoliated metamorphic rocks. Call on individual students to describe what their sketches show.

EXTENSION

For students who have mastered this section, use the **Reinforcement** and **Enrichment** masters or other OPTIONS provided.

3 CLOSE

▶ Ask questions 1-3 and the **Apply** Question in the Section Review.

▶ Invite a sculptor into class to discuss the type of rocks he or she uses when sculpting. Ask the sculptor to discuss why marble is a good sculpting material.

SECTION REVIEW ANSWERS

1. The temperature and pressure that cause metamorphism are lower than those needed to form igneous rocks. Melting does not occur during metamorphism.

2. Metamorphic rocks are classified by texture. Foliated rocks are banded; nonfoliated rocks are not.

3. Marble metamorphoses from limestone. The heat and pressure necessary to change limestone into marble destroy fossils.

4. Apply: Slate is a foliated metamorphic rock that can be broken into thin, flat plates. Water can't penetrate slate.

Another nonfoliated metamorphic rock is marble. Marble forms from the sedimentary rock limestone which 4 is composed of calcite. The calcite crystals give marble its glassy, shiny luster that makes it a popular material for sculpturing. Usually, marble contains several other minerals besides calcite which color it. For example, hornblende and serpentine give it a greenish tone whereas hematite makes it red.

So far, we've traveled through only a portion of the rock cycle. We still haven't observed how sedimentary rocks are formed and how igneous and metamorphic rocks evolve from them. The next section will complete our investigation of the rock cycle.

Figure 4-11. Sculptors often work with marble because it's soft and easy to shape. Its calcite crystals also give it a glassy, shiny luster.

SECTION REVIEW

1. How is the formation of igneous rock different from that of metamorphic rock?
2. How are metamorphic rocks classified? What are the characteristics of rocks in each of these classifications?
3. Marble rarely contains fossils even though limestone does. Explain.
4. **Apply:** Slate is sometimes used as roofing tiles for houses. What properties of slate make it useful for this purpose?

Skill Builder: Sequencing

Put the following events in a sequence that could explain how a metamorphic rock might form from an igneous rock. (HINT: Start with *igneous rock forms.*) Use each event just once. If you need help, refer to Sequencing in the **Skill Handbook** on page 680.

Events: *sedimentary rock forms, weathering occurs, heat and pressure are applied, igneous rock forms, metamorphic rock forms, erosion occurs, sediments are formed, deposition occurs*

Skill Builder

Igneous rock forms. Weathering occurs. Sediments are formed. Erosion occurs. Deposition occurs. Sedimentary rock forms. Heat and pressure are applied. Metamorphic rock forms.

ACTIVITY 4-2
Sedimentary Rocks

Problem: *How can you classify sedimentary rocks?*

Materials  

- unknown sedimentary rock samples
- marking pen
- 5% hydrochloric acid (HCl)
- dropper
- hand lens
- paper towels
- water

Procedure

1. On your paper, make a Data and Observations chart similar to the one shown below.
2. Determine the types of sediments in each sample. What size are the sediments in the clastic rocks? Classify them as pebbles, sand, silt, or clay.
3. Put a few drops of HCl on each rock sample. **CAUTION:** *HCl is an acid and can cause burns. Wear goggles. Rinse spills with water.* "Bubbling" on a rock indicates the presence of carbonate minerals.
4. Look for fossils and describe them if any are present.
5. Classify your samples as clastic, chemical, or organic. Identify each rock sample.

Analyze

1. Why did you test the rocks with hydrochloric acid?
2. What mineral reacts with hydrochloric acid?
3. What is needed in order for sedimentary rocks to form from fragments?

Conclude and Apply

4. How do clastic sedimentary rocks differ from nonclastics?
5. How can you classify sedimentary rocks?

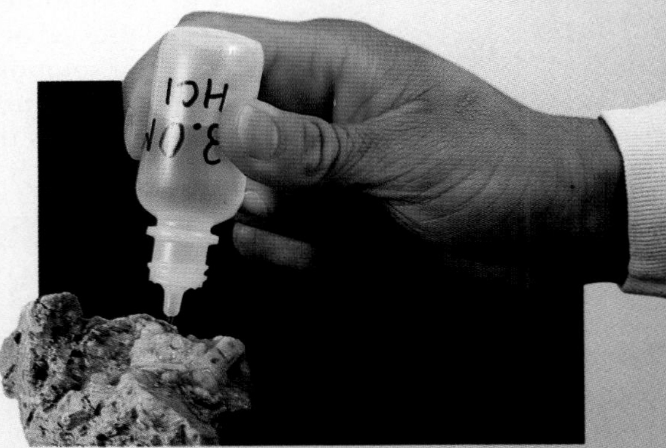

Data and Observations

Sample Data

Sample	Observations	Minerals or fossils present	Sediment size	Clastic, Chemical, or Organic	Rock name
A	fizzes in HCl	calcite, fossils	usually silt	organic	limestone
B		quartz, feldspar, hematite	sand	clastic	sandstone
C		kaolinite, feldspar	clay	clastic	shale
D		pebbles composed of any mineral or rock	sand and pebble	clastic	conglomerate
E	tastes salty	halite	varies	chemical	rock salt

ACTIVITY 4-2
50 minutes

OBJECTIVE: Identify and **describe** ways in which sedimentary rocks are classified.

PROCESS SKILLS applied in this activity:
▶ **Observing** in Procedure Steps 2, 3, and 4.
▶ **Communicating** in Procedure Steps 1 and 6.
▶ **Classifying** in Procedure Step 5.
▶ **Inferring** in Analyze Questions 1 and 3, and Conclude and Apply Question 4.

COOPERATIVE LEARNING Use the Science Investigation strategy to have students perform this activity.

TEACHING THE ACTIVITY

▶ Divide sedimentary rock samples into kits of known and unknown rocks. Sample kits should be the same for each laboratory group.

Troubleshooting: Be sure students are wearing goggles when using hydrochloric acid. If the activity is going to be done more than once, check that rock kits did not get mixed up.

PROGRAM RESOURCES

From the **Teacher Resource Package** use:
Activity Worksheets, pages 32-33, Activity 4-2: Sedimentary Rocks.

ANSWERS TO QUESTIONS

1. to determine if calcite was present; calcite effervesces in the presence of HCl
2. calcite
3. fragments and a cementing agent
4. Clastic sedimentary rocks are made of fragments of other rocks, minerals, and/or shells. Nonclastics are either chemically or organically formed.
5. Sedimentary rocks are classified as clastics or nonclastics. Clastics can be classified according to particle size and shape. Nonclastic sedimentary rocks can be classified as having formed from solutions or by organic processes.

SECTION 4-4

PREPARATION

SECTION BACKGROUND

▶ Sediment carried by water and other agents of erosion is sorted by size. As the agent loses energy, larger pieces are deposited. Finer sediments are transported further.

▶ Generally, sedimentary rocks are the only rocks that contain fossils. The high temperatures and pressures involved in forming igneous and metamorphic rocks destroy any fossils present in parent rocks.

PREPLANNING

▶ To prepare for the Mini-Lab and the proposed demonstrations, obtain different-sized sediments, including sand, silt, clay, and rounded and angular pebbles.

▶ Obtain boxed and labeled samples of sedimentary rocks to be used for class demonstrations and in Activity 4-2.

1 MOTIVATE

Cooperative Learning: Form Science Investigation groups with three students per group. Supply each group with containers of clay, fine sand, coarse sand, and rounded and angular pebbles. Make samples of shale, siltstone, sandstone, conglomerate, and sedimentary breccia available to each group. Have students use a hand lens to match sediment type with the appropriate rock sample. One student should prepare a report of the conclusions drawn by the group.

4-4 Sedimentary Rocks

New Science Words

sedimentary rocks
sediments
compaction
cementation

Objectives

▶ Explain how sedimentary rocks form from sediments.
▶ Classify sedimentary rocks as clastic, chemical, or organic in origin.

Origin of Sedimentary Rocks

Most of the rocks below Earth's surface are igneous rocks. Igneous rocks are the most common rocks on Earth. But chances are, you've seen more sedimentary rocks than igneous rocks. Seventy-five percent of the rocks at Earth's surface are sedimentary rocks.

Define *sediments.*

Sedimentary rocks form when sediments become pressed or cemented together or when sediments fall out of solution. **Sediments** are loose materials such as rock fragments, mineral grains, and bits of plant and animal remains that have been transported. Minerals that are

Table 4-2

SEDIMENT SIZES

Sediment	Clay	Silt	Sand	Pebbles
Size range	< 0.004 mm	0.004 - 0.06 mm	0.06 - 2 mm	2 - 64 mm
Examples of rock formed from	Mudstone	Siltstone	Sandstone	Conglomerate

OPTIONS

Meeting Different Ability Levels

For Section 4-4, use the following **Teacher Resource Masters** depending upon individual students' needs.

◆ **Study Guide Master** for all students.

● **Reinforcement Master** for students of average and above average ability levels.

▲ **Enrichment Master** for above average students.

Additional Teacher Resource Package masters are listed in the OPTIONS box throughout the section. The additional masters are appropriate for all students.

◆ **STUDY GUIDE 20**

NAME ______ DATE ______ CLASS ______

STUDY GUIDE — Chapter 4

Sedimentary Rocks — Text Pages 100–107

Answer the following questions on the lines provided.

1. What are sediments? **Sediments are loose materials such as rock fragments, mineral grains, and bits of plant and animal remains that have been transported by erosion processes.**
2. What are sedimentary rocks? **They are rocks that form when sediments are pressed or cemented together or fall out of solution.**
3. What is compaction? **Compaction is the process by which small sediments are pressed together to form solid rock.**
4. What is cementation? **Cementation is the process by which large sediments are glued together to form solid rock.**
5. What are clastic sedimentary rocks? **They are rocks made of broken fragments of plants, animals, and other rocks.**
6. What is conglomerate? **Conglomerate is a clastic rock formed from large, well-rounded sediments.**
7. What is breccia? **Breccia is a clastic rock formed from large sediments with sharp angles.**
8. What are chemical sedimentary rocks? **They are rocks formed from minerals dissolved in solution.**
9. What are organic sedimentary rocks? **They are rocks formed from the remains of once-living things.**
10. What is coquina? **Coquina is limestone formed from large shell fragments.**
11. What is chalk? **Chalk is limestone formed from tiny shells.**

20

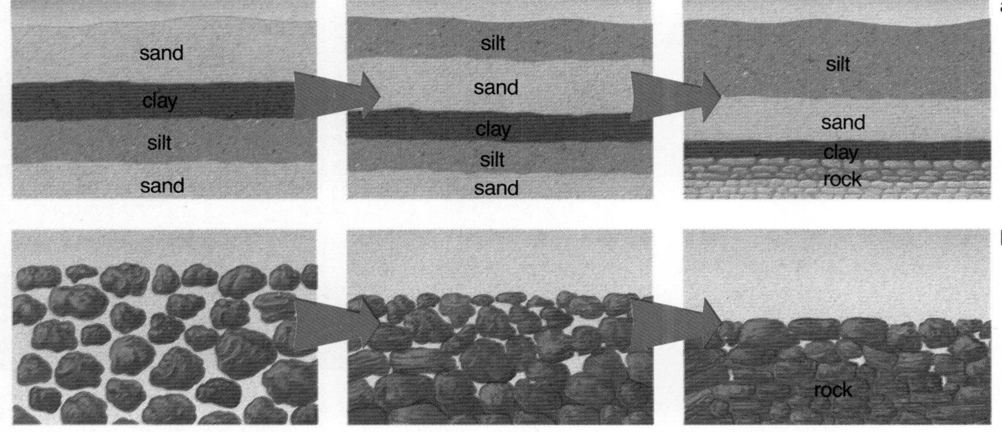

Figure 4-12. Two processes that form sedimentary rocks are compaction (a) and cementation (b).

dissolved in water are also sediments. But where do sediments come from? If you look at the model of the rock cycle, you will see that they come from already-existing rocks that are weathered and eroded.

Weathering is the process that breaks rocks into smaller pieces. Table 4-2 shows how these pieces are classified by size. These sediments are usually moved by water, wind, ice, or gravity. The movement of sediments is called erosion. You will learn more about these processes in Chapters 5 and 6.

Erosion moves sediments to a new location, where they are then deposited. Here, layer upon layer of sediment builds up. Pressure from the upper layers pushes down on the lower layers. If the sediments are very small, they can stick together and form solid rock. This process is called **compaction.**

You've compacted sediments if you've ever made "mud pies." Mud is made of small, clay-sized sediments. They easily stick together under the pressure applied by your hands. However, if you tried the same thing with large particles, such as driveway gravel, you couldn't make them compact into one mass.

If sediments are large, like sand and pebbles, pressure alone can't make them stick together. Large sediments have to be cemented together. **Cementation** (see men TAY shun) occurs in the following way. Water soaks through soil and rock. As it moves, it dissolves minerals in the rock such as quartz and calcite. These minerals

MINI-Lab

What are rocks made of?

Spread some sediments on a sheet of paper. Using tweezers or a dissecting probe, separate the sediments into three piles based on size—large, medium, or small. Now separate each of these piles into two piles based on shape: rounded or angular. You should now have six piles. Describe each of the six types of sediments you have.

TYING TO PREVIOUS KNOWLEDGE: Have students recall from Chapter 3 the physical properties of quartz. Lead a discussion that will help students conclude that the hardness of quartz makes it resistant to weathering. Point out that most of the sand-sized grains found in many sandstones are quartz.

OBJECTIVES AND SCIENCE WORDS: Have students review the objectives and science words to become familiar with this section.

MINI-Lab

Materials: mixtures of different-sized and shaped sediments such as sand grains, pebbles, and silt or clay-sized grains; tweezers or dissecting probe

Teaching Tips

►Students will not be able to physically manipulate the silt or clay with tweezers. Suggest that it be swept into a pile with the hand.

►If a powerful binocular scope is available, students will be able to observe that silt-sized particles are angular.

►**Answer:** Students should describe their sediments by size and angularity.

PROGRAM RESOURCES

From the **Teacher Resource Package** use:

Activity Worksheets, page 37, Mini-Lab: What are rocks made of?

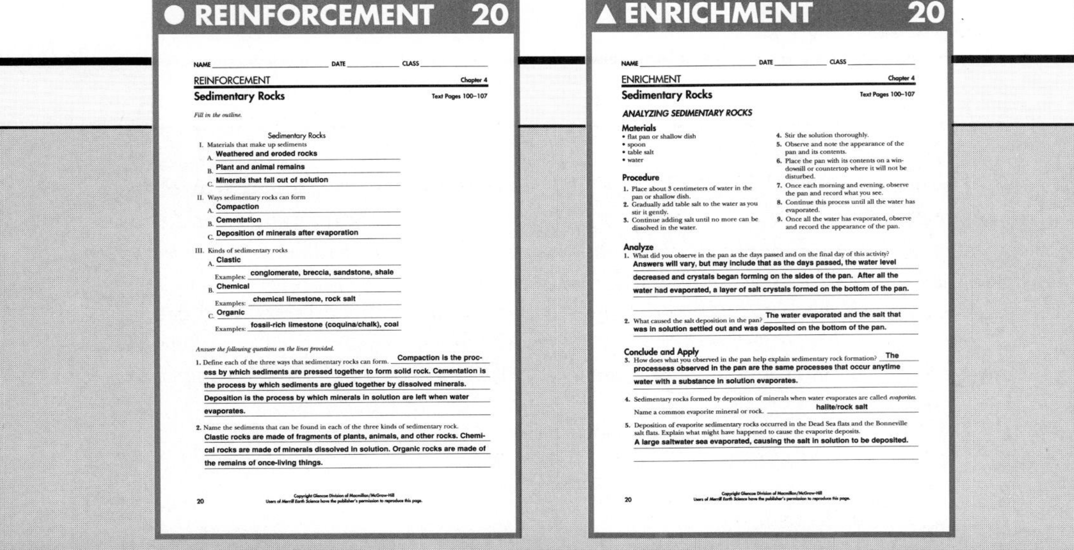
● REINFORCEMENT 20

NAME ______ DATE ______ CLASS ______

REINFORCEMENT — Chapter 4

Sedimentary Rocks — Text Pages 100–107

Fill in the outline.

Sedimentary Rocks

I. Materials that make up sediments
   A. **Weathered and eroded rocks**
   B. **Plant and animal remains**
   C. **Minerals that fall out of solution**

II. Ways sedimentary rocks can form
   A. **Compaction**
   B. **Cementation**
   C. **Deposition of minerals after evaporation**

III. Kinds of sedimentary rocks
   A. **Clastic**
      Examples: **conglomerate, breccia, sandstone, shale**
   B. **Chemical**
      Examples: **chemical limestone, rock salt**
   C. **Organic**
      Examples: **fossil-rich limestone (coquina/chalk), coal**

Answer the following questions on the lines provided.

1. Define each of the three ways that sedimentary rocks can form. **Compaction is the process by which sediments are pressed together to form solid rock. Cementation is the process by which sediments are glued together by dissolved minerals. Deposition is the process by which minerals in solution are left when water evaporates.**

2. Name the sediments that can be found in each of the three kinds of sedimentary rock. **Clastic rocks are made of fragments of plants, animals, and other rocks. Chemical rocks are made of minerals dissolved in solution. Organic rocks are made of the remains of once-living things.**

20

▲ ENRICHMENT 20

NAME ______ DATE ______ CLASS ______

ENRICHMENT — Chapter 4

Sedimentary Rocks — Text Pages 100–107

ANALYZING SEDIMENTARY ROCKS

Materials
- flat pan or shallow dish
- spoon
- table salt
- water

Procedure
1. Place about 3 centimeters of water in the pan or shallow dish.
2. Gradually add table salt to the water as you stir it gently.
3. Continue adding salt until no more can be dissolved in the water.
4. Stir the solution thoroughly.
5. Observe and note the appearance of the pan and its contents.
6. Place the pan with its contents on a windowsill or countertop where it will not be disturbed.
7. Once each morning and evening, observe the pan and record what you see.
8. Continue this process until all the water has evaporated.
9. Once all the water has evaporated, observe and record the appearance of the pan.

Analyze
1. What did you observe in the pan as the days passed and on the final day of this activity? **Answers will vary, but may include that as the days passed, the water level decreased and crystals began forming on the sides of the pan. After all the water had evaporated, a layer of salt crystals formed on the bottom of the pan.**
2. What caused the salt deposition in the pan? **The water evaporated and the salt that was in solution settled out and was deposited on the bottom of the pan.**

Conclude and Apply
3. How does what you observed in the pan help explain sedimentary rock formation? **The processess observed in the pan are the same processes that occur anytime water with a substance in solution evaporates.**
4. Sedimentary rocks formed by deposition of minerals when water evaporates are called *evaporites.* Name a common evaporite mineral or rock. **halite/rock salt**
5. Deposition of evaporite sedimentary rocks occurred in the Dead Sea flats and the Bonneville salt flats. Explain what might have happened to cause the evaporite deposits. **A large saltwater sea evaporated, causing the salt in solution to be deposited.**

20

2 TEACH

Key Concepts are highlighted.

CONCEPT DEVELOPMENT

▶ Have a volunteer compare and contrast *cementation* and *compaction*.

▶ Place a "pet rock," Conrad Conglomerate, in front of the class. Have students examine the rock and write a brief geologic history that explains how the conglomerate formed. Then, have students hypothesize what might happen to Conrad if he is exposed to Earth processes. Remind students to use their knowledge of the rock cycle.

▶ Ask students the following questions. **How do sedimentary cements form?** *Certain minerals are dissolved in water. When the solution moves through sediments, the minerals can be deposited around the sediments, causing the pieces to stick together to form rocks.* **What are sediments?** *fragments of rocks, minerals, plants, and animals*

Figure 4-13. These sedimentary rock layers formed from the compaction and cementation of many layers of sediments.

are natural cements. The solution of water and dissolved minerals moves through open spaces between sediments. The natural cements are deposited around the pieces of sediment and they stick together. A group of sediments cemented together in this way forms a sedimentary rock.

How do sedimentary rock layers form?

Sedimentary rocks often form as layers. The older layers are on the bottom because they were deposited first. Then, more sediments pile up and they, too, become compacted and cemented together to form another layer of rock.

Sedimentary rock layers are a lot like the papers in your locker. The oldest papers are on bottom and the ones you get back today will be deposited on top of them. If, however, you disturb the papers, searching through them for a pencil at the bottom of the pile, the older ones may come to the top. Sometimes layers of rock are disturbed by forces within Earth. The layers are overturned, and the oldest are no longer on the bottom. The forces that cause such disturbances will be discussed in Chapter 13.

Classification of Sedimentary Rocks

Sedimentary rocks can be composed of just about anything. Sediments come from weathered and eroded igneous, metamorphic, and sedimentary rocks. Sediments also come from plants, insects, and animals. The composition of a sedimentary rock depends on the composition of the rocks and living things its sediments came from.

OPTIONS

INQUIRY QUESTIONS

▶ **How are sediments held together in sedimentary rocks?** *As water containing dissolved minerals moves through spaces in the sediment, minerals are deposited, harden, and become cements that hold the sediments together.*

▶ **What generalization can you draw about clastic sedimentary rocks?** *All clastic sedimentary rocks are composed of sediments such as plants, animals, and/or minerals and rocks that are joined by compaction and cementation.*

▶ **Describe the shape and size of the sediments in the sedimentary rock shown on page 103.** *The sediments are well rounded and are relatively large.*

▶ **How do conglomerates and breccias differ?** *The components of conglomerates are well rounded, whereas the components in a breccia are angular.*

Like igneous and metamorphic rocks, sedimentary rocks are classified by their composition and by the way they formed. Sedimentary rocks are usually classified as clastic, chemical, or organic.

Clastic Sedimentary Rocks

The word *clastic* comes from the Greek word *klastos*, which means "broken." Clastic sedimentary rocks are made of the broken fragment of plants, animals, and other rocks. These sediments are compacted and cemented together.

The shape and size of the sediments are used to name a clastic rock. For example, conglomerate and breccia both form from large sediments. If the sediments have been well rounded, the rock is called conglomerate. If the sediments are not rounded and have sharp angles, the rock is called breccia.

The pebble-sized sediments in both conglomerate and breccia may consist of any type of rock or mineral. Often, they are chunks of the minerals quartz or feldspar. They can also be pieces of rocks such as gneiss, granite, or limestone. The cement holding them all together is usually quartz or calcite.

Have you ever looked at the concrete in sidewalks and driveways. It's made of pebbles and sand grains that have been cemented together. Since concrete is made by people, it's not a rock, but it does have a structure similar to that of naturally occurring conglomerate.

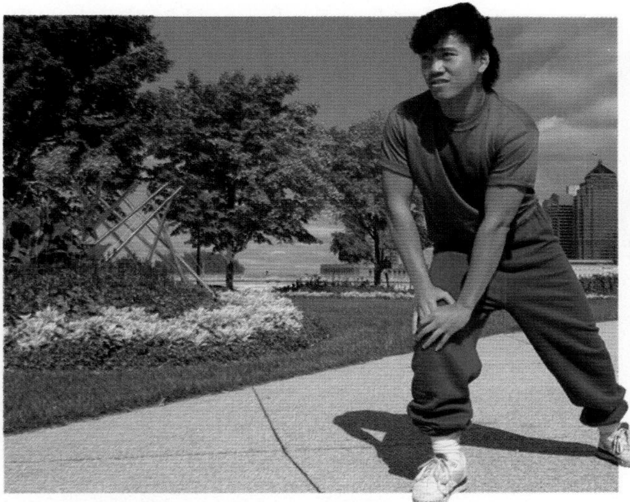

Figure 4-14. The concrete making up the sidewalk is similar to naturally occurring conglomerate (above).

CONCEPT DEVELOPMENT

▶ After students read pages 103 and 104, ask the following questions. **What are the three groups of sedimentary rocks?** *clastic, chemical, and organic* **What's the difference between conglomerates and breccias?** *Sediments that compose conglomerates are well rounded. If the sediments are angular, the rock is a breccia.*

TEACHER F.Y.I.

▶ Agents capable of transporting the pebbles found in conglomerates and breccias include water, glaciers, and gravity. The rounded pebbles of conglomerates form from grinding and abrasion. Therefore, the depositional environments for conglomerates include stream channels and alluvial fans. The angular fragments of breccias were not subjected to turbulent long-distance transport prior to deposition. Depositional environments of breccias include talus slopes and glacial moraines.

PROGRAM RESOURCES

From the **Teacher Resource Package** use:
Critical Thinking/Problem Solving, page 10, Rocks All Around You.
Use **Laboratory Manual,** page 35, Concretions.

CHECK FOR UNDERSTANDING

Have students write a brief paragraph describing how sediment sizes vary among a shale, a sandstone, and a conglomerate.

RETEACH

Demonstration: Pass samples of shale, sandstone, and conglomerate around the room. Once all students have examined the rocks, place the rocks on a cement slab behind a safety screen. When students have moved well out of your way, crush the rocks with a hammer. Have the students pick up and examine the sediments that composed each rock. **CAUTION:** *Wear safety goggles while performing this demonstration.*

EXTENSION

For students who have mastered this section, use the **Reinforcement** and **Enrichment** masters or other OPTIONS provided.

REVEALING MISCONCEPTIONS

▶ Ask students where oil and natural gas are found. Many students probably think oil and natural gas exist underground in cavelike chambers. Point out that oil and natural gas often exist in openings among the sediments in sandstone or in limestones.

Figure 4-15. Rock salt is a chemical sedimentary rock.

Sandstone is formed from smaller particles than conglomerates and breccias. Its sand-sized sediments are usually grains of the minerals quartz and feldspar, but can be just about any mineral. These sand grains can be compacted together if clay particles are also present, or they can be cemented.

1 Layers of sandstone beneath Earth's surface transport large volumes of groundwater. Groundwater is rain or surface water that has soaked into the ground. It reaches the sandstone deposits and moves through them. People drill wells into sandstone deposits and pump the groundwater to the surface to use as drinking water.

Shale is a clastic sedimentary rock that requires no cementation to hold its particles together. Its sediments are clay-sized particles. Clay-sized sediments are compacted together by pressure from overlying layers.

Chemical Sedimentary Rocks

2 Chemical sedimentary rocks form from minerals dissolved in solution. In rock formation these minerals separate from the water. Think back to our discussion of solutions in Chapter 2. We found that sugar is deposited in the bottom of a glass when tea evaporates. In a similar way, minerals collect when seas or lakes evaporate. The deposits of minerals that fall out of solution form rocks.

The mineral calcite is carried in solution in ocean water. When calcite comes out of solution and its many crystals grow together, limestone is formed. Limestone may also contain other minerals and sediments, but it's at least 50

Figure 4-16. Why does this sandstone look so much like desert sand dunes? This rock formed from sand deposited in layers by desert winds.

OPTIONS

INQUIRY QUESTIONS

▶ **Why can groundwater flow through sandstone but not through shale?** *Sand-sized grains have larger spaces between them than clay-sized sediments. The clay particles are so small and so tightly compacted that water isn't able to permeate them.*

▶ **Why is rock salt classified as a chemical sedimentary rock?** *Rock salt forms as water containing minerals in solution evaporates.*

▶ **What can be said about the geologic history of an area in which most of the rock is limestone?** *The area was probably covered by an ocean at some time in the past because most limestones form in salt water.*

PROBLEM SOLVING

A Geology Trip in the City

While on a class field trip in the city, Peter and his classmates observed rocks used as building materials. In the city square Peter noticed flowers arranged in a rock terrace. The rocks were light-colored and contained many small fossils.

Soon, the class left the square and entered a historical district with an assortment of buildings. The first building Peter noticed was light pink with small crystals of quartz that felt gritty to the touch. Continuing down the street, he observed another building with columns. This building was constructed of a light-colored rock containing large mineral grains. Next, he saw a wooden building with a roof made of dark tiles. Some of the tiles had been broken off in layers.

On the bus trip back to school, students were asked to describe and name the rocks they observed on the field trip.

Think Critically: Using what you have learned about minerals and rocks, name the rocks that Peter observed. What rocklike materials do people make and use for buildings and other structures?

percent calcite. Limestone is usually deposited on ocean floors. Large areas of the United States are underlain by limestone because oceans once covered much of the United States for millions of years.

When lakes and seas evaporate, they often deposit the mineral halite. Halite, mixed with a few other minerals, forms rock salt. Rock salt deposits range in thickness 3 from a few meters to over 400 meters. People mine these deposits because rock salt is an important resource. It's used in the manufacturing of glass, paper, soap, and dairy products. The halite in rock salt is even used as table salt.

How does rock salt form?

Organic Sedimentary Rocks

When rocks form from the remains of once-living things, they are organic sedimentary rocks. One of the 4 most common organic sedimentary rocks is fossil-rich limestone. Like chemical limestone, fossil-rich limestone is made of the mineral calcite. But fossil-rich limestone

CONCEPT DEVELOPMENT

► **Demonstration:** Have students gather around a large table or desk. Place samples of calcite, limestone, and marble on the table for students to observe. Ask a volunteer to explain how the samples are alike and how they differ. Place a few drops of dilute HCl acid on each sample. Students will observe that all samples "fizz" when the acid is applied.

► Ask the following questions based on the demonstration above. **Why do all three samples react to acid?** *Calcite reacts to HCl. Limestone and marble contain calcite.* **How do the two rocks differ?** *Limestone forms when calcite precipitates from seawater or when seashells are cemented together. The sedimentary rock limestone can be changed to marble if the limestone is subjected to increases in temperature and pressure.*

MINI QUIZ

Use the Mini Quiz to check students' recall of chapter content.

1. **Water that soaks into Earth's crust is called _____ .** *groundwater*
2. **_____ rocks are sedimentary rocks that form from minerals dissolved in solution.** *Chemical sedimentary*
3. **Rock salt is an example of a(n) _____ sedimentary rock.** *chemical*
4. **Sedimentary rocks that form from the remains of once-living things are _____ sedimentary rocks.** *organic*

PROBLEM SOLVING

Think Critically: Limestone was used to construct the rock terrace. The first building was made of sandstone; the building with columns was made of granite; and the roof tiles of slate. Concrete, bricks, and tiles are rocklike materials used as building materials.

PROGRAM RESOURCES

From the **Teacher Resource Package** use:
Cross-Curricular Connections, page 8, Roots, Prefixes, and Suffixes.
Technology, page 7, Digging and Shaping Stone.

TEACHER F.Y.I.

▶ The Bonneville Salt Flats are composed of chemical sedimentary rocks that formed as the ancient Lake Bonneville evaporated. A present-day remnant of this lake is the Great Salt Lake in Utah.

CONCEPT DEVELOPMENT

▶ Explain that coal forms when dead plants become buried under sediment for millions of years. Use the time needed for coal to form to help students realize the need for energy conservation and alternative energy resources.

CROSS CURRICULUM

▶ **Geography:** Have students make a map that shows the coal reserves of the United States. A map key or legend should include the type of coal deposits and how long the deposits are expected to last. Some students might want to determine what percentage of the world's coal reserves are located in the United States.

TEACHER F.Y.I.

▶ The organic sedimentary rock coquina can also be classified as a clastic rock because it is composed of broken shells from sea animals.

Figure 4-17. The White Cliffs of Dover, England, are composed mostly of chalk.

also contains remains of once-living ocean animals instead of just calcite that has separated from ocean water.

Animals such as mussels, coral, and snails make their shells from the mineral calcite. When they die, their shells accumulate on the ocean floor. These calcite shells are compacted and cemented together and fossil-rich limestone is formed. If the shell fragments are relatively large, the rock is called coquina (koh KEE nuh). If the shells are microscopic, the rock is called chalk. When your teachers use naturally occurring chalk to write with, they're actually crushing and smearing the calcite shells of once-living ocean animals.

Another very useful sedimentary rock is coal. Coal forms when pieces of dead plants are buried under other sediments. These plant materials are chemically changed by microorganisms. The resulting sediments are compacted over millions of years to form coal. In Chapter 18, you will learn how we use coal as a source of energy.

EcoTip

Instead of rock salt, try using regular cat litter to deice sidewalks. Halite is composed of the elements sodium and chloride, which pollute water and soil.

Another Look at the Rock Cycle

You have seen that the rock cycle has no beginning and no end. Rocks are continually changing from one form to another. Sediments come from rocks and other objects that have been broken apart. Even the magma and lava that form igneous rocks come from the melting of rocks that already exist.

All of the rocks that you've learned about in this chapter evolved because of the processes of the rock cycle. And all of the rocks around you, including those used to build houses and monuments, are part of the rock cycle. They are all changing.

OPTIONS

ENRICHMENT

▶ Have students devise a chart that enables them to classify rocks in all three of the major groups. This chart should be related to the rock cycle.

PROGRAM RESOURCES

From the **Teacher Resource Package** use: **Activity Worksheets,** page 5, Flex Your Brain.

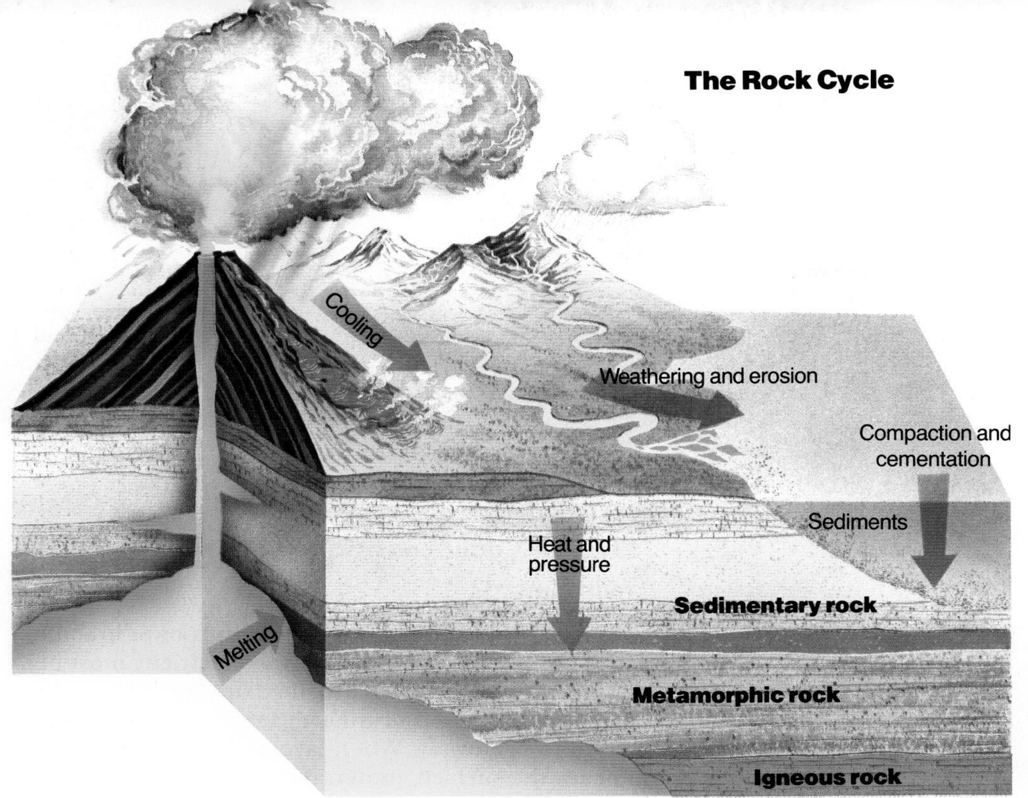

SECTION REVIEW

1. Where do sediments come from?
2. Explain why limestone can be classified as a chemical or organic sedimentary rock.
3. **Apply:** Use the rock cycle to explain how pieces of granite and slate could be found in the same piece of conglomerate.

Interpreting Data

You are told that a clastic sedimentary rock is composed of sediments of the following sizes: pebbles, sand, and silt. The larger sediments are surrounded by the smaller sediments which are cemented together by quartz. What is the name of this rock? If you need help, refer to Interpreting Data in the **Skill Handbook** on page 687.

Skill Builder

The observation that the rock contains sediments of greatly varying sizes indicates that it's a conglomerate. The observation that larger particles (the pebbles) are held together by silica cement and compacted small sediments (sand and silt) indicates the rock is clastic. The specimen can be classified as a conglomerate.

CHECK FOR UNDERSTANDING

Ask the following question. **What sedimentary processes were involved in forming the White Cliffs of Dover, England?** *Microscopic calcite shells of dead sea animals settled to the bottom of the ocean floor where they accumulated and became cemented together. Compaction by overlying sediments was also involved in the chalk formation.*

RETEACH

Demonstrate that chalk is made of calcite by placing a few drops of HCl acid on white chalk. The chalk will "fizz" as the calcite reacts with the acid.

EXTENSION

For students who have mastered this section, use the **Reinforcement** and **Enrichment** masters or other OPTIONS provided.

3 CLOSE

▶ Ask questions 1-2 and the **Apply** Question in the Section Review.

FLEX Your Brain

Use the Flex Your Brain activity to have students explore CLASTIC, CHEMICAL, or ORGANIC SEDIMENTARY ROCKS.

SECTION REVIEW ANSWERS

1. rocks, minerals, and plant and animal remains

2. Chemical limestone contains calcite that precipitated out of solution. Organic limestone contains remains of once-living ocean organisms.

3. Apply: If granite and slate were both exposed to weathering at Earth's surface, fragments of both rocks could become sediments that eventually were cemented and compacted to form a conglomerate.

SECTION 4-5

PREPARATION

SECTION BACKGROUND

▶ The Surface Mining Control and Reclamation Act of 1977 controls environmental hazards caused by strip mining.

▶ There are two methods used to mine coal below Earth's surface. In some mines, large pillars of coal are left to help support the roof. In other mines, continuous mining machines are used to hold up the roof during mining, and allow it to cave in as the seam is mined.

▶ Coal forms when plant remains fall into swamps and are quickly buried. Because of the lack of oxygen in swamp water, total decay cannot occur. Bacteria attack the plant remains and cause partial decay. The partly decayed plant material, called peat, contains a large amount of water. As the peat is buried deeper under sediment, moisture and other materials are released to form lignite, a woody material with little water. Further burial changes lignite into bituminous coal. Bituminous coal is darker, harder, and contains more carbon than lignite. Increased temperatures and pressures can change bituminous coal into anthracite.

1 MOTIVATE

FLEX Your Brain

Use the Flex Your Brain activity to have students explore OPERATION OF A STRIP MINE.

▶ Have students research the working conditions of present-day miners. Encourage students to compare and contrast these conditions to the working conditions 50 years ago.

4-5 Environmental Effects of Coal Mines

New Science Words

strip mine

Objectives

- ▶ Contrast characteristics of strip mines and underground coal mines.
- ▶ List several environmental effects associated with coal mining.

How Are Coal Mines Harmful to the Environment?

Every day of your life, you use electric power in some way. The coal used to generate the electricity must be taken from Earth. Two basic methods are used to remove the coal. If the coal is near Earth's surface, strip mining is used to remove it. When layers of coal are deeper beneath the surface, underground mines are used to take it out.

In a **strip mine,** layers of soil and rock above the coal are removed. These materials are piled up to one side. The exposed coal is then removed and loaded into trucks or trains to be moved elsewhere. A large open pit exists where the coal, soil, and rock were removed.

Mining companies are required to return the soil and rock to the open pit and cover it with topsoil. Usually, they plant trees and grass as well. This process is called land reclamation.

In underground mining, tunnels are dug 1
to reach the coal. Large amounts of coal can be removed, but some must be left behind as walls or pillars to support the rocks and soil above. Otherwise, the mine would cave in.

Removal of coal by either method causes problems with the environment. Strip mining requires the removal of all

OPTIONS

Meeting Different Ability Levels

For Section 4-5, use the following **Teacher Resource Masters** depending upon individual students' needs.

◆ **Study Guide Master** for all students.

● **Reinforcement Master** for students of average and above average ability levels.

▲ **Enrichment Master** for above average students.

Additional Teacher Resource Package masters are listed in the OPTIONS box throughout the section. The additional masters are appropriate for all students.

◆ STUDY GUIDE 21

NAME ______ DATE ______ CLASS ______

STUDY GUIDE — Chapter 4

Environmental Effects of Coal Mines — Text Pages 108–110

Write each term in the box after its definition.

strip mine	underground mine	land reclamation

1. The process of returning rock, soil, trees, and grass to land that has been mined **land reclamation**
2. A method for mining coal near Earth's surface in which layers of soil and rock are removed to expose the coal **strip mine**
3. A method for mining coal far below Earth's surface in which tunnels are dug to reach the coal **underground mine**

Put an X by each statement that does not agree with your textbook.

X 4. Strip mining is used to remove coal far below Earth's surface.
____ 5. Soil exposed by mining washes into streams, which then become so polluted that fish cannot survive.
____ 6. Vegetation, soil, and rock are removed to expose coal for a strip mine.
X 7. After a strip mine is closed, the land can always be restored to its original form.
____ 8. Tunnels are dug to reach coal in an underground mine.
____ 9. Water made acidic by sulfur from coal can pollute drinking water.
X 10. Land reclamation is the removal of the rock and soil that cover layers of coal.
____ 11. Abandoned underground mines can be a danger when they collapse.
X 12. Underground mining is used to take out coal near Earth's surface.
____ 13. Mining is important because it provides coal used to generate electricity and it provides jobs for many people.
X 14. Both strip mining and underground mining methods are good for the environment.
X 15. Mining companies are not required to reclaim the land they mine.
X 16. Wildlife is not affected by coal mining operations.

 21

vegetation. It temporarily scars the land with open pits. Wildlife lose their habitats.

Abandoned underground coal mines can collapse, causing large pits on Earth's surface. If people built homes above a mine, their homes would end up at the bottom of a pit when the mine collapsed.

Both mining methods pollute streams and kill fish and other wildlife. Since the vegetation has been removed, the soil is exposed. Heavy rains wash exposed soil into streams. The water can become so polluted with sediments that fish can no longer survive. ❷

An even bigger problem occurs when water flows through mines and then into streams or lakes. The water dissolves sulfur from the coal and carries it in solution. Such water is acidic. The acidic water kills wildlife and severely pollutes drinking water.

From 1930 to 1970, only 40 percent of the mines in the United States were reclaimed. Since then, states have passed laws that require mining companies to reclaim the land. Today, almost all the land affected by mining is reclaimed. Mining companies put great effort and money into making the land as it was before they mined it. But the land can't always be restored to its original form. Forests take hundreds of years to develop, and wildlife that left the area when the mines came in may never return. ❸

Differentiate between strip mines and underground mines.

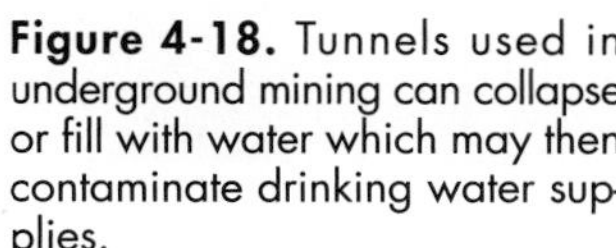

Figure 4-18. Tunnels used in underground mining can collapse or fill with water which may then contaminate drinking water supplies.

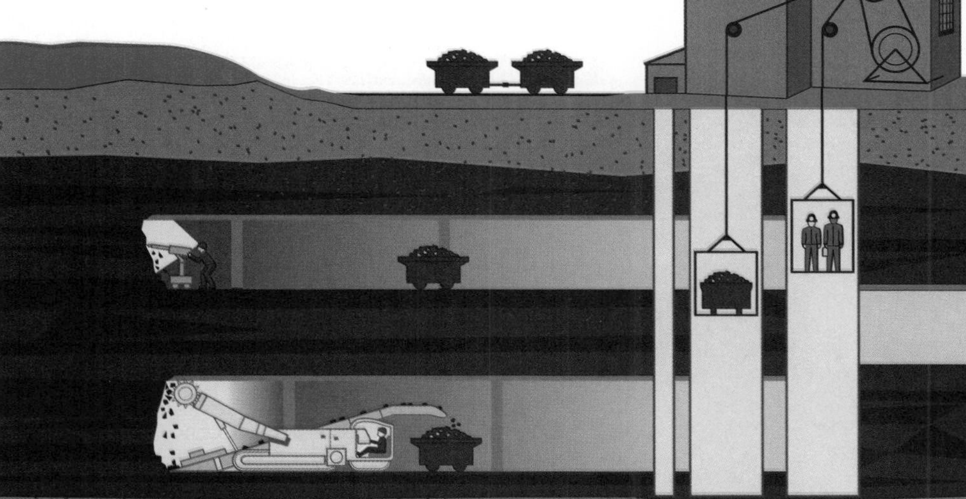

TYING TO PREVIOUS KNOWLEDGE: Ask students to recall what they know about coal. Most students will know that coal is black, can leave a residue on the hands, and can be burned for energy.

OBJECTIVES AND SCIENCE WORDS: Have students review the objectives and science words to become familiar with this section.

2 TEACH

Key Concepts are highlighted.

CONCEPT DEVELOPMENT

Cooperative Learning: Use the Paired Partner strategy to set up debating teams. After allowing time for the teams to study the pros and cons of strip mining and underground mining, have volunteers debate strip mining and underground mining.

▶ Show samples of peat, lignite, bituminous coal, and anthracite to the students in the order stated. Demonstrate how each sample is a little more difficult to break apart and a little blacker than the preceding sample.

CHECK FOR UNDERSTANDING

Use the Mini Quiz to check for understanding.

MINI QUIZ

Use the Mini Quiz to check students' recall of chapter content.

❶ **In which type of coal mine are tunnels dug to reach the coal?** *underground mines*

❷ **Why can heavy rains be a problem during mining operations?** *Because vegetation has been removed during mining, soil can easily be eroded by heavy rains.*

❸ **What percentage of coal mines in the United States were reclaimed between 1930 and 1970?** *40 percent*

● **REINFORCEMENT 21**

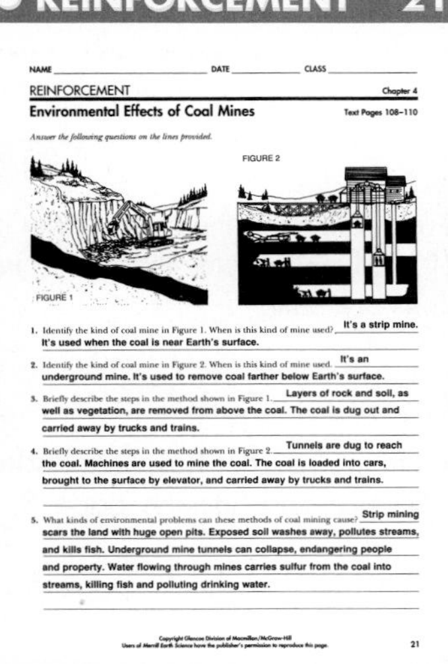

NAME ______ DATE ______ CLASS ______

REINFORCEMENT — Chapter 4

Environmental Effects of Coal Mines — Text Pages 108–110

Answer the following questions on the lines provided.

1. Identify the kind of coal mine in Figure 1. When is this kind of mine used? **It's a strip mine. It's used when the coal is near Earth's surface.**
2. Identify the kind of coal mine in Figure 2. When is this kind of mine used. **It's an underground mine. It's used to remove coal farther below Earth's surface.**
3. Briefly describe the steps in the method shown in Figure 1. **Layers of rock and soil, as well as vegetation, are removed from above the coal. The coal is dug out and carried away by trucks and trains.**
4. Briefly describe the steps in the method shown in Figure 2. **Tunnels are dug to reach the coal. Machines are used to mine the coal. The coal is loaded into cars, brought to the surface by elevator, and carried away by trucks and trains.**
5. What kinds of environmental problems can these methods of coal mining cause? **Strip mining scars the land with huge open pits. Exposed soil washes away, pollutes streams, and kills fish. Underground mine tunnels can collapse, endangering people and property. Water flowing through mines carries sulfur from the coal into streams, killing fish and polluting drinking water.**

21

▲ **ENRICHMENT 21**

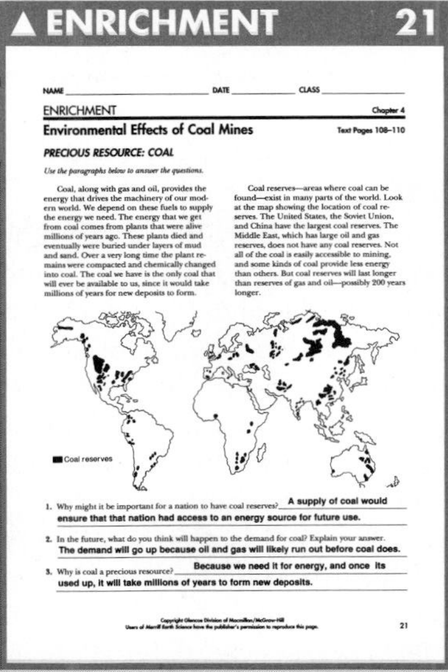

NAME ______ DATE ______ CLASS ______

ENRICHMENT — Chapter 4

Environmental Effects of Coal Mines — Text Pages 108–110

PRECIOUS RESOURCE: COAL

Use the paragraphs below to answer the questions.

Coal, along with gas and oil, provides the energy that drives the machinery of our modern world. We depend on these fuels to supply the energy we need. The energy that we get from coal comes from plants that were alive millions of years ago. These plants died and eventually were buried under layers of mud and sand. Over a very long time the plant remains were compacted and chemically changed into coal. The coal we have is the only coal that will ever be available to us, since it would take millions of years for new deposits to form.

Coal reserves—areas where coal can be found—exist in many parts of the world. Look at the map showing the location of coal reserves. The United States, the Soviet Union, and China have the largest coal reserves. The Middle East, which has large oil and gas reserves, does not have any coal reserves. Not all of the coal is easily accessible to mining, and some kinds of coal provide less energy than others. But coal reserves will last longer than reserves of gas and oil—possibly 200 years longer.

1. Why might it be important for a nation to have coal reserves? **A supply of coal would ensure that that nation had access to an energy source for future use.**
2. In the future, what do you think will happen to the demand for coal? Explain your answer. **The demand will go up because oil and gas will likely run out before coal does.**
3. Why is coal a precious resource? **Because we need it for energy, and once its used up, it will take millions of years to form new deposits.**

21

RETEACH

Cooperative Learning: Using the Paired Partners strategy, have students collaborate on a brief written report of the harmful effects of mining operations. Have each team determine which kind of mine is less damaging to the environment. Each team must support its choices.

EXTENSION

For students who have mastered this section, use the **Reinforcement** and **Enrichment** masters or other OPTIONS provided.

3 CLOSE

▶ Ask questions 1-2 in the Section Review.

FLEX Your Brain

Use the Flex Your Brain activity to have students explore THE ENVIRONMENTAL IMPACT OF COAL MINING.

▶ Invite a geologist from your state geological survey to visit your class and explain how reclamation is handled in your region of the country.

SECTION REVIEW ANSWERS

1. strip mine

2. Answers will vary but could include pollution of streams and lakes and subsidence of land overlying old mines.

YOU DECIDE!

Before answering the questions posed, have each student make a list of 12 personal uses of electricity. Then have each student cut the list in half and in half again to determine his or her three electrical priorities. Have students discuss similarities and differences among lists.

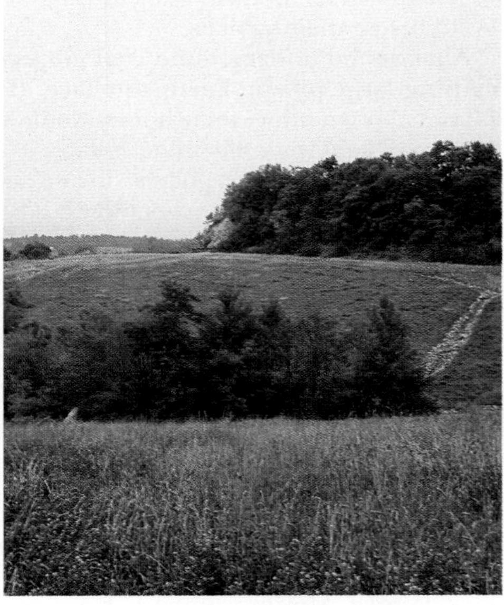

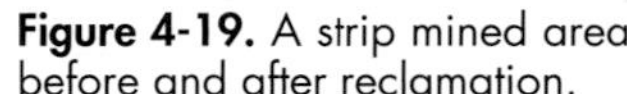

Figure 4-19. A strip mined area before and after reclamation.

Mines exist because we all want the energy that comes from coal. Would you be willing to give up electricity so that our environment didn't suffer? Probably not. Whole communities rely on mining operations for their survival. Men and women work in mines to make money to support themselves and their families. Mines are an important economic and energy resource for all of us.

SECTION REVIEW

1. What type of mine removes coal by removing overlying vegetation, soil, and rock?
2. List two environmental problems caused by underground mining.

You Decide!

Should you be required to use less electricity so that less damage is done to our environment? Should you have to wash dishes only by hand and reduce the use of your TV and stereo? Should people be required to give up energy-using luxuries such as hot tubs and air conditioners? What would you be willing to give up in order to conserve energy and protect our environment?

OPTIONS

ENRICHMENT

▶ Have students find out which areas of the United States remove coal by strip mining and which areas use underground mining methods. Have students hypothesize why some areas use one method of mining over the other. Students should realize the amount of overburden that must be removed varies from one geographic region to another. In some regions, the coal is quite close to the surface and can easily be removed by strip mining techniques. In other places, the coal is deep. Removing the overburden is more difficult and expensive, therefore, underground mines are built.

PROGRAM RESOURCES

From the **Teacher Resource Package** use:
Science and Society, page 8, Cleaning Up Coal.
Activity Worksheets, page 5, Flex Your Brain.

CHAPTER

REVIEW

SUMMARY

4-1: The Rock Cycle

1. A rock is a mixture of one or more minerals.
2. The rock cycle includes all processes by which rocks form. A model of the rock cycle shows how rocks change into other rocks.

4-2: Igneous Rocks

1. Magma and lava are molten materials that harden to form igneous rocks.
2. Intrusive igneous rocks form when magma cools below Earth's surface. Extrusive igneous rocks form when lava cools at Earth's surface.
3. Basaltic rocks are dense, heavy, dark-colored rocks. Granitic rocks are light-colored and less dense than basalts. Andesitic rocks are intermediate between basaltics and granitics.

4-3: Metamorphic Rocks

1. Increases in heat and pressure can cause metamorphic rocks to form.
2. Slate and gneiss are classified as foliated, or banded, metamorphic rocks. When banding is not visible, as in quartzite, metamorphic rocks are classified as nonfoliated.

4-4: Sedimentary Rocks

1. Sedimentary rocks form when fragments of rocks, minerals, and/or organic materials are compacted and cemented together.
2. Clastic sedimentary rocks form when sediments are compacted and/or cemented together. Chemical sedimentary rocks form from minerals dissolved in solution. Organic sedimentary rocks are made mostly of once-living organisms.

4-5: Science and Society: Environmental Effects of Coal Mines

1. Strip mines are mines in which vegetation, rocks, and soil are removed from an area. Tunnels are dug to reach resources in underground mines.
2. Both strip and underground mining pollute the environment and kill wildlife.

KEY SCIENCE WORDS

a. **basaltic**
b. **cementation**
c. **compaction**
d. **extrusive**
e. **foliated**
f. **granitic**
g. **igneous rocks**
h. **intrusive**
i. **lava**
j. **metamorphic rocks**
k. **nonfoliated**
l. **rock**
m. **rock cycle**
n. **sedimentary rocks**
o. **sediments**
p. **strip mine**

UNDERSTANDING VOCABULARY

Match each phrase with the correct term from the list of Key Science Words.

1. mixture of one or more minerals
2. processes that form and change rocks
3. molten material at Earth's surface
4. igneous rocks that form when lava cools
5. rocks formed by heat and pressure
6. quartzite has this kind of texture
7. fragments of rocks, minerals, plants, and animals
8. process by which sediments are pressed together
9. process by which sediments become glued together
10. a mine at Earth's surface

CHAPTER

REVIEW

SUMMARY

Have students read the summary statements to review the major concepts of the chapter.

UNDERSTANDING VOCABULARY

1. l
2. m
3. i
4. d
5. j
6. k
7. o
8. c
9. b
10. p

ASSESSMENT

To assess student understanding of material in this chapter, use the resources listed.

COOPERATIVE LEARNING

Consider using cooperative learning in the THINK AND WRITE CRITICALLY, APPLY, and MORE SKILL BUILDERS sections of the Chapter Review.

PROGRAM RESOURCES

From the **Teacher Resource Package** use:
Chapter Review, pages 11-12.
Chapter and Unit Tests, pages 24-27, Chapter Test.
Chapter and Unit Tests, pages 28-29, Unit Test.

CHAPTER

REVIEW

CHECKING CONCEPTS

1. d
2. d
3. a
4. d
5. a
6. b
7. a
8. c
9. c
10. d

UNDERSTANDING CONCEPTS

11. Temperature, pressure
12. less dense
13. rapid
14. breccias
15. increased

THINK AND WRITE CRITICALLY

16. Rocks are constantly changing due to Earth processes. Thus, the rock cycle has no starting point or end point.
17. Both are molten materials that cool and harden to form igneous rocks. Both form from the melting of existing rock.
18. All are sedimentary rocks that form at or near Earth's surface. Clastic rocks are made of fragments of rocks, minerals, and/or organic matter. Chemical rocks form either from solution or by evaporation. Organic rocks contain an abundance of organic matter.
19. Vegetation is removed, which increases soil erosion and reduces edible plants. Many kinds of wildlife lose their habitats. Nearby water bodies can become polluted with acidic waters.
20. First, the company would have to replace the removed soil. Vegetation could then be planted and nurtured until it was well established. Wildlife that lost their habitats could then be reintroduced into the area.

CHAPTER

REVIEW

CHECKING CONCEPTS

Choose the word or phrase that completes the sentence or answers the question.

1. Which process is a part of the rock cycle?
   a. weathering **c.** melting
   b. deposition **d.** all of these
2. Igneous rocks form from ______ rocks.
   a. sedimentary **c.** other igneous
   b. metamorphic **d.** all of these
3. ______ rocks have large mineral grains.
   a. Intrusive **c.** Obsidian
   b. Extrusive **d.** All of these
4. During metamorphism, minerals can ______.
   a. partly melt **c.** grow larger
   b. become new minerals **d.** all of these
5. Gneiss is a(n) ______ rock.
   a. foliated **c.** intrusive
   b. nonfoliated **d.** extrusive
6. ________ is a rock made of large, angular pieces of sediments.
   a. Conglomerate **c.** Limestone
   b. Breccia **d.** Chalk
7. Which of these is not an organic rock?
   a. shale **c.** chalk
   b. coal **d.** coquina
8. A(n) ______ mine removes overlying rocks and soil to get to the material being mined.
   a. underground **c.** strip
   b. tunnel **d.** none of these
9. ______ mines scar Earth's surface because they require the removal of all vegetation.
   a. Underground **c.** Strip
   b. Tunnel **d.** Reclaimed
10. ______ forms when water carries sulfur from coal in solution.
    a. An open pit **c.** Strip
    b. Soil **d.** Acidic water

UNDERSTANDING CONCEPTS

Complete each sentence.

11. ______ and ______ can cause metamorphic rocks to form from sedimentary rocks.
12. Magma reaches Earth's surface because it is ______ than the surrounding rocks.
13. Rocks with fine-grained textures are the result of ______ cooling.
14. Conglomerates form in much the same way as shales, sandstones, and ______.
15. Erosion of soil is often ______ due to strip mining.

THINK AND WRITE CRITICALLY

16. Explain why the rock cycle has no beginning and no end.
17. Compare magma and lava.
18. Compare and contrast clastic rocks with organic and chemical rocks.
19. How do strip mines harm wildlife?
20. List the steps from first to last that a mining company would have to take to reclaim an area that was strip mined.

APPLY

21. Granite, pumice, and scoria are igneous rocks. Why doesn't granite have air holes like the other two?
22. Contrast the process that forms igneous rocks with the process that forms metamorphic rocks.
23. Why are only a few fossils found in marble?
24. Recall that a mineral is an inorganic solid with a definite structure. Rocks are mixtures of one or more minerals. Why do some scientists not consider coal a rock?
25. Explain why coquina could also be classified as a clastic rock.

MORE SKILL BUILDERS

If you need help, refer to the Skill Handbook.

1. **Concept Mapping:** Copy and complete the concept map shown. Add ovals and connecting lines so you can include examples of each classification of rock.

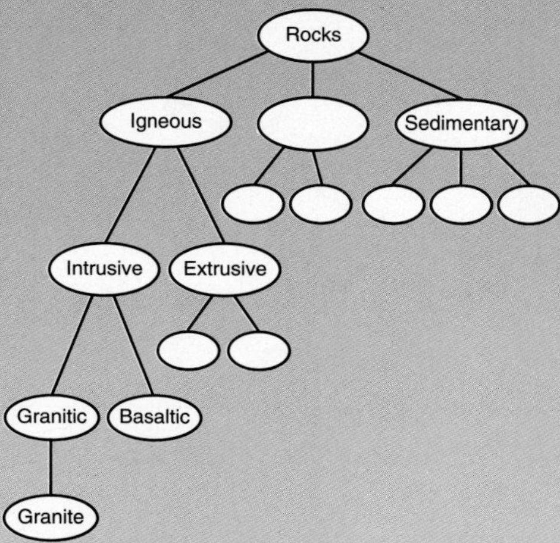

2. **Comparing and Contrasting:** Compare and contrast basaltic and granitic magmas.
3. **Hypothesizing:** A geologist found a sequence of rocks in which 200 million year-old shales were lying on top of 100 million year-old sandstones. Hypothesize how this could happen.
4. **Measuring in SI:** The rock shown below is a limestone that contains fossils. Find the average length of the fossils.
5. **Recognizing Cause and Effect:** Explain the cause and effects of pressure and temperature on shale.

PROJECTS

1. Use sand, gravel, mud, clay, and a salt solution to make at least three igneous, three metamorphic, and three sedimentary "rocks." Label your "rocks" and explain how each forms in nature.
2. Do some research to find out where coal is mined in the United States. Include the type of mining that is done for each deposit. Also include a discussion of how successful the reclamation efforts of the area have been.

APPLY

21. Granite is an intrusive rock that forms deep within Earth. The magma from which it forms is not exposed to air. Most of the other gases are squeezed from the magma due to the immense pressures at these depths.

22. Complete melting must occur for igneous rocks to form. During metamorphism, partial melting or no melting occurs.

23. Marble is a metamorphic rock. The processes that form it often destroy any organic remains.

24. Coal is formed from plant remains, which are organic. Rocks, by definition, are made of minerals. A mineral is an inorganic solid.

25. Coquina is made of broken shells that are cemented together. Because the shells are organic remains, the rock can be classified as an organic rock. But, because of its texture, coquina can be called a clastic rock.

MORE SKILL BUILDERS

1. Concept Mapping: See one possible solution below.

2. Comparing and Contrasting: Both are molten materials that form deep within Earth due to high pressures and temperatures. Basaltic magma is dense, and is rich in iron and magnesium. Granitic magmas are less dense than basaltic magmas. Granite magmas are thick and stiff and contain a lot of silicon and oxygen.

3. Hypothesizing: The sequence has been disturbed since it was deposited because younger rocks overlie older rocks in most rock sequences.

4. Measuring in SI: Answers will vary but should be approximately 1.5 cm.

5. Recognizing Cause and Effect: Pressure and temperature increases caused by overlying rocks can cause the minerals in shale to rearrange. Over time, the effects of the temperature and pressure will produce a slate.

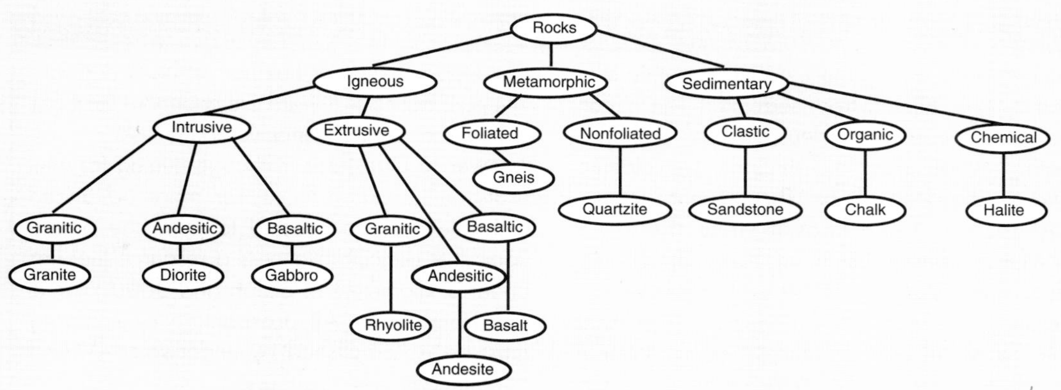

UNIT 2 GLOBAL CONNECTIONS

Objectives

In this unit ending feature, the unit topic, "Rocks and Minerals," is extended into other disciplines. Students will see how the study of rocks and minerals and their properties relate to other disciplines.

Motivate

Cooperative Learning: Assign one Connection to each group of students. Using the Expert Teams strategy, have each group research to find out more about the geographic location of the Connection—its climate, culture, flora, and fauna. Also include what kinds of minerals are found in each place.

Wrap-Up

► After students have reviewed all the boxes on these pages, ask them to form a hypothesis about why diamonds are found in so few places on Earth.

HEALTH

Background: Minerals other than those mentioned in the Health Connection are needed by the human body. These include iodine, required for the production of the hormone made by the thyroid gland and potassium and sodium, both important minerals for the transmission of nerve impulses.
Discussion: Discuss with students the importance of sodium in the functioning of the body. Sodium helps to sustain cell activities throughout the body and is critical to the transport of water and other substances in and out of cells. However, point out that prepared foods now have a very high sodium content. Sodium can raise the blood pressure abnormally.
Answer to Question: The body usually obtains the amount of minerals it needs from foods. Some people take pills to supplement the minerals in food.
Extension: Have students compile a table of the recommended daily allowance of minerals such as calcium, iron, and zinc.

UNIT 2

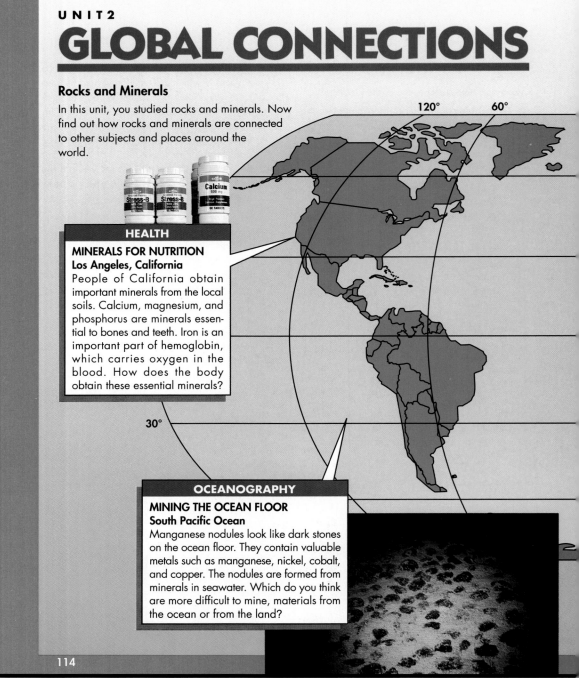

GLOBAL CONNECTIONS

Rocks and Minerals

In this unit, you studied rocks and minerals. Now find out how rocks and minerals are connected to other subjects and places around the world.

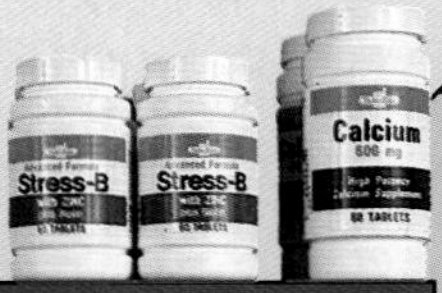

HEALTH

MINERALS FOR NUTRITION
Los Angeles, California
People of California obtain important minerals from the local soils. Calcium, magnesium, and phosphorus are minerals essential to bones and teeth. Iron is an important part of hemoglobin, which carries oxygen in the blood. How does the body obtain these essential minerals?

OCEANOGRAPHY

MINING THE OCEAN FLOOR
South Pacific Ocean
Manganese nodules look like dark stones on the ocean floor. They contain valuable metals such as manganese, nickel, cobalt, and copper. The nodules are formed from minerals in seawater. Which do you think are more difficult to mine, materials from the ocean or from the land?

OCEANOGRAPHY

Background: Manganese nodules contain substances precipitated from seawater. The minerals gather around a nucleus, such as a shark's tooth, a small piece of fish bone, or volcanic lava on the ocean floor. The presence of the nodules has been known since the *HMS Challenger* dredged them up 100 years ago.
Discussion: Discuss that the biggest problem in the mining of manganese nodules is a political one: To whom do the nodules belong? Internationally accepted legal controls for the ownership of the resources of the continental shelf have been established, but the question of the ownership of the deep ocean floor has not yet been decided. The possibilities of reward are enormous for those nations that devote themselves to the task.
Answer to Question: Although mining for minerals on land is difficult, far more advanced technologies are needed to mine the ocean floor. It is difficult to access a resource that lies under 5 kilometers of ocean and 3000 kilometers from shore. All prospecting and mining must be accomplished by underwater TV and remote controlled grabbers.
Extension: Have students determine the location of manganese deposits on a map of the ocean floor.

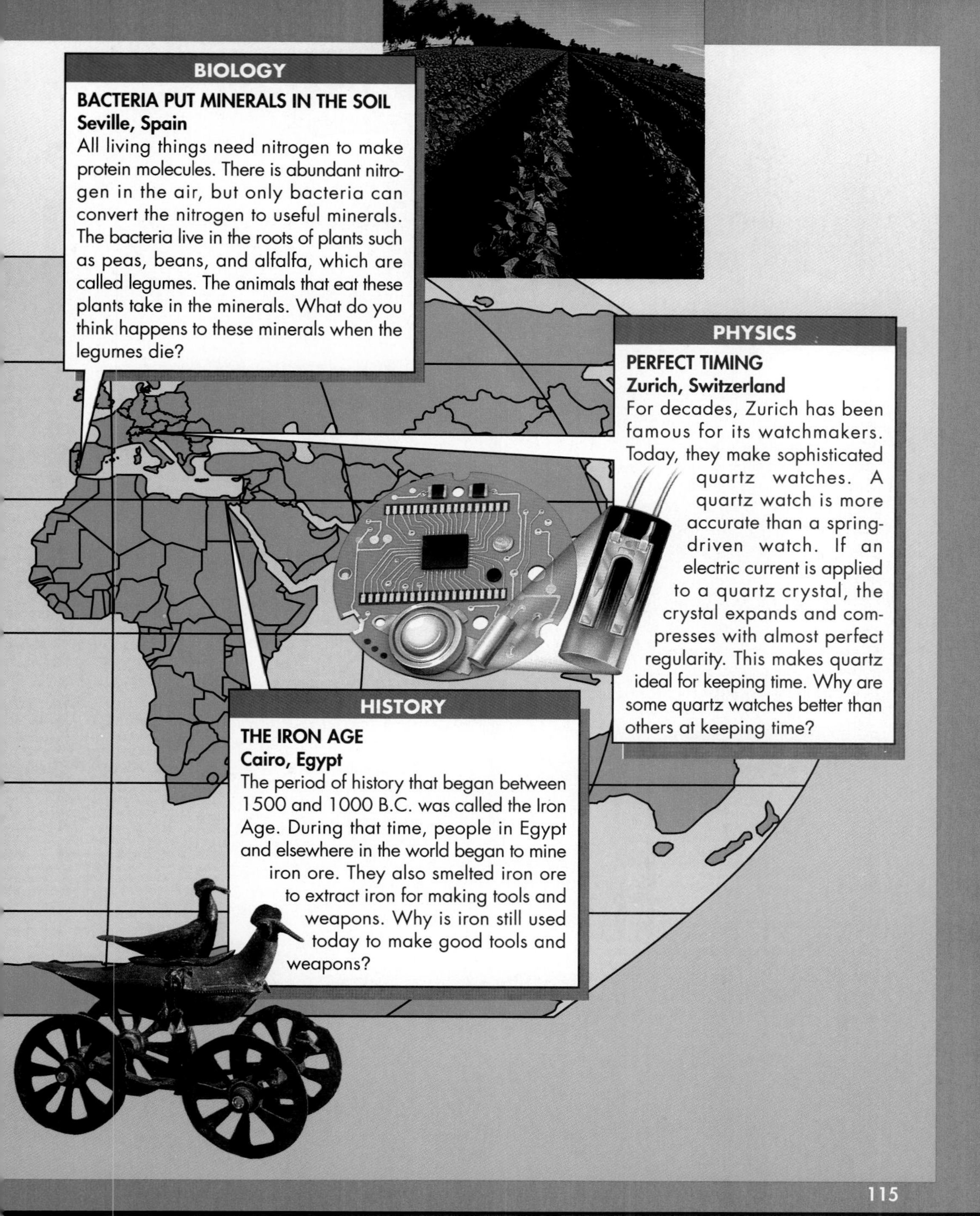

BIOLOGY

BACTERIA PUT MINERALS IN THE SOIL
Seville, Spain
All living things need nitrogen to make protein molecules. There is abundant nitrogen in the air, but only bacteria can convert the nitrogen to useful minerals. The bacteria live in the roots of plants such as peas, beans, and alfalfa, which are called legumes. The animals that eat these plants take in the minerals. What do you think happens to these minerals when the legumes die?

PHYSICS

PERFECT TIMING
Zurich, Switzerland
For decades, Zurich has been famous for its watchmakers. Today, they make sophisticated quartz watches. A quartz watch is more accurate than a spring-driven watch. If an electric current is applied to a quartz crystal, the crystal expands and compresses with almost perfect regularity. This makes quartz ideal for keeping time. Why are some quartz watches better than others at keeping time?

HISTORY

THE IRON AGE
Cairo, Egypt
The period of history that began between 1500 and 1000 B.C. was called the Iron Age. During that time, people in Egypt and elsewhere in the world began to mine iron ore. They also smelted iron ore to extract iron for making tools and weapons. Why is iron still used today to make good tools and weapons?

115

HISTORY

Background: Some people in the Middle East began to smelt iron ore and to use iron for tools as early as 3000 B.C. It was not until the Iron Age in that region, however, that the wide use of iron for tools became prevalent. Iron was cheap because it was plentiful.

Discussion: Discuss the dual effect the possession of iron had on the people who used it. First, they were able to build military power. Second, iron tools allowed people to clear large tracts of land for farming.

Answer to Question: Iron can be hammered into thin sheets or drawn into thin wires. If carbon is added to iron, steel can be made. Both iron and steel are hard and make strong tools.

Extension: Have students make a pie graph comparing the amount of iron ore mined in various sections of the United States.

PHYSICS

Background: Quartz has an interesting property called piezoelectricity, which means that pressure applied to a quartz crystal produces an electric current. Using this property, quartz can be used to make gauges that measure high pressures. The higher the pressure, the stronger the current produced by the quartz.

Discussion: Discuss the accuracy of quartz crystals. The number of vibrations of the quartz wafer to which an electric current is applied is about 100 000 vibrations per second. The vibrating crystals are off by no more than one vibration out of 10 billion. Some precision quartz clocks lose or gain no more than one second every ten years.

Answer to Question: The mechanical parts of some quartz watches are better made than those parts in other quartz watches.

Extension: Have students research how the piezoelectricity property of quartz is used in watches to generate pulses one second apart.

BIOLOGY

Background: The bacteria that take in nitrogen from the air are called nitrogen-fixing bacteria. The bacteria convert the nitrogen to ammonia, which is a product containing nitrogen that is needed by plants. Other bacteria convert the ammonia to important minerals—nitrites and nitrates—needed by plants and other living things.

Discussion: Discuss the practice of crop rotation to resupply minerals to the soil. Explain that some plants, such as corn, are not able to convert nitrogen to ammonia. Instead, corn uses up the ammonia products in the soil. Farmers all over the world rotate crops by growing corn during one season and growing one of the legumes during the next growing season. The legumes restore the minerals taken out by the corn.

Answer to Question: When the plants die and decay, these minerals are released into the soil.

Extension: Have students research nitrogen-fixing bacteria and list useful compounds that have nitrogen fixed to them.

METALLURGICAL ENGINEER

Background: Usually, a metallurgical engineer specializes in one of three branches. The work of extractive and physical metallurgists is described in the Career feature. Mechanical metallurgical engineers develop and improve metal-working processes, such as casting and forging.

Career Issue: Competition from imported steel has caused some American steel mills to close. Those mills that have remained open have been forced to modernize their equipment in order to compete more favorably with foreign steel.

Related Career	Education
Mining Engineer	college
Iron Worker	on-site training
Electroplating	technical school

What do you think? Ask students to discuss why imported steel is able to compete successfully with steel made in the United States.

GEMOLOGIST

Background: A gemologist may work for a large jewelry company. These companies purchase precious stones in bulk. Only after the gemologist categorizes the stones according to value can the jeweler decide what kind of setting is appropriate for each gem.

Career Issue: Many precious gems are held in collections owned by governments of the world. Some people think that the collections should be sold to provide for needy people in those countries. Others think that as long as the governments own the jewels, they belong to all the people of the country. If the jewels were sold, the people would lose a great national treasure.

Related Career	Education
Jeweler	high school
Jewelry Designer	college
Diamond Cutter	trade school

What do you think? Have students use Archimedes' Principle to determine the specific gravity of corundum and amethyst quartz.

CAREERS

METALLURGICAL ENGINEER

Metallurgical engineers develop new types of metals with properties required for special tasks. For example, they may produce a material that is heat resistant for use in machinery that operates at very high temperatures. Metallurgical engineers also search for new ways to extract metals from their ores. Some of them determine ways to convert metals into useful products.

Metallurgical engineers usually have a degree in engineering with a specialty in metallurgy. A student interested in becoming a metallurgical engineer should take courses in mathematics, chemistry, and physics.

For Additional Information

Contact the Minerals, Metals, and Materials Society, 420 Commonwealth Drive, Warrendale, PA 15086.

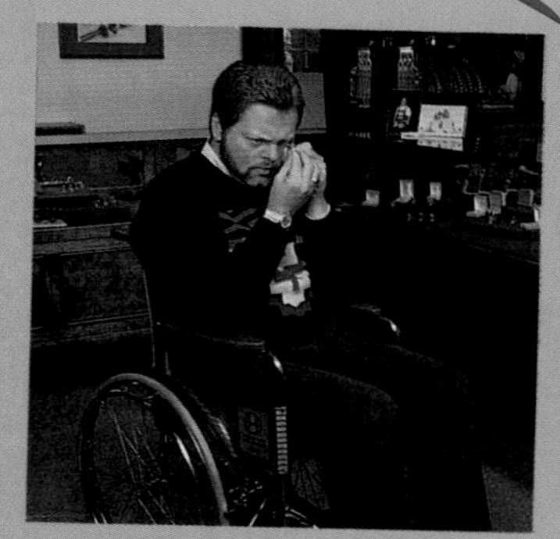

GEMOLOGIST

A *gemologist* examines gems to grade them for purity and to estimate their value. Jewelers depend on the expertise of gemologists to appraise gems at a fair price. One benefit of being a gemologist is that you can look at and enjoy the beauty of precious stones.

Most gemologists receive training at a trade school after high school. Students learn to use a refractometer to measure how light passing through the gems is refracted, or bent. They also use a stone's specific gravity for identification purposes.

For Additional Information

Contact the Jewelers of America, Time-Life Building, Suite 650, 1271 Avenue of the Americas, New York, NY 10020.

UNIT READINGS

►Amato, Ivan. "Diamond Fever." *Science News,* August 4, 1990, p. 72.
►Pough, Frederick H. *Rocks and Minerals.* Boston: Houghton Mifflin, 1983.
►"Trapping Wastes in Glass." *Popular Science,* November 1990.

116

UNIT READINGS

Background

► "Diamond Fever" shows unique electron micrographs of synthetic diamonds.

► *Rocks and Minerals* is an excellent field guide to the rocks and minerals mentioned in the text.

More Readings

1. Fisher, Arthur. "A Gem of an Idea." *Popular Science,* October, 1990, p. 25. This is an article on synthetic diamonds that helps students understand how diamonds form in nature.

2. "Mining with Microbes: A Labor of Bug." *Science News,* April 14, 1990, p. 236. This interesting article discusses how bacteria can be used to mine for copper, gold, cobalt, and uranium.

Classics

► Cuvier, G. *Essay on the theory of the earth with mineralogical notes by Professor Jameson.* 1818. This essay is interesting to read to find out what was known about minerals in the beginning of the last century.

► *Report on HMS Challenger Expedition,* 1895. The total report filled 50 volumes.

SCIENCE & ART

Native American Pottery

In Chapters 3 and 4, you read about the properties of rocks and minerals. As you read the following paragraphs about Maria Martinez and her pottery, you'll discover that rocks and minerals can be used to fashion works of art.

The Pueblo people of the Southwest had one of the most highly developed civilizations to ever inhabit North America. Like other Native Americans, the Pueblos have always had a good understanding of how to make use of the natural resources of their environment. They employed minerals and rocks to produce useful and artistic products. Of particular interest are the beautiful hand-painted pieces of pottery fashioned by Pueblo craftspeople.

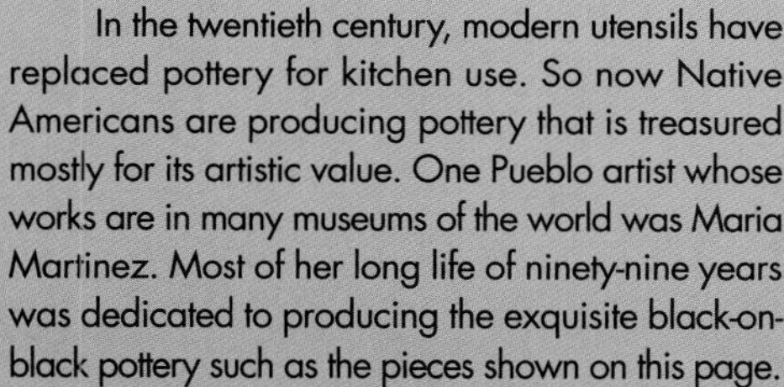

In the twentieth century, modern utensils have replaced pottery for kitchen use. So now Native Americans are producing pottery that is treasured mostly for its artistic value. One Pueblo artist whose works are in many museums of the world was Maria Martinez. Most of her long life of ninety-nine years was dedicated to producing the exquisite black-on-black pottery such as the pieces shown on this page.

Black pottery had not been produced by Native Americans for over 700 years until an archaeologist discovered some black pottery shards in an excavation of an ancient Native American village near San Ildefonso. He brought them to Maria who had already become well known for her multicolored pottery. Maria began working with a clay, rich in several minerals, found near her home, hoping to find the secret of how to make black pottery. Then one day she and her husband smothered the flames while the clay pots were being fired. When they removed the pots, they found that the clay had blackened! They had finally discovered how to duplicate the ancient black pottery.

Maria later devised a way to make the black pots shine by polishing the surface with a smooth stone before firing. After awhile, she combined polished designs with a flat finish called matte.

When demands for her black-on-black pottery exceeded her ability to produce them, Maria taught others in her village the secret. Soon Maria Martinez's black-on-black pottery replaced the earlier styles in several villages. Other Native Americans, influenced by Maria, have received recognition for their artistic pottery: Grace Medicine Flower, Cristina Naranjo, Joy "Frogwoman" Navasie, Blue Corn, and Nampeyo (a Hopi artist).

In Your Own Words

▶ Maria Martinez's rediscovery of an ancient skill came after many trials and errors. Write an essay to compare and contrast the techniques of artists and scientists. Explain how both must experiment, observe, and analyze results to achieve their goals.

Source: *Masterpieces of Fifty Centuries: The Metropolitan Museum of Art.* New York: E.P. Dutton and Company, Inc., 1970.

Biography: Theodore Rousseau was the Vice-Director and Curator in Chief of the Metropolitan Museum of Art at the time of the exhibition of the Masterpieces of Fifty Centuries. His efforts gave shape to the exhibition. According to Rousseau, "Every work of art is a mirror, reflecting the time and the place in which it was made, and the feelings of the human being who created it....To see and understand this in a work of art is one of the most satisfying aspects of its enjoyment....There is no 'ancient art,' no 'modern art.' There are simply human instincts and emotions constantly recurring and inspiring different peoples at different times."

TEACHING STRATEGY

Cooperative Learning: Have groups of students work together to discuss Theodore Rousseau's ideas expressed in the Biography. Ask them to explain how the works of art discussed in "Science and the Arts" are a mirror, reflecting the time and place in which they were made.

▶ **Writing an Essay:** Explain why there is no "ancient art," no "modern art."

▶ Ask the students if they think "human instincts and emotions are constantly recurring and inspiring different peoples at different times."

▶ Discuss the materials of which each of the statues was made: *King Sahure and a Divinity*—diorite; *Statue of Mitry*—wood, covered with plaster, *Seated Figure of Hatshepsut*—white limestone. Ask students why they think these materials were good choices.

Cooperative Learning: Have students discuss if the statues shown seem to be of real people. Have them role play, as the subject of each piece of sculpture plans with the sculptor the kind of statue to be made.

Other Works

▶ Other books about ancient sculptures include:

Craven, Thomas. *The Rainbow Book of Art.* New York: The World Publishing Company, 1956.

Ruskin, Ariane. *History of Art.* New York: Franklin Watts, Inc., 1974.

UNIT

3

THE CHANGING SURFACE OF EARTH

In Unit 3, students are introduced to the processes and agents that change Earth's surface, as well as the surface features formed by these processes. The physical and chemical processes of weathering and the agents of erosion, including gravity, water, glaciers, and wind, are described.

CONTENTS

ADVANCE PREPARATION

Activities

▶ **Activity 5-1, page 125,** requires 100 g limestone and shale samples.

▶ **Activity 6-1, page 161,** requires a stream table with sand.

▶ **Activity 6-2, page 166,** requires 5 flat pans, a hair dryer, and a sprinkling can.

▶ **Activity 7-1, page 180,** requires a stopwatch and a stream table with sand.

▶ **Activity 8-1, page 213,** requires a plastic model landform.

Field Trips and Speakers

▶ Ask a farmer to visit class to discuss how erosion affects his or her crops.

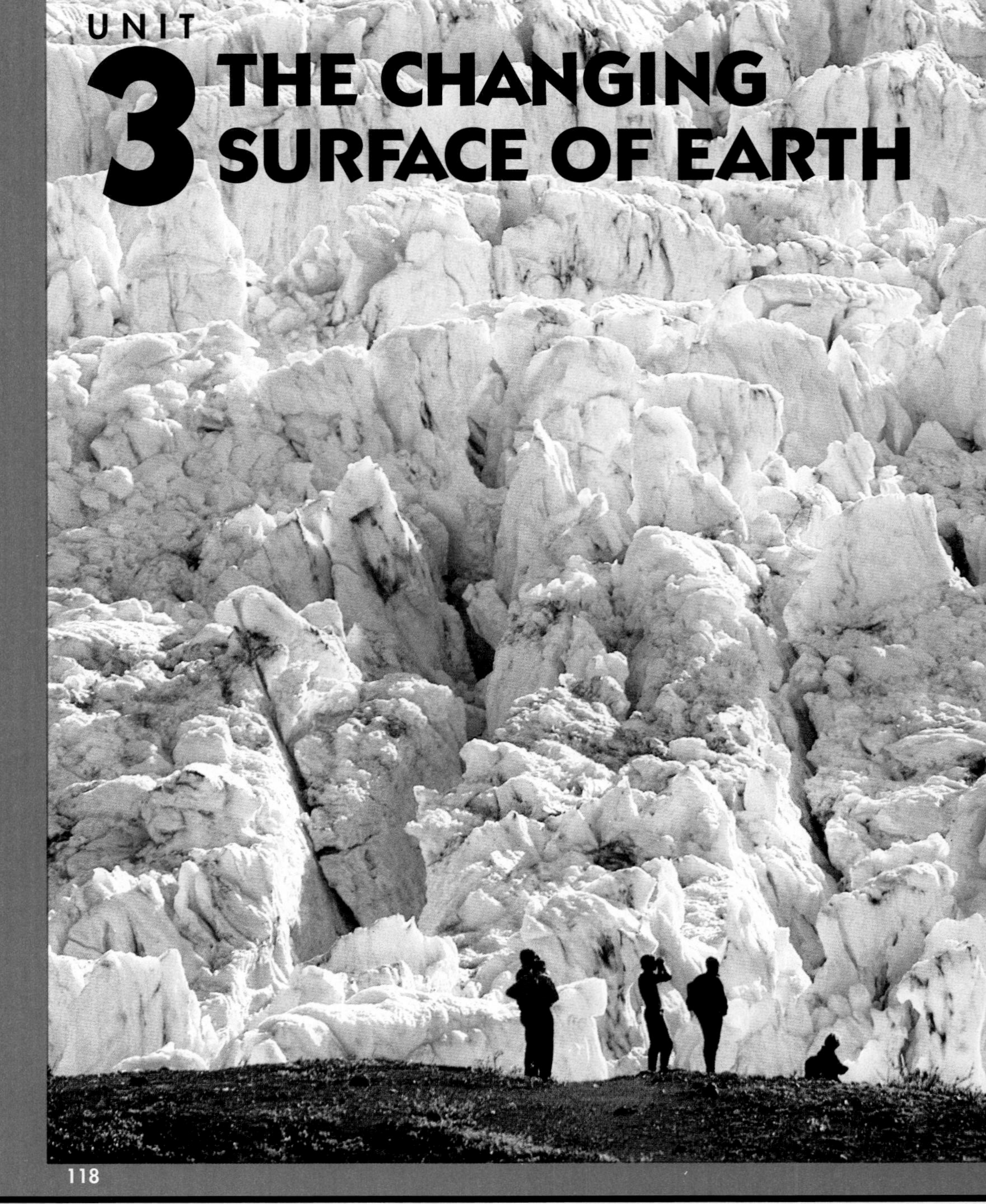

118

OPTIONS

Cross Curriculum

▶ Have students in horticulture or domestic arts class report to students on which type of soil is best for a flower garden or a vegetable garden.

▶ Have students determine which areas of the United States are most affected by wind erosion.

▶ As students study geography, have them determine the type of maps used to locate positions on Earth's surface.

Science at Home

▶ Have students select an area near their homes that would have the greatest amount of erosion. Ask students to explain why they chose the areas they did.

Cooperative Learning: Using the Paired Partners strategy, have students devise methods that would minimize erosion of soil from a garden or flower bed at their homes.

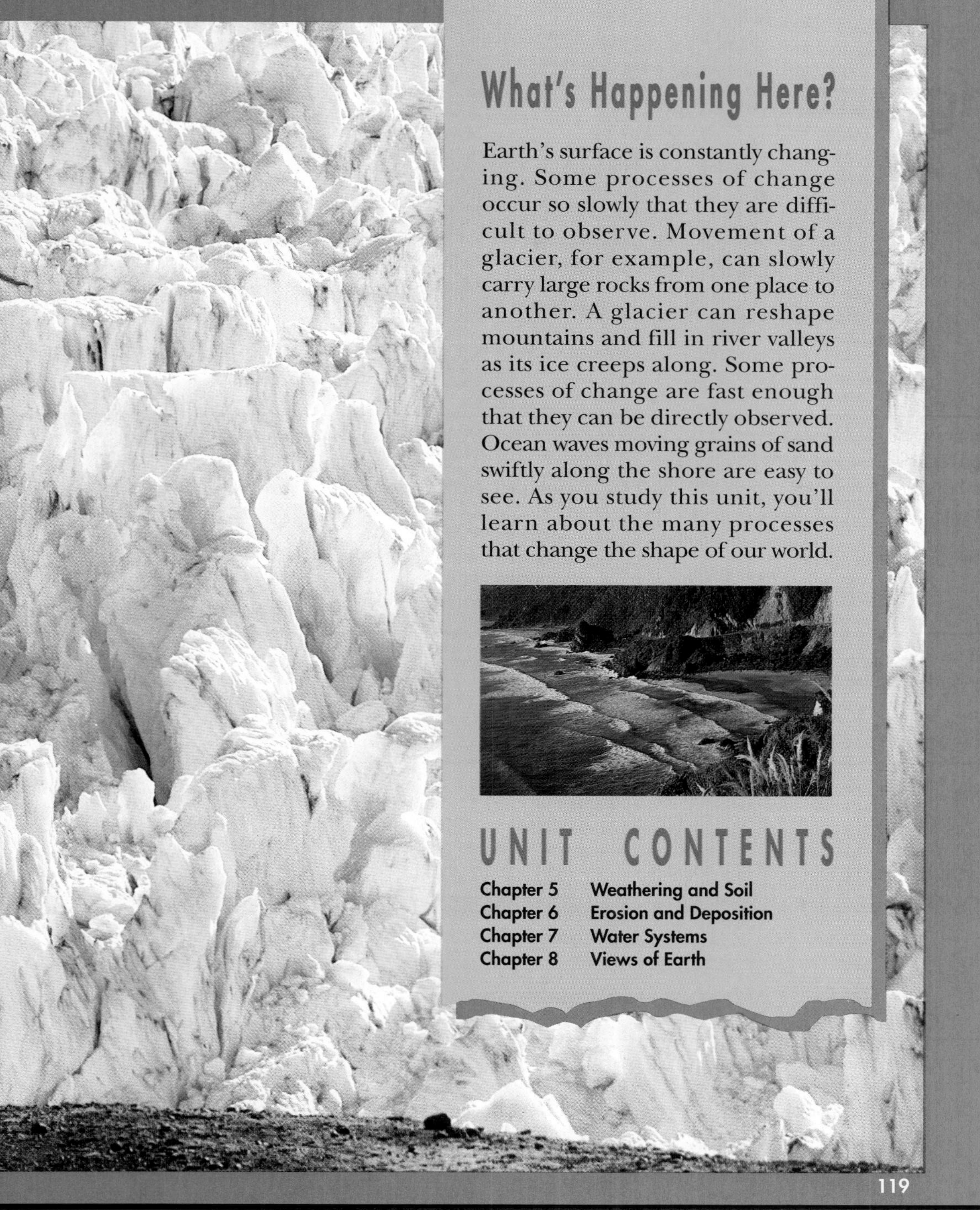

What's Happening Here?

Earth's surface is constantly changing. Some processes of change occur so slowly that they are difficult to observe. Movement of a glacier, for example, can slowly carry large rocks from one place to another. A glacier can reshape mountains and fill in river valleys as its ice creeps along. Some processes of change are fast enough that they can be directly observed. Ocean waves moving grains of sand swiftly along the shore are easy to see. As you study this unit, you'll learn about the many processes that change the shape of our world.

UNIT CONTENTS

INTRODUCING THE UNIT

What's Happening Here?

▶ Have students look at the photos and read the text. Ask them to tell you what's happening here. Point out to students that in this unit they will be studying Earth's surface features as well as how they change because of weathering, erosion, and deposition processes.

▶ **Background:** Many large boulders, called glacial erratics, have been transported as far as 500 km from their source area. In a few cases, glacial erratics have been carried over 1000 km from their source by moving ice. Glaciers are capable of transporting huge volumes of sediment at a very slow rate. Moving water, such as the water along a coastline, erodes large volumes of sediments at a faster rate.

Previewing the Chapters

▶ Have students search through Chapter 6 for figures that show examples of erosion caused by gravity, water, ice, and wind.

▶ Have students participate in a scavenger hunt through the unit looking for photographs of soil evolution (page 128), the soil profile (page 131), deposition by water (page 151), the water cycle (page 173), and the four types of mountains (pages 199-201).

Tying to Previous Knowledge

▶ Ask how many students have ever helped to plant a shrub or a tree. Have one student describe what the soil was like as it was removed from the ground.

▶ Have students recall evidence of erosion they have observed while walking near the school or their homes. Ask students what probably caused the erosion they observed.

▶ Ask a volunteer to describe what happened to water that fell on the ground during a recent rainstorm.

▶ Use the **Inquiry Questions** in the OPTIONS box to the left to investigate with students how sediment is formed by weathering and carried away by the agents of erosion.

Multicultural Awareness

Have students research the practices of various cultures regarding the use of river systems. Many cultures have built up centers of civilization around rivers. Other cultures look on rivers in their area as part of a religious background.

Inquiry Questions

Use the following questions to focus a discussion of how sediment is formed by weathering and transported by agents of erosion.

1. How could alternating freezing and thawing temperatures cause rocks to break?
2. What happens to sediments that fall into a stream?
3. Why do beaches continually change shape?
4. Where do sand particles that collect on a beach originate?

CHAPTER

Weathering and Soil

CHAPTER SECTION	OBJECTIVES	ACTIVITIES
5-1 Weathering (3 days)	1. **Contrast** mechanical weathering and chemical weathering. 2. **Explain** the effects of climate on weathering.	**Activity 5-1:** *Weathering Rocks,* p. 125 **MINI-Lab:** *How does rust form?* p. 126
5-2 Soil (2 days)	1. **Explain** how soil evolves from rock. 2. **Describe** soil by comparing A, B, and C soil horizons. 3. **Discuss** how environmental conditions affect the evolution of soils.	**MINI-LAB:** *What is soil made of?* p. 129 **Activity 5-2:** *Soil Characteristics,* p. 130
5-3 Soil Loss Science & Society (1 day)	1. **Explain** the importance of soil. 2. **Identify** and **describe** activities that lead to soil loss.	
Chapter Review		

ACTIVITY MATERIALS

FIND OUT	ACTIVITIES		MINI-LABS	
Page 121 several samples of different rocks for each student	**5-1 Weathering Rocks, p. 125** 100 g limestone or shale samples plastic bottle with cap wire strainer pan balance water	**5-2 Soil Characteristics, p. 130** soil sample sand clay gravel hand lens water paper scissors plastic coffee can lids (3) cheese cloth squares rubber bands pencil 250-mL beakers (3) thumbtack large polystyrene cups (3) graduated cylinder	**How does rust form? p. 126** piece of steel wool paper towels water shallow pan	**What is soil made of? p. 129** soil samples dissecting probe sheet of white paper plastic bags microscope or magnifying glass light source

CHAPTER FEATURES	TEACHER RESOURCE PACKAGE	OTHER RESOURCES
Problem Solving: *Jamie's Frozen Failure,* p. 124 **Skill Builder:** *Recognizing Cause and Effect,* p. 127	**Ability Level Worksheets** ◆ ***Study Guide,*** p. 22 ● ***Reinforcement,*** p. 22 ▲ ***Enrichment,*** p. 22 **Activity Worksheet,** pp. 39-40 **MINI-Lab Worksheet,** p. 45 **Concept Mapping,** pp. 15-16	**Lab Manual:** *Chemical Weathering,* p. 37
Technology: *Knock on Wood!* p. 132 **Skill Builder:** *Concept Mapping,* p. 133	**Ability Level Worksheets** ◆ ***Study Guide,*** p. 23 ● ***Reinforcement,*** p. 23 ▲ ***Enrichment,*** p. 23 **Activity Worksheet,** pp. 41-42 **MINI-Lab Worksheet,** p. 46 **Critical Thinking/Problem Solving,** p. 11 **Cross-Curricular Connections,** p. 9 **Transparency Master,** pp. 13-14	**Color Transparency 7,** Soil Evolution **Lab Manual:** *Transporting Soil Materials by Runoff,* p. 39 **Lab Manual:** *Soil Infiltration by Groundwater,* p. 41
You Decide! p. 136	**Ability Level Worksheets** ◆ ***Study Guide,*** p. 24 ● ***Reinforcement,*** p. 24 ▲ ***Enrichment,*** p. 24 **Science and Society,** p. 9	
Summary Key Science Words Understanding Vocabulary Checking Concepts Understanding Concepts Think & Write Critically Apply More Skill Builders Projects	**Chapter Review,** pp. 13-14 **Chapter Test,** pp. 35-38	**Chapter Review Software** **Test Bank**

◆ **Basic** ● **Average** ▲ **Advanced**

ADDITIONAL MATERIALS

SOFTWARE	AUDIOVISUAL	BOOKS/MAGAZINES
Landslides, IBM. *Weathering and Erosion,* Queue. *Water on the Land,* Queue.	*Soils: An Introduction,* film, BFA. *Erosion and Weathering,* film, EBEC. *Erosion—Leveling the Land,* film, EBEC. *Strata: Earth's Changing Crust,* film, BFA.	Lutgens, Frederick K. and Edward J. Tarbuck. *Essentials of Geology* 3rd ed. Columbus, OH: Merrill Publishing, 1989. Ollier, C.D. *Weathering* 2nd ed. NY: John Wiley and Sons, Inc., 1986. Trudgill, Stephen T. *Weathering and Erosion Sources and Methods in Geography*. Stoneham, MA: Butterworth Publishing, 1982.

CHAPTER

5

WEATHERING AND SOIL

THEME DEVELOPMENT: Energy and evolution are two of the major themes emphasized in this chapter. The importance of the transfer of mechanical and chemical energy in weathering processes should be a major focus of your teaching the chapter. Equally important is an emphasis on the evolution of weathered rock into soil.

CHAPTER OVERVIEW

- ▶**Section 5-1:** This section discusses mechanical and chemical weathering and the effects of climate on weathering.
- ▶**Section 5-2:** The evolution of soil from weathered rock is introduced. Soil horizons are contrasted and factors that affect the evolution of different soil types are briefly discussed.
- ▶**Section 5-3: Science & Society** Human activities that cause soil loss are discussed. The You Decide feature asks students whether public land should be better protected against soil erosion.

CHAPTER VOCABULARY

weathering
mechanical weathering
ice wedging
chemical weathering
oxidation
soil
humus
soil profile
horizon
leaching
desertification

CHAPTER

5 Weathering and Soil

120

OPTIONS

For Your Gifted Students

Have students research and construct a compost pile that can be added to, compared to the surrounding soil, and analyzed throughout the year. Students can transfer it to a garden plot in the spring to enrich the soil. Interested students should contact the state Department of Natural Resources for information on what should be included in the compost pile. Students could also enlist the services of the Industrial Technology department to help construct a storage bin.

These stone carvings stand guard on tiny Easter Island in the South Pacific Ocean. They show the results of being exposed to weathering for hundreds of years. What happens to rock that is weathered?

FIND OUT!

Do this simple activity to find out what happens to different types of rocks when they are exposed to weather.

Obtain small samples of several different types of rocks. You could use sandstone, shale, granite, and basalt. Hold any two of the rocks above a piece of white paper and rub them together.

Observe the small particles of rock that fell to the white paper. Which rock broke apart more easily when rubbed? Repeat this process with the other rocks. Which rocks do you think would last the longest if exposed to wind and rain?

Gearing Up

Previewing the Chapter

Use this outline to help you focus on important ideas in this chapter.

Section 5-1 Weathering
- About Weathering
- Mechanical Weathering
- Chemical Weathering
- Effects of Climate on Weathering

Section 5-2 Soil
- Formation of Soil
- Soil Profiles
- Types of Soil

Section 5-3 Science and Society
Soil Loss
- Human Activities and Soil Loss

Previewing Science Skills

- In the **Skill Builders**, you will recognize cause and effect and make a concept map.
- In the **Activities**, you will observe, infer, interpret data, and measure.
- In the **MINI-Labs**, you will observe, and compare and contrast.

What's next?

Now that you've seen how rocks can break down, you'll learn about the processes that cause rocks to break down. You will have a better understanding of the rock cycle by studying these processes.

For Your Mainstreamed Students

Students can simulate the effects of erosion. Have students find a spot outside the school close enough to the building to be within reach of an extension cord. Have volunteers pour two piles of sand or potting soil on the ground. Cover one pile with leaves or grass clippings and leave the other uncovered. With students well out of the way, hook up an electric fan and turn it on so that the air hits both piles equally. Have students observe and discuss the erosion that takes place. Next, try hooking up a sprinkler that waters both piles. If time permits, leave the piles exposed to wind, rain, and other elements of weather for several weeks and have students compare the results.

INTRODUCING THE CHAPTER

Use the Find Out activity to introduce students to mechanical weathering. Inform students that they will be learning more about how rocks weather and how soils evolve as they read the chapter.

FIND OUT!

Preparation: Have several samples of different types of rocks on hand including sandstones, shales, granites, and basalts.

Materials: several samples of different rocks for each student.

Cooperative Learning: Have Paired Partners look at the small particles with a hand lens or microscope. Then ask: **In what ways are these small particles similar to the rocks?** *Similarities may include color and texture. Differences might include size and shape. Also, perhaps only certain minerals from the rock were broken off.*

Teaching Tips

- Most students will probably say that the rocks that did not easily break would last the longest if exposed to wind and rain. Explain that this may not be true. The rate of weathering is affected by the composition of a rock and the degree to which it is consolidated, among other things.

Gearing Up

Have students study the Gearing Up feature to familiarize themselves with the chapter. Discuss the relationships of the topics in the outline.

What's Next?

Have a student read What's Next aloud. Before beginning the first section, make sure students understand the connection between the Find Out activity and the topics to follow.

SECTION 5-1

PREPARATION

SECTION BACKGROUND

▶Generally, the smaller the object, the greater its surface area per unit of volume. Mechanical weathering exposes more surface area of a rock to chemical weathering by breaking large masses of rock into smaller units.

▶Minerals in metamorphic rocks generally weather more rapidly than the minerals in igneous rocks.

▶In igneous rocks, the first minerals to crystallize from magma or lava weather the fastest. Quartz, which is the last mineral to form, is very resistant to weathering.

▶The sedimentary rocks shale and limestone weather rapidly in humid environments.

PREPLANNING

▶To prepare for Activity 5-1, obtain limestone or shale samples, plastic bottles with caps, wire strainers, and pan balances.

▶To prepare for the Mini-Lab, obtain steel wool and shallow pans.

1 MOTIVATE

Cooperative Learning: Have Paired Partners list humanmade objects they believe are deteriorating. Their lists might include sidewalks, bridges, roads, buildings, and other structures. Ask students what agents may be causing the breakdown of these structures. Lead students to realize that several factors may be responsible for the breakdown of a single structure. Explain that many of the same agents are at work weathering Earth's rocks.

▶Have students collect pictures of objects that are being weathered. Photographs might include cracks in rocks, sidewalks, buildings, and so on.

5-1 Weathering

New Science Words

weathering
mechanical weathering
ice wedging
chemical weathering
oxidation

Objectives

- ▶ **Contrast mechanical weathering and chemical weathering.**
- ▶ **Explain the effects of climate on weathering.**

About Weathering

Have you ever noticed, while you've been walking down a sidewalk, that there is sand and grit along the sidewalk and the curb? Also, there always seems to be a layer of gritty dirt on the sidewalk at the bottom of stone or concrete buildings. Where do you suppose this dirt comes from? Actually, it is made up of small particles that break loose from the concrete in the curbs and the stones or concrete in the buildings.

Conditions and processes in the environment cause stone and concrete to break apart. In Chapter 4, the rock cycle showed you how sedimentary rocks form from pieces of other rocks. But you haven't investigated the conditions and processes that create these sediments. Let's see how it all happens.

Figure 5-1. Weathering changes sharp, jagged mountains into smooth, rolling mountains and hills over long periods of time.

OPTIONS

Meeting Different Ability Levels

For Section 5-1, use the following **Teacher Resource Masters** depending upon individual students' needs.

- ◆ **Study Guide Master** for all students.
- ● **Reinforcement Master** for students of average and above average ability levels.
- ▲ **Enrichment Master** for above average students.

Additional Teacher Resource Package masters are listed in the OPTIONS box throughout the section. The additional masters are appropriate for all students.

◆ STUDY GUIDE 22

NAME ______ DATE ______ CLASS ______

STUDY GUIDE — Chapter 5

Weathering — Text Pages 122–127

Use the words in the box to fill in the blanks of the paragraphs.

plants	tropical	mechanical
freezing	moisture	acids
climate	oxidation	air
sediments	desert	minerals
chemical	ice wedging	cracks
dissolves	temperatures	carbonic acid

Weathering is the breaking of rocks into __sediments__. There are two main types of weathering. __Mechanical__ weathering involves breaking rocks without changing their chemical composition. For example, rocks may collide with other rocks and break apart. In __ice wedging__, water trapped in rock cracks freezes and expands, forcing the rocks apart. __Plants__ can also cause mechanical weathering. As their roots grow and put pressure on rocks, __cracks__ widen and rock fragments may fall off. __Chemical__ weathering involves water, air, and other substances reacting with the minerals in the rocks. Water __dissolves__ the minerals in rocks or combines with compounds in the __air__. When metal is exposed to water and oxygen, __oxidation__ occurs and rust forms. __Acids__ in plant roots and mosses can also dissolve the __minerals__ in rocks. Water and carbon dioxide combine to form __carbonic acid__, which dissolves minerals such as calcite in limestone.

How rapidly weathering occurs in an area depends on the __climate__. In __tropical__ regions, chemical weathering is most rapid. Chemical weathering happens more slowly in __desert__ areas and polar regions due to a lack of __moisture__ and/or low __temperatures__. Whenever __freezing__ and thawing alternate, mechanical weathering becomes an important form of weathering.

22

Weathering is the term used to describe the breaking of rocks into smaller fragments. Weathering changes things around us gradually over long periods of time. It wears mountains down to hills over thousands of years. Weathering affects both naturally formed rocks and human-made structures such as buildings and streets. There are two main types of weathering processes—mechanical and chemical.

What is weathering?

Mechanical Weathering

Mechanical weathering is weathering that breaks apart rocks without changing their chemical composition. This can happen in many different ways. Suppose you are sitting beside a swiftly moving river. As you watch the swift water move by, you can only imagine what's happening below the surface. There, water is lifting rocks from the bottom and forcing them to collide with other rocks. When they hit, tiny pieces break off of the rocks. In this example, the force of the water creates the energy necessary to cause mechanical weathering.

You've probably seen the results of another type of mechanical weathering if you've ever ridden a skateboard on an old sidewalk. Some old sidewalks near trees are so cracked that you can't ride on them. Can you guess what causes this to happen? As trees grow, their roots spread through the soil. As roots grow under the sidewalks, they expand and force the concrete to break. Roots can break up naturally formed rocks the same way. This is how plant roots cause mechanical weathering.

How can plants cause weathering?

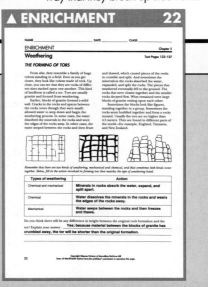

Figure 5-2. Tree roots break up naturally formed rocks the same way that they break up sidewalks.

TYING TO PREVIOUS KNOWLEDGE: Have students recall from Chapter 3 that minerals have different hardnesses. Have students determine which minerals listed on Mohs' Scale of Hardness would be the most resistant to mechanical weathering.

OBJECTIVES AND SCIENCE WORDS: Have students review the objectives and science words to become familiar with this section.

2 TEACH

Key Concepts are highlighted.

CONCEPT DEVELOPMENT

▶Refer students to Figure 5-1. Ask how the two ranges differ. Then ask: **What do you think the Appalachian Mountains will look like in several thousands of years?** *They will be worn down into hills.* **In the same amount of time, what will the Rockies look like?** *They will probably resemble the present-day Appalachians.*

▶**What are the two main types of weathering?** *mechanical and chemical*

▶**Explain why there is sand at the bottom of many river beds?** *The sand formed by mechanical weathering of the rocks in the river.*

● REINFORCEMENT 22

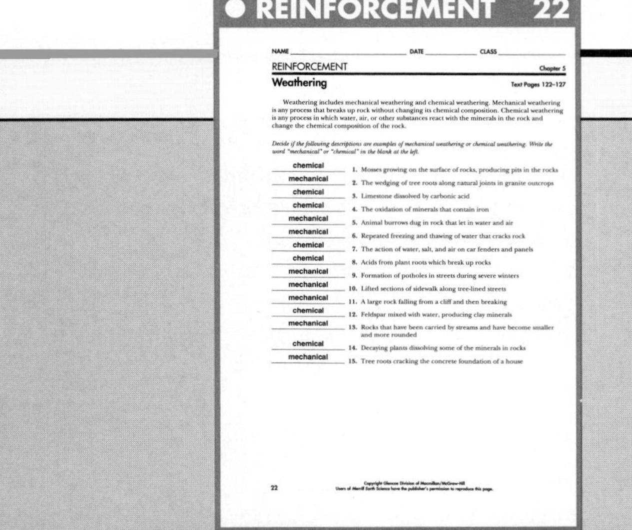

NAME ______ DATE ______ CLASS ______

REINFORCEMENT — Chapter 5

Weathering — Text Pages 122–127

Weathering includes mechanical weathering and chemical weathering. Mechanical weathering is any process that breaks up rock without changing its chemical composition. Chemical weathering is any process in which water, air, or other substances react with the minerals in the rock and change the chemical composition of the rock.

Decide if the following descriptions are examples of mechanical weathering or chemical weathering. Write the word "mechanical" or "chemical" in the blank at the left.

chemical 1. Mosses growing on the surface of rocks, producing pits in the rocks
mechanical 2. The wedging of tree roots along natural joints in granite outcrops
chemical 3. Limestone dissolved by carbonic acid
chemical 4. The oxidation of minerals that contain iron
mechanical 5. Animal burrows dug in rock that let in water and air
mechanical 6. Repeated freezing and thawing of water that cracks rock
chemical 7. The action of water, salt, and air on car fenders and panels
chemical 8. Acids from plant roots which break up rocks
mechanical 9. Formation of potholes in streets during severe winters
mechanical 10. Lifted sections of sidewalk along tree-lined streets
mechanical 11. A large rock falling from a cliff and then breaking
chemical 12. Feldspar mixed with water, producing clay minerals
mechanical 13. Rocks that have been carried by streams and have become smaller and more rounded
chemical 14. Decaying plants dissolving some of the minerals in rocks
mechanical 15. Tree roots cracking the concrete foundation of a house

22

▲ ENRICHMENT 22

NAME ______ DATE ______ CLASS ______

ENRICHMENT — Chapter 5

Weathering — Text Pages 122–127

THE FORMING OF TORS

From afar, they resemble a family of huge robots standing in a field. Even as you get closer, they look like robots made of rock. Up close, you can see that they are rocks of different sizes stacked upon one another. This kind of landform is called a tor. Tors are usually granite and formed from weathering.

Earlier, blocks of granite formed a solid wall. Cracks in the rocks and spaces between the rocks (even though they were small) allowed water to seep down and begin the weathering process. In some cases, the water dissolved the minerals in the rocks and wore the edges of the rocks away. In other cases, the water seeped between the rocks and then froze and thawed, which caused pieces of the rocks to crumble and split. And sometimes the minerals in the rocks absorbed the water, expanded, and split the rocks. The pieces that weathered eventually fell to the ground. The rocks that were closest together and the smaller rocks decayed first. What remained were large blocks of granite resting upon each other.

Sometimes the blocks look like figures, standing together in a group. Sometimes the rocks seem huddled together and form a rocky mound. Usually the tors are no higher than 4.5 meters. They are found in different parts of the world—for example, England, Tanzania, and New Zealand.

Remember that there are two kinds of weathering, mechanical and chemical, and that sometimes both kinds occur together. Below, fill in the action involved in forming tors that matches the type of weathering listed.

Types of weathering	Action
Chemical and mechanical	Minerals in rocks absorb the water, expand, and split apart.
Chemical	Water dissolves the minerals in the rocks and wears the edges of the rocks away.
Mechanical	Water seeps between the rocks and then freezes and thaws.

Do you think there will be any difference in height between the original rock formation and the tor? Explain your answer. **Yes; because material between the blocks of granite has crumbled away, the tor will be shorter than the original formation.**

22

CONCEPT DEVELOPMENT

▶**What causes many roads to have potholes?** Water gets into cracks in road pavement, freezes, and expands, forcing the pavement apart.

▶Have students contrast chemical weathering with mechanical weathering.

PROBLEM SOLVING

Think Critically: The water in the lemonade expanded when it froze, pushing out on the glass container and causing it to break. This process is similar to ice wedging. Ice wedging occurs as water repeatedly freezes and thaws.

CONCEPT DEVELOPMENT

▶ **How could you tell which of two tombstones, both made of limestone, was older without looking at the dates?** *It is often more difficult to read the engravings on an older tombstone because chemical weathering has caused more damage to the older stone.*

▶ Stress that moisture and temperature are important factors of both mechanical and chemical weathering.

▶ **How do plants cause chemical weathering?** *They produce acids that dissolve some minerals.*

▶ **How do plants cause mechanical weathering?** *Roots of plants can cause mechanical weathering.*

PROGRAM RESOURCES

From the **Teacher Resource Package** use:

Concept Mapping, pages 15-16.

Use **Laboratory Manual,** page 37, Chemical Weathering.

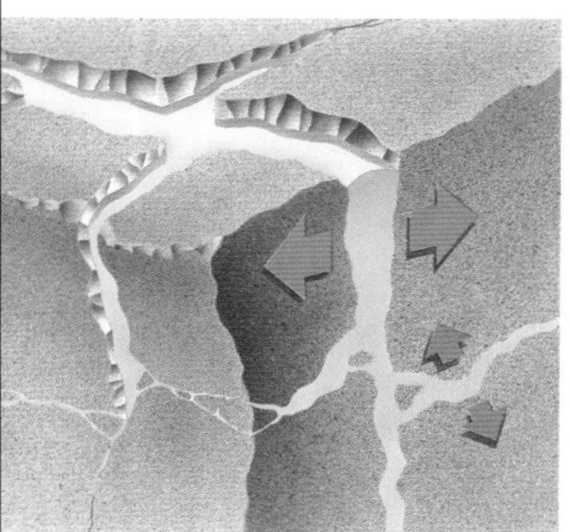

Figure 5-3. When water gets into cracks in rock and freezes, it expands, forcing the rock apart.

A third example of mechanical weathering occurs when water gets into the cracks in rocks and freezes. **Ice wedging** occurs when water freezes in cracks, expands, and forces the rocks apart. This process repeats itself when the ice thaws and the water freezes again. Mountain peaks are weathered rapidly by this process because they are often exposed to warm temperatures during the day and freezing temperatures at night. This cycle of freezing and thawing also breaks up roads and highways. When water gets into cracks in road pavement and freezes, it forces the pavement apart. This can lead to the formation of "potholes" in roads.

Chemical Weathering

The second main type of weathering occurs when water, air, and other substances react with the minerals in rocks. This type of weathering is called **chemical weathering** because the mineral composition of the rock is changed. Let's see how chemical weathering can happen.

PROBLEM SOLVING

Jamie's Frozen Failure

Jamie had promised her dad she would cut the lawn before he got home from work. She had heard on the weather report that the temperature might reach a record high on that day. Jamie found that the weather report was right. It was a very hot afternoon and she knew she would be very thirsty by the time she finished such a big job. She decided to make herself a jar of lemonade. She poured the lemonade into a glass jar, put a lid on it, and put it in the freezer to make it really cold.

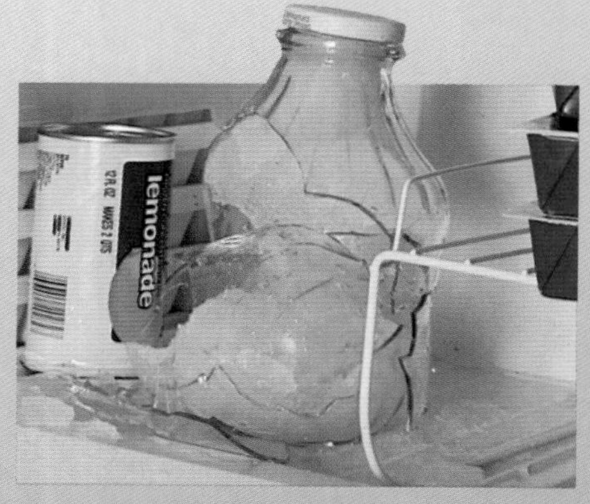

At the end of two hours she finally returned for a glass of lemonade. She opened the freezer to find the glass jar broken. It didn't take Jamie long to guess what had caused the glass to break.

Think Critically: What do you think caused the glass to break? How does the same process weather rocks?

OPTIONS

INQUIRY QUESTIONS

▶**Explain how wind causes mechanical weathering.** *Wind picks up sand and other particles and hurls them against buildings and rock surfaces. Small pieces of the buildings and rocks break off or become scratched and pitted due to this type of weathering.*

▶**Why do people sandblast building exteriors made of stones or brick?** *Sandblasting "weathers away" the dirty outer surfaces of the rocks, exposing a clean surface.*

▶**What would happen if you didn't empty a concrete birdbath of its water before the temperature dropped to freezing?** *When water freezes, it expands and can break concrete.*

ACTIVITY 5-1
Weathering Rocks

Problem: *How can physical weathering break down rocks?*

Materials 

- 100 g limestone or shale samples
- plastic bottle with cap
- wire strainer
- pan balance
- water

Procedure

1. Determine the mass of the presoaked limestone or shale using the pan balance.
2. Place the chips into the plastic bottle and add enough water so that the bottle is about half filled. Seal the bottle with the cap.
3. Before continuing, make a list of the factors that you think will affect the weathering rate of the rocks.
4. Shake the bottle vigorously for two minutes. Uncap the bottle and pour the water and rock through the strainer. Rinse the rocks off, and again determine the mass of the rock material. Record this measurement.
5. Repeat Steps 2 and 4 until 20 minutes of shaking time have been completed, broken into shaking intervals of two minutes each. Record the original mass and the final mass of the rock material at each shaking time. Extend your data table to include 10-, 12-, 14-, 16-, and 18-minute shaking times.

Analyze

1. What happened to the mass of the rock material after each period of shaking?
2. What was the total change in mass of the rock from the beginning to the end of the 20-minute shaking time?
3. What were some of the factors in this activity that affected the rate that the rock was physically weathered?

Conclude and Apply

4. Where on Earth would you find rocks undergoing weathering similar to this activity?
5. What are some factors that would affect the physical weathering rate of rocks in a natural weathering situation outside of your classroom?

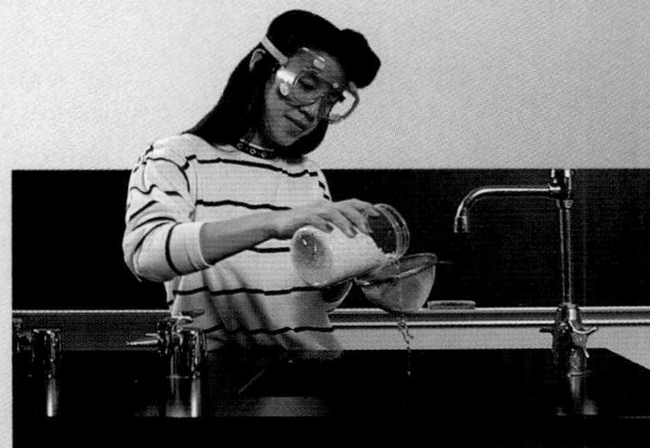

Data and Observations

Sample Data

Shaking Time	2 min.	4 min.	6 min.	8 min.	10 min.	12 min.	14 min.	16 min.	18 min.	20 min.
Original mass	100	98	96	95	94.2	93.6	93.2	93	92.9	92.8
Final mass	98	96	95	94.5	93.6	93.2	93	92.9	92.8	92.7
Change in mass	2	2	1	0.8	0.6	0.4	0.2	0.1	0.1	0.1

ACTIVITY 5-1
80 minutes

OBJECTIVE: Identify factors that affect the rate at which certain rocks are physically weathered by water.

PROCESS SKILLS applied in this activity:
▶ Measuring in Procedure Steps 1 and 4.
▶ **Predicting** in Procedure Step 3.
▶ **Controlling Variables** in Procedure Steps 4 and 5.
▶ **Using Numbers** in Analyze Questions 1 and 2.
▶ **Interpreting Data** in Analyze Questions 1 and 3.
▶ **Inferring** in Conclude and Apply Questions 4 and 5.

COOPERATIVE LEARNING Use the Science Investigation strategy with three students per group to have students perform this activity.

TEACHING THE ACTIVITY

Alternate Materials: The addition of a few marble or quartz chips to the rock chips will accelerate the rate at which the rocks abrade.

▶ **Troubleshooting:** Presoak the rock chips for at least several hours before performing this activity. If this is not done, the chips may have more mass after shaking than before.

▶ When shaken, the angular rock chips become rounded, which reduces the rate at which they abrade. Thus, the rock chips should not be reused by other students or groups.

▶ Have students express the loss of mass as a percentage of loss of original mass rather than the actual amount using the following equation:
% of mass loss = change in mass/original mass × 100

▶ Although individual data may vary considerably, compiled results for an entire class should show an increase in total loss of rock with time. The rate of loss will be greater during the earlier shaking intervals when the rock chips are more angular.

ANSWERS TO QUESTIONS

1. It decreased—more rapidly at the beginning, and at a slower rate as the chips became more rounded.
2. Answers will vary.
3. Variables such as the shaking rate; the amounts of rock chips and water; shaking vigor applied by the students; the hardness, size, and angularity of the chips; the shape and size of the plastic bottle; and the temperature and acidity of the water are all factors that may affect the weathering rate of the rocks used.
4. in a rapidly moving stream or as waves break against a beach or coastline
5. The composition, hardness, and angularity of the rock particles and the force, temperature, and acidity of the water acting upon the rock are some factors that affect the weathering rate of Earth's rocks.

PROGRAM RESOURCES

From the **Teacher Resource Package** use:
Activity Worksheet, pages 39-40, Activity 5-1: Weathering Rocks.

MINI-Lab

Materials: piece of steel wool, paper towels, water, shallow pan

Teaching Tips: Ask students to predict which type of weathering—chemical or physical—will produce the most noticeable effects. A short discussion should lead to the conclusion that chemical weathering, although often the more pervasive process, tends to occur at a much slower rate, making it often quite difficult to detect.

▶ Rust will form as the steel wool oxidizes in the presence of the water.

▶ Iron, the major component of steel, is chemically weathered and forms iron oxide or rust.

CHECK FOR UNDERSTANDING

Use the Mini Quiz to check for understanding.

MINI QUIZ

Use the Mini Quiz to check students' recall of chapter content.

1. **Ice wedging is a type of _____ weathering.** *mechanical*
2. **_____ weathering occurs when the mineral composition of the rock is changed.** *Chemical*
3. **What is the main cause of chemical weathering?** *water*
4. **_____ occurs when a metal is exposed to oxygen and water.** *Oxidation*

RETEACH

Have students refer to the photo on page 120. Ask them to explain how weathering may have affected these statues over time.

EXTENSION

For students who have mastered this section, use the **Reinforcement** and **Enrichment** masters or other OPTIONS provided.

MINI-Lab

How does rust form?

Put a piece of steel wool in a shallow pan containing about 1 cm of water. Observe it for several days. What changes are occurring? How can you explain these changes?

Figure 5-4. Oxidation causes rocks that contain iron to "rust," giving them a reddish color.

3 Water is the main cause of chemical weathering. What happens to a sugar cube when you put it in a cup of tea? The water dissolves the cube. Water does the same thing to some minerals in rock. It dissolves them and carries them away. The rock that is left behind now has a different composition.

Sometimes compounds in the air combine with water. When this water comes in contact with some minerals in rocks, new minerals are formed. For example, when water mixes with the mineral feldspar, clay minerals such as kaolinite are formed.

Oxygen also helps cause chemical weathering. Have you ever seen a rusty car? **Oxidation** occurs when a metal
4 such as iron is exposed to oxygen and water. Paint usually protects metal and keeps it from rusting, but if the metal under the paint gets exposed to oxygen and water, rust forms. Rocks that contain iron also "rust."

Another type of chemical weathering occurs when naturally formed acids come in contact with rocks. When water mixes with carbon dioxide from the air, a very weak acid called carbonic acid forms. This acid dissolves minerals such as calcite, the main mineral in the rock limestone. Over thousands of years, the acid can dissolve enough limestone to form caves as shown in Figure 5-5.

Acids are also given off by some plant roots and decaying plants. These acids dissolve some of the minerals in the rocks. When these minerals are gone, the rock is weaker and will eventually break into smaller pieces. The next time you find a moss-covered rock, peel back the moss and you'll find small pits in the rock. These pits are caused by the plant root acids.

Effects of Climate on Weathering

Mechanical and chemical weathering occur all around the world. However, the climate of a particular region determines how fast weathering happens. Climate is the pattern of weather an area has over many years. Climate also has an effect on what types of weathering are occurring. For example, in regions where freezing and thawing occur frequently, rocks weather rapidly because of the expansion of freezing water. You may have seen the effects of this type of weathering on the streets in your neighborhood. The pavement cracks and buckles during the winter, and potholes seem to be everywhere.

OPTIONS

INQUIRY QUESTIONS

▶ **The Statue of Liberty has to be repaired periodically because of damage caused by weathering. What could be done to help slow down this damage?** *The statue could be coated with a protective material that will prevent chemicals in the air from reacting with its metal.*

▶ **Paint contains certain minerals. Can you explain why old paint on some houses and cars is powdery like chalk?** *The minerals in the paint have been chemically weathered.*

PROGRAM RESOURCES

From the **Teacher Resource Package** use:

Activity Worksheets, page 45, Mini-Lab: How does rust form?

Figure 5-5. Chemical weathering dissolves limestone, forming caves.

Chemical weathering is most rapid in regions with lots of moisture and warm temperatures. Thus, chemical weathering is very rapid in tropical areas such as the Amazon River region of South America. In desert areas and polar regions, the lack of moisture and low temperatures keep chemical weathering at a minimum.

Why is chemical weathering rapid in the Amazon region?

Now that you know what weathering is, you can see its results in many places. You also know that weathering does more than just break up rocks. Weathering contributes to the rock cycle by making sediment. When you see a broken sidewalk near a tree, you know that roots caused mechanical weathering. Roots break up rocks, forming sediments that form sedimentary rocks.

Science and WRITING

The rate of chemical weathering in the Amazon River region is very different from that in Antarctica. Find information on these two places in an encyclopedia and write a short paper describing reasons for their different climates and their different rates of chemical weathering.

SECTION REVIEW

1. What is the difference between mechanical and chemical weathering?
2. How is mechanical weathering affected by climate?
3. How do some plant roots cause chemical weathering?
4. **Apply:** How can water cause both mechanical and chemical weathering?

Recognizing Cause and Effect

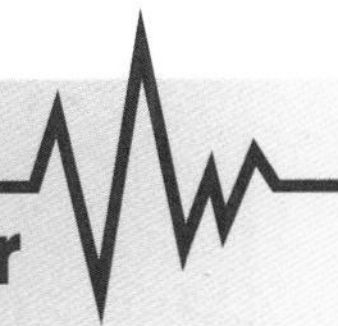

Skill Builder

Identify the cause and effect in each of these examples of weathering. If you need help, refer to Recognizing Cause and Effect in the **Skill Handbook** on page 683.

1. Acid rain has turned a bronze statue green in a major city.
2. Tree roots are exposed in cracks in your sidewalk.
3. A piece of limestone has a honeycomb appearance.

TEACHER F.Y.I.

▶ Chemical changes occur even in deserts because moisture from the air condenses on rocks during the cool nights.

CROSS CURRICULUM

▶ **Social Studies:** Have students research how weathering affects your local economy.

3 CLOSE

Ask questions 1-3 and the **Apply** Question in the Section Review.

▶ Have students find evidence of weathering around the outside of the school. If the school building is made of rock, have them examine the effects of weathering by comparing exposed surfaces with surfaces that are protected from weathering processes.

SECTION REVIEW ANSWERS

1. Mechanical weathering breaks a rock into smaller pieces without changing its composition. Chemical weathering changes a rock's composition.

2. In areas with temperate climates, the alternate freezing and thawing of water increases mechanical weathering.

3. Some plant roots produce acids that dissolve some of the minerals in rocks. When the minerals are gone, the rocks break into smaller pieces.

4. Apply: Water mechanically pushes rocks into other rocks, creating sediments, or it chemically reacts with the minerals either to dissolve them or to change them into new minerals.

OPTIONS

ENRICHMENT

▶ Have students report on local problems involving weathering.

▶ Have students use tombstone dates to determine the rate of weathering of markers made of limestone and marble.

Skill Builder

1. Acid rain was the cause. The effect on the statue was a discoloration.

2. The tree roots may have caused the cracks. Or, the cracks may have formed due to other types of weathering, thus exposing the roots.

3. Movement of water over the limestone caused chemical weathering. The effect of the chemical weathering is the appearance of the rock.

SECTION 5-2

PREPARATION

SECTION BACKGROUND

▶ Residual soils are soils that form in place by the gradual weathering of bedrock. These soils are especially thick on gentle slopes.

▶ Some soils have no relation to the underlying bedrock. These soils are eroded from the areas where they formed and deposited in new locations. Soil horizons in these transported soils are usually poorly defined or absent.

PREPLANNING

▶ To prepare for the Mini-Lab, have digging tools, buckets, and magnifying glasses or microscopes available.

▶ To prepare for Activity 5-2, have available the materials listed on page 130.

1 MOTIVATE

▶ Take students to an area near the school where they can examine an exposed soil profile. Badly eroded gullies, road cuts, and steep slopes are good places to observe soil horizons.

Cooperative Learning: Have Paired Partners examine and sample exposed soils at three different locations in your community. Have them compare and contrast the textures, grain sizes, and colors of their samples. To determine the texture, have them rub a small amount between their fingers and describe it as smooth or rough. Depending on their results, ask them why they think the soils at these locations are similar or dissimilar.

TYING TO PREVIOUS KNOWLEDGE: Ask students to recall what happens to plants after they die and fall to the ground. Explain that as the plants decay, humus is formed.

5-2 Soil

New Science Words

soil
humus
soil profile
horizon
leaching

Objectives

- ▶ Explain how soil evolves from rock.
- ▶ Describe soil by comparing the A, B, and C soil horizons.
- ▶ Discuss how environmental conditions affect the evolution of soils.

Formation of Soil

How often have you been told, "Take off those dirty shoes before you come into this house"? Ever since you were a young child, you've had many experiences with dirt. Usually, this dirt is actually soil. You can find soil in lots of places. An empty lot may have exposed soil in it. A garden or a flower bed has soil.

But what is soil and where does it come from? As you learned in Section 5-1, weathering gradually breaks rocks into smaller and smaller fragments. When plants and animals live in these fragments, organic matter, such as leaves, twigs, and dead worms and insects, is added. When organic matter is gradually added to the weathered rock, soil evolves. **Soil** is a mixture of weathered rock and organic matter. Most soil is made up of about 50 percent rock and mineral fragments and 50 percent air, water, and

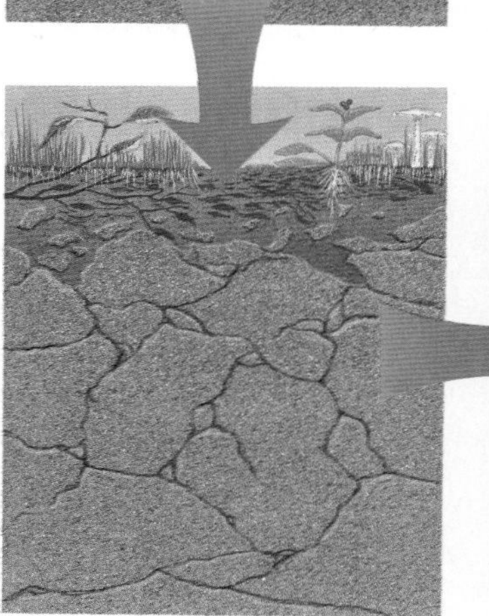

Figure 5-6. Soil evolves from weathered rock.

OPTIONS

Meeting Different Ability Levels

For Section 5–2, use the following **Teacher Resource Masters** depending upon individual students' needs.

◆ **Study Guide Master** for all students.

● **Reinforcement Master** for students of average and above average ability levels.

▲ **Enrichment Master** for above average students.

Additional Teacher Resource Package masters are listed in the OPTIONS box throughout the section. The additional masters are appropriate for all students.

◆ STUDY GUIDE 23

NAME ______ DATE ______ CLASS ______

STUDY GUIDE — Chapter 5

Soil — Text Pages 128–133

Use the terms in the box to complete the sentences. Use the information in your textbook.

soil	humus	A horizon
horizons	composition	below
topsoil	solid rock	top
evolve	bottom	leaching
soil profile	water	

1. **Soil** is a mixture of sediments of weathered rock and organic matter.
2. Organic matter that contains pieces of decaying plants and animals is called **humus**.
3. Due to weathering, different layers, or **horizons**, of soil form.
4. Soil generally has three layers, and these make up a **soil profile**.
5. The *A* horizon is the **top** layer and is also known as **topsoil**.
6. The *B* horizon is the layer **below** the *A* horizon.
7. The *C* horizon is the **bottom** layer in a soil profile; it contains partly weathered rock but no humus.
8. Below the bottom horizon is **solid rock**.
9. You can tell that the **A horizon** is the most fully evolved soil layer because it has more humus and smaller rock fragments than the other layers.
10. **Water** moving downward through the horizons dissolves and carries minerals into lower horizons by the process of **leaching**.
11. The thickness of the soil layers and their **composition** depend on the climate, slope of the land, and the type of rock in an area and how long the soil has been evolving.
12. Soil horizons **evolve** more slowly in an area that has little rainfall because chemical weathering occurs slowly in a dry climate.

23

Figure 5-7. Soil is a mixture of weathered rock and organic matter.

organic matter. Soil can take hundreds of years to form and can range in thickness from 60 meters in some areas to just a few centimeters in others.

As rock weathers into smaller and smaller fragments, plants begin to grow in the weathered rock. Then worms, insects, bacteria, and fungi begin living among the plant roots. These organisms don't just live in the weathered rock, they help it evolve into soil by adding organic matter. When the plants and animals that live in the soil eventually die, they break down in a process called decay. The dark-colored organic matter made of pieces of decaying plants and animals is called **humus.** 1 As worms and insects burrow throughout the soil, they mix the humus with the fragments of rock. As you can see, weathered rock is constantly evolving into soil.

MINI-Lab

What is soil made of?

Collect a sample of soil. Observe it closely with a magnifying glass or microscope. Try to identify the different particles by describing them. Do any of the materials appear to be remains of once-living organisms? Compare your samples to those of other students in your class. In what ways are those samples different or similar to yours?

Soil Profiles

You may have seen layers of soil if you've ever been near a steep slope such as a road cut where the soil and rock are exposed. You might have noticed that plants grow in the top layer of soil, which is a darker color than the other soil layers below it. These different layers of soil make up what is called a **soil profile.** 2 Each layer in the soil profile is called a **horizon.** There are generally three horizons, and they are labeled A, B, and C.

● REINFORCEMENT 23

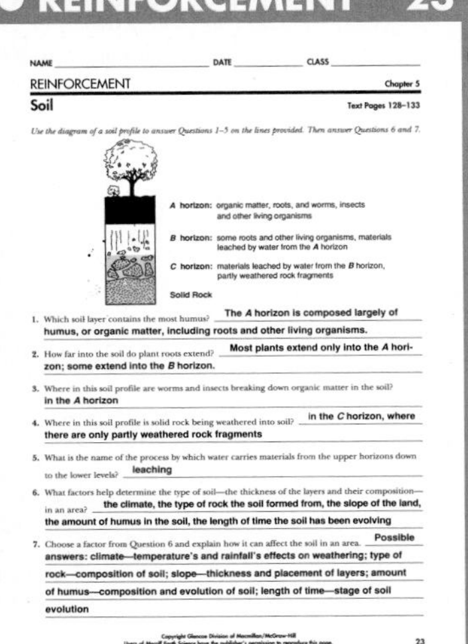

NAME ____ DATE ____ CLASS ____

REINFORCEMENT — Chapter 5

Soil — Text Pages 128–133

Use the diagram of a soil profile to answer Questions 1–5 on the lines provided. Then answer Questions 6 and 7.

1. Which soil layer contains the most humus? **The *A* horizon is composed largely of humus, or organic matter, including roots and other living organisms.**
2. How far into the soil do plant roots extend? **Most plants extend only into the *A* horizon; some extend into the *B* horizon.**
3. Where in this soil profile are worms and insects breaking down organic matter in the soil? **in the *A* horizon**
4. Where in this soil profile is solid rock being weathered into soil? **in the *C* horizon, where there are only partly weathered rock fragments**
5. What is the name of the process by which water carries materials from the upper horizons down to the lower levels? **leaching**
6. What factors help determine the type of soil—the thickness of the layers and their composition—in an area? **the climate, the type of rock the soil formed from, the slope of the land, the amount of humus in the soil, the length of time the soil has been evolving**
7. Choose a factor from Question 6 and explain how it can affect the soil in an area. **Possible answers: climate—temperature's and rainfall's effects on weathering; type of rock—composition of soil; slope—thickness and placement of layers; amount of humus—composition and evolution of soil; length of time—stage of soil evolution**

23

▲ ENRICHMENT 23

NAME ____ DATE ____ CLASS ____

ENRICHMENT — Chapter 5

Soil — Text Pages 128–133

ANALYZING SOIL

The hydrangea is a bush with snowball-like flowers on it. When a certain kind of hydrangea grows on the East Coast, the flowers are blue. When that same kind of hydrangea grows in the Midwest, the flowers are pink. What causes the flowers to be two different colors? The answer is the soil. In much of the East Coast the soil is acidic. In the Midwest, some of the soil is alkaline—it has more calcium in it than acid soil does.

Some plants grow best in fairly acidic soil—blueberries, cranberries, and pineapples, for example. Other plants, like cotton and alfalfa, need a soil that is neutral—neither acidic nor alkaline. Most plants seem to do well in a mildly acidic soil.

Material can be added to soil to make it the right acidity for the crop that will be grown. To know what and how much material to add, the soil has to be tested. Samples of soil are analyzed by a machine to measure the soil's pH—the measure of how acidic or alkaline it is. Soil that has a pH between 0 and 7 is acidic; the lower the number, the more acidic the soil. Soil that has a pH of 7 is neutral. Soil that has a pH between 7 and 14 is alkaline; the higher the number, the more alkaline the soil. Actually, in nature, soils don't seem to reach the extremes of 0 and 14. They range between about 3.5 and 11.

If the soil needs to be more alkaline, then lime—a chalky material (not the fruit) containing calcium—is added to the soil. If the soil needs to be made more acidic, sulfur can be added to the soil. Most of the time, the soil needs to be made more alkaline rather than more acidic.

1. How would you classify a soil that has a pH of 8? **an alkaline soil**
2. Suppose a soil has a pH of 5.5, but the crop to be grown does best in a soil with a pH of 6. What would you do? **raise the pH level by adding lime**
3. If a hydrangea has flowers that are part pink and part blue, in what kind of soil would you suspect it was planted? **neutral soil, or soil with a pH of about 7**
4. Why is it important for a farmer to know the pH of soil? **so the farmer will know what to add to the soil to make his or her crop grow better, or so the farmer can choose a crop that will do well in that soil**

23

2 TEACH

Key Concepts are highlighted.

CONCEPT DEVELOPMENT

▶ Make sure students understand the definition of *soil.* The terms *topsoil, sand, clay,* and *humus* are not soil types but rather components of certain soils. For example, a soil rich in clay may contain sand but little humus.

▶ After students have read pages 128 and 129, pose these questions:

▶ **What important soil component would be missing if plants and animals did not decay?** *humus*

▶ **Why is the top layer of certain soil profiles darker in color than the horizons below?** *The top layer in such soils contains humus.*

MINI-Lab

Materials: soil samples, pin or dissecting probe, sheet of white paper, plastic bags or envelopes to store samples, microscope or magnifying glass, light source.

Teaching Tips: Make sure soil samples are completely dry to facilitate probing.

▶ Have students closely examine their samples on the sheet of paper under magnification in bright light.

Cooperative Learning: Form Numbered Heads Together groups based on the similarities of students' samples. Provide each group with soil samples from other geographic regions. Students will discover that the local soil samples, which they thought were different, are really quite similar compared to soil samples of other geographic areas.

Answers: Depending on location, some of the soil samples will have greater or lesser amounts of organic matter present. Have students identify some of the sources of any organic material in the samples.

PROGRAM RESOURCES

From the **Teacher Resource Package** use:

Activity Worksheet, page 46, MiniLab: What is Soil Made of?

ACTIVITY 5-2
two class periods

OBJECTIVE: Compare and contrast different soils.

PROCESS SKILLS applied in this activity:
▶**Observing** in Procedure Steps 1, 2, and 3.
▶**Classifying** in Analyze Question 2.
▶**Communicating** in Procedure Step 3 and Analyze Question 1.
▶**Inferring** in Conclude and Apply Questions 3 and 4.
▶**Experimenting** in Procedure Steps 4-11.
▶**Interpreting Data** in Analyze Question 2 and Conclude and Apply Questions 3 and 4.

TEACHING THE ACTIVITY

▶Have a bucket of fresh soil for students to use in this activity.
▶Be sure students punch the same number of holes in each cup. Emphasize that these holes are a control device. Different numbers of holes would introduce another variable into the experiment.
▶**Alternate Materials:** Binocular microscopes will show more of the details of the soil than will hand lenses.
▶**Troubleshooting:** Have students check to be sure that the cheesecloth is securely fastened to the bottom of the cups before they start.

PROGRAM RESOURCES

From the **Teacher Resource Package** use:

Activity Worksheet, pages 41-42, Avtivity 5-2: Soil Characteristics.

ACTIVITY 5-2
Soil Characteristics

Problem: *What are the characteristics of soil?*

Materials 

- soil sample
- sand
- clay
- gravel
- hand lens
- water
- paper
- watch
- scissors
- plastic coffee can lids (3)
- cheesecloth squares
- rubber bands
- pencil
- 250-mL beakers (3)
- thumbtack
- large polystyrene cups (3)
- graduated cylinder

Procedure

1. Describe the color of the soil sample.
2. Spread some of the sample on a sheet of paper and examine it with a hand lens. Name or describe some of the different particles you see.
3. Place a small amount of soil in your hand and rub it between your fingers. Describe the texture (how it feels).
4. Punch the same number of holes in the bottom and around the lower part of each of three polystyrene cups with a thumbtack.
5. Cover the holes in each cup with a square of cheesecloth. Secure the cloth with a rubber band.
6. Cut a hole in each plastic lid so that a cup will fit just inside the hole.
7. Place each cup in a lid and place each lid over a beaker.
8. Label the cups A, B, and C.
9. Fill cup A half full of dry sand, cup B half full of clay. Half fill cup C with an equal mixture of sand, gravel, and clay.
10. Use the graduated cylinder to pour 100 mL of water into each cup. Record the time when the water is first poured into each cup and when the water first drips from each cup.
11. Allow the water to drip for 25 minutes, then measure and record the amount of water in each beaker.

Analyze

1. Based on your examination of the soil sample in Steps 1-3, describe your soil sample in as much detail as possible.
2. Permeability refers to the ability of water to move through a substance. Which substance that you tested in Steps 4-11 is most permeable? least permeable?

Conclude and Apply

3. How does the addition of gravel affect the permeability of clay?
4. What are three characteristics of soil?

ANSWERS TO QUESTIONS

1. Answers will vary by soil samples used. Characteristics should include color, types and percentages of particles, organisms, texture, and drainage.
2. The sand, gravel, and clay mixture is probably the most permeable, although if the sand is very coarse it may be more permeable. Clay is least permeable.
3. It increases the permeability.
4. color, types and percentages of particles, types and amounts of organisms, texture, and permeability

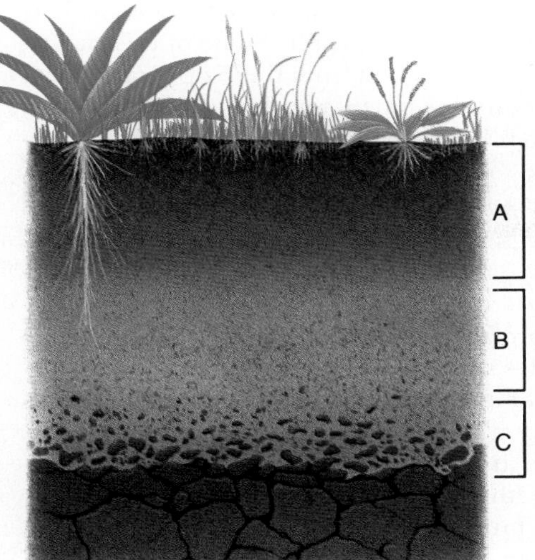

The A horizon is the top layer of soil. It's also known as topsoil. If you could dig up a scoop of topsoil from the top of that steep slope and look at it very closely, what would you see? The soil would be dark in color and would contain sediments, decayed leaves, the roots of plants, and even insects and worms. The A horizon is the most fully evolved soil layer in a soil profile. This means that the A horizon has changed the most since it was just weathered rock. It generally has more humus and smaller sediments in it than the other, less evolved layers in a soil profile.

The next layer below the A horizon is the B horizon. This layer is less evolved and lighter in color than the A horizon because it has little or no humus. Some plant roots reach into this layer. This horizon usually contains minerals that were washed down from the A horizon. The process in which minerals are dissolved in water and carried down in a soil profile is called **leaching.** The process of leaching is similar to how coffee is made in an automatic drip coffee maker. Like water seeping into the A horizon, hot water drips into coffee grounds in a filter. There, like water dissolving minerals in the B horizon, the water absorbs flavor and color from the coffee grounds. Then, like water carrying the dissolved minerals to the C horizon, water in a coffee maker flows through the filter and into the pot.

Figure 5-8. A soil profile is divided in layers called horizons. Each horizon represents a different stage in the evolution of soil. Horizons A, B, and C are identified above.

EcoTip

Roses and azaleas love an acid soil. Coffee grounds acidify soil. Recycle coffee grounds by placing them around these acid-loving plants.

Why does the B horizon contain minerals from the A horizon?

CROSS CURRICULUM

▶ **Life Science:** Have students research why plants grow better in humus-rich soils. Students might want to actually plant three identical plants in various soils and display how growth is affected by soil type.

TEACHER F.Y.I.

▶ In one kilogram of soil, the total number of organisms, including billions of bacteria, is greater than one hundred billion.

REVEALING MISCONCEPTIONS

▶ Students might think that all soil profiles are equally well developed. Explain that sometimes soil profiles do not show distinct A, B, and C horizons because of disturbances that have occurred or because the soils are too young.

CONCEPT DEVELOPMENT

▶ Stress that leaching allows minerals from the A and B horizons to be carried to lower horizons.

▶ Have a volunteer compare and contrast the A and B horizons in a soil profile.

CHECK FOR UNDERSTANDING

Use the Mini Quiz to check for understanding.

MINI QUIZ

Use the Mini Quiz to check students' recall of chapter content.

1. **____ is the dark-colored organic matter made of decaying organisms.** *Humus*
2. **Each layer in a soil profile is called a ____.** *horizon*
3. **The ____ soil horizon is the least evolved.** *C*

INQUIRY QUESTIONS

▶ **Why do you think some soils are only a few centimeters thick?** *Wind and water erode soils from some regions and deposit them elsewhere. Soil thickness is also affected by the slope of the land. Soils won't form on steep slopes because weathered rock will slide down the slopes. In some areas, weathering is very slow because there is little moisture; therefore, soils in dry areas evolve very slowly.*

▶ **Explain why topsoil is fertile.** *Humus is full of nutrients.*

▶ **How can chemicals such as fertilizers and herbicides dumped onto topsoil pollute groundwater?** *The chemicals are leached and eventually enter the groundwater supply.*

RETEACH

Cooperative Learning: Prior to this activity, number and label four buckets as follows: (1) large gravel, (2) pea-sized gravel, (3) topsoil containing humus, and (4) light-colored sand and clay. Fill each bucket with the appropriate sediment(s). Give each group of Paired Partners a clear plastic tube or graduated cylinder to use. Ask the partners to use these sediments and their tube to make a soil profile with four horizons, arranged in order. The arrangement of sediments should be, from bottom to top: The large gravel, which represents the bedrock; the pea gravel, which represents the C horizon; the sand and clay, which make up the B horizon; and the topsoil, which is included in the A horizon.

EXTENSION

For students who have mastered this section, use the **Reinforcement** and **Enrichment** masters or other OPTIONS provided.

TECHNOLOGY

Think Critically: Much soil is lost due to the clearing of forests. Tree removal causes soil erosion. Using reconstituted lumber saves trees and thus helps to preserve soil.

▶Explain that engineered wood is able to make use of younger trees that aren't structurally satisfactory for many lumber needs. Help students to conclude that reconstituted wood can reduce the demand for old-growth timber and thus preserve many mature trees.

▶For more information, see "Reinventing Wood," *Popular Science,* May 1990, pp. 96-99+.

Figure 5-9. This scientist is analyzing soil.

Below the B horizon you will find the C horizon. This is the bottom layer in a soil profile. Some of the materials in this layer were leached from the B horizon. The C horizon also contains partly weathered rock, but no
3 humus. This rock is just beginning the long, slow process of evolving into soil. What do you suppose you will find if you dig all the way to the bottom of the C horizon? As you might have guessed, there will be solid rock.

Types of Soil

Are all soil profiles the same no matter where you dig? No, soil profiles vary greatly from one location to the next. The thickness of the horizons and the soil composition depend on many conditions. These include the climate of the area and the type of rock the soil has evolved from. Other factors include the slope of the land, the amount of humus in the soil, and the length of time the soil has been evolving.

TECHNOLOGY

Knock on Wood!

Soil is estimated to be lost from about 56 000 square kilometers of land per year around the world. Some of this soil loss is caused by the cutting of trees.

Engineers and scientists have developed a way to reduce the number of trees that must be cut to provide lumber. "Reconstituted lumber" is wood that is made from logs that aren't long enough or in good enough shape to be cut for lumber. These logs are ground up into small chips; and then the chips are glued together. Because it is dried in special kilns, reconstituted lumber is less prone to shrinkage, warping, and bowing. The manufacturers of this engineered lumber also say that their products can be up to 2.5 times stronger than natural wood.

Think Critically: How does using reconstituted lumber help conserve soil? What are the benefits of reconstituted lumber?

OPTIONS

INQUIRY QUESTIONS

▶**Why are sediments in the A horizon smaller than those in the B and C horizons?** *They have been exposed to more agents of weathering.*

ENRICHMENT

▶Have students research to find out about different types of soils in your state.

▶Have students find out how soils are classified.

PROGRAM RESOURCES

Use Laboratory Manual, page 39, Transporting Soil Materials by Runoff, and page 41, Soil Infiltration by Groundwater.

For example, if you consider just the climate of an area, you can see how one factor affects the soil. Soil in an area where there is little rainfall is very different from soil in an area with a lot of rainfall. Chemical weathering is slower in the area where there is little rainfall, so the soil horizons there are thinner than horizons from a rainy climate. Soil from a rainy climate with a lot of plant life is thick with humus. So as you can see, soil profiles are quite different depending on many factors.

Figure 5-10. Soils in cold, dry climates have thin horizons (a). Soils in warm, humid climates have well-developed horizons because of chemical weathering (b).

SECTION REVIEW

1. How do organisms help soils to evolve?
2. What is the difference between the A horizon and the C horizon?
3. Why does horizon B contain minerals from horizon A?
4. **Apply:** Why aren't all soil profiles the same?

Concept Mapping

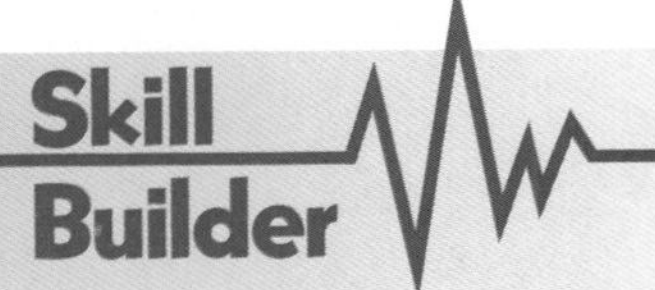

Make an events chain map that explains how soil evolves. Use the following terms and phrases: soil is formed, humus develops, rock is weathered, plants grow, worms and insects added, humus mixes with weathered rock. If you need help, refer to Concept Mapping in the **Skill Handbook** on pages 688 and 689.

3 CLOSE

FLEX Your Brain

Use the Flex Your Brain activity to have students explore SOIL.

▶Have a farmer, soil analyst, or agricultural consultant come to class and talk about local soils. Have the person discuss how different soils affect crop yields.

▶Ask questions 1-3 and the **Apply** Question in the Section Review.

SECTION REVIEW ANSWERS

1. Organisms create humus, mix the humus with fragments of rock, churn the soil and thus allow air to get between the soil particles, and add organic materials to the soil.

2. The A horizon is composed of fine sediments, humus, the roots of plants, and organisms. The C horizon is mostly leached material from the B horizon and partly weathered rock.

3. Minerals in the A horizon become dissolved in water, which moves down into the B horizon. This process is called leaching.

4. Apply: Soil profiles are different because the thicknesses and compositions of their horizons are different. Soil horizons are affected by the environmental conditions of the area in which soil evolves. Environmental conditions include the climate, type of bedrock, slope of the land, vegetation present, and the absence or presence of other organisms.

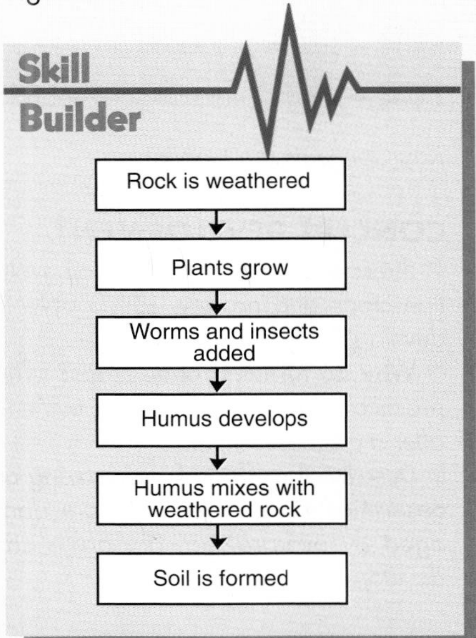

OPTIONS

PROGRAM RESOURCES

From the **Teacher Resource Package** use:

Critical Thinking/Problem Solving, page 11, Hydroponics: Growing Plants Without Soil.

Cross-Curricular Connections, page 9, Weathering and Soil.

Transparency Masters, page 13-14, Soil Evolution.

Use **Color Transparency** number 7, Soil Evolution.

PROGRAM RESOURCES

From the **Teacher Resource Package** use:

Activity Worksheets, page 5, Flex your Brain.

SECTION 5-3

PREPARATION

SECTION BACKGROUND

▶ Clear-cutting involves cutting down all trees of all sizes in an area. Selective cutting involves removing only particular sizes or types of trees. Clear-cutting leads to erosion and disrupts soil evolution much more than does selective cutting.

1 MOTIVATE

▶ Lead a class discussion of how students think human activities like farming and building affect soil formation and loss.

▶ Invite a city planner to meet with your class and discuss ways in which land is used locally.

TYING TO PREVIOUS KNOWLEDGE: Students should know that farmers and gardeners often use fertilizers on soil. Have students explain why fertilizers are used.

OBJECTIVES AND SCIENCE WORDS: Have students review the objectives and science words to become familiar with this section.

2 TEACH

Key Concepts are highlighted.

CONCEPT DEVELOPMENT

▶ Stress that, without plants, soil evolution stops and no new soil is able to develop.

▶ **Why do farmers rotate crops?** *This practice allows soil to recover nutrients after a crop uses them.*

▶ **Describe the effect of overgrazing on desertification.** *When soils are damaged by overgrazing, dry areas can develop into deserts.*

SCIENCE & SOCIETY 5-3 Soil Loss

New Science Words

desertification

Objectives

- ▶ Explain the importance of soil.
- ▶ Identify and describe activities that lead to soil loss.

Human Activities and Soil Loss

Why is soil important to us?

You probably don't realize how important soil is. Have you ever thought about where bread comes from? How about the paper in this book or the cotton fabric in your clothes? Bread, paper, and cotton fabric all have a direct connection to soil. Bread comes from grains that grow in soil. Paper is made from trees that need soil to grow in. Cotton comes from another plant that grows in soil. Without soil, we simply couldn't grow food and other resources. You can see how important soil is.

We've seen the results of soil loss in the past. In the 1930s, poor farming practices and a drought in the Great Plains area of the United States led to what is known as
1 the "dust bowl." It was called the dust bowl because topsoil was carried away by the wind, creating dust storms. Thousands of metric tons of soil were carried away by wind during the dust bowl.
2 One of the poor farming practices that contributed to the dust bowl was overgrazing. Overgrazing occurs when livestock such as cattle or sheep eat every bit of grass off of the land. Without grass on the land, wind and water

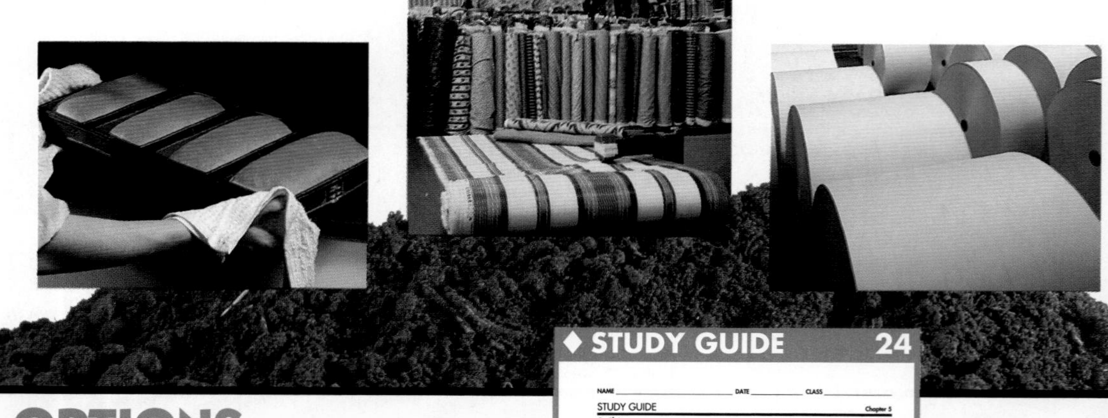

Figure 5-11. Many products we use and depend on come from resources grown in soil.

OPTIONS

Meeting Different Ability Levels

For Section 5-3, use the following **Teacher Resource Masters** depending upon individual students' needs.

◆ **Study Guide Master** for all students.

● **Reinforcement Master** for students of average and above average ability levels.

▲ **Enrichment Master** for above average students.

Additional Teacher Resource Package masters are listed in the OPTIONS box throughout the section. The additional masters are appropriate for all students.

◆ STUDY GUIDE 24

NAME ________ DATE ________ CLASS ________

STUDY GUIDE — Chapter 5

Soil Loss — Text Pages 134–136

Match the items in Column I with the terms in Column II. Write the letter of the correct term in the blank at the left.

	Column I	Column II
b	1. The Great Plains area during the 1930s	a. rain forest
c	2. Livestock eating all the grass off of the land	b. dust bowl
a	3. Trees and plants in tropical regions	c. overgrazing
d	4. Desert formation	d. desertification
e	5. Practice of planting a different crop in the same area every year	e. crop rotation

Decide whether each of the following statements is true or false. Write the word "true" or "false" in the blank. If the statement is false, rewrite it so that it is true.

true 6. Overgrazing removes the grass that holds the topsoil in place.

true 7. Plants are important to soil, because without them, soil evolution stops and no new soil develops.

false 8. Desertification is a slow process that affects very little land each year.
Desertification is a rapid process that affects a lot of land each year.

false 9. During the dust bowl in the 1930s, floods washed away the topsoil.
During the dust bowl in the 1930s, wind carried away the topsoil.

false 10. Soil can easily recover the nutrients that crops use up.
Soil takes years to recover the nutrients that crops use up.

24

carry away the valuable topsoil. Also, without plants, soil evolution stops and no new soil develops. In some places around the world, when one area is overgrazed, livestock are simply moved to a new location to overgraze again.

Another poor farming practice is growing crops every year in the same area until all of the soil nutrients are used up. When this soil is no longer good for growing crops, the crops are moved to a new area and all of the soil nutrients there are used up. These ruined soils can take many years to recover. It takes 10 to 30 years for 1 mm of soil to evolve! Rotating crops so that an area doesn't have the same crop every year allows soil to recover nutrients after a crop uses them.

When soils are damaged by overgrazing in areas that receive little rain, a desert can form. Desert formation, also called **desertification,** is currently happening in some areas of Africa, China, and the United States. Desertification is so rapid that each year it claims an area of land that is nearly the size of the state of Maine. 3

Another human activity that is destroying soil is the clearing of forests for farming. Each year, thousands of square kilometers of tropical rain forest are cleared for farming and grazing. That soil depends on the rich nutrients provided by the lush rain forest. When the rain forest is removed, the soil is useful to farmers for only a few years before the nutrients are gone. Then the productivity of the soil is lost, and farmers clear more rain forest, repeating the process.

Figure 5-12. Poor farming practices and drought turned the Great Plains into a "dust bowl" in the 1930s.

How does rotating crops help soil?

Did You Know?

Each year about 146 000 square kilometers of tropical rain forest is destroyed. This area is roughly the same size as the state of Illinois.

TEACHER F.Y.I.

▶ In the United States, poor agricultural practices contribute to a loss of six billion tons of topsoil each year.

MINI QUIZ

Use the Mini Quiz to check students' recall of chapter content.

1. **Why were the Great Plains states called the "dust bowl" in the 1930s?** *All the topsoil was eroded due to a drought and poor farming practices.*
2. **What is overgrazing?** *the result of animals eating every bit of grass off the land*
3. **Desertification means _____ .** *the formation of deserts*

CHECK FOR UNDERSTANDING

Have students write essays on how soil loss can be prevented. Their ideas might include eliminating overgrazing, engaging in good farming practices, and planting trees, among other methods.

RETEACH

Cooperative Learning: Form Science Investigation groups and have them sketch the school yard, noting the locations of all buildings, parking lots, sidewalks, and so on. Ask each group to estimate the amount of land being used for human activities, and answer this question: How do these activities affect the soil?

EXTENSION

For students who have mastered this section, use the **Reinforcement** and **Enrichment** masters or other OPTIONS provided.

● REINFORCEMENT 24

NAME ______ DATE ______ CLASS ______

REINFORCEMENT — Chapter 5

Soil Loss — Text Pages 134–136

In the following statements, words have been scrambled. Unscramble the words and write them on the lines provided.

soil loss 1. Poor farming practices can lead to **liso slos.**

overgrazing 2. Soil erosion can be caused by **gongzarvire.**

dust bowl 3. Soil blown away by wind created dust storms in the **tuds wolb.**

desertification 4. Some countries, including Ethiopia, China, and the United States, are experiencing **fatisodertineic.**

crop rotation 5. Different crops are grown in the same areas each year in **porc toorniat.**

rain forest 6. Soil is destroyed by the clearing of hundreds of acres of **ianr setrof.**

Answer the following questions on the lines provided.

7. Why is it important that soil evolution continue? **The continuing evolution of soil ensures that there will be new soil to replace old, worn-out or damaged soil. If no new soil is allowed to develop, eventually there will be no usable soil left.**
8. What effect does overgrazing have on topsoil? **Overgrazing removes all the grass from the land. Once the grass is gone, the topsoil is blown away by wind or washed away by water.**
9. Why shouldn't more land be cleared for farming and grazing as old land is worn out? **If land is continually cleared, used up, and abandoned, and nothing is done to restore the land to usefulness, eventually there will be no more land to clear or use. Land is not an endless resource.**
10. Why do people need soil? **Our food and many of our resources are ultimately derived from plants. Plants cannot grow without soil. Therefore, without soil, we would not have food or other resources.**
11. What do many of the activities that cause soil loss have in common? **People are responsible for many activities that cause soil loss. They damage the land through overgrazing, lack of crop rotation, and other poor farming practices. They cut down forests for farms, roads, and buildings, often without thinking about the impact this will have on the land.**

24

▲ ENRICHMENT 24

NAME ______ DATE ______ CLASS ______

ENRICHMENT — Chapter 5

Soil Loss — Text Pages 134–136

NO-TILL FARMING

One image of a farmer that comes to mind is of a farmer plowing fields of rich, dark earth in the springtime. But that image simply doesn't fit some farmers. These farmers practice a method of farming called no-till farming. In no-till farming, the farmer drives a machine that makes slits in the ground, spreads fertilizer, and plants the seeds. Sometimes the farmer does this all in one operation. Sometimes the farmer plants the seeds in a separate operation. What the farmer does NOT do is plow the soil.

When the crop has been harvested, the remains of the plants are left on the field. They act as a covering called a mulch. The mulch helps to prevent the loss of soil. This is a major advantage of the no-till method. The mulch prevents the loss of as much as 90 to 95 percent of the soil that would normally be blown or washed away in a plowed field. The mulch also allows the farmer to plant on hillsides without causing excessive soil loss.

The no-till method has other advantages as well. It helps keep the ground moist; it requires fewer machines than the usual plowing method; and, in comparison to the plowing method, the farmer spends less time in planting crops.

The no-till method is well suited to crops such as corn, which have large seeds, but it doesn't work as well with plants such as tomatoes, which have tiny seeds.

Disadvantages include an increase in the amount of weeds and the large quantity of weed killer that is required to deal with those weeds.

1. In the no-till method, farmers often spread fertilizer over the remains of the old crop. How do you think the fertilizer gets into the ground? **Rainwater carries the fertilizer into the ground.**
2. Who do you think uses more fertilizer—a no-till farmer or a farmer who uses the traditional plowing method? Why? **No-till farmers have to use more. Spreading fertilizer over the old crops rather than directly on the ground means that some of the fertilizer never gets into the ground, and so more has to be used to compensate for the unused fertilizer.**
3. What are some advantages of using less farm machinery in planting? **Answers will vary. Students might suggest saving money by not buying equipment, using less energy, saving money by not having to buy fuel, causing less pollution.**
4. Why is using a large quantity of weed killer a disadvantage? **The weed killer goes into the soil and could possibly pollute nearby wells and streams. It might also poison organisms living in the soil that enrich the soil.**

24

3 CLOSE

FLEX Your Brain

Use the Flex Your Brain activity to have students explore what is meant by PUBLIC LAND.

▶ Ask questions 1-2 in the Section Review.

SECTION REVIEW ANSWERS

1. Soils are important because without them plants couldn't grow. People depend on plants for food and products such as paper and cotton.

2. Answers may include overgrazing, poor farming, and clearing forests for farming, buildings, and roads.

YOU DECIDE!

Some students might say that the government should prohibit private use of public land because soil loss is likely. Other students may suggest that the government allow private use of public land, but carefully monitor the amount of grazing that takes place in order to prevent the land from being overgrazed. Other students may say that if the government didn't allow for overgrazing, many livestock owners would not be able to stay in business because of the high costs to rent private land. The costs of meat and leather products would increase and some consumers wouldn't be able to afford to buy them.

PROGRAM RESOURCES

From the **Teacher Resource Package** use:

Activity Worksheets, page 5, Flex Your Brain.

Science and Society, page 9, The Destruction of the Tropical Rain Forests.

Figure 5-13. Clear cutting of forests leads to soil loss.

Developers in many locations clear forests to make way for buildings and roads. This type of development stops the evolution of soil also.

Overgrazing is one of the largest causes of soil loss in the United States. There are almost 2.5 million square kilometers acres of public land in the U.S. This is land that the federal government controls but lets people use for different purposes. Some of this land is used by ranchers for grazing cattle and other livestock. Grazing livestock on this public land costs ranchers about half as much as it would if they had to rent private land.

SECTION REVIEW

1. Why are soils important?
2. What are some human activities that destroy soils and prevent the evolution of new soils?

You Decide!

Public land is overgrazed. In Colorado, 84 percent of the public land is overgrazed, making soil loss very likely. On the other hand, the low grazing fees make it cheaper for ranchers to raise livestock. People benefit by paying lower prices for products made from cattle such as meat and leather products. What do you think? Should public land be better protected against soil erosion?

OPTIONS

INQUIRY QUESTIONS

▶ **In addition to the examples of human activities discussed in this text, what are other things people do that create soil problems?** *Answers might include mining, dumping wastes, and moving soil from one place to another.*

ENRICHMENT

▶ Have students research how contour plowing, strip cropping, and terracing maintain soil fertility and reduce erosion.

▶ Have students research how soil farms could be used to naturally and artificially create soils.

▶ Have students find evidence that desertification is occurring in Africa, China, and the United States.

CHAPTER

REVIEW

SUMMARY

5-1: Weathering

1. Mechanical weathering breaks apart rocks without changing their chemical composition. Chemical weathering changes the composition of the rock. Ice and plant roots are two things that can cause mechanical weathering. Chemical weathering can be caused by water, oxygen, and acids.

2. Climate affects the rate and type of weathering in an area.

5-2: Soil

1. When rock is weathered and organic matter is added, soil evolves.

2. In a soil profile, the A horizon, or topsoil, is dark in color, and contains weathered rock and organic matter such as leaves, roots, insects, and worms. The B horizon has little or no humus and usually contains minerals leached from the A horizon. The C horizon contains partly weathered rock and some minerals leached from the B horizon.

3. Soil characteristics depend on the climate of the area, the type of rock the soil formed from, the slope of the land, the amount of humus in the soil, and the length of time the soil has been evolving.

5-3: Science and Society: Soil Loss

1. Soil is important because we use things such as grain and wood that grow in soil.

2. Soil loss is due to poor farming practices, overgrazing, the clearing of forests, and construction.

KEY SCIENCE WORDS

a. **chemical weathering**
b. **desertification**
c. **horizon**
d. **humus**
e. **ice wedging**
f. **leaching**
g. **mechanical weathering**
h. **oxidation**
i. **soil**
j. **soil profile**
k. **weathering**

UNDERSTANDING VOCABULARY

Match each phrase with the correct term from the list of Key Science Words.

1. breaking down rocks without changing their chemical composition
2. weathering in which the composition of the rock is changed
3. mixture of weathered rock and organic matter
4. decayed organic matter
5. all layers that make up a soil
6. each layer in a soil profile
7. a process that carries dissolved minerals downward in soil
8. desert formation
9. rock is forced apart by ice
10. chemical weathering due to exposure to water and oxygen

OPTIONS

ASSESSMENT

To assess student understanding of material in this chapter, use the resources listed.

COOPERATIVE LEARNING

Consider using cooperative learning in the THINK AND WRITE CRITICALLY, APPLY, and MORE SKILL BUILDERS sections of the Chapter Review.

PROGRAM RESOURCES

From the **Teacher Resource Package** use:

Chapter Review, pages 13 to 14.

Chapter and Unit Tests, pages 35 to 38, Chapter Test.

CHAPTER

REVIEW

SUMMARY

Have students read the summary statements to review the major concepts of the chapter.

UNDERSTANDING VOCABULARY

1. g
2. a
3. i
4. d
5. j
6. c
7. f
8. b
9. e
10. h

CHAPTER REVIEW

CHECKING CONCEPTS

1. d
2. c
3. b
4. a
5. d
6. c
7. a
8. b
9. c
10. d

UNDERSTANDING CONCEPTS

11. Sediments
12. leaching
13. desertification
14. Overgrazing
15. C horizon

THINK AND WRITE CRITICALLY

16. Both change rocks. Mechanical weathering changes the size of a rock whereas chemical weathering changes a rock's composition.

17. Rock is exposed to air and water and Earth processes. All of these factors can cause rocks to change physically and chemically. When humus is added over time, these changes result in the formation of soil.

18. A burrowing worm churns the soil, causing mechanical weathering. Substances released by the worm can cause chemical weathering.

19. The B horizon contains very little organic matter, if any, and is not exposed to air and water as the A horizon is.

20. By removing trees, soil nutrients are lost. Such "poor" soil is useful for only a short period of time. When the soil's productivity is lost, more rain forest is cleared and the process continues.

CHAPTER REVIEW

CHECKING CONCEPTS

Choose the word or phrase that completes the sentence.

1. ______ break(s) rocks into sediments.
a. Water **b.** Other rocks **c.** Roots **d.** All of these

2. Freezing and thawing weathers rocks because water ______ as it freezes.
a. contracts **b.** gets less dense **c.** expands **d.** none of these

3. Air, water, and other substances react with rocks to produce ______ weathering.
a. mechanical **b.** chemical **c.** physical **d.** all of these

4. ______ causes rust to form.
a. Oxygen **b.** Carbon dioxide **c.** Feldspar **d.** Paint

5. ______ determines how fast weathering takes place.
a. Acid **b.** Slope of the land **c.** Water **d.** Climate

6. Chemical weathering is most rapid in ______ regions.
a. cold, dry **b.** cold, moist **c.** warm, moist **d.** warm, dry

7. ______ is a mixture of weathered rock and organic matter.
a. Soil **b.** Limestone **c.** Carbon dioxide **d.** All of these

8. Decayed organic matter is called ______ .
a. leaching **b.** humus **c.** soil **d.** sediment

9. The ______ has little or no humus.
a. A horizon **b.** B horizon **c.** C horizon **d.** D horizon

10. ______ is destroying the world's soils.
a. Overgrazing **b.** Construction **c.** Clearing of trees **d.** All of these

UNDERSTANDING CONCEPTS

Complete each sentence.

11. ______ are formed as the result of mechanical weathering.

12. Minerals are washed to lower soil horizons in a process called ______.

13. Poor farming practices in areas that receive little rain results in ______.

14. ______ occurs when livestock eat all of the grass off the land.

15. The ______ in a soil profile is the least weathered layer.

THINK AND WRITE CRITICALLY

16. Compare and contrast mechanical weathering and chemical weathering.

17. Explain how soil evolves from rock.

18. How can a worm help soil to evolve?

19. Hypothesize why the B horizon is less weathered than the A horizon.

20. Explain how the clearing of tropical rain forests contributes to soil loss.

APPLY

21. Which type of weathering, mechanical or chemical, would you expect to be more effective in a desert region? Explain.
22. How does ice wedging damage roads and streets in areas that have cold temperatures?
23. Why does some metal rust?
24. Why are some areas around the world changing to deserts?
25. Explain how chemical weathering can form a cavern.

MORE SKILL BUILDERS

If you need help, refer to the Skill Handbook.

1. **Outlining:** Make an outline of Section 5-2, Soil.
2. **Concept Mapping:** Make an events chain concept map that shows two ways in which acids can cause chemical weathering.

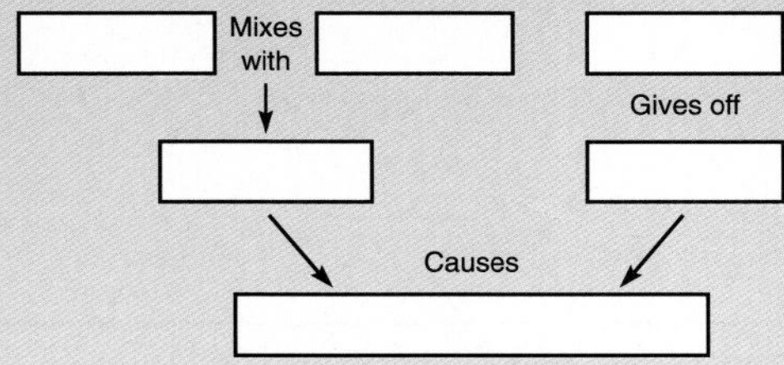

3. **Using Variables, Constants, and Controls:** Juan Carlos did an activity to test the ability of water to wash away soil. He put the same amount and kind of soil in three identical pans. He was careful to pour the same amount of water at the same rate over two pans: one that contained only soil and another that contained soil and grass. What is Juan Carlos' control? Which factors in his activity are constants? What is the independent variable? the dependent variable?
4. **Recognizing Cause and Effect:** In Juan Carlos' activity, he found that in the pan containing soil and grass, the least amount of soil washed away. What are the cause and the effect in his observation?
5. **Sequencing:** Sequence the following types of soil in proper soil profile order from top to bottom: light colored soil with little humus, weathered rock, topsoil. Label the soils A, B, and C horizon.

PROJECTS

1. Obtain several different soil samples from around your community. Compare and contrast the samples, looking at color, texture, composition, number of organisms present, and the permeability. Construct a table on posterboard of your findings. Include an actual sample of each soil in the table.
2. Use reference books and current magazines to find out what is being done to prevent desertification. Prepare a written report that summarizes your findings.

APPLY

21. Due to the lack of moisture, mechanical weathering would be more effective in a desert than chemical weathering.
22. As water freezes and thaws in cracks in the pavement, the pavement is forced apart, creating gaps and potholes on streets and roads.
23. When certain metals are exposed to oxygen and water, chemical reactions occur to form rust.
24. Poor farming practices and the clearing of forests cause nutrients to become depleted from the soil. When the nutrients are gone, the soil is unable to support vegetation. The lack of vegetation causes massive erosion.
25. Groundwater flowing through underground rock bodies can dissolve rocks. Over time, the dissolution can create a large cavity, or cavern.

MORE SKILL BUILDERS

1. Outlining: Students' outlines will vary slightly. Have them refer to the section objectives to help them get started.
2. Concept Mapping:
Possible Solution: See below.
3. Using Variables, Constants, and Controls: The control is the pan to which nothing was done. Constants are the kind of soil, the amount of soil and water, and the rate of water flow. The independent variable is the pan containing grass. The dependent variable is the amount of soil that washed away.
4. Recognizing Cause and Effect: The grass had an effect on the amount of soil that washed away.
5. Sequencing: The topsoil is in the A horizon. The light-colored soil with little humus is the B horizon. Weathered rock forms the C horizon.

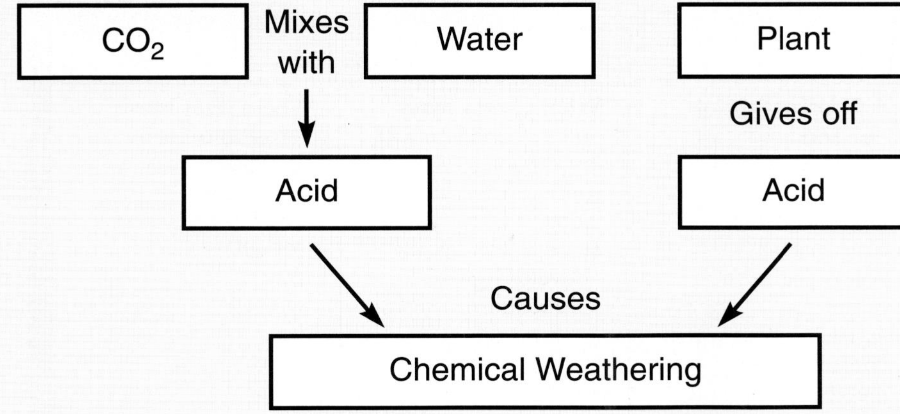

CHAPTER

6 Erosion and Deposition

CHAPTER SECTION	OBJECTIVES	ACTIVITIES
6-1 Gravity (1 day)	1. **Define** *erosion* and *deposition*. 2. **Compare** and **contrast** slumps, creep, rockslides, and mudflows.	**MINI-Lab:** *What causes mass movements?* p. 147
6-2 Running Water (1 day)	1. **Compare** rill, gully, and sheet erosion. 2. **Describe** how alluvial fans and deltas form.	**MINI-LAB:** *Where does most erosion occur?* p. 150
6-3 Developing Land Prone to Erosion Science & Society (1 day)	1. **Explain** why problems develop when people live in places where land is prone to excessive erosion. 2. **Describe** ways that erosion can be reduced in some high risk areas.	
6-4 Glaciers (2 days)	1. **Describe** how plucking occurs. 2. **Explain** how striations are created. 3. **Compare** and **contrast** till and outwash.	**Activity 6-1:** *Glacial Erosion,* p. 161
6-5 Wind (2 days)	1. **Explain** how wind causes deflation and abrasion. 2. **Discuss** how loess and dunes form.	**Activity 6-2:** *Wind Erosion,* p. 166
Chapter Review		

ACTIVITY MATERIALS

FIND OUT	ACTIVITIES		MINI-LABS	
Page 141 sand gravel	**6-1 Glacial Erosion, p. 161** stream table with sand pail ice block containing sand, clay, and gravel wood block metric ruler overhead ligh source with reflector	**6-2 Wind Erosion, p. 166** goggles flat pans fine sand clay, gravel hair dryer protractor sprinkling can, water cardboard sheet metric ruler	**What causes mass movements? p. 147** large pan sand water camera with instant developing film (optional)	**Where does most erosion occur? p. 150** large pan sand gravel soil water

CHAPTER FEATURES	TEACHER RESOURCE PACKAGE	OTHER RESOURCES
Skill Builder: *Concept Mapping,* p. 147	**Ability Level Worksheets** ◆ ***Study Guide,*** p. 25 ● ***Reinforcement,*** p. 25 ▲ ***Enrichment,*** p. 25 **MINI-Lab Worksheet,** p. 54	**Lab Manual:** *Mass Movements,* pp. 43-44
Skill Builder: *Comparing and Contrasting,* p. 151	**Ability Level Worksheets** ◆ ***Study Guide,*** p. 26 ● ***Reinforcement,*** p. 26 ▲ ***Enrichment,*** p. 26 **MINI-Lab Worksheet,** p. 55	
You Decide! p. 153	**Ability Level Worksheets** ◆ ***Study Guide,*** p. 27 ● ***Reinforcement,*** p. 27 ▲ ***Enrichment,*** p. 27 **Critical Thinking/Problem Solving,** p. 12 **Science and Society,** p. 10	
Technology: *Bergy Bits?* p. 158 **Skill Builder:** *Outlining,* p. 160	**Ability Level Worksheets** ◆ ***Study Guide,*** p. 28 ● ***Reinforcement,*** p. 28 ▲ ***Enrichment,*** p. 28 **Activity Worksheet,** pp. 48-49 **Transparency Masters,** pp. 15-18	**Lab Manual:** *Model Glacier,* pp. 45-46 **Lab Manual:** *Glaciation and Sea Level,* pp. 47-50 **Color Transparency 8,** Glacial Erosional Features **Color Transparency 9,** Glacial Depositional Features
Problem Solving: *A Trip Across the Desert,* p. 164 **Skill Builder:** *Sequencing,* p. 165	**Ability Level Worksheets** ◆ ***Study Guide,*** p. 29 ● ***Reinforcement,*** p. 29 ▲ ***Enrichment,*** p. 29 **Activity Worksheet,** pp. 50-51 **Concept Mapping,** pp. 17-18 **Cross-Curricular Connections,** p. 10	
Summary Key Science Words Understanding Vocabulary Checking Concepts Understanding Concepts Think & Write Critically Apply More Skill Builders Projects	**Chapter Review,** pp. 15-16 **Chapter Test,** pp. 39-42	**Chapter Review Software** **Test Bank**

◆ **Basic** ● **Average** ▲ **Advanced**

ADDITIONAL MATERIALS

SOFTWARE	AUDIOVISUAL	BOOKS/MAGAZINES
Stratigraphy, Aquarius, Inc. *Glaciers,* COMPress. *Energy and Environment,* Educational Materials and Equipment Co. *Glacial Landforms,* IBM. *Surface Water,* IBM.	*Strata: Earth's Changing Crust,* film, BFA. *Evidence for the Ice Age,* films, EBEC. *Glacier on the Move,* film, EBEC. *Rise and Fall of the Great Lakes,* film, Pyramid. *Erosion—Each Moving Grain,* film, UEVA.	Bramwell, Martys. *Glaciers and Ice Caps.* NY: Watts, Franklin, Inc., 1986. Walker, Sally M. Glaciers: *Ice on the Move.* Minneapolis, MN: Carolrhoda Books, Inc., 1990.

CHAPTER

6 EROSION AND DEPOSITION

THEME DEVELOPMENT: Energy and change are two prevalent themes of this chapter. Gravity, moving water, glaciers, and wind provide the energy that changes Earth's landforms.

CHAPTER OVERVIEW

- **Section 6-1:** Section 6-1 describes agents of erosion and deposition. Different types of mass movement are also discussed.
- **Section 6-2:** This section discusses water as the most pervasive agent of erosion and deposition.
- **Section 6-3: Science and Society:** Living on land prone to erosion is described. The You Decide feature asks students to discuss whether or not communities should be able to control where people live.
- **Section 6-4:** This section discusses how water in the form of ice—glaciers—is an agent of erosion and deposition.
- **Section 6-5:** Moving air, or wind, as an agent of erosion and deposition is presented in this closing section.

CHAPTER VOCABULARY

erosion	terraces
deposition	glacier
slump	plucking
creep	till
rill erosion	outwash
gully erosion	deflation
sheet erosion	abrasion
alluvial fan	loess
delta	

CHAPTER

6 Erosion and Deposition

140

OPTIONS

For Your Gifted Students

- Have students develop a crossword puzzle using the new science words presented in this chapter. They can use definitions from the chapter for clues.
- Ask students to design an experiment to simulate one type of erosion discussed in the chapter.

The water in the waterfall you see here looks clear and clean. But it's actually carrying tonnes of sediments.

There are little bits and pieces of rocks, soil, plants, insects, and animals all around you. These sediments don't just stay in one place—they are continually moving from one location to another. Your world is constantly changing because these bits and pieces are part of a cycle that keeps them moving and changing.

FIND OUT!

Do this simple activity to find out how sediments are moved from one location to another.

Place a small pile of sand and gravel on your desk. Now move the pile across your desk without touching any of the grains with your hands. How many ways can you think of to move the particles? Compare each of your methods with a force in nature that might cause sediments to move.

Gearing Up

Previewing the Chapter

Use this outline to help you focus on important ideas in this chapter.

Previewing Science Skills

- In the **Skill Builders**, you will make concept maps, compare and contrast, recognize cause and effect, outline, and sequence.
- In the **Activities**, you will observe, infer, and analyze.
- In the **MINI-Labs**, you will design experiments, observe, and infer.

What's next?

Now that you've experimented with moving sediments, learn how the forces in nature transport sediments. You will explore how sediments are moved and dropped off at new locations by the agents of erosion.

INTRODUCING THE CHAPTER

Use the Find Out activity to introduce students to different ways in which sediments can be moved. Inform students that they will be learning more about agents of erosion and deposition as they read this chapter.

FIND OUT!

Preparation: Obtain sand and gravel for students to use.

Materials: sand, gravel, and safety goggles

Cooperative Learning: Have students work as Paired Partners to perform this activity.

Teaching Tips

- Have all students wear safety goggles at all times during this activity.
- Instruct students to take care when moving the sediments so that they do not disturb the work of their classmates.
- Ideas for moving the sediments might include flushing them with water, blowing on them, tilting the surface on which the sediments are lying, or taking a piece of paper and pushing them along.
- Have students relate the amount of energy they exerted to the distance the sediments were moved.

Gearing Up

Have students study the Gearing Up feature to familiarize themselves with the chapter. Discuss the relationships of the topics in the outline.

What's Next?

Before beginning the first section, make sure students understand the connection between the Find Out activity and the topics to follow.

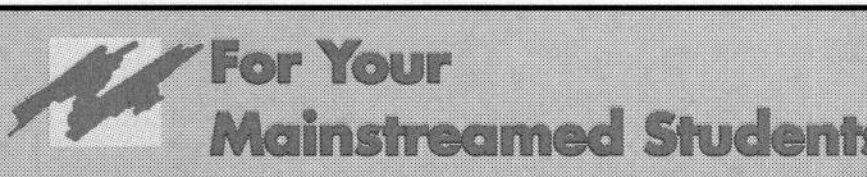

For Your Mainstreamed Students

- Allow students to use a variety of materials to create three-dimensional models of different types of erosion discussed in the chapter. Or, they can make models that show the effects of the various types of erosion.
- Have students make a dictionary of erosion terminology discussed in the chapter.

SECTION 6-1

PREPARATION

SECTION BACKGROUND

▶ Landscapes undergo constant change as materials are moved from one location to another.

▶ All geological processes consist of a change in energy from one form to another, or of the transfer of matter from one location to another.

PREPLANNING

▶ To prepare for the Mini-Lab on page 147, obtain large pans and sand for each group of students.

1 MOTIVATE

▶ Have students search the school grounds for sediments that have been transported. They may find grit on curbs, dust on leaves, and fine sediments on the windowsills. Have students think about the sources of the sediments and how the sediments were transported.

▶ Lead students in a discussion of the types of agents they think carry sediments away from one location and deposit them elsewhere.

6-1 Gravity

New Science Words

erosion
deposition
slump
creep

Objectives

▶ Define erosion and deposition.
▶ Compare and contrast slumps, creep, rockslides, and mudflows.

Erosion and Deposition

Have you ever ridden your bike by a river just after a heavy rain? The water was so muddy that it looked like chocolate milk. Where do you suppose all of the mud came from? As you might guess, some of it came from dirt along the river's bank, but the rest of it was carried to the river from much more distant sources.

1 Mud is a product of erosion. **Erosion** (ih ROH zhun) is the process that moves weathered sediments from one location to another. As you investigate the processes of

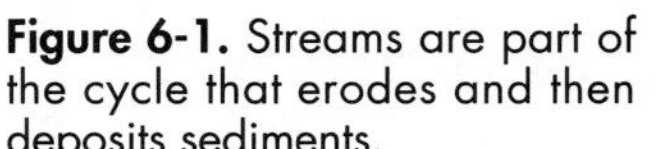

Figure 6-1. Streams are part of the cycle that erodes and then deposits sediments.

OPTIONS

Meeting Different Ability Levels

For Section 6-1, use the following **Teacher Resource Masters** depending upon individual students' needs.

◆ **Study Guide Master** for all students.

● **Reinforcement Master** for students of average and above average ability levels.

▲ **Enrichment Master** for above average students.

Additional Teacher Resource Package masters are listed in the OPTIONS box throughout the section. The additional masters are appropriate for all students.

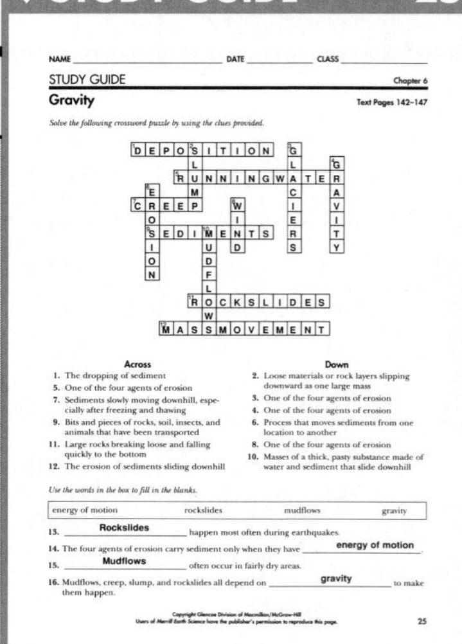

◆ STUDY GUIDE 25

NAME ______ DATE ______ CLASS ______

STUDY GUIDE — Chapter 6

Gravity — Text Pages 142–147

Solve the following crossword puzzle by using the clues provided.

DEPOSITION
SLUMP
GLACIERS
GRAVITY
RUNNINGWATER
EROSION
CREEP
WIND
SEDIMENTS
MUDFLOW
ROCKSLIDES
MASSMOVEMENT

Across
1. The dropping of sediment
5. One of the four agents of erosion
7. Sediments slowly moving downhill, especially after freezing and thawing
9. Bits and pieces of rocks, soil, insects, and animals that have been transported
11. Large rocks breaking loose and falling quickly to the bottom
12. The erosion of sediments sliding downhill

Down
2. Loose materials or rock layers slipping downward as one large mass
3. One of the four agents of erosion
4. One of the four agents of erosion
6. Process that moves sediments from one location to another
8. One of the four agents of erosion
10. Masses of a thick, pasty substance made of water and sediment that slide downhill

Use the words in the box to fill in the blanks.

energy of motion	rockslides	mudflows	gravity

13. Rockslides happen most often during earthquakes.
14. The four agents of erosion carry sediment only when they have energy of motion.
15. Mudflows often occur in fairly dry areas.
16. Mudflows, creep, slump, and rockslides all depend on gravity to make them happen.

25

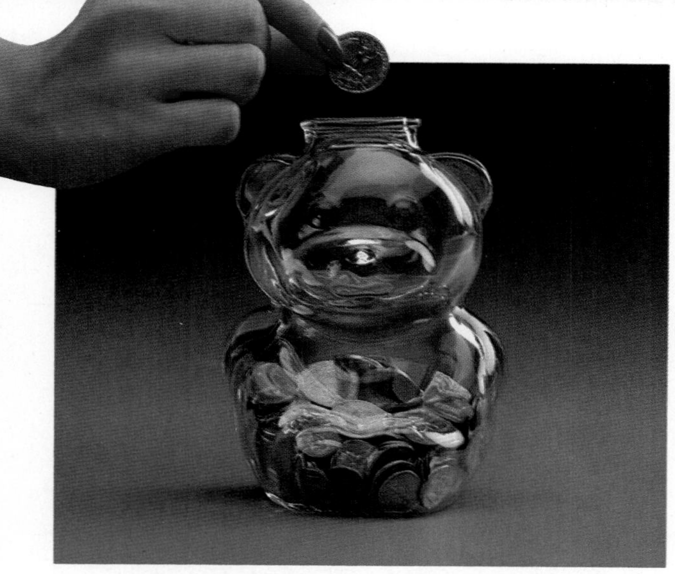

Figure 6-2 . You are an agent of erosion when you transport coins and then deposit them in your bank.

erosion, you will see that eroded sediments are eventually deposited. But what moves the sediments in the first place? The four major agents of erosion are gravity, running water, glaciers, and wind.

As you investigate these four agents of erosion, you will notice that they have several things in common. For one thing, they all carry sediments only when they have enough energy of motion. For example, air doesn't have the ability to erode sediments as long as it's standing still. But once air begins moving and develops into wind, it can carry dust, soil, and even large rocks along with it.

Another thing that the agents of erosion have in common is that they all drop their load of sediments when their energy of motion decreases. This dropping of sediments is called **deposition** (dep uh ZIHSH un). Now let's take a look at how gravity, running water, glaciers, and wind erode and deposit sediments.

Erosion and Deposition by Gravity

Gravity causes loose materials to move down a slope. When gravity alone causes materials to move downslope, it's called mass movement. Some mass movements are very slow; you hardly notice that they're happening. Other types, however, happen very quickly. Let's examine some different types of mass movements.

What is mass movement?

TYING TO PREVIOUS KNOWLEDGE: Have students recall from Chapter 1 that gravity is the force that pulls everything toward Earth. Elicit that this same force causes loose material to move down a slope.

OBJECTIVES AND SCIENCE WORDS: Have students review the objectives and science words to become familiar with this section.

2 TEACH

Key Concepts are highlighted.

CONCEPT DEVELOPMENT

▶ After students have read pages 142 and 143, pose the following question. **What are two characteristics that all agents of erosion have in common?** *They carry sediments only when they have enough energy of motion and they drop their load of sediments as the energy of motion decreases.*

▶ Discuss the role of gravity as a driving force of each agent of erosion. Be sure that students realize that gravity alone is considered an erosional agent. Additionally, it causes the other agents of erosion to move. For example, water runs downslope because of gravity. Likewise, glaciers move because gravity causes a mass of ice to have weight and to move downslope.

● REINFORCEMENT 25

NAME ____________ DATE ________ CLASS ________

ENRICHMENT — Chapter 6

Gravity — Text Pages 142–147

HOW DOES SLOPE AFFECT THE RATE OF DESCENT OF AN OBJECT?

Complete the activity and then answer the questions.

Materials
- one 2-meter-long piece of cove molding or two metersticks
- masking tape and 4 meters of about 1 1/2-inch-wide cardboard strips, if you use metersticks
- playing marble
- stopwatch
- boxes, books, or low tables
- pen or pencil

Advance Preparation
If cove molding is unavailable, use masking tape to securely tape the ends of two metersticks together. Tape cardboard strips to the sides of the metersticks to create edges that will prevent the marble from falling off the metersticks.

Procedure
1. Prop the molding on boxes, books, or tables so that it very gently inclines.
2. Ask a partner to use the stopwatch to time the descent of the marble from the time it is released to the time it falls to the floor.
3. Drop the marble from the top of the stick.
4. In the table below, record the height and time of the descent.
5. Repeat Steps 3 and 4 three times, increasing the slope of the molding each time.

Data and Observations

Slope	Height	Time	Slope	Height	Time
A			C		
B			D		

Analyze
1. Study your data. When did the marble move the fastest? When did the marble move the slowest? **The marble moved fastest when the slope was steepest. The marble moved slowest when the slope was shallowest.**
2. Can you identify a relationship between steepness and time? What is it? **Increased slope increases the rate of descent.**

Conclude and Apply
3. Why does the amount of slope affect the rate of descent? **At greater inclines the force of gravity is greater and causes materials to drop from top to bottom more quickly.**
4. What effect would you expect the amount of slope to have on a rockslide or mudflow? **The steeper the slope, the more likely a rockslide or mudflow will occur.**

 25

▲ ENRICHMENT 25

NAME ____________ DATE ________ CLASS ________

REINFORCEMENT — Chapter 6

Gravity — Text Pages 142–147

Complete the items on the lines provided.

1. Identify the types of mass movement described below.
   a. It causes sediments to slowly move downhill. It happens in areas where the ground freezes and thaws. As the ground freezes, expanding water in the soil pushes up sediments. When the ground thaws, the sediments fall downslope. This is a slow process. **creep**
   b. These are common in mountainous areas. A sign that these have occurred is a pile of rocks at the bottom of a hill. They occur most often after heavy rains or during earthquakes. **rockslides**
   c. This takes place on steep slopes. It happens when underlying material is weakened and can no longer support material on top of it. Loose material slips downward as a large mass. **slump**
   d. These are likely to happen in relatively dry areas where weathering forms thick layers of dry sediment. They occur after heavy rains fall. Sediments and water mix together to form paste that slides downhill. **mudflows**
2. What do these four types of erosion have in common? **They are all mass movements. All occur on slopes. All are most likely to happen after a heavy rain. All erode sediments from the top of a slope to farther downhill.**
3. Identify the type of mass movement from the clues provided.
   a. A cone-shaped deposit **mudflows**
   b. Leaning fenceposts **creep**
   c. "Beware of falling rock" signs **rockslides**
   d. A curved scar where eroded material once was located **slump**
4. Answer the following questions in complete sentences.
   a. Hawaii consists of a chain of tropical islands. Would you expect to see evidence of creep there? Explain. **No, creep occurs most commonly in areas where the ground freezes.**
   b. To provide privacy, a landscape architect built a hill around a new housing development. Clay and dirt were used to build the hill, and trees and grass were planted on it. Do you think the area would experience rockslides? Why or why not? **Since rocks were not used to build the hill, rockslides would not occur.**

 25

CONCEPT DEVELOPMENT

▶ **What do slump and creep have in common?** *Slump and creep are very slow types of mass movement.*

▶ **Do you think creep occurs in our area?** *Answers will depend upon your climate and the topography of your area.*

CROSS CURRICULUM

▶ **Language Arts:** Have students use dictionaries to look up the meaning of *slump*. Ask volunteers to read aloud the definitions when describing a person's physical appearance and the condition of economic activity. Then ask students what all meanings of the word have in common. They should be able to conclude, that in every case, *slump* describes a decline or collapse of something.

EXTENSION

▶ Have interested students discover the relationship between slope and occurrences of slump. Slump often occurs when slopes have been oversteepened. Slopes are commonly oversteepened when construction workers remove materials near the base of a slope. The materials near the top of a slope are held in place by the materials nearer the base of the slope. When these basal materials are removed, the slope becomes unstable, and gravity pulls the mass downward. Slopes can also be made unstable (oversteepened) when overburden from a construction project is piled up. The overload causes stress on underlying layers. When the underlying layers are too weak to anchor the overlying materials, slumps result.

Figure 6-3. Slumps occur when material slips downslope as one large mass.

Slump

A **slump** is a type of mass movement that takes place on steep slopes. It occurs when loose materials or rock layers slip downward as one large mass. The material doesn't travel very fast or very far, but when it happens, a curved scar is left where the slumped material originally rested. Slumps occur because the material underlying the slumped material weakened. It could no longer support the overlying material, so it slipped downslope.

Figure 6-4. When the ground freezes, soil particles are lifted at a right angle to the slope. Upon thawing, they fall downslope resulting in soil creep.

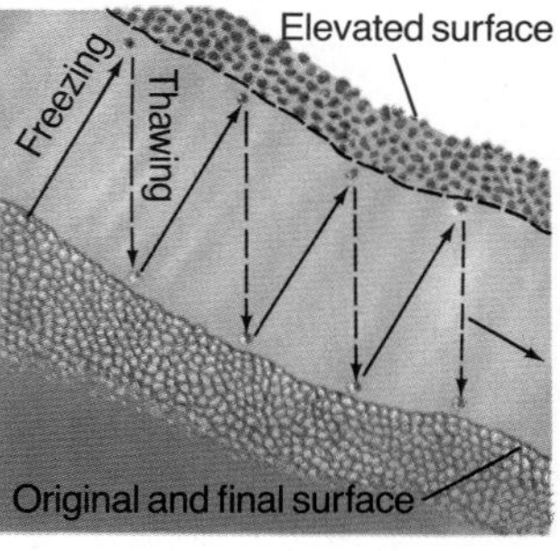

Creep

The next time you travel by car or bus, look along the roadway for slopes where trees, utility poles, and fenceposts lean downhill. These indicate that another type of mass movement is happening. It's called creep. **Creep** gets its name from the way sediments slowly creep down a hill. It is especially common in areas where freezing and thawing occur. As the ground freezes, small sediments are pushed up by the expanding water in the soil. Then, when the soil thaws, the sediments fall downslope, often less than a millimeter at a time. Several years of soil creeping downslope can cause objects such as utility poles and fenceposts to lean.

OPTIONS

INQUIRY QUESTIONS

▶ **What evidence would you look for to find out whether a particular slope has undergone slump or creep?** *Curved scars indicate slump. Trees, utility poles, and fenceposts that lean downhill indicate creep.*

▶ **Slumps occur when underlying material weakens and the weight of overlying sediments causes slippage. What causes the underlying materials to weaken?** *Weathering is often a cause of weakening.*

PROGRAM RESOURCES

Use **Laboratory Manual,** pages 43-44, Mass Movements.

Rockslides

You may have seen signs along the road warning you to "Beware of Falling Rocks." Falling rocks are a type of mass movement called a rockslide. A rockslide happens when large blocks of rock break loose from steep slopes and tumble quickly to the bottom. As they fall, these rocks crash into other rocks, and they too break loose. Rockslides commonly occur in mountainous areas. They happen most often after heavy rains or during earthquakes, but they can happen on any rocky slope at any time without warning. Piles of broken rock at the bottom of a cliff tell you that rockslides have occurred there in the past and are likely to occur there again.

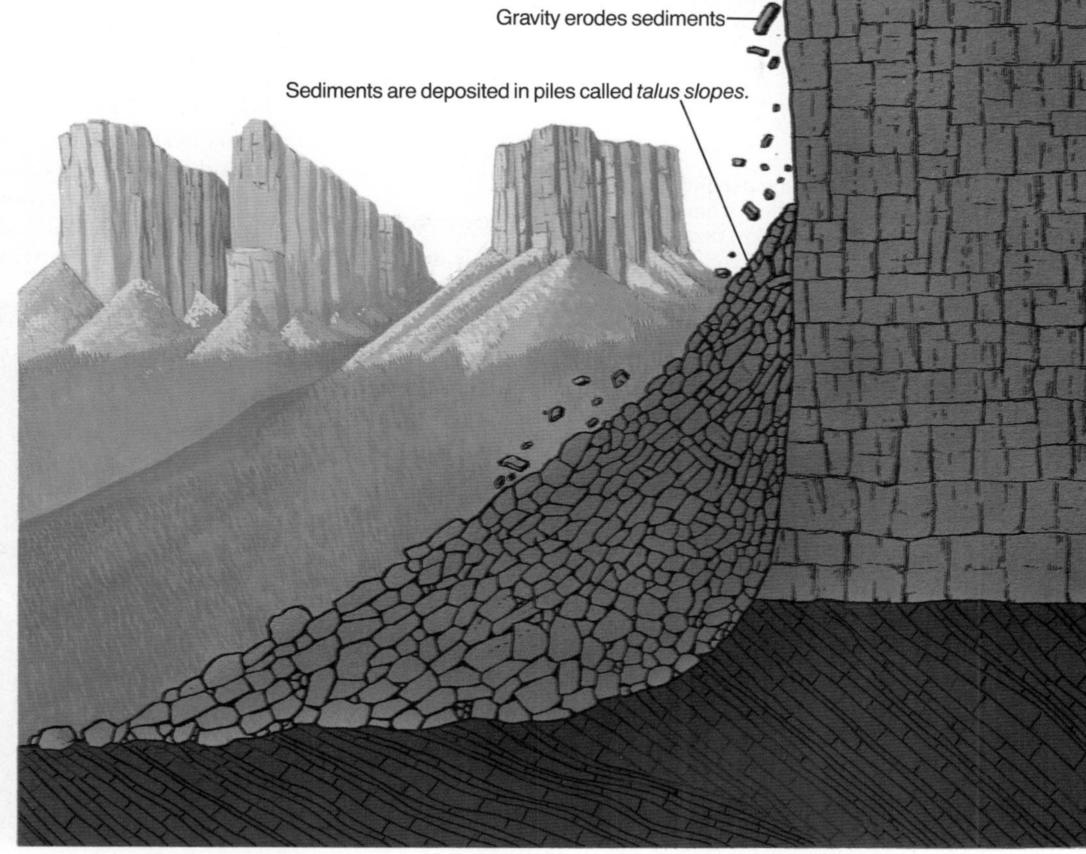
Weathering breaks rocks apart
Gravity erodes sediments
Sediments are deposited in piles called *talus slopes.*

CONCEPT DEVELOPMENT

▶ Invite an engineer to the class to speak about the importance of knowing about mass movements, weathering, and erosion when considering building sites for roads, dams, and buildings.

TEACHER F.Y.I.

▶ The material that accumulates at the bottom of a slope as a result of mass movement is called talus.

EXTENSION

▶ Have students explore the connection between weathering and erosion as they relate to rockslides. Students should infer that materials on a slope (or cliff) do not fall unless they are unconsolidated. A solid rock cliff is fragmented by weathering processes. Chemical and mechanical weathering processes break the rocks of a slope into small, unconsolidated pieces. Erosional agents (in the case of a rockfall—gravity) cause the pieces to fall.

CONCEPT DEVELOPMENT

▶ Use the figure on this page to illustrate how mass movements result in less steep slopes. Compare the slope of the cliff prior to weathering and erosion to its slope after materials have been removed near the top.

INQUIRY QUESTIONS

▶ **How are avalanches and rockslides similar?** *Both occur on steep slopes where large blocks of material break loose and tumble quickly to the bottom of the slope. Both events occur in mountainous areas. Finally, both result in piles of loose material that accumulate at the bottom of the slopes.*

▶ **Suppose you were purchasing property on a hillside. Why should you examine the bottom of the hill?** *Sediment piles at the bottoms of slopes indicate there have been previous landslides and there will likely be more.*

▶ **Look at the figure on page 145. Explain what talus slopes are and how they form.** *Talus slopes are piles of loose material that often form at the bases of very steep rock outcrops. They are composed of the materials that were weathered and eroded from the outcrop.*

CHECK FOR UNDERSTANDING

Use the Mini Quiz to check for understanding.

MINI QUIZ

Use the Mini Quiz to check students' recall of chapter content.

1. **What is erosion?** *the process that moves sediments from one place to another*
2. **How do climatic conditions affect mass movements?** *All mass movements occur more often after a heavy rain because water adds mass to the sediments and makes them slippery.*
3. **How do mass movements affect the angle of a slope?** *Mass movments make a slope less steep.*

RETEACH

Have students use information in the text to make a table contrasting the speed and evidence of movement of slump, creep, landslides, and mudflows. Assist students, if necessary.

EXTENSION

For students who have mastered this section, use the **Reinforcement** and **Enrichment** masters or other OPTIONS provided.

Did You Know?

Mudflows have moved 85-ton boulders hundreds of meters downslope.

Mudflows

Can you imagine being in a car traveling along a mountain road during a storm, when suddenly a wall of chocolate pudding slides down a slope and covers your car? This is similar to what might happen if you were caught in a mudflow. Instead of chocolate pudding, a thick mixture of sediments and water would flow down the slope in a type of mass movement called a mudflow.

Mudflows usually occur in relatively dry areas where weathering forms thick layers of dry sediments. When heavy rains fall in these areas, the water mixes with the sediments and forms a thick, pasty substance. Gravity causes this mass to slide downhill. A mudflow has enough energy to move almost anything in its path, including houses, cars, and large rocks. When a mudflow finally reaches the bottom of a slope, it loses its energy of motion and deposits all the sediments and debris it has been carrying. These deposits are usually a cone-shaped mass.

Why do mudflows eventually deposit sediments?

Now that you've thought about mudflows, rockslides, creep, and slump, think about how all these mass movements are similar. They're all more likely to happen where there are steep slopes. They all depend on gravity to make
2 them happen. And, regardless of the type of mass movement, it will occur more often after a heavy rain because the water adds mass and makes the sediments slippery.

Figure 6-5. How does the deposit from a mudflow differ from deposits from slumps, creeps, and rockslides?

OPTIONS

ENRICHMENT

▶ Have students research to find out how rockslides, mudflows, avalanches, creep, and slump can be prevented.

▶ Refer students to the Technology feature on page 398. After they have read this feature and examined the photograph, have students explain the purpose of the concrete structures shown. Ask students how these reduce destruction due to mudflows.

PROGRAM RESOURCES

From the **Teacher Resource Package** use:

Activity Worksheets, page 54, Mini-Lab: What causes mass movements?

MINI-Lab

What causes mass movements? Using a large pan and moist sand, construct model landforms that will show how the mass movements of sediments or loose materials can be demonstrated. Try to set up situations where each of the four types of mass movements is created. If a camera is available, take before and after pictures that will show the effects of these movements. What factors must be present for mass movements to occur? In what ways are each of these forms of mass movements similar?

Now, can you think of one more way they are all alike? All mass movements are the erosion of sediments from the top of a slope to a place farther downslope. The result is that mass movements constantly change the shape of a 3
slope so that it becomes less steep.

SECTION REVIEW

1. Define erosion and deposition.
2. What is the difference between slump and creep?
3. What characteristics do all types of mass movements have in common?
4. **Apply:** People pile up dirt or cut into the sides of hills when they build houses and roads. Why does this speed up erosion by mass movement?

Concept Mapping

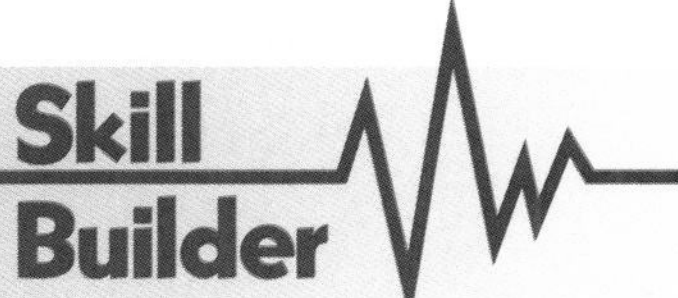

Make a concept map about mass movements using these terms: gravity, slump, creep, rockslides, mudflows, curved scar, leaning trees and poles, rock piles, and cone-shaped mass. If you need help, refer to Concept Mapping in the **Skill Handbook** on pages 688 and 689.

Skill Builder

Possible Solution:

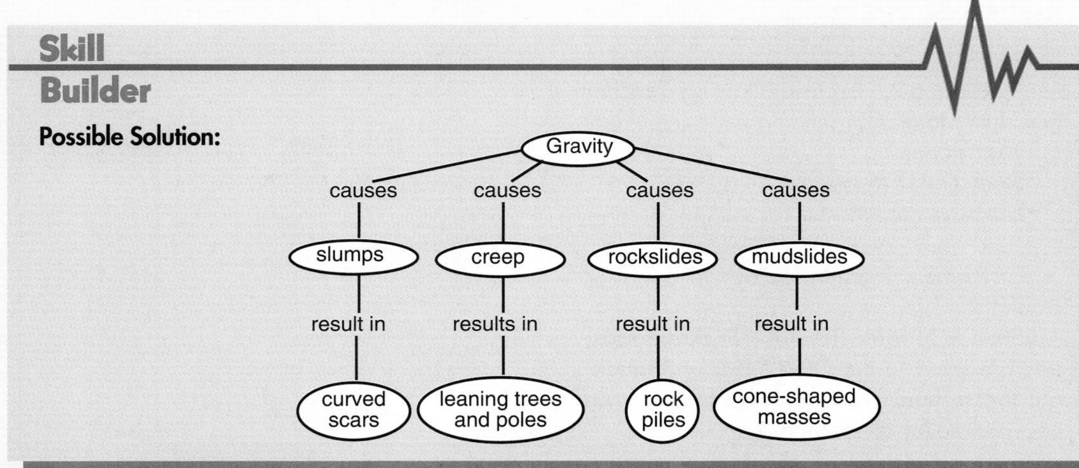

MINI-Lab

Materials: large pan or basin, sand, water, camera with instant developing film (optional)

Teaching Tips

Cooperative Learning: Form Science Investigation groups of three or four students per group. Have each group duplicate each type of mass movement with the moist sand.

▶"Before" and "after" photos of each landform will provide an excellent basis for discussing mass movements.

▶Have a mop, bucket, and plenty of paper towels available for clean-up of spills.

▶**Answers:** Mass movements occur in areas where both steep slopes and lots of water are present. All forms of mass movement result from gravity. Mass movement moves loose materials from higher to lower elevations.

3 CLOSE

▶ Ask questions 1-3 and the **Apply** Question from the Section Review.

▶ Have students report on problems involving local mass movements.

SECTION REVIEW ANSWERS

1. Erosion is a process that moves weathered sediments from one location to another. Deposition is the dropping of sediments.

2. Slump occurs when loose material and rock layers slip downhill as one large mass, leaving behind a curved scar. Creep occurs when sediments slowly slide down a slope, causing trees, telephone poles, and fenceposts to lean downhill.

3. All happen on steep slopes; all depend on gravity to make them happen; and they occur more often after a heavy rain.

4. Apply: Piling up dirt and cutting into the sides of hills create steep slopes. Steep slopes are more unstable than shallow slopes and are more prone to erosion.

SECTION 6-2

PREPARATION

SECTION BACKGROUND

- Braided stream systems form when a channel is overloaded with sediment that builds up as bars, forcing the water to flow around the obstructions.
- An alluvial fan is a cone-shaped, gently sloping mass of rock debris that is deposited by a stream at a point where the stream emerges from a narrow mountain valley onto a plain.
- Even in a desert area, the chief erosional agent is water, usually from flash floods.

PREPLANNING

- To prepare for the Mini-Lab on page 150, obtain large pans and sand, gravel, or soil.

1 MOTIVATE

- Take students outside to look for evidence of water erosion around the school grounds. Some things they might find include small channel scars on the sides of slopes or low, flat areas where fine sediments have been deposited.
- Have students collect photos that show features formed by water erosion.

TYING TO PREVIOUS KNOWLEDGE: Have students recall from Chapter 5 the importance of water in weathering sediments. In this section, they will learn that once weathered, sediments also can be eroded by water.

6-2 Running Water

New Science Words

rill erosion
gully erosion
sheet erosion
alluvial fan
delta

Objectives

- Compare rill, gully, and sheet erosion.
- Describe how alluvial fans and deltas form.

Figure 6-6. Cross Section of a Stream Channel

Water Erosion

1 Water erodes more sediments than any other agent of erosion. It's easy to see why—running water has great energy of motion. Usually, water moves downslope because of gravity's pull. As long as it has its energy of motion, water carries its load of sediments. But when it loses some of its energy, water must deposit the sediments that it's eroding.

As the water in a stream moves along, it constantly picks up sediments from the bottom and sides of its channel. Water picks up and carries some of the lightweight sediments, while large, heavy sediments just roll along the bottom of the stream channel. All of these different-sized materials scrape against the bottom and sides of the channel, where they knock loose even more sediments. Because of this, a stream continually cuts a deeper and wider channel.

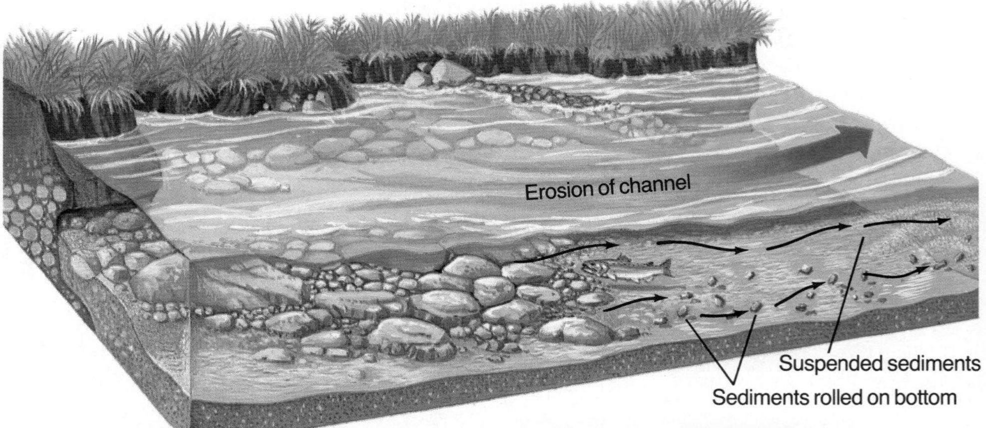

OPTIONS

Meeting Different Ability Levels

For Section 6-2, use the following **Teacher Resource Masters** depending upon individual students' needs.

◆ **Study Guide Master** for all students.
● **Reinforcement Master** for students of average and above average ability levels.
▲ **Enrichment Master** for above average students.

Additional Teacher Resource Package masters are listed in the OPTIONS box throughout the section. The additional masters are appropriate for all students.

◆ STUDY GUIDE 26

NAME ______ DATE ______ CLASS ______

STUDY GUIDE — Chapter 6

Running Water — Text Pages 148–151

After each statement is a word that has been scrambled. Unscramble the word and write it on the line provided to complete the sentence.

1. More sediments are eroded by **water** than by any other agent of erosion. **tawre**
2. A scar or small channel on the side of a slope is evidence of **rill** erosion. **lirl**
3. Rainwater flowing into lower elevations outside of a channel and carrying sediments with it causes **sheet** erosion. **hetes**
4. Shaped like a triangle, an **alluvial** fan is one type of deposit resulting from water erosion. **lauvilla**
5. The alluvial fan resulting from water erosion of the Mississippi River is known as the Mississippi **delta**. **taled**
6. The Grand Canyon evolved from **gully** erosion. **lugly**
7. As it moves along a stream, water constantly picks up **sediment** from the bottom and sides of its channel. **mensidet**
8. The rill erosion of a **stream** that frequently flows in the same path may evolve into gully erosion. **marets**
9. Water usually loses energy of motion as it moves **downstream**. **stonedwarm**
10. When water begins flowing on a **level** surface, it slows down, loses energy of motion, and drops its sediments. **velle**
11. The pull of **gravity** causes water to move downslope. **varygit**
12. Because of erosion, a stream continually cuts a deeper and wider **channel**. **henlanc**
13. Rill erosion begins when a small stream forms during a heavy **rain**. **rina**
14. When the Mississippi River reaches the Gulf of Mexico, it loses much of its **energy** of motion. **greney**
15. A delta is formed when water does not **deposit** its sediments until it empties into an ocean, lake, or gulf. **topside**
16. Sediments in a slow-moving stream may settle at the **bottom** of the stream. **toombt**

26

Figure 6-7. As the Colorado River flows, it erodes a huge load of sediments. Over the past several million years, the Colorado River has carved out the Grand Canyon by carrying away the rock and soil that were once there.

Rill and Gully Erosion

Suppose you and several friends walk the same way to school each day. Perhaps you cross the same field or empty lot, always walking in the same footsteps as you did the day before. By now, you've worn a path through the lot. Water also wears a path as it travels down a slope.

You may have seen a scar or small channel on the side of a slope that was left behind by running water. If you have, then you've seen evidence of rill erosion. **Rill erosion** ② begins when a small stream forms during a heavy rain. As this stream flows along, it has enough energy to carry away plants and soil. There's a scar left on the slope where the water eroded the plants and soil. If a stream frequently flows in the same path, rill erosion may evolve into gully erosion.

How do rill and gully erosion differ?

In **gully erosion,** a stream channel becomes broader and deeper, and large amounts of soil are removed from an area. Deep canyons, such as the Grand Canyon in Arizona, evolve from this type of erosion. ③

Sheet Erosion

Water often erodes without being in a stream channel. For example, when it rains over a fairly flat area, the rainwater accumulates until it eventually begins moving down a gentle slope. **Sheet erosion** happens when this rainwater flows into lower elevations, carrying sediments with it. In these lower elevations, the water loses some of its energy of motion and it drains into the soil or slowly evaporates. The sediments left behind cover the soil like a sheet.

Science and READING

Research recent news articles to find which planets in the solar system have evidence of erosion by running water.

OBJECTIVES AND SCIENCE WORDS: Have students review the objectives and science words to become familiar with this section.

2 TEACH

Key Concepts are highlighted.

CONCEPT DEVELOPMENT

▶ After students have read pages 148-149, ask the following questions: **Suppose a rapidly flowing stream is carrying gravel, sand, and silt. Which sediment will be deposited when the stream loses some of its energy?** *gravel, because it is the largest* **Explain how rill erosion could evolve into gully erosion.** *If a stream flows along the same path for a substantial amount of time, the channel becomes wider and deeper.*

Science and READING

Sources of information include *Astronomy,* which has printed all of the data available from the *Voyager* missions.

TEACHER F.Y.I.

▶ Several rivers have been named for the color of the sediments they carry. The Colorado River has the Spanish name for "red" because of the reddish sandstone it erodes from the Grand Canyon. China's Yellow River carries yellowish, wind-deposited silt.

MINI QUIZ

Use the Mini Quiz to check students' recall of chapter content.

1. **____ erodes more sediments than any other agent of erosion.** *Water*
2. **Which type of erosion begins when a small stream forms during a heavy rain?** *rill erosion*
3. **How has the Grand Canyon evolved?** *It began as a small channel due to rill erosion by the Colorado River. The channel became a gully and finally a canyon.*

● REINFORCEMENT 26

NAME ________ DATE ________ CLASS ________

REINFORCEMENT — Chapter 6

Running Water — Text Pages 148–151

In the spaces provided, write the term that matches the description.

1. D [E] L T A
2. G U L L Y E [R] O S I O N
3. S E D I M E [N] T S
4. M I S S I S S I P P I [R] I V E R
5. S H E E T E R [O] S I O N
6. A L L U V I A L F [A] N
7. G R A N D C A N Y [O] N
8. L O U I [S] I A N A
9. C H A N N [E] L
10. [W] A T E R
11. R I L L E R O S [I] O N
12. E N E R G Y O F M O [T] I O N

1. This kind of alluvial fan forms where a stream empties into a lake.
2. This form of erosion can result from rill erosion.
3. A stream constantly picks these up from the sides and bottom of a channel.
4. This forms a delta as it empties into the Gulf of Mexico.
5. This is water erosion that doesn't flow in a channel.
6. This is a triangular-shaped deposit of sediment.
7. This spectacular sight in Arizona was formed by gully erosion.
8. The Mississippi Delta is located on the coast of this state.
9. This becomes deeper and wider as materials scrape its sides and bottom.
10. This is an agent of erosion.
11. This begins when a small stream forms during a heavy rain.
12. When water loses this, the water deposits its sediments.

Some of the letters in the answers are in boxes. Write those letters on the line below. Then unscramble the letters to make two words that are the topic of the above activity.

ERNROAOSEWIT WATER EROSION

26

▲ ENRICHMENT 26

NAME ________ DATE ________ CLASS ________

ENRICHMENT — Chapter 6

Running Water — Text Pages 148–151

HOW DOES VEGETATION DECREASE EROSION?

Complete the activity and answer the questions.

Materials
- 2 shoe boxes
- plastic wrap or foil
- soil
- 2 buckets
- sod or grass seed
- water in a container
- scissors
- low table or desk
- ruler
- 2 blocks of wood, about 2.5 cm high

Advance Preparation
1. Line the shoe boxes with plastic wrap or foil.
2. Fill one of the shoe boxes halfway with soil. Throw grass seed on the soil and water it. Allow the grass to grow about 5 cm before performing the activity.
3. Cut triangles out of the ends of the boxes as shown.
4. Place plastic wrap or foil under the boxes.

Procedure
1. Fill one shoe box about half full of soil, and fill the other shoe box half full of soil and sod.
2. Place the shoe boxes at the end of a low table or desk, with the "triangle" end extending about 7.5 cm over the edge.
3. Put buckets underneath the shoe boxes. Place a block of wood under the back of each shoe box, so that the boxes are sloping slightly toward the buckets.
4. Slowly pour about 1 L of water down each box. Pour the water at the same rate for each box.
5. Examine the water in the buckets and note which bucket contains the most sediment.
6. Repeat the activity again, but this time pour the water quickly over the soil.

Analyze
1. How does the rate of water flow affect the amount of erosion? **The faster-running water erodes more soil.**
2. Does the bucket for the box with just soil have more sediments than the other bucket? **Yes.**

Conclude and Apply
3. How does the vegetation affect erosion? What evidence helps you draw this conclusion? **Plants slow erosion by holding soil in place. The bucket for the box with soil and grass has less sediment than the other bucket.**
4. Would you recommend planting vegetation in areas with exposed soil? Explain. **Planting uncovered areas would help reduce erosion of the soil.**

26

MINI-Lab

Materials: large pan or basin; sand, gravel, or soil; water

Teaching Tips

Cooperative Learning: Form Science Investigation groups of four students per group.

►Explain to students that they should observe the erosion that occurs on the inside and the outside of the stream channel as it turns.

►Have cleanup materials available.

Answer: Erosive action in streams occurs at a much greater rate on the outside of channel curves because the water exerts its greatest force here. The amount of erosion on the inside of the curves is minimal.

CHECK FOR UNDERSTANDING

Cooperative Learning: Using the Paired Partner strategy and Appendix G, have students explain how sediments on a hillside in Memphis, Tennessee might end up in the Mississippi Delta. Students should conclude that sediments eroded from the hillside by rill and gully erosion are carried to a local stream, which eventually feeds into the Mississippi River. When the river enters the Gulf of Mexico, it loses its energy of motion and deposits the sediments from Tennessee.

RETEACH

Cooperative Learning: Have students work in Science Investigation groups. Instruct each group to do the following. Pour water into the deep end of a paint tray and cover the top of the tray with fine soil. Gently pour water from a beaker onto the soil at the top of the tray and observe what happens. Students will observe the evolution of a "delta."

EXTENSION

For students who have mastered this section, use the **Reinforcement** and **Enrichment** masters or other OPTIONS provided.

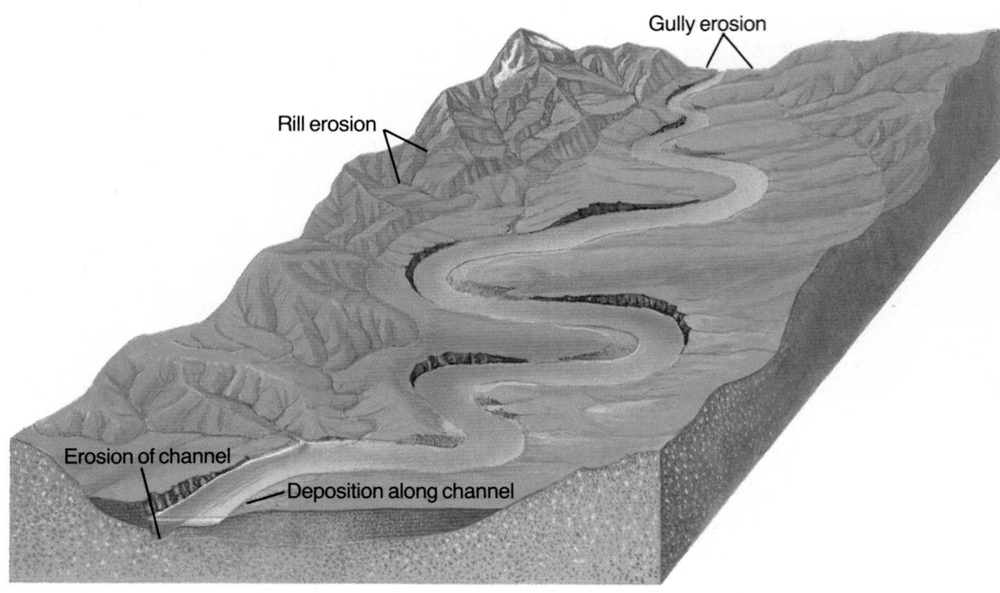

Figure 6-8. Streams are eroding and depositing material at the same time.

MINI-Lab

Where does most erosion occur?

In a large pan with sand, gravel, or soil, make a channel for a stream of water to flow through. Put several bends or turns in the channel so that the water will not be able to flow along a straight path. Start the water moving and observe where the stream erodes most rapidly. Describe how the path of a stream of running water affects the rate at which erosion takes place.

Deposition by Water

Where do you suppose the sediments from sheet, rill, and gully erosion end up? Why doesn't the stream just carry the sediments forever?

Some stream sediments aren't carried very far before being deposited. In fact, many sediments are deposited within the stream channel itself. Whenever the water in a stream isn't moving fast enough to carry sediments, they settle to the bottom.

Some stream sediments travel great distances before they are deposited. Sediments picked up when rill and gully erosion occur are examples. Water usually has a lot of energy of motion as it moves down a steep slope. When the water begins flowing on a level surface, it slows down, loses energy of motion, and drops its sediments.

One type of deposit that results, an **alluvial fan,** is shaped like a triangle. If the sediments are not deposited until the water empties into an ocean, gulf, or lake, the alluvial fan is known as a **delta.**

Let's use the Mississippi River as an example to tie all of this together. Thousands of small streams flow into the Mississippi. These streams are causing rill or gully erosion as they pick up sediments and dump them into the

OPTIONS

INQUIRY QUESTIONS

► **Why do deltas make very good farmlands?** *They contain a lot of topsoil from various locations.*

► **What size sediments are found at the narrow end of an alluvial fan?** *The coarsest sediments are deposited at the narrow end of the fan because as the energy of motion begins to decrease, the heavier sediments are dropped.*

Mississippi River. The Mississippi is quite large and has a lot of energy. It can erode many sediments. As it flows, it cuts into its banks and picks up more sediments. In other places, where the land is flat, the river deposits some of its sediments in its own channel.

Eventually, the Mississippi River reaches the Gulf of Mexico. There, it flows into the gulf, loses most of its energy of motion, and dumps its sediments in a large triangular deposit on the Louisiana coast. This deposit, shown in Figure 6-9, is the Mississippi Delta.

Describe how the Mississippi Delta grows.

SECTION REVIEW

1. What causes rill erosion?
2. How do alluvial fans and deltas form?
3. **Apply:** How can rill erosion evolve into gully erosion?

Figure 6-9. This satellite image of the Mississippi Delta shows how sediments accumulate when the Mississippi River empties into the Gulf of Mexico.

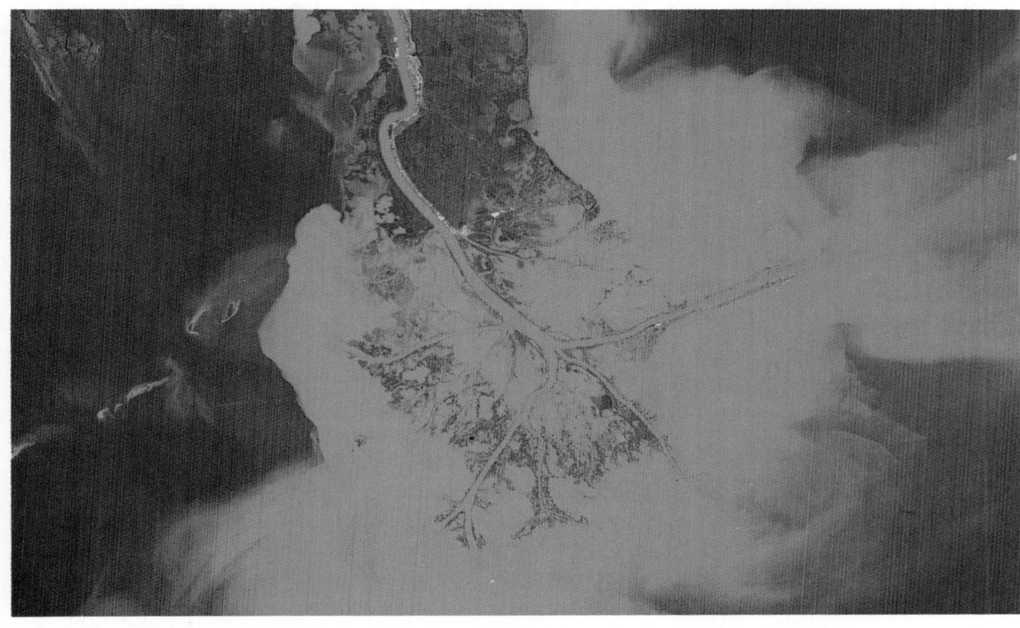

Comparing and Contrasting

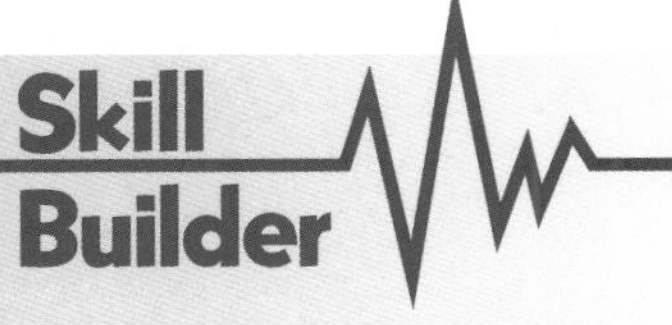

Compare and contrast sheet, rill, and gully erosion. If you need help, refer to Comparing and Contrasting in the **Skill Handbook** on page 683.

CROSS CURRICULUM

▶ **Language Arts:** Have students find out how deltas got their name. They will learn that both the Greek capital letter delta (Δ) and the deposit have a triangular shape.

3 CLOSE

FLEX Your Brain

Use the Flex Your Brain activity to have students explore ALLUVIAL FANS.

▶ Ask questions 1-2 and the **Apply** Question in the Section Review.

SECTION REVIEW ANSWERS

1. Small streams called rills form during heavy rains and erode the land over which they flow.

2. Both form when water flows onto a level surface, loses velocity, and deposits sediments. Deltas form where water empties into an ocean, gulf, or lake.

3. Apply: If a stream continues to flow over an area, sediments will continue to be carried away. The rill will erode the channel deeper and wider, and eventually a gully will form.

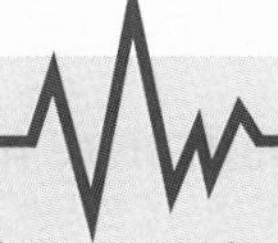

All are examples of erosion by water. Sheet erosion occurs when rainwater has enough energy to suspend sediments above the ground. Rill erosion also occurs during heavy rains, but unlike sheet erosion, rill erosion has enough energy to carry away plants and soil. Gully erosion cuts a stream channel deeper and wider and removes large amounts of soil from an area.

ENRICHMENT

▶ Have students report on the evolution of the Mississippi Delta. The relationship between sediment size and distance from the source should be stressed.

▶ Have students research the erosional effects of the Colorado or Mississippi rivers.

▶ Have students photograph places where water erosion has occurred in the community.

PROGRAM RESOURCES

From the **Teacher Resource Package** use:

Activity Worksheets, page 55, Mini-Lab: Where does most erosion occur?

Activity Worksheets, page 5, Flex Your Brain.

SECTION 6-3

PREPARATION

SECTION BACKGROUND

▶ For centuries, in some mountainous regions, terraces have been used as places to live and grow crops. In Peru, the Philippines, Japan, and China, vast numbers of people live and produce crops on terraces.

1 MOTIVATE

▶ Invite a real-estate agent in to talk about how the view affects the value of property.

▶ Show students photographs of houses crowded on the sides of hills or mountains, or beside lakes, rivers, or oceans. Ask students why they think people want to live in these locations.

TYING TO PREVIOUS KNOWLEDGE: Remind students that early American pioneers first settled areas along rivers. Lead students to conclude that the water was used for transportation, washing, cooking, drinking, and trapping.

OBJECTIVES AND SCIENCE WORDS: Have students review the objectives and science words to become familiar with this section.

2 TEACH

Key Concepts are highlighted.

TEACHER F.Y.I.

▶ Approximately 12 percent of the population of the United States lives on land that periodically floods.

6-3 Developing Land Prone to Erosion

New Science Words

terraces

Objectives

▶ Explain why problems develop when people live in places where land is prone to excessive erosion.

▶ Describe ways that erosion can be reduced in some high risk areas.

Should We Develop Land Prone to Erosion?

Have you noticed that many people live in houses and apartments beside rivers and lakes and on the sides of hills and mountains? If you ask real-estate agents, they'll tell you that people like to live where there's a good view. People like to look down on a valley or watch boats sail along a river. However, when you think of the effects of gravity and water, do you think steep slopes and river banks are good places for people to live? Perhaps not.

When people settle in these locations, they must constantly battle erosion problems. They have to deal not only with erosion that occurs naturally, but sometimes with additional problems they create themselves. When people make a slope steeper or remove vegetation, they are speeding up the erosion process.

EcoTip

In nature areas, stay on marked trails. You will protect fragile plant life and prevent excessive erosion.

There are a variety of things that people can do to reduce erosion. Planting vegetation is one of the best ways because not only do roots hold soil, but plants absorb a lot of water. A person living on a steep slope might also build terraces or retaining walls.

Why do terraces reduce erosion?

Terraces are broad, steplike cuts made into the side of a slope. When water flows onto a terrace, it is slowed down and its energy of motion is reduced, so it can't erode as much. Retaining walls are often made of concrete, stones, wood, or railroad ties. Their purpose is to keep soil and rocks from sliding downhill. These walls can also be built along stream channels, lakes, or ocean beaches to reduce erosion caused by flooding, running water, or waves.

OPTIONS

Meeting Different Ability Levels

For Section 6-3, use the following **Teacher Resource Masters** depending upon individual students' needs.

◆ **Study Guide Master** for all students.

● **Reinforcement Master** for students of average and above average ability levels.

▲ **Enrichment Master** for above average students.

Additional Teacher Resource Package masters are listed in the OPTIONS box throughout the section. The additional masters are appropriate for all students.

◆ STUDY GUIDE 27

NAME ______ DATE ______ CLASS ______

STUDY GUIDE Chapter 6

Excessive Erosion Text Pages 152–153

Use the code given to decode the message. Note that in the code, one letter simply stands for another. Write your answer in the spaces provided, placing one letter on each space. The first word of the message is decoded for you.

A B C D E F G H I J K L M N O P Q R S T U V W X Y Z
Code: B C D E F G H I J K L M N O P Q R S T U V W X Y Z A

PEOPLE **CAN HELP REDUCE EROSION**
QFPQMF DBO IFMQ SFEVDF FSPTJPO
IN MANY WAYS. THEY CAN PLANT
JO NBOZ XBZT. UIFZ DBO QMBOU
VEGETATION. PLANT ROOTS HOLD
WFHFUBUJPO. QMBOU SPPUT IPME
SOIL AND PLANTS ABSORB LOTS OF
TPJM BOE QMBOUT BCTPSC MPUT PG
WATER. PEOPLE WHO LIVE ON
XBUFS. QFPQMF XIP MJWF PO
SLOPES CAN BUILD TERRACES.
TMPQFT DBO CVJME UFSSBDFT.
TERRACES CAN SLOW THE ENERGY
UFSSBDFT DBO TMPX UIF FOFSHZ
OF MOTION OF WATER. PEOPLE ON
PG NPUJPO PG XBUFS. QFPQMF PO
SLOPES AND NEAR STREAMS, LAKES,
TMPQFT BOE OFBS TUSFBNT, MBLFT,
AND OCEANS CAN BUILD RETAINING
BOE PDFBOT DBO CVJME SFUBJOJOH
WALLS. THEY CAN KEEP SOIL AND
XBMMT. UIFZ DBO LFFQ TPJM BOE
ROCKS FROM SLIDING DOWNHILL.
SPDLT GSPN TMJEJOH EPXOIJMM.

 27

People who live in areas with erosion problems spend a lot of time and money trying to preserve their land. Sometimes they're successful in slowing down erosion, but they can never eliminate it. Eventually, cliffs cave in and streams overflow their banks. Sediments constantly move from place to place, changing the shape of the land forever.

Figure 6-10. Building on steep slopes can have severe consequences.

SECTION REVIEW

1. How do people increase erosion when they develop an area?
2. How can erosion be reduced in areas where there are steep slopes?

You Decide!

Suppose you live beside a river. You love it there. It's beautiful, and there's so much to do. The only problem is that the river frequently floods. Several times your family has been evacuated to higher ground. One day, the mayor informs your family that you must move. She tells you that living along the river is not only dangerous, but it costs the city too much money each time you're evacuated. Do you think this is fair? Should communities be able to control where people live?

● REINFORCEMENT 27

NAME ______ DATE ______ CLASS ______

REINFORCEMENT Chapter 6

Excessive Erosion Text Pages 152–153

A cause is something that makes something else happen. An effect is what happens. For each of the items, write C in front of the cause and E in front of the effect.

1. __C__ A house builder removes trees from a lot.
   __E__ Topsoil is removed during a heavy rain.
2. __E__ Rainwater slows down.
   __C__ Terraces are built on a hillside.
3. __E__ Terraces are built on a hillside.
   __C__ A person living on a hillside does not want the land to erode.
4. __E__ The shape of the land changes.
   __C__ Sediments constantly move from place to place.
5. __C__ People building on a hill make the slope steeper.
   __E__ The erosion process is sped up.
6. __C__ Trees are planted in an area that was treeless.
   __E__ The erosion process in the area is slowed.

Read each of the following situations and write a recommendation based on your understanding of erosion and deposition.

Situation 1: Lakewood County has a money shortage, and so the county commissioners are thinking about selling one of the county's forest preserves. All of the forest preserves are on sloped land. A land developer would like to buy the preserve and build a housing development there.

What decision would you recommend to the board? Explain. **Responses should indicate an understanding of the ways people can speed up the erosion process. Students might recommend that the board refuse to sell the land or that the board require the developer to take steps that would help prevent erosion.**

Situation 2: The Petersons live in a low-lying area near a river. Almost every year, the river overflows and floods the Petersons' home. What steps do you think the Petersons should take to help prevent flood damages? **Answers will vary. Students might recommend that the Petersons build a retaining wall and plant vegetation to help prevent flood damages to their home.**

27

▲ ENRICHMENT 27

NAME ______ DATE ______ CLASS ______

ENRICHMENT Chapter 6

Excessive Erosion Text Pages 152–153

HOW PEOPLE AFFECT THE ENVIRONMENT

You already learned about erosion and weathering. And you learned that erosion can occur as a result of natural causes and as a consequence of actions that people take—for example, bulldozing land.

Weathering too occurs naturally and can also be caused by people, even though people don't cause it directly. For example, smoke that contains sulfur dioxide is frequently released into the air by factories that burn coal. The sulfur dioxide mixes with rain, and the acid that forms is strong enough to weather rocks. Irrigation can lead to another kind of weathering. In some places, irrigation water seeps into the land and dissolves salt in the soil. The saltwater solution evaporates into the air and can cause severe damage to brick and stone.

Subsidence is a problem that almost always is caused by people. When a large amount of material has been removed from beneath the ground, the land above has lost much of its support and sometimes sinks, or subsides. This frequently occurs in land above mines and in regions where oil or water has been pumped from beneath the ground.

Read the following cases and complete the table. Then answer the question below.

- In the Sahel region of Africa, wells have been sunk into the ground to tap aquifers below the surface. Livestock gather by the wells to eat the vegetation that grows there. They leave the ground bare. As a result, topsoil blows away and the land becomes a desert.
- In Pakistan, archaeologists unearthed a 4500-year-old settlement known as Mohenjo-Daro, revealing villages and towns with brick buildings and stone steps. At about the same time that the archaeologists discovered Mohenjo-Daro, irrigation was introduced into the region. Now, much of the stone and brick has disintegrated.
- For years, underground water was pumped from beneath the city of Venice, Italy. As a result, the city began to sink at a rate of about 5 mm a year. Venice stopped sinking in the 1970s when limits were placed on the amount of water that could be pumped.

Environmental problem	Place	Cause
Erosion	**Sahel region**	**wells which encourage vegetation, which attract animals, which eat vegetation**
Weathering	**Mohenjo-Daro**	**salts from irrigation water attacking stone and brick**
Subsidence	**Venice, Italy**	**pumping too much water from beneath the ground**

Venice, Italy, lies on the coast of the Adriatic Sea. Flooding from the Adriatic has always been a problem. But it has grown worse in this century. Why do you think that has happened? **Because of subsidence, Venice has sunk and is lower than it was in the past. And so the likelihood of it being flooded is increased.**

27

CHECK FOR UNDERSTANDING

Have students explain why people can be successful in slowing down erosion, but not in eliminating it. Students should conclude that planting vegetation, terracing, and using walls only postpone the inevitable. There is no way to completely stop erosion.

RETEACH

Cooperative Learning: Have students work as Paired Partners to draw a picture showing what might have been done to help protect the house shown in Figure 6-10 from falling down the slope.

EXTENSION

For students who have mastered this section, use the **Reinforcement** and **Enrichment** masters or other OPTIONS provided.

3 CLOSE

▶ Ask questions 1-2 in the Section Review.

SECTION REVIEW ANSWERS

1. When they remove vegetation or make slopes steeper, people increase erosion.

2. People can plant vegetation and construct terraces and retaining walls to reduce erosion.

YOU DECIDE!

Some students will feel that people should have the right to decide for themselves where to live. Other students will argue that there should be limitations imposed by a community when other people, safety, and money are involved.

PROGRAM RESOURCES

From the **Teacher Resource Package** use:

Science and Society, page 10, Erosion and Deposition.

Critical Thinking/Problem Solving, page 12, A Disappearing Civilization.

SECTION 6-4

PREPARATION

SECTION BACKGROUND

▶ Glaciers can move on a horizontal surface when the mass of the ice exerts enough pressure to cause the molecules at the bottom to flow.

▶ Glacial deposits in the United States are found from the northern border of the United States to the Ohio and Missouri rivers and in the mountains of the west.

▶ The most recent ice age took place during the Pleistocene Epoch. During this epoch, there were four ice advances, known as the Nebraskan, the Kansan, the Illinoian, and the Wisconsinian glaciations. Each glaciation was followed by an interval of warmer climate called the interglacial period.

▶ Valley glaciers tend to create a rugged topography, whereas continental glaciers smooth the landscape by eroding high spots and filling low places.

1 MOTIVATE

▶ Have students examine maps that show the bottom of the ocean. Have them identify the position of the continental shelves. Inform students that when the last ice age was at its peak, sea level was 110 meters lower than it is today. Many of the structures on the continental shelf would have been at or above sea level. This should lead to a discussion of the effects of glaciation.

▶ **Demonstration:** Demonstrate how a solid, like ice, can flow by mixing cornstarch with water. The mixture will look like a solid. Have a volunteer pick up a handful and tilt his or her hand to deposit the mixture into a cup. Have other students observe that the mixture flows like a liquid. When the mixture reaches the bottom of the cup, it again resembles a solid. Relate the plasticlike cornstarch solution to the base of a glacier.

6-4 Glaciers

New Science Words

glacier
plucking
till
outwash

Objectives

- ▶ Describe how plucking occurs.
- ▶ Explain how striations are created.
- ▶ Compare and contrast till and outwash.

Continental and Valley Glaciers

Does it snow where you live? Does it snow only a few months out of the year? In some areas of the world, temperatures are low enough that it snows year-round. If the snow doesn't melt, it begins piling up. When it accumulates, the weight of the snow is great enough to compress the bottom layers into ice. When the snow piles up to 50 to 60 meters high, the ice on bottom partially melts and becomes putty-like. The whole mass begins to slide on this putty-like layer and it moves downhill. This moving mass of ice and snow is a **glacier.**

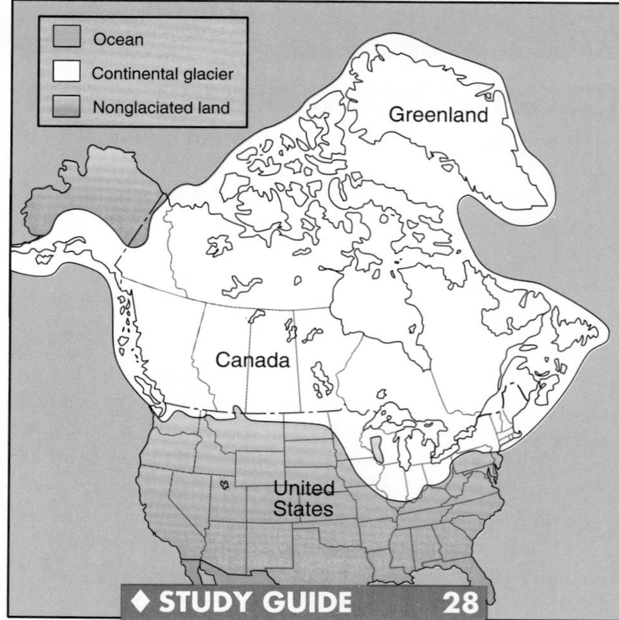

Figure 6-11. This map shows the extent of continental glaciation in North America.

OPTIONS

Meeting Different Ability Levels

For Section 6-4, use the following **Teacher Resource Masters** depending upon individual students' needs.

◆ **Study Guide Master** for all students.

● **Reinforcement Master** for students of average and above average ability levels.

▲ **Enrichment Master** for above average students.

Additional Teacher Resource Package masters are listed in the OPTIONS box throughout the section. The additional masters are appropriate for all students.

◆ **STUDY GUIDE 28**

NAME ______ DATE ______ CLASS ______

STUDY GUIDE — Chapter 6

Glaciers — Text Pages 154–161

Determine whether each of the following statements is true or false. Write the word "true" or "false" in the blank. If the statement is false, change the italicized term to make the statement true.

true 1. The glaciers in Greenland and Antarctica are *continental* glaciers. ______

false 2. The usually long, parallel scars gouged into bedrock by glaciers are known as *cirques*. striations

false 3. Valleys eroded by glaciers are usually *V-shaped*. U-shaped

true 4. *Till* is the sediments that drop from the base of a glacier as it stops moving. ______

false 5. Moraines are mounds of material formed by deposits of glacial *outwash*. till

true 6. Meltwater forms a winding ridge of sand and gravel known as an *esker*. ______

true 7. Glacial *plucking* can create a cirque, or bowl-shaped basin, on a mountainside. ______

false 8. One type of *till* deposits is an alluvial fan of glacially eroded sediments. outwash

true 9. *Icebergs* are sources of fresh water. ______

true 10. *Plucking* is the process by which rocks and soil are added to the sides and bottom of a glacier when water freezes and melts. ______

false 11. Very large striations are called glacial *cracks*. grooves

true 12. The two types of glacial *deposits* are till and outwash. ______

false 13. Scientists have been studying ways to tow *valley glaciers*. icebergs

true 14. The Great Lakes were gouged out by *glacial ice*. ______

28

a

b

Figure 6-12. A continental glacier in Antarctica (a) and a valley glacier (b).

Glaciers, along with gravity, running water, and wind, are agents of erosion. There are two types of glaciers: continental glaciers and valley glaciers. Continental glaciers are huge masses of ice and snow found near Earth's polar regions. Today, they are found only in Greenland and Antarctica. But during past ice ages, continental glaciers covered large portions of the world. An ice age is a period of time when ice and snow cover much of Earth's surface. The most recent ice age began 2 million years ago and ended about 12 000 years ago. During that time, the average temperature on Earth was about 4°C lower than it is today.

When did the last ice age occur?

Valley glaciers are fairly common even in today's warmer climate. They are located in mountainous areas where the average temperature is low enough that snow doesn't melt over the summer season. The glaciers of Glacier National Park in Montana are valley glaciers.

How is it possible that something as fragile as snow or ice can erode something as hard as rock? It may not seem likely, but much of Earth's landscape has been shaped by glacial ice. Let's explore how this is possible.

● REINFORCEMENT 28

NAME ______ DATE ______ CLASS ______

REINFORCEMENT — Chapter 6

Glaciers — Text Pages 154–160

Complete the following tables to show the similarities and differences between continental glaciers and valley glaciers.

Similarities

Valley glaciers	Continental glaciers
All glaciers are thick masses of ice that slowly move on land; form where temperatures are cold enough for snow to remain all year; erode by moving loose sediments and by plucking; leave till and outwash deposits as they lose their energy of motion.	

Differences

Valley glaciers	Continental glaciers
Valley glaciers form in mountainous areas that have snow year-round; flow down mountain slopes and valleys causing erosion; may create cirques in the side of a mountain and erode valleys in a *U*-shape.	Continental glaciers form near the Earth's polar regions and are found only in Greenland and Antarctica today. During an ice age, continental glaciers cover much of the Earth. Icebergs break off continental glaciers in water.

Now that you have finished the table, use it to identify the glaciers described below.

1. It has pieces that break off as icebergs. **continental**
2. They are the kind of glaciers found in Montana. **valley**
3. They deposit till and outwash. **continental and valley**
4. They cover much of Earth during ice ages. **continental**
5. They form *U*-shaped valleys. **valley**
6. They are now located only in the polar regions. **continental**
7. They form in areas that have cold temperatures all year. **continental and valley**
8. They weather rocks by plucking. **continental and valley**
9. They can create cirques on the side of mountains. **valley**
10. They are slow-moving, thick masses of ice. **continental and valley**

28

▲ ENRICHMENT 28

NAME ______ DATE ______ CLASS ______

ENRICHMENT — Chapter 6

Glaciers — Text Pages 154–161

Many terms are used to describe glaciers, their movement, and their erosive and depositing impact. Some of the terms are given below. Use dictionaries, encyclopedias, and library books to define or describe these glacier-related terms.

1. Basal sliding **Basal sliding is the movement of glaciers that occurs when a layer of water and sediments is present at the base of the glacier. The water lets the glaciers move over the layers of rock beneath it.**
2. Plastic flow **Plastic flow is movement that occurs within a glacier and results from internal pressure. The weight of the ice in the glacier causes ice crystals to slide against one another, and this sliding causes the ice to bend and flow.**
3. Zone of accumulation **The zone of accumulation is the area of the glacier that gains ice and snow. The ice and snow accumulates because more snow falls in the winter than can melt in the summer.**
4. Zone of ablation **The zone of ablation is the part of a glacier that loses snow and ice. The loss usually occurs from melting and evaporation.**
5. Calving **Calving is the process of large chunks of a glacier breaking off after part of the glacier ends up in water. Icebergs are the result of calving.**
6. Ice sheets **Ice sheets is another name for continental glaciers.**
7. Drumlins **Drumlins are spoon-shaped hills formed by glaciers. Scientists are not certain about how drumlins are formed.**
8. Rock flour **Rock flour is a finely ground powder of rocks that is deposited by meltwater and gives the meltwater the look of milk.**
9. Kettles **Kettles are bowl-shaped holes that form when huge masses of ice are buried in outwash sediments. The ice melts and the holes remain. Sometimes the holes fill with water to form lakes.**

28

TYING TO PREVIOUS KNOWLEDGE: Have students recall from Chapter 2 that water exists in all three states on Earth. A glacier is, for the most part, a solid, but its bottom layers are partially melted because of the pressure of the overlying ice.

OBJECTIVES AND SCIENCE WORDS: Have students review the objectives and science words to become familiar with this section.

2 TEACH

Key Concepts are highlighted.

CROSS CURRICULUM

▶ **History:** Inform students that during the last ice age, people traveled from Asia to North America across the Bering land bridge. Have students locate the Bering Strait on a map. Ask students why there was a bridge there then but not today. During the last ice age, much of Earth's water was in glaciers and sea level was much lower. A strip of land connected Asia and North America. Today, this area is below sea level.

STUDENT TEXT QUESTION

▶ Page 155, paragraph 3: **How is it possible that something as fragile as snow or ice can erode something as hard as rock?** *Rocks and sediments loosened by ice are carried along by the glacier. These sediments erode the land over which the glacier moves.*

REVEALING MISCONCEPTIONS

▶ Ask students to guess how much the average world temperature would have to drop before Earth would experience another ice age. They will likely guess a large number of degrees. Actually, the answer is by only 2.3°C in the ocean and 6.5°C on land.

CONCEPT DEVELOPMENT

▶ After students have read page 156, ask the following questions: **How does plucking occur?** *Glacial snow and ice melt and flow down into cracks in rocks. When the water refreezes in these cracks, it expands and breaks the rock into pieces.* **What are striations?** *long parallel scars left in rocks by glaciers*

▶ Explain to students that core samples of ocean sediments are used to study Earth's ancient climate. Shells of small sea organisms found in these sediments are used to determine the temperature of the water in which they lived. Thus, scientists can tell how much ice existed on Earth during different geologic periods.

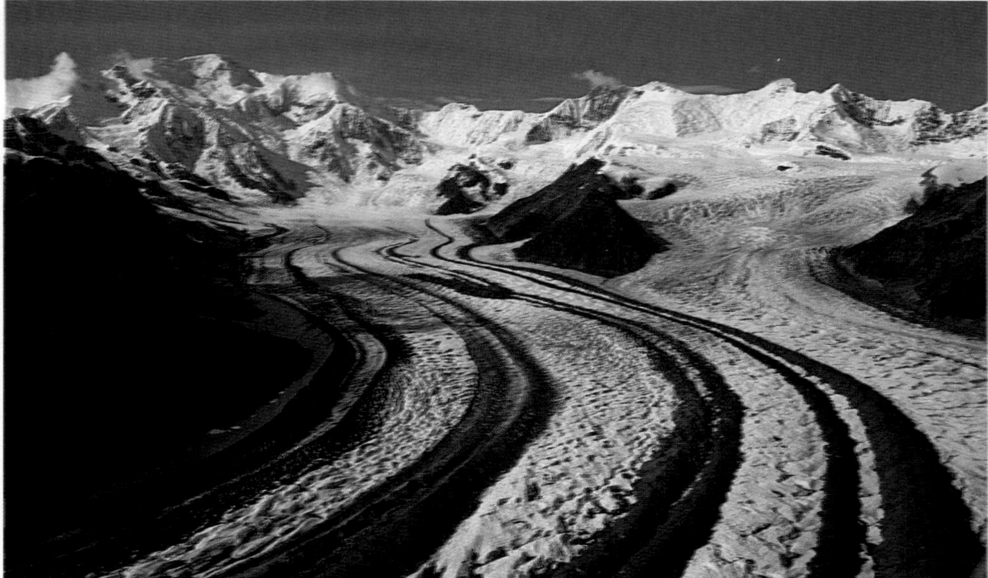

Figure 6-13. The material plucked from the sides and bases of valleys can flow within glaciers as streams of rock and soil.

Glacial Erosion

As they move over land, glaciers act like bulldozers, pushing any loose materials out of their path. These eroded sediments are added to the mass of the glacier or piled up along its sides.

But glaciers do more than just move loose sediments. They also weather and erode rock and soil that isn't loose. Glacial snow and ice melt and the water flows down into cracks in rocks. Later, the water refreezes in these cracks, expands, and breaks the rock into pieces. The rock fragments are moved along with the glacial ice. This process,
1 called **plucking,** results in boulders, gravel, and sand being added to the bottom and sides of a glacier.

These materials at the base of a glacier act like the blades of a plow. They scrape the soil and bedrock that the glacier moves over. They cause the glacier to erode even more than the ice and snow alone could.

Why do striations form?

When bedrock is gouged by rock fragments being dragged across it, marks are left behind. These striations (stri AY shunz) are usually long, parallel scars in rocks.
2 Very large striations are called glacial grooves. Figure 6-14 shows a set of glacial grooves.

OPTIONS

INQUIRY QUESTIONS

▶ **Layers of ice can be distinguished in glaciers. Explain why.** *The layers form when annual snow deposits are followed by dry seasons during which dust is deposited.*

▶ **Icebergs form from continental glaciers. Why do icebergs float?** *The density of ice is less than that of liquid water.*

ENRICHMENT

▶ Have students use a map or globe to predict what the future shoreline of North America might be if all of the ice in Greenland and Antarctica melted. Have them draw diagrams that show this predicted future shoreline. The sketches should show much of the present-day east and Gulf coasts underwater.

Did You Know?

The Great Lakes were gouged out of rock by glacial ice that covered the area from about 250 000 to 11 000 years ago.

Figure 6-14. This set of grooves at Kelleys Island, Ohio, are 10 m wide and 5 m deep.

If you live in the mountains and want to know if there were ever valley glaciers in your area, how could you find out? You might begin by looking for striations. But what other evidence of glacial erosion could you find? Glacial plucking often occurs near the top of a mountain, where a glacier is in contact with a wall of rock. A bowl-shaped basin, called a cirque (SURK), is created in the side of 3 the mountain. If two or more glaciers erode a mountain summit from several directions, a ridge or sharpened peak forms.

Figure 6-15. Plucking by valley glaciers produces characteristic landforms.

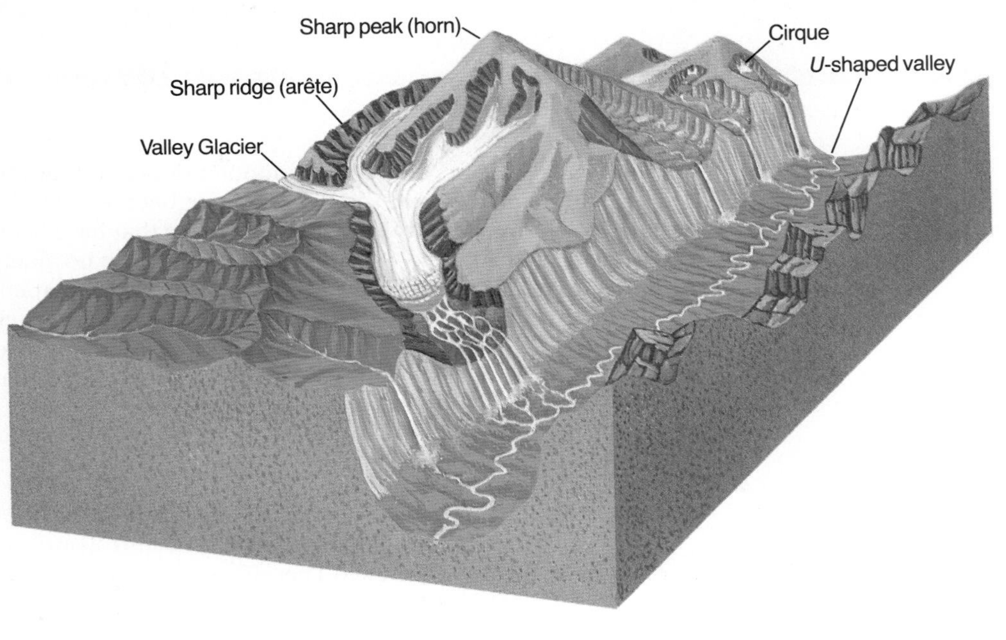

CONCEPT DEVELOPMENT

▶ **What is a cirque and how does it form?** *A cirque is a bowl-shaped basin that is created in the side of a mountain where glacial plucking has occurred.*

▶ **Where do you think most of the water in the Great Lakes came from?** *The water accumulated as the glaciers that formed the lakes melted.*

▶ Have students discuss the reasons for the different topographic features left as the result of valley glaciation versus continental glaciation. The discussion should include the fact that valley glaciers create a more rugged topography. Continental glaciers tend to smooth the landscape by removing high spots and filling low places.

▶ Explain to students that valley glaciers often occupy channels originally cut by what were once called youthful streams. The glacier erodes the sides of the channel as well as the bottom, changing the *V*-shape of the youthful stream valley to the broad *U*-shape of the glaciated valley.

PROGRAM RESOURCES

From the **Teacher Resource Package** use:

Transparency Masters, pages 15-16, Glacial Erosional Features.

Use **Color Transparency** number 8, Glacial Erosional Features.

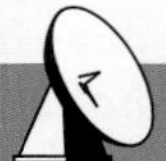

TECHNOLOGY

Have students brainstorm to list potential problems with towing icebergs. One logistical concern is melting, which would be reduced by insulating the icebergs during travel.

Think Critically: Places should be close to oceans or ports and might include Saudi Arabia, western Australia, the Sahara Desert, the Yuma Desert of California, and the Atacama Desert of Chile.

CHECK FOR UNDERSTANDING

Use the Mini Quiz to check for understanding.

MINI QUIZ

Use the Mini Quiz to check students' recall of chapter content.

1. **_____ causes sediments to be added to the sides and bottom of a glacier.** *Plucking*
2. **Large striations are called _____ .** *glacial grooves*
3. **Cirques are created by ____ glaciers.** *valley*

RETEACH

Demonstration: In order to show students how glacial plucking occurs, submerge a brick in water for one full day. Then, place the water-soaked brick in a freezer overnight. Show the frozen brick to students. They will observe that part of the brick has crumbled.

EXTENSION

For students who have mastered this section, use the **Reinforcement** and **Enrichment** masters or other OPTIONS provided.

TEACHER F.Y.I.

▶ During valley glaciation, as much as 2000 kilometers of ice can flow down a valley, causing it to be eroded as much as 600 meters below its original elevation.

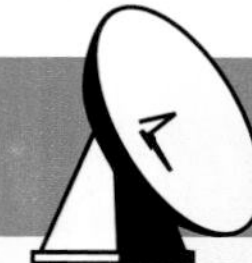

TECHNOLOGY

Bergy Bits?

Icebergs are large chunks of ice that break loose from continental glaciers. In the North Atlantic each year, about 16 000 icebergs break loose from Greenland's glaciers. As these vast chunks of ice move southward, the warmer waters and heat from the sun cause pieces to break off from the icebergs. Pieces the size of an average house are called bergy bits. Smaller pieces of ice are called growlers due to the noises they make as they float in the water.

Because more than 75 percent of Earth's fresh water is locked up in glacial ice, scientists have been studying ways to tow icebergs to areas that need fresh water. It has been estimated that an iceberg about 270 square kilometers in area would provide over 7080 million cubic meters of fresh water! A supertanker tug could tow an iceberg of this size at a rate of about 32 kilometers per day. This may be the only way to bring drinking water to some areas of the world.

Think Critically: What area of the world would benefit most from using icebergs as a source of fresh water?

Valley glaciers flow down mountain slopes and valleys, eroding as they go. Valleys that have been eroded by glaciers are a different shape from those that have been eroded by streams. Stream-eroded valleys are normally *V*-shaped; glacially eroded valleys are usually *U*-shaped. This is because glaciers pluck and scrape soil and rock along their sides as well as on their bottoms. Streams tend to erode downward into underlying rock more than glaciers do. Figure 6-17 shows a *U*-shaped valley.

Deposition by Glaciers

As you might guess, when glaciers begin to melt, they no longer have enough energy of motion to continue carrying many sediments. Therefore, these materials are deposited. Glacial deposits are classified into two major

OPTIONS

PROGRAM RESOURCES

Use **Laboratory Manual,** pages 45-46, Model Glacier.

Use **Laboratory Manual,** pages 47-50, Glaciation and Sea Level.

ENRICHMENT

▶ Have students research and summarize the origin of the Great Lakes and the Matterhorn in Switzerland.

▶ Have students describe changes that might occur in daily living when the next ice age begins.

▶ Have students find out how each of the following glacial deposits forms: ground moraines, terminal moraines, drumlins, and kames.

types. One is a jumble of different-sized sediments that is deposited from the glacial ice and snow. This mixture of boulders, sand, clay, and silt is called **till.** When a glacier stops moving, till begins dropping from its base. These sediments cover huge areas of land. In fact, during the last ice age, continental glaciers moving across the northern United States dropped so much till that it completely filled valleys and covered hills. Today, these areas appear quite flat.

Till is also deposited in front of a glacier when it stops moving forward. Unlike the till that is dropped from a glacier's base, this type of deposit doesn't cover a very wide area. Because it's made of the rocks and soil that the glacier has been pushing along, it looks like a big ridge of material left behind by a bulldozer. Similar ridges are deposited along the sides of glaciers. These mounds of material are called moraines.

The other major type of glacial deposit is outwash. **Outwash** is deposited from the glacier's melted ice. This meltwater carries sediments and deposits them much like a river does. For example, one type of outwash deposit

Science and WRITING

An erratic is a rock fragment deposited by a glacier. The word *erratic* comes form the Latin word *errare*, which means "to wander." Research how erratics are eroded and deposited by glaciers. Then, write a poem about the "life" of an erratic.

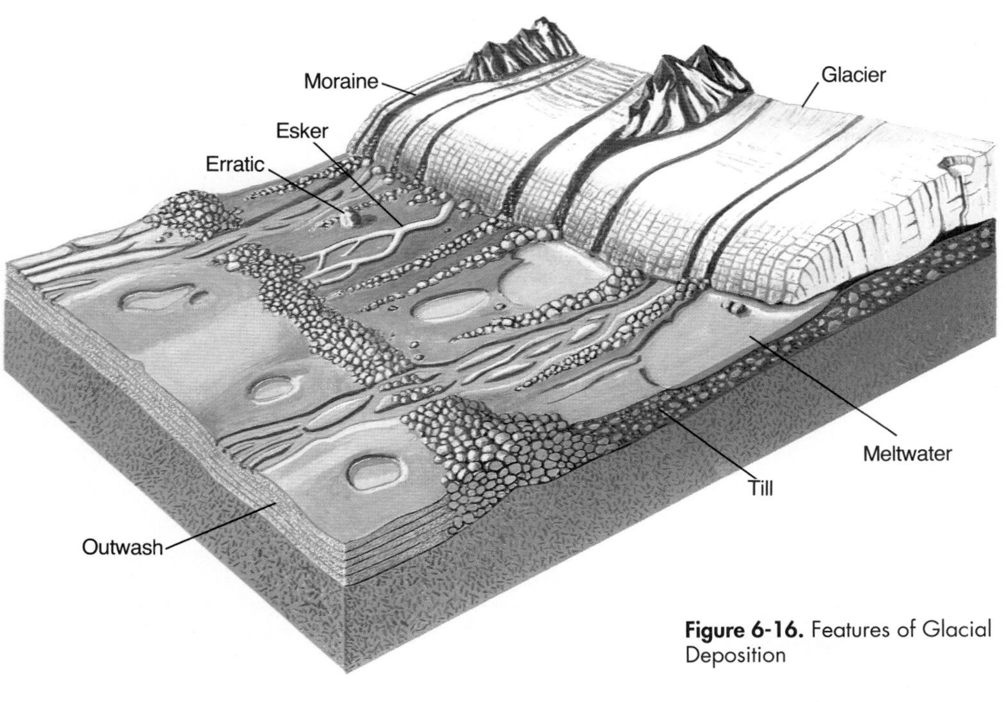

Figure 6-16. Features of Glacial Deposition

CONCEPT DEVELOPMENT

▶ Inform students that in Wisconsin a small area known as the Driftless Area escaped glaciation as the continental glacier was diverted around it. The Driftless Area has buttes, rock pillars, and outcrops of sedimentary rock in great contrast to the surrounding landscape covered with glacial till.

▶ **Compare and contrast till and outwash.** *Both are glacial deposits. Till is a mixture of boulders, sand and silt that is deposited over large areas of land. Outwash is sediment that is deposited by glacial meltwater, depositing this smaller sediment like a river does.*

Science and WRITING

▶ Geologists can often infer the source of an erratic from its mineral composition. If an erratic closely resembles rocks of an area known to have been visited by the glacier that deposited the erratic, geologists infer that the erratic was carried by the glacier from that area. One of the largest known erratics rests in Germany. Its dimensions are 4 km by 2 km by 120 m. The United States contains many erratics transported from Canada. They range in size from pebbles to house-size chunks.

▶ Erratics are picked up by glaciers (often by plucking) and entrained by the ice. They can be carried along the top, sides, or bottom of the glacier, or within its body. Erratics that are dragged along the base of a glacier may scour bedrock over which the ice is passing. Thus, erratics may carve striations or grooves as they are eroded. Once a glacier begins to melt, it drops its load. Erratics are left behind as the glacier retreats. Students' poems should include some of these points.

INQUIRY QUESTIONS

▶ **List two ways continental glaciers change the underlying land.** *They erode the land much like bulldozers, and they deposit till.*

PROGRAM RESOURCES

From the **Teacher Resource Package** use:

Transparency Masters, pages 17-18, Glacial Depositional Features.

Use Color Transparency number 9, Glacial Depositional Features.

3 CLOSE

▶ Ask questions 1-3 and the **Apply** Question in the Section Review.

▶ If you are in an area where glacial features can be seen, plan a field trip to study these features.

▶ Inform students that the Alps, Sierra Nevadas, Rockies, and Himalayas were all greatly eroded by glaciers during the last ice age. Have students locate these mountain ranges on a map and describe some of the glacial features they are likely to find in each locale.

SECTION REVIEW ANSWERS

1. When water gets into cracks in rock, it freezes and expands, which causes the rocks to break into pieces. These pieces become trapped in the glacier and are therefore "plucked" from their original position.

2. Rocks dragged along by a glacier gouge scratches into the underlying bedrock.

3. Till is all sizes of glacial sediment including boulders and large rocks; outwash is smaller. Till is deposited directly from glacial ice; outwash is deposited by meltwater.

4. Apply: A glacier may have plucked the boulder out of bedrock in Canada and carried it along as the glacier moved south. When the glacier melted in Indiana, its energy of motion was too weak to carry the boulder any farther. Thus, the boulder was deposited. Students should realize the boulder is an example of an erratic.

Figure 6-17. A *U*-shaped valley formed by a glacier looks much different than a valley cut by a river.

is an alluvial fan made of sediments eroded by the glacier. It forms when a stream of meltwater drops sand and gravel in front of the glacier.

Another type of outwash deposit looks like a long winding ridge. This deposit forms beneath a melting glacier. Meltwater forms rivers within the ice. These rivers carry sand and gravel and deposit them within their channels. When the glacier melts, a winding ridge of sand and gravel, called an esker, is left behind.

SECTION REVIEW

1. How does the expansion of water when it freezes result in plucking?
2. How do striations form?
3. Explain how till and outwash are different. Which one is deposited directly from ice? Which is deposited from meltwater?
4. **Apply:** Suppose you find a large boulder in the middle of a field in Indiana. Later, you find out that it's a type of rock normally found in Canada but not in Indiana. Give one explanation of how it got there.

Skill Builder — ☑ Outlining

Make an outline of Section 6-4. If you need help, refer to Outlining in the **Skill Handbook** on page 681.

Skill Builder

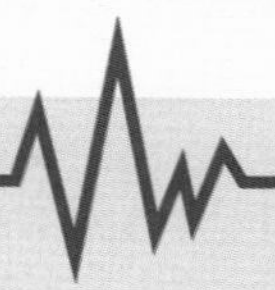

Outlines will vary but should include points on how a glacier erodes by abrading and plucking. Points listed under a head entitled "Deposition by Glaciers" should include the terms *till* and *outwash*.

ACTIVITY 6-1
Glacial Erosion

Problem: *How do valley glaciers affect the surface?*

Materials

- stream table with sand
- pail
- ice block containing sand, clay, and gravel
- wood block
- metric ruler
- overhead light source with reflector

Procedure

1. Set up the stream table as shown.
2. Make a river channel. Measure and record its width and depth. Draw a sketch that includes these measurements.
3. Position the light source so that the light shines on the stream bed as shown.
4. Place the ice block in the river channel at the upper end of the stream table.
5. Gently push the "glacier" along the river channel until it's halfway between the top and bottom of the stream table and is positioned directly under the light.
6. Turn on the light and allow the ice to melt. Observe and record what happens.
7. Measure and record the width and depth of the glacial channel. Draw a sketch of the channel and include these measurements.

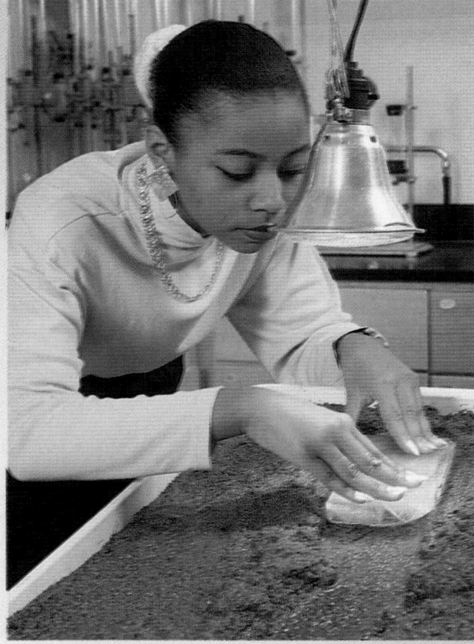

Analyze

1. Explain how you can determine the direction from which a glacier traveled by considering the shape of the channel and location of deposits.

Conclude and Apply

2. Can you determine the direction of glacial movement from sediments deposited by meltwater? Explain.
3. How do valley glaciers affect the surface over which they move?

Data and Observations Sample Data

	Width	Depth	Observations
River	6 cm	3 cm	Stream channel looked U-shaped
Glacier	8 cm	3.5 cm	after "glacier" was pushed down it.

ACTIVITY 6-1
50-60 minutes

OBJECTIVE: Observe how valley glaciers affect a surface.

PROCESS SKILLS applied in this activity:
▶ **Observing** in Procedure Step 6.
▶ **Communicating** in Procedure Steps 2, 6, and 7.
▶ **Interpreting Data** in Analyze Question 1 and Conclude and Apply Question 2.
▶ **Hypothesizing** in Analyze Question 1.
▶ **Formulating Models** in Conclude and Apply Questions 2 and 3.

COOPERATIVE LEARNING Have students perform this activity as Science Investigation groups.

TEACHING THE ACTIVITY

▶ You will need to prepare freezer trays of sand, gravel, and clay a day or two before the students perform this activity.
Troubleshooting: Be sure that students adjust the overhead light so that it provides enough energy to melt the ice. Warn students of the danger of being burned by the overhead light.

PROGRAM RESOURCES

From the **Teacher Resource Package** use:
Activity Worksheets, pages 48-49, Activity 6-1: Glacial Erosion.

ANSWERS TO QUESTIONS

1. The channel will be *U*-shaped to the point where the glacier stopped. From that point on, the valley will be *V*-shaped. A row of small hills of till marks the end position of the glacier. Using this evidence, the direction from which a glacier traveled can be determined.
2. Yes, the larger outwash sediments are deposited closest to the glacial front. Smaller sediments are carried farther from the glacial front.
3. Valley glaciers have a "bulldozing" effect, which produces a *U*-shaped valley with steep sides and a relatively flat bottom.

SECTION 6-5

PREPARATION

SECTION BACKGROUND

▶ Sand-sized particles move along the ground by a series of intermittent bounces or leaps of varying lengths that depend on grain size, mass, and wind velocity.

▶ Falling sand-sized particles may strike and displace other sand grains, thus increasing the total number of particles that are horizontally displaced.

▶ Like water, abrasion by the wind depends on the availability of suspended fragments that can be used as scouring tools.

▶ Each time the wind blows over a sand dune, sand is carried up the windward side and dropped on the leeward side. When the sand becomes too high, a sheetlike mass of sand slips down the leeward side of the dune, causing dune migration.

PREPLANNING

▶ To prepare for Activity 6-2, obtain the materials listed on page 166.

1 MOTIVATE

▶ Take students outdoors to observe the direction from which the wind is blowing and the materials being carried by the wind. Ask students how wind speed affects the amount and kind of material that the wind is able to transport.

FLEX Your Brain

Use the Flex Your Brain activity to have students explore SANDBLASTING.

6-5 Wind

New Science Words

deflation
abrasion
loess

Objectives

- ▶ **Explain how wind causes deflation and abrasion.**
- ▶ **Discuss how loess and dunes form.**

Wind Erosion

Wind erodes sediments in two ways—by deflation and by abrasion. Both types occur over all of Earth's land surface. However, they are most common in deserts, beaches, and plowed fields. In these places, the sediments are exposed to the wind because there aren't many plants to protect them.

Wind easily picks up and moves small sediments such as clay, silt, and sand. Pebbles and boulders too heavy to
1 move are left behind. This type of erosion is **deflation.**

Figure 6-18. Deflation produces airborne sediments (a) and leaves behind what is called *desert pavement* (b).

OPTIONS

Meeting Different Ability Levels

For Section 6-5, use the following **Teacher Resource Masters** depending upon individual students' needs.

◆ **Study Guide Master** for all students.

● **Reinforcement Master** for students of average and above average ability levels.

▲ **Enrichment Master** for above average students.

Additional Teacher Resource Package masters are listed in the OPTIONS box throughout the section. The additional masters are appropriate for all students.

◆ STUDY GUIDE 29

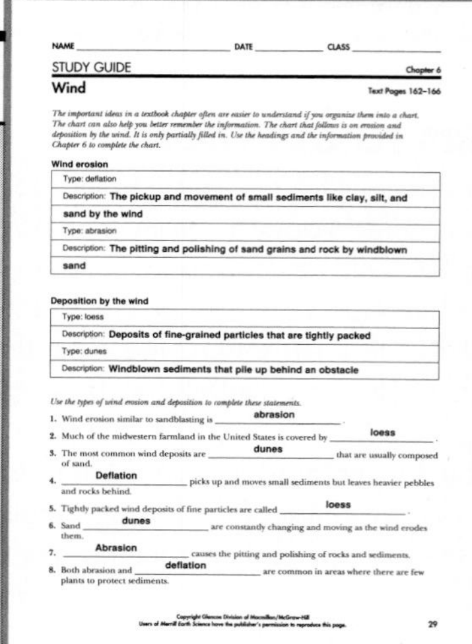

NAME ______ DATE ______ CLASS ______

STUDY GUIDE Chapter 6

Wind Text Pages 162–166

The important ideas in a textbook chapter often are easier to understand if you organize them into a chart. The chart can also help you better remember the information. The chart that follows is on erosion and deposition by the wind. It is only partially filled in. Use the headings and the information provided in Chapter 6 to complete the chart.

Wind erosion

Type: deflation
Description: **The pickup and movement of small sediments like clay, silt, and sand by the wind**
Type: abrasion
Description: **The pitting and polishing of sand grains and rock by windblown sand**

Deposition by the wind

Type: loess
Description: **Deposits of fine-grained particles that are tightly packed**
Type: dunes
Description: **Windblown sediments that pile up behind an obstacle**

Use the types of wind erosion and deposition to complete these statements.

1. Wind erosion similar to sandblasting is **abrasion**.
2. Much of the midwestern farmland in the United States is covered by **loess**.
3. The most common wind deposits are **dunes** that are usually composed of sand.
4. **Deflation** picks up and moves small sediments but leaves heavier pebbles and rocks behind.
5. Tightly packed wind deposits of fine particles are called **loess**.
6. Sand **dunes** are constantly changing and moving as the wind erodes them.
7. **Abrasion** causes the pitting and polishing of rocks and sediments.
8. Both abrasion and **deflation** are common in areas where there are few plants to protect sediments.

29

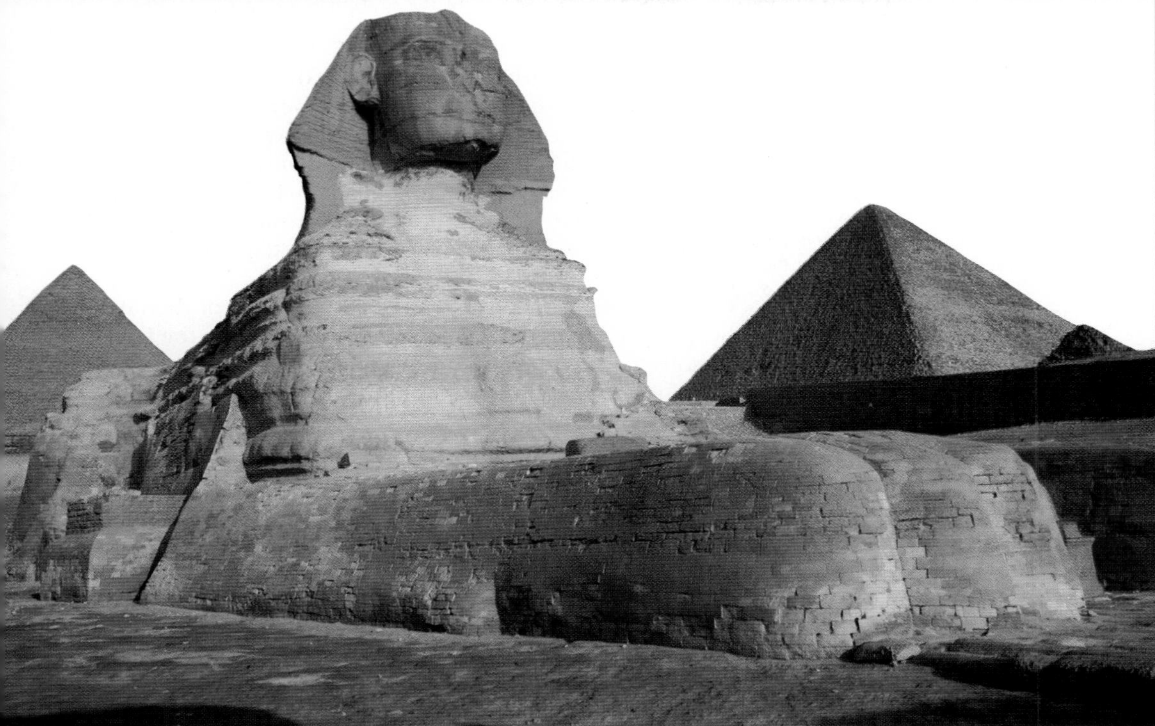

The second type of wind erosion is abrasion. It's similar to the action of a crew of restoration workers sandblasting a building. These workers use machines that spray a mixture of sand and water against a building. The blast of sand removes dirt from stone, concrete, or brick walls. It also polishes the building walls by breaking away small pieces and leaving an even, smooth finish. Wind is like a sandblasting machine at work.

Wind makes sand grains roll and skip along the ground. As the grains move along, they bump into other grains. The sand grains and the rocks they strike become pitted and polished when small fragments are broken off. This sandblasting is a type of erosion called **abrasion.** 1

Figure 6-19. Egypt's desert winds, carrying sand-sized sediments, have abraded this sculpture of a sphinx.

Define deflation and abrasion.

Deposition by Wind

What do you think happens to the sediments that are blown away when deflation and abrasion occur? Eventually, they are deposited. These windblown deposits form several types of landforms.

● REINFORCEMENT 29

NAME ____ DATE ____ CLASS ____

REINFORCEMENT — Chapter 6

Wind — Text Pages 162–165

Write the word that best completes the statement.

1. **Abrasion** is wind erosion that can be compared to sandblasting.
2. When windblown sediments pile up behind obstacles, **dunes** are formed.
3. Wind erosion that picks up small particles and leaves heavier particles behind is called **deflation**.
4. **Loess** is sediment that is as fine as talcum powder.
5. Wind erosion called **abrasion** causes sand grains to pit and polish rocks when the grains hit them.
6. Dunes are made up mostly of **sand**.
7. Much of the midwestern United States is on fertile soil that evolved from **loess** deposits.
8. **Dunes** are the most common form of wind deposit, and they constantly change and move as the wind erodes them.
9. Abrasion and deflation are forms of **wind** erosion.
10. Loess and dunes are **deposits** of wind-eroded sediments.
11. The wind erodes sediments in **two** ways.
12. One of the largest loess deposits is near the **Mississippi** River.
13. Wind erosion is most common in **deserts**, beaches, and plowed fields.
14. When wind blows sediments against an **obstacle**, sediment builds up behind it.
15. Erosion and deposition are part of a **cycle** that shapes and reshapes the land.

Using your understanding of wind erosion, draw a two-step picture that shows how a dune is formed.

Drawings will vary, but the first picture should show mounds building up behind an obstacle. The second picture should show the mounds increasing in size to become a dune.

29

▲ ENRICHMENT 29

NAME ____ DATE ____ CLASS ____

ENRICHMENT — Chapter 6

Wind — Text Pages 162–166

Hector and Heather devised an activity to demonstrate how dunes are formed and how the rate of the wind affects the amount of erosion. This is what they've done:

Materials
- large cardboard box
- sand
- one or more large rocks
- hair dryer
- safety goggles

Safety Procedures
1. Wear safety goggles when blowing the sand with the hair dryer.
2. Make sure the hair dryer is properly plugged in and do not place it too close to the sand.

Procedure
1. Fill a box about one third full of sand.
2. Put the rock or rocks about one third of the way from the back end of the box.
3. Put on the safety goggles.
4. Turn on the dryer on the low setting and aim the air flow toward the sand at the front of the box.
5. Observe what happens as the air flow blows the sand against the rocks.
6. Smoothe out the sand in the box so it is distributed evenly, and repeat Steps 3–6, but this time operate the dryer at high speed.

If possible, perform the activity they devised. Then base your answers to the following questions on your observations. If you cannot perform the activity, hypothesize the answers.

Conclude and Apply
1. What happened to the sand when the dryer was at a low speed? **The sand piled up behind the rocks.**
2. What happened to the sand when the dryer was at high speed? **The sand piled up higher and more quickly.**
3. What caused the sand to pile up? **The rock or rocks served as a windbreak. The sand was deposited when the wind could no longer carry it.**
4. How does an increased wind affect erosion? **The stronger wind picks up more sediments and thus erodes more land.**

29

TYING TO PREVIOUS KNOWLEDGE: Lead a discussion during which students conclude from their own experiences that wind can have a lot of energy of motion. Effects of this energy include trees swaying in a breeze, dust blowing into their eyes, and having been blown sideways when trying to walk in a stiff breeze.

OBJECTIVES AND SCIENCE WORDS: Have students review the objectives and science words to become familiar with this section.

2 TEACH

Key Concepts are highlighted.

CONCEPT DEVELOPMENT

▶ Have a volunteer compare and contrast deflation and abrasion.

▶ After students read pages 162-163, ask the following questions: **How does vegetation affect erosion by the wind?** *Where there are no plants to protect sediments, there will be more deflation and abrasion.* **How can you tell if rocks have been abraded?** *They are pitted and have shiny surfaces due to abrasion by sand grains.*

▶ Direct students to the caption for Figure 6-18. Have students operationally define *desert pavement.* Desert pavement is wind-polished, densely packed pebbles left behind when smaller particles have been removed by the wind. Desert pavement often protects underlying materials from further deflation.

PROGRAM RESOURCES

From the **Teacher Resource Package** use:

Activity Worksheets, page 5, Flex Your Brain.

CONCEPT DEVELOPMENT

▶ **From where did the loess deposits near the Mississippi River come?** *They came from the northern United States and Canada.*

▶ Ask students to describe how obstacles such as clumps of vegetation can cause sand dunes to form.

Science and WRITING

The Dust Bowl was the result of poor farming practices combined with a severe drought. Vegetation died and no longer held the soil in place. In some places, more than one meter of topsoil was carried away by winds. Some of this soil was blown eastward toward the Atlantic Coast. The land, laid bare by removal of the topsoil, was of little value for farming for many years. Many people were forced to leave the Great Plains as a result of the conditions that developed physiographically and economically.

CROSS CURRICULUM

▶ **Geography:** Have students locate China and the Gobi and Ordos deserts on a world map. Then have them determine the direction of the wind that forms the loess deposits in China.

MINI QUIZ

Use the Mini Quiz to check students' recall of chapter content.

1. **The wind erosion called ____ leaves behind pebbles and boulders that are too heavy to move.** *Deflation*
2. **____ is similar to sandblasting a building.** *Abrasion*
3. **____ is a fine-grained wind deposit.** *Loess*

PROBLEM SOLVING

Think Critically: Rocks were piled around the bases of telephone poles to protect the bottoms of the poles from abrasion. Fences were placed along the desert highways to control deposition. The fences caused the sand to collect and form dunes before sand reached the highways.

Science and WRITING

Pretend you are a radio news reporter during the great dust storms in the Dust Bowl of the 1930's. Research the cause of the Dust Bowl and the effects on the land and people. Then, give a report to your class as if you were broadcasting on the radio.

One of the largest deposits of windblown sediments in the world is near the Mississippi River. The small sediments in this deposit were carried by strong winds that blew from the continental glaciers that once covered the northern United States and Canada. When the sediments finally settled, they fell onto hilltops and into valleys. Once there, the particles were packed together, creating a thick deposit known as **loess** (LES).

3 Loess is as fine as talcum powder. Many of the farmlands of the midwestern United States are on the fertile soils that have evolved from loess deposits. Loess is also found in China, where the sand and silt blow in from the Gobi and Ordos deserts.

What happens when wind blows sediments against an obstacle such as a rock or a clump of vegetation? The sediments settle behind the obstacle. More and more

PROBLEM SOLVING

A Trip across the Desert

Emmanuel and Jason had been best friends for years. But two years ago Emmanuel moved to southern California with his family. One day Emmanuel's father announced he was taking a business trip to their old hometown, where Jason still lived. When his father said he could come with him, Emmanuel was excited at the prospect of seeing Jason again.

Soon, Emmanuel and his father were on their way. As they crossed the desert of the southwestern United States, Emmanuel noticed large rocks had been piled up at the bases of utility poles. Rocks had also been stacked up along the bases of some houses. His father said the rocks had been put there by people. Emmanuel also noticed that sand dunes were forming on parts of the highway. However, where fences had been built along the highways, no sand dunes formed.

Think Critically: Why had people piled rocks at the bases of poles and houses? How did fences help control the natural deposition of sand on the desert highways?

OPTIONS

INQUIRY QUESTIONS

▶ **Along some beaches, people lay old Christmas trees in the sand to keep the sand from eroding. Large dunes develop in these areas. Why?** *The trees act as barriers to the wind and trap the sand grains, which eventually form dunes.*

▶ **An oasis is a fertile, vegetated area within a desert. How could deflation cause an oasis to form?** *Occasionally, winds erode material down to a depth where water is present. When water is available near the surface, vegetation can grow. Trees, shrubs, and grasses take root and form an oasis. The vegetation acts as a barrier against further erosion. Sometimes, however, sand dunes bury an oasis. Oases prove that where water is available, a desert can be fertile.*

sediments build up and eventually a dune is formed. Dunes are the most common wind deposits and are usually composed of sand. These sand dunes form in deserts and beaches where sand is abundant. They are constantly changing and moving as wind erodes them.

When dunes and loess form, the landscape is changed. Wind, like gravity, running water, and glaciers, shapes the land as it erodes sediments. But the new landforms created by these agents of erosion are themselves being eroded. Erosion and deposition are part of a cycle of change that constantly shapes and reshapes the land around us.

Figure 6-20. Sand dunes typically have a gentle slope on one side and a steep slope on the other side.

EcoTip

Don't disturb grass or other plants on beach sand dunes. These plants prevent excessive beach erosion by slowing running water and by holding the sediments together with their roots.

SECTION REVIEW

1. How does deflation happen? What is abrasion?
2. How do loess deposits form?
3. **Apply:** You notice that snow is piling up behind a fence outside your apartment building. The wind is blowing strong but it's depositing snow when it comes to the fence. Why?

Sequencing

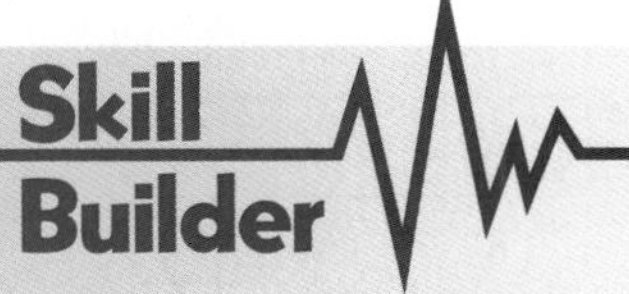

Sequence the following events that describe how a sand dune forms. If you need help, refer to Sequencing in the **Skill Handbook** on page 680.

a. Grains collect to form a mound.
b. Wind blows sand grains until they hit an obstacle.
c. Wind blows over an area and causes deflation.
d. Vegetation grows on the dune.

ENRICHMENT

Have students find out why off-highway vehicles are so damaging to desert soils. One reference is *National Geographic Magazine,* January, 1987, pp. 42-76.

PROGRAM RESOURCES

From the **Teacher Resource Package** use:

Concept Mapping, pages 17-18.

Cross-Curricular Connections, page 10, Erosion and Historical Events.

Activity Worksheets, page 5, Flex Your Brain.

CHECK FOR UNDERSTANDING

Ask questions 1-2 and the **Apply** Question in the Section Review.

RETEACH

Cooperative Learning: Have students work in Science Investigation groups to find out the effects of clumps of grass on the development of sand dunes. Each team will need the following items: safety goggles, a flat pan half-filled with sand, a hair dryer, and clumps of grass.

EXTENSION

For students who have mastered this section, use the **Reinforcement** and **Enrichment** masters or other OPTIONS provided.

3 CLOSE

FLEX Your Brain

Use the Flex Your Brain activity to have students explore SAND DUNES. Students may discover that dunes can be classified according to shape. Shapes include: barchan, transverse, parabolic, longitudinal, and star-shaped.

SECTION REVIEW ANSWERS

1. Deflation occurs when wind picks up and transports small sediments, leaving behind heavier sediments such as pebbles and boulders. Abrasion occurs when sand-sized grains scour and polish rocks. Abrasion also causes pits to form in the rocks being eroded.
2. Loess is wind-blown dust that settles to the ground. The small, dust particles pack together to form a dense deposit.
3. Apply: When the wind strikes the fence, it loses some of its energy of motion and can carry much of the snow no farther.

Skill Builder

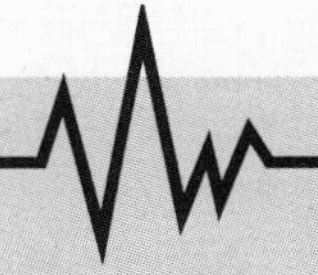

The ordering of events from start to finish as c, b, a, and d is the most logical sequence.

ACTIVITY 6-2
60 minutes

OBJECTIVE: Observe how wind erodes different materials.

PROCESS SKILLS applied in this activity:
▶ **Observing** in Procedure Steps 3, 6, and 8.
▶ **Inferring** in Conclude and Apply Question 4.
▶ **Communicating** in Procedure Steps 3, 6, and 8.
▶ **Interpreting Data** in Analyze Questions 1 and 2 and Conclude and Apply Questions 3 and 4.
▶ **Hypothesizing** in Analyze Question 1.
▶ **Separating and Controlling Variables** in Procedure Steps 1-4, 6, and 8.
▶ **Experimenting** in Procedure Steps 1-8.

COOPERATIVE LEARNING Use the Science Investigation strategy to have students complete this activity.

TEACHING THE ACTIVITY

▶ Ask one student from each group to bring a hair dryer from home to use in this activity.
▶ Be sure that all pans used by a particular team are the same size.
▶ Have cardboard pre-cut to fit the back of the pans. Taping cardboard on three sides of the pans will prevent some of the sand from blowing out into the room.

Troubleshooting: Remind students to use the same speed setting on their hair dryers for all the angles. This will serve as one of the constants in the experiment.

ACTIVITY 6-2
Wind Erosion

Problem: *Which factors affect wind erosion of different materials?*

Materials

- goggles
- flat pans (5)
- 1250 mL fine sand
- 1000 mL clay
- 250 mL gravel
- hair dryer
- protractor
- sprinkling can
- water
- cardboard sheet
- metric ruler

Procedure

1. Put 500 mL sand into pans A and B. Put 500 mL clay into C and D. Mix 250 mL sand and 250 mL gravel and put mixture into pan E.
2. Use the sprinkling can to dampen the material in pans A and C.
3. Hold the hair dryer 10 cm from pan A at an angle of 45°. Tape the cardboard to the other end of the pan. Direct a stream of air onto the pan for 1 minute. **CAUTION:** *Wear your goggles.* Record in your table every effect of the air that you observe.
4. Repeat Step 3 for pans B, C, D, and E.
5. Smooth out the "soil" in each pan.
6. Change the angle of the hair dryer to 10°. Repeat Step 3 for all pans using this new angle. Record all observations. **CAUTION:** *Wear your goggles.*
7. Smooth out the "soil" in each pan.
8. Repeat Steps 3 through 6 for all pans from a distance of 20 cm. Hold the hair dryer at an angle of 45°. (The distance of the hair dryer to the pan represents the force.) **CAUTION:** *Wear your goggles.* You may need to redampen the "soil" in pans A and C before completing this step. Record your results in the table.

Data and Observations Sample Data

Pan	10cm		20cm	
	45°	10°	45°	10°
A	movement of dry particles		movement of only a few dry grains	
B	much sand movement		slight sand movement	
C	little movement		little movement	
D	small particles close to wind source moved		no movement	
E	sand moved		little movement	

Analyze

1. How do dry sand and clay react to the wind?
2. How does the addition of gravel to the sand affect its reaction to the wind?

Conclude and Apply

3. How does the change in force (distance of hair dryer to pan) affect movement of sediment grains? The angle of the wind?
4. Is wind a more effective erosional agent in wet or dry climates? Which pans give evidence to support your answer?

ANSWERS TO QUESTIONS

1. Dry materials are more easily eroded by wind. Moisture retards erosion.
2. Gravel helps hold sand in place by creating obstacles, which cause the sand to collect.
3. the greater the force, the more material eroded; the more directly the wind blows on the material, the greater the effect of the wind
4. Wind is more effective in dry climates, as shown in Pans B, D, and E.

PROGRAM RESOURCES

From the **Teacher Resource Package** use:

Activity Worksheets, pages 50-51, Activity 6-2: Wind Erosion.

CHAPTER
REVIEW

SUMMARY

6-1: Gravity

1. Erosion is the process that moves weathered sediments. Deposition occurs when an agent of erosion can no longer transport its load.
2. Slump, creep, rockslides, and mudflows are all mass movements.

6-2: Running Water

1. Rill and gully erosion create stream channels on slopes. Large canyons can eventually evolve from gully erosion. Sheet erosion occurs outside of a stream channel.
2. Alluvial fans and deltas are triangular-shaped deposits that form when water loses energy of motion.

6-3: Science and Society: Developing Land Prone to Erosion

1. Increasing slopes and removing vegetation increase erosion.
2. Vegetation, terraces, and retaining walls can reduce erosion on slopes.

6-4: Glaciers

1. Plucking adds rock and soil to a glacier's sides and bottom as water freezes and thaws in surrounding rocks.
2. Striations are formed when bedrock is gouged by rock fragments being transported by a glacier.
3. Till is a jumble of sediments deposited directly from glacial ice and snow. Outwash is glacial debris deposited by melted ice.

6-5: Wind

1. Deflation occurs when wind erodes only small-sized sediments and pebbles and boulders are left behind. The pitting and polishing of rocks and sediments by windblown sediments is called abrasion.
2. Deposits of fine-grained particles that are tightly packed are called loess. Dunes begin to form when windblown sediments pile up behind an obstacle.

KEY SCIENCE WORDS

a. **abrasion**
b. **alluvial fan**
c. **creep**
d. **deflation**
e. **delta**
f. **deposition**
g. **erosion**
h. **glacier**
i. **gully erosion**
j. **loess**
k. **outwash**
l. **plucking**
m. **rill erosion**
n. **sheet erosion**
o. **slump**
p. **terraces**
q. **till**

UNDERSTANDING VOCABULARY

Match each phrase with the correct term from the list of Key Science Words.

1. process of moving weathered sediments
2. slow movement of sediments downhill because of freezing and thawing
3. steplike cuts in the side of a slope
4. mass movement in which materials move as one large mass
5. erosion caused by freezing and thawing of glacial ice
6. wind erosion that leaves large sediments
7. mixture of rocks and sediments deposited by glacial snow and ice
8. sediments deposited by glacial meltwater
9. erosion caused by natural sandblasting
10. thick, densely packed deposits of dust

CHAPTER
REVIEW

SUMMARY

Have students read the summary statements to review the major concepts of the chapter.

UNDERSTANDING VOCABULARY

1. g
2. c
3. p
4. o
5. l
6. d
7. q
8. k
9. a
10. j

OPTIONS

ASSESSMENT

To assess student understanding of material in this chapter, use the resources listed.

COOPERATIVE LEARNING

Consider using cooperative learning in the THINK AND WRITE CRITICALLY, APPLY, and MORE SKILL BUILDERS sections of the Chapter Review.

PROGRAM RESOURCES

From the **Teacher Resource Package** use:
Chapter Review, pages 15-16.
Chapter and Unit Tests, pages 39-42, Chapter Test.

CHAPTER

REVIEW

CHECKING CONCEPTS

1. a	**6.** d
2. b	**7.** c
3. b	**8.** d
4. d	**9.** a
5. b	**10.** c

UNDERSTANDING CONCEPTS

11. Creep
12. increases
13. water
14. increases
15. esker

THINK AND WRITE CRITICALLY

16. Gravity and steep slopes cause materials or rock layers to slip downward as a large mass. Curved scars along the slopes are the effects of slumping.
17. Some of the lightweight sediments are carried by the water. The more massive sediments are rolled along the bottom of the channel.
18. Both are massive bodies of ice in motion that change Earth's surface by erosion and deposition. Continental glaciers are much bigger than valley glaciers, which are restricted to mountain valleys.
19. Till is dropped from the front and base of a glacier. Outwash is deposited by meltwater.
20. clay, silt, sand, pebbles, boulders

APPLY

21. Striations are made by glacial debris embedded in the bottom of the ice. The debris gouges the bedrock as the glacier moves, thus recording the movement of the glacier. Striations are generally parallel to glacial movement.
22. A fine mesh wire will only prevent larger particles such as pebbles and boulders from eroding. Smaller sediments like sand, silt, and dust will fall through the mesh.

CHAPTER

REVIEW

CHECKING CONCEPTS

Choose the word or phrase that completes the sentence or answers the question.

1. Which of the following is not a type of mass movement?
   a. abrasion **c.** slump
   b. creep **d.** mudflow
2. ______ is not an agent of erosion.
   a. Gravity **c.** A glacier
   b. A rockslide **d.** Wind
3. Which of these is not a type of erosion by water?
   a. rill erosion **c.** sheet erosion
   b. abrasion **d.** plucking
4. ______ reduces erosion.
   a. Planting vegetation **c.** Making terraces
   b. Building a wall **d.** All of these
5. A mass of snow and ice in motion is a(n) ______.
   a. loess deposit **c.** outwash
   b. glacier **d.** abrasion
6. ______ glaciers are found in Greenland.
   a. *U*-shaped **c.** Outwash
   b. Till **d.** None of these
7. Glacial valleys are ______.
   a. *V*-shaped **c.** *U*-shaped
   b. *L*-shaped **d.** None of these
8. Glaciers have changed Earth by ______.
   a. erosion **c.** deposition
   b. plucking **d.** all of these
9. Wind erosion in which pebbles and boulders are left behind is called ______.
   a. deflation **c.** abrasion
   b. loess **d.** sandblasting
10. A(n)______ is a bowl-shaped erosional feature formed by glacial plucking.
    a. striation **c.** cirque
    b. esker **d.** moraine

UNDERSTANDING CONCEPTS

Complete each sentence.

11. ______ is the slowest type of mass movement.
12. Water ______ the chances of mass movement on a slope.
13. Deltas differ from alluvial fans because deltas are deposited in ______.
14. Building by people often ______ erosion.
15. A(n) ______ is a long, winding ridge formed by deposits from outwash.

THINK AND WRITE CRITICALLY

16. Discuss the causes and effects of slumping.
17. Explain how a river carries its load of sediments.
18. Compare and contrast continental and valley glaciers.
19. How does the deposition of till differ from the deposition of outwash?
20. Arrange these sediments according to size from smallest to largest: boulders, clay, sand, pebbles, and silt. (HINT: Refer to Table 4-2 in Chapter 4.)

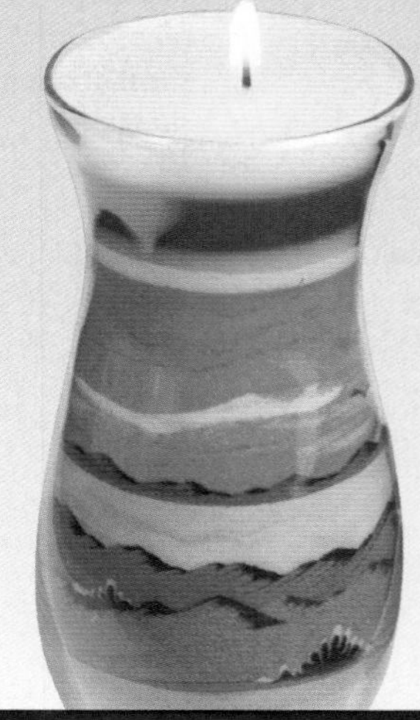

APPLY

21. How can striations give information about the direction of movement of a glacier?
22. How effective would a retaining wall made of fine wire mesh be against erosion?
23. Sand dunes often migrate. What can be done to prevent the migration of beach dunes?
24. Scientists have found evidence of movement of ice within a glacier. Explain how this may occur. (HINT: Recall how putty-like ice forms at the base of a glacier.)
25. Often the front end of a valley glacier is at a lower elevation than the tail end. How does this explain melting at its front end while snow is still accumulating at its tail end?

MORE SKILL BUILDERS

If you need help, refer to the Skill Handbook.

1. **Making and Using Tables:** Make a table that contrasts rockslides and mudflows.
2. **Designing an Experiment:** Explain how you could test the effect of glacial thickness on a glacier's ability to erode.
3. **Concept Mapping:** Copy and complete the cycle map to show how sediments form from and result in sedimentary rocks.

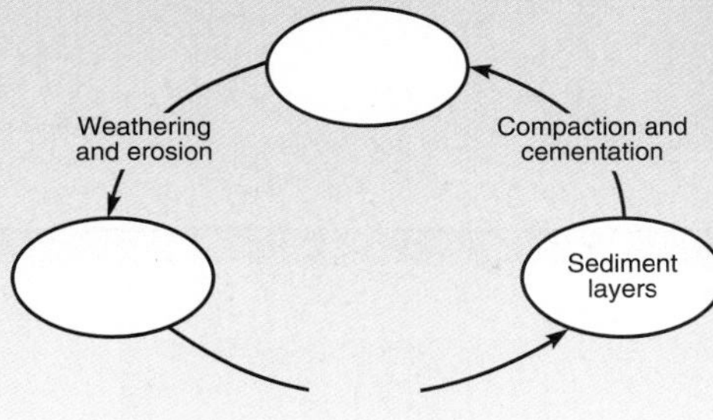

4. **Hypothesizing:** Hypothesize why most of the silt in the Mississippi Delta is found farther out to sea than the sand-sized particles.
5. **Interpreting Scientific Illustrations:** Look at the map of Ohio below. In which part of Ohio would you find erosion and deposition caused by glaciers of the last ice age? How would you expect the terrains to differ throughout the state?

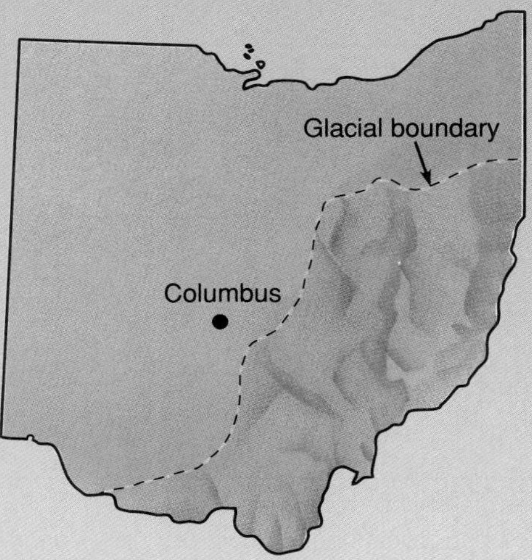

PROJECTS

1. Design an experiment to study the effects of a thin layer of oil on the ability of wind to erode sand.
2. Obtain a map of your area and find the local streams that drain into a major river in the area. Compute the area in square kilometers that is eroded by the main river and the smaller streams.

23. Planting vegetation or erecting fences can reduce or even prevent dune migration.
24. The mass of the overlying snow and ice compresses the underlying layers into ice. This pressure can cause the ice to partially melt. The melting then causes movement not only at the glacier's bottom, but also within the glacier.
25. Warmer weather could cause the front end to melt and appear to retreat. Colder temperatures would allow the snow and ice to accumulate and cause the glacial front to advance.

MORE SKILL BUILDERS

1. Making and Using Tables: See one possible solution below.
2. Designing an Experiment: Two ice blocks, one thicker than the other, could be guided with the same amount of force over a pan containing a certain amount of sand.
3. Concept Mapping See one possible solution below.
4. Hypothesizing: The river loses some of its kinetic energy when it empties into the Gulf. It is able to carry only small sediments as it flows into open water. Silt, because it is smaller than sand, will be transported farther into the Gulf than the sand and other large sediments.
5. Interpreting Scientific Illustrations: Glacial deposits and erosional features would be found in areas north of the glacial boundary line. Glaciers were not present south of this line. The terrain of the glaciated region is much smoother and flatter than the nonglaciated area. The glaciers smoothed the land by weathering and eroding hills and by filling lowlands with till. The glaciated area contains gently rolling hills and depositional features such as eskers and terminal morains. Till covers large areas. The nonglaciated area has much greater relief and sleep stream valleys. Some outwash deposits are found there.

	Rockslides	Mudflows
Composition	large pieces of rock	small sediments mixed with water
Occurrence	mountainous regions	mountainous dry regions after rainfalls

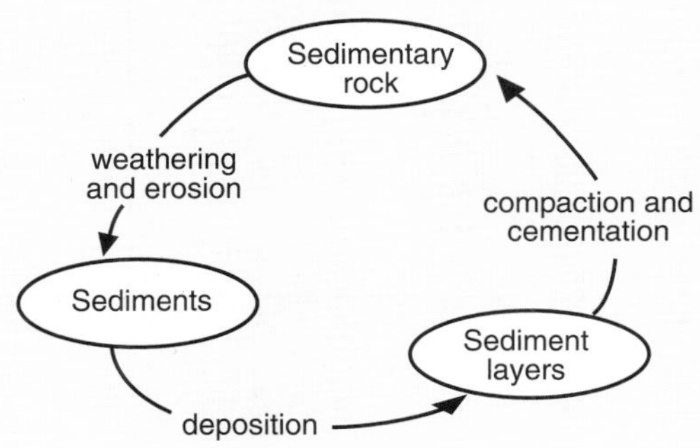

CHAPTER

7 Water Systems

CHAPTER SECTION	OBJECTIVES	ACTIVITIES
7-1 Water on Earth (1 day)	1. **Describe** the water cycle. 2. **Explain** what happens to water that doesn't soak into the ground or evaporate. 3. **List** three factors that affect runoff.	**MINI-Lab:** *How does the water cycle work?* p. 173
7-2 Development of River Systems (2 days)	1. **Describe** how a river system is like a tree. 2. **Explain** what a drainage basin is. 3. **Discuss** the three different stages of river development.	**Activity 7-1:** *Stream Velocity,* p. 180
7-3 The Action of Groundwater (3 days)	1. **Explain** what happens to water when it soaks into the ground. 2. **Describe** the relationship between the water table and springs. 3. **Explain** the cause of geysers and how caves form.	**MINI-Lab:** *How can you measure pore space?* p. 184 **Activity 7-2:** *Artesian Wells,* p. 185
7-4 Water Wars Science & Society (1 day)	1. **Give examples** of ways people use water. 2. **Explain** why some communities must rely on water diversion methods for their water supply. 3. **Identify** a problem caused by water diversion.	**Technology:** *Water shortage in Florida?* p. 189
Chapter Review		

ACTIVITY MATERIALS

FIND OUT	ACTIVITIES		MINI-LABS	
Page 171 waxed paper pieces of cardboard eye droppers water	**7-1 Stream Velocity, p. 180** stream table plastic pails (2) rubber tubing meterstick wooden blocks (2) stopwatch small cork sand to fill stream table books (2)	**7-2 Artesian Wells, p. 185** 30-cm plastic or rubber tube funnel protractor water scissors sink beaker tape	**How does the water cycle work? p. 173** water large beaker small beaker marble rubber band plastic wrap	**How can you measure pore space? p. 184** 250-mL beakers (2) 100 mL sand 100 mL gravel graduated cylinder water

CHAPTER FEATURES	TEACHER RESOURCE PACKAGE	OTHER RESOURCES
Skill Builder: *Sequencing,* p. 175	**Ability Level Worksheets** ◆ ***Study Guide,*** p. 30 ● ***Reinforcement,*** p. 30 ▲ ***Enrichment,*** p. 30 **MINI-Lab Worksheet,** p. 63 **Cross-Curricular Connections,** p. 11 **Transparency Masters,** pp. 19-20	**Color Transparency 10,** Water Cycle
Problem Solving: *Washed Out,* p. 178 **Skill Builder:** *Concept Mapping,* p. 181	**Ability Level Worksheets** ◆ ***Study Guide,*** p. 31 ● ***Reinforcement,*** p. 31 ▲ ***Enrichment,*** p. 31 **Activity Worksheet,** pp. 57-58	**Lab Manual:** *Stream Patterns,* p. 51 **Lab Manual:** *Rivers,* p. 55
Skill Builder: *Comparing and Contrasting,* p. 187	**Ability Level Worksheets** ◆ ***Study Guide,*** p. 32 ● ***Reinforcement,*** p. 32 ▲ ***Enrichment,*** p. 32 **MINI-Lab Worksheet,** p. 64 **Activity Worksheet,** pp. 59-60 **Critical Thinking/Problem Solving,** p. 13 **Concept Mapping,** pp. 19-20	**Lab Manual:** *Capillary Action,* p. 57 **Lab Manual:** *Permeability,* p. 59 **Lab Manual:** *Carbon Dioxide and Limestone,* p. 61
You Decide! p. 190	**Ability Level Worksheets** ◆ ***Study Guide,*** p. 33 ● ***Reinforcement,*** p. 33 ▲ ***Enrichment,*** p. 33 **Science and Society,** p. 11 **Technology,** pp. 9-10	
Summary Key Science Words Understanding Vocabulary Checking Concepts Understanding Concepts Think & Write Critically Apply More Skill Builders Projects	**Chapter Review,** pp. 17-18 **Chapter Test,** pp. 43-46	**Chapter Review Software** **Test Bank**

◆ **Basic** ● **Average** ▲ **Advanced**

ADDITIONAL MATERIALS

SOFTWARE	AUDIOVISUAL	BOOKS/MAGAZINES
Streams and Rivers, Aquarius. *Stream Erosion,* Teach Yourself by Computer Software. *Hydrologic Cycle,* IBM. *Ground Water,* IBM. *The Earth's Water,* Queue.	*Flow in Alluvial Channels,* film, USGS. *Men at Bay,* film, BFA. *Return to the Sea: Mississippi, 150 Years of Work,* film, U.S. Army Corps of Engineers. *Water Below,* film, USGS. *The Water Cycle,* film, EBEC. *The Earth and Its Wonders: The Story of Rivers,* filmstrip/cassette, EBEC. *The Blue Planet,* video, NOVA (PBS).	Dunne, Thomas and Luna B. Leopold. *Water in Environmental Planning.* NY: W.H. Freeman and Co., 1978. Manning, John. *Applied Principles of Hydrology.* Columbus, OH: Merrill Publishing Co., 1987. Patrick, Ruth et al. *Groundwater Contamination in the United States.* Philadelphia, PA: University of Pennsylvania Press, 1987.

CHAPTER

7 WATER SYSTEMS

THEME DEVELOPMENT: Two themes emphasized in this chapter are systems and interactions, and energy. Systems and interactions discussed include that water flowing along Earth's surface is part of the water cycle; streams join to eventually form river systems; and water flowing through pores in rocks forms the groundwater system. How the sun's energy powers the water cycle and how a river's energy is affected by the slope of the channel are also presented.

CHAPTER OVERVIEW

- **Section 7-1:** This section describes the water cycle. Factors that affect runoff are introduced.
- **Section 7-2:** The various stages in the development of river systems are discussed.
- **Section 7-3:** This section defines *groundwater* and explains how it flows through and changes soil and rocks.
- **Section 7-4: Science and Society:** The problem of a limited water supply in some regions is discussed. The You Decide feature asks students whether or not a canal should be built to divert water from the Great Lakes.

CHAPTER VOCABULARY

hydrosphere
water cycle
runoff
drainage basin
meander
floodplain
groundwater
permeable
impermeable
aquifer
zone of saturation
water table
artesian well
spring
hot spring
geyser
cave
water diversion

CHAPTER

7 Water Systems

OPTIONS

For Your Gifted Students

Have students discuss water shortage problems and propose possible solutions. Then, have students add salt to a test tube of water. Instruct them to carefully cork the tube with a rubber stopper containing a hole through which a drop or two of dish soap has been added. They should then carefully run a short piece of glass tubing through the hole and into the test tube of water. A piece of plastic tubing should be run from the other end of the glass tubing to a beaker. Have students heat the salt water to boiling and observe the condensation that occurs in the tube. Also have them observe the liquid that accumulates in the beaker.

You've probably seen pictures of a river like this one. What determines the direction a river takes? Does the surface of the land have any effect on the water?

FIND OUT!

Do this activity to find out about water systems.

Place a piece of waxed paper on top of a piece of cardboard. Then, using eye droppers, place water droplets onto the waxed paper as close as you can without having them touch. Next, gently tip the cardboard and observe what happens. Repeat the procedure, using cardboard covered with a paper towel instead of waxed paper. What happens to the water droplets on the waxed paper when the cardboard is tilted? What differences are there between the two types of surfaces? How could the surface of Earth affect how water flows?

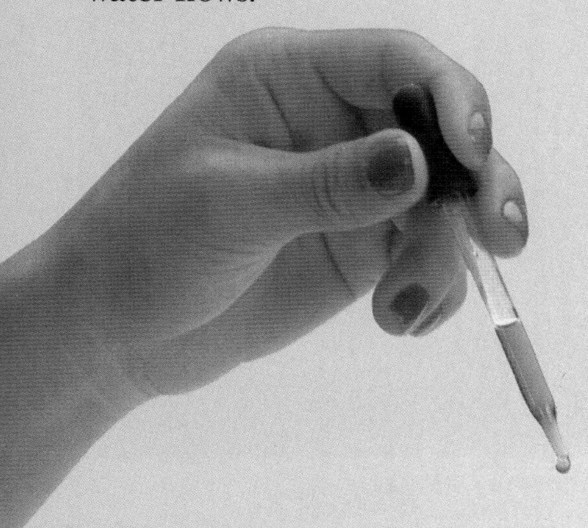

Gearing Up

Previewing the Chapter

Use this outline to help you focus on important ideas in this chapter.

Section 7-1 Water on Earth
- ▶ The Water Planet
- ▶ The Water Cycle
- ▶ Runoff

Section 7-2 Development of River Systems
- ▶ River System Development
- ▶ Stages of Stream Development

Section 7-3 The Action of Groundwater
- ▶ Groundwater Systems
- ▶ Wells and Springs
- ▶ Hot Springs and Geysers
- ▶ Caves and Sinkholes

Section 7-4 Science and Society Water Wars
- ▶ Water As a Resource
- ▶ Water Diversion

Previewing Science Skills

- ▶ In the **Skill Builders,** you will sequence, compare and contrast, and make a concept map.
- ▶ In the **Activities,** you will observe and record data.
- ▶ In the **MINI-Labs,** you will make a model, observe and infer, and record observations.

What's next?

In Chapter 6, you learned that water is the primary agent of erosion. You just saw in the Find Out activity some things that can happen to water on Earth's surface. In this chapter, you'll learn more about how water interacts with Earth.

INTRODUCING THE CHAPTER

Use the Find Out activity to introduce students to the ways in which different surfaces affect the flow of water. Inform students that they will be learning how water flows at and below Earth's surface in this chapter.

FIND OUT!

Preparation: Obtain waxed paper, cardboard, paper towels, and eye droppers for students to use.

Materials: waxed paper, pieces of cardboard, eye droppers, paper towels, and water

Teaching Tips

▶ Students will observe how absorbent materials like paper towels soak up water, while waxy surfaces do not.

▶ Have students experiment to find out how the slope affects the flow of the water. They will discover that there is little change with the paper towel. Water is soaked up by the towel regardless of the slope. But on the waxed paper, the greater the slope, the more quickly the droplets will join and begin to flow.

Gearing Up

Have students study the Gearing Up feature to familiarize themselves with the chapter. Discuss the relationships of the topics in the outline.

What's Next?

Before beginning the first section, make sure students understand the connection between the Find Out activity and the topics to follow.

For Your Mainstreamed Students

▶ Arrange for a local contractor or a city engineer to visit the class. Ask the person to explain how construction areas are evaluated in terms of runoff and drainage. The students may be able to visit a construction site to see the work firsthand. This would be a good opportunity to discuss career options in this area.

▶ Discuss groundwater pollution problems caused by fertilizers and by salt used on highways to melt ice.

SECTION 7-1

PREPARATION

SECTION BACKGROUND

▶ During evaporation, water is changed from a liquid to a gas because energy causes the molecules to move apart.

▶ During condensation, water is changed from a gas to a liquid because as the molecules cool, they move closer together.

PREPLANNING

▶ To prepare for the Mini-Lab on page 173, obtain marbles, rubber bands, plastic wrap, and small beakers that fit inside of large beakers.

1 MOTIVATE

▶ Tell students that worldwide each year, about 517 000 cubic kilometers of water evaporate. Of this amount, about 108 000 cubic kilometers fall as precipitation on land. Ask students to discuss what happens to the water Earth receives. Students should be able to conclude that some is absorbed by plants, some filters into the soil, some fills ponds and lakes, but most of the excess is runoff that eventually flows to the ocean.

FLEX Your Brain

Use the Flex Your Brain activity to have students explore THE WATER CYCLE.

PROGRAM RESOURCES

From the **Teacher Resource Package** use:

Activity Worksheets, page 5, Flex Your Brain.

Activity Worksheets, page 63, Mini-Lab: How does the water cycle work?

7-1 Water on Earth

New Science Words

hydrosphere
water cycle
runoff

Objectives

- ▶ Describe the water cycle.
- ▶ Explain what happens to water that doesn't soak into the ground or evaporate.
- ▶ List three factors that affect runoff.

The Water Planet

Earth is very different from the other planets in the solar system. Unlike the other planets, Earth's surface is about 70 percent covered with water. Most of this water is in the oceans. But water can also be found in lakes, streams, rivers, underground, and frozen in glaciers. All the water on Earth's surface is called the **hydrosphere**. Even though there's a lot of water on Earth, 97 percent of it is salt water. Of the remaining three percent, two-thirds of it is frozen in ice caps at the north and south poles. Therefore, only

Figure 7-1. Most of the water in the hydrosphere is salt water (a). Earth's surface is about 70 percent water (b).

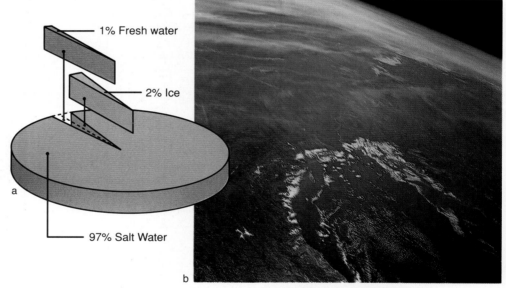

1% Fresh water
2% Ice
97% Salt Water
a
b

OPTIONS

Meeting Different Ability Levels

For Section 7-1, use the following **Teacher Resource Masters** depending upon individual students' needs.

◆ **Study Guide Master** for all students.

● **Reinforcement Master** for students of average and above average ability levels.

▲ **Enrichment Master** for above average students.

Additional Teacher Resource Package masters are listed in the OPTIONS box throughout the section. The additional masters are appropriate for all students.

◆ STUDY GUIDE 30

NAME ____ DATE ____ CLASS ____

STUDY GUIDE — Chapter 7

Water on Earth — Text Pages 172–175

Use the words in the box to fill in the blanks.

atmosphere	precipitation	vapor
oceans	sun	lakes
soaks	evaporates	runs
condenses	rivers	water cycle

Water moves between Earth and the **atmosphere**. This movement of water is called the **water cycle**. Heat from the **sun** causes water on Earth to change from a liquid to a **vapor** as it **evaporates**, rising from Earth's **oceans**, **rivers**, and **lakes**. Eventually this water **condenses**, or forms drops, and falls to Earth as **precipitation**.

Much of the rain that falls **soaks** into the ground. The rest either **runs** along the ground or evaporates and begins the process again.

In the blank at the left, write a term from the box to complete each statement.

erosion	vegetation
runoff	time span

runoff 1. Water that does not soak into the ground or evaporate is called ____.

time span 2. Two factors that determine whether rain soaks into the ground or runs off are the amount of rainfall and the ____ of the rainfall.

vegetation 3. Two factors that affect the amount of runoff are the kind of ____ that grows on the land and the slope of the land.

erosion 4. ____ may result if rain runoff is too fast.

30

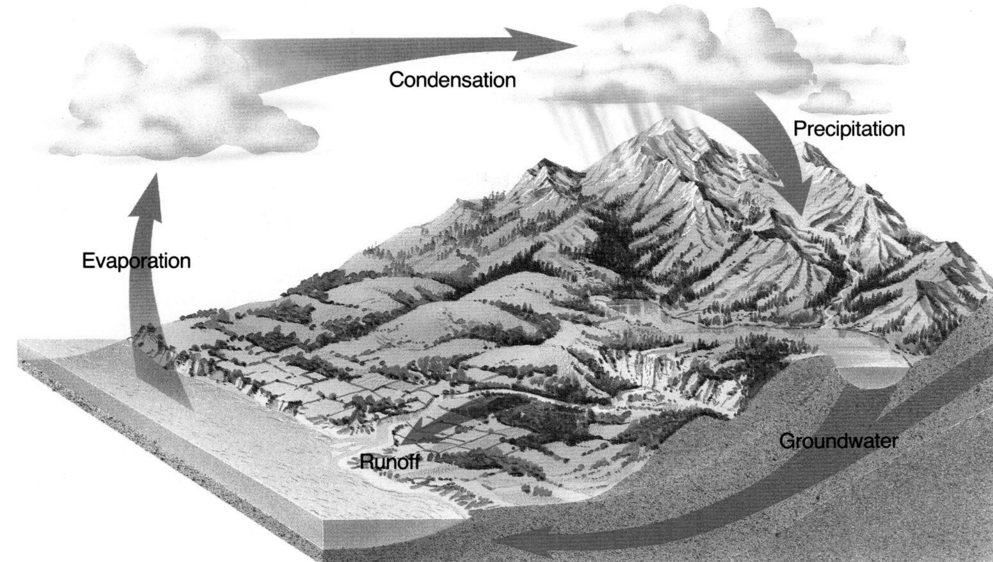

about one percent of the water in the hydrosphere is water we can drink and use to grow food.

Figure 7-2. Water moves from Earth to the atmosphere and back to Earth again in the water cycle.

The Water Cycle

Think back to the last time you experienced a hard rain. You could see it forming puddles on the grass and in the streets. Where did the water go after it rained? How did the water get in the atmosphere in the first place?

Water constantly moves between the atmosphere and Earth in the **water cycle,** as seen in Figure 7-2. The sun provides the energy for the water cycle. 1 Heat from the sun causes water to change to a gas called water vapor. This process is called evaporation. Water evaporates from lakes, streams, and oceans and rises into Earth's atmosphere.

In the next step of the water cycle, water vapor changes back into a liquid in the atmosphere. This process is called condensation and forms clouds. Clouds are made of tiny droplets of water that have condensed.

The third step in the water cycle is precipitation. When the clouds can no longer hold the condensed water vapor, it falls back to Earth as precipitation such as rain. 2 Rain can do three things when it falls to Earth. It either soaks into the ground, runs along the ground to someplace

MINI-Lab

How does the water cycle work?

Pour 2 cm of water into a large beaker. Place a small beaker in the center of the large beaker. Cover the large beaker loosely with plastic wrap and seal it with a rubber band. Put a marble in the middle of the plastic wrap. Place the beaker in direct sunlight for several hours. How does this simulate the water cycle?

● REINFORCEMENT 30

NAME ______ DATE ______ CLASS ______

REINFORCEMENT — Chapter 7

Water on Earth — Text Pages 172–175

Answer the following questions on the lines provided.

1. What term refers to the stages that water goes through as it moves between the atmosphere and Earth? **water cycle**
2. What provides the energy that causes water to evaporate? **sun**
3. What is precipitation? **water or ice that falls to Earth**
4. What three things may water do after it falls to Earth? **soak into the ground, run off, or evaporate**
5. What is the term for water that does not soak into the ground and does not evaporate? **runoff**
6. How does the slope of the land affect the amount of runoff after a rain? **Gentle slopes and flat land hold water until it has had time to soak into the ground. Steeper slopes cause more water to run off.**
7. Why is there more runoff after a heavy rain than after a light rain? **Heavy rainfall does not allow time for rain to soak into the ground, which causes more runoff.**
8. How do grass and other plants affect runoff? **Plants and their roots absorb water. This slows the runoff.**
9. What happens to runoff water? **Water that runs off fills streams, which then form rivers and become part of the river system.**
10. Write the correct terms in the blanks in the drawing of the water cycle.

Clouds cool
evaporation
precipitation
Water table
runoff
groundwater flows into ocean

30

▲ ENRICHMENT 30

NAME ______ DATE ______ CLASS ______

ENRICHMENT — Chapter 7

Water on Earth — Text Pages 172–175

WATER IN THE ATMOSPHERE

You know that the water cycle is water in motion. Evaporation distributes large amounts of moisture into the air. Every minute, more than 12 billion cubic kilometers of water circulates into the atmosphere. About 84 percent of the rising moisture is from oceans. The rest is from other bodies of water and from soil, plants, and animals. This experiment shows how soil and plants add to the water in Earth's atmosphere.

Materials
- soil in a flowerpot
- flowering plant, such as a geranium
- large plastic bag
- small plastic bag
- tape or twist tie (2)
- pencil and paper

Procedures
1. Place the flowering plant in the pot.
2. Water thoroughly.
3. Put a small plastic bag around the pot and seal it around the stem of the plant as shown in the illustration.
4. Cover the entire pot and plant with a large plastic bag. Seal the bag so it is airtight.
5. Observe the plant for two days.

Data and Observations

Day	Soil	Flowering plant
1		
2		

Analyze
1. Was moisture released from the soil? **yes** Was moisture released from the plant? **yes**

Conclude and Apply
1. How does this experiment show that plants and soil add to the water cycle? **The plastic bags were dry to begin with. The droplets of water that condensed on the bags had to come from the soil and the plants.**
2. Water is considered a renewable resource. Think about the experiment you just did. Why do you think water is called "renewable"? **Even though it evaporates, it condenses again into water which means it can be used again.**

30

TYING TO PREVIOUS KNOWLEDGE: Have students recall from Chapter 2 the three most common states of matter: solids, liquids, and gases. Explain that water that circulates through Earth's water cycle exists in all three states.

OBJECTIVES AND SCIENCE WORDS: Have students review the objectives and science words to become familiar with this section.

2 TEACH

Key Concepts are highlighted.

CONCEPT DEVELOPMENT

Cooperative Learning: Form Numbered Heads Together groups. Use Figure 7-2 to describe a sequence of events—either correct or incorrect—and have students either agree or disagree with your descriptions. If groups disagree, have them explain why.

REVEALING MISCONCEPTIONS

▶ Ask students: **When water evaporates, do the molecules expand?** *Although some students will answer "yes," explain that the molecules do not change size, but rather move farther away from one another.*

MINI-Lab

Materials: water, large beaker, small beaker, marble, rubber band, and plastic wrap for each group of students

Teaching Tips

Cooperative Learning: Have students perform this activity as Science Investigation teams.

Answer: Water evaporates due to the energy of the sunlight. It condenses on the cooler plastic wrap and returns to the smaller beaker in much the same way that precipitation returns water to Earth's surface.

CONCEPT DEVELOPMENT

▶ After students have read the information about runoff, pose the questions. **What happens to water that doesn't soak into the ground or evaporate?** *It becomes runoff.* **What factors affect runoff?** *amount of rain, time that rain falls, slope of land, amount of vegetation*

MINI QUIZ

Use the Mini Quiz to check students' recall of chapter content.

1. **Heat from the sun ____ water.** *evaporates*
2. **When water vapor condenses, it falls back to Earth as ____ .** *precipitation*
3. **____ slopes hold water in place until it evaporates or sinks into the ground.** *Gentle*

CROSS CURRICULUM

▶ **Biology:** Grasses have many shallow roots that spread laterally across soil. A pine tree has a few long roots. Ask students to write a short essay describing which plant would better reduce runoff and help prevent soil erosion. *Grasses' roots can soak up more surface water.*

else, or evaporates to repeat the cycle. In this chapter, you will look closely at what water does while it is on Earth.

Runoff

What happens to water that doesn't soak into the ground or evaporate?

Water that doesn't soak into the ground or evaporate flows across Earth's surface and is called **runoff.** If you've ever spilled milk while pouring it, you've experienced something similar to runoff. You can picture it in your mind. You start pouring yourself a glass of milk, and it overflows and spills all over the table. Then, before you can grab a towel to clean up the mess, it runs off the table onto the floor. This is similar to rainwater that doesn't soak into the ground or evaporate. It runs along the ground and eventually enters streams.

But what factors determine whether rain soaks into the ground or runs off? The amount of rain and the time span over which it falls are two factors that affect the amount of runoff. Light rain falling over several hours will probably have time to soak into the ground. Heavy rain falling in just an hour or so will run off because it doesn't have time to soak in.

Another factor that affects the amount of runoff is the
3 slope of the land. Gentle slopes and flat areas hold water

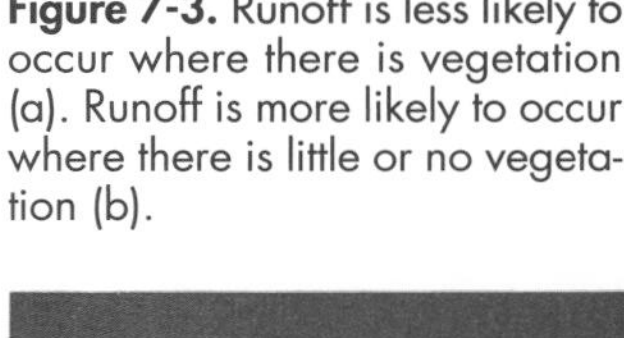

Figure 7-3. Runoff is less likely to occur where there is vegetation (a). Runoff is more likely to occur where there is little or no vegetation (b).

a

b

OPTIONS

INQUIRY QUESTIONS

▶ **Look at Figure 7-3. Which land probably has more problems with erosion of the soil? Why?** *The land on the right has no vegetation to anchor the soil, thus, erosion is greater here than on the other lot.*

▶ **Predict what happens to the amount of runoff from an area when an asphalt parking lot is built on top of the soil.** *Runoff increases because the asphalt prevents water from soaking into the ground.*

PROGRAM RESOURCES

From the **Teacher Resource Package** use:

Cross-Curricular Connections, page 11, Using Photographs and Illustrations.

Transparency Masters, pages 19-20, Water Cycle.

Use **Color Transparency** number 10, Water Cycle.

Figure 7-4. Runoff can cause erosion.

in place until it has a chance to evaporate or sink into the ground. On steep slopes, however, water runs off before these things can happen.

The amount of vegetation, such as grass, also affects the amount of runoff. Just like milk running off the table, water will tend to run off smooth surfaces with little or no vegetation. Plants and their roots act like sponges to soak up and hold water. By slowing down runoff, plants and roots help prevent the erosion of soil.

How do plants slow down runoff?

Runoff is just one part of the water cycle. This water will pass through many stages on its trip through the cycle. In the next stage, runoff enters streams and rivers and becomes a part of a water system, which you will learn about in Section 7-2.

EcoTip

Adopt a stream or pond. Keep it clean by picking up trash along the banks. Recycle the trash you collect.

SECTION REVIEW

1. What does the sun do in the water cycle?
2. What are three things water can do on Earth's surface?
3. What are three factors that affect runoff?
4. **Apply:** How does the water cycle keep river systems full of water?

Sequencing — Skill Builder

Sequence the events in the water cycle beginning with rain falling to Earth. If you need help, refer to Sequencing in the **Skill Handbook** on page 680.

CHECK FOR UNDERSTANDING

Have students contrast the runoff from paved streets and grassy fields during both a thunderstorm and a gentle rain.

RETEACH

Cooperative Learning: Have students work in Science Investigation groups to see how different surfaces affect runoff. Each team will need a paint tray half full of soil, a piece of cardboard, a clump of grass, and a beaker of water. Have students design and execute an experiment using the cardboard to simulate a paved street, and the clump of grass to simulate a grassy field.

EXTENSION

For students who have mastered this section, use the **Reinforcement** and **Enrichment** masters or other OPTIONS provided.

3 CLOSE

▶ Ask questions 1-3 and the **Apply** Question in the Section Review.

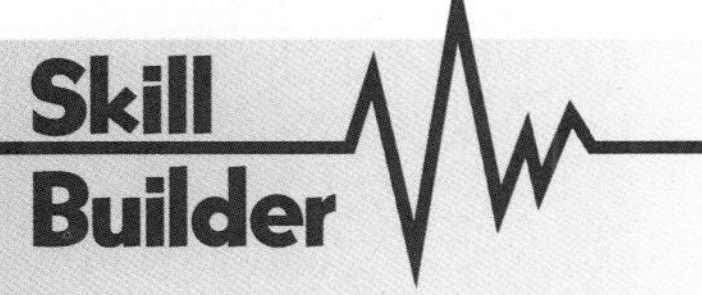

FLEX Your Brain

Use the Flex Your Brain activity to have students explore RUNOFF.

SECTION REVIEW ANSWERS

1. It provides energy for the cycle.
2. soak into the ground, run along the ground, or evaporate into air
3. amount of rain, time span over which the rain falls, slope of the land, amount of vegetation
4. Apply: Precipitation and runoff supply river systems with water.

Skill Builder

1. Rain falls to Earth.
2. Some of it soaks into ground; some becomes runoff.
3. Water that doesn't become runoff or groundwater evaporates.
4. Evaporated water condenses to form clouds.
5. Precipitation falls from clouds.

ENRICHMENT

▶ Have students research what happens to local runoff.

▶ Have students experiment with growing a variety of plants on a constant slope. The purpose of their experiments is to see which plants are best in reducing runoff and soil erosion.

PROGRAM RESOURCES

From the **Teacher Resource Package** use:

Activity Worksheets, page 5, Flex Your Brain.

SECTION 7-2

PREPARATION

SECTION BACKGROUND

▶ A drainage basin is separated from other basins by high ground called a divide. As a river system evolves, rills and gullies erode the divide. With time, the divide becomes more and more narrow.

▶ Major drainage patterns include: dendritic drainage, which resembles a tree; rectangular drainage, which forms when bedrock is cracked; trellis drainage, which results from an area's being covered with hard and soft bedrock; and radial drainage, which forms when a central structure is a part of the landscape.

PREPLANNING

▶ To prepare for Activity 7-1, obtain a stream table, sand, plastic pails, rubber tubing, a meterstick, a plastic sheet, wooden blocks, and a stopwatch for each team.

1 MOTIVATE

▶ Take students to a local stream. Have them determine the velocity both at the middle and at the edge of the stream by measuring 10 meters along the bank and timing how long it takes a fishing bob to float the 10 meters. Velocity equals distance divided by time. Tell students erosion is greatest where the velocity is greatest. Have them determine where in the stream erosion is greatest.

▶ Have students examine Figure 7-6, which shows the Mississippi River and its tributaries. Have them trace the pattern of this drainage system from its source to its mouth. They should use Appendix G on page 670 to name several of the major tributaries to the Mississippi. Have students discuss why the main river follows the path it does.

7-2 Development of River Systems

New Science Words

drainage basin
meander
floodplain

Objectives

- ▶ **Describe how a river system is like a tree.**
- ▶ **Explain what a drainage basin is.**
- ▶ **Discuss the three different stages of river development.**

River System Development

Do you know of a stream in your neighborhood or town? Maybe you've been fishing or swimming in that stream. Each day, thousands of liters of water flow through your neighborhood or town in that stream. But just where does that water come from?

The stream in your neighborhood is really a part of a river system. The water in the stream came from smaller channels located upstream. Just as a tree is a system

a

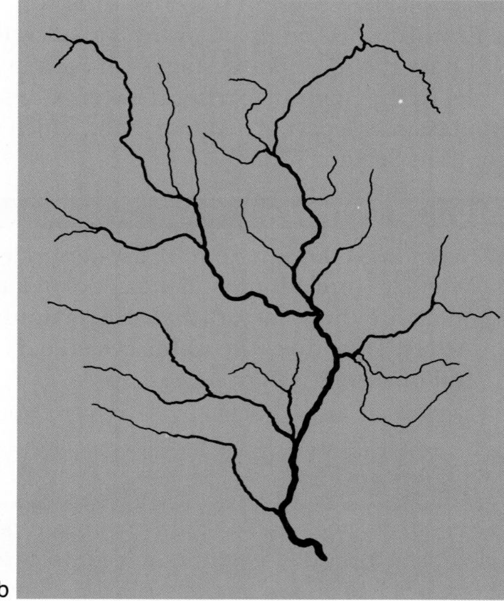
b

Figure 7-5. The system of twigs, branches, and a trunk that make up a tree (a) is similar to a river system (b).

OPTIONS

Meeting Different Ability Levels

For Section 7-2, use the following **Teacher Resource Masters** depending upon individual students' needs.

◆ **Study Guide Master** for all students.

● **Reinforcement Master** for students of average and above average ability levels.

▲ **Enrichment Master** for above average students.

Additional Teacher Resource Package masters are listed in the OPTIONS box throughout the section. The additional masters are appropriate for all students.

◆ **STUDY GUIDE 31**

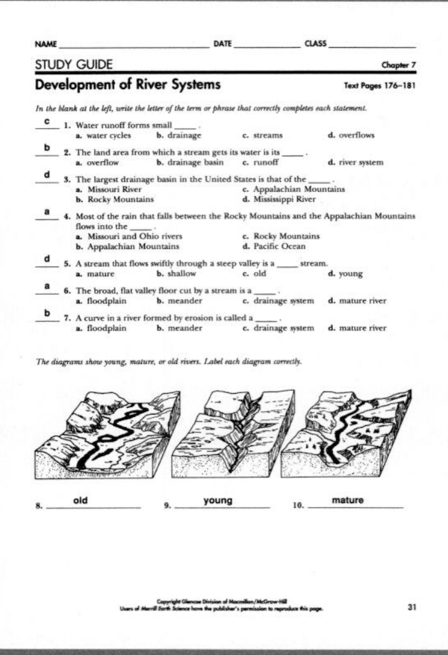

NAME ______ DATE ______ CLASS ______

STUDY GUIDE — Chapter 7

Development of River Systems — Text Pages 176–181

In the blank at the left, write the letter of the term or phrase that correctly completes each statement.

c 1. Water runoff forms small ____.
a. water cycles b. drainage c. streams d. overflows

b 2. The land area from which a stream gets its water is its ____.
a. overflow b. drainage basin c. runoff d. river system

d 3. The largest drainage basin in the United States is that of the ____.
a. Missouri River c. Appalachian Mountains
b. Rocky Mountains d. Mississippi River

a 4. Most of the rain that falls between the Rocky Mountains and the Appalachian Mountains flows into the ____.
a. Missouri and Ohio rivers c. Rocky Mountains
b. Appalachian Mountains d. Pacific Ocean

d 5. A stream that flows swiftly through a steep valley is a ____ stream.
a. mature b. shallow c. old d. young

a 6. The broad, flat valley floor cut by a stream is a ____.
a. floodplain b. meander c. drainage system d. mature river

b 7. A curve in a river formed by erosion is called a ____.
a. floodplain b. meander c. drainage system d. mature river

The diagrams show young, mature, or old rivers. Label each diagram correctly.

8. old 9. young 10. mature

31

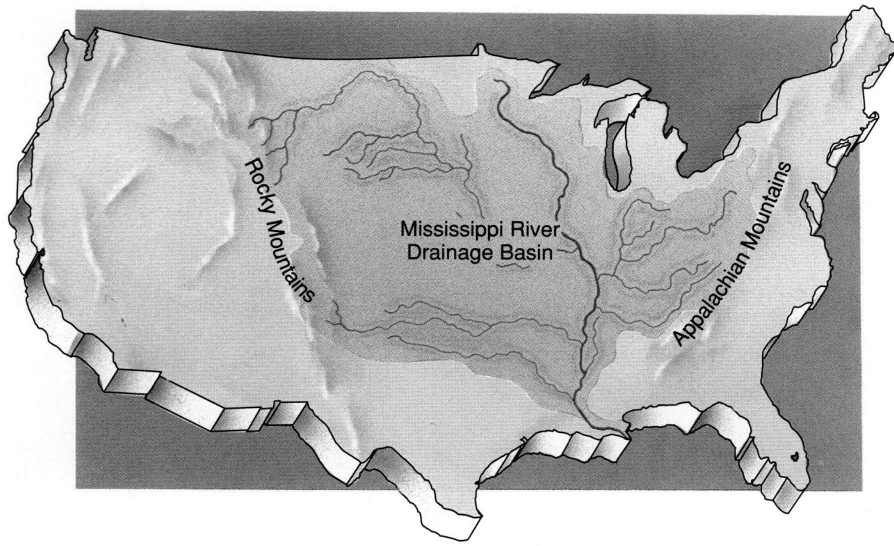

containing stems, twigs, branches, and a trunk, a river system also has many parts. Water runs off of the ground and enters small streams. Where small streams join, a larger stream forms. Finally, where streams merge, a larger body of water called a river forms. 1

The land area from which a stream gets its water is called a **drainage basin.** 2 A drainage basin can be compared to a bathtub. Water that collects in a bathtub flows toward the drain. Likewise, all of the water in a river system eventually flows to one location—the main river. The largest drainage basin in the United States is the Mississippi River drainage basin. Most of the rain that falls between the Rocky Mountains and the Appalachian Mountains drains into the Missouri and Ohio rivers. These rivers and others flow into the Mississippi River, as seen in Figure 7-6.

Figure 7-6. Water from a large portion of the United States drains into the Mississippi River.

Where does rain that falls between the Rocky Mountains and the Appalachian Mountains go?

Stages of Stream Development

There are many different types of streams. Some are narrow and swift-moving, and others are very wide and slow-moving. Streams differ because they are in different stages of development. These stages depend on the slope of the ground over which the stream flows. Streams are classified as young, mature, or old.

TYING TO PREVIOUS KNOWLEDGE: Have students recall from Chapter 6 that running water causes erosion. In this section, they will find out that this erosional energy causes some tributaries in a river system to change the shapes of their channels.

OBJECTIVES AND SCIENCE WORDS: Have students review the objectives and science words to become familiar with this section.

2 TEACH

Key Concepts are highlighted.

CONCEPT DEVELOPMENT

▶ After students have read pages 176 and 177, ask the following questions. **What is the largest drainage basin in the United States?** *the Mississippi drainage basin* **How are streams classified?** *Streams can be classified as young, mature, or old.*

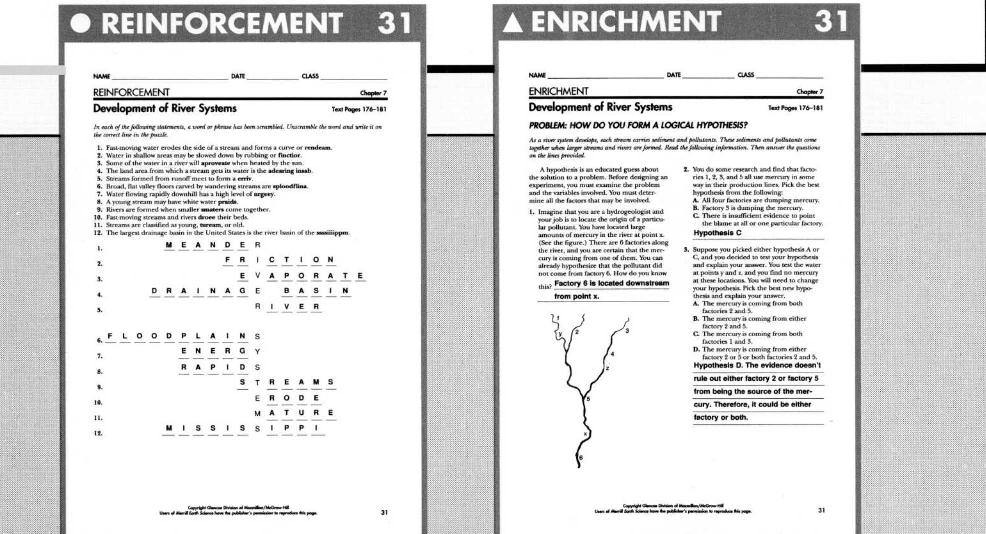

● REINFORCEMENT 31

NAME ______ DATE ______ CLASS ______

REINFORCEMENT — Chapter 7

Development of River Systems — Text Pages 176–181

In each of the following statements, a word or phrase has been scrambled. Unscramble the word and write it on the correct line in the puzzle.

1. Fast-moving water erodes the side of a stream and forms a curve or **rendeam**.
2. Water in shallow areas may be slowed down by rubbing or **finctior**.
3. Some of the water in a river will **aproveate** when heated by the sun.
4. The land area from which a stream gets its water is the **adearing insab**.
5. Streams formed from runoff meet to form a **erriv**.
6. Broad, flat valley floors carved by wandering streams are **sploodflina**.
7. Water flowing rapidly downhill has a high level of **nrgeey**.
8. A young stream may have white water **praids**.
9. Rivers are formed when smaller **smaters** come together.
10. Fast-moving streams and rivers **droee** their beds.
11. Streams are classified as young, **tuream**, or old.
12. The largest drainage basin in the United States is the river basin of the **sssiiiippm**.

1. M E A N D E R
2. F R I C T I O N
3. E V A P O R A T E
4. D R A I N A G E B A S I N
5. R I V E R
6. F L O O D P L A I N S
7. E N E R G Y
8. R A P I D S
9. S T R E A M S
10. E R O D E
11. M A T U R E
12. M I S S I S S I P P I

Copyright Glencoe Division of Macmillan/McGraw-Hill
Users of Merrill Earth Science have the publisher's permission to reproduce this page. 31

▲ ENRICHMENT 31

NAME ______ DATE ______ CLASS ______

ENRICHMENT — Chapter 7

Development of River Systems — Text Pages 176–181

PROBLEM: HOW DO YOU FORM A LOGICAL HYPOTHESIS?

As a river system develops, each stream carries sediment and pollutants. These sediments and pollutants come together when larger streams and rivers are formed. Read the following information. Then answer the questions on the lines provided.

A hypothesis is an educated guess about the solution to a problem. Before designing an experiment, you must examine the problem and the variables involved. You must determine all the factors that may be involved.

1. Imagine that you are a hydrogeologist and your job is to locate the origin of a particular pollutant. You have located large amounts of mercury in the river at point x. (See the figure.) There are 6 factories along the river, and you are certain that the mercury is coming from one of them. You can already hypothesize that the pollutant did not come from factory 6. How do you know this? **Factory 6 is located downstream from point x.**

2. You do some research and find that factories 1, 2, 3, and 5 all use mercury in some way in their production lines. Pick the best hypothesis from the following:
   A. All four factories are dumping mercury.
   B. Factory 3 is dumping the mercury.
   C. There is insufficient evidence to point the blame at all or one particular factory.
   Hypothesis C

3. Suppose you picked either hypothesis A or C, and you decided to test your hypothesis and explain your answer. You test the water at points y and z, and you find no mercury at these locations. You will need to change your hypothesis. Pick the best new hypothesis and explain your answer.
   A. The mercury is coming from both factories 2 and 5.
   B. The mercury is coming from either factory 2 and 5.
   C. The mercury is coming from both factories 1 and 3.
   D. The mercury is coming from either factory 2 or 5 or both factories 2 and 5.
   Hypothesis D. The evidence doesn't rule out either factory 2 or factory 5 from being the source of the mercury. Therefore, it could be either factory or both.

Copyright Glencoe Division of Macmillan/McGraw-Hill
Users of Merrill Earth Science have the publisher's permission to reproduce this page. 31

CONCEPT DEVELOPMENT

▶ **Why do streams in the mountains have such high levels of energy?** *The water is flowing rapidly downhill.*

PROBLEM SOLVING

Think Critically: The river had flooded due to runoff from the land in the northern areas of David's state. The river next to the ball field was a part of the same drainage system as the streams farther north. Locations downstream from heavy rainfall are subject to flooding.

CONCEPT DEVELOPMENT

▶ Have a volunteer compare and contrast young and mature streams.

▶ Stress that as a stream matures, its erosional energy is no longer concentrated along its bottom. Streams begin meandering because the velocity of the water varies throughout the width of the channel. On the side of the stream where the current is strongest, erosion is greatest.

PROGRAM RESOURCES

Use **Laboratory Manual,** page 51, Stream Patterns.

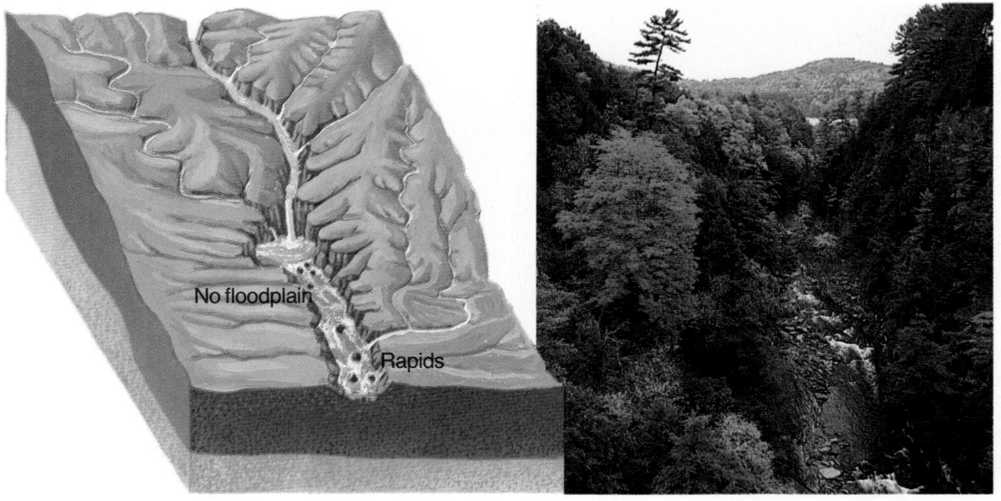

Figure 7-7. The characteristics of a young stream can be seen in the diagram and in the photo.

A stream that flows swiftly through a steep valley and has steep sides is a young stream. These streams are found in mountainous or hilly regions. The water is flowing rapidly down a steep slope. A young stream may have white water rapids and waterfalls. Because the water is flowing rapidly downhill, it has a high level of energy and
3 erodes the stream bottom more than its sides.

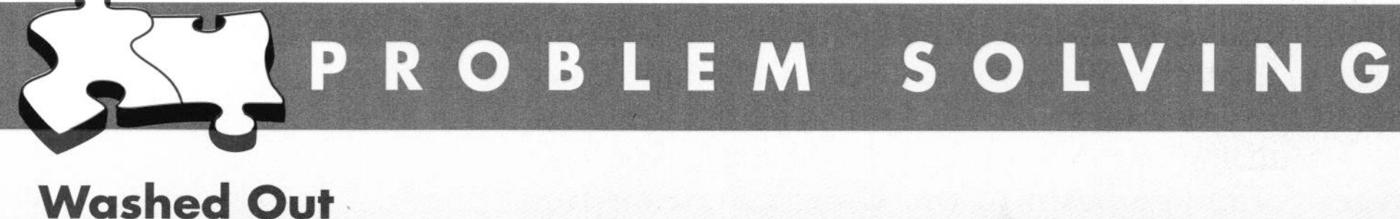

PROBLEM SOLVING

Washed Out

David stared at the cloudy sky. He knew from weather reports that northern areas of the state had received heavy rain.

However, his hometown had not received a drop. He hoped the rain would come and go by the weekend so the baseball game would not be rained out. His team was in the playoffs, and the day of the big game was almost here.

It never did rain that week. Saturday morning arrived and David had hardly slept. He arrived at the field early and could not believe his eyes. The playing field next to the river was underwater.

Think Critically: How could the field be flooded if it didn't rain?

OPTIONS

INQUIRY QUESTIONS

▶ **Explain why most white-water rafting is done in young rivers.** *These rivers flow downhill with enough energy to form rapids. Older rivers cannot provide the thrilling rides that young rivers can.*

▶ **Examine Figure 7-6. Where are the youngest parts of the drainage system? Where are the older rivers?** *The young rivers are at the outer edges of the system in the mountains and hills. The mature rivers are those with meanders. The oldest part of the system is the Mississippi River itself.*

The next stage in the development of a stream is the mature stage. A curving stream that flows down a gradual slope and erodes its sides is a mature stream. A mature stream flows less swiftly through its valley. Most of the rocks in the stream bed that cause waterfalls and rapids have been eroded away.

The erosional energy of a mature stream is no longer concentrated on its bottom. Now, the stream starts to erode its sides, developing curves. These curves form because the speed of the water varies throughout the width of a channel. Water in shallow areas of a stream is slowed down by the friction created by the bottom of the river. In deep areas, less of the water comes in contact with the bottom. This means that deep water has less friction with the bottom of the stream and therefore flows faster.

This faster moving water erodes the side of the stream where the current is strongest, forming curves. A curve that forms in this way is called a **meander.** Figure 7-8 shows 4
what a meandering stream looks like from the air.

When a stream enters its mature stage and starts to meander, it erodes the valley walls and widens the valley floor. This broad, flat valley floor carved by a meandering stream is called a **floodplain.** When a stream floods, it 5
often covers a part of or the whole floodplain.

Did You Know?

It's taken the Colorado River 10 to 15 million years to carve the Grand Canyon, which ranges from 6 to 29 km wide and is more than $1\frac{1}{2}$ km deep.

Why does water flow faster in an area of deeper water?

Figure 7-8. The characteristics of a mature stream can be seen in the diagram and in the photo.

CROSS CURRICULUM

▶ **History:** Have students do some research to find out that because the Rio Grande meanders, the border between the United States and Mexico, which is formed by the river, has changed over time. Mexico has had to cede some land to the U.S.

MINI QUIZ

Use the Mini Quiz to check students' recall of chapter content.

1. **A(n) _____ consists of small and large merging streams.** *river system*
2. **The land area where a stream gets its water is a(n) _____ .** *drainage basin*
3. **The erosional energy of a(n) _____ stream is concentrated on the bottom of the channel.** *young*
4. **Curves in mature streams are called _____ .** *meanders*
5. **A broad, flat valley floor carved by a meandering stream is a(n) _____ .** *floodplain*

ENRICHMENT

▶ Have students do research that will enable them to make sketches of dendritic, rectangular, trellis, and radial drainage patterns.

▶ Have students construct a river profile by plotting elevations along the stream bed from its headwaters to its mouth. Then have them construct a cross section of a river by plotting its elevation across the stream valley.

ACTIVITY 7-1
50-60 minutes

OBJECTIVE: Observe how the slope of a stream affects its velocity.

PROCESS SKILLS applied in this activity:
▶ **Observing** in Procedure Steps 6 and 8.
▶ **Communicating** in Procedure Step 1.
▶ **Measuring** in Procedure Steps 3 and 9.
▶ **Interpreting Data** in Analyze Questions 1 and 2.
▶ **Hypothesizing** in Conclude and Apply Question 4.
▶ **Separating and Controlling Variables** in Procedure Step 10.
▶ **Experimenting** in Procedure Steps 1-10.
▶ **Formulating Models** in Conclude and Apply Question 3.

TEACHING THE ACTIVITY

▶ Create a curved stream channel and allow water to flow. Ask students to compare the velocity of the straight stream to the meandering stream.
▶ Students may not be familiar with the term *load* in reference to streams. Load refers to the amount of sediment a stream is carrying.

Troubleshooting: The tube that carries excess water out of the stream may become clogged with sand. To prevent this, be sure that the stream channel is deep enough near the tube opening that the tube is above the sand, but not so high that the water cannot reach it.

PROGRAM RESOURCES

From the **Teacher Resource Package** use:

Activity Worksheets, pages 57-58, Activity 7-1: Stream Velocity.

ACTIVITY 7-1
Stream Velocity

Problem: *How does the slope of a stream affect its velocity and load?*

Materials
- stream table
- plastic pails (2)
- rubber tubing
- meterstick
- wooden blocks (2)
- stopwatch
- small cork
- sand to fill stream table
- books (2)
- plastic sheet
- water

Procedure
1. Arrange the stream table as shown.
2. Make a stream channel down the center of the sand so that it ends at the short length of rubber tubing.
3. Measure and record the length of the stream channel.
4. Fill the pail at the top of the table with water. Set up a siphon using a long piece of rubber tubing.

5. Put one block of wood under the upper end of the stream table.
6. Put the cork at the upper end of the stream bed. Start the water into the stream bed.
7. Record the time the cork takes to travel the length of the stream channel.
8. Observe and record whether or not the water carries material other than the cork downstream. Stop the flow of water. Allow excess water to drain from the stream table.
9. Repeat the procedure in Steps 6-8 two more times. Record the average flow time in a table.
10. Stack another block on top of the first at the upper end of the stream table.
11. Repeat Steps 6, 7, 8, and 9 and record all observations in a table.

Data and Observations
Sample Data

Slope	Stream length	Flow time	Observations
one block	1.9 m	5.2 seconds	
two blocks	1.9 m	2.7 seconds	

Analyze
1. Calculate the velocity of the stream for a slope of one block and for a slope of two blocks.

$$\text{velocity} = \frac{\text{distance}}{\text{time}}$$

2. Did your stream meander?

Conclude and Apply
3. How does the increase in slope affect the amount of sediment the stream carries?
4. What was the purpose of the cork?
5. How does the velocity of the stream change when you increase the slope?

ANSWERS TO QUESTIONS

1. Answers will vary with the height of the blocks and the time recorded.
2. Answers will vary. The velocity of the water may be too great for meanders to develop in this activity.
3. An increase in the slope increases the amount of sediment carried by the stream.
4. The purpose of the cork is to aid in determining the flow of the stream.
5. Answers will vary with the height of the blocks and the time recorded. Velocity will probably increase more than students would expect.

Figure 7-9. The characteristics of an old stream can be seen in the diagram and in the photo.

The last stage in the development of a stream is the old stage. An old stream flows very slowly through a very broad, flat floodplain that it has carved. A river in this stage erodes its sides mostly causing changes in its meanders. The lower Mississippi River is a river in the old stage of development.

River systems usually contain streams in all stages of development. At the outer edges of a river system, you find white water streams moving swiftly down mountains and hills. At the bottom of mountains and hills, you find streams that are starting to meander and are in the mature stage of development. These streams meet at the lowest point in the drainage basin to form a major river, which is usually in the old stage of development.

What kind of stream is found at the bottoms of hills and mountains?

SECTION REVIEW

1. Why can a river be described as a system?
2. What is a drainage basin?
3. In which stage of development is a stream that erodes its sides?
4. **Apply:** How is a stream's rate of flow related to the amount of erosion it causes?

Concept Mapping — Skill Builder

Make an events chain concept map showing the stages of stream development. Use the following words or phrases: *old stream, mature stream, young stream, slow-moving, meanders, waterfalls.* If you need help, refer to Concept Mapping in the **Skill Handbook** on page 688.

CHECK FOR UNDERSTANDING

Ask questions 1-3 and the **Apply** Question in the Section Review.

RETEACH

Have students examine rivers shown on maps or in photographs. Ask students to classify these rivers as being young, mature, or old rivers.

EXTENSION

For students who have mastered this section, use the **Reinforcement** and **Enrichment** masters or other OPTIONS provided.

3 CLOSE

FLEX Your Brain

Use the Flex Your Brain activity to have students explore the COLORADO RIVER DRAINAGE SYSTEM.

SECTION REVIEW ANSWERS

1. A river contains water carried to it from small and large merging streams. The tributaries and the main river are all parts of the same system.
2. the land area from which a stream gets its water
3. in the mature and old stage
4. Apply: the greater the stream's rate of flow, the greater the amount of erosion

Skill Builder

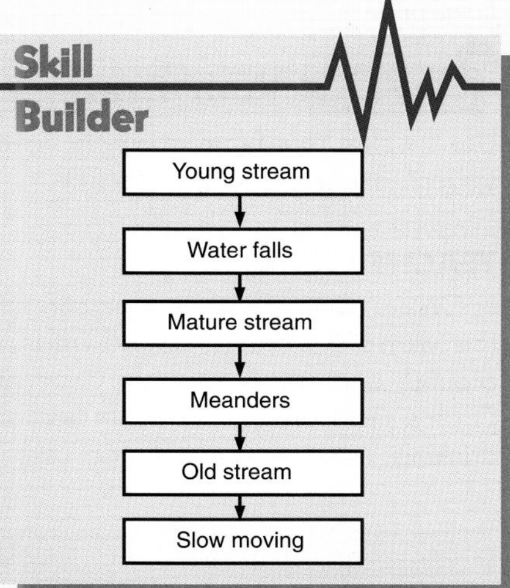

PROGRAM RESOURCES

From the **Teacher Resource Package** use:
Activity Worksheets, page 5, Flex Your Brain.
Use **Laboratory Manual,** page 55, Rivers.

SECTION 7-3

PREPARATION

SECTION BACKGROUND

▶ Most natural water contains carbonic acid because rainwater dissolves carbon dioxide from the air and from decaying plants. When groundwater comes in contact with limestone, the carbonic acid reacts with calcite in the rocks to form soluble calcium bicarbonate.

PREPLANNING

▶ To prepare for the Mini-Lab on page 184, obtain sand, gravel, beakers, and graduated cylinders.

▶ Obtain plastic tubing, funnels, protractors, scissors, and beakers for Activity 7-2.

1 MOTIVATE

▶ **Demonstration:** Explain to students that groundwater often dissolves subsurface limestones. Half fill a beaker with limestone chips. Pour carbonated water over the chips and have students observe what happens. Help them conclude that the carbonated water represents groundwater and weathers the limestone.

FLEX Your Brain

Use the Flex Your Brain activity to have students explore GROUNDWATER.

TEACHER F.Y.I.

▶ Only about 3/5 of one percent of the world's water is found underground; and yet, this water is one of Earth's most important resources for drinking, washing, and industrial uses.

PROGRAM RESOURCES

From the **Teacher Resource Package** use:

Activity Worksheets, page 5, Flex Your Brain.

7-3 The Action of Groundwater

New Science Words

groundwater
permeable
impermeable
aquifer
zone of saturation
water table
artesian well
spring
hot spring
geyser
cave

Objectives

- ▶ **Explain what happens to water when it soaks into the ground.**
- ▶ **Describe the relationship between the water table and springs.**
- ▶ **Explain the cause of geysers and how caves form.**

Groundwater Systems

What would have happened if the spilled milk from Section 7-1 had run off the table onto a carpeted floor? It would have quickly soaked into the carpet. Water that falls on Earth can also soak into the ground.

But what happens to water then? Water that soaks into the ground becomes a part of a system, just as water that stays above ground becomes a part of a river system. You already know that soil is made up of many small rock fragments and that there is weathered rock beneath the soil. Between these fragments and pieces of weathered rock are spaces called pores. Water that soaks into the ground
collects in these pores and becomes part of what is called 1
groundwater.

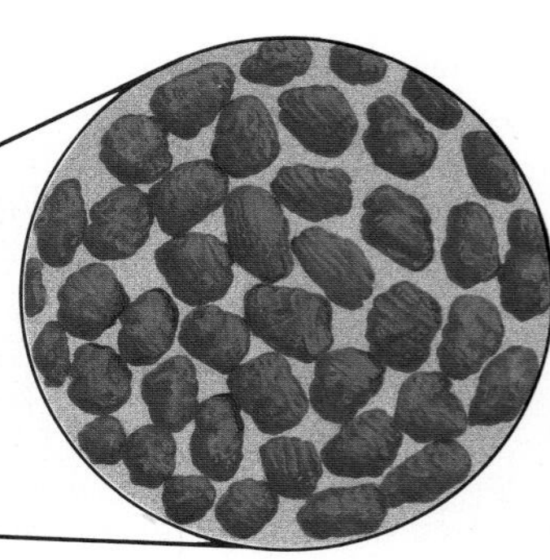

Figure 7-10. Water disappears into soil because it has pore spaces.

OPTIONS

Meeting Different Ability Levels

For Section 7-3, use the following **Teacher Resource Masters** depending upon individual students' needs.

◆ **Study Guide Master** for all students.

● **Reinforcement Master** for students of average and above average ability levels.

▲ **Enrichment Master** for above average students.

Additional Teacher Resource Package masters are listed in the OPTIONS box throughout the section. The additional masters are appropriate for all students.

◆ STUDY GUIDE 32

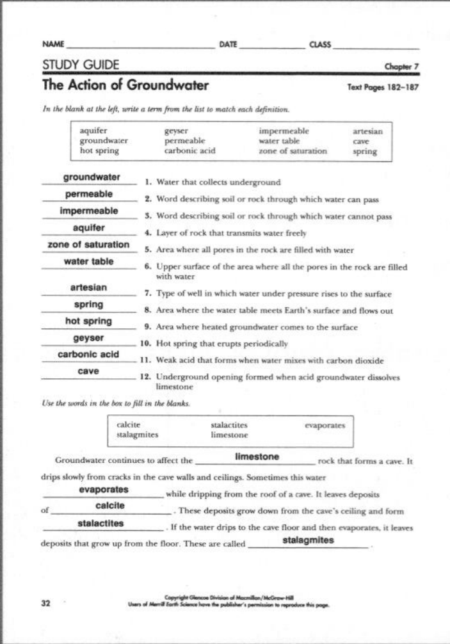

NAME ______ DATE ______ CLASS ______

STUDY GUIDE — Chapter 7

The Action of Groundwater — Text Pages 182–187

In the blank at the left, write a term from the list to match each definition.

aquifer	geyser	impermeable	artesian
groundwater	permeable	water table	cave
hot spring	carbonic acid	zone of saturation	spring

groundwater 1. Water that collects underground
permeable 2. Word describing soil or rock through which water can pass
impermeable 3. Word describing soil or rock through which water cannot pass
aquifer 4. Layer of rock that transmits water freely
zone of saturation 5. Area where all pores in the rock are filled with water
water table 6. Upper surface of the area where all the pores in the rock are filled with water
artesian 7. Type of well in which water under pressure rises to the surface
spring 8. Area where the water table meets Earth's surface and flows out
hot spring 9. Area where heated groundwater comes to the surface
geyser 10. Hot spring that erupts periodically
carbonic acid 11. Weak acid that forms when water mixes with carbon dioxide
cave 12. Underground opening formed when acid groundwater dissolves limestone

Use the words in the box to fill in the blanks.

calcite	stalactites	evaporates
stalagmites	limestone	

Groundwater continues to affect the **limestone** rock that forms a cave. It drips slowly from cracks in the cave walls and ceilings. Sometimes this water **evaporates** while dripping from the roof of a cave. It leaves deposits of **calcite**. These deposits grow down from the cave's ceiling and form **stalactites**. If the water drips to the cave floor and then evaporates, it leaves deposits that grow up from the floor. These are called **stalagmites**.

32

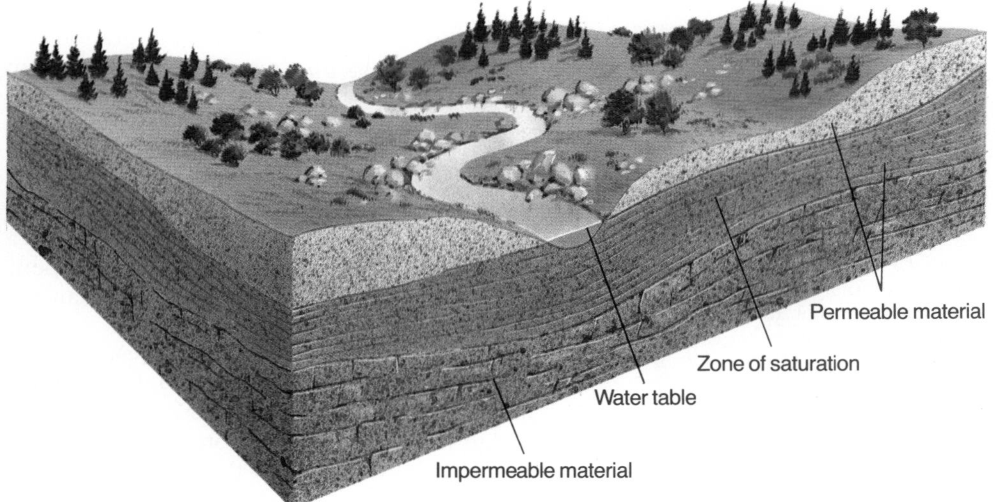

Figure 7-11. A stream's surface is the level of the water table in that area.

The groundwater system is similar to a river system. However, instead of having channels that connect different parts of the drainage basin, the groundwater system has connecting pores. Some soils and rock have connecting pores, as shown in Figure 7-10, that water can move through. Soils and rock are **permeable** if water can pass through them this way. Sandstone is a common permeable rock.

Soil or rock that has many large connected pores is very permeable. Water can pass through it easily. Soil or rock that has few or small pores is less permeable because water can't easily pass through. Some material, such as
2 clay, has very small pores or no pores at all. Water can't pass through this **impermeable** material.

How deep into Earth's crust do you suppose groundwater can go? That depends on the permeability of the soil and rock. Groundwater will keep going to lower elevations until it reaches a layer of impermeable rock. When this happens, the impermeable rock acts like a dam and the water can't move down any deeper. So, it begins filling up the pores in the rocks above the impermeable
3 layer. A layer of permeable rock that transmits water freely is an **aquifer.** The area where all of the pores in the rock
4 are completely filled with water is the **zone of saturation.** The upper surface of this zone is the **water table.**

Science and MATH

In an experiment, you find that 100 mL of gravel (Total Volume) can hold 31 mL (Volume of Pore Spaces, VPS) of water. Calculate the percentage of pore space (porosity) using the following formula.

$$\frac{\text{VPS}}{\text{Total Volume}} \times 100 = \text{\% Porosity}$$

● REINFORCEMENT 32

NAME ____ DATE ____ CLASS ____

REINFORCEMENT — Chapter 7

The Action of Groundwater — Text Pages 182–187

Use the terms in the box to label the diagrams below.

artesian well	aquifer	column	stalactite
stalagmite	water table	zone of saturation	

1. stalactite
2. stalagmite
3. column

limestone
cave

4. water table
5. zone of saturation

Soil
Saturated with groundwater
Impermeable

6. aquifer
7. artesian well

Impermeable layer
Saturated permeable layer
Impermeable layer

32

▲ ENRICHMENT 32

NAME ____ DATE ____ CLASS ____

ENRICHMENT — Chapter 7

The Action of Groundwater — Text Pages 182–187

Do the activity and answer the questions on the lines provided.

Materials
- dropper
- water
- clear plastic cups or jars (3)
- 250 mL each of gravel, sand, and clay

Procedure
1. Half fill one cup or jar with gravel, the second with sand, and the third with clay.
2. Use the dropper and a small cup of water to place drops of water onto each material.
3. Record what happens to the water for each sample.
4. Note the rate at which each absorbed water.

Analyze and Conclude
1. Define the terms *permeable* and *impermeable.* **Permeable means that a substance has pores or openings that allow fluid to pass through. Impermeable means that a substance has pores that do not interconnect and fluids do not pass through.**
2. Which material was the most permeable? Least permeable? **Gravel is the most permeable. Clay is the least permeable.**
3. Define an aquifer. **An aquifer is a permeable rock layer with water filling its pores.**
4. Shale is a very impermeable rock made of clay. Sandstone is very permeable. Which of these two rocks would make the best aquifer? Explain. **Sandstone would because it is permeable.**

32

TYING TO PREVIOUS KNOWLEDGE: Have students recall from Chapter 5 that some substances in soil are leached from the *A* horizon to the *B* horizon, and from the *B* horizon to the *C* horizon. This would not be possible if soil were impermeable.

OBJECTIVES AND SCIENCE WORDS: Have students review the objectives and science words to become familiar with this section.

2 TEACH

Key Concepts are highlighted.

CONCEPT DEVELOPMENT

▶ **Since groundwater has no channels, how is water transferred to different locations within a groundwater system?** *It travels through interconnecting pores.*

▶ **What causes the speed of groundwater to vary from place to place?** *The permeability of the rocks affects the speed.*

MINI QUIZ

Use the Mini Quiz to check students' recall of chapter content.

1. **Water that collects in pores in soils and rocks is _____ .** *groundwater*
2. **Soils and rocks are _____ if water cannot pass through them.** *impermeable*
3. **A permeable rock that transmits water freely is a(n) _____ .** *aquifer*
4. **The area where all pores in a rock body are completely filled with water is the _____ .** *zone of saturation*

Science and MATH

The answer is 31 percent porosity. Challenge students to use this formula with different variables.

Wells and Springs

What's so important about the zone of saturation and the water table? Many people get drinking water from groundwater in the zone of saturation. Water wells are drilled down into the zone of saturation. Water flows into the well, and a pump brings it to the surface. A well must go down at least past the water table to reach water. Sometimes during dry seasons, a well goes dry because the water table drops. Having too many wells in one area can also cause the water table to drop. This happens because more water is taken out of the ground than can be replaced by rain.

There is another type of well that doesn't need a pump to bring water to the surface. An **artesian** (ar TEE zhun) **well** is a well in which water under pressure rises to the surface. Artesian wells are less common than other wells because of the unique conditions they require.

An artesian well requires a sloping aquifer located between two impermeable layers. Water must be able to enter the aquifer at the high part of the sloping aquifer. Water in the higher part of the aquifer puts pressure on the water in the lower part. If a well is drilled into the lower part of the aquifer, the pressurized water will come to the surface. Sometimes there is enough pressure to force the water into the air, forming a fountain.

In some places, the water table meets Earth's surface. When this happens, water flows out and forms a **spring.** Springs can be found on hillsides or any other place where the water table is exposed at the surface. Springs can be used as a source of fresh water.

MINI-Lab

How can you measure pore space?

Put 100 mL of sand in one beaker and 100 mL of gravel in another beaker. Fill a graduated cylinder with 100 mL of water. Pour the water slowly into the gravel and stop when the water just covers the top of the gravel. Record the volume of water used. Repeat the procedure with the sand. Which substance has more pore space—gravel, or sand? Why?

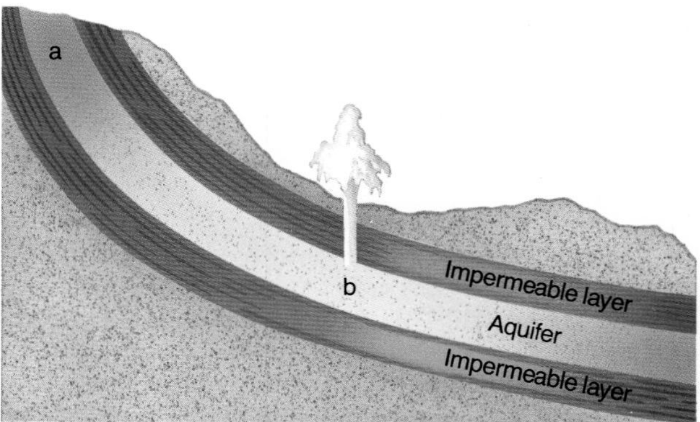

Figure 7-12. Water is forced out of the artesian well (b) because of pressure applied by the water in the aquifer at (a) above the well.

MINI-Lab

Materials: two 250-mL beakers, 100 mL sand, 100 mL gravel, graduated cylinder, water

Teaching Tips

▶The sand and the gravel mixtures should be of relatively uniform grain size and perfectly dry for best results.

▶Ask students to predict which material will allow more water to be poured in before reaching capacity.

Answers: Results averaged from the whole class should show that it takes about the same amount of water for either material. The two substances will be about equal in total amount of pore space. Although the individual pore spaces are larger among gravel grains, there are fewer of them when compared to the smaller but more numerous pore spaces among the sand grains.

CROSS CURRICULUM

▶**Health:** Ask students to discuss how pollutants from landfills, agriculture, and industry might affect the water quality of groundwater. Pesticides, solvents, degreasers, septic tank cleaners, and other toxic wastes get into soil and permeable rocks from runoff. Some of these pollutants become dissolved in groundwater. Pollutants in groundwater can cause harm to all organisms that use the water.

CONCEPT DEVELOPMENT

▶**What are two factors that can cause the water table to drop?** *Lack of rain and having too many wells in one area are two possible causes.*

▶Have a volunteer compare and contrast artesian wells and springs.

OPTIONS

PROGRAM RESOURCES

From the **Teacher Resource Package** use:

Activity Worksheets, page 64, Mini-Lab: How can you measure pore space?

Use **Laboratory Manual,** page 57, Capillary Action.

Use **Laboratory Manual,** page 59, Permeability.

ACTIVITY 7-2
Artesian Wells

Problem: *How does an artesian well work?*

Materials
- 30-cm plastic or rubber tube
- funnel
- protractor
- water
- scissors
- sink
- beaker
- tape

Procedure
1. Use the scissors to cut a hole 2 mm in diameter in the tube 2 cm from the end.
2. Put tape over the end nearest the hole you just made.
3. Copy the Data and Observations table.
4. Place the tube in the sink at a 45° angle as shown below. Put the end with the 2-mm hole down first.
5. Place a funnel into the top end and use a beaker to pour water in the tube in a steady stream.
6. Be careful not to pour water down the outsides of the tube.
7. Observe what happens at the 2-mm hole. Record your observations in the table.
8. Reduce the angle that you hold the tube to 20°. Record what happens at the hole.
9. Repeat Steps 3-6 for angles of 30° and 40°. Record your observations.
10. Increase the angle that you hold the tube to 60°. Record what happens at the hole.

Analyze
1. Which angle allowed the greatest flow of water out of the hole? Which allowed the least?

Conclude and Apply
2. Compare the inside of the tube to an aquifer. How are they similar?
3. Compare the rubber sides of the tube to impermeable rock. How are they similar?
4. What does the 2-mm hole represent?

Data and Observations

Angle	Observations
45°	
20°	
30°	
40°	
60°	

ACTIVITY 7-2
35-40 minutes

OBJECTIVE: Construct a model of an artesian well and **explain** how it works.

PROCESS SKILLS applied in this activity:
▶ **Observing** in Procedure Steps 7-10.
▶ **Forming Models** in Conclude and Apply Questions 2-4.
▶ **Inferring** in Conclude and Apply Question 5.
▶ **Interpreting Data** in Analyze Question 1.
▶ **Experimenting** in Procedure Steps 1-10.

COOPERATIVE LEARNING Form Science Investigation groups with three students per team. Have one pour the water, one measure the angle of the tubing, and one observe the 2-mm hole.

TEACHING THE ACTIVITY
▶ Have the tubing already cut to 30-cm lengths.

Troubleshooting: It is important that when water is poured into the tube, it completely fills the diameter of the tube. Use plastic tubing with a small diameter. If this is not possible, have the students hold end A of the tubing directly onto the faucet and do not use the funnel and beaker.

PROGRAM RESOURCES

From the **Teacher Resource Package** use:

Activity Worksheets, pages 59-60, Activity 7-2: Artesian Wells.

ANSWERS TO QUESTIONS
1. The angle with the greatest flow is 60°. The one with the least flow is 20°.
2. The inside of the tube is like permeable rocks in the aquifer. Water flows under pressure through the tube and the aquifer.
3. The plastic sides are like impermeable rocks through which the water cannot flow.
4. The hole represents the opening at the surface through which water flows.
5. Groundwater flowing between layers of impermeable rock is under pressure similar to water in a pipe. The water flows between the layers until it exits through a hole at the surface. If the outlet is lower than the intake, water will flow out as an artesian well.

CONCEPT DEVELOPMENT

▶ **How can cracks in limestone evolve into caves?** *Groundwater in the cracks dissolves the rock. Over time, the cracks enlarge to become caves.*

▶ **What is a stalactite?** *a long, pointed deposit that hangs from the roof of a cave*

Science and READING 

▶ Students will find out that geothermal energy is energy that comes from the internal heat of Earth. Sources of the energy include volcanoes, magma bodies, and certain tectonic boundaries.

▶ Limitations include restricted geographic areas, problems with salt and thermal pollution, and cost, among others.

Science and READING 

Read an article about geothermal energy and draw a diagram explaining how it works. Also, list the limitations of this energy source.

Hot Springs and Geysers

The water from most springs is cold. But in some places, groundwater is heated and comes to the surface as a **hot spring.** The groundwater is heated by rocks that come in contact with molten material under Earth's surface.

One of these places where groundwater is heated is Yellowstone National Park in Wyoming. In Yellowstone, there are hot springs and geysers. A **geyser** is a hot spring that erupts periodically, shooting water and steam into the air. Water is heated to very high temperatures, causing it to expand underground. This expanding water forces some of it out of the ground, taking the pressure off of the remaining water. The remaining water boils quickly, with much of it turning to steam. The steam shoots out of the opening like steam out of a tea kettle, forcing the remaining water out with it. Yellowstone's famous geyser, Old Faithful, shoots about 45 000 liters of water and steam into the air once each hour.

Caves and Sinkholes

Just as water is the most powerful agent of erosion on Earth's surface, it can also have a great effect underground. As mentioned in Chapter 5, when water mixes with carbon dioxide in the air, it forms a weak acid. This carbonic acid eventually becomes groundwater. One type of rock that is easily dissolved by this acid is limestone. As this acidic groundwater moves through natural cracks in limestone, it dissolves the rock. Gradually, the cracks in the limestone are enlarged until an underground opening called a **cave** is formed.

You've probably seen a picture of the inside of a cave, or perhaps you've visited one. Groundwater not only dissolves limestone to make caves, but it also can make spectacular deposits on the insides of caves. The long, pointed objects hanging from the roof of the cave in Figure 7-14 are stalactites.

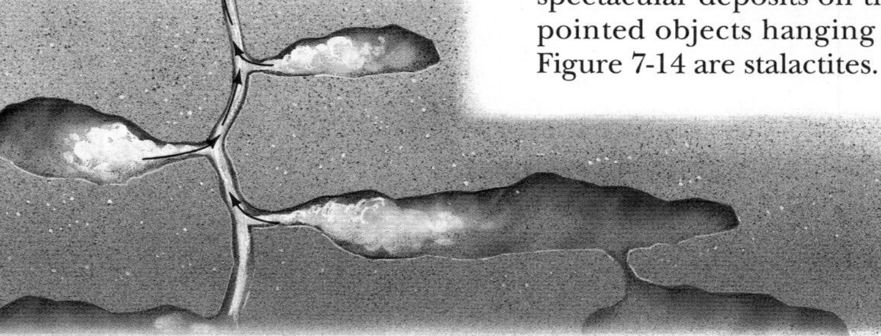

Figure 7-13. After a geyser erupts, water runs back into the underground openings where it is heated and erupts again.

OPTIONS

INQUIRY QUESTIONS

▶ **What is the difference between a geyser and other types of hot springs?** *Geysers erupt periodically. Other types of hot springs do not.*

▶ **Why don't geysers continuously spout?** *Water must trickle back down below the water table and become heated to form steam. The steam rises and makes the geyser spout. These processes take time.*

▶ **Describe how a cave can evolve into a sinkhole.** *As groundwater dissolves a limestone cave, the cave ceiling can become so thin that it eventually collapses. This new structure is a sinkhole.*

▶ **How would excessive pumping of groundwater by cities affect sinkhole development?** *The water table would drop and the ground above the drained area would collapse, creating a sinkhole.*

a

b

Figure 7-14. This large sinkhole in Florida caused major damage (a). Water containing dissolved calcite forms interesting features in caves. (b).

Water often drips slowly from cracks in the cave walls and ceilings. This water contains calcite dissolved from the limestone. If this water evaporates while hanging from the roof of a cave, a deposit of calcite is left behind. Stalactites form when this process happens over and over. Where drops of water fall to the floor of the cave, a stalagmite forms. Sometimes a stalactite and a stalagmite grow together to form a column.

If underground rock is dissolved near the surface, a sinkhole may form. A sinkhole is a depression that forms when the roof of a cave collapses. You probably never thought that all these things could happen to water. You can see that this portion of the water cycle is very complex. When rain falls and becomes groundwater, it might dissolve a cave, erupt from a geyser, or be pumped from a well to be used at your house.

How do sinkholes form?

SECTION REVIEW

1. How does water enter the groundwater system?
2. What causes a geyser to erupt?
3. What is the difference between a stalagmite and a stalactite?
4. **Apply:** Explain how a well can go dry.

Comparing and Contrasting — Skill Builder

Compare and contrast wells, geysers, and hot springs. If you need help, refer to Comparing and Contrasting in the **Skill Handbook** on page 683.

CHECK FOR UNDERSTANDING

▶ Ask questions 1-3 and the **Apply** Question in the Section Review.

▶ Have students describe how cave deposits form.

RETEACH

Cooperative Learning: Have Paired Partners use shoe boxes and salt-flour mixtures to make models of limestone caves and their deposits.

EXTENSION

For students who have mastered this section, use the **Reinforcement** and **Enrichment** masters or other OPTIONS provided.

3 CLOSE

▶ If possible, take students on a field trip to a local limestone cave.

▶ Under adult supervision, have students collect "stalactites" from places where water has percolated through cement structures. The roofs of underground parking garages and the underside of cement bridges may have these structures. Have students compare the origin of these deposits with true stalactites.

SECTION REVIEW ANSWERS

1. It soaks into the ground and collects among pores.

2. Water is heated to very high temperatures underground. As the water changes to steam, some of the water spews from the ground.

3. Stalagmites form on cave floors. Stalactites hang from cave ceilings.

4. Apply: This can occur when the water table drops either because of drought or because too much water was pumped from the ground.

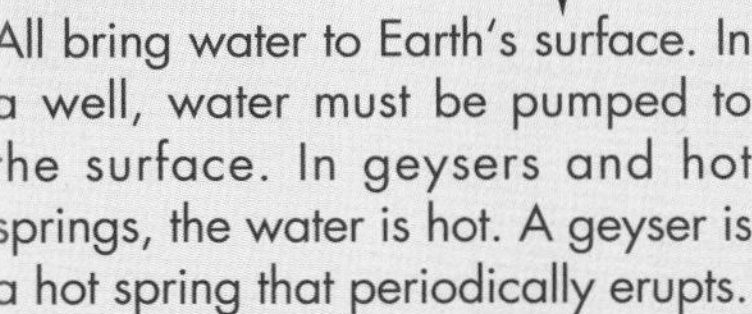

Skill Builder

All bring water to Earth's surface. In a well, water must be pumped to the surface. In geysers and hot springs, the water is hot. A geyser is a hot spring that periodically erupts.

ENRICHMENT

▶ Have students write short reports on Old Faithful and other features in Yellowstone National Park.

▶ Have groups of students make models that show how the position of the water table affects the formation of a well, geyser, hillside spring, stream, lake, hot spring, and artesian well.

PROGRAM RESOURCES

From the **Teacher Resource Package** use:

Critical Thinking/Problem Solving, page 13, Water Systems - Natural Resources.

Concept Mapping, pages 19-20.

Use **Laboratory Manual,** page 61, Carbon Dioxide and Limestone.

SCIENCE & SOCIETY

SECTION 7-4

PREPARATION

SECTION BACKGROUND

▶ According to the U.S. Water Council, by the year 2000, there will be an inadequate supply of water in 17 of the nation's 106 water supply regions.

1 MOTIVATE

▶ Take your class on a tour of the local water treatment plant.

▶ Lead a discussion about the need to conserve fresh water even in areas with adequate supplies.

TYING TO PREVIOUS KNOWLEDGE: Have students recall from Chapter 6 that many people live in areas prone to flooding. Explain that one way to reduce flooding is to build dams. Dams also make available large quantities of water to nearby communities.

OBJECTIVES AND SCIENCE WORDS: Have students review the objectives and science words to become familiar with this section.

7-4 Water Wars

New Science Words

water diversion

Objectives

- ▶ Give examples of ways people use water.
- ▶ Explain why some communities must rely on water diversion methods for their water supply.
- ▶ Identify a problem caused by water diversion.

Water As a Resource

How much water do you use each day? An average person in the United States uses about 227 liters each day. That's equal to the amount of liquid in 678 soft drink cans. How could you possibly use that much water? Think about it. You use it whenever you shower, bathe, and flush the toilet. Also, you use a lot of water indirectly. Water is used in making paper, plastic, and metal products that you use, and to irrigate crops that become your food. You can see that you use a lot of water each day.

Why is it easy to underestimate the amount of water you use every day?

Just imagine how much water a whole community of people uses each day. Do you know where your town gets its water? Some towns use nearby rivers and lakes, or they have wells. But, many communities don't have enough water to supply all their needs. Where do they get their water?

Figure 7-15. Water is a resource that many people take for granted.

OPTIONS

Meeting Different Ability Levels

For Section 7-4, use the following **Teacher Resource Masters** depending upon individual students' needs.

◆ **Study Guide Master** for all students.

● **Reinforcement Master** for students of average and above average ability levels.

▲ **Enrichment Master** for above average students.

Additional Teacher Resource Package masters are listed in the OPTIONS box throughout the section. The additional masters are appropriate for all students.

◆ STUDY GUIDE 33

NAME ______ DATE ______ CLASS ______

STUDY GUIDE Chapter 7

Water Wars Text Pages 188–190

Match the definitions in Column I with the terms in Column II. Write the letter of the correct term in the blank on the left.

Column I	Column II
e 1. Use of water for fishing or boating	a. agricultural use
c 2. Use of water for manufacturing	b. fresh water
d 3. Change of the natural flow of water	c. industrial use
b 4. Water that is not salt water	d. water diversion
a 5. Use of water to grow crops	e. recreational use

Read the sentences that follow and unscramble the terms.

1. When the natural flow of water is changed by people, it is called **trewa verdision.** water diversion
2. As the population grows, greater demand is put on Earth's **rewfserath** supply. freshwater
3. One reason people divert water is because they have a water **gheators.** shortage

Answer the following questions on the lines provided.

1. What change in population has made some people think about diverting water from the Great Lakes? The centers of greatest population growth are in the South.
2. How would that water diversion affect the states on the Great Lakes? There would be less water available for industry, agriculture, recreation, and home use.

 33

Figure 7-16. Reservoirs are constructed to hold water for when it is needed.

Water Diversion

Many towns are forced to get water from other locations. Dams and pipelines are used to divert water to other locations. When the natural flow of water is changed by people, it is called **water diversion.** Dams and pipelines have been used successfully in many places around the world. However, taking water from one location for another town leaves less water for the people at the original location.

TECHNOLOGY

Water Shortage in Florida?

The southern tip of Florida receives between 102 and 165 centimeters of rain per year. However, after evaporation and runoff, only one-fifth, or about 26 cm, of the rain seeps into the ground and shallow lakes. In addition to the loss of fresh water by natural processes, daily usage of water in some areas of southern Florida is about 6000 liters per person! This is a little over 14 times the national average.

In order to preserve and protect the much needed fresh water, a new technique has been implemented. Some farmers are now using purified sewage water to irrigate their crops. This water-cycling method is an alternative to irrigating crops with fresh water from wells.

Think Critically: What environmental factors contribute to a water shortage in Florida? What human factors contribute to the water shortage?

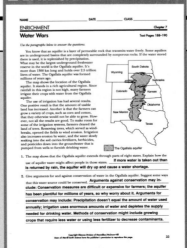

2 TEACH

Key Concepts are highlighted.

CONCEPT DEVELOPMENT

▶ Ask students these questions. **What is water diversion?** *people's changing of the natural flow of water* **What are two ways people divert water?** *by building dams and pipelines* **Why do some people think that water diversion is "unfair?"** *It leaves less water for people who would have originally received the water before the water was diverted.*

TEACHER F.Y.I.

▶ Almost all U.S. flatlands west of the 100th meridian (from Texas to North Dakota) receive too little precipitation to sustain agriculture without irrigation.

TECHNOLOGY

For more information, see "South Florida Water: Paying the Price" by Nicole Duplaix, *National Geographic Magazine,* July 1990, pp. 89-114.

▶ Have students compute the national water average usage based on the data given here. By dividing 6000 liters per person/day by 14, students should calculate the national average to be about 429 L per person/day.

Think Critically: Florida has a high rate of evaporation due to intense sunshine. Water usage per person is about 14 times the national average.

● REINFORCEMENT 33

NAME ________ DATE ________ CLASS ________

REINFORCEMENT — Chapter 7

Water Wars — Text Pages 188–190

Determine whether each of the following statements is true or false. Write "true" or "false" in the blank. Rewrite each false statement correctly on the lines provided.

true 1. An average person in the United States uses more than 200 liters of water each day.

false 2. All communities get their water from nearby lakes or rivers. **Some communities get their water from nearby lakes or rivers.**

false 3. Changing the natural flow of water is called water wars. **Changing the natural flow of water is called water diversion.**

true 4. Some farmers use purified sewage water for watering crops.

true 5. Pipelines are used to take water from one location to another.

false 6. Water diversion is not used now, but plans are being made to use it in the future. **Water diversion is used now.**

false 7. The southern part of the United States needs less water than it did in the past. **The southern part of the United States needs more water than it did in the past.**

true 8. Some people would like to bring Great Lakes water to states with a dry climate.

 33

▲ ENRICHMENT 33

NAME ________ DATE ________ CLASS ________

ENRICHMENT — Chapter 7

Water Wars — Text Pages 188–190

Use the paragraphs below to answer the questions.

You know that an aquifer is a layer of permeable rock that transmits water freely. Some aquifers are in underground basins that are completely surrounded by nonporous rocks. If the water stored there is used, it is replenished by precipitation. What may be the largest underground freshwater reserve in the world is the Ogallala aquifer. It's more than 1300 km long and holds over 2.5 trillion liters of water. The Ogallala aquifer was formed millions of years ago.

The map shows the location of the Ogallala aquifer. It stands in a rich agricultural region. Since rainfall in this region is not high, many farmers irrigate their crops with water from the Ogallala aquifer.

The use of irrigation has had several results. One positive result is that the amount of usable land has increased. Another is that the farmers can grow a variety of crops, such as corn and cotton, that they otherwise would not be able to grow. However, not all the results are good. To make room for some of the irrigation systems, farmers cleared the land of trees. Removing trees, which served as windbreaks, opened the fields to wind erosion. Irrigation also increases erosion by water, and the water slowly soaking into the soil carries fertilizers, herbicides, and pesticides down into the groundwater that is pumped from wells to furnish drinking water.

South Dakota
Wyoming
Nebraska
Colorado
Kansas
Oklahoma
New Mexico
Texas
The Ogallala aquifer

1. The map shows that the Ogallala aquifer extends through parts of eight states. Explain how the use of aquifer water might affect people in those states. **If more water is taken out than is returned by rain, the aquifer will dry up and cause a water shortage.**

2. Give arguments for and against conservation of water in the Ogallala aquifer. Suggest some ways that this water source could be conserved. **Arguments against conservation may include: Conservation measures are difficult or expensive for farmers; the aquifer has been plentiful for millions of years, so why worry about it. Arguments for conservation may include: Precipitation doesn't equal the amount of water used annually; irrigation uses enormous amounts of water and depletes the supply needed for drinking water. Methods of conservation might include growing crops that require less water or using less fertilizer to decrease contaminants.**

 33

CHECK FOR UNDERSTANDING

Ask students to explain the advantage and disadvantage of water diversion.

RETEACH

Divide the class into two groups. One group will represent people from a city that wants to build a dam to divert water to their community. The other group represents people living downstream from the proposed dam site. Have students role-play various people: city officials, farmers, industrial leaders, homeowners, and so on.

EXTENSION

For students who have mastered this section, use the **Reinforcement** and **Enrichment** masters or other OPTIONS provided.

3 CLOSE

Use the Flex Your Brain activity to have students explore WATER RIGHTS.

▶ Have students answer questions 1 and 2 in the Section Review.

SECTION REVIEW ANSWERS

1. consuming foods and beverages that contain water, flushing toilets, taking baths and showers, using products manufactured with it, eating foods that come from irrigated fields, relying on it to treat wastewater

2. Their demand for water is greater than their supply.

YOU DECIDE!

SCIENCE & SOCIETY

Some students will say that the canal should be built because people in the southwest need the water. Also, the Great Lakes contain a tremendous amount of water. The states that surround the lakes would probably do fine without some of the water. Others will feel that it would be unfair to divert the water as this could hurt these states economically.

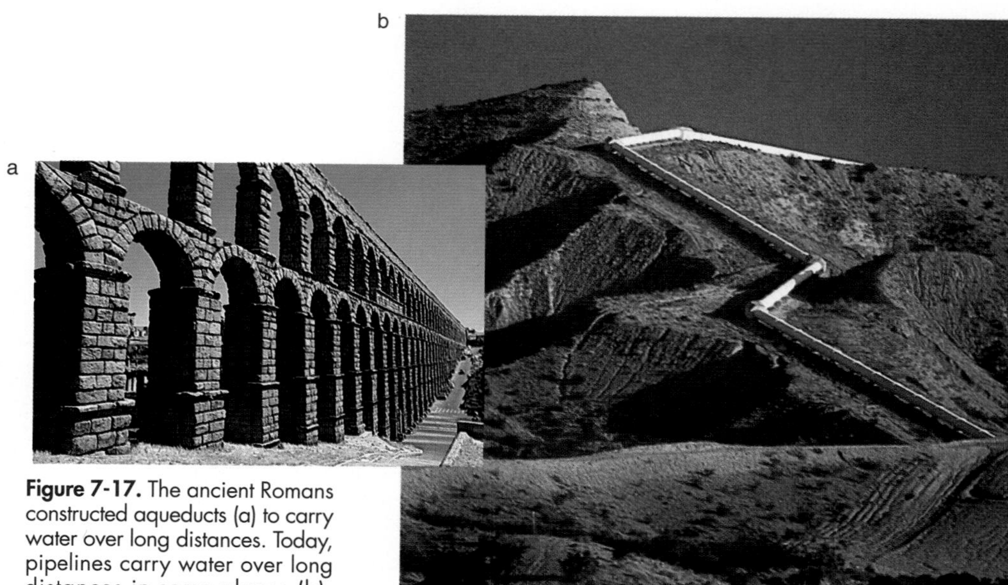

a b

Figure 7-17. The ancient Romans constructed aqueducts (a) to carry water over long distances. Today, pipelines carry water over long distances in some places (b).

Water diversion is becoming a big issue. In some areas of the United States, individuals, communities, and even states have gone to court over water rights. As Earth's population continues to increase, more and more demands are placed on Earth's freshwater supply. With more people, water needed for industrial, agricultural, and recreational uses increases.

SECTION REVIEW

1. What are four ways that you use water each day?
2. Why must some communities rely on water diversion methods for their water supply?

You Decide!

Each year, more and more people move to the southern United States. As a result, a large and growing quantity of water is needed in an already dry climate. To solve this problem, some people would like to build a giant canal to divert water from the Great Lakes. However, if the lakes are slowly drained, their states will suffer economically. Industries, recreation, and agriculture will be affected. Do you think a canal should be built?

OPTIONS

ENRICHMENT

▶ Have students research the effects that Boulder Dam has on Colorado River communities.

▶ Have students research the effects that communities like Miami, Florida are having on the water in the Everglades.

PROGRAM RESOURCES

From the **Teacher Resource Package** use:

Activity Worksheets, page 5, Flex Your Brain.

Technology, pages 9-10, City Water Systems.

Science and Society, page 11, Protecting an Aquifer.

CHAPTER

REVIEW

SUMMARY

7-1: Water on Earth
1. The water cycle is the movement of water between Earth and its atmosphere.
2. When water from the atmosphere doesn't soak into the ground or evaporate, it flows across Earth's surface as runoff.
3. The amount of runoff in an area depends on the amount of rain that falls and the time period over which it falls. Runoff is also affected by slope of the land and the amount of vegetation.

7-2: Development of River Systems
1. A river system can be compared to a tree whose "branches" include small streams. The main river can be compared to the tree trunk.
2. A drainage basin is the land area from which a river system gets its water.
3. Young streams flow swiftly through steep-sided valleys and erode the bottoms of their channels more than the sides. Mature streams erode the sides of their channels and form meanders. A stream in the old stage has less energy than a young stream because it moves very slowly. Broad, carved floodplains are common along old streams.

7-3: The Action of Groundwater
1. Water that soaks into the ground becomes part of an underground system called groundwater.
2. When the water table reaches Earth's surface, a spring forms.
3. Geysers are eruptions of steam and water caused by the heating of water underground. Caves form when water dissolves limestone.

7-4: Science and Society: Water Wars
1. People use water by drinking it, bathing, showering, and flushing the toilet.
2. Because many communities don't have enough water to meet their needs, they must divert water from other places.
3. Water diversion takes water away from other places that may need it.

KEY SCIENCE WORDS

a. **aquifer**
b. **artesian well**
c. **cave**
d. **drainage basin**
e. **floodplain**
f. **geyser**
g. **groundwater**
h. **hot spring**
i. **hydrosphere**
j. **impermeable**
k. **meander**
l. **permeable**
m. **runoff**
n. **spring**
o. **water cycle**
p. **water diversion**
q. **water table**
r. **zone of saturation**

UNDERSTANDING VOCABULARY

Match each phrase with the correct term from the list of Key Science Words.

1. water that flows over Earth's surface
2. land area drained by a river system
3. a curve in a stream channel
4. water that soaks into the ground
5. rocks through which fluids are unable to pass
6. the upper surface of the zone of saturation
7. hot springs that erupt
8. a large underground opening formed when limestone dissolves
9. the low flat part of a river valley
10. the changing of natural water flow by people

CHAPTER

REVIEW

SUMMARY

Have students read the summary statements to review the major concepts of the chapter.

UNDERSTANDING VOCABULARY

1. m
2. d
3. k
4. g
5. j
6. q
7. f
8. c
9. e
10. p

OPTIONS

ASSESSMENT

To assess student understanding of material in this chapter, use the resources listed.

COOPERATIVE LEARNING

Consider using cooperative learning in the THINK AND WRITE CRITICALLY, APPLY, and MORE SKILL BUILDERS sections of the Chapter Review.

PROGRAM RESOURCES

From the **Teacher Resource Package** use:

Chapter Review, pages 17-18.

Chapter and Unit Tests, pages 43-46, Chapter Test.

CHAPTER
REVIEW

CHECKING CONCEPTS

1. c
2. d
3. a
4. c
5. d
6. a
7. b
8. d
9. a
10. d

UNDERSTANDING CONCEPTS

11. stalagmite
12. young
13. carbonic
14. friction
15. hydrosphere

THINK AND WRITE CRITICALLY

16. More runoff would be produced from the lot. Plants in the yard would minimize runoff.
17. All the valleys are alike in that they are eroded by the river. The valleys differ, though, in that young river valleys have very steep sides, whereas mature and old valleys are broad and flat.
18. Both contain moving water. A groundwater system, however, has no channels like a river system.
19. Groundwater moves downward to the zone of saturation. The upper surface of this zone is the water table. Groundwater fills permeable rocks to create aquifers. Aquifers are bounded by impermeable rocks.
20. Water is evaporated from bodies of water on Earth. Then water vapor forms clouds in the atmosphere. The water vapor then condenses and falls to Earth as precipitation.

CHAPTER
REVIEW

CHECKING CONCEPTS

Choose the word or phrase that completes the sentence or answers the question.

1. The movement of water between Earth and the air is the ______.
   a. groundwater **c.** water cycle
   b. floodplain **d.** drainage basin
2. ______ affects the runoff in an area.
   a. Amount of rain **c.** Slope of the land
   b. Vegetation **d.** All of these
3. A layer of rock that water flows through is a(n) ______.
   a. aquifer **c.** well
   b. pore **d.** artesian well
4. The network formed by a river and all the smaller streams that contribute to it is a ______.
   a. water cycle **c.** drainage basin
   b. water table **d.** zone of saturation
5. Soils through which fluids can easily flow are ______.
   a. impermeable **c.** saturated
   b. geysers **d.** permeable
6. Underground rocks completely filled with water belong to the ______.
   a. zone of saturation **c.** lower water table
   b. limestone caves **d.** water diversion

7. A(n) ______ forms when the water table is exposed at the surface.
   a. meander **c.** aquifer
   b. spring **d.** all of these
8. Heated groundwater that reaches Earth's surface is a(n) ______.
   a. water table **c.** aquifer
   b. cave **d.** hot spring
9. At the outer edge of a drainage basin, streams are in the ______ stage.
   a. young **c.** old
   b. mature **d.** none of these
10. Water rises in an artesian well because of ______.
    a. a pump **c.** gravity
    b. none of these **d.** pressure

UNDERSTANDING CONCEPTS

Complete each sentence.

11. When water containing dissolved calcite drips in a cave, a(n) ______ can form on the cave floor.
12. A V-shaped valley is typical of a river in the ______ stage of development.
13. When water mixes with carbon dioxide, ______ acid is formed.
14. Water in a shallow part of a stream is slowed by ______.
15. Water on Earth's surface makes up the ______.

THINK AND WRITE CRITICALLY

16. Would you expect more runoff from a parking lot or a backyard with the same slope? Explain.
17. Compare and contrast the valleys of young, mature, and old rivers.
18. Compare a river system to a groundwater system.
19. Explain the relationship among the zone of saturation, the water table, and an aquifer.
20. Sequence the major events in the water cycle.

APPLY

21. Explain why the Mississippi River has meanders.
22. What determines whether a stream erodes its bottom or its sides?
23. Why would you be concerned if developers of a new housing project started drilling wells near your well?
24. If you had an artesian well, would the water come from a higher or lower elevation? Explain.
25. How is a tea kettle like a geyser?

MORE SKILL BUILDERS

If you need help, refer to the Skill Handbook.

1. **Making and Using Tables:** Use the table below to answer these questions. Which river has the highest flow? Which has the lowest flow rate? Which two rivers have nearly the same flow rate?

River	Waterflow (m^3/sec)
Mississippi	17 500
Brahmaputra	19 800
La Plata	79 300
Ganges	18 700
Congo	39 600
Yangtze	21 800
Amazon	113 330

2. **Interpreting Data:** Compare the rates of flow of the Brahmaputra and the La Plata Rivers.
3. **Making and Using Graphs:** Make a bar graph showing the flow of the five slowest rivers listed in the table at left.
4. **Outlining:** Make an outline that explains the three stages of stream development.
5. **Using Variables, Constants, and Controls:** Explain how you could test the effect of slope on the amount of runoff produced.

PROJECTS

1. Use the map of North America in Appendix G to locate the source and mouth of the Mississippi River. Then, carefully outline the boundaries of the Mississippi drainage basin and compute its approximate area.
2. Research the topic of water diversion. Discover as many pros and cons of this technique of supplying water to places as you can. Choose a stance and then debate the topic with a classmate.

APPLY

21. The Mississippi River is in the old stage of development and thus has meanders, which begin to form in a river's mature stage.
22. The energy of the moving water, which is related to a river's stage of development, determines whether a stream erodes its bottoms or its sides. Young streams erode downward; old streams erode their sides.
23. Water from your well could become diverted to the other wells, which could pose water shortage problems or a decrease in water pressure for you.
24. An artesian well is a well in which the source of the water is upslope from the point where the water flows to the surface.
25. In both a teakettle and a geyser, water is heated and turned into steam, which rises rapidly through a small opening.

MORE SKILL BUILDERS

1. Making and Using Tables: The Amazon has the highest flow; the Mississippi the lowest. The Brahmaputra and Ganges have similar flow rates.
2. Interpreting Data: The LaPlata is about 4 times faster than the Brahmaputra.
3. Making and Using Graphs: Students should use the Mississippi, the Ganges, the Brahmaputra, the Yangtze, and the Congo rivers in their graph. The range of waterflow shown on the graph is between 17 500 and 39 600 m^3/sec.
4. Outlining: Answers will vary, but students' outlines should include a detailed display of the three stages of development of a river.
5. Using Variables, Constants, and Controls: Answers may vary but a simple activity to measure runoff could be done using a shallow cake pan, some water, a timepiece, and a protractor. A horizontal pan with a certain amount of water could be the control. Constants would include the amount of water used and the rate at which it is poured. The dependent variable is the time it takes the water to reach the bottom of the pan. The independent variable is the slope.

CHAPTER

8 Views of Earth

CHAPTER SECTION	OBJECTIVES	ACTIVITIES
8-1 Landforms (2 days)	1. **Differentiate** between plains and plateaus. 2. **Compare** and **contrast** folded, upwarped, fault–block, and volcanic mountains.	**MINI-Lab:** *What does a profile of the landforms of the United States look like?* p. 198
8-2 Viewpoints (2 days)	1. **Differentiate** between latitude and longitude. 2. **Describe** how latitude and longitude are used to identify locations. 3. **Calculate** the time and date in different time zones.	**MINI-Lab:** *How do you use latitude and longitude?* p. 203
8-3 Maps (3 days)	1. **Differentiate** among Mercator, Robinson, and conic projections. 2. **Describe** how contour lines and contour intervals are used to illustrate elevation on a topographic map. 3. **Explain** why topographic maps have scales.	**Activity 8-1:** *Determining Elevation,* p. 213
8-4 Secret Maps Science & Society (3 days)	1. **Explain** why some maps have been intentionally distorted. 2. **Recognize** why some maps of the ocean floor have been classified as secret and why these maps would be valuable to some people.	**Activity 8-2:** *Reading Topographic Maps* p. 216
Chapter Review		

ACTIVITY MATERIALS

FIND OUT	ACTIVITIES		MINI-LABS	
Page 195 one globe or world map	**8-1 Determining Elevation, p. 213** plastic model landform water transparency clear plastic storage box with lid beaker metric ruler tape transparency marker	**8-2 Reading Topographic Maps, p. 216** Figure 8-16 paper Appendix H	**What does a profile of the landforms of the U.S. look like? p. 198** graph paper metric ruler paper pencil	**How do you use latitude and longitude? p. 203** world map or globe pencil paper

CHAPTER FEATURES	TEACHER RESOURCE PACKAGE	OTHER RESOURCES
Skill Builder: *Concept Mapping,* p. 201	**Ability Level Worksheets** ◆ ***Study Guide,*** p. 34 ● ***Reinforcement,*** p. 34 ▲ ***Enrichment,*** p. 34 **MINI-Lab Worksheet,** p. 74 **Concept Mapping,** pp. 21-22 **Transparency Masters,** pp. 21-22	**Color Transparency 11,** U.S. Physiographic Regions
Skill Builder: *Interpreting Scientific Illustrations,* p. 205	**Ability Level Worksheets** ◆ ***Study Guide,*** p. 35 ● ***Reinforcement,*** p. 35 ▲ ***Enrichment,*** p. 35 **MINI-Lab Worksheet,** p. 75 **Transparency Masters,** pp. 23-26	**Color Transparency 12,** Latitude and Longitude **Color Transparency 13,** World Time Zones **Lab Manual:** *Determining Latitude,* pp. 63-66 **Lab Manual:** *Time Zones,* pp. 67-68
Technology: *Rocks in 3-D!,* p. 209 **Problem Solving:** *A Climb to the Top,* p. 211 **Skill Builder:** *Measuring in SI,* p. 212	**Ability Level Worksheets** ◆ ***Study Guide,*** p. 36 ● ***Reinforcement,*** p. 36 ▲ ***Enrichment,*** p. 36 **Activity Worksheet,** pp. 66-67 **Critical Thinking/Problem Solving,** p. 14 **Cross-Curricular Connections,** p. 12	**Lab Manual:** *Comparing Maps,* pp. 69-72
You Decide! p. 215	**Ability Level Worksheets** ◆ ***Study Guide,*** p. 37 ● ***Reinforcement,*** p. 37 ▲ ***Enrichment,*** p. 37 **Activity Worksheet,** pp. 68-70 **Science and Society,** p. 12	**Lab Manual:** *Using a Clinometer,* pp. 73-76
Summary Key Science Words Understanding Vocabulary Checking Concepts Understanding Concepts Think & Write Critically Apply More Skill Builders Projects	**Chapter Review,** pp. 19-20 **Chapter Test,** pp. 47-50 **Unit Test,** pp. 51-52	**Chapter Review Software** **Test Bank**

◆ **Basic** ● **Average** ▲ **Advanced**

ADDITIONAL MATERIALS

SOFTWARE	AUDIOVISUAL	BOOKS/MAGAZINES
Latitude and Longitude, Teach Yourself by Computer. *Maps and Globes,* MICRO-ED, Inc. *Mapping the Earth,* Queue.	*Latitude, Longitude, and Time Zones,* film, Coronet/MTI. *Map Skills,* film, Coronet/MTI. *Landforms on the Earth's Crust,* slides, SVE.	Press, Frank and Raymond Siever. *Earth.* NY: Freeman, W.H. and Company, 1986. Sahu, Dibaker. *Land Forms, Hydrology and Sedimentation.* Columbia, MO: South Asia Books, 1990. Strahler, Arthur N. *Physical Geography.* NY: John Wiley & Sons, Inc., 1989.

CHAPTER

8

VIEWS OF EARTH

THEME DEVELOPMENT: Scale and structure are the major themes emphasized in this chapter. The structural differences among major landforms are the focus of Section 8-1. In the remaining three sections, students focus on understanding the scale and structure of maps.

CHAPTER OVERVIEW

- ▶**Section 8-1:** This section presents the structural differences among plains, plateaus, and mountains.
- ▶**Section 8-2:** Concepts discussed in this section include latitude and longitude. Determining the time and date in different time zones is also explored.
- ▶**Section 8-3:** Mercator, Robinson, and conic projections are defined and discussed. Students are introduced to interpreting and using topographic maps.
- ▶**Section 8-4: Science and Society:** Maps that have been intentionally distorted are described. The You Decide feature asks students to consider whether the United States government should release all Sea Beam maps to the public.

CHAPTER VOCABULARY

plains	International Date Line
plateaus	Mercator projection
folded mountains	Robinson projection
upwarped mountains	conic projection
fault-block mountains	topographic map
volcanic mountains	contour line
equator	contour interval
latitude	map scale
prime meridian	sonar
longitude	Sea Beam

CHAPTER

8 Views of Earth

194

OPTIONS

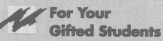

For Your Gifted Students

Have students draw a scale map of the school. They can measure the dimensions of the school with a meter wheel and then scale their drawings appropriately. For an additional challenge, have students add the school grounds to their maps.

This astronaut is using a jet powered maneuvering unit outside the space shuttle during a space walk. It's hard to imagine what it would be like to view Earth from space. Astronauts can see the outlines of some land masses from space. How can you become familiar with views of Earth?

FIND OUT!

Do this simple activity to find out more about views of Earth.

Using a globe or a world map, first look for natural features such as rivers and lakes that you may have heard of before. Can you find the Amazon, the Ganges, or the Mississippi River? Next, look at the bodies of water on Earth. Where is the Indian Ocean, the Sea of Japan, and the Baltic Sea? Then try to identify the continents. Where is Australia, South America, and North America? Locate your country. Where is your home on this view of Earth?

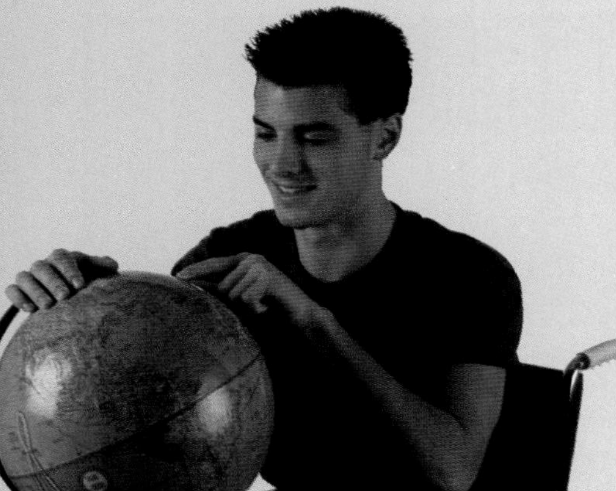

Gearing Up

Previewing the Chapter

Use this outline to help you focus on important ideas in this chapter.

Section 8-1 Landforms
- Plains
- Plateaus
- Mountains

Section 8-2 Viewpoints
- Latitude and Longitude
- Earth Time

Section 8-3 Maps
- Map Projections
- Topographic Maps
- Map Scale and Legends

Section 8-4 Science and Society
Secret Maps
- Intentional Distortion of Maps
- Sea Beam

Previewing Science Skills

- In the **Skill Builders**, you will make a concept map, interpret a scientific illustration, and measure in SI.
- In the **Activities**, you will observe, measure, use numbers, and interpret data.
- In the **MINI-Labs**, you will interpret a scientific illustration and make a scientific illustration.

What's next?

Now that you've seen one view of Earth, you should be ready to explore some others. You'll first learn about some landscapes found on Earth's surface. Then you'll see how exact locations on Earth are found using longitude and latitude. Section 8-3 shows you how Earth's irregular surface can be captured on a topographic map.

For Your Mainstreamed Students

Have students make dioramas of the different physiographic features of Earth. One diorama could represent a plain; another, folded mountains; and so on. Have students omit labels and allow other students to guess which landscape is being represented.

INTRODUCING THE CHAPTER

Use the FIND OUT activity to review basic geography with students. Inform them that they will be learning more about landforms and maps as they read the chapter.

FIND OUT!

Preparation: Obtain enough globes or world maps for each group of three students.

Materials: one globe or world map for every three students

Cooperative Learning: Form Science Investigation groups with three students per group. Have groups assist each other, if necessary.

Teaching Tips

- If time allows, have students locate places that are currently in the news.
- Have students locate their homes in at least four different ways. For example, "My home is east of city Y, west of city X, south of Canada, and north of the equator" might be one response.

Gearing Up

Have students study the Gearing Up feature to familiarize themselves with the chapter. Discuss the relationships of the topics in the outline.

What's Next?

Before beginning the first section, make sure students understand the connection between the Find Out activity and the topics to follow.

SECTION 8-1

PREPARATION

SECTION BACKGROUND

▶ Plateaus are one of the effects of mountain building. The Colorado Plateau of Arizona, New Mexico, Utah, and Colorado is associated with the Rocky Mountains. The Allegheny and Cumberland Plateaus of Pennsylvania, Kentucky, and Tennessee are associated with mountain building processes that formed the Appalachians.

▶ In this text, mountains are classified according to their most dominant characteristics. It should be noted that folding, faulting, upwarping, and igneous and metamorphic activity are processes involved in all mountain building.

1 MOTIVATE

▶ Display a relief map of North America. Have students compare and contrast the different landforms.

Cooperative Learning: Use the Numbered Heads Together strategy to have students compare local land features with other types of landforms they've seen or read about.

8-1 Landforms

New Science Words

plains
plateaus
folded mountains
upwarped mountains
fault-block mountains
volcanic mountains

Objectives

- ▶ Differentiate between plains and plateaus.
- ▶ Compare and contrast folded, upwarped, fault-block, and volcanic mountains.

Plains

What is a landform?

1 There are a lot of interesting landforms around the world. A landform is a feature that makes up the shape of the land at Earth's surface. Three basic types of landforms are plains, plateaus, and mountains.

What do you think of when you hear the word *plains*? You might think of endless flat fields of wheat or grass. That's true, many plains are used to grow crops. **Plains** are large, relatively flat areas that cover much of the United States. About one-half of all the land in the United States is plains.

Coastal Plains

2 Coastal plains are broad areas along coastlines that are called lowlands because of their low elevations. Elevation refers to distance above or below sea level. Sea level has zero elevation. The Atlantic Coastal Plain stretches along the East Coast of the United States. This area is characterized by low rolling hills, swamps, and marshes. A marsh is grassy wetland, usually flooded with water.

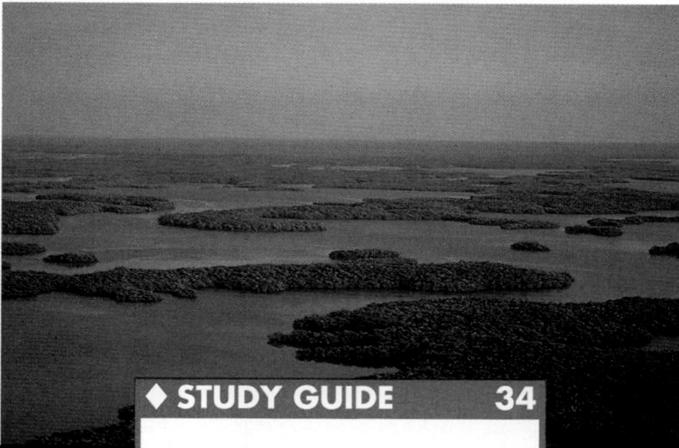

Figure 8-1. The Florida Everglades is a marsh area on a coastal plain.

OPTIONS

Meeting Different Ability Levels

For Section 8-1, use the following **Teacher Resource Masters** depending upon individual students' needs.

◆ **Study Guide Master** for all students.

● **Reinforcement Master** for students of average and above average ability levels.

▲ **Enrichment Master** for above average students.

Additional Teacher Resource Package masters are listed in the OPTIONS box throughout the section. The additional masters are appropriate for all students.

◆ STUDY GUIDE 34

NAME ______ DATE ______ CLASS ______

STUDY GUIDE — Chapter 8

Landforms — Text Pages 196–201

Answer the following questions on the lines provided.

1. What are the three basic types of landforms? **plains, plateaus, and mountains**
2. What are the four types of mountains? **folded, upwarped, fault-block, and volcanic**

Match each description in Column I with the correct term in Column II. Write the letter of the correct term in the blank at the left.

	Column I	Column II
b	3. Large, relatively flat areas of land	a. folded mountains
f	4. Large areas of horizontal rocks that have been uplifted and that rise steeply above the land around the rocks	b. plains
e	5. Distance above or below sea level	c. marshes
c	6. Grassy wetlands usually flooded with water	d. fault-block mountains
i	7. Broad, flat lowlands along coastlines	e. elevation
h	8. Land features that rise high above the surrounding land	f. plateaus
a	9. Type of mountains formed when rock layers are squeezed from opposite sides	g. volcanic mountains
j	10. Type of mountains formed when crust was pushed up by forces inside Earth	h. mountains
d	11. Type of mountains formed when huge tilted blocks of rocks are separated from surrounding rock by faults	i. coastal plains
g	12. Type of mountains formed when molten material reaches Earth's surface through a weak area in the crust	j. upwarped mountains

34

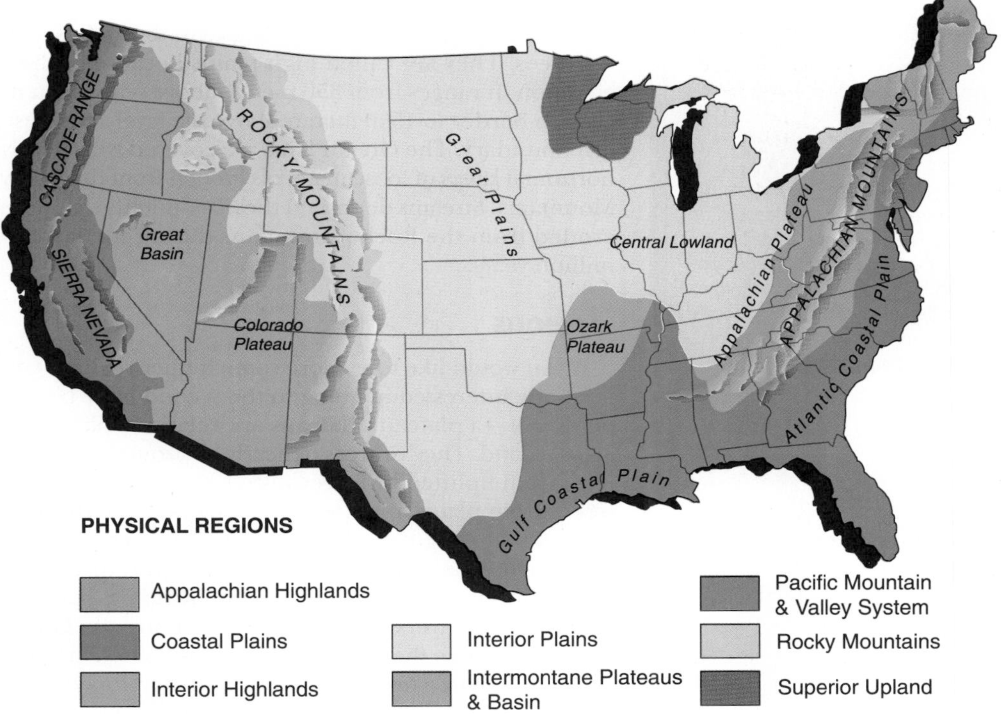

Figure 8-2. The United States is made up of eight major types of landforms called physical regions.

If you hiked along this plain, you would realize it isn't perfectly flat. Many low hills and valleys have been carved by rivers. What do you suppose caused the Atlantic Coastal Plain to form? It formed as land emerged from the Atlantic Ocean during the last few million years.

Another coastal plain is the Gulf Coastal Plain. It includes the lowland in the southern United States that surrounds the Gulf of Mexico.

Interior Plains

A large portion of the center of the United States is called the interior plains. They extend from the Appalachian Mountains in the east, to the Rocky Mountains in the west, to the Gulf Coastal Plain in the south. The interior plains include the rolling hills of the
3 Great Lakes area and the central lowland around the Missouri and Mississippi rivers.

What are the boundaries of the interior plains?

TYING TO PREVIOUS KNOWLEDGE: Have students recall from Chapters 5 and 6 that weathering, erosion, and deposition are constantly changing Earth's surface. In this section, students will see how these forces have helped create and/or change plains, plateaus, and mountains.

OBJECTIVES AND SCIENCE WORDS: Have students review the objectives and science words to become familiar with this section.

2 TEACH

Key Concepts are highlighted.

CONCEPT DEVELOPMENT

▶ After students have read pages 196 and 197, ask: **What created many of the low hills and valleys on the Atlantic Coastal Plain?** *rivers*

▶ Help students locate the Atlantic Coastal Plain, the Gulf Coastal Plain, and the Colorado Plateau on a map.

● REINFORCEMENT 34

NAME ______ DATE ______ CLASS ______

REINFORCEMENT Chapter 8

Landforms Text Pages 196–201

Use the words in each box to fill in the blanks of the paragraph below it.

plateaus	plains	Atlantic Coastal Plain	Gulf Coastal Plain
Great Plains	landforms	mountains	Coastal
Rocky Mountains	lowlands	flat	Interior

Features that make up the shape of the land at Earth's surface are called **landforms**. There are three basic types of landforms, **plains**, **plateaus** and **mountains**. Plains are large, relatively **flat** areas. In the United States, plains cover about one-half of all the land areas. **Coastal** plains are broad areas along coastlines. These plains are called **lowlands** because of their low elevation. The coastal plain along the East Coast of the United States is called the **Atlantic Coastal Plain**. The plain that surrounds the Gulf of Mexico is the **Gulf Coastal Plain**. **Interior** plains extend across the center of the United States. The **Great Plains** are high, flat, grassy, dry plains. They have been formed by sediment eroded from the **Rocky Mountains** over the last few million years.

plateaus	River	Colorado Plateau	Grand Canyon	uplifted

Relatively flat areas of land that rise steeply from the land around them are called **plateaus**. They are areas of nearly horizontal rocks that have been **uplifted** by forces within Earth. An example of a plateau in the United States is the **Colorado Plateau**, which lies just west of the Rocky Mountains. Here the Colorado **River** has cut deep into the rock layers, forming the **Grand Canyon**.

Name the four kinds of mountains and give examples of each.

1. **Answers for examples will vary; folded — Appalachians**
2. **upwarped — Black Hills**
3. **fault block — Grand Tetons**
4. **volcanic — Mount St. Helens**

34

▲ ENRICHMENT 34

NAME ______ DATE ______ CLASS ______

ENRICHMENT Chapter 8

Landforms Text Pages 196–201

BUILDING NEW LANDFORMS

Through the years people have changed the land. Pit mining has changed hills into basins. In some places, people have built mountains of trash. San Francisco, New York City, and Boston are examples of places where people have filled in bays with soil to extend their land area. Mexico City is built on an old lake that has been filled in with soil.

One of the best known examples of extending a coastal plain is The Netherlands. Over the centuries, the Dutch have built polders, or tracts of lowland reclaimed from the sea, lakes, or swamps. They have pumped water out of the area and built dikes made of sand and large rocks to hold the water back. Almost half of the country is formed from polders. The polders contain the richest farmland and the largest cities. The Netherlands has a population density of 393 people per km^2 (1989) compared to 26 people per km^2 in the United States.

0 25 50 75 km
North Sea
Waddenzee
Dike
POLDERS
Polder under construction
IJsselmeer
Side view below
SAND DUNES
Amsterdam
SAND PLAINS

Sand dune
North Sea
Sea level
Dike to the north
Waddenzee (sea)
Wieringermeer Polder
Dike
IJsselmeer (lake)
Northeast Polder
Dike
IJssel River
Polders
Salt water
Fresh water
12 m
6
0
-6
0 25 50 75 100 km

Study the map and the diagram that shows a side view of the elevation of the polders. Then answer the questions.

1. From the diagram, what is the approximate elevation of the Wieringermeer and Northeast polders? **6 m below sea level**
2. Of the area shown on the map, how much is made up of polders? **approximately two thirds**
3. Why do you think the Dutch are changing part of a freshwater lake into a polder? **With the high population density, they probably need space for people to live on and land to grow crops to feed the people.**

34

MINI-Lab

Materials: Figure 8-2, graph paper, metric ruler, paper and pencil

Teaching Tips

▶Before students begin, you may wish to demonstrate the technique by using an overhead projector, a transparency of Figure 8-2, a clear transparency to represent the student's paper, and a marking pen to show how the cross section should be made.

▶As an optional extension to this activity, you may want to have students construct a profile of the topographic map they develop in Activity 8-1. This will provide them with the opportunity to match their profiles with a three-dimensional model.

CONCEPT DEVELOPMENT

▶ Ask a volunteer to compare and contrast plains and plateaus.

▶ Have another volunteer make a rough sketch differentiating a plain from a nearby plateau.

TEACHER F.Y.I.

▶ The Colorado Plateau has been rising by about 0.03 cm a year for more than 10 million years. Today, it is nearly 2 km higher than surrounding areas.

MINI-Lab

What does a profile of the landforms of the United States look like?

Draw a cross section profile of the United States from the west coast to the east coast. Use Figure 8-2, Appendix G, and the descriptions of the landforms in Section 8-1. Place the edge of a piece of paper along Figure 8-2 and mark where the different landforms are located. Draw a profile of the landforms.

To the west of the Mississippi lowlands lie the Great Plains. The Great Plains are flat, grassy, dry plains with few trees. They are called high plains because of their elevation. It ranges from 350 meters above sea level at its eastern border to 1500 meters above sea level at its western boundary. The Great Plains are covered with nearly horizontal layers of loose materials eroded from the Rocky Mountains. Streams deposited these sediments that were eroded from the Rocky Mountains during the last few million years.

Plateaus

How are plateaus different from plains?

If you would like to explore some higher regions, you might be interested in going to the second basic type of 4 landform—a plateau. **Plateaus** are relatively flat raised areas of land. They're areas of nearly horizontal rocks that have been uplifted by forces within Earth. They are different from plains in that they rise steeply from the land around them. A good example of a plateau in the United States is the Colorado Plateau that lies just west of the Rocky Mountains. Here, the Colorado River has cut deep into the rock layers of the plateau, forming the Grand Canyon. Because the Colorado Plateau is located in a very dry region, only a few river systems have developed on its surface. If you hiked around on this plateau, you'd see a desert landscape.

Figure 8-3. Rivers cut deep into the Colorado Plateau.

OPTIONS

INQUIRY QUESTIONS

▶ **Explain how erosion helped create the Great Plains.** *Loose materials eroded from the Rocky Mountains were deposited by streams into horizontal layers over the last few million years.*

PROGRAM RESOURCES

From the **Teacher Resource Package** use:

Activity Worksheets, page 74, Mini-Lab: What does a profile of the United States look like?

Transparency Masters, pages 21 and 22, U.S. Physiographic Regions.

Use **Color Transparency** number 11, U.S. Physiographic Regions.

Mountains

Are plateaus still not high enough? How about hiking on a mountain ridge, or climbing steep rock faces? To do these activities, you must go to the third basic type of landform—mountains. Mountains rise high above the surrounding land, providing a spectacular view from the top. The world's highest peak is Mt. Everest in the Himalayan Mountains. It's more than 8800 meters above sea level. Mountain peaks in the United States reach just a little more than 4000 meters high. Mountains vary greatly in size and in how they are formed.

Folded Mountains

The first mountains we'll investigate are folded mountains. If you ever travel through a road cut in the Appalachian Mountains, you'll see rock layers that are folded. Folded rock layers look like a rug that has been pushed up against a wall. What do you think caused this to happen? Tremendous forces inside Earth force rock layers together. When rock layers are squeezed from opposite sides, rock layers buckle and fold into **folded mountains.** You'll learn more about the forces that create mountains in Chapters 13, 14, and 15.

How do folded mountains form?

The Appalachian Mountains are folded mountains that were formed in this way between 450 and 200 million years ago. They are the oldest mountains in North America and also one of the longest ranges, stretching from Quebec, Canada, south to Alabama. The Appalachians were higher than the Rocky Mountains at one time, but weathering and erosion have worn them down to less than 2000 meters above sea level.

Did You Know?

The highest mountain in the world is Mt. Everest in the Himalayan Mountains of Asia. At over 8800 meters, it is more than 19 times as tall as the Empire State Building in New York City.

Figure 8-4. The Appalachian Mountains are folded mountains.

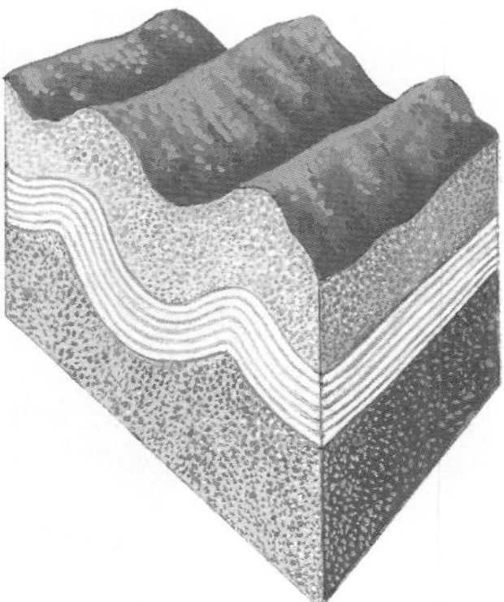

CROSS CURRICULUM

▶ **Social Studies:** Have students determine why more than half of the world's human population lives on plains. Students should discover that plains are often fertile farmlands.

MINI QUIZ

Use the Mini Quiz to check students' recall of chapter content.

1. **A _____ is a feature that makes up the shape of the land at Earth's surface.** *landform*
2. **The Great Lakes area is part of the _____ plains.** *interior*
3. **_____ plains are lowlands along coastlines.** *Coastal*
4. **Relatively flat raised areas of land are _____ .** *plateaus*

CONCEPT DEVELOPMENT

▶ Help students locate the Himalayan, Appalachian, and Rocky Mountains on a world map.

▶ **Why aren't the Appalachian Mountains as high as the Rocky Mountains?** *They are much older and weathering and erosion have worn them down.*

ENRICHMENT

▶ Several of the world's highest peaks are located in the Himalayas. Have students investigate this mountainous region. Have them investigate the following questions: Where are the Himalayas? What other famous peaks are near Mount Everest? What is it like to climb Mount Everest?

CONCEPT DEVELOPMENT

▶ Have students contrast the processes that formed the Appalachians with those that formed the Black Hills. Students should realize that the difference involves the direction of force—lateral forces formed the Appalachians while vertical forces were responsible for the formation of the Black Hills.

▶ **What is a fault?** *a large crack in rocks along which there has been movement*

CHECK FOR UNDERSTANDING

Have a volunteer explain that fault-block mountains form when huge blocks of rock become separated from surrounding rock by faults.

RETEACH

Use wooden blocks cut at various angles to demonstrate the formation of fault-block mountains.

EXTENSION

For students who have mastered this section, use the **Reinforcement** and **Enrichment** masters or other OPTIONS provided.

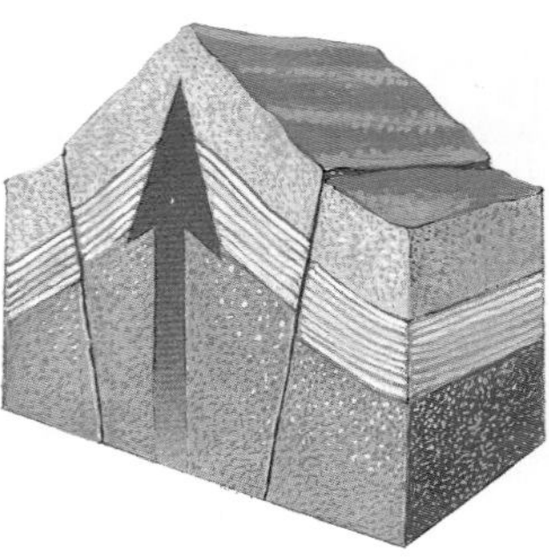

Figure 8-5. Some parts of the Rocky Mountains are upwarped mountains.

Upwarped Mountains

The southern Rocky Mountains in Colorado and New Mexico, the Black Hills in South Dakota, and the Adirondak Mountains in New York are **upwarped mountains.** These mountains were formed when crust was pushed up by forces inside Earth. Over time, the sedimentary rock on top of the crust was eroded, leaving behind the igneous and metamorphic rock underneath. These igneous and metamorphic rocks were then eroded to form sharp peaks and ridges as found in the southern Rockies.

How do upwarped mountains become sharp peaks?

Fault-Block Mountains

The Grand Teton Mountains of Wyoming and the Sierra Nevada Mountains in California formed in yet another way. **Fault-block mountains** are made of huge tilted blocks of rocks that are separated from surrounding rock by faults. A fault is a large crack in rocks along which there is movement. When the Grand Tetons were formed, one block was tilted and pushed up. The other block was pushed down. If you decide to go to the Tetons or the Sierra Nevadas, you'll see the sharp, jagged peaks that are characteristic of these mountains.

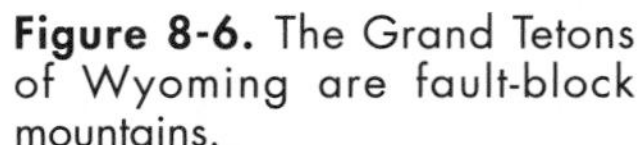

Figure 8-6. The Grand Tetons of Wyoming are fault-block mountains.

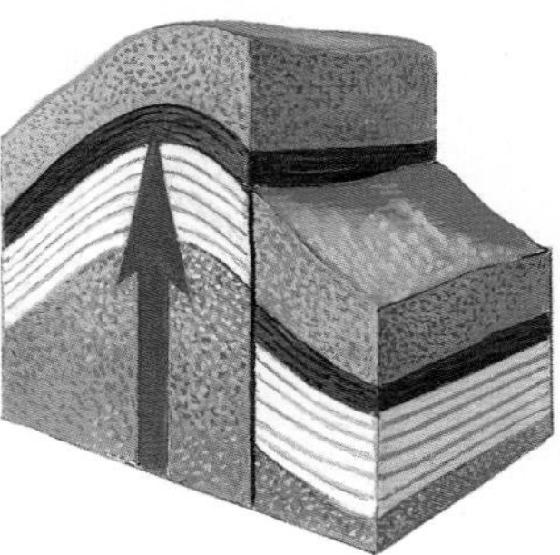

OPTIONS

INQUIRY QUESTIONS

▶ **What type of rocks make up the cores of upwarped mountains?** *igneous and metamorphic rocks*

ENRICHMENT

▶ Have students research the evolution of the Sierra Nevada Range in the western United States.

▶ Have students research the evolution of the Hawaiian Islands and present their findings as a pictorial report.

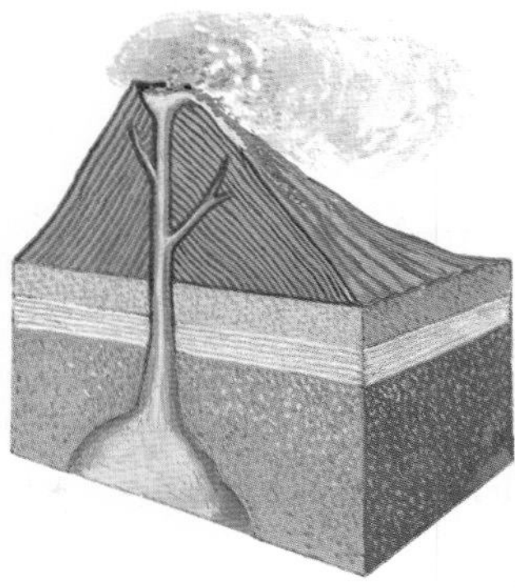

Figure 8-7. Mountains in the Cascade range of Washington and Oregon are volcanic mountains.

Volcanic Mountains

The last type of mountain that you could choose to explore is a volcano. Mount St. Helens in Washington state and Mauna Loa in Hawaii are two of the many volcanic mountains in the United States. **Volcanic mountains** begin when molten material reaches the surface through a weak area of the crust. The materials pile up, one layer on top of another, until a cone-shaped structure forms. The Hawaiian Islands are volcanic mountains formed on the floor of the Pacific Ocean. The islands are just the peaks of huge volcanoes that stick out above the water.

Plains, plateaus, and mountains offer a wide variety of landforms to explore. They range from low coastal plains, high desert plateaus, to mountain ranges thousands of meters high. Have you made up your mind yet? Where would you like to go?

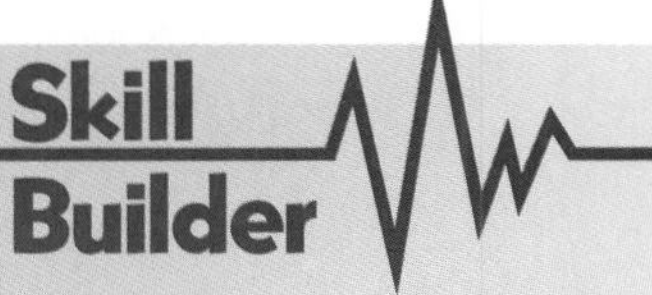

EcoTip

When camping in the woods, always make sure your campfire is out before leaving the campsite. Douse the fire with water and then cover it with dirt.

SECTION REVIEW

1. How do folded mountains form?
2. What's the difference between a plain and a plateau?
3. **Apply:** If you climbed the volcano Mauna Loa in Hawaii, why would it be inaccurate to say that you climbed from the bottom to the top of the mountain?

Concept Mapping — Skill Builder

Make a concept map that explains how upwarped mountains form. If you need help, refer to Concept Mapping in the **Skill Handbook** on pages 688 and 689.

CONCEPT DEVELOPMENT

► Use a world map to show students where major volcanic mountain chains are located.

► Demonstrate the spectacular nature of volcanoes by showing a film on volcanic eruptions.

3 CLOSE

► Ask questions 1-2 and the **Apply** Question in the Section Review.

► Obtain photos of the three basic kinds of landforms. Have students classify each landscape as a plain, plateau, or mountainous region. *National Geographic* is a good source of landscape photography.

SECTION REVIEW ANSWERS

1. They form when rocks squeezed from opposite sides buckle and fold.

2. A plain is a large, relatively flat area of land. A plateau is also flat, but it rises steeply from the land around it.

3. Apply: The base of this mountain is below sea level.

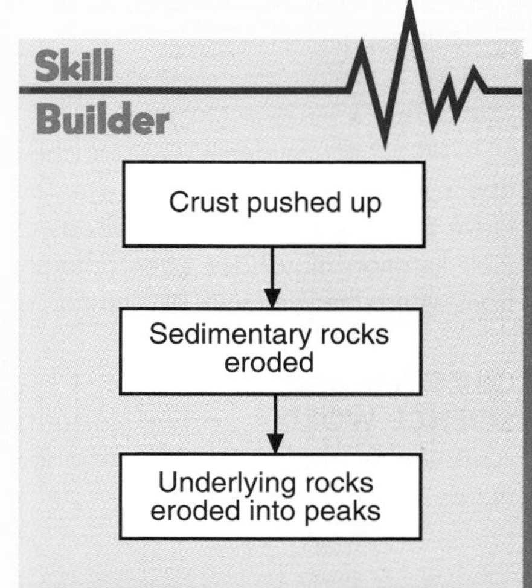

PROGRAM RESOURCES

From the **Teacher Resource Package** use:
Concept Mapping, page 21.

SECTION 8-2

PREPARATION

SECTION BACKGROUND

▶ *Latitude* is defined as the angle formed between the zenith line of any given point on Earth's surface and the plane of Earth's equator.

1 MOTIVATE

Cooperative Learning: Have globes available that Paired Partners can look at, touch, and explore. Ask one of the students from each pair to describe the location of an interesting place that he or she has visited or read about. The other student must locate the place from clues given by the partner.

FLEX Your Brain

Use the Flex Your Brain activity to have students explore LATITUDE.

TYING TO PREVIOUS KNOWLEDGE: Students have watched live sports and news events on TV. Have them recall that the time of day at their location may have been different from where the live event originated.

OBJECTIVES AND SCIENCE WORDS: Have students review the objectives and science words.

2 TEACH

Key Concepts are highlighted.

CONCEPT DEVELOPMENT

▶ **Lines of latitude are also called parallels. Why?** *The lines are parallel to one another.*

▶ **Demonstration:** Use a large map or globe to show students how to use latitude and longitude.

8-2 Viewpoints

New Science Words

equator
latitude
prime meridian
longitude
International Date Line

Objectives

- ▶ **Differentiate between latitude and longitude.**
- ▶ **Describe how latitude and longitude are used to identify locations.**
- ▶ **Calculate the time and date in different time zones.**

Latitude and Longitude

If you're going to explore landforms, you might want to learn how to find locations on Earth. If you wanted to go to the Hawaiian Islands, how would you describe their location? You might say that they're located in the Pacific Ocean. That's correct, but there's a more precise way to locate places on Earth. You could use lines of latitude and longitude. These lines form an imaginary grid system that enables points on Earth to be located exactly.

First, look at Figure 8-8. The **equator** is an imaginary line that circles Earth exactly halfway between the North and South Poles. The equator separates Earth into two

Figure 8-8. The degree value used for latitude is the measurement of the imaginary angle created between the equator, the center of Earth, and that location (a). Likewise, longitude is the measurement of the angle created between the prime meridian, the center of Earth, and that location.

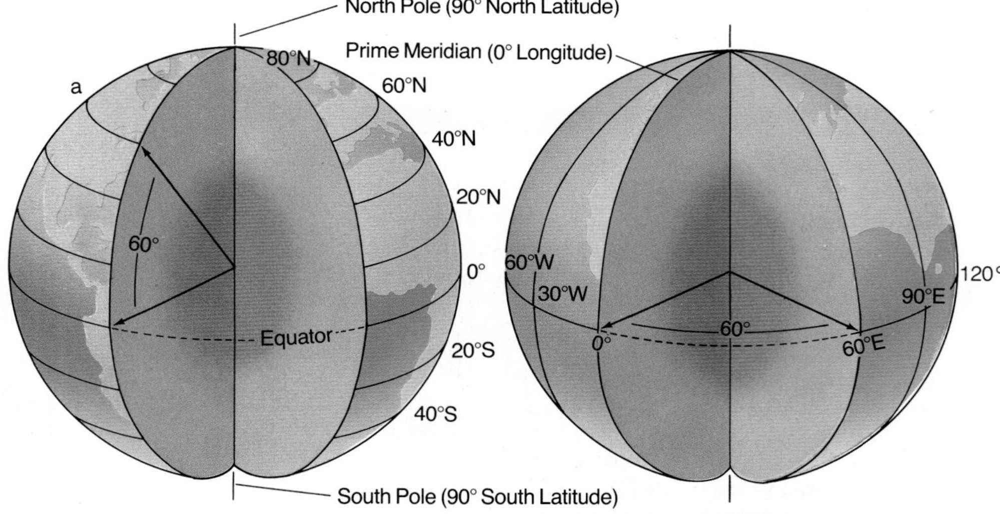

OPTIONS

Meeting Different Ability Levels

For Section 8-2, use the following **Teacher Resource Masters** depending upon individual students' needs.

◆ **Study Guide Master** for all students.
● **Reinforcement Master** for students of average and above average ability levels.
▲ **Enrichment Master** for above average students.

Additional Teacher Resource Package masters are listed in the OPTIONS box throughout the section. The additional masters are appropriate for all students.

◆ STUDY GUIDE 35

NAME ________ DATE ________ CLASS ________

STUDY GUIDE — Chapter 8

Viewpoints — Text Pages 202–205

Match the descriptions in Column I with the terms in Column II. Write the letter of the correct term in the blank on the left.

Column I

c 1. An imaginary line that circles Earth exactly halfway between the North and South poles
d 2. A reference point for east/west grid lines that runs through Greenwich, England, from the North Pole to the South Pole
e 3. A line at the 180 degree meridian
b 4. Lines that run north and south and determine locations east or west of the prime meridian
a 5. Lines that run parallel to the equator and determine north and south locations

Column II

a. latitude
b. longitude
c. equator
d. prime meridian
e. International Date Line

Use the words in the box to fill in the blanks.

15	24	spinning	lost
one	nighttime	gained	longitude

When it is daytime for half of Earth, it is **nighttime** for the other half. Time is always changing because Earth is constantly **spinning**. Earth is divided into **24** time zones. Each division is **15** degrees wide and has a **one** -hour difference in time from the previous 15° meridian. A meridian is a line of **longitude**. At the International Date Line, one day is **lost** going west, and one day is **gained** going east across the line.

 35

equal halves, called the Northern Hemisphere and the Southern Hemisphere. The lines running parallel to the equator are called lines of latitude. Because these lines are parallel to each other, they are also called parallels.
1 **Latitude** refers to distance in degrees either north or south of the equator. This system uses numbers with degree symbols, such as 59° north latitude.

The equator is numbered 0° latitude. The poles are each numbered 90°. Therefore, latitude is measured from 0° at the equator to 90° at the poles. Locations north of the equator are referred to by degrees north latitude. Locations south of the equator are referrred to by degrees south latitude. For example, Minneapolis, Minnesota, is located at 45° north latitude.

Latitude lines are used for locations north and south of the equator, but what about locations in east and west directions? These vertical lines seen in Figure 8-8 have two names—meridians and lines of longitude. Just as the equator is used as a reference point for north/south grid lines, there's a reference point for east/west grid lines. This reference point is the **prime meridian.** This imaginary line runs through Greenwich (GREN itch), England, and represents 0° longitude. In 1884, astronomers decided the prime meridian should go through the Greenwich Observatory near London. The observatory has since been moved, but the prime meridian remains in its original location in
2 Greenwich. **Longitude** refers to distances in degrees east or west of the prime meridian. Points west of the prime meridian have west longitude measured from 0° to 180°, while points east of the prime meridian have east longitude, also measured from 0° to 180°.

The prime meridian does not circle Earth like the equator does. It runs from the North Pole through Greenwich, England, to the South Pole. The line of longitude on the opposite side of Earth from the prime meridian where east lines of longitude meet west lines of longitude is the 180°
3 meridian. This line is also known as the International Date Line, which you will learn about on page 205.

Using latitude and longitude, you can locate Hawaii more accurately as seen in Figure 8-9. Hawaii is located at 20° north latitude and about 155° west longitude. Read on to see how longitude lines are used to tell time on Earth.

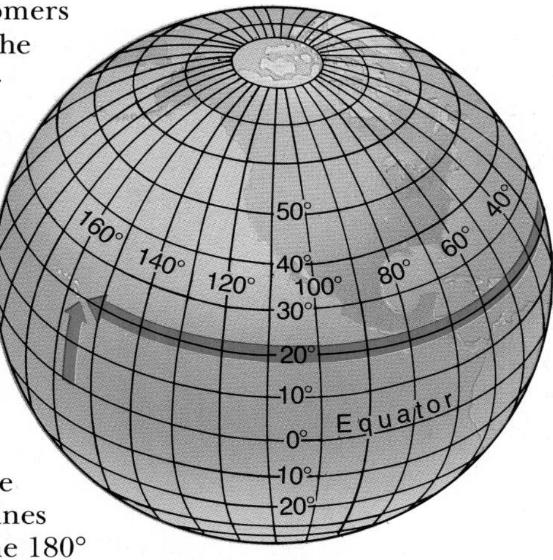

Figure 8-9. Hawaii is located at about 20°N, 155°W.

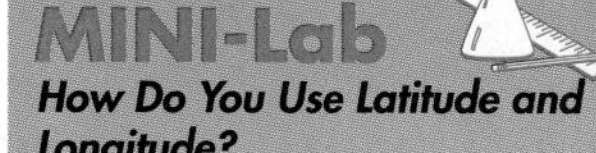

MINI-Lab

How Do You Use Latitude and Longitude?

On a world map that shows latitude and longitude, identify the cities that have the following coordinates:

1. 56°N; 38°E 4. 13°N; 101°E
2. 34°S; 18°E 5. 38°N; 9°W
3. 23°N; 82°W

Now determine the latitude and longitude coordinates of the following cities:

6. London, England
7. Melbourne, Australia
8. Buenos Aires, Argentina
9. Paris, France
10. Anchorage, Alaska

List your answers on a sheet of paper and compare them with your classmates'.

● REINFORCEMENT 35

NAME ________ DATE ________ CLASS ________

REINFORCEMENT Chapter 8

Viewpoints Text Pages 202–205

Study the map. Write the letter of each map feature or location on the line provided.

West (W) 180° 150° 120° 90° 60° 30° 0° 30° 60° 90° 120° 150° 180° East (E)

90° 60° 45° 30° 15° 0° 15° 30° 45° 60° 90°

A B C D E F G H I J K L M N O

N W E S

A 1. equator
C 2. prime meridian
F 3. International Date Line
K 4. 90° east longitude
J 5. 15° north latitude
I 6. 45° south latitude
L 7. 165° west longitude
N 8. 15° south latitude, 60° east longitude
M 9. 30° north latitude, 120° west longitude
O 10. 30° south latitude, 15° east longitude

The map shows longitude in the 15 degree increments that are approximate to the time zones. Use the lines of longitude to estimate the time for the following places.

6:00 A.M. 11. You're at point B on the map. It's 7:00 A.M. What time would it be at point E?

10:00 A.M. 12. You're at point H on the map. It's 5:00 P.M. What time would it be at point G?

12 midnight 13. You're at point H on the map. It's 7:00 P.M. What time would it be at point D?

gain 14. You're at point J and you travel eastward to point L. Do you lose or gain a day?

 35

▲ ENRICHMENT 35

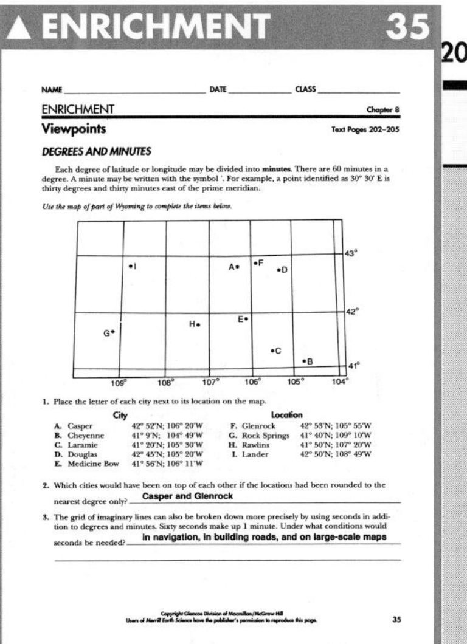

NAME ________ DATE ________ CLASS ________

ENRICHMENT Chapter 8

Viewpoints Text Pages 202–205

DEGREES AND MINUTES

Each degree of latitude or longitude may be divided into **minutes**. There are 60 minutes in a degree. A minute may be written with the symbol '. For example, a point identified as 30° 30' E is thirty degrees and thirty minutes east of the prime meridian.

Use the map of part of Wyoming to complete the items below.

43° 42° 41°
109° 108° 107° 106° 105° 104°
I A F D G H E C B

1. Place the letter of each city next to its location on the map.

City	Location	City	Location
A. Casper	42° 52'N; 106° 20'W	F. Glenrock	42° 53'N; 105° 55'W
B. Cheyenne	41° 9'N; 104° 49'W	G. Rock Springs	41° 40'N; 109° 10'W
C. Laramie	41° 20'N; 105° 30'W	H. Rawlins	41° 50'N; 107° 20'W
D. Douglas	42° 45'N; 105° 20'W	I. Lander	42° 50'N; 108° 49'W
E. Medicine Bow	41° 56'N; 106° 11'W		

2. Which cities would have been on top of each other if the locations had been rounded to the nearest degree only? **Casper and Glenrock**

3. The grid of imaginary lines can also be broken down more precisely by using seconds in addition to degrees and minutes. Sixty seconds make up 1 minute. Under what conditions would seconds be needed? **in navigation, in building roads, and on large-scale maps**

 35

MINI-Lab

Materials: world map or globe, pencil and paper

Teaching Tips

► Have students complete this activity as Paired Partners.

► After students have found the answers to the questions given, have them compare them to the answers obtained by other groups.

► **Answers**: (1) Moscow, Russia; (2) Cape Town, South Africa; (3) Havana, Cuba; (4) Bangkok, Thailand; (5) Lisbon, Portugal; (6) 51°N; 1°W; (7) 38°S; 145°E, (8) 35°S; 59°W, (9) 49°N; 2°E, (10) 63°N; 150°W

REVEALING MISCONCEPTIONS

Ask students whether or not lines of longitude and latitude intersect at right angles. Have students examine a globe to determine that although lines of latitude are parallel to one another, lines of longitude are not. Lines of longitude converge at the poles and are farthest apart at the equator.

MINI QUIZ

Use the Mini Quiz to check students' recall of chapter content.

1. **Lines of _____ are used to locate places north and south of the equator.** *latitude*
2. **Lines of _____ are used to locate points east and west of the prime meridian.** *longitude*
3. **The 180° meridian is also called the _____.** *International Date Line*

PROGRAM RESOURCES

From the **Teacher Resource Package** use:

Activity Worksheets, page 75, Mini-Lab: How do you use Latitude and Longitude?

Transparency Masters, pages 23 and 24, Latitude and Longitude.

Use **Color Transparency** number 12, Latitude and Longitude.

Use **Laboratory Manual,** page 63, Determining Latitude.

CONCEPT DEVELOPMENT

▶ **How many time zones are there in the world? Why?** *Earth rotates once every 24 hours. Thus, there are 24 time zones.*

▶ **How many time zones are there in the United States?** *five*

▶ **Demonstration:** Demonstrate the concept of Earth time using a rotating globe and a bright light to represent the sun. Point out that noon, midnight, 6 PM, and 6 AM remain stationary with respect to the sun, while positions on Earth's surface rotate toward or away from a specific time.

TEACHER F.Y.I.

▶ Daylight saving time was established in 1918, during World War I, as a way to save fuel. It is observed by adjusting clocks ahead in the spring to extend daylight hours.

CROSS CURRICULUM

▶ **Biology:** Have students research how organisms use biological clocks to tell time.

CHECK FOR UNDERSTANDING

▶ Ask questions 1-3 and the **Apply** Question in the Section Review.

Cooperative Learning: Have Paired Partners determine the time differences between cities with similar latitudes but different longitudes and cities with the same longitude but different latitudes.

RETEACH

To help students with the concept of time zones, obtain a globe that has an indicator showing time zones.

EXTENSION

For students who have mastered this section, use the **Reinforcement** and **Enrichment** masters or other OPTIONS provided.

What is Earth time based on?

Earth Time

What time is it right now? That depends on where you are on Earth. We keep track of time by measuring Earth's movement in relation to the sun. Earth rotates one full turn every 24 hours. When one half of Earth is facing the sun, the other half is facing away from it. For the half facing the sunlight, it's daytime. For the half in darkness, it's nighttime. Half of Earth is experiencing sunlight, while the other half is in darkness. And because Earth is constantly spinning, time is always changing.

How can you know what time it is at any particular location on Earth? Earth is divided into time zones. Because Earth takes 24 hours to rotate once, it is divided into 24 time zones, each one hour different. Each time zone is 15 degrees wide. There are six different time zones in the United States. Because Earth is rotating, the sun rises earlier in Atlanta, Georgia, than it does in Los Angeles, California. When the sun is rising in Atlanta at 7:00 AM, it's still dark in Los Angeles, and the time is earlier—4:00 AM. If you lived in Los Angeles, and were in your first or second period class, a student in Atlanta would be at lunch.

Did You Know?

If you left London on the Concord jet airplane, at 8 AM, London time, you would arrive in New York at 6 AM, New York time. The Concord can make the trip through five time zones in just three hours, which means you would gain two hours.

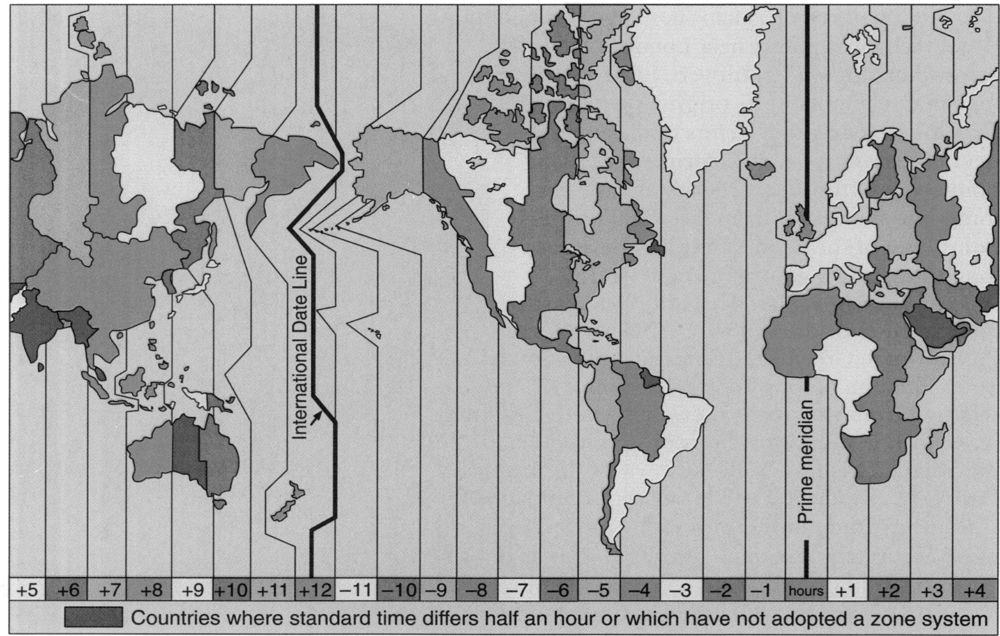

Figure 8-10. Time zones are roughly determined by lines of longitude.

OPTIONS

INQUIRY QUESTIONS

▶ **Explain why each time zone is 15° wide.** *Because Earth is nearly circular, there are 360° of longitude. Each time zone is 1/24 of 360°, or 15° wide.*

▶ **How many degrees of longitude separate two cities that are five hours apart in time?** *75°*

PROGRAM RESOURCES

From the **Teacher Resource Package** use:

Transparency Masters, pages 25 and 26, World Time Zones.

Use **Color Transparency** number 13, World Time Zones.

Use **Laboratory Manual,** page 67, Time Zones.

As you can see in Figure 8-10, the time zones do not strictly follow lines of longitude. Time zone boundaries have been adjusted in local areas. For example, if a city were split by a time zone boundary, great confusion would result. In such a situation, the time zone boundary is moved to outside of the city.

We all know that a day ends and the next day begins at 12 midnight. If it is 11:59 PM Tuesday, two minutes later it is 12:01 AM Wednesday. Over the period of a day, every time zone experiences this transition from one day to the next. The calendar advances to the next day in each time zone at midnight.

But if you were traveling around the world, you'd have a harder time keeping track of the days. You gain or lose time at each time zone you travel through until at some point you gain or lose a whole day. The **International Date Line** is the 180 degree meridian that is the transition line for calendar days. The International Date Line is one-half of one day, or 12 time zones, from the prime meridian. If you were traveling west across the International Date Line, you would lose one day. If you were traveling east across the International Date Line, you would gain one day.

Exploring different locations on Earth could be tricky. If you moved from Los Angeles to Atlanta without changing your watch, you would be three hours late to school the first day.

Science and MATH

Moscow, Soviet Union, is the third time zone east of the prime meridian, and Washington D.C. is the fifth time zone west of the prime meridian. If both presidents work in their offices from 8 AM to 5 PM, what time must the President of the United States call Moscow to reach the President of the Soviet Union?

What meridian is directly opposite the prime meridian?

SECTION REVIEW

1. What is the difference between latitude and longitude?
2. What is the longitude and latitude of New Orleans, Louisiana?
3. If it's 9:00 AM in Maine, what time is it in California?
4. **Apply:** How could you go fishing on Monday, fish for an hour on Sunday, and return on Monday.

Interpreting Scientific Illustrations — Skill Builder

Use Appendix F on page 668 to find the approximate longitude and latitude of the following locations: the Hawaiian Islands; Sri Lanka; Tokyo, Japan; London, England; and the Falkland Islands. If you need help, refer to Interpreting Scientific Illustrations in the **Skill Handbook** on page 693.

Science and MATH

There is a time difference of 8 hours between Moscow and Washington. The call must be made between 8 AM and 9 AM EST.

3 CLOSE

▶ Invite a travel agent or an airplane pilot to talk to your class about why understanding time zone differences is important to his or her job.

FLEX Your Brain

Use the Flex Your Brain activity to have students explore the INTERNATIONAL DATE LINE.

SECTION REVIEW ANSWERS

1. Latitude refers to distances north and south of the equator. Longitude is a measure of distances east and west of the prime meridian.
2. 90° west longitude, 30° north latitude
3. 6:00 AM
4. Apply: If you lived just west of the International Date Line, you could fish in waters just east of the International Date Line, and return home back across the date line at night.

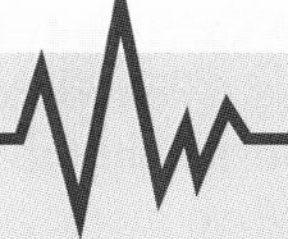

Skill Builder

Hawaii: 20°N, 157°W
Sri Lanka: 8°N, 82°E
Tokyo: 35°N, 139°E
London: 51°N, 0.1°W
Falkland Islands: 50°S, 61°W

INQUIRY QUESTIONS

▶ **Look at Figure 8-10. If it's Friday, May 10 in Japan, what day is it in California?** *Thursday, May 9*

▶ **Suppose you lived in Washington, DC, and you wanted to watch a live volleyball match on TV between Russia and the U.S. The game was being played in Moscow on January 6 at 8:00 PM. What would be the local time in Washington, DC, at the start of the game?** *1:00 PM on January 6*

ENRICHMENT

▶ Have students research jet lag.

▶ Have students research when and why time zones were created, and why Greenwich, England, was chosen as the location for the prime meridian.

PROGRAM RESOURCES

From the **Teacher Resource Package** use:

Activity Worksheets, page 5, Flex Your Brain.

SECTION 8-3

PREPARATION

SECTION BACKGROUND

▶ The major publisher of topographic maps in the U.S. is the United States Geological Survey (USGS). Other map publishers include the Department of Defense, the Department of Agriculture, and the Forest Service.

▶ Standard maps produced by the USGS are called quadrangles. Quadrangle maps are bounded by parallels and meridians. The maps are named for obvious features within the area shown on the map. No two quadrangles of the same series in the same state can have the same name.

PREPLANNING

▶ To prepare for Activity 8-1, obtain the following items for each group of students: plastic model landforms, transparencies, clear plastic storage boxes with lids, beakers, metric rulers, tape, and glass markers.

1 MOTIVATE

Cooperative Learning: Have Paired Partners sketch a map of the neighborhood around the school. When maps are completed, have partners exchange with other partners. Allow students to compare and contrast at least three or four maps. After examining the maps, students should realize the need for a uniform system of representing features at Earth's surface and the importance of accurate observations and measurements.

▶ Use a photo of Earth from space to discuss why, due to Earth's size, globes and maps must be used to represent physical and cultural features of the planet's surface.

8-3 Maps

New Science Words

Mercator projection
Robinson projection
conic projection
topographic map
contour line
contour interval
map scale

Objectives

- ▶ **Differentiate between Mercator, Robinson, and conic projections.**
- ▶ **Describe how contour lines and contour intervals are used to illustrate elevation on a topographic map.**
- ▶ **Explain why topographic maps have scales.**

Map Projections

One of the things that you would take with you if you went hiking is a map. It would sure be hard to get to a certain mountain without a map showing where it is. There are road maps, political maps showing the boundaries between states and countries, and maps that show physical features such as mountains and valleys. They all have one thing in common. They are models of Earth's surface. But because Earth's surface is curved, it's not easy to represent on a flat piece of paper.

Maps are made using projections. A map projection is made when points and lines on a globe's surface are transferred onto paper. There are several different ways to

Figure 8-11. A Mercator projection exaggerates the areas near the poles.

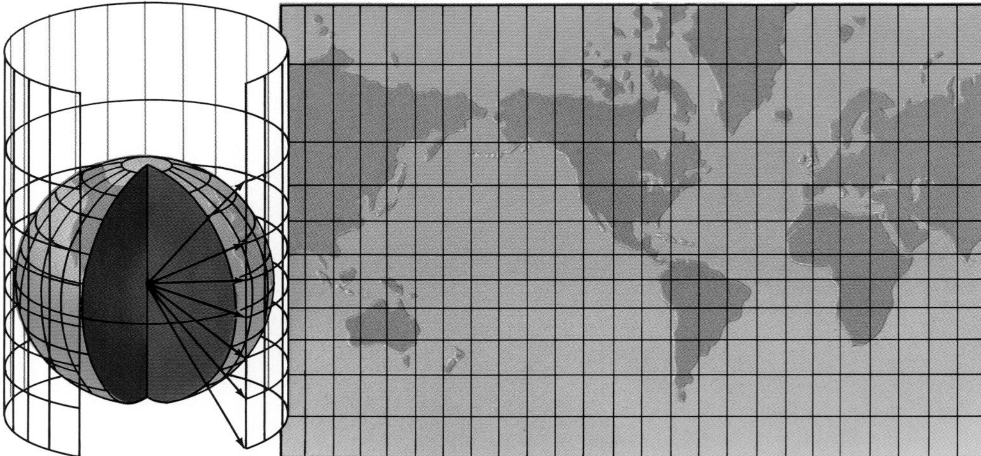

OPTIONS

Meeting Different Ability Levels

For Section 8-3, use the following **Teacher Resource Masters** depending upon individual students' needs.

◆ **Study Guide Master** for all students.

● **Reinforcement Master** for students of average and above average ability levels.

▲ **Enrichment Master** for above average students.

Additional Teacher Resource Package masters are listed in the OPTIONS box throughout the section. The additional masters are appropriate for all students.

◆ STUDY GUIDE 36

NAME ________ DATE ________ CLASS ________

STUDY GUIDE — Chapter 8

Maps — Text Pages 206–212

Use the words in the box to fill in the blanks.

models	small areas	distorted	larger
legend	projection	Robinson projection	contour
Mercator projection	globe	topographic	scale
flat	curved	contour interval	conic projection

Maps are **models** of Earth's surface. The best model, because of Earth's shape, would be a **globe**. A convenient paper model of Earth, however, would be a map **projection**. On a map projection, the points and lines of Earth's **curved** surface are transferred onto a **flat** piece of paper. A **Mercator projection** shows all lines of latitude and all lines of longitude as parallel lines. This projection distorts areas near the poles, showing them **larger** than they actually are. On a **Robinson projection**, lines of latitude are parallel and lines of longitude are curved. Landmasses near the poles are not **distorted** on this type of map projection. By projecting points and lines from a globe onto a cone, a **conic projection** may be drawn. This projection is used to make accurate maps of **small areas**.

A **topographic** map shows the changes in elevation of Earth's surface. This map shows **contour** lines which connect points on Earth's surface of equal elevation. The lines are drawn at specific intervals. The distance between the contour lines is the **contour interval**. A map **scale** gives the relationship between the distances on the map and the actual distances on Earth's surface. The map **legend** explains what the symbols used on the topographic map mean.

36

Figure 8-12. A Robinson projection is less distorted near the poles.

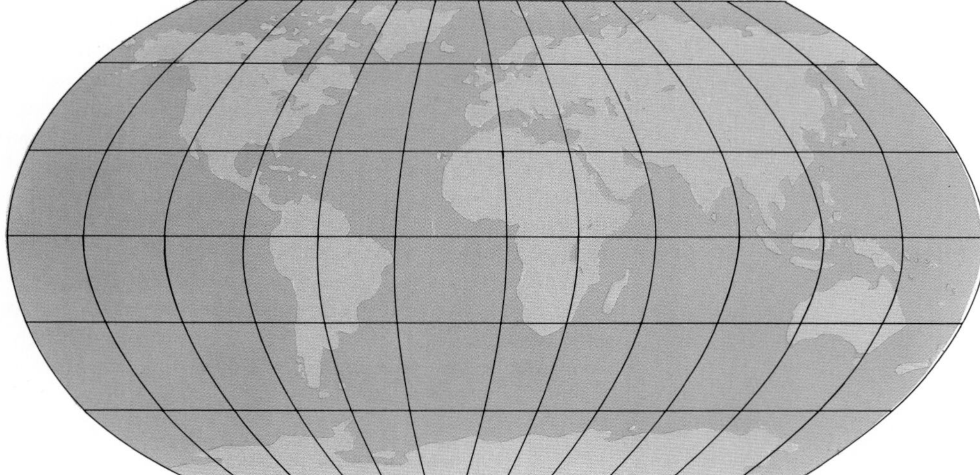

make map projections. But all types of projections have some sort of distortion in either the shapes of land masses or their areas.

One type is a Mercator (mur KAYT ur) projection. A **Mercator projection** has correct shapes of continents, but their areas are distorted. Lines of longitude are projected onto the map parallel to each other. As you learned earlier, only latitude lines are parallel. Longitude lines meet at the poles. When longitude lines are projected parallel, areas near the poles are exaggerated. Look at Greenland in the Mercator projection in Figure 8-11. It appears larger than South America. Greenland is actually much smaller than South America. Mercator projections are mainly used on ships and airplanes.

A map that has accurate continent shapes and shows accurate land areas is the **Robinson projection.** Here, lines of latitude remain parallel, and lines of longitude are curved as they would be on a globe. This results in less distortion near the poles.

A third type of projection is a conic projection. You use this type of projection whenever you look at a road map or a weather map. A **conic projection** is used to produce a map of small areas. They're made by projecting points and lines from a globe onto a cone.

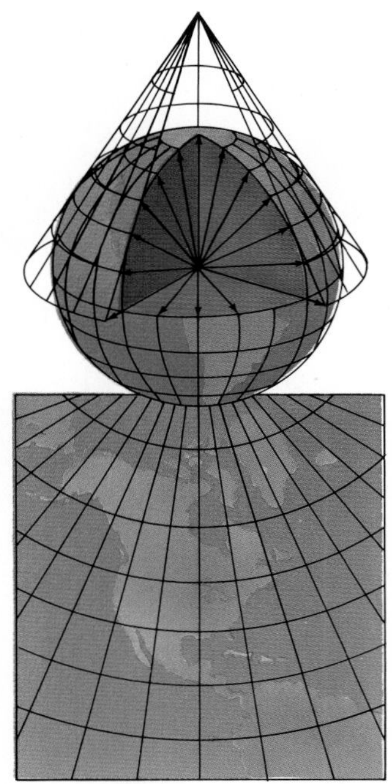

Figure 8-13. A conic projection is very accurate for small areas of Earth.

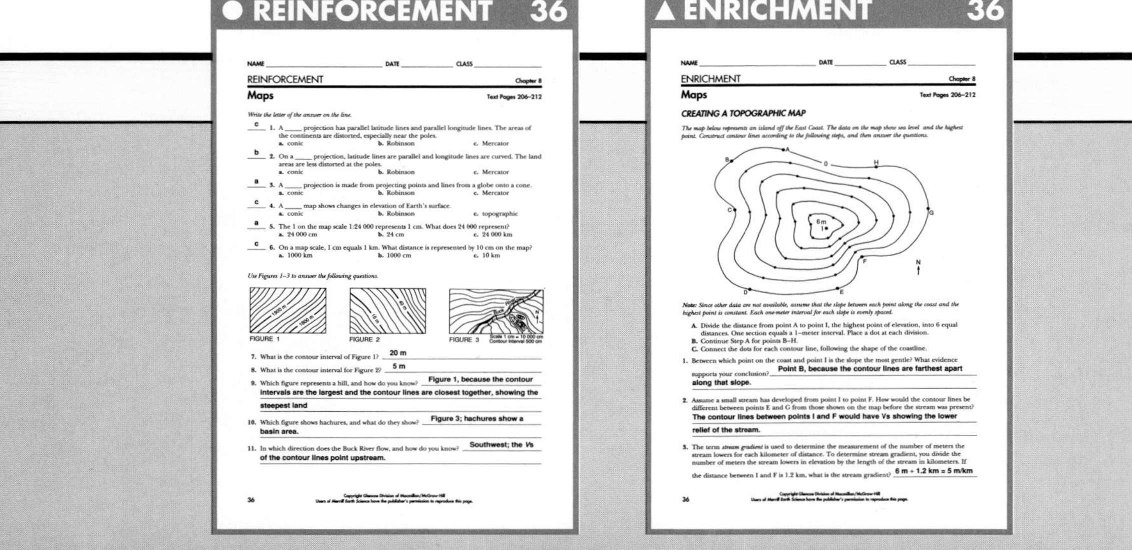

● REINFORCEMENT 36

NAME ______ DATE ______ CLASS ______

REINFORCEMENT — Chapter 8

Maps — Text Pages 206–212

Write the letter of the answer on the line.

c 1. A ____ projection has parallel latitude lines and parallel longitude lines. The areas of the continents are distorted, especially near the poles.
a. conic b. Robinson c. Mercator

b 2. On a ____ projection, latitude lines are parallel and longitude lines are curved. The land areas are less distorted at the poles.
a. conic b. Robinson c. Mercator

a 3. A ____ projection is made from projecting points and lines from a globe onto a cone.
a. conic b. Robinson c. Mercator

c 4. A ____ map shows changes in elevation of Earth's surface.
a. conic b. Robinson c. topographic

a 5. The 1 on the map scale 1:24 000 represents 1 cm. What does 24 000 represent?
a. 24 000 cm b. 24 cm c. 24 000 km

c 6. On a map scale, 1 cm equals 1 km. What distance is represented by 10 cm on the map?
a. 1000 km b. 1000 cm c. 10 km

Use Figures 1–3 to answer the following questions.

7. What is the contour interval of Figure 1? 20 m
8. What is the contour interval for Figure 2? 5 m
9. Which figure represents a hill, and how do you know? Figure 1, because the contour intervals are the largest and the contour lines are closest together, showing the steepest land
10. Which figure shows hachures, and what do they show? Figure 3; hachures show a basin area.
11. In which direction does the Buck River flow, and how do you know? Southwest; the Vs of the contour lines point upstream.

36

▲ ENRICHMENT 36

NAME ______ DATE ______ CLASS ______

ENRICHMENT — Chapter 8

Maps — Text Pages 206–212

CREATING A TOPOGRAPHIC MAP

The map below represents an island off the East Coast. The data on the map show sea level and the highest point. Construct contour lines according to the following steps, and then answer the questions.

Note: *Since other data are not available, assume that the slope between each point along the coast and the highest point is constant. Each one-meter interval for each slope is evenly spaced.*

A. Divide the distance from point A to point I, the highest point of elevation, into 6 equal distances. One section equals a 1–meter interval. Place a dot at each division.
B. Continue Step A for points B–H.
C. Connect the dots for each contour line, following the shape of the coastline.

1. Between which point on the coast and point I is the slope the most gentle? What evidence supports your conclusion? Point B, because the contour lines are farthest apart along that slope.
2. Assume a small stream has developed from point I to point F. How would the contour lines be different between points E and G from those shown on the map before the stream was present? The contour lines between points I and F would have Vs showing the lower relief of the stream.
3. The term *stream gradient* is used to determine the measurement of the number of meters the stream lowers for each kilometer of distance. To determine stream gradient, you divide the number of meters the stream lowers in elevation by the length of the stream in kilometers. If the distance between I and F is 1.2 km, what is the stream gradient? 6 m ÷ 1.2 km = 5 m/km

36

TYING TO PREVIOUS KNOWLEDGE: Have a map of your city available for students to examine. Although the students are very familiar with the city, they may have never used a city map to get around. Use the map to locate familiar places—your school, the mall, and so on.

OBJECTIVES AND SCIENCE WORDS: Have students review the objectives and science words to become familiar with this section.

2 TEACH

Key Concepts are highlighted.

CONCEPT DEVELOPMENT

▶ **How are map projections made?** *Points and lines on a globe's surface are transferred onto paper.*

▶ Emphasize that Mercator projections are distorted the most in the polar areas.

▶ Have students contrast the three types of projections described on this page.

CROSS CURRICULUM

▶ **Vocational:** Have some blueprints of houses and other structures available for students to examine. Have students compare and contrast maps and blueprints.

PROGRAM RESOURCES

Use **Laboratory Manual,** page 69, Comparing Maps.

CONCEPT DEVELOPMENT

▶ **List several natural and cultural features you would find on topographic maps.** *mountains, hills, plains, lakes, rivers, roads, dams, and houses*

▶ **How does Figure 8-14 show how topographic maps represent land surfaces?** *Part b of Figure 8-14 shows how points of equal elevation are projected onto a flat surface. These points form contour lines on a topographic map. These contour lines have a numerical value indicating height above sea-level.*

▶ **What do contour lines that come together to form circles or loops indicate?** *They indicate a hill or, if accompanied with hachures, a depression.*

▶ Use the above question to challenge your students about contour lines that close. Use this as a preview. They will learn about contour lines that close and hachures on page 210.

▶ If possible, obtain a topographic map of your state for students to examine.

TEACHER F.Y.I.

▶ Most USGS quadrangles use the English System of units rather than SI. Therefore, contour intervals are given in feet above or below sea level instead of meters on most topographic maps.

Topographic Maps

What does a topogaphic map show?

After you used a conic map projection to get to the mountain, you would also want a detailed map showing the hills
1 and valleys of that specific area. A **topographic map** shows the changes in elevation of Earth's surface. With this map, you could tell how steep the mountain trail is. It also shows natural features such as mountains, hills, plains, lakes, and rivers and cultural features such as roads, cities, dams, and other structures built by people. Thus, topographic maps are models of a small part of Earth's surface.

If you were starting your hike up the mountain, you would look at the contour lines on your topographic map to see the changes in elevation that the trail goes through.
2 A **contour line** is a line on a map that connects points of

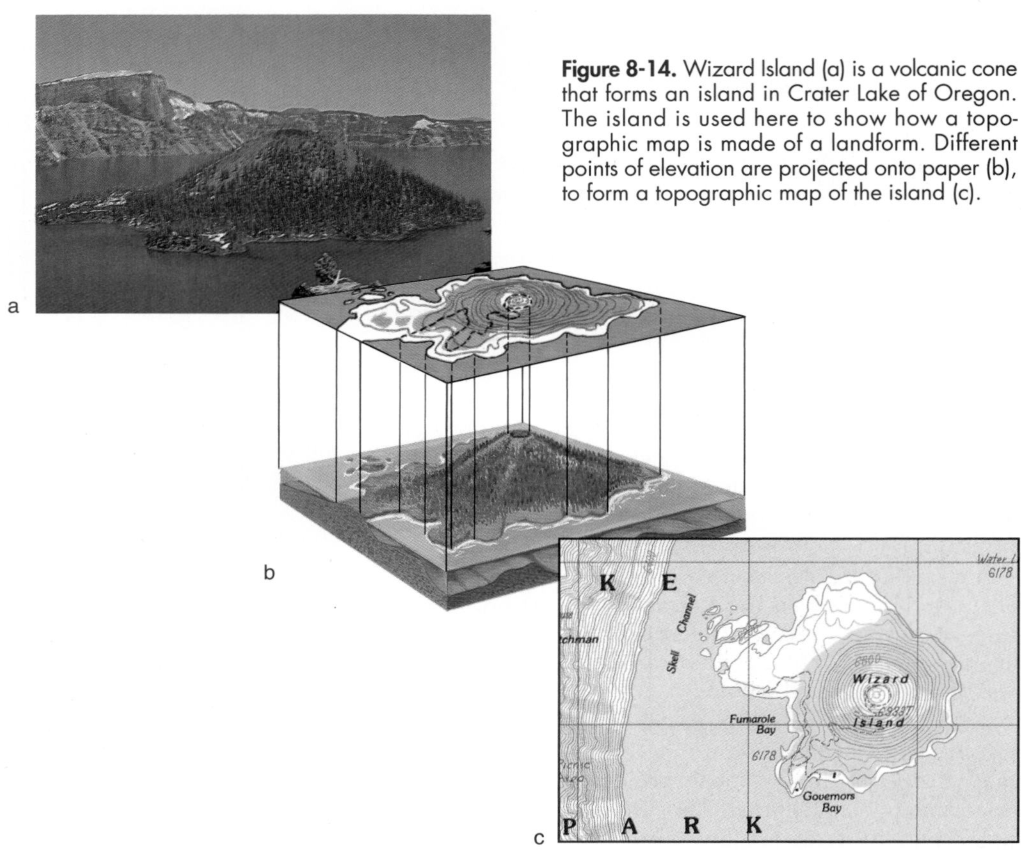

Figure 8-14. Wizard Island (a) is a volcanic cone that forms an island in Crater Lake of Oregon. The island is used here to show how a topographic map is made of a landform. Different points of elevation are projected onto paper (b), to form a topographic map of the island (c).

OPTIONS

INQUIRY QUESTIONS

▶ **Examine the Mercator map projection on page 206. Why do you suppose Australia is considered a continent while Greenland is not?** *On Mercator maps, Greenland appears to be much bigger than Australia. In reality, Greenland is a much smaller island that appears bigger because of the distortion of the map.*

▶ **Why are conic maps more accurate than Mercator maps?** *Conic maps more closely approximate the curvature of Earth for a smaller geographic area.*

▶ **Suppose you were a pilot flying from New York, NY, to Los Angeles, CA. Which type of projection would be most useful in navigating your route?** *Mercator*

▶ **Suppose you were driving from New York to Los Angeles. Which projection would you use to find your way?** *conic*

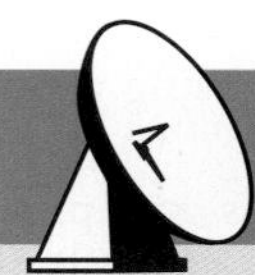

TECHNOLOGY

Rocks in 3-D!

You have learned that topographic maps are two-dimensional models of Earth. On such maps, contour lines connect points of equal elevation. Topographic maps are used to study features on Earth's surface.

To unravel Earth's complex structure, however, geologists also need to know what the rock beds "look like" in three dimensions. Using computers, topographic maps are digitized to get the "top layer" of data for the 3-D maps. Digitizing is a process by which points are located on a coordinate grid. Geologists then use data from wells drilled into the crust to obtain information about other "layers" of rocks beneath the surface. The computer analyzes all the data and generates a 3-dimensional map that shows what the rocks of an area look like. The map shown in the photograph shows how the drainage basin of an ancient river system was changed when forces at Earth's surface and forces within Earth acted on the river in Montana.

Think Critically: List one advantage a 3-D map has over a 2-D map.

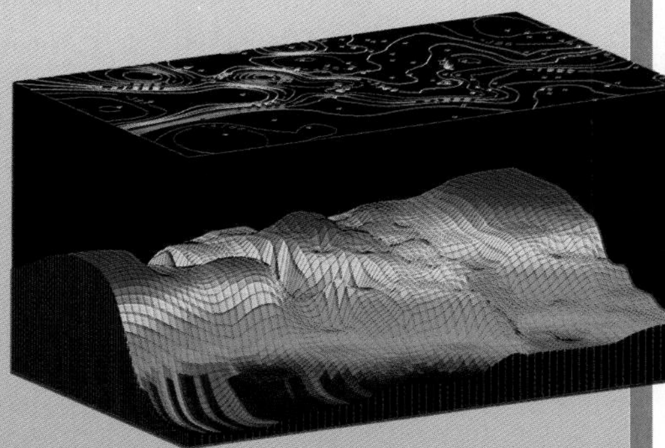

equal elevation. As you know, elevation refers to the distance above or below sea level. The difference in elevation between two side-by-side contour lines is called the **contour interval**. If the contour interval was 10 meters, then you would know that when you walked between those two lines on the trail, you would have climbed 10 meters.

The size of the contour interval can vary. If the land is very steep like in mountains, the contour lines might be very close and the contour interval might be as great as 100 meters. This would tell you that the land is very steep there because there is a large change in elevation between lines. However, if there isn't a great change in elevation and the contour lines are far apart, your map might have a contour interval of 5 meters.

What does a small contour interval tell you about land?

Some contour lines, called index contours, are marked with their elevation. If you know the contour interval, you can tell the elevation of other lines around the index contour by adding or subtracting the known contour interval from the elevation indicated on the index contour.

TECHNOLOGY

▶ Show students a photo of an outcrop. Have them use clay to construct a 3-D model of the rocks. Then, have students hypothesize what the rock beds look like in the third dimension.

▶ For more information, see "Geologic Models in Three Dimensions" by Nick Van Driel, *Geotimes*, September, 1989, pp. 12-13.

Think Critically: Answers may vary but students should realize that 3-D maps allow geologists to "see" subsurface structures.

CONCEPT DEVELOPMENT

▶ **What is the difference between a contour line and a contour interval?** *A contour line connects points of equal elevation on a topographic map. A contour interval is the difference in elevation between two side-by-side contour lines.*

▶ **What is the contour interval on a map if two side-by-side contour lines are labeled as 200 meters and 300 meters?** *The contour interval is 100 meters.*

▶ **How can you distinguish between an index contour and a regular contour line?** *An index contour is marked with its elevation. A regular contour line is not labeled.*

▶ **Why wouldn't a 5-meter contour interval be used on a topographic map of a mountainous region?** *The map would not be readable because the lines would be too close together.*

ENRICHMENT

▶ Have students research the history of Crater Lake in Oregon. Students will discover that Crater Lake is located atop a volcano known as Mount Mazama. Crater Lake formed some 7000 years ago after an eruption much larger than the famous Vesuvius eruption. Rainwater filled the caldera, forming Crater Lake.

PROGRAM RESOURCES

From the **Teacher Resource Package** use:
Critical Thinking/Problem Solving, page 14, A Change of Projection.
Use **Laboratory Manual,** page 73, Using a Clinometer.

CONCEPT DEVELOPMENT

▶ How can you tell a hill from a depression on a contour map? *Depressions are marked with hachures. Reading the elevation numbers can also help distinguish a hill from a depression.*

CHECK FOR UNDERSTANDING

Use the Mini Quiz to check for understanding.

MINI QUIZ

Use the Mini Quiz to check students' recall of chapter content.

1. **A _____ map shows the changes in elevation of Earth's surface.** *topographic*
2. **A _____ is a line on a map that connects points of equal elevation.** *contour line*
3. **Short lines at right angles to contour lines that are used to show depressions are called _____ .** *hachures*
4. **Contour lines form Vs that point _____ whenever they cross streams.** *upstream*
5. **A map's _____ explains what symbols used on the map mean.** *legend*

RETEACH

Obtain topographic maps of your area from the USGS. Take students to a specific area of the map and point out the actual features and their representations on the map. Students will find this exercise useful in their attempts to understand and interpret topographic maps.

EXTENSION

For students who have mastered this section, use the **Reinforcement** and **Enrichment** masters or other OPTIONS provided.

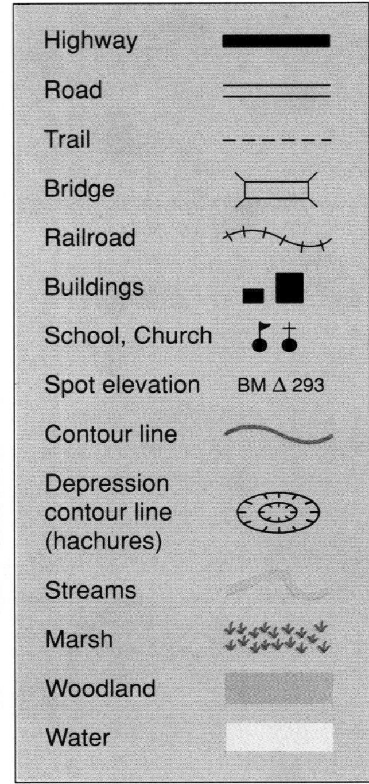

Figure 8-15. Here are some typical symbols used on topographic maps.

Here are some rules to remember when using topographic maps.

1. **Contour lines close around hills and basins or depressions.** To decide whether you're looking at a hill or basin, you can either read the elevation numbers or 3 look for hachures (ha SHOORZ). Hachures are short lines at right angles to the contour line that are used to show depressions. These lines point toward lower elevations.
2. **Contour lines never cross.** If they did, it would mean that the spot where they cross would have two different elevations.
3. 4 **Contour lines form Vs that point upstream whenever they cross streams.** This is because streams flow in depressions that are beneath the elevation of the surrounding land surface. When the contour lines follow the depression, they appear as Vs pointing upstream on the map.

Map Scale and Legends

Another thing you would want to know before you set out on your hike is, "How far is it to the top of the mountain?" Since maps are small models of Earth's surface, distances and sizes of things on a map should be proportional to the real thing on Earth. This is accomplished using "scale" distances. The **map scale** is the relationship between the distances on the map and actual distances on Earth's surface. For example, a topographic map of the Grand Canyon may have a scale that reads "1 : 80 000 ." This means that one unit on the map represents 80 000 units on land. If the unit you wanted to use was a centimeter, then one cm on the map would equal 80 000 cm on land. A map scale may also be in the form of a small bar graph that's divided into a number of units. The units are the scaled-down equivalent distances to real distances on Earth.

What is the purpose of a legend?

Topographic maps and most other maps have a legend. As you can see in Figure 8-15, topographic maps are covered with different colored lines, dots, letters, and 5 odd shapes. A map's legend explains what the symbols used on the map mean. Some frequently used symbols for topographic maps are shown in Figure 8-15 and Appendix H on page 672.

OPTIONS

INQUIRY QUESTIONS

▶ Explain the meaning of a topographic map scale of 1:62 500. *One unit (inch, foot, centimeter, or kilometer) of any distance on the map equals 62 500 of the same unit on the area that has been mapped.*

▶ Why is the marsh topographic symbol sometimes found with contour lines with hachures? *Water gathers in low spots, indicated on a topographic map by hachures. A marsh is a watery lowland.*

▶ If you see a small triangle with numbers next to it on a topographic map, what does it mean? *spot elevation, the exact elevation above sea level at that spot*

PROBLEM SOLVING

A Climb to the Top

The map below is a topographic map of an area in California. One sunny day, three hikers started from the point marked with the + in the center of the map. One hiker headed for the peak of Cedar Mountain, another for the peak of Orr Mountain, while the third intended to climb to the top of Garner Butte.

All three would travel at the same rate on flat or gentle slopes. The climb would be slower on the steeper slope. If each hiker could choose any route to take to the top of the intended goals, which one do you think would reach the top first? Explain.

Think Critically: Could the three hikers see each other at the top? Why or why not?

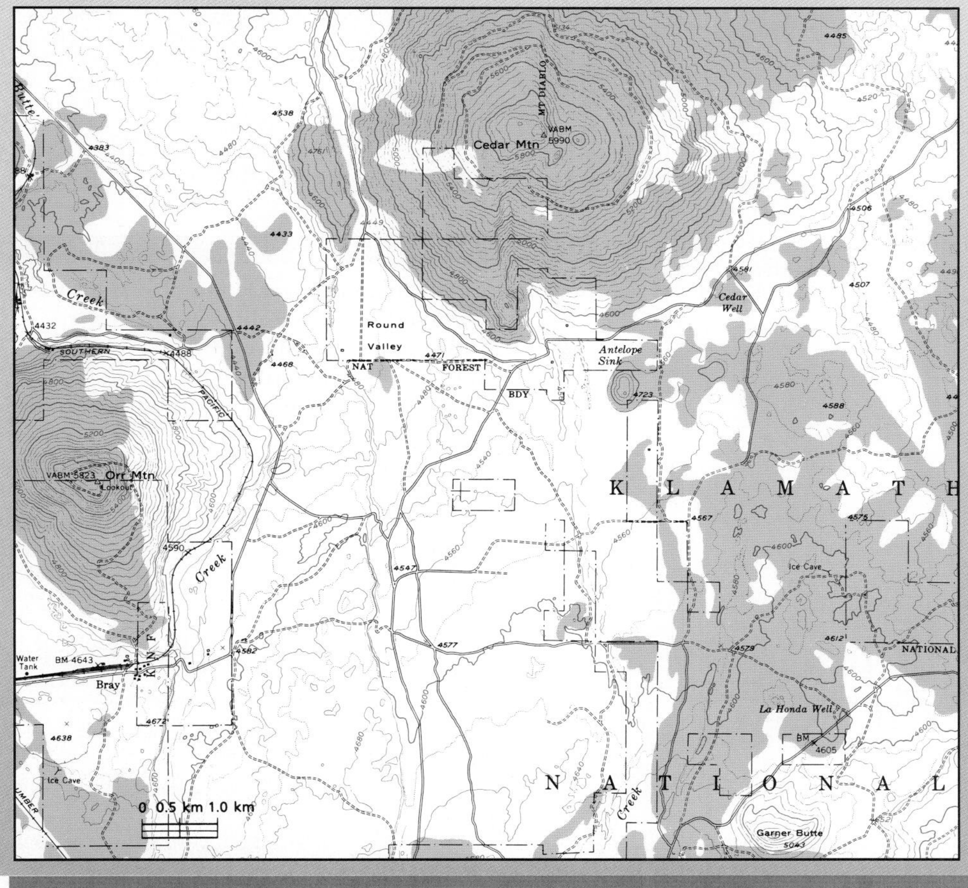

PROBLEM SOLVING

▶ Since a straight line path is probably not the quickest way to the top of these landforms because of steep slopes, forests, streams, and lack of direct trails, use of available trails would probably save time. The hiker heading for the top of Orr Mountain would be most likely to reach the top first, using available trails. If the straight line path is used, the Garner Butte hiker has a chance because of having to spend less time climbing steep slopes.

Think Critically: Once at the top, all three hikers would have unobstructed views of the other two summits. But, because of the distances, each would need strong binoculars to see the others.

INQUIRY QUESTIONS

▶ **What is the contour interval of the topographic map above?** *40 feet*

▶ **How far is it from Cedar Mountain to Garner Butte?** *about 10 kilometers*

▶ **What is the height of Orr Mountain?** *5823 feet above sea level*

PROGRAM RESOURCES

From the **Teacher Resource Package** use:
Cross-Curricular Connections, page 12, Uncovering the past.

3 CLOSE

▶ Ask questions 1-3 and the **Apply** Question in the Section Review.
▶ Have students do Activity 8-1.

FLEX Your Brain

Use the Flex Your Brain activity to have students explore MAP LEGENDS.

SECTION REVIEW ANSWERS

1. In a Mercator projection, lines of longitude are parallel to one another. Thus, a Mercator map distorts regions near the poles, making them appear much larger than they really are.
2. It shows the relationship between the distances on the map and actual distances on Earth's surface.
3. One spot cannot have two different elevations.
4. Apply: They are 8 km apart. The change in elevation is 200 m.

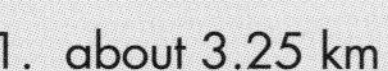

Skill Builder

1. about 3.25 km
2. It's about 2.25 km from the westernmost shore of Factory Pond to the westernmost shore of Mill Pond.
3. about 1.25 km

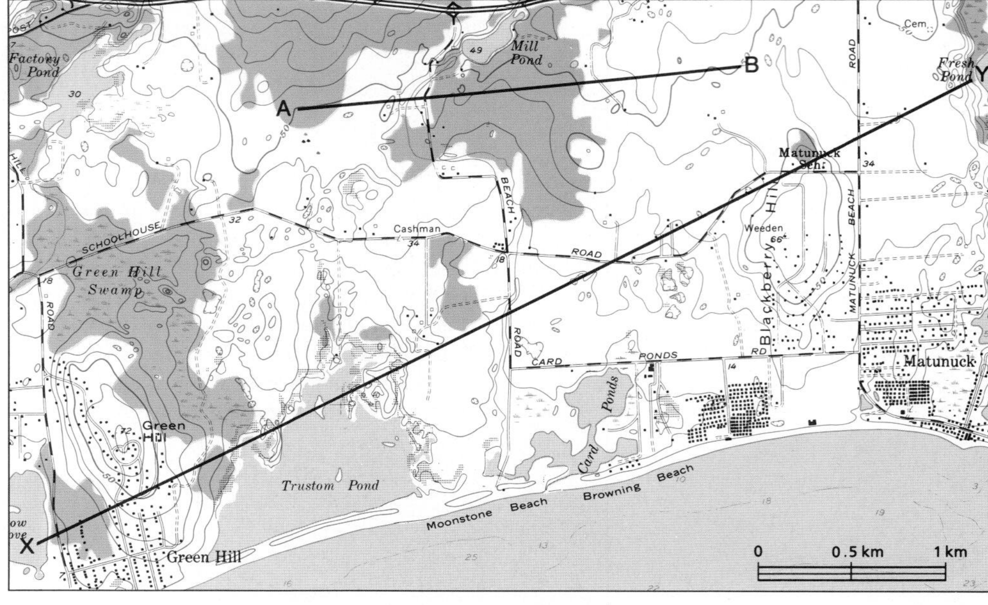

Figure 8-16. This topographic map of Kingston, Rhode Island shows many common features of topographic maps.

SECTION REVIEW

1. Why does Greenland appear larger on a Mercator projection than it does on a Robinson projection?
2. What does a map scale tell you?
3. Why can't contour lines cross?
4. **Apply:** Suppose you have a topographic map with a contour interval of 50 m. The scale is 1 cm on the map equals 1 km on Earth. The distance between point A and point B on the map is 8 cm. Four contour lines lie between points A and B. How far apart are the points and what is the change in elevation between them?

Skill Builder

☑ Measuring in SI

Use Figure 8-16 to practice measuring in SI.
1. How long is Matunuck Beach Road?
2. How far is it from Factory Pond to Mill Pond?
3. How big is Trustom Pond at its widest place?

If you need help, refer to Measuring in SI in the **Skill Handbook** on page 684.

OPTIONS

ENRICHMENT

▶ Have students use topographic maps to identify landforms in your state or your part of the country.
▶ Have students use the legend shown in Figure 8-15 and Appendix H to interpret information about features shown on the topographic maps in this chapter.
▶ Have students research other types of map projections besides Mercator, Robinson, and conic maps. Have them report their results in a table.

PROGRAM RESOURCES

From the **Teacher Resource Package** use:
Activity Worksheets, page 5, Flex Your Brain.

ACTIVITY 8-1
Determining Elevation

Problem: *How is elevation indicated on a topographic map?*

Materials 

- plastic model landform
- water
- transparency
- clear plastic storage box with lid
- beaker
- metric ruler
- tape
- transparency marker

Procedure

1. Using the ruler and the transparency marker, make marks up the side of the storage box 2 cm apart.
2. Secure the transparency to the outside of the box lid with tape.
3. Place the plastic model in the box. The bottom of the box will be zero elevation.
4. Using the beaker, pour water into the box to a height of 2 cm. Place the lid on the box.
5. Use the transparency marker to trace the top of the water line on the transparency.
6. Using the scale 2 cm = 10 m, mark the elevation on the line.
7. Remove the lid and add water until a depth of 4 cm is reached.
8. Map this level on the storage box lid and record the elevation.
9. Repeat the process of adding water and tracing until you have the hill mapped.
10. Transfer the tracing of the hill onto a white sheet of paper.

Analyze

1. What is the contour interval of this topographic map?
2. How does the distance between contour lines on the map show the steepness of slope on the landform model?
3. What is the total elevation of the hill?
4. How was elevation represented on your map?

Conclude and Apply

5. How are elevations shown on topographic maps?
6. Must all topographic maps have a 0-m elevation contour line? Explain.
7. How would the contour interval of an area of high relief compare to one of low relief on a topographic map?

ACTIVITY 8-1
45 minutes

OBJECTIVE: Demonstrate and **explain** how elevation is indicated on a topographic map.

PROCESS SKILLS applied in this activity:
▶ **Recognizing and Using Spatial Relationships** in Steps 5 and 9.
▶ **Measuring** in Steps 1, 4, and 7.
▶ **Interpreting Data** in Analyze Questions 1-4 and Conclude and Apply Question 5.
▶ **Forming Hypotheses** in Conclude and Apply Questions 6 and 7.
▶ **Experimenting** in Steps 1-10.
▶ **Formulating Models** in Step 9.

TEACHING THE ACTIVITY

▶ Keep paper towels on hand to mop up spills.
▶ Some students may need extra help in understanding the scale to be used.
▶ A few drops of food coloring added to the water make it easier to detect the model/water contact when tracing.
▶ Use beakers or cups to remove some of the water when done, before attempting to move the full box to the sink to pour out the water.

Alternate Materials: If plastic model landforms are unavailable, a hill can be made using clay. Water-soluble flow pens are good replacements for glass marking pencils, provided the transparency is kept dry.

Troubleshooting: For acceptable results, students must be directly over the model when tracing the contour lines. Best results are obtained when one eye is closed. If they do not trace from the same position each time, a difference in tracing angle can cause the traced lines to touch or even cross.

ANSWERS TO QUESTIONS

1. 10 m
2. The closer together the contour lines are on the map, the steeper the slopes on the model. Increased distances between contour lines indicate relatively flat areas of the model.
3. The elevation of students' hills will vary, but will always equal the height of the model in centimeters times 1000.
4. Elevation above sea level is indicated by the lines drawn on the transparencies. These lines are called contour lines.
5. by contour lines
6. No, the 0 m contour line is only on maps with elevations at sea level.
7. Generally, the greater the relief of an area, the larger the contour interval. Relatively flat areas of low relief are represented by smaller contour intervals.

PROGRAM RESOURCES

From the **Teacher Resource Package** use:

Activity Worksheets, page 66-67, Activity 8-1, Determining Elevation.

SECTION 8-4

PREPARATION

SECTION BACKGROUND

▶ In 1988, the Soviet Union admitted that for 50 years its government deliberately falsified all public maps.

1 MOTIVATE

TYING TO PREVIOUS KNOWLEDGE: Have students recall that when they first came to school, they had to find their classes by using either a map or verbal directions. Ask them how successful they would have been if the map or directions hadn't been accurate.

OBJECTIVES AND SCIENCE WORDS: Have students review the objectives and science words to become familiar with this section.

2 TEACH

Key Concepts are highlighted.

CONCEPT DEVELOPMENT

▶ **How does sonar work?** *A sound wave is sent from the bottom of a ship to the ocean floor. The wave is reflected or bounced off the bottom and is picked up by a receiving device. A computer calculates the distance to the bottom using the speed of sound in water and the time it takes for the sound to be reflected.*

PROGRAM RESOURCES

From the **Teacher Resource Package** use:

Science and Society, page 12, Northwest Passage Controversy.

8-4 Secret Maps

New Science Words

sonar
Sea Beam

Objectives

- ▶ Explain why some maps have been intentionally distorted.
- ▶ Recognize why some maps of the ocean floor have been classified as secret and why these maps would be valuable to some people.

Intentional Distortion of Maps

Over the years, several countries in the world have intentionally distorted maps. Early Romans designed maps to greatly exaggerate the size of the Roman Empire. This made them appear even more powerful than they actually were to their enemies. The Soviet Union has also distorted and falsified public maps. Rivers, mountains, roads, and towns were misplaced. The purpose of distorting their maps was to confuse spies from other countries. Throughout history, countries have tried to keep some maps secret for security reasons. Even today, many maps are classified "secret."

Sea Beam

Using a new technology called Sea Beam, scientists are making detailed, accurate maps of the ocean floor in the coastal areas around the United States.

Figure 8-17. Sea Beam sonar, shown at left, can make very accurate maps of the ocean floor—right.

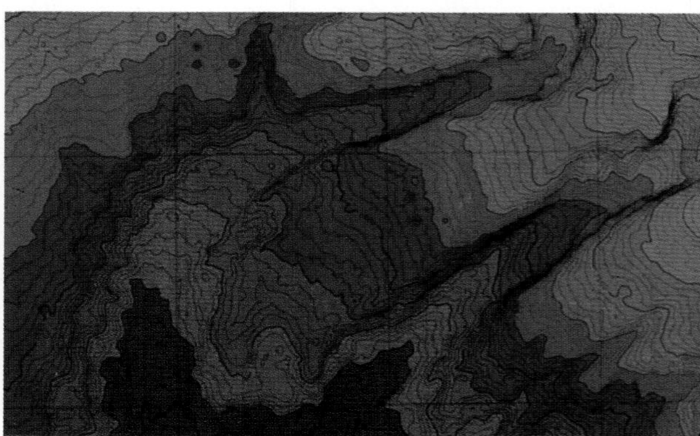

OPTIONS

Meeting Different Ability Levels

For Section 8-4, use the following **Teacher Resource Masters** depending upon individual students' needs.

◆ **Study Guide Master** for all students.

● **Reinforcement Master** for students of average and above average ability levels.

▲ **Enrichment Master** for above average students.

Additional Teacher Resource Package masters are listed in the OPTIONS box throughout the section. The additional masters are appropriate for all students.

◆ STUDY GUIDE 37

NAME ____________ DATE ________ CLASS ________

STUDY GUIDE — Chapter 8

Secret Maps — Text Pages 214–215

Use the words in the box to complete the statements.

deposits	receiving	speed	sixteen
Sonar	secret	canyons	map
ocean	Sea Beam	echo	depth
sound	calculated	distance	time
study			

1. Throughout history, countries in the world have intentionally falsified maps or kept some maps **secret** for security purposes.
2. **Sea Beam** is a new sonar technology.
3. **Sonar** refers to the use of sound waves to detect structures on the ocean bottom.
4. Sea Beam sends a **sound** wave from the bottom of the ship toward the **ocean** floor.
5. The sound wave bounces off the ocean floor and an **echo** of the sound wave is picked up by a **receiving** device.
6. The **distance** the sound wave traveled is **calculated** by a computer.
7. The computer uses the **speed** of the sound in the water and the **time** it takes for the sound to be reflected to make the calculations.
8. An equipped Sea Beam has **sixteen** sonar devices.
9. The ship gathers **depth** readings as the ship moves above the seafloor.
10. Computers take depth readings and make a detailed continuous **map** of the ocean floor.
11. Sea Beam maps are used to **study** parts of the ocean floor not known about before.
12. If Sea Beam maps were not secret, people could use them to locate underwater **canyons** where certain fish might be found or to find oil-bearing **deposits**.

 37

Sea Beam is a new type of sonar technology. **Sonar** refers to the use of sound waves to detect ocean bottom structures. First a sound wave is sent from the bottom of a ship toward the ocean floor. A receiving device then picks up the returning echo when it bounces off the bottom. The distance to the bottom is calculated by a computer on the ship using the speed of sound in water and the time it takes for the sound to be reflected.

A ship with **Sea Beam** sonar has 16 of these sonar devices. The sonar devices are each "aimed" at different parts of the seafloor, gathering depth readings from a wide swath as the ship moves. As the ship goes back and forth across the seafloor, readings of depth overlap. Computers take this information and make a detailed continuous map of the ocean floor.

These new Sea Beam maps are very useful. For example, fishing companies can use them to locate underwater canyons where certain fish might be found. Petroleum engineers use them to find oil-bearing deposits. Oceanographers use them to study parts of the ocean floor that previously they didn't know existed.

At first, all of the new Sea Beam maps were classified as secret. Because Sea Beam maps are so accurate, government officials didn't want other countries to have detailed maps of the ocean floor around the United States. They feared that enemy submarines could use the maps to navigate in United States coastal areas. Now most of the Sea Beam maps have been released to the public.

SECTION REVIEW

1. Why are some maps intentionally distorted?
2. How do Sea Beam's maps aid people who fish and look for oil?

Science and MATH

Sea Beam sends a sonar signal toward the ocean floor. The sound wave travels at 1454 meters per second, reflects off the ocean floor, and returns to the sonar receiver in 2.25 seconds. How deep is the ocean at that point?

Why are Sea Beam maps so desirable?

You Decide!

There are Sea Beam maps of the ocean floor near navy bases that are still classified secret. The government wants to keep this area of the ocean floor a secret because submarines navigate in these areas. This means that fishing companies, petroleum engineers, and oceanographers can't benefit from these maps. What do you think? Should all Sea Beam maps be released to the public?

● REINFORCEMENT 37

NAME ______ DATE ______ CLASS ______

REINFORCEMENT — Chapter 8

Secret Maps — Text Pages 214–215

The word *sonar* comes from the phrase "sound navigation ranging." When a ship has sonar, its navigator can figure the distance from the ship to any solid object. The object may be the bottom of the ocean above which the ship is sailing or another ship. In the early days of sailing, navigators measured the depth of the water by letting a weighted rope over the side of the ship. The rope was marked in sections and when it touched bottom, they could measure the depth. If the rope did not reach bottom, they knew only that the water was very deep.

Answer the questions on the lines provided.

1. Name a new type of sonar technology. **Sea Beam**
2. How does this new technology differ from older forms? **A ship with Sea Beam sonar has 16 sonar devices aimed at different parts of the seafloor.**
3. Explain how sonar uses sound to take the place of the long rope used by navigators of the past. **Instead of letting a rope down to the floor of the ocean, navigators use sonar which sends a sound wave to the bottom. The wave's echo is then picked up by a device on the ship.**
4. What equipment translates the information into map form? **computers**
5. What research people make educational use of the maps? **oceanographers**
6. Name two groups who might use the maps for business reasons. **fishing companies and oil companies**
7. What use has the United States government made of the new sonar technology? **It has mapped the floors of the oceans near the coastlines of the United States.**

Make a puzzle that uses words and phrases from the lesson on secret maps and Sea Beam. In the puzzle, letters forming the words Sea Beam read down. Share your completed puzzle with a classmate.

S **sonar** **Answers will vary.**
E **echo**
A **accurate**
B **bottom of the ocean**
E **engineers**
A **aimed at seafloor**
M **maps**

 37

▲ ENRICHMENT 37

NAME ______ DATE ______ CLASS ______

ENRICHMENT — Chapter 8

Secret Maps — Text Pages 214–215

SOLVING A MAP PUZZLE

In 2990, Mies and Rhonda found a map fragment in the ruins of a library of 1990. They were thrilled to see a paper map. But what region did it represent? One word gave them a clue. Mies had read that people used to drive gasoline-powered cars and that some people held car races. He recognized the word "speedway" on the map fragment. Mies and Rhonda decided to research that and other clues from the map. They found out what the clues meant. Then they used their clues to find out which place is shown on the map.

Odd 2-digit numbers = north-south freeways
Even 2-digit numbers = east-west freeways
Three-digit numbers = routes around a city
(wavy line) = major rivers

School for the blind
White River
69
65
70
Speedway
465
N
0 1 2 3 4 km

Use the key and clues on the map to read the map and answer the questions.

1. Mies and Rhonda decided the map was of a city. What evidence did they have of that? **The line that forms a rough circle around the area represents a limited-access highway forming a route around a city.**
2. What did the double lines represent on this map? **the White River**
3. What was the approximate distance formed by the rough circle around this region? **approximately 82 km**
4. Rhonda used the rough circle as a circumference and found the approximate area of the region. What is it? **approximately 530 km²**
5. What other symbols gave Rhonda and Mies clues about the region? **Four schools can be identified since one symbol is labeled as a school. Two airports are marked, symbolized by the airplanes.**
6. What sources could Mies and Rhonda use to check out their clues? **an old atlas of road maps**
7. Where is the place represented by the map fragment? **Indianapolis, Indiana**

 37

Science and MATH

Distance equals the velocity of the sound wave multiplied by time.

$d = vt$

$= 1454\ m/s \times 2.25\ s$

$= 3198.8$ m that the wave traveled

The distance to the bottom is half the traveled distance or 1599.4 m.

CHECK FOR UNDERSTANDING

Have a volunteer explain why Sea Beam maps can be so detailed. They should respond that the depth readings overlap to provide much data.

RETEACH

Have students stand beside their desks and look down at their books. Then, have them move to different distances while still looking at the books. Ask students to describe how observing an object from different angles allows them to see more or fewer details of the object. Then have them compare what they've observed with how Sea Beam works.

EXTENSION

For students who have mastered this section, use the **Reinforcement** and **Enrichment** masters.

3 CLOSE

▶ Ask the questions 1-2 in the Section Review and the You Decide question.
▶ Have students perform Activity 8-2.

SECTION REVIEW ANSWERS

1. for political advantage over their enemies
2. Maps are used to locate canyons that harbor fish and oil-bearing deposits.

YOU DECIDE!

Some students will think it is reasonable for the government to classify these maps in order to protect national security. Other students will feel that Sea Beam maps should be released because people could greatly benefit from these maps.

ACTIVITY 8-2
45 minutes

OBJECTIVE: Determine the distance between any two points on a topographic map and **interpret** various features of a landscape.

PROCESS SKILLS applied in this activity:
▶ **Using Numbers** in Procedure Step 3 and Analyze Questions 1-8.
▶ **Measuring** in Procedure Steps 1-3 and Analyze Questions 1 and 2.
▶ **Interpreting Data** in Conclude and Apply Questions 9-14.

TEACHING THE ACTIVITY
▶ If a topographic map of the local area is available, apply these procedures and similar questions as an extension. Using an area with which the students are familiar can assist greatly in the acquisition of these mapping concepts.
▶ **Alternate Materials:** With minimal wording changes, these same questions and procedures can be used for almost any topographic quadrangle map that is available.

PROGRAM RESOURCES

From the **Teacher Resource Package** use:
Activity Worksheets, page 68-70, Activity 8-2, Reading Topographic Maps.

ACTIVITY 8-2
Reading Topographic Maps

Problem: *How can distances and features be determined on a topographic map?*

Materials
- Figure 8-16
- paper
- Appendix H

NOTE: The contour interval on Figure 8-16 is expressed in feet above sea level.

Procedure
1. Lay a piece of paper along a straight line between Matunuck and Green Hill. Use the first letter of each name for the measurement.
2. Make a mark on the paper where the two towns are located.
3. Move the paper to the scale and determine the distance.

Analyze
1. What is the distance between the two towns? Is this measurement the same distance you would cover if you traveled by car between the two cities? Explain.
2. How would you measure this same distance using a ratio scale?
3. What is the contour interval of this map?
4. What is the approximate elevation of the Matunuck School?
5. What is the distance between the Matunuck School and the intersection of Moonstone Beach Road and Schoolhouse Road?
6. What is the approximate elevation of Mill Pond?
7. What is the approximate elevation of Green Hill Swamp?
8. What is the elevation of Schoolhouse Road where it intersects Green Hill Road?

Conclude and Apply
9. How can you determine the distance between two points on a topographic map?
10. How many closed contour lines would Green Hill have if the contour interval were 50 feet?
11. Would a contour interval of 50 feet give more or less detail? Explain.
12. If sea level rose 50 feet, would the State Trout Hatchery be covered by water?
13. What is the relief of the area south of Post Road?
14. Locate the closed contour line just northeast of the intersection of Moonstone Beach Road and Card Ponds Road. Is this feature a hill or a depression? Explain.

ANSWERS TO QUESTIONS
1. 4.2 km, or slightly more than 4 km; This distance is much shorter than what you would have to travel if you went by car from one city to the other.
2. To use a ratio scale, measure the scale distance between the two points and multiply by the actual distance provided in the scale.
3. 10 feet
4. 55 feet
5. approximately 1.7 km
6. approximately 50 feet
7. below 20 feet
8. approximately 20 feet
9. Distances can be determined using the scale provided on the map and by determining the scale distance between the points by measuring.
10. one
11. less detail, because this is an area of very low relief
12. No, it is at 70 feet.
13. The relief is very low south of Post Road.
14. This feature is a depression, as it contains hachure marks on the contour lines.

CHAPTER

REVIEW

SUMMARY

8-1: Landforms

1. Plains are large, flat areas that cover much of the United States. Plateaus are high, relatively flat areas next to mountains.
2. Folded mountains are formed when rocks are squeezed from opposite sides. Upwarped mountains form when Earth's crust is pushed up and then eroded. Fault-block mountains are tilted blocks that are bounded by at least one fault. Volcanic mountains are made of layers of molten material that pile up to form cone-shaped structures.

8-2: Viewpoints

1. Latitude refers to the distance in degrees north or south of the equator. Longitude refers to distance in degrees east or west of the prime meridian.
2. Lines of latitude and longitude form an imaginary grid that enables points on Earth to be located exactly.
3. Earth is divided into 24 time zones, each one hour ahead or behind the adjacent zone.

8-3: Maps

1. On a Mercator projection, landmasses near the poles are distorted, appearing larger than they actually are. Robinson projections have curved lines of longitude resulting in less distortion near the poles. Conic projections are used for maps of small areas. Road maps and weather maps are conic projections.
2. A contour line on a topographic map connects points of equal elevation. The difference in elevation between contour lines is the contour interval.
3. Because maps are small models of Earth's surface, a scale is used to show the relationship between map distances and the actual distances on Earth's surface.

8-4: Science and Society: Secret Maps

1. Maps are sometimes distorted to exaggerate the size of a country.
2. Some maps of the ocean floor are secret even though people would benefit from them.

KEY SCIENCE WORDS

a. **conic projection**
b. **contour interval**
c. **contour line**
d. **equator**
e. **fault-block mountains**
f. **folded mountains**
g. **International Date Line**
h. **latitude**
i. **longitude**
j. **map scale**
k. **Mercator projection**
l. **plains**
m **plateaus**
n. **prime meridian**
o. **Robinson projection**
p. **Sea Beam**
q. **sonar**
r. **topographic map**
s. **upwarped mountains**
t. **volcanic mountains**

UNDERSTANDING VOCABULARY

Match each phrase with the correct term from the list of Key Science Words.

1. high, flat areas next to mountains
2. mountains formed when Earth's crust is squeezed from opposite sides
3. imaginary line parallel to the equator
4. 0° longitude
5. projections used mainly for navigation
6. map that shows changes in elevation
7. line connecting points of equal elevation
8. change in elevation between adjacent contour lines
9. instrument that uses sound waves to detect features
10. system using 16 sonar devices

CHAPTER

REVIEW

SUMMARY

Have students read the summary statement to review the major concepts of the chapter.

UNDERSTANDING VOCABULARY

1. m
2. f
3. h
4. n
5. k
6. r
7. c
8. b
9. q
10. p

OPTIONS

ASSESSMENT

To assess student understanding of material in this chapter, use the resources listed.

COOPERATIVE LEARNING

Consider using cooperative learning in the THINK AND WRITE CRITICALLY, APPLY, and MORE SKILL BUILDERS sections of the Chapter Review.

PROGRAM RESOURCES

From the **Teacher Resource Package** use:
Chapter Review, pages 19-20.
Chapter and Unit Tests, pages 47–50, Chapter Test.
Chapter and Unit Tests, pages 51-52, Unit Test.

CHAPTER

REVIEW

CHECKING CONCEPTS

1. b	**6.** d
2. d	**7.** b
3. b	**8.** b
4. a	**9.** c
5. c	**10.** d

UNDERSTANDING CONCEPTS

11. longitude
12. equator
13. 90 degrees north
14. volcanic
15. fault-block

THINK AND WRITE CRITICALLY

16. Both are large, relatively flat regions of land. A plateau, however, is a flat area next to mountains and has a relatively high elevation.
17. Both are imaginary lines that enable the precise location of any point on Earth. Lines of latitude are parallel to one another and to the equator. Lines of longitude come together near the poles and run north-south on a map.
18. Mercator projections distort landmasses near the poles. Because it is near the South Pole, Antarctica would appear larger than it actually is.
19. There is little relief on the Great Plains. Thus, because the area is so flat, a topographic map of the Great Plains would have a small contour interval.
20. Ships using Sea Beam sonar have 16 data-collecting devices as opposed to just one device on conventional ships. Thus, Sea Beam systems can gather more data. Also, because Sea Beam readings overlap, more complete maps can be made.

CHAPTER

REVIEW

CHECKING CONCEPTS

Choose the word or phrase that completes the sentence.

1. ______ make up about 50 percent of all land areas in the United States.
a. Plateaus
b. Plains
c. Folded mountains
d. Volcanoes

2. The Grand Canyon is part of the ______.
a. Great Plains
b. Rocky Mountains
c. Appalachians
d. none of these

3. ______ mountains form when Earth's crust is pushed up into a dome shape by internal forces.
a. Fault-block
b. Upwarped
c. Volcanic
d. Folded

4. Lines parallel to the equator are ______.
a. lines of latitude
b. prime meridians
c. lines of longitude
d. contour lines

5. Earth can be divided into 24 time zones that are ______ degrees apart.
a. 10
b. 34
c. 15
d. 25

6. ______ projections are distorted at the poles.
a. Conic
b. Topographic
c. Robinson
d. Mercator

7. A ______ map shows changes in elevation at Earth's surface.
a. conic
b. topographic
c. Robinson
d. Mercator

8. ______ is measured with respect to sea level.
a. Contour interval
b. Elevation
c. Conic projection
d. Sonar

9. ______ are used to show depressions.
a. Vs
b. Scales
c. Hachure lines
d. Legends

10. Sea Beam sonar can be used to find ______.
a. schools of fish
b. submarine hiding places
c. oil deposits
d. all of these

UNDERSTANDING CONCEPTS

Complete each sentence.

11. Lines east or west of the prime meridian are lines of ______.
12. The ______ is an imaginary line halfway between the North and South Poles.
13. The North Pole is located at ______ latitude.
14. The Hawaiian Islands are ______ mountains.
15. Mountains, tilted and bounded by faults, are ______ mountains.

THINK AND WRITE CRITICALLY

16. Compare and contrast plains and plateaus.
17. Compare and contrast lines of latitude and lines of longitude.
18. Why would Antarctica be larger on a Mercator map than it actually is?
19. Would a topographic map of the Great Plains have a large or small contour interval? Explain.
20. How does the information gathered by ships using Sea Beam sonar differ from that collected with standard methods which use one sonar device?

APPLY

21. How would a topographic map of the Atlantic Coastal Plain differ from a topographic map of the Rocky Mountains?
22. If it was Wednesday and you were flying east across the Soviet Union, what day would it be when you reached Alaska?
23. If you were flying directly south from the North Pole and reached 70° north latitude, how many more degrees of latitude would be left to pass over before reaching the South Pole?
24. Why can't two contour lines overlap?
25. What does a map scale of 1 : 50 000 mean?

MORE SKILL BUILDERS

If you need help, refer to the Skill Handbook.

1. **Concept Mapping:** Make a network tree concept map that explains how topographic maps are used. Use the following terms: *topographic maps, mountains, rivers, natural features, contour lines, changes in elevation, equal elevation, hills, plains.*

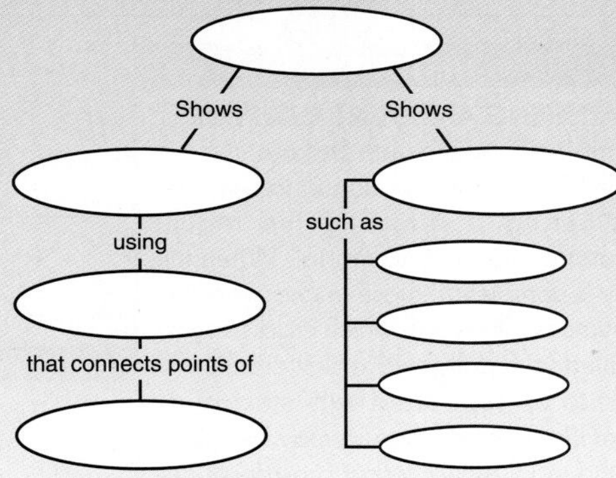

2. **Measuring in SI:** What is the area in square kilometers of the topographic map in the Problem Solving feature on page 211?
3. **Outlining:** Outline the major points in Section 8-2, Viewpoints.
4. **Sequencing:** Arrange these cities in order from the city with the earliest time to that with the latest time on a given day: Anchorage, AK; San Francisco, CA; Bangor, ME; Columbus, OH; Houston, TX.
5. **Interpreting Data:** If a map has a scale of "1 cm = 80 000 cm," how far on the map would two cities be if they were 300 km apart on Earth's surface?

PROJECTS

1. Use modeling clay to construct a physiographic map to scale of the United States. Be sure to include all the landforms shown in Figure 8-2.
2. Determine the actual area of each continent. Then, compute the difference in size between the actual size of each and its size on a Mercator, Robinson, and a conic projection. Make a table to display your results. Which projection is the most accurate for each of the continents?
3. Find out what daylight savings time is and why it was implemented. Also find out why some states do not use this plan.

APPLY

21. The map of the Atlantic Coastal Plain would show little change in elevation. The contour interval would be small. The map of the Rockies would show many closed contours indicating mountain peaks. The contour interval would be very large due to the rugged topography.
22. Tuesday
23. 160°
24. Contour lines connect points of equal elevation. A particular point on Earth's surface cannot be at two different elevations. Therefore, the lines can't overlap.
25. One unit on the map equals 50,000 of the same unit on Earth's surface.

MORE SKILL BUILDERS

1. Concept Mapping: Possible solution is given.

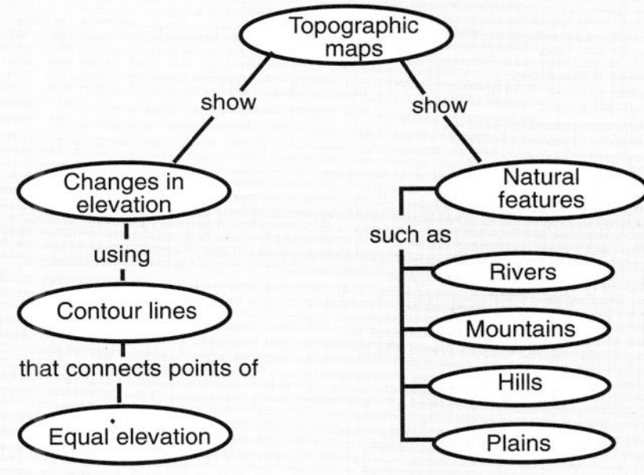

2. Measuring in SI: The area covered is approximately 138 km^2.
3. Outlining: Students' outlines will vary. There are 90 degrees of latitude between the equator and the South Pole. Directions north or south of the equator and east or west of the prime meridian are needed when stating latitude and longitude.
4. Sequencing: Bangor and Columbus have the same time, Houston, San Francisco, Anchorage
5. Interpreting Data: 300 000 cm ÷ 80 000 cm = 3.75 cm

UNIT 3
GLOBAL CONNECTIONS

Objective

In this unit ending feature, the unit topic, "The Changing Surface of Earth," is extended into other disciplines. Students will see how the study of the processes of weathering, soil formation, erosion, and deposition are important to the progress of other disciplines.

Motivate

Cooperative Learning: Assign one Connection to each group of students. Using the Expert Teams strategy, have each group research to find out more about the geographic location of the Connection—its climate, culture, flora, and fauna, and any geological issues.

Wrap-Up

After students have reviewed all the boxes on these pages, ask them to form a hypothesis about how location affects the types of erosion and deposition that occur.

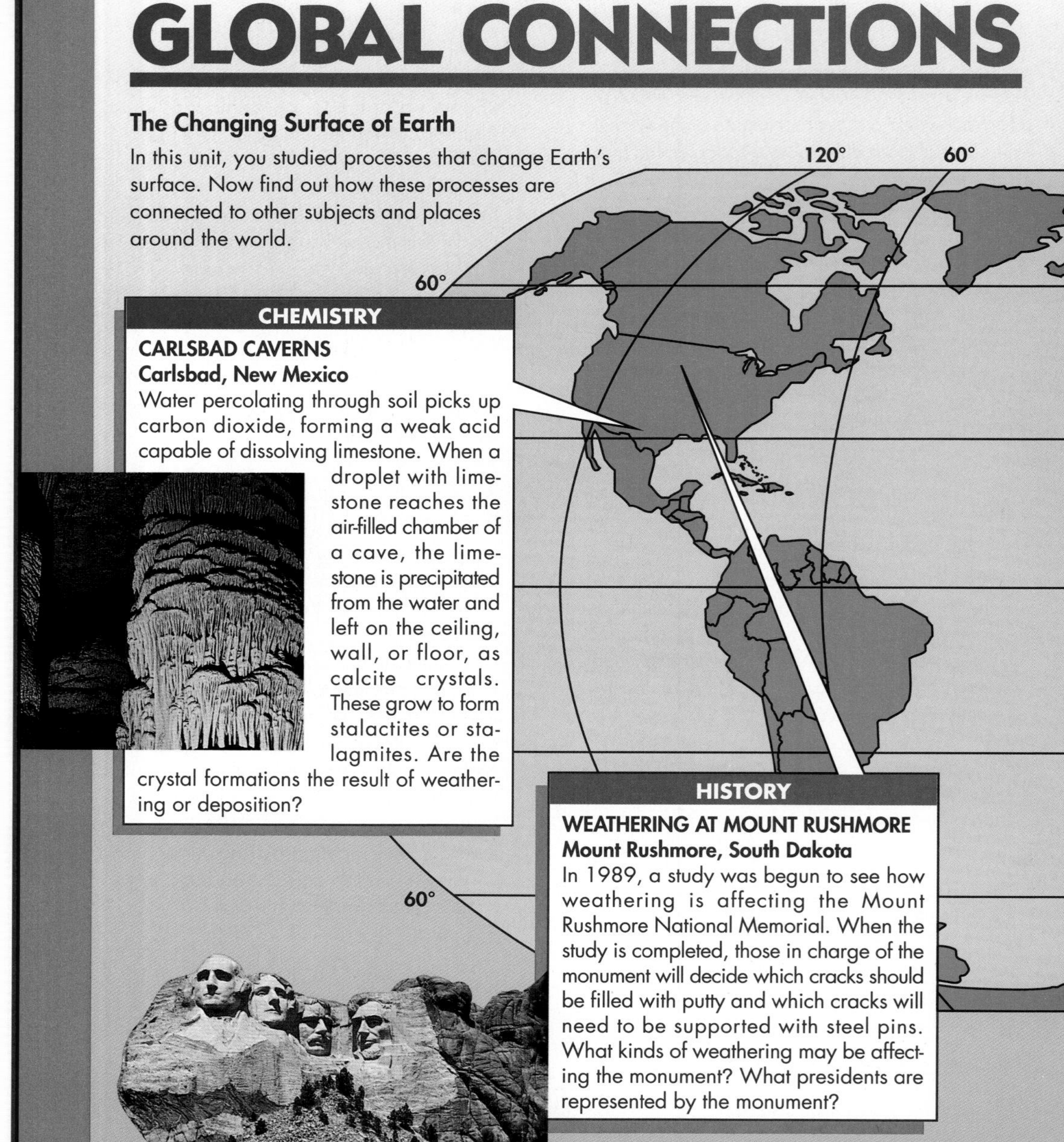

UNIT 3
GLOBAL CONNECTIONS
The Changing Surface of Earth
In this unit, you studied processes that change Earth's surface. Now find out how these processes are connected to other subjects and places around the world.
120°
60°
60°
60°
CHEMISTRY
CARLSBAD CAVERNS
Carlsbad, New Mexico
Water percolating through soil picks up carbon dioxide, forming a weak acid capable of dissolving limestone. When a droplet with limestone reaches the air-filled chamber of a cave, the limestone is precipitated from the water and left on the ceiling, wall, or floor, as calcite crystals. These grow to form stalactites or stalagmites. Are the crystal formations the result of weathering or deposition?
HISTORY
WEATHERING AT MOUNT RUSHMORE
Mount Rushmore, South Dakota
In 1989, a study was begun to see how weathering is affecting the Mount Rushmore National Memorial. When the study is completed, those in charge of the monument will decide which cracks should be filled with putty and which cracks will need to be supported with steel pins. What kinds of weathering may be affecting the monument? What presidents are represented by the monument?
220

CHEMISTRY

Background: The rocks on which the caverns formed are the product of an ancient reef that once flourished along the edge of an inland sea. Tiny lime-secreting algae created a favorable place for other plants and animals to live. Their limestone remains grew to massive proportions. As uplift occurred in the region, groundwater drained away from where the caves are located, creating air-filled openings.

Discussion: Use the picture of the Giant Dome for a discussion of stalactites and stalagmites. When these grow directly opposite each other, they connect and form a column. The Giant Dome is an extraordinary example of a column.

Answer to Question: The actual formations are formed by deposition of limestone on the ceiling, wall, or floor.

Extension: Have students observe the dissolving of limestone by placing a few drops of weak HCl acid on a sample of the rock.

HISTORY

Background: In 1941, sculptor Gutzon Borglum completed the Mount Rushmore National Memorial. He told spectators that he expected the heads of the presidents to last for thousands of years. Although everyone hopes that his expectations will be true, a geotechnical survey has begun to find and fix any trouble spots.

Discussion: Discuss why carving the monuments of George Washington, Thomas Jefferson, Theodore Roosevelt, and Abraham Lincoln, was a great achievement. Ask students why they think each of these four presidents was chosen to be portrayed in granite.

Answer to Question: Mechanical weathering by rain and ice wedging and chemical weathering by carbonic acid may wear down the monuments. Presidents George Washington, Thomas Jefferson, Theodore Roosevelt, and Abraham Lincoln are memorialized by the monument.

Extension: Have students research the birthplaces and accomplishments of the four presidents carved into Mount Rushmore.

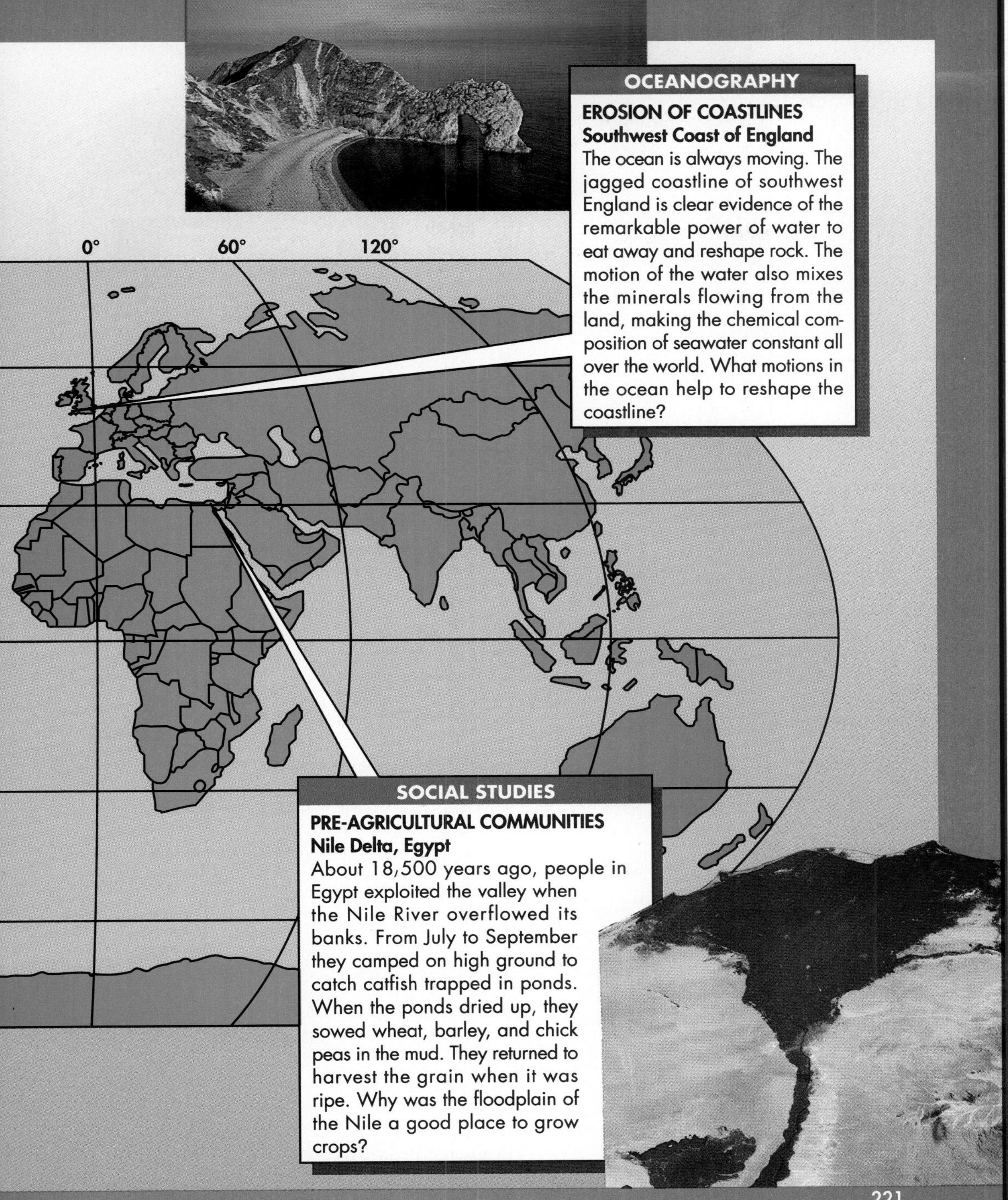

OCEANOGRAPHY

EROSION OF COASTLINES
Southwest Coast of England
The ocean is always moving. The jagged coastline of southwest England is clear evidence of the remarkable power of water to eat away and reshape rock. The motion of the water also mixes the minerals flowing from the land, making the chemical composition of seawater constant all over the world. What motions in the ocean help to reshape the coastline?

SOCIAL STUDIES

PRE-AGRICULTURAL COMMUNITIES
Nile Delta, Egypt
About 18,500 years ago, people in Egypt exploited the valley when the Nile River overflowed its banks. From July to September they camped on high ground to catch catfish trapped in ponds. When the ponds dried up, they sowed wheat, barley, and chick peas in the mud. They returned to harvest the grain when it was ripe. Why was the floodplain of the Nile a good place to grow crops?

OCEANOGRAPHY

Background: When waves break near shore, the greatest wave energy is concentrated on the short stretches of shore around a headland—high land jutting into a body of water. The waves bend around the headland, causing erosion. Where the shore is recessed, wave force is diminished and material is deposited.

Discussion: Discuss the role of currents in carrying material from the land with them, especially on smoothly curving coasts.

Answer to Question: The motions in the ocean that cause the water to eat away and reshape the coastline are currents, tides, and waves.

Extension: Have students make a model coastline in a flat pan. Add water to the pan and vibrate it to simulate wave action.

SOCIAL STUDIES

Background: The first agricultural villages did not appear in Egypt until around 5000 B.C. This is considered the beginning of Egyptian civilization. The bands of people described in the Social Studies Connection combined hunting and gathering with agriculture, but they did not settle down and build a village. It is interesting to note, however, that both the pre-agricultural visitations and the true agricultural villages both occurred in the area of the delta of the Nile and in the flooded Nile River valley.

Discussion: Have students discuss the importance of establishing permanent villages as the cornerstone for the beginning of civilization. Only after people began to live in villages did they have a highly organized society.

Answers to Question: The river deposits many sediments when it overflows its banks. As a result, the Nile floodplain is composed of rich, fertile soil.

Extension: Have students use topographic maps to measure the size of a rich, fertile floodplain of a nearby river.

SOIL ENGINEER

Background: Soil engineers work for large construction companies, government agencies, or private materials laboratories. For someone who enjoys working outdoors, this may be a good career.

Related Career	Education
Soil Conservation Technician	high school
Civil Engineer	college
Excavating Contractor	trade school
Bulldozer Operator	trade school

Career Issue: There are usually ways to make less safe soil secure enough to build on. If the builders dig deeper until they reach a harder layer of soil, they can pour concrete caissons. These will make the soil safe for building a road or bridge.

What do you think? Lead students in a discussion of the concerns builders and soil engineers have in making buildings safe.

FOREST TECHNICIAN

Background: Most forest technicians work for the federal government, although large companies that own timberlands may also employ technicians, especially to help protect against forest fires.

Career Issue: A forest technician working for the Federal Government generally receives good fringe bene-

Related Career	Education
Forest Ranger	college
Wildlife Manager	college
Forest Fire Aide	high school
Rancher	high school

fits—for example, pension and retirement plans, health and life insurance, and paid vacations. Sometimes these benefits are more important to a worker than earning a higher salary.

What do you think? Have students list the pros and cons of a career as a forest technician.

CAREERS

SOIL ENGINEER

A *soil engineer* tests the soil during every stage of excavation for buildings, roads, tunnels, and bridges. In areas of the country where there is a danger of earthquakes, the importance of a soil engineer is greatly increased. At each level during the excavation, a sample of the soil is taken. Every sample is subjected to several tests: a hammer is used to pound the soil. A soil that has a density of 1.8 g/cm^3 may be compacted to a density of 0.2 g/cm^3. The tests help the soil engineer to decide whether or not it's safe to build on the land. They may prevent a later disaster.

A soil engineer usually obtains a degree as a civil engineer and then specializes in geotechnical subjects. A student interested in becoming a soil engineer should take courses in mathematics and physics.

For Additional Information

Contact the American Society of Civil Engineers, 345 E. 47th Street, New York, NY 10017.

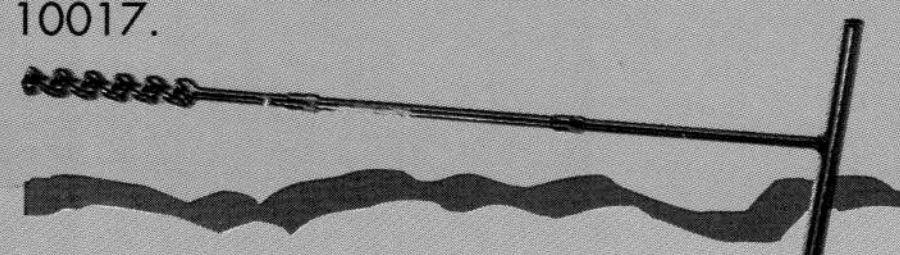

FOREST TECHNICIAN

A *forest technician* may assist forest rangers in the work of preserving our national parks. Sometimes the work involves protecting the national monuments in the parks. For example, the technicians may check that no visitor to the Mount Rushmore National Memorial causes any harm to the monument. They also monitor damage done to the monuments by acid rain.

A forest technician usually has a two-year associate degree. In some states, a high school diploma followed by extensive on-the-job training is sufficient to become a forest technician.

For Additional Information

Contact the Society of American Foresters, 5400 Grovenor Lane, Bethesda, MD 20814.

UNIT READINGS

► Albright, Horace M., Russ Dickenson, and William Penn Mott, Jr. *National Park Service: The Story Behind the Scenery 1916-1986.* Las Vegas, Nevada: KC Publications, 1986.

► "Saving Face: Mount Rushmore National Memorial." *Life,* February 1990, pp. 50-52.

READINGS

Background

► Both *Grand Canyon: The Story Behind the Scenes* and *National Park Service and Grand Canyon: The Story Behind the Scenery* are beautifully illustrated books that provide the reader with an understanding of the greatness of the land preserved in our national parks.

► "Saving Face: Mount Rushmore National Memorial" describes the study being carried out to preserve the memorial.

More Readings

1. Tuttle, S. D. *Landforms and Landscapes.* Dubuque, Iowa: Wm. C. Brown Publishers, 1980. This book covers in a comprehensive way the story of erosion and deposition.
2. Chodorow, Stanley, et al. *A History of the World.* San Diego: Harcourt Brace Jovanovich, Inc., 1986, pp. 18, 33-34. This book contains much interesting information about pre-agricultural societies.

SCIENCE & LITERATURE

Los Angeles, A Mobile Society

by Art Buchwald

The excerpt that follows gives Art Buchwald's humorous account of life in Los Angeles.

Los Angeles—I came to Los Angeles last week for rest and recreation, only to discover that it had become a rain forest.

I didn't realize how bad it was until I went to dinner at a friend's house. I had the right address, but when I arrived there was nothing there. I went to a neighboring house where I found a man bailing out his swimming pool.

"I beg your pardon," I said. "Could you tell me where the Cables live?"

"They used to live above us on the hill. Then about two years ago, their house slid down in the mud, and they lived next door to us. I think it was last Monday, during the storm, that their house slid down there. We were sorry to see them go—they were really nice neighbors."

I thanked him and slid straight down the hill to the new location of the Cables' house....

"Cable," I said, "You and your wife are intelligent people, why do you build your house on the top of a canyon, when you know that during a rainstorm it has a good chance of sliding away?"

"It's hard for people who don't live in California to understand how we people out here think. Sure we have floods, and fire and drought, but that's the price you have to pay for living the good life. When Esther and I saw this house, we knew it was a dream come true. It was located right on the tippy top of the hill, way up there. We would wake up in the morning and listen to the birds, and eat breakfast out on the patio and look down on all the smog.

"Then, after the first mudslide, we found ourselves living next to people. It was an entirely different experience. But by that time we were ready for a change. Now we've slid again and we're in a whole new neighborhood. You can't do that if you live on solid ground. Once you move into a house below Sunset Boulevard, you're stuck there for the rest of your life."

In Your Own Words

▶ Why do you think Art Buchwald wrote a humorous article about such a serious topic? Write an essay to explain your reasoning.

223

Source: Syndicated column by Art Buchwald.

Biography: Art Buchwald (1925-) is a syndicated newspaper columnist, humorist, and author, well-known for his witty commentaries about whatever is in the news. His newspaper columns are syndicated in 550 newspapers throughout the world. Buchwald received the Pulitzer Prize for outstanding commentary.

TEACHING STRATEGY

▶ Ask students to discuss the opinions they expressed in the essay about whether a humorist should discuss such a serious topic as a mudslide in a light-hearted way.

Cooperative Learning: Have students work together to identify in Art Buchwald's essay other problems besides mudslides that are due to natural causes and that people in California are often subjected to.

Cooperative Learning: Have students work together to list ways in which a humorous work can achieve the same goal as a serious piece of literature.

▶ Possible essay topics for students to write about include erosion of a favorite rock, erosion at the seashore, deposition on a river bank.

▶ Ask students to look for Art Buchwald's column in the newspapers. Have them share their findings.

Other Works

▶ Other essays by Art Buchwald pertaining to mudslides or other earth science issues:

Buchwald, Art. "The Hazards of EPA." *While Reagan Slept.* New York: G.P. Putnam's Sons, 1983. Buchwald, Art. "The U.S. Garage Sale." *While Reagan Slept.* New York: G.P. Putnam's Sons, 1983.

Classics

▶ Barnett, John. *Carlsbad Caverns National Park.* Salt Lake City, Utah: Deseret Press. Spectacular photography makes this book an unforgettable, vicarious visit to the caverns. John Barnett, a former park naturalist, takes the reader to his favorite haunts.

▶ Sharpe, C.F.S. *Landslides and Related Phenomena.* New York: Columbia University Press. Reprinted in 1960 by Pageant Press. This is a classic that is well worth the time of any student interested in landslides.

UNIT

4

EARTH'S AIR AND WATER

In Unit 4, students are introduced to Earth's atmosphere and oceans. The characteristics and movement of Earth's air and water are presented.

CONTENTS

ADVANCE PREPARATION

Activities

▶ **Activity 9-1, page 235,** requires small coffee cans. Have your students save them and bring them from home.

▶ **Activity 11-2, page 297,** requires a 3-speed electric fan.

▶ **Activity 12-1, page 311,** requires samples of sand from three different beaches.

Audiovisuals

▶ **Section 10-2, page 262:** Arrange to show the video "Miracle Planet—Patterns in the Air," KCTS Television.

▶ **Section 11-1, page 282:** Arrange to show the filmstrip/cassette "The Oceans: Exploring Earth's Last Frontier," National Geographic.

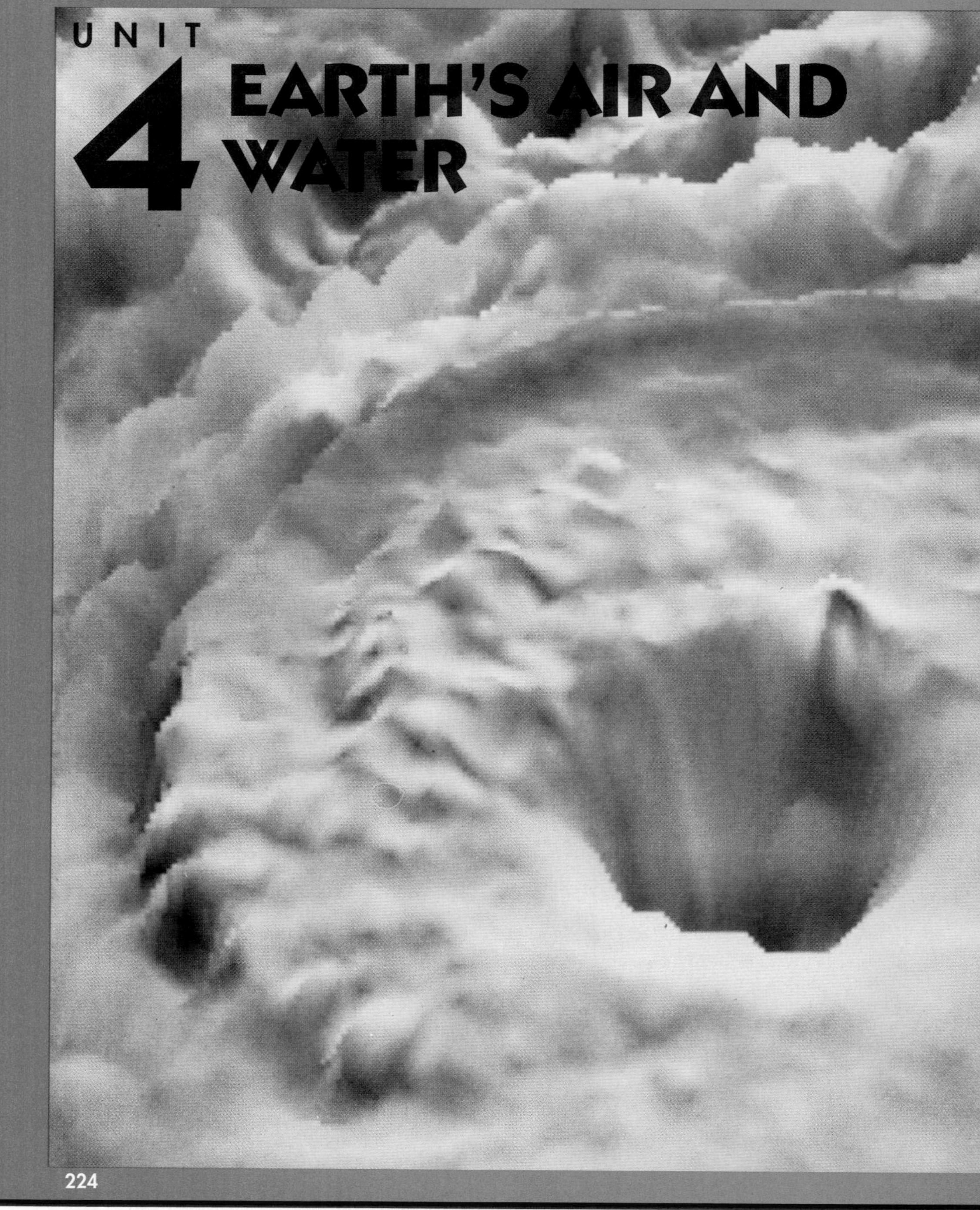

OPTIONS

Cross Curriculum

▶ Have students write papers that describe how access to ocean shipping routes has caused political disputes between neighboring countries, as well as countries far apart.

▶ Have students discuss how winds in Earth's atmosphere might affect the flight time of commercial airliners.

Science at Home

▶ Have students observe the cloud cover each afternoon after class. Ask them to draw a picture of the type of cloud they observe and to use Table 10-1 on page 258 to name each type they observe.

Cooperative Learning: Using the Paired Partners strategy, have students draw the major cloud types on flash cards. On the reverse of each card, students can identify each cloud type. Partners can then test each other using the flash cards.

What's Happening Here?

Hurricanes, the largest and most powerful storms in Earth's atmosphere, form over tropical regions of the oceans. As long as they remain over water, they gain energy and become stronger. Satellite photographs from space enable scientists to track these storms. When hurricanes reach land, they can cause tremendous destruction. People can be warned to evacuate, but their homes and businesses often can't be saved. As you read the chapters in Unit 4, you'll discover how Earth's atmosphere and oceans interact to generate storms and other weather.

UNIT CONTENTS

Multicultural Awareness

Have students research cultural differences, emphasizing eating and working habits, of people living near the shore compared with those of people living farther inland in the United States. Have students continue with a comparison of cultural differences between people who live near the shore in industrialized countries and those living near the shore in agricultural countries.

Inquiry Questions

Use the following questions to focus a discussion of how movement of air in Earth's atmosphere affects the movement of water in Earth's oceans.

1. Compare Figure 9-13 (page 247) and Figure 11-5 (page 288). What relationship do major wind systems in Earth's atmosphere have to surface currents in Earth's oceans?
2. How do large bodies of water cause small-scale sea breezes and land breezes?
3. What process causes water to begin to move, which in turn forms ocean currents?

INTRODUCING THE UNIT

What's Happening Here?

▶ Have students look at the photos and read the text. Ask them to tell you what's happening here. Point out to students that in this unit they will be studying the interaction of air and water in Earth's atmosphere and oceans. Point out to students that the large photo shown is a computer-generated image. It was constructed from data collected by a satellite of an actual hurricane.

▶ **Background:** Hurricanes are given names for scientific and safety reasons. Scientists refer to hurricanes by name rather than by position and it is easier to alert the public about the approach of a hurricane when referring to it by name. The earlier method of identifying hurricanes by longitude and latitude proved too confusing for radio reports.

Previewing the Chapters

▶ Have students read the objectives for each lesson and then search for charts and photographs that relate to each objective.

▶ Have students read the captions to several figures in the unit. Have volunteers briefly describe what they see in each photograph or illustration.

▶ Prior to reading each chapter, have students read the section review questions to help them determine what the key concepts of each lesson are.

Tying to Previous Knowledge

▶ Ask if any students have ever experienced severe thunderstorms, tornadoes, or hurricanes. Have volunteers describe what happened and what precautions they and other people around them took to protect themselves.

▶ Ask students, "How many of you have ever been to a beach near a large body of water?" Call on a volunteer to describe the topography of the land near the beach. Ask students who have visited different beaches to share their experience with the class. You might suggest that they describe the characteristics of the sand found on the beach.

▶ Use the **Inquiry Questions** in the OPTIONS box to the left to investigate with students how movement of air in Earth's atmosphere affects movement of water in the oceans.

CHAPTER 9 Air

CHAPTER SECTION	OBJECTIVES	ACTIVITIES
9-1 Earth's Atmosphere (2 days)	1. **Name** the common gases in Earth's atmosphere. 2. **Describe** the structure of Earth's atmosphere. 3. **Explain** what causes air pressure.	**MINI-Lab:** *Does air have mass?* p. 232 **Activity 9-1:** *Air Pressure,* p. 235
9-2 The Ozone Layer Science & Society (1 day)	1. **Explain** why exposure to ultraviolet radiation can be a problem for plants and animals. 2. **Describe** how chlorofluorocarbons destroy ozone molecules.	
9-3 Energy from the Sun (2 days)	1. **Describe** three things that happen to the energy Earth receives from the sun. 2. **Contrast** radiation, conduction, and convection.	**Activity 9-2:** *Heating Differences of Soil and Water,* p. 243
9-4 Movement of Air (1 day)	1. **Explain** why different latitudes receive different amounts of solar energy. 2. **Describe** causes of the Coriolis effect, sea breezes, and land breezes. 3. **Locate** the positions of the doldrums, trade winds, prevailing westerlies, and polar easterlies.	**MINI-LAB:** *What do convection currents look like?* p. 246
Chapter Review		

ACTIVITY MATERIALS

FIND OUT	ACTIVITIES		MINI-LABS	
Page 227 water metal can w/cap hot plate or other burner	**9-1 Air Pressure, p. 235** coffee can drinking straw rubber balloon heavy paper transparent tape scissors metric ruler rubber band	**9-2 Heating Differences of Soil and Water, p. 243** ring stand soil metric ruler graph paper clear plastic boxes overhead light with reflector thermometers water masking tape colored pencils	**Does air have mass? p. 232** pan balance football, basketball, or volleyball air pump w/ball inflation needle	**What do convection currents look like? p. 246** 500-mL glass beaker or 2-L glass saucepan water food coloring hot plate or stove

CHAPTER FEATURES	TEACHER RESOURCE PACKAGE	OTHER RESOURCES
Skill Builder: *Making and Using Graphs,* p. 234	**Ability Level Worksheets** ◆ ***Study Guide,*** p. 38 ● ***Reinforcement,*** p. 38 ▲ ***Enrichment,*** p. 38 **MINI-Lab Worksheet,** p. 83 **Activity Worksheet,** pp. 77-78 **Transparency Masters,** pp. 27-30	**Color Transparency 14,** Composition of the Atmosphere **Color Transparency 15,** Layers of the Atmosphere **Lab Manual:** *Air,* pp. 77-78 **Lab Manual:** *Air Pressure,* pp. 79-80
You Decide! p. 237	**Ability Level Worksheets** ◆ ***Study Guide,*** p. 39 ● ***Reinforcement,*** p. 39 ▲ ***Enrichment,*** p. 39 **Critical Thinking/Problem Solving,** p. 15 **Cross-Curricular Connections,** p. 13 **Science and Society,** p. 13	
Skill Builder: *Concept Mapping,* p. 242	**Ability Level Worksheets** ◆ ***Study Guide,*** p. 40 ● ***Reinforcement,*** p. 40 ▲ ***Enrichment,*** p. 40 **Activity Worksheet,** pp. 79-80	**Lab Manual:** *Temperature of the Air,* pp. 81-82
Problem Solving: *The Coriolis-go-around,* p. 245 **Skill Builder:** *Comparing and Contrasting,* p. 248	**Ability Level Worksheets** ◆ ***Study Guide,*** p. 41 ● ***Reinforcement,*** p. 41 ▲ ***Enrichment,*** p. 41 **MINI-Lab Worksheet,** p. 84 **Concept Mapping,** pp. 23-24 **Transparency Masters,** pp. 31-32	**Color Transparency 16,** Major Air Circulation **Lab Manual:** *Air in Motion,* pp. 83-84
Summary Key Science Words Understanding Vocabulary Checking Concepts Understanding Concepts Think & Write Critically Apply More Skill Builders Projects	**Chapter Review,** pp. 21-22 **Chapter Test,** pp. 62-65	**Chapter Review Software** **Test Bank**

◆ **Basic** ● **Average** ▲ **Advanced**

ADDITIONAL MATERIALS

SOFTWARE	AUDIOVISUAL	BOOKS/MAGAZINES
Your Universe, SVE. *Earth Science 2,* Texas Instruments, Data Systems Group. *Moisture in the Atmosphere,* IBM. *Earth's Atmosphere,* Queue.	*Above the Horizon,* film, UEVA. *Heat and Temperature,* film, Coronet/MTI. *What Makes the Wind Blow?* film, EBEC. *The Atmosphere in Motion,* film, EBEC. *What Makes Clouds?/What Makes the Wind Blow?,* laserdisc, EBEC.	Barry, Roger B. and Richard J. Chorley. *Atmosphere, Weather, and Climate.* NY: Routledge, Chapman, and Hall, Inc., 1988. Jones, R. Russell ed. and T. Wigley. *Ozone Depletion and Health.* NY: John Wiley and Sons, Inc., 1989. Riehl, Herbert. *Introduction to the Atmosphere.* NY: McGraw-Hill Publishing Co., 1978.

CHAPTER

AIR

THEME DEVELOPMENT: Three foci of the energy theme are: the sun is the source of energy for atmospheric heat; energy transfer is by radiation, conduction, and convection; and temperature differences on the surface result in wind. Scale and structure are emphasized through a discussion of the composition and structure of the atmosphere.

CHAPTER OVERVIEW

- **Section 9-1:** This section discusses the composition and structure of the atmosphere.
- **Section 9-2: Science and Society:** The You Decide feature asks students to consider which conveniences they would give up if these things proved to cause holes in Earth's ozone layer.
- **Section 9-3:** Energy transfer by radiation, conduction, and convection is described.
- **Section 9-4:** The roles of solar energy and the Coriolis effect on the movement of air are explained. Major wind systems are described.

CHAPTER VOCABULARY

troposphere	doldrums
ionosphere	trade winds
ozone layer	prevailing westerlies
ultraviolet radiation	polar easterlies
chlorofluorocarbons	jet streams
radiation	sea breezes
conduction	land breezes
convection	
Coriolis effect	

CHAPTER 9 Air

226

OPTIONS

For Your Gifted Students

Have students work in small groups to write plays or skits about how different "wild things" might be affected by the depletion of the ozone layer. The characters in the skits can be old or young and living or nonliving. Each "wild thing" could discuss how it feels about all the changes that it is experiencing and its concerns for the future. Costumes can be made and the skits performed for the class. Encourage creativity, yet insist on scientific accuracy.

How do these hot-air balloons float in the atmosphere? How is the atmosphere inside a giant balloon different from the atmosphere outside of it? Heat makes molecules of air inside the balloon move away from each other. Therefore, the air inside the balloon has less density than the colder air around it. The cold air pushes the balloon up into the atmosphere.

FIND OUT!

Your teacher will perform this simple activity to demonstrate how temperature affects the density of air.

Your teacher will pour a small quantity of water into a metal can. Then, with the cap still off, he or she will heat the can over a hot plate or other burner. When the water begins to boil, the heat source is turned off and the cap is screwed on the metal can. Watch what happens as the can cools. Why does the can collapse in on itself?

Gearing Up

Previewing the Chapter

Use this outline to help you focus on important ideas in this chapter.

Previewing Science Skills

- In the **Skill Builders,** you will make and use graphs, make concept maps, and compare and contrast.
- In the **Activities,** you will record and analyze data and observations and draw conclusions.
- In the **MINI-Labs,** you will measure in SI, observe, and infer.

What's next?

Now that you've seen how the density of air increases and decreases because of changes in its temperature, you can see how this affects air pressure within our atmosphere. You'll also explore the composition and structure of Earth's atmosphere and how air pressure changes within it.

INTRODUCING THE CHAPTER

Use the Find Out activity to introduce students to air pressure. Inform students that they will be learning more about air pressure as they read this chapter.

FIND OUT!

Preparation: Obtain one clean, empty metal can with a cap for each class you teach.

Materials: one clean metal can with cap, water, hot plate or other burner

Teaching Tips

- Use steel cans with tightly fitting caps for best results.
- Explain to students that when the water begins to boil, water vapor molecules escape from the can; thus, the density of molecules in the can is reduced. Then, when the can is capped, the air molecules outside the can cannot get in to replace the molecules that escaped. As the air inside the can cools, the molecules cluster together, creating very little pressure against the inside of the can. The air pressure outside the can is greater than the pressure inside; thus, the can collapses.

Gearing Up

Have students study the Gearing Up feature to familiarize themselves with the chapter. Discuss the relationships of the topics in the outline.

What's Next?

Before beginning the first section, make sure students understand the connection between the Find Out activity and the topics to follow.

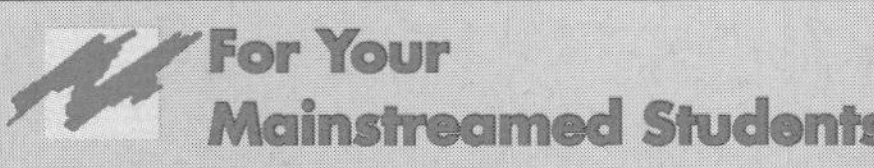

For Your Mainstreamed Students

Have students chart the movement of air within the classroom. Carefully light the end of a wax taper or piece of string and have students observe the smoke patterns created. Make sure that the class is very still and the movement of bodies does not disrupt the air flow. Then have students make a diagram of the room and include the pattern of air flow within the room.

SECTION 9-1

PREPARATION

SECTION BACKGROUND

▶ Earth's original atmosphere was probably composed mostly of methane and ammonia. This primitive atmosphere changed over geologic time as erupting volcanoes emitted gases such as water vapor, carbon dioxide, and nitrogen. As Earth continued to cool after its formation, the water vapor condensed and absorbed most of the carbon dioxide. Oxygen was probably formed from the dissociation of water molecules and by photosynthesis of primitive plants.

▶ The gases of Earth's atmosphere are selective absorbers of energy from the sun. The type of energy absorbed by the atmosphere depends on the kinds of gases that are present.

PREPLANNING

▶ To prepare for the Mini-Lab on page 232, obtain pan balances, inflatable balls, and an air pump with a ball inflation needle.

▶ To prepare for Activity 9-1, obtain small coffee cans, drinking straws, rubber balloons, heavy paper, transparent tape, scissors, metric rulers, and rubber bands.

1 MOTIVATE

▶ Ask students what they know about air pollution. Ask them how they think pollutants affect the atmosphere. This exercise will logically lead to a discussion of the composition of the atmosphere.

9-1 Earth's Atmosphere

New Science Words

troposphere
ionosphere

Objectives

- ▶ Name the common gases in Earth's atmosphere.
- ▶ Describe the structure of Earth's atmosphere.
- ▶ Explain what causes air pressure.

Composition of the Atmosphere

It's early morning and you're getting dressed for work. As you eat breakfast, you read the weather report coming over the computer screen. The report says "Smog levels are higher than normal, temperatures will near 38°C, and the ozone layer in the stratosphere is thinner than yesterday." You realize you'll need your filter mask to protect your lungs from the smog. Pollution in the atmosphere has raised the temperature, so you'll have to wear clothes designed to keep you cool. The thin ozone layer means you'll have to use a strong sunblock lotion to protect yourself from skin cancer. It's an average day in the city.

Does this sound like your future? It's one possible future you may face. Your life depends on the air you breathe and the condition of the atmosphere that you live in. But what do you know about the atmosphere? You

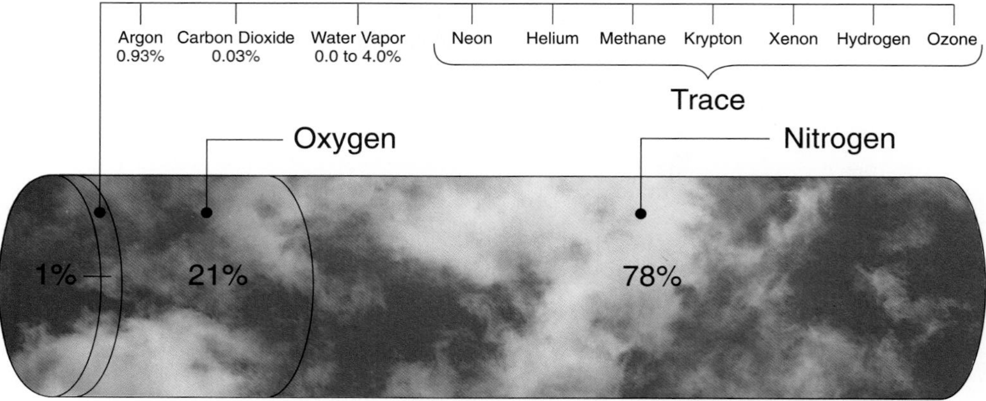

Figure 9-1. This graph illustrates the percentages of gases in our atmosphere.

OPTIONS

Meeting Different Ability Levels

For Section 9-1, use the following **Teacher Resource Masters** depending upon individual students' needs.

◆ **Study Guide Master** for all students.

● **Reinforcement Master** for students of average and above average ability levels.

▲ **Enrichment Master** for above average students.

Additional Teacher Resource Package masters are listed in the OPTIONS box throughout the section. The additional masters are appropriate for all students.

◆ STUDY GUIDE 38

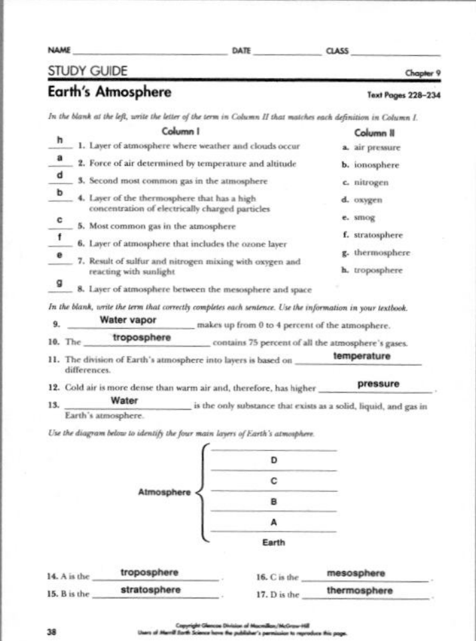

NAME ______ DATE ______ CLASS ______

STUDY GUIDE Chapter 9

Earth's Atmosphere Text Pages 228–234

In the blank at the left, write the letter of the term in Column II that matches each definition in Column I.

	Column I	Column II
h	1. Layer of atmosphere where weather and clouds occur	a. air pressure
a	2. Force of air determined by temperature and altitude	b. ionosphere
d	3. Second most common gas in the atmosphere	c. nitrogen
b	4. Layer of the thermosphere that has a high concentration of electrically charged particles	d. oxygen
c	5. Most common gas in the atmosphere	e. smog
f	6. Layer of atmosphere that includes the ozone layer	f. stratosphere
e	7. Result of sulfur and nitrogen mixing with oxygen and reacting with sunlight	g. thermosphere
g	8. Layer of atmosphere between the mesosphere and space	h. troposphere

In the blank, write the term that correctly completes each sentence. Use the information in your textbook.

9. Water vapor makes up from 0 to 4 percent of the atmosphere.
10. The troposphere contains 75 percent of all the atmosphere's gases.
11. The division of Earth's atmosphere into layers is based on temperature differences.
12. Cold air is more dense than warm air and, therefore, has higher pressure.
13. Water is the only substance that exists as a solid, liquid, and gas in Earth's atmosphere.

Use the diagram below to identify the four main layers of Earth's atmosphere.

Atmosphere: D, C, B, A; Earth

14. A is the troposphere.
15. B is the stratosphere.
16. C is the mesosphere.
17. D is the thermosphere.

38

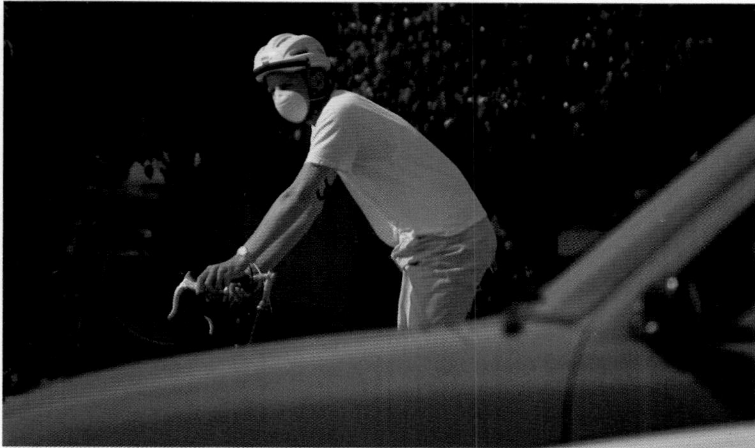

Figure 9-2. When pollution levels are high, it's necessary to protect ourselves from the harmful side effects of breathing smog.

learned in Chapter 2 that the atmosphere is a mixture. What types of substances make up this mixture? Learning about the composition and structure of the atmosphere will help you make decisions to protect it for your future.

The atmosphere surrounding Earth is a mixture of solids, liquids, and gases. In Figure 9-1 you see a graph of the gases in Earth's atmosphere. Nitrogen is the most common gas. Water vapor can make up from zero to four percent of the atmosphere. When the volume of water vapor is high, the percentages of other gases is slightly lower.

The smog in the atmosphere is a mixture of compounds that include sulfur, nitrogen, and oxygen. When we burn coal, gasoline, and other fossil fuels, we produce sulfur and nitrogen. The sulfur and nitrogen combine with oxygen in the atmosphere, and sunlight then reacts with these gases to produce smog.

Smog is a type of pollution. It's visible as a smoke-like haze hanging over cities and towns. One component of smog is called ozone. As you'll learn in Section 9-2, ozone is a compound that occurs naturally higher up in the atmosphere. But when it's present where plants and animals come in contact with it, it can be very harmful.

Gases aren't the only thing making up Earth's atmosphere. Dust and ice are two common solids found in the atmospheric mixture. Dust gets into the atmosphere when wind picks it up off the ground and erodes it. Ice is common in the form of hailstones and snowflakes.

Did You Know?

Earth's original atmosphere had almost no oxygen. Organisms called cyanobacteria, living about 3.5 billion years ago, produced oxygen as part of their life processes. Eventually, enough oxygen existed in the atmosphere that lifeforms that use oxygen could evolve.

TYING TO PREVIOUS KNOWLEDGE: Ask students to explain why they may suffer earaches when riding in an airplane. Earaches occur when the air pressure is not equal on both sides of the eardrum. If the airplane cabin is properly pressurized, earaches will not occur.

OBJECTIVES AND SCIENCE WORDS: Have students review the objectives and science words to become familiar with this section.

2 TEACH

Key Concepts are highlighted.

CONCEPT DEVELOPMENT

▶ Stress that even though carbon dioxide, water vapor, and ozone make up a small percentage of the air, they are important in terms of weather and atmospheric processes.

▶ After students read pages 228 and 229, pose the following questions. **What is the most common gas in the atmosphere?** *nitrogen* **What is smog?** *a type of pollution created when sulfur, nitrogen, and oxygen mix and then react with sunlight*

● REINFORCEMENT 38

NAME ______ DATE ______ CLASS ______

REINFORCEMENT — Chapter 9

Earth's Atmosphere — Text Pages 228–234

Use the chart to answer Questions 1–4.

Gas	Percent by volume	Gas	Percent by volume
A	78.09	Helium	trace
B	20.95	Methane	trace
Argon	0.93	Krypton	trace
Carbon dioxide	0.03	Xenon	trace
C	0.0 to 4.0	Hydrogen	trace
Neon	trace	Ozone	trace

1. What information does the chart show? **the names and percentages of the gases found in Earth's atmosphere**
2. A, B, and C, represent three different gases. What is A? **nitrogen** How do you know? **Nitrogen is the most abundant gas in air.**
3. What is B? **oxygen** How do you know? **Oxygen is the second most abundant gas in air.**
4. What is C? **water vapor** How do you know? **Water vapor amounts in air can vary between 0.0 and 4.0%**

The diagram below represents the layers of Earth's atmosphere. Write the names of the layers in the space provided.

5. **thermosphere** / **ionosphere**
6. **mesosphere**
7. **stratosphere**
8. **troposphere**

Earth

Atmosphere

9. In which layer(s) does the temperature increase? **thermosphere, ionosphere, and stratosphere**
10. In which layer(s) does the temperature decrease? **mesosphere, troposphere**
11. Which layer contains electrically charged particles that reflect radio waves? **ionosphere**

38

▲ ENRICHMENT 38

NAME ______ DATE ______ CLASS ______

ENRICHMENT — Chapter 9

Earth's Atmosphere — Text Pages 228–234

OBSERVING THE EFFECTS OF AIR PRESSURE

The activity at the beginning of the chapter showed how temperature affects the density of air. When the air in a closed can became heated by boiling water, it expanded and much of it escaped out of the can before the top was put on. As the air that was left inside cooled, it became more dense and took up less space. Because the air pressure on the outside of the can was higher than the pressure inside the can, the sides of the can collapsed. You could see what a powerful force air pressure can be. Here's another experiment about the power of air pressure.

Materials

- glass bottle
- sheet of paper
- long match or paper drinking straw and match
- hard-boiled egg, peeled

Procedure

1. Be sure that the opening at the top of the glass bottle is slightly smaller than the diameter of the egg.
2. Crumple the sheet of paper into a ball and drop it into the bottle.
3. Light the end of the paper drinking straw or the long match and hold the burning end on the paper in the bottle until the paper begins to burn.
4. Let the paper burn until the flame burns out.
5. Set the peeled hard-boiled egg over the opening at the top of the bottle with the pointed end of the egg down.

Analyze

1. What happened to the egg? **It was sucked into the bottle.**
2. What caused the egg to do this? **The burning paper burned up the available oxygen in the bottle and the heat made the molecules in the remaining air move farther apart or become less dense. The air pressure on the inside of the bottle became lower than the air pressure on the outside. The outside air pressure pushed the egg into the bottle.**

Conclude and Apply

3. How can you get the egg out? **Increase the air pressure inside of the bottle. Hold the bottle upside down at an angle with the egg's small end over the opening. Blow hard into the bottle. This should increase the air pressure. Quickly turn the bottle completely upside down with the egg over the opening. If you increase the air pressure enough, the egg will be pushed out.**

38

CONCEPT DEVELOPMENT

▶ Use Figure 9-3 to stress that each layer of Earth's atmosphere has unique characteristics.

▶ As a component of the stratosphere, the ozone layer is several kilometers thick. Looking at Figure 9-3, students may infer that there is an abundance of ozone molecules. Inform students that the ozone layer is thick because the molecules are widely dispersed in the stratosphere. If all the ozone molecules in the atmosphere were brought down to sea level, where pressure is greater, it would form a layer less than 3.0 mm thick.

▶ After students have read the Science and Society feature, which discusses the ozone layer, refer back to Figure 9-3 to discuss the scale and structure of the ozone layer and the stratosphere.

TEACHER F.Y.I.

▶ The uppermost portion of the thermosphere is called the exosphere. The exosphere, extending from about 500 km outward, marks the transition from Earth's atmosphere to the extremely sparse interplanetary gas.

▶ At the exosphere, molecules of hydrogen and helium leave the atmosphere. These light molecules, which have absorbed radiation from the sun, move so fast they escape Earth's gravitational field. As a result, there is a constant seepage of gases into outer space.

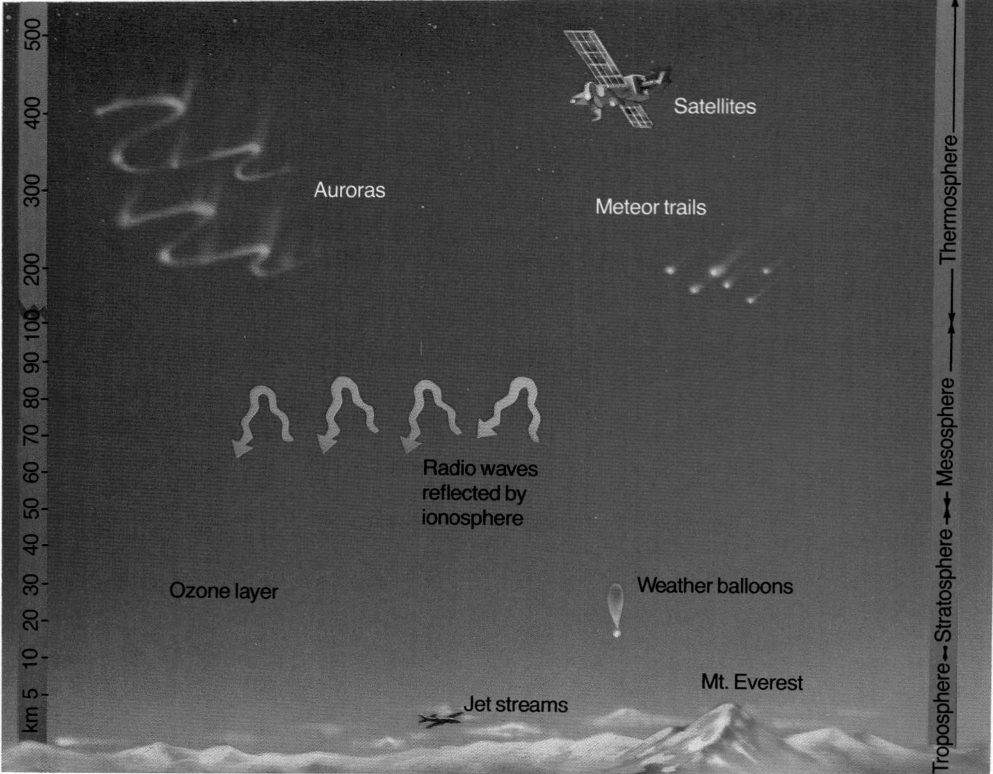

Figure 9-3. Although Earth's atmosphere extends nearly 700 kilometers upward, 75 percent of all its gases are in the lowest 15 kilometers.

The other components of the atmosphere are liquids. The most common liquid in the atmosphere is water. Water is the only substance that exists as a solid, liquid, and gas in Earth's atmosphere.

Structure of the Atmosphere

The weather forecast on this morning in your future said that the smog was heavy and the ozone layer in the stratosphere was thin. Both will affect how you're able to spend your day. But what do you know about smog and the ozone layer? Where do each of these occur in the atmosphere?

Earth's atmosphere has four main layers, each with its own unique characteristics. In Figure 9-3 you see that the 1 names of these layers are troposphere, stratosphere, mesosphere, and thermosphere.

OPTIONS

INQUIRY QUESTIONS

▶ **What substances besides gases make up the atmosphere?** *Solids such as dust and ice and liquid water are parts of the atmosphere.*

PROGRAM RESOURCES

From the **Teacher Resource Package** use:

Transparency Masters, pages 27-28, Composition of the Atmosphere.

Transparency Masters, pages 29-30, Layers of the Atmosphere.

Use **Color Transparency** number 14, Composition of the Atmosphere.

Use **Color Transparency** number 15, Layers of the Atmosphere.

You live in the troposphere. It's the layer closest to the 2
ground. The **troposphere** contains 75 percent of all the atmosphere's gases, as well as dust, ice, and liquid water. This layer is where weather and clouds occur. It's also where smog is found.

Above the troposphere lies the stratosphere. Within the stratosphere a layer of ozone exists. It's this ozone 3
layer that was mentioned in this morning's forecast. As you already know, the ozone layer in the stratosphere is important because it directly affects your health. You'll learn more about this layer in Section 9-2 later in this chapter.

Where is the ozone layer located?

Beyond the stratosphere are the mesosphere and thermosphere. One important layer of the thermosphere is the **ionosphere.** It's a layer of electrically charged particles. When these particles are bombarded by energy from space, ions and free electrons are created. These particles are useful for communications because they reflect radio waves. Radio transmissions from one side of the globe can be received on the other side of the globe because they bounce off the ionosphere. Figure 9-4 illustrates how this is possible.

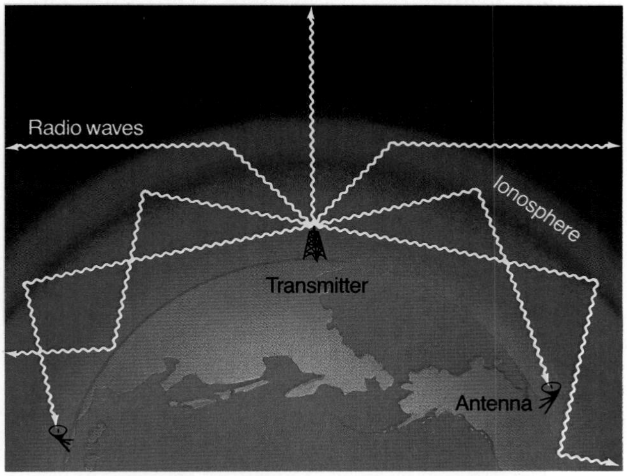

Figure 9-4. Radio waves that strike the ionosphere at sharp angles pass through to space. Some strike at lower angles and are reflected. These may be received by antennas around the globe.

When particles of matter from the sun strike the ionosphere, the ions glow in different colors. The result is visible bands of shimmering light called auroras. The famous Northern and Southern Lights are auroras.

CONCEPT DEVELOPMENT

▶ Ask the following questions. **In which layer of the atmosphere are weather, clouds, and smog found?** *They're in the troposphere.* **Where is Earth's ozone layer?** *in the stratosphere*

▶ Inform students that the data in Figure 9-1 represent the composition of Earth's atmosphere at sea level. The amounts and types of gases change with an increase in altitude.

CROSS CURRICULUM

▶ **Language Arts:** Have students use dictionaries to determine the meanings of the prefixes *meso, thermo,* and *iono. Meso* means middle, *thermo* means heat, and *iono* refers to a charged particle.

INQUIRY QUESTIONS

▶ **How is the ionosphere useful for communications?** *This layer reflects radio waves; thus, radio transmissions from one side of the world can be received on the other.*

MINI-Lab

Does air have mass?
On a pan balance determine the total mass of an inflatable ball that is completely deflated. Before proceeding, predict what the mass of the ball will be if it is fully inflated. Next, inflate the ball to its maximum recommended inflation pressure and determine the mass of the fully inflated ball. Does any change occur in the mass of the ball when it is inflated? Does air have mass? Explain how the pressure of air at Earth's surface compares to the pressure of air near the top of the atmosphere.

The thermosphere is the uppermost part of Earth's atmosphere. Beyond it lies space. There's no clear boundary between the thermosphere and space. If you were an 4 astronaut, you would encounter fewer and fewer molecules and ions as you traveled upward through the thermosphere. Eventually, you would find so few molecules and ions that, for all practical purposes, you would be out of Earth's atmosphere.

Temperatures in the Atmosphere

The division of Earth's atmosphere into layers is based on temperature differences. Figure 9-5 illustrates the temperature changes throughout the layers.

Earth's atmospheric gases heat up when they absorb energy from the sun. For example, the molecules of ozone in the stratosphere absorb the sun's ultraviolet radiation, heating the stratosphere. While some layers contain gases that easily absorb the sun's energy, other layers do not. As a consequence, the various layers have different amounts of thermal energy.

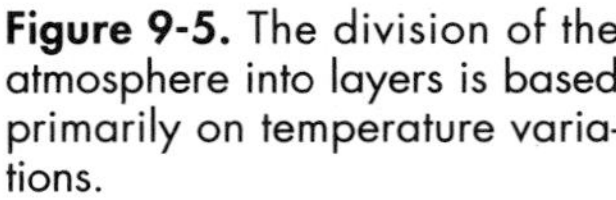

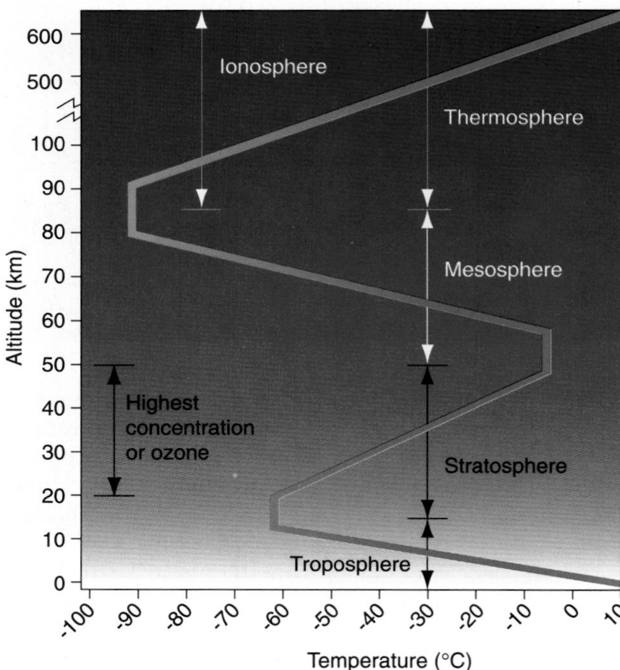

Figure 9-5. The division of the atmosphere into layers is based primarily on temperature variations.

MINI-Lab

Materials: pan balance; football, basketball, or volleyball; air pump with ball inflation needle

Teaching Tips

▶ Perform the activity beforehand to make sure that the ball being used is large enough to cause a detectable change in mass when air is added to the ball.

Answers

▶ The mass of the inflated ball is greater than the mass of the uninflated ball. Since the addition of air was the only variable in this activity, it provides evidence that air has mass. Air near Earth's surface would be "squeezed" by the mass of the air above it; thus, air nearer Earth's surface is more dense than air near the top of the atmosphere.

CONCEPT DEVELOPMENT

▶ Be certain students are aware that density of the atmosphere decreases with altitude.

REVEALING MISCONCEPTIONS

▶ Students might think that temperature decreases with altitude in the atmosphere. Have them carefully examine Figure 9-5 to see that this is not true.

TEACHER F.Y.I.

▶ Estimates are that the temperature of the thermosphere at 500 km may be in excess of 1370°C in the daytime and cool to 150°C at night.

MINI QUIZ

Use the Mini Quiz to check students' recall of chapter content.

1. **The layer of air between the stratosphere and the thermosphere is the _____ .** *mesosphere*
2. **The layer of the atmosphere closest to Earth's surface is the _____ .** *troposphere*
3. **The ozone layer is located in the _____ .** *stratosphere*
4. **Beyond Earth's thermosphere is _____ .** *space*

OPTIONS

INQUIRY QUESTIONS

▶**Use Figure 9-5 to determine the temperature at an altitude of 60 km above sea level.** *−30°C*

▶**Use Figure 9-5 to determine the altitude of the coldest air in Earth's atmosphere.** *The coldest air lies between 80 and 90 km above Earth.*

PROGRAM RESOURCES

From the **Teacher Resource Package** use:

Activity Worksheets, page 83, Mini-Lab: Does air have mass?

Use **Laboratory Manual,** pages 77-78, Air.

Atmospheric Pressure

Gases in the atmosphere, like all matter, have mass. The gravitational attraction between Earth and the atoms and molecules of gas causes the gas to be pulled toward Earth's surface. Atoms and molecules of the gas are pushed together because of the weight of the atmosphere above them. This increase in density causes the molecules to collide more often, causing pressure on each other.

Where do you hypothesize that pressure is greater: at the top of a mountain or at sea level? The pressure is greater at sea level because there are more molecules of air pushing down from above. In general, atmospheric pressure is greatest near Earth's surface and decreases as you move out toward space. But pressure can vary from one location to another even if the locations are at the same elevation. This happens because the density of air varies from one location to another.

How does pressure change with altitude?

TECHNOLOGY

Barometers

A barometer is an instrument used by scientists and weather forecasters to measure air pressure. One common type of barometer is pictured here. Aneroid barometers often consist of a sealed metal can with an attached pen. All of the air is removed from the can, leaving a vacuum inside. As air pressure outside of the vacuum changes, the can expands and contracts, which causes the pen to rise or fall.

A record of the changing air pressure is made as the pen marks on a chart attached to a spinning drum. Usually the drum turns one full turn in a 24-hour period.

You may be familiar with mercurial barometers. They consist of a long tube closed at one end. The tube is partially placed in a dish of mercury. As air pushes down on the mercury in the dish, more mercury is forced into the tube. The level of mercury in the tube is measured in centimeters and rises with rising air pressure.

Think Critically: How can barometers be used to measure elevation?

CHECK FOR UNDERSTANDING

Have students explain why air exerts pressure. Students should respond that atoms and molecules in the atmosphere are pushed together because of the mass of the air above them. Because the molecules become more densely packed, they collide more often. These collisions cause air to exert pressure.

RETEACH

Demonstration: Show that air exerts pressure by obtaining a large jar from the school cafeteria. The jar should be large enough that a student can stick his or her hand into it easily. Also obtain a plastic bag with an opening large enough to fit over the rim of the jar. Secure the plastic bag to the rim of the jar. Be sure that the bag fits tightly. Have a student make a fist and try to push the plastic bag gently into the jar. Air in the jar will resist the student's attempts to push on the bag.

EXTENSION

For students who have mastered this section, use the **Reinforcement** and **Enrichment** masters or other OPTIONS provided.

TECHNOLOGY

Think Critically: Barometers measure air pressure. Air pressure changes with altitude. Thus, barometers can be used to measure elevation.

ENRICHMENT

▶ Have students find out how space shuttles are able to withstand the high temperatures of the thermosphere when they leave and reenter the atmosphere.

▶ Have students research the effects that solar flares have on the atmosphere.

▶ Have students write brief reports explaining how an aneroid barometer called an altimeter is used to determine an airplane's altitude.

PROGRAM RESOURCES

Use **Laboratory Manual,** pages 79-80, Air Pressure.

3 CLOSE

▶Ask questions 1-3 and the **Apply** Question in the Section Review.

▶Display a mercury or aneroid barometer in the classroom. Provide students with a chance to observe the barometer each day and observe pressure differences. Discuss what would happen to the barometer if it were placed on a different floor of the school.

SECTION REVIEW ANSWERS

1. nitrogen and oxygen

2. The troposphere is the part of Earth's atmosphere that contains 75 percent of all the atmosphere's gases, plus dust, ice, and liquid water. It is also the layer where weather, clouds, and smog are found.

3. The temperature is dependent on the amount of energy absorbed by the particles within it. Because the layers contain different proportions of compounds, the amount of radiation absorbed varies.

4. Apply: The pressure exerted at the bottom of the pile would be the greatest. This is like the pressure exerted by Earth's troposphere. Moving upward in the pile of players is similar to moving to higher levels of the atmosphere; that is, the pressure exerted decreases.

EcoTip

Helium-filled balloons rising up into the atmoshere are fun to watch, but they are also a hazard to wildlife. They reach the ocean where turtles and whales eat them, thinking they are jellyfish. Dead turtles and whales have been found with balloons in their intestines. If you know of a group planning to release balloons into the atmosphere, alert them to the hazards they create.

When the density of air is high, there are more molecules above a particular location exerting their weight on those below. Cold air is more dense than warm air and, therefore, has higher pressure. At any one time, one area of the United States may be covered by a high-pressure air while areas surrounding it are covered by low-pressure air. Because these masses of air are almost always moving, scientists measure the pressure changes in an area to make weather forecasts. In the Technology section of this chapter and in Chapter 10, you'll read how we measure air pressure and make forecasts based on those measurements.

Forecasting the weather allows us to plan how we will spend our day. We know whether to bring an umbrella or to plan a picnic. Understanding the composition and structure of Earth's atmosphere also helps us know when we are making changes to it. In the next section, you will read how we may be changing Earth's atmosphere and how it may affect how we all live.

SECTION REVIEW

1. What are the two most common gases in our atmosphere?
2. What are some characteristics of the troposphere?
3. Why doesn't the temperature in the atmosphere steadily increase or decrease as you move from Earth's surface toward space?
4. **Apply:** Imagine you're a football player running with the ball. You're tackled and, soon, six other players pile on top of you. Relate the pressure that you and each player above you feels to the pressure in the layers of the atmosphere.

Skill Builder

Making and Using Graphs

Use Figure 9-1 to answer the following questions. If you need help, refer to Making and Using Graphs in the **Skill Handbook** on page 691.

1. What is the most abundant gas in Earth's atmosphere?
2. What percentage of the total volume of gases is argon?
3. What percentage of the total volume is nitrogen and oxygen? Argon and carbon dioxide?

Skill Builder

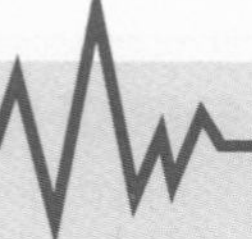

You may wish to have students construct a pie graph using the data in Figure 9-1. Students should calculate the degrees of a circle represented by nitrogen, oxygen, and trace gases. For example, nitrogen represents 78 percent of 360 degrees, or 281 degrees. Oxygen is represented by 76 degrees and the trace gases by 3 degrees. Have students calculate the above given proportions and construct graphs.

1. nitrogen
2. 0.93 percent
3. 99 percent; 0.96 percent

ACTIVITY 9-1
Air Pressure

Problem: *How does a barometer work?*

Materials

- small coffee can
- drinking straw
- rubber balloon
- heavy paper (28 cm × 21.5 cm)
- transparent tape
- scissors
- metric ruler
- rubber band

Procedure

1. Using the figure below as a guide, draw a line 8 cm from the right edge of the paper. Draw a second line lengthwise through the center of the paper. The second line should extend 20 cm from the left edge to the 8-cm line.
2. Cut the paper along the 20-cm line. Cut away the section shown in blue.
3. Fold the paper along the 8-cm line.
4. Wrap the section shown in dark blue around the can and fasten with tape. The long edge of the paper should stick up above the can to form a gauge.
5. Cover the top of the coffee can with the rubber balloon. The balloon must be stretched tightly over the top of the can in order for the barometer to function correctly. Secure the balloon with a rubber band.
6. Trim one tip of the straw to a point. Position the straw so that the pointed end is alongside the gauge. Tape the other end of the straw to the balloon. DO NOT tape the straw to the gauge.
7. Make a horizontal mark on the gauge showing the position of the straw. Write "high pressure" above this mark, and write "low pressure" below this mark.
8. Keep track of the movement of the straw over a period of a week. Also record the weather conditions each day. Record your observations in a data table similar to the one shown.

Data and Observations

Date	Barometric readings (high or low)	Weather conditions

Analyze

1. Explain how your barometer works.
2. What type of barometric readings would you expect if you brought your barometer to the top of a mountain? The mesosphere?

Conclude and Apply

3. What type of weather is usually associated with high pressure? With low pressure?
4. How can a weather forecaster use the barometric reading to help formulate a forecast?

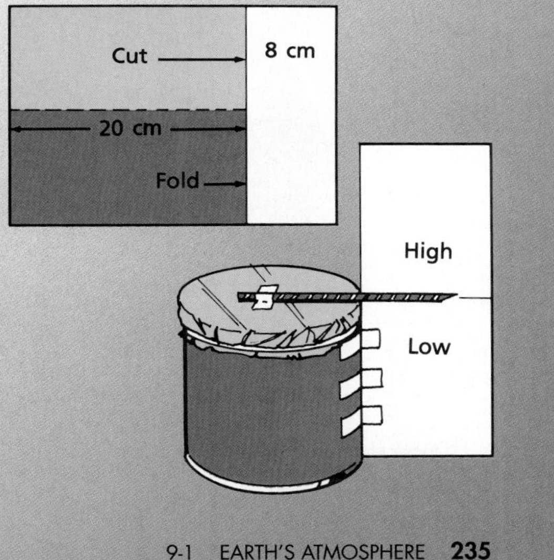

ACTIVITY 9-1
45 minutes

OBJECTIVE: Construct modified aneroid barometers and **use** them to make daily measurements of atmospheric pressure.

PROCESS SKILLS applied in this activity:
▶ **Observing** in Procedure Step 8.
▶ **Measuring** in Procedure Step 1.
▶ **Using Numbers** in Procedure Steps 1-3, and 8.
▶ **Formulating Models** in Procedure Steps 4-7.
▶ **Inferring** in Analyze Questions 1 and 2 and Conclude and Apply Questions 3 and 4.

COOPERATIVE LEARNING Have Paired Partners perform this activity.

TEACHING THE ACTIVITY

▶ Cut heavy paper into 28 cm x 21.5 cm sheets ahead of time.

Alternate Materials: You may substitute any wide-mouthed can if coffee cans are not available. A broom straw may be substituted for the drinking straw.

Troubleshooting: Remind students that once the coffee can is sealed, it should not be reopened. If the barometer is constructed during periods of extreme high or low pressures, the indicator (straw) either may not move up, if constructed under high pressure; or down, if made under low pressure.

▶ If possible, have students compare their data with a barometer in the classroom.

▶ You may want to obtain a barograph for classroom use. A barograph is a barometer that is designed to continuously record daily atmospheric pressure.

PROGRAM RESOURCES

From the **Teacher Resource Package** use:

Activity Worksheets, pages 77-78, Activity 9-1: Air Pressure.

ANSWERS TO QUESTIONS

1. Air presses down on the balloon on the can. When air pressure is high, the balloon is depressed, and the straw points toward "high." When air pressure is low, less pressure is applied to the balloon, and the straw points toward "low."
2. The pressures measured would be lower both at the top of the mountain and in the mesosphere.
3. Fair weather is usually associated with high pressure and stormy weather with low pressure.
4. Changes in air pressure indicate changes in approaching weather.

SECTION 9-2

PREPARATION

SECTION BACKGROUND

▶ Before ozone was present in Earth's atmosphere, much ultraviolet radiation reached Earth's surface. At that time in Earth's past, if life were present at all, it must have been confined to deep water where it was protected from the ultraviolet radiation.

1 MOTIVATE

FLEX Your Brain

Use the Flex Your Brain activity to have students explore THE EFFECTS OF SUNBATHING.

TYING TO PREVIOUS KNOWLEDGE: Students learned in Chapter 2 that atoms combine to form molecules and compounds. The oxygen molecules we breathe each have two atoms. Ozone is composed of three atoms of oxygen.

OBJECTIVES AND SCIENCE WORDS: Have students review the objectives and science words to become familiar with this section.

2 TEACH

Key Concepts are highlighted.

PROGRAM RESOURCES

From the **Teacher Resource Package** use:

Critical Thinking/Problem Solving, page 15, Protecting the Ozone Layer.

Cross-Curricular Connections, page 13, Ultraviolet Rays.

Science and Society, page 13, The Revised Clean Air Act of 1990.

Activity Worksheets, page 5, Flex Your Brain.

9-2 The Ozone Layer

New Science Words

ozone layer
ultraviolet radiation
chlorofluorocarbons

Objectives

- ▶ Explain why exposure to ultraviolet radiation can be a problem for plants and animals.
- ▶ Describe how chlorofluorocarbons destroy ozone molecules.

Do We Need to Protect the Ozone Layer?

About 24 kilometers above your head lies the ozone layer. You can't see, feel, smell, or observe it in any way. It's out of reach and unobservable, yet your life depends on it. The ozone layer is a shield between you and harmful energy coming from the sun.

Ozone is a compound whose molecules are composed of three oxygen atoms bonded together. The **ozone layer** is a layer in the stratosphere where concentrations of ozone are high. Ozone absorbs most of the ultraviolet radiation that enters the atmosphere. **Ultraviolet radiation** is one of the many types of energy that comes to Earth from the sun. Ultraviolet radiation can cause you to tan or sunburn. Too much exposure to this radiation, however, causes people to develop skin cancer. It causes cancer and other health problems in many types of plants and animals.

What would happen if the ozone layer disappeared? Already, about 27 000 Americans develop skin cancer annually, and 6000 die from it. If the ozone layer disappeared, these numbers would probably

Hole in ozone layer
Troposphere
Antarctica
Lower stratosphere
Upper stratosphere

Figure 9-6. What's causing the ozone layer to disappear?

OPTIONS

Meeting Different Ability Levels

For Section 9-2, use the following **Teacher Resource Masters** depending upon individual students' needs.

◆ **Study Guide Master** for all students.

● **Reinforcement Master** for students of average and above average ability levels.

▲ **Enrichment Master** for above average students.

Additional Teacher Resource Package masters are listed in the OPTIONS box throughout the section. The additional masters are appropriate for all students.

◆ STUDY GUIDE 39

NAME ________ DATE ________ CLASS ________

STUDY GUIDE — Chapter 9

The Ozone Layer — Text Pages 236–237

Choose the correct term in the box and write each term after its definition.

chlorofluorocarbons	ozone layer	ultraviolet radiation

1. Layer in the stratosphere containing ozone, which absorbs ultraviolet radiation
   ozone layer
2. Type of energy from the sun that can be harmful in large amounts
   ultraviolet radiation
3. Chemicals used in some aerosol sprays, refrigerants, and some foam products
   chlorofluorocarbons

Determine whether each of the following statements is true or false. Write the word "true" or "false" in the blank. If the statement is false, rewrite it so that it's true.

false 4. The kind of oxygen we breathe can absorb ultraviolet radiation.
The kind of oxygen we breathe can't absorb ultraviolet radiation.

false 5. Scientists know exactly what is causing the ozone layer to disappear.
Scientists don't know exactly what's causing the ozone layer to disappear.

false 6. Chlorofluorocarbons are making the ozone layer thicker.
Chlorofluorocarbons are making the ozone layer thinner.

true 7. The ozone layer acts as a shield between us and ultraviolet radiation.

true 8. Holes in the ozone layer have been found over Antarctica and the North Pole.

false 9. Ozone molecules destroy chlorofluorocarbon molecules.
Chlorofluorocarbon molecules destroy ozone molecules.

39

increase. But that may be exactly what's happening. In 1986, scientists found areas in the stratosphere where almost no ozone existed. One very large hole was over Antarctica. A smaller hole was discovered over the North Pole. Since that time, every year, these holes appear during certain seasons, and disappear during others. Not only is the ozone layer missing over the poles, but the entire ozone layer has become thinner around the world.

We don't know for sure why the ozone layer is disappearing, but some scientists hypothesize that pollutants in the environment are the cause. Chlorofluorocarbons are a group of chemicals that are being blamed. **Chlorofluorocarbons** are used in making refrigerants, some aerosol sprays, and some foam products. They enter the atmosphere when these products are manufactured and used.

Chlorofluorocarbon molecules destroy ozone molecules when they come in contact with each other. Recall that an ozone molecule is composed of three oxygen atoms bonded together. When a chlorine atom from a chlorofluorocarbon molecule comes near a molecule of ozone, the ozone molecule breaks apart. It forms the same type of oxygen that you breathe in the troposphere. This oxygen can't absorb ultraviolet radiation. The result is that more ultraviolet radiation reaches the plants and animals of Earth's surface.

1 UV light breaks up CFC

2 A chlorine atom breaks up ozone

3 A free oxygen atom breaks the chlorine-oxygen bond

4 Oxygen forms; the chlorine is free to destroy more ozone

Figure 9-7. One atom of chlorine can destroy 10 000 ozone molecules.

SECTION REVIEW

1. Why is exposure to too much ultraviolet radiation a problem?
2. How do chlorofluorocarbons destroy ozone molecules?
3. Why do people other than those living near the poles need to be concerned about the ozone layer?

You Decide!

The use of chlorofluorocarbons has provided us with many conveniences including refrigerators, air conditioners, spray paints, and foam cups and fast food containers. However, when we use these products, we may be destroying the ozone layer. Is the risk worth it? Which of these conveniences would you be willing to give up if it were proven that they cause holes in the ozone layer?

● REINFORCEMENT 39

NAME ______ DATE ______ CLASS ______

REINFORCEMENT — Chapter 9

The Ozone Layer — Text Pages 236–237

Answer the following questions on the lines provided.

1. What is ozone? **Ozone is a compound whose molecules are composed of three oxygen atoms bonded together.**
2. Why is the ozone layer particularly important to life on Earth? **It absorbs most of the ultraviolet radiation that comes from the sun.**
3. What is ultraviolet radiation? **Ultraviolet radiation is a type of energy from the sun.**
4. Why is too much ultraviolet radiation harmful to plants and animals? **Too much ultraviolet radiation can cause cancer and other problems in plants and animals.**
5. What makes scientists think that the ozone layer is disappearing? **In recent years scientists have found areas in the stratosphere where the ozone layer is getting thinner or disappearing altogether.**
6. Why is the ozone layer's disappearance a problem? **Because the ozone layer protects us from exposure to too much ultraviolet radiation, its disappearance means we will be exposed to greatly increased amounts of ultraviolet radiation. Occurrences of skin cancer and other health problems will also increase.**
7. What chemicals are being blamed for damaging the ozone layer? **Chlorofluorocarbons are being blamed.**
8. What are these chemicals used in? **Chlorofluorocarbons are used in refrigerants for refrigerators and air conditioners, in aerosol sprays such as spray paints, and in foam products such as cups and other fast-food containers.**
9. How do chlorofluorocarbons destroy ozone? **Ozone molecules are composed of three oxygen atoms. A chlorine atom from a chlorofluorocarbon molecule can break apart many ozone molecules.**

 39

▲ ENRICHMENT 39

NAME ______ DATE ______ CLASS ______

ENRICHMENT — Chapter 9

The Ozone Layer — Text Pages 236–237

OBSERVING PHOTOCHEMICAL SMOG

Ozone in the upper atmosphere acts as a shield against 95 to 99 percent of the ultraviolet radiation coming from the sun. Without ozone, life would not be possible on Earth. But ozone in the lower atmosphere is a pollutant, and a dangerous one that can damage materials such as plastic and rubber and cause eye irritation, headaches, and respiratory problems in people.

In the lower atmosphere, ozone is often a component of photochemical smog. Exhaust gases from the burning of gasoline, oil, and other fuels react with sunlight and produce gases called oxidants. One of these is ozone. Heavy concentrations of smog can be caused by mountain ranges near cities which trap and hold the smog in one place. Weather conditions can also contribute to smog concentration. A lack of wind or a warm air layer over a cool layer can prevent the smog from rising and dispersing.

Try this experiment to see how smog can be trapped at ground level by atmospheric conditions.

Materials
- large glass jar
- aluminum foil
- salt
- ice cubes
- small pieces of paper
- matches

Procedure
1. Light a piece of paper with a match and drop the paper into the jar.
2. Cover the jar with the aluminum foil. Put the ice cubes on top of the foil. Sprinkle the salt on the ice cubes.
3. Record what happens to the air in the jar.
4. Remove the salt, ice, and foil. Wash out the jar. Leave a little water on the sides of the jar.
5. Light another piece of paper and drop it into the jar. Repeat Step 2.
6. Record what happens to the air and smoke in the jar.

Analyze
1. What happened in the jar after you burned the first piece of paper? **Smoke filled the jar.**
2. What happened in the jar after you burned the second piece of paper? **The moisture in the jar combined with the smoke and made smog which became thicker and thicker as the air cooled.**
3. What did the jar look like at the end of the experiment? **The jar was coated with a smoky residue.**

Conclude and Apply
4. How does the data from this experiment relate to the information about smog? Explain. **The smoke, air, and water in the jar represent smog. The ice cubes cool the air at the top of the jar, forming the cool air layer that keeps smog trapped at ground level. As the cool conditions continue, the smog gets worse.**

 39

CHECK FOR UNDERSTANDING

▶ Ask questions 1-3 in the Section Review.

▶ Ask each student to write a paragraph describing the relationship among ozone, ultraviolet radiation, and chlorofluorocarbons.

RETEACH

Have five volunteers go to the front of the class. Have three of them join hands to form a "molecule" of ozone. A fourth person is to represent ultraviolet radiation. The fifth person represents chlorofluorocarbons. Have students role-play the effects of chlorofluorocarbons in allowing UV to penetrate the atmosphere.

EXTENSION

For students who have mastered this section, use the **Reinforcement** and **Enrichment** masters or other OPTIONS provided.

3 CLOSE

Cooperative Learning: Have Paired Partners make a bulletin board display of products that contain chlorofluorocarbons (CFCs) like polystyrene foam, air conditioners, and refrigerators.

SECTION REVIEW ANSWERS

1. Too much UV causes severe sunburn, cancers, and other health problems in humans.

2. Chlorofluorocarbons break the bonds of the oxygen molecules.

3. The most dramatic depletion of the ozone layer is found near the poles. However, most scientists agree that the layer is becoming thinner everywhere on the globe.

YOU DECIDE!

SCIENCE & SOCIETY

Most students will probably feel that giving up spray paints, foam cups, and fast-food containers produced with CFCs would be easier than giving up refrigerators and air conditioners. Encourage students, however, to think about how they could adjust their lifestyles to living without refrigeration and air conditioning as their ancestors may have done.

SECTION 9-3

PREPARATION

SECTION BACKGROUND

▶ Matter is not involved during the transfer of energy by radiation.

▶ Convection currents distribute energy until equilibrium is reached. On Earth, however, equilibrium is never attained. The tropics always receive more radiant energy than the rest of Earth. Therefore, atmospheric energy transfer is always occurring.

PREPLANNING

▶ To prepare for Activity 9-2, obtain the materials listed on page 243.

1 MOTIVATE

FLEX Your Brain

Use the Flex Your Brain activity to have students explore THE GREENHOUSE EFFECT IN THE ATMOSPHERE OF VENUS.

▶ Ask students the following questions. **Why does a metal spoon get hot if you leave it in a pot on top of a hot burner? Why does it get very hot inside a closed car on a hot sunny day? Why is an attic very warm in the springtime, while the ground floor is cool?** Answers will lead to a discussion of energy transfer. Inform students that they will learn that the methods of transfer for the questions asked above are *conduction, radiation,* and *convection,* respectively.

PROGRAM RESOURCES

From the **Teacher Resource Package** use:

Activity Worksheets, page 5, Flex Your Brain.

9-3 Energy from the Sun

New Science Words

radiation
conduction
convection

Objectives

- ▶ **Describe three things that happen to the energy Earth receives from the sun.**
- ▶ **Contrast radiation, conduction, and convection.**

Figure 9-8. Most radiation entering Venus' atmosphere is trapped by thick gases and clouds. On Mars, a thin atmosphere allows much radiation to escape. Earth's atmosphere creates a delicate balance between energy received and energy lost.

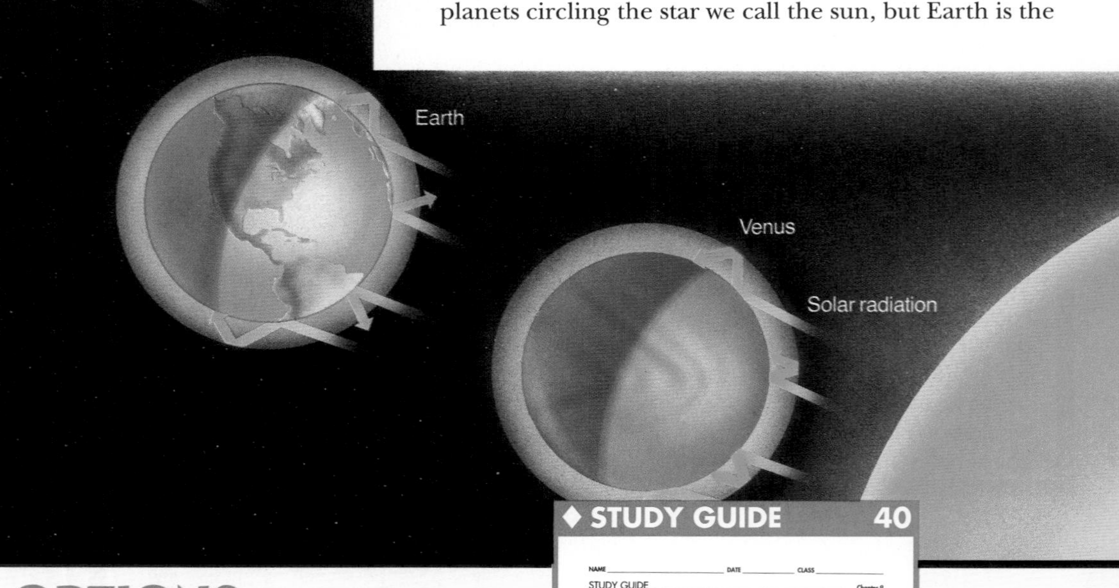

Energy Transfer in the Atmosphere

After returning from work, you eat dinner and sit down to read the evening news as it's transmitted on the computer network. You see that the Space Agency is still trying to create a hospitable atmosphere on Mars. It's studying the atmospheres of Earth and Venus to understand how they work and how an Earthlike atmosphere might be produced on Mars. The atmosphere on Mars is currently too thin to support life or to hold much heat from the sun. As a result, Mars is a cold, lifeless world. Venus' atmosphere is so dense that almost no heat coming in from the sun can escape. Venus is so hot that a living thing would instantly melt if put on its surface.

After finishing the story, you decide to go for a walk. You think about Mars and Venus and how Earth is different from them. In our solar system, there are many planets circling the star we call the sun, but Earth is the

OPTIONS

Meeting Different Ability Levels

For Section 9-3, use the following **Teacher Resource Masters** depending upon individual students' needs.

◆ **Study Guide Master** for all students.

● **Reinforcement Master** for students of average and above average ability levels.

▲ **Enrichment Master** for above average students.

Additional Teacher Resource Package masters are listed in the OPTIONS box throughout the section. The additional masters are appropriate for all students.

◆ STUDY GUIDE 40

NAME ______ DATE ______ CLASS ______

STUDY GUIDE — Chapter 9

Energy from the Sun — Text Pages 238–242

Use the words in the box to fill in the blanks.

heat	three	absorb	radiation
sun	lower	reflects	density
waves	current	contact	conduction
rises	campfire	environment	temperature
space	surfaces	atmosphere	convection

The **sun** is the source of all energy on Earth. **Three** different things happen to the solar energy that Earth receives. Some escapes back into **space**, some is absorbed by the **atmosphere**, and some is absorbed by land and water **surfaces**. Energy reaches Earth in the form of radiant energy, or **radiation**. This process is the transfer of energy by **waves**. You experience radiation when you sit by a **campfire** and your skin becomes warm. The molecules of your skin **absorb** the energy and you feel **heat**. Heat is the transfer of energy from an object with a higher **temperature** to an object with a **lower** temperature. Some radiation isn't absorbed by the atmosphere or surface objects; it **reflects** off the atmosphere or surface.

Conduction is the transfer of energy that occurs when molecules bump into one another. Heat is transferred through direct **contact**. **Convection** is the transfer of heat that occurs because of **density** differences in the air. Because warm air has a lower density, it **rises**, while cold air, which has a higher density, sinks. This rise and fall of air sets up a circular movement called a convection **current**. Convection currents and other processes that transfer energy control the **environment** we live in.

40

only one known to support life. Why is this the case? How does the interaction between Earth's atmosphere and the sun provide an environment suitable for life?

The sun is the source of all energy on Earth. Three different things happen to the energy Earth receives from the sun. Some of it escapes back into space, some is absorbed by the atmosphere, and some is absorbed by land and water surfaces. The balance among these three events controls the characteristics of the atmosphere and the life that it supports. Let's take a look at what happens to the energy that reaches Earth.

What three things may happen to energy from the sun?

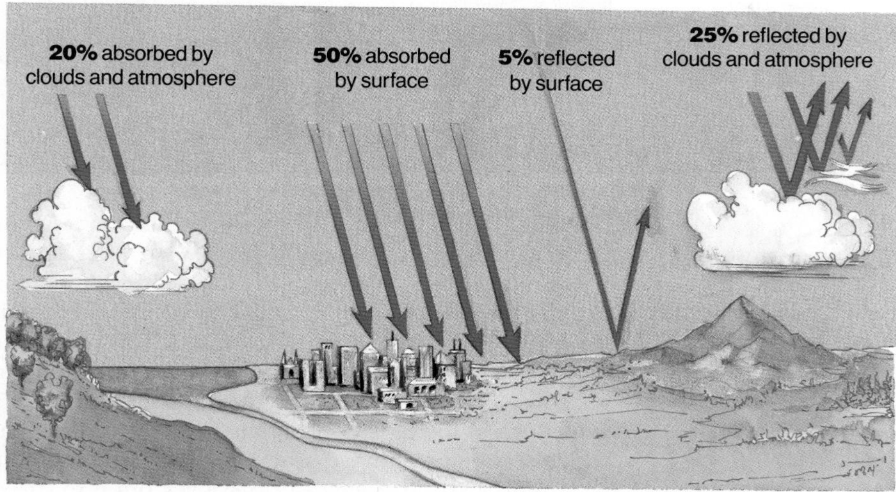

Figure 9-9. Thirty percent of the incoming radiation is reflected back into space. Only 20 percent is absorbed by the atmosphere directly. Most atmospheric heating is from heat radiated from the surface back to the atmosphere.

Radiation

Energy from the sun reaches our planet in the form of radiant energy, or radiation. **Radiation** is the transfer 1
of energy by electromagnetic waves. Radiation from the sun travels through empty space as well as through our atmosphere. You experience radiation when you sit by a campfire and the side of your body facing the fire becomes warm. You aren't in direct contact with the fire, but its energy still reaches you.

When radiation from the fire reaches you, the molecules of your skin absorb the energy and you feel heat. Heat is the transfer of energy from an object with a higher temperature to an object with a lower temperature. You know that the ozone layer absorbs ultraviolet

TYING TO PREVIOUS KNOWLEDGE: Students learned in Chapter 2 that matter is made of atoms and molecules. Energy transfer via conduction and convection involves movements of atoms and molecules.

OBJECTIVES AND SCIENCE WORDS: Have students review the objectives and science words to become familiar with this section.

2 TEACH

Key Concepts are highlighted.

CONCEPT DEVELOPMENT

▶ Stress that the sun is the source of almost all energy on Earth. Some energy is generated by the radioactive decay of atoms contained in Earth's rocks and magma.

▶ After students have read pages 238 and 239, pose these questions. **What happens to the energy Earth receives from the sun?** *Some escapes back into space; some is absorbed by the atmosphere; and some is absorbed by land and water surfaces.* **What is heat?** *Heat is the transfer of energy from an object with a higher temperature to an object with a lower temperature.*

▶ Make sure students use the terms *heat* and *energy* correctly. The terms are often incorrectly interchanged—they are *not* synonymous.

● REINFORCEMENT 40

NAME ____ DATE ____ CLASS ____

REINFORCEMENT — Chapter 9

Energy from the Sun — Text Pages 238–242

Complete the chart on the three types of heat transfer and their causes. Then answer the following questions on the lines provided.

Types of heat transfer	How they are produced
Radiation	produced by **waves**
Conduction	produced by **contact of molecules**
Convection	produced by **density differences in air**

1. In some home heating systems, warm air rises on one side of a room and forces cold air across the room where it sinks to the floor. What type of heat transfer is this? **convection**
2. When you get in a closed car on a sunny day and the temperature inside is much warmer than outside, what type of heat transfer has taken place? **radiation**
3. If you put a frying pan on a burner on a stove and turn the burner on, the bottom of the frying pan gets hot. What type of heat transfer has occurred? **conduction**

Answer the following questions using the information from the graph.

What happens to radiation coming to Earth from the sun?

Reflected by Earth's surface 5%
Absorbed by clouds and atmosphere 20%
Absorbed by Earth's surface 50%
Scattered by clouds and air 25%

4. Why doesn't all radiation directed at Earth reach the surface? **Some of the energy is absorbed, scattered, and/or reflected.**
5. What percent of radiation is lost before reaching Earth's surface? **45%**
6. What percent of radiation is lost after reaching Earth's surface? **5%**
7. What factor in the atmosphere seems to have the greatest effect on radiation coming from the sun? **clouds**

40

▲ ENRICHMENT 40

NAME ____ DATE ____ CLASS ____

ENRICHMENT — Chapter 9

Energy from the Sun — Text Pages 238–242

DETERMINING TEMPERATURE CHANGE

Materials

- dark-colored, small block of wood
- thermometer
- water
- electric teapot or teapot and hot plate
- coffee mug
- ice cubes
- room heater or register
- clock or watch

Procedure

1. Place the wooden block on a windowsill in direct sunlight.
2. Use the thermometer to determine the temperature of the block. Record the temperature.
3. After two hours in direct sunlight, determine the temperature of the block and record it.
4. Carefully heat some water in the teapot. Pour the water into the coffee mug.
5. Place a thermometer in the water and record its temperature.
6. Put two ice cubes in the mug of hot water.
7. Wait ten minutes; then place the thermometer in the water and record its temperature.
8. Record the temperature of the air in a room. This is displayed on the thermostat.
9. Ask an adult to turn up the thermostat.
10. Stand near the room heater or register and record your observations.
11. Stand near the cold air return. Record what you notice.
12. After 20 minutes, record the temperature of the air in the room as shown on the thermostat.

Analyze and Conclude

1. What happened to the wood block? **It warmed up after being in direct sunlight.**
2. What type of heat transfer caused what you noticed? **Heat transfer was by radiation from the sun to the wood block.**
3. What happened to the temperature of the water when ice cubes were added? **The temperature decreased.**
4. Explain the method of heat transfer demonstrated by the ice in the water. **Heat transfer was by conduction. Heat was transferred from the fast-moving molecules of the hot water to the slow-moving molecules of the ice. The molecules try to reach the same speed in both the water and the ice.**
5. Explain what happened in the room when the thermostat was turned up. **Hot air came out of the register and cooler air was pulled into the cold air return. The circulation of air set up a current of rising hot air that cooled and sank toward the cold air return.**
6. Which method of heat transfer is demonstrated by the heating of the room? **convection**

40

CONCEPT DEVELOPMENT

▶ Have volunteers compare and contrast the atmospheres of Earth and Venus. Then ask: **Why is Venus so hot?** *Very little radiation is able to escape back to space.*

▶ Have a picture of Venus available so students can see its dense cloud cover.

CROSS CURRICULUM

▶ **Industrial Technology:** Invite a speaker to talk about the effect that the color of an object has on its ability to absorb or reflect energy. Have him or her describe ways industry uses this effect in manufacturing items like solar panels.

Science and MATH

$$\frac{150\ 000\ 000 \text{ km}}{300\ 000 \text{ km/s}} = 500 \text{ s or } 8.3 \text{ minutes}$$

Figure 9-10. Pollution can change the proportions of radiation that enter and leave the atmosphere. Some types of pollution prevent radiation from escaping back into space, possibly causing Earth's temperature to rise.

radiation. When ozone and other gases absorb radiation, the temperature of the atmosphere rises. Vegetation, rocks, and surfaces such as asphalt also absorb radiation.

Once objects at Earth's surface have absorbed radiation, they can transfer heat back to the atmosphere. Heated surfaces give off radiation, but the radiation they give off is slightly different than that coming from the sun. Much of the radiation coming from the sun can pass through the atmosphere, whereas most radiation coming from Earth's surface can't pass back out into space.

On Venus, even less radiation is able to escape back to space. As a result, Venus is extremely hot. On Earth, there is a delicate balance between heat received from the sun and heat escaping back to space. In your future weather forecast this morning, you read that temperatures were going to be very high. This may be because smog and other pollutants in the atmosphere keep radiation from returning to space. You'll learn more about this one-way flow of energy in Chapter 10.

Some radiation from the sun isn't absorbed by Earth's atmosphere or surface objects. Instead, it simply reflects off the atmosphere and surface, like a ball bouncing off a wall. Figure 9-9 illustrates the percentages of radiation absorbed and reflected by Earth's surface and atmosphere.

Science and MATH

Earth is about 150 000 000 km from the sun. The radiation coming from the sun travels at 300 000 km/second. About how long does it take for the radiation leaving the sun to reach Earth?

OPTIONS

INQUIRY QUESTIONS

▶ **Contrast the radiation received from the sun with radiation transferred from objects at Earth's surface.** *Radiation from the sun can pass through the atmosphere, while most radiation coming from Earth's surface cannot pass back out into space.*

▶ **What effect do smog and other pollutants in the atmosphere have on Earth's temperature?** *Pollutants cause the temperature to increase because they keep radiation from returning to space.*

▶ **If you burn yourself by touching a hot stove, what type of energy transfer are you experiencing?** *conduction*

▶ **If you were to open a hot oven, you would feel a blast of warm air on your face. What type of energy transfer is this?** *radiation*

Conduction

When you walk barefoot on asphalt during a hot summer day, your feet heat up because of conduction. The asphalt was heated by radiation from the sun, but your feet are heated because they're in direct contact with the asphalt. In a similar way, objects on Earth's surface transfer energy directly to the atmosphere. As air moves over hot land, oceans, and roads, it's heated by conduction.

Conduction is the transfer of energy that occurs when 2
molecules bump into one another. Molecules are always in motion, but molecules in heated objects move more rapidly than those in cooler objects. Energy is transferred from the fast-moving molecules to slow-moving molecules until all molecules are moving at about the same rate.

How is air heated by conduction?

Convection

After the atmosphere is warmed by radiation or conduction, the heat is transferred throughout the atmosphere by a third process. This process is convection. **Convection** is the transfer of heat that occurs because 3
of density differences in the air. Let's see how this works.

When air is warmed, the air molecules move apart. This increases the volume of the air, which, in turn reduces its density. With lower density, there is less air

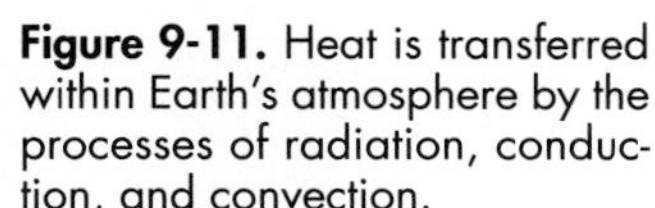

Figure 9-11. Heat is transferred within Earth's atmosphere by the processes of radiation, conduction, and convection.

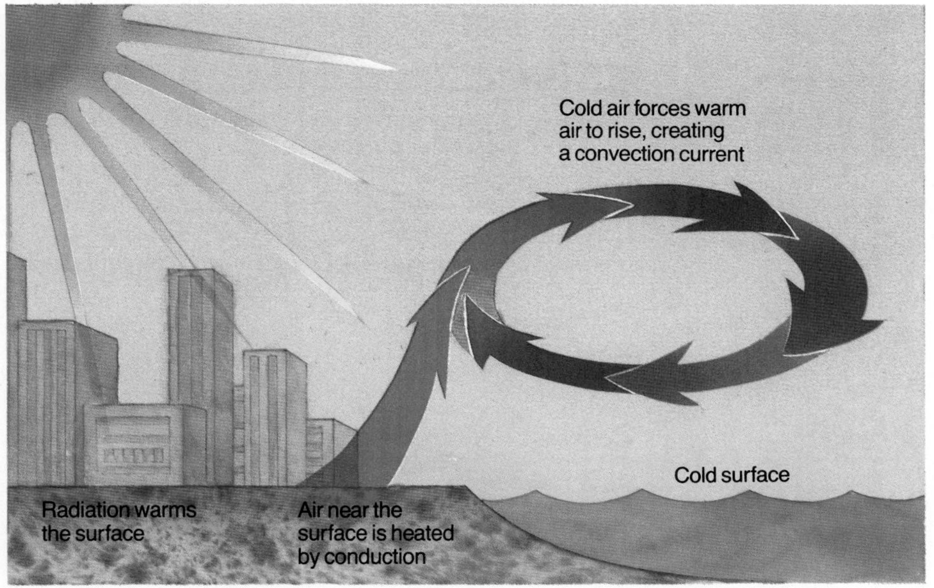
Cold air forces warm air to rise, creating a convection current
Cold surface
Radiation warms the surface
Air near the surface is heated by conduction

CONCEPT DEVELOPMENT

▶ Ask students to contrast conduction and convection.

▶ **How does the movement of molecules in warm objects compare with the movement of molecules in cooler objects?** *Molecules move more rapidly in warmer objects.*

CHECK FOR UNDERSTANDING

Use the Mini Quiz to check for understanding.

MINI QUIZ

Use the Mini Quiz to check students' recall of chapter content.

1. **____ is the transfer of energy by waves.** *Radiation*
2. **____ is the transfer of energy that occurs when molecules bump into one another.** *Conduction*
3. **____ is the transfer of energy that occurs because of density differences in the air.** *Convection*

RETEACH

Lead a class discussion of experiences students have had with radiation, conduction, and convection.

EXTENSION

For students who have mastered this section, use the **Reinforcement** and **Enrichment** masters or other OPTIONS provided.

ENRICHMENT

▶ Have students find out how a car radiator works. Ask them why *radiator* is an appropriate term for this part of a car.

▶ Have students make drawings showing how a convection oven works.

PROGRAM RESOURCES

Use **Laboratory Manual,** pages 81-82, Temperature of the Air.

3 CLOSE

►Ask questions 1-3 and the **Apply** Question in the Section Review.

FLEX Your Brain

Use the Flex Your Brain activity to have students explore CONVECTION.

Cooperative Learning: Have Science Investigation Groups use thermometers to find the temperatures of five stations in the classroom. Have students describe energy transfer in the room.

SECTION REVIEW ANSWERS

1. Space contains very little matter. The particles of matter in space between the Sun and Earth are separated by voids. Conduction is only possible when matter is continuous.

2. a circular movement of air that results when hot, less dense air rises and cold, dense air sinks

3. Pollution may trap radiation within our atmosphere, preventing it from escaping back into space. This would cause Earth's overall average temperatures to rise.

4. Apply: It will shrink. The cold air inside the freezer has a greater density and pressure than the warm air inside the balloon. The colder air pushes against the balloon. Also, as the air inside the balloon cools, the molecules move closer together, causing the balloon to deflate.

PROGRAM RESOURCES

From the **Teacher Resource Package** use:

Activity Worksheets, page 5, Flex Your Brain.

Science and WRITING

Mars and Venus are similar to Earth in size and structure, but have atmospheres very different from Earth's. Write a report about how the atmospheres of these three planets differ. Include in your report a discussion of the possibility of "terra-forming," or creating an Earthlike atmosphere, on Mars.

pressure because there are fewer molecules pressing in on each other. Cold temperatures affect the air density in just the opposite way. Molecules move closer together and the density and air pressure increase.

Because warm air has low density, it rises as cold air moves in and pushes it up. A circular movement of air, called a convection current, results.

Our Unique Atmosphere

Convection currents and other processes that transfer energy control the environment that we all live in. As you have seen, radiation from the sun can escape back into space, be absorbed by the atmosphere, or be absorbed by bodies on Earth's surface. Once it's been absorbed, heat can be transferred by radiation, conduction, or convection. Just how much and what type of radiation is absorbed determines the type of life, if any, that can exist on this planet. Other planets in the solar system similar to Earth, such as Venus and Mars, don't absorb and lose radiation like Earth does. Their atmospheres aren't able to support life as we know it. Many factors determine whether a planet will have an atmosphere capable of supporting life. But one thing is for certain, learning about our atmosphere will help us protect it so it can support life for years to come.

SECTION REVIEW

1. Why doesn't the sun transfer energy to Earth through the process of conduction?
2. What is a convection current?
3. Pollution may be making our atmosphere more like Venus'. How might this affect temperatures on Earth?
4. **Apply:** Suppose you fill a balloon with air, and then put it into a freezer. Will the balloon shrink, expand, or stay the same size? Why?

Skill Builder — Concept Mapping

Make a cycle concept map that explains what happens to energy that reaches Earth as radiant energy. If you need help, refer to Concept Mapping in the **Skill Handbook** on pages 688 and 689.

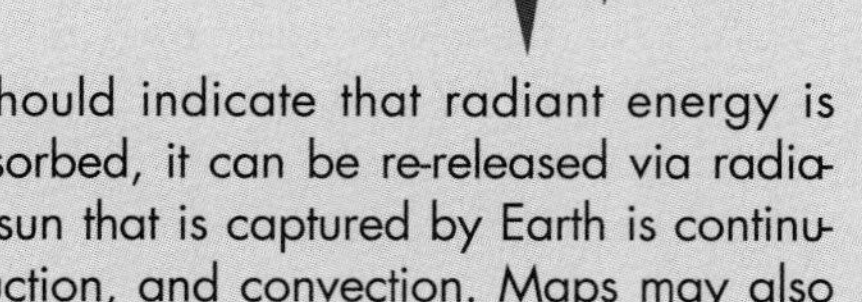

Skill Builder

Many solutions are possible. Most concept maps should indicate that radiant energy is absorbed by Earth's surface or atmosphere. Once absorbed, it can be re-released via radiation, conduction, or convection. Thus, energy from the sun that is captured by Earth is continuously cycled through the processes of radiation, conduction, and convection. Maps may also indicate that some energy escapes Earth's atmosphere.

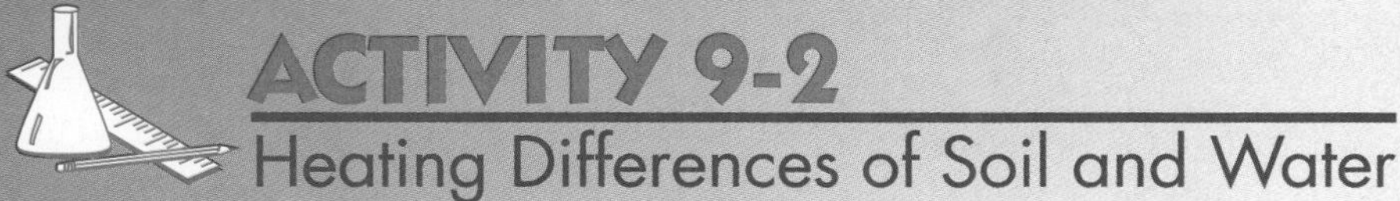

ACTIVITY 9-2
Heating Differences of Soil and Water

Problem: *How do soil and water compare in their abilities to absorb and release heat?*

Materials 

- ring stand
- soil
- metric ruler
- graph paper
- clear plastic boxes (2)
- overhead light with reflector
- thermometers (4)
- water
- masking tape
- colored pencils (4)

Procedure

1. Fill one box two-thirds full of soil.
2. Place one thermometer in the soil with the bulb barely covered. Use masking tape to fasten the thermometer to the side of the box as shown.
3. Position a second thermometer in the box with its bulb about 1 cm above the soil. Tape the thermometer in place.
4. Fill the second box two-thirds full of water.
5. Position the remaining two thermometers the same way as you did in the soil box.
6. Attach the light source to the ring stand. Place the two boxes about 2 cm apart below the light. The light should be about 25 cm from the tops of the boxes.
7. Record the temperature of all four thermometers with the light turned off.
8. Turn on the light. Check to make sure that the bulbs of the thermometers are shielded from direct light.
9. Take temperature readings every two minutes for 14 minutes and record.
10. Turn off the light. Take temperature readings every two minutes for 14 minutes and record.
11. Using temperature units on the vertical axis and time in minutes on the horizontal axis, graph your data. Use a different colored pencil to plot the data from each different thermometer.

Analyze

1. Did the air heat up faster over water or soil?
2. When the light was turned off, which lost heat faster, water or soil?
3. Compare the temperatures of the air above the water and above the soil after the light was turned off.

Conclude and Apply

4. Explain how the information you gathered relates to land and sea breezes.

Data and Observations Sample Data

Light on				
Time (minutes)	Temperature (°C)			
	1	2	3	4
0	25	25	24	25
2	27	27	25	27
Light off				
Time (minutes)	Temperature (°C)			
	1	2	3	4
0	34	33	32	33
2	31	30	32	30

ANSWERS TO QUESTIONS

1. over soil
2. Soil loses heat faster than water.
3. At first, the temperature above the soil was higher. After 7 to 8 minutes, the temperature above the water was higher.
4. When the light was on, daytime effects were being demonstrated. The air was warmer above the soil (land). This air would be replaced by the denser, cool air from above the water, forming a sea breeze. At night, demonstrated with the light off, the breeze would be off the land.

ACTIVITY 9-2
45 minutes

OBJECTIVE: Contrast the abilities of soil and water to absorb and release heat.

PROCESS SKILLS applied in this activity:
▶ **Observing** in Analyze Question 1.
▶ **Inferring** in Conclude and Apply Question 4.
▶ **Measuring** in Procedure Steps 1, 4, 6, 7, 9, and 10.
▶ **Interpreting Data** in Analyze Questions 2 and 3.
▶ **Separating and Controlling Variables** in Procedure Steps 1-11.
▶ **Using Numbers** in Procedure Step 11.
▶ **Experimenting** in Procedure Steps 1-11.
▶ **Defining Operationally** in Conclude and Apply Question 4.

COOPERATIVE LEARNING
Form Science Investigation Teams of four students per group for this activity.

TEACHING THE ACTIVITY

▶ Calibrate all thermometers ahead of time. Check to be sure all overhead lights have bulbs and reflectors.
Alternate Materials: Any transparent box may be used, including aquariums. However, be sure that both boxes being used by a student team are identical. Aluminum foil may be wrapped around the bulb to make a reflector.
Troubleshooting: Check students' setups to ensure proper placement of thermometers and positioning of the light over the containers. If thermometers have not been calibrated, students' results may not be accurate.

PROGRAM RESOURCES
From the **Teacher Resource Package** use:
Activity Worksheets, pages 79-80, Activity 9-2: Heating Differences in Soil and Water.

SECTION 9-4

PREPARATION

SECTION BACKGROUND

► The doldrums are areas of permanent low pressure that occur in zones of maximum solar heating with a weak horizontal pressure gradient.

► The easterlies are relatively steady winds. Westerlies are more complex because their flow is impeded by mountains and valleys. Friction between land and air creates local eddies that slow wind movement.

► Land and sea breezes occur because the specific heat of water is much higher than that of land. This means much more solar radiation must be absorbed by water in order for its temperature to rise. Also, water loses its heat to the atmosphere more slowly than land.

PREPLANNING

► To prepare for the Mini-Lab on page 246, obtain glass beakers or saucepans, hot plates, and food coloring.

1 MOTIVATE

FLEX Your Brain

Use the Flex Your Brain activity to have students explore WIND.

►**Demonstration:** Tape a piece of paper to a phonograph turntable. On top of the paper, tape a piece of carbon paper, carbon side down. Turn on the phonograph. While the turntable is rotating, roll a steel ball bearing straight across the carbon paper. Remove the carbon paper and have students observe the mark on the paper. Use this activity to introduce the Coriolis effect.

9-4 Movement of Air

New Science Words

Coriolis effect
doldrums
trade winds
prevailing westerlies
polar easterlies
jet streams
sea breezes
land breezes

Objectives

- ► Explain why different latitudes receive different amounts of solar energy.
- ► Describe causes of the Coriolis effect, sea breezes, and land breezes.
- ► Locate the positions of the doldrums, trade winds, prevailing westerlies, and polar easterlies.

The Coriolis Effect

Have you ever watched a tree swaying in the breeze and wondered where wind comes from? Wind is the movement of air molecules from an area of high pressure to an area of lower pressure. In this section, you'll learn how temperature differences on Earth's surface create areas of different pressure and the winds that circulate the air on our planet.

What causes temperature differences at Earth's surface? Because Earth's surface is curved rather than flat, not all areas receive the same amount of radiation. Figure 9-12 illustrates why more radiation is received at the equator than at any other latitude. Thus, the air above the

Figure 9-12. Near the poles, the sun's rays are spread out more than at the equator. So, equal amounts of energy don't heat equally—each square meter of land at the poles receives less energy than each square meter at the equator.

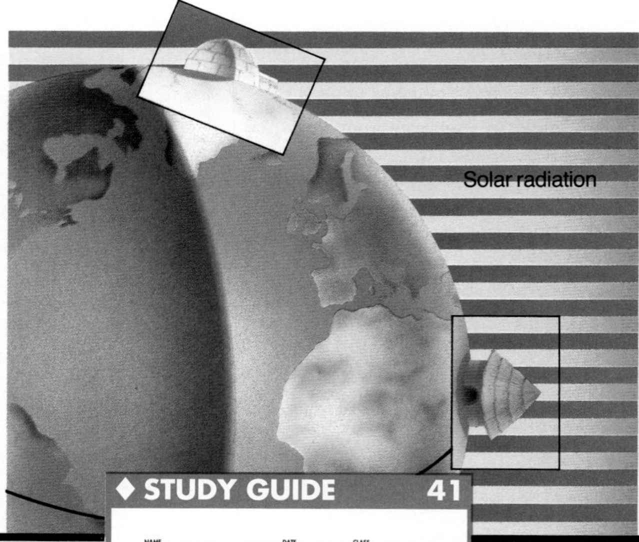

OPTIONS

Meeting Different Ability Levels

For Section 9-4, use the following **Teacher Resource Masters** depending upon individual students' needs.

◆ **Study Guide Master** for all students.

● **Reinforcement Master** for students of average and above average ability levels.

▲ **Enrichment Master** for above average students.

Additional Teacher Resource Package masters are listed in the OPTIONS box throughout the section. The additional masters are appropriate for all students.

◆ STUDY GUIDE 41

NAME ______ DATE ______ CLASS ______

STUDY GUIDE — Chapter 9

Movement of Air — Text Pages 244–248

Use the diagrams below to identify the following terms: doldrums, land breeze, polar easterlies, prevailing westerlies, trade winds, sea breeze. Write each term next to the appropriate number.

1. polar easterlies
2. prevailing westerlies
3. trade winds
4. doldrums
5. trade winds
6. prevailing westerlies
7. polar easterlies

FIGURE 1 (60°, 30°, 0°, 30°, 60°)

FIGURE 2 (Warm air, Cool air) — FIGURE 3 (Cool air, Warm air)

8. land breeze
9. sea breeze

In the blank on the left, write the term that matches each definition.

Coriolis effect — 10. The turning of air masses from their original paths because of Earth's rotation

jet streams — 11. High altitude winds that occur in places where trade winds and polar easterlies meet prevailing westerlies

wind systems — 12. Air movement patterns on Earth's surface as shown in Figure 1

convection current — 13. Circular movement of air that causes the winds shown in Figure 2

 41

equator is heated more than at any other place on Earth. As you know, heated air has low density and low pressure, so it rises.

Because less radiation is received at the poles, air there is much cooler. This dense, high pressure air sinks and moves along the surface.

1 Because Earth rotates, the **Coriolis** (kohr ee OH lus) **effect** is created. This effect causes air masses moving in the northern hemisphere to be turned westward from their original paths. Imagine a volume of cold, dense air from the North Pole moving toward the equator. To someone standing at the equator, the southbound air appears to be turning to the west because Earth is moving to the east. Just the opposite is true in the southern hemisphere. When seen from space, overall air movement appears to be from northeast to southwest in the northern hemisphere, whereas airflow in the southern hemisphere is from southeast to northwest. The flow of air caused by differences in heating and by the Coriolis effect has created distinct wind patterns on Earth's surface. Not only do these wind systems determine the weather, but they also determine when and where ships and planes can travel.

Name two things that are responsible for Earth's major wind patterns.

PROBLEM SOLVING

The Coriolis-go-round

Ricardo and Sam were playing on a merry-go-round when they made an interesting observation. Sam sat in the middle of the spinning merry-go-round and threw a rubber ball to Ricardo. To Ricardo, the ball appeared to travel in a straight line from Sam to him. But to Sam, the ball appeared to be curving as it traveled from him to Ricardo.

Think Critically: Was the ball actually curving as it traveled to Ricardo? Why did it appear to Sam, on the spinning merry-go-round, to follow a curved path?

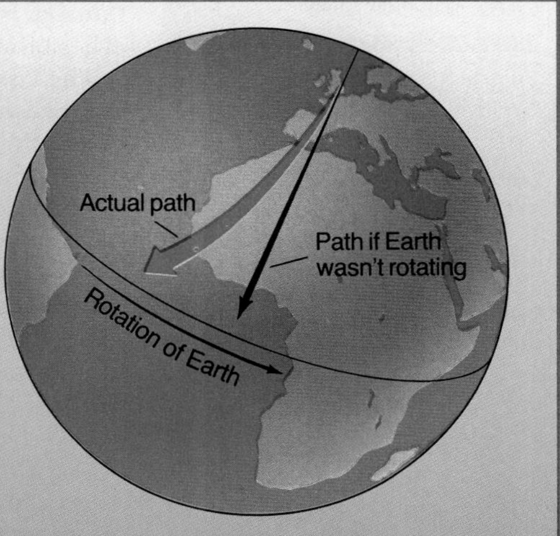

TYING TO PREVIOUS KNOWLEDGE: All students have seen and felt the effects of wind. Now students will learn what causes wind.

OBJECTIVES AND SCIENCE WORDS: Have students review the objectives and science words to become familiar with this section.

2 TEACH

Key Concepts are highlighted.

CONCEPT DEVELOPMENT

▶ **Why does air sink at the poles and rise at the equator?** *At the poles, air is cold and dense. Dense air tends to sink. At the equator, the air is warm and less dense. A less dense substance will overlie denser substances.* **In which direction do air masses in the Southern Hemisphere turn?** *They turn eastward from their original paths.*

PROBLEM SOLVING

Think Critically: No, the ball appeared to be deflected due to the Coriolis effect experienced by Sam as he spun on the merry-go-round. Sam's point of reference changed because he was in motion.

● REINFORCEMENT 41

NAME ________ DATE ________ CLASS ________

REINFORCEMENT — Chapter 9

Movement of Air — Text Pages 244-248

Write the term that matches each description below on the spaces provided. Write one letter in each space. Use the letters in the boxes to write a phrase related to the lesson. Use your textbook as a reference.

1. C O R [I] O L I S E F F E C T
2. T [R] A D E W I N D S
3. S E [A] B R E E Z E S
4. P R E [V] A I L I N G W E S T E R L I E S
5. [E] Q U A T O R
6. J E T S T R E A [M] S
7. D O L D R U [M] S
8. P [O] L A R E A S T E R L I E S
9. W I [N] D
10. W I N D S Y S [T] E M S
11. L A N D B R [E] E Z E S

1. The turning of air masses resulting from Earth's eastward rotation
2. Winds that provide a route for sailing ships from Europe to the Americas
3. Cool breezes during the day caused by differences in heating and cooling rates of land and water
4. Winds generally responsible for the movement of weather across the United States and Canada
5. Imaginary line around the middle of Earth
6. Narrow belts of strong winds at high altitudes which flow from west to east
7. Windless zone at the equator which sailing vessels try to avoid
8. Winds that blow from the North and South Poles
9. Movement of air molecules from an area of high pressure to an area of lower pressure
10. Patterns of air movement on Earth's surface caused by the Coriolis effect and differences in heating
11. Cool breezes at night caused by differences in heating and cooling rates of land and water

Unscramble the letters in the boxes to make a phrase.

The phrase is: air movement

 41

▲ ENRICHMENT 41

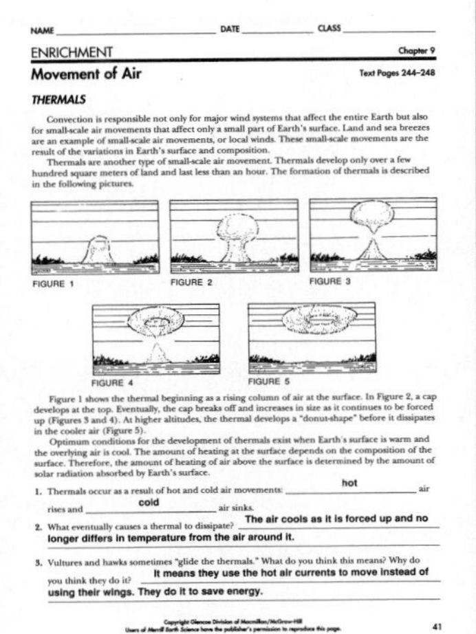
NAME ________ DATE ________ CLASS ________

ENRICHMENT — Chapter 9

Movement of Air — Text Pages 244-248

THERMALS

Convection is responsible not only for major wind systems that affect the entire Earth but also for small-scale air movements that affect only a small part of Earth's surface. Land and sea breezes are an example of small-scale air movements, or local winds. These small-scale movements are the result of the variations in Earth's surface and composition.

Thermals are another type of small-scale air movement. Thermals develop only over a few hundred square meters of land and last less than an hour. The formation of thermals is described in the following pictures.

FIGURE 1 FIGURE 2 FIGURE 3

FIGURE 4 FIGURE 5

Figure 1 shows the thermal beginning as a rising column of air at the surface. In Figure 2, a cap develops at the top. Eventually, the cap breaks off and increases in size as it continues to be forced up (Figures 3 and 4). At higher altitudes, the thermal develops a "donut-shape" before it dissipates in the cooler air (Figure 5).

Optimum conditions for the development of thermals exist when Earth's surface is warm and the overlying air is cool. The amount of heating at the surface depends on the composition of the surface. Therefore, the amount of heating of air above the surface is determined by the amount of solar radiation absorbed by Earth's surface.

1. Thermals occur as a result of hot and cold air movements: hot air rises and cold air sinks.
2. What eventually causes a thermal to dissipate? The air cools as it is forced up and no longer differs in temperature from the air around it.
3. Vultures and hawks sometimes "glide the thermals." What do you think this means? Why do you think they do it? It means they use the hot air currents to move instead of using their wings. They do it to save energy.

 41

STUDENT TEXT QUESTION

► Page 246, paragraph 2: **Actually, the air in the doldrums is rising almost straight up. Do you remember why this happens?** *The air at the equator is very hot and not very dense, and thus, rises.*

MINI QUIZ

Use the Mini Quiz to check students' recall of chapter content.

1. **Air masses moving in the Northern Hemisphere turn westward due to the ____ .** *Coriolis effect*
2. **The ____ are the windless zone at the equator.** *doldrums*
3. **The ____ blow weather across the United States and Canada.** *prevailing westerlies*

MINI-Lab

Materials: 500-mL glass beaker or a 2-L glass saucepan, water, food coloring, hot plate or stove

Teaching Tips

► Emphasize that only a few drops of food coloring should be added at any one time since it is important to be able to observe what happens. Too much food coloring makes it impossible to see anything.

►Have students focus their observations on the motions that occur at the top and bottom of the water in the container.

►**CAUTION:** *Do not let the water be heated to the point where it is unsafe for students to handle.* It is not necessary for the water to be very hot.

►**Answers:** The currents are due to density differences caused by unequal heating of the container. The atmosphere receives most of its energy in a similar fashion—at its bottom near Earth's surface. The movement of air along Earth's surface, as it moves from an area of higher density to an area of lower density, is wind.

MINI-Lab

What do convection currents look like?

Have an adult help you with this activity. Place a clear glass beaker or saucepan on a hot plate or stove. Fill the container to within 2 cm of the top and turn the heat source to high. As the water becomes warm, add a few drops of food coloring. Describe the motion of the food coloring as the water continues to warm. Explain how this motion is similar to air circulation in the atmosphere. If the bottom of the container represented Earth's surface and the water represented air in the atmosphere, what term would accurately describe the motion of the current across the bottom of the container? Make sure you turn off the heat source before the water becomes too hot to handle safely.

Wind Systems

Earlier, you read a possible forecast from your future. Now, let's venture into the past. Suppose you're sailing the oceans during the time of Christopher Columbus and the explorers who followed him.

You don't have any motors to propel your ship. You depend entirely on the winds for energy. As an experienced explorer of the oceans, you know you must avoid getting into the doldrums. The **doldrums** are the windless zone at the equator. There, the air seems motionless. Actually, the air in the doldrums is rising almost straight up. Do you remember why this happens? 2

A better place to sail is 15° north or south of the equator. There, air that has descended to Earth's surface creates steady winds that blow to the southwest. In the southern hemisphere, they blow toward the northwest. You know these winds as the **trade winds.** The northern trade winds provide a route for ships sailing from Europe to the Americas.

Between 30° and 60° north and south of the equator, winds blow in the opposite direction from the trade winds. These winds are called the **prevailing westerlies.** As a sailor, you use the prevailing westerlies to go east from the Americas to Europe. The prevailing westerlies blow from the southwest to the northeast in the northern hemisphere, and they are responsible for much of the movement of weather across the United States and Canada. 3 In the southern hemisphere, the prevailing westerlies blow from the northwest to the southeast.

What are the names of the major wind systems?

The last major wind systems at Earth's surface are the **polar easterlies.** These winds blow from the northeast to the southwest near the North Pole and from the southeast to the northwest in the southern hemisphere.

The trade winds, prevailing westerlies, and polar easterlies are the major wind systems at Earth's surface. There are also winds at higher altitudes. Narrow belts of winds, called **jet streams,** are located near the top of the troposphere. Flowing from west to east, they occur over locations where the trade winds and polar easterlies meet the prevailing westerlies. Thus, there are two jet streams in each hemisphere. These streams of air resemble very fast-moving, winding rivers. Their speeds range between 8 and 200 km/h, and their positions in latitude and altitude change from day to day and season to season.

OPTIONS

INQUIRY QUESTIONS

►**Why do you think the trade winds are called such?** *These steady winds were used by trade ships to sail from Europe to the Americas.*

►**Explain why the term *doldrums* is a good description of the air near the equator.** *A doldrums is a state of inactivity, stagnation, or slump. Air in the doldrums seems motionless.*

►**Why does water in a swimming pool feel cool on a hot, summer day, but warm that same night?** *During the day, the water temperature is cooler than the air temperature, because land heats up faster than water and releases much of its heat to the surrounding air. At night, the land cools down faster than the water and so does the surrounding air. Therefore, the water temperature is higher than the air temperature during the night.*

Just as sailors seek the trade winds, prevailing westerlies, and polar easterlies to help propel their ships, jet pilots take advantage of the jet streams when flying east. They save both time and fuel by using the energy of these winds.

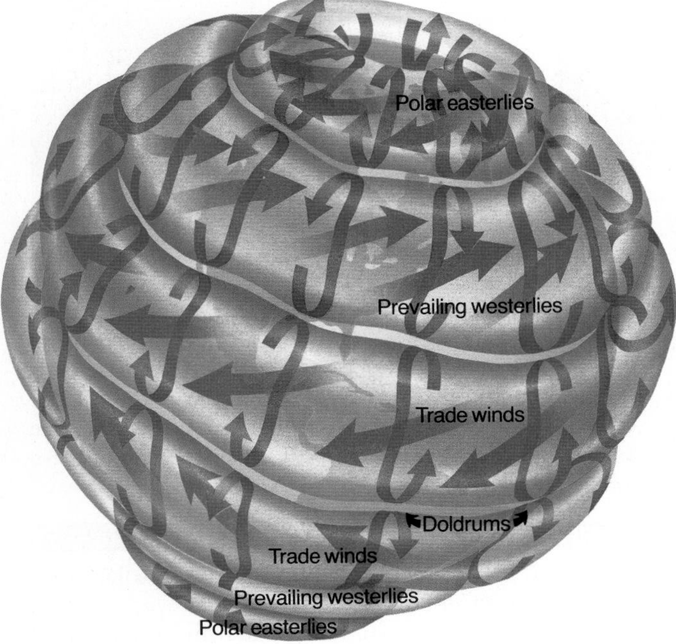

Figure 9-13. The purple arrows show the many convection currents resulting from differential heating of the latitudes. The blue arrows show the world's major wind systems created when air moving across the surface is deflected eastward or westward due to the Coriolis effect.

Sea Breezes and Land Breezes

The wind systems you've just read about determine weather patterns for the entire globe. But there are much smaller wind systems that determine local weather. If you live near a large body of water, you're familiar with two such wind systems—land breezes and sea breezes.

Convection currents over areas where the land meets the sea cause sea breezes and land breezes. **Sea breezes** are created during the day because solar radiation warms the land more than the water. Air over the land is heated by conduction. This heated air becomes less dense and is forced upward by cooler denser air moving inland from the ocean. A convection current results.

How are sea breezes and land breezes similar?

CHECK FOR UNDERSTANDING

Ask students to explain why winds blow inland off the ocean during the day. Students should conclude that the air over land heats up faster than air over the water, becomes less dense, and rises. The air over the ocean then moves inland to replace it.

RETEACH

Demonstration: Fill one 1000-mL beaker with soil and another with water. Pour 10 mL of ammonium hydroxide into a small beaker and place this small beaker into the middle of an empty, glass aquarium. Place the beakers of soil and water into the aquarium on either side of the small beaker. Next, add several drops of concentrated hydrochloric acid to the ammonium hydroxide. Smoke will appear. Quickly cover the aquarium with a glass lid. Then place an overhead light source above the lid. Be careful that the light is not too close to the glass or the heat will crack the glass. Students will observe a convection current within the aquarium similar to that formed during a sea breeze. If there is not enough smoke to observe the air movement, remove the lid, add more drops of HCl to the ammonium hydroxide, and replace the lid.

EXTENSION

For students who have mastered this section, use the **Reinforcement** and **Enrichment** masters or other OPTIONS provided.

CROSS CURRICULUM

▶**History:** Have students draw maps showing the routes that early explorers took across the oceans. Then have them compare these routes with the wind systems shown in Figure 9-13.

ENRICHMENT

▶ Have students research and report on some local winds, such as the Santa Anas, mistrals, siroccos, boras, and chinooks.

▶ Have students make models of anemometers and do some research to find out how actual anemometers work.

▶ Have students keep track of the movements of the jet streams by watching daily weather reports on television.

PROGRAM RESOURCES

From the **Teacher Resource Package** use:

Activity Worksheets, page 84, Mini-Lab: What do convection currents look like?

Transparency Masters, pages 31-32, Major Air Circulation.

Use **Color Transparency** number 16, Major Air Circulation.

3 CLOSE

►Ask questions 1-3 and the **Apply** Question in the Section Review.

►Have a pilot come to class to discuss how winds affect flying.

SECTION REVIEW ANSWERS

1. Because Earth is curved, solar energy strikes Earth most directly at the equator. Therefore, lower latitudes receive more energy, while higher latitudes receive lesser amounts.

2. Sailors took advantage of the direction in which the wind was blowing.

3. A jet is flying against the jet streams when it flies from South Carolina to Arizona. Therefore, more fuel is used and the trip takes longer than when the jet flies in the opposite direction.

4. Apply: During the day, the air above the land becomes warmer than the air over the water. The warm air over the land rises, and the cool, dense air over the water moves in to replace it. After the sun sets, the land cools more quickly than the water does. Thus, the air above the land is more dense and moves out over the water, pushing the warmer, less dense air aloft.

Skill Builder

Both are caused by convection currents that form over areas where landmasses are next to bodies of water. They differ, however, in that sea breezes form during the day when air over the land is warmer than air over the water. A land breeze forms at night when the conditions are reversed.

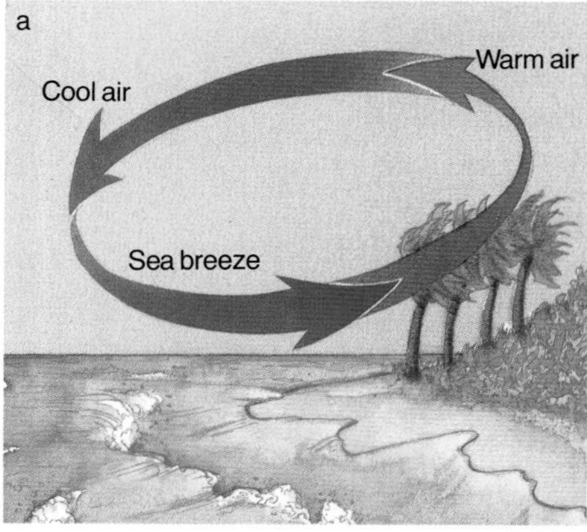

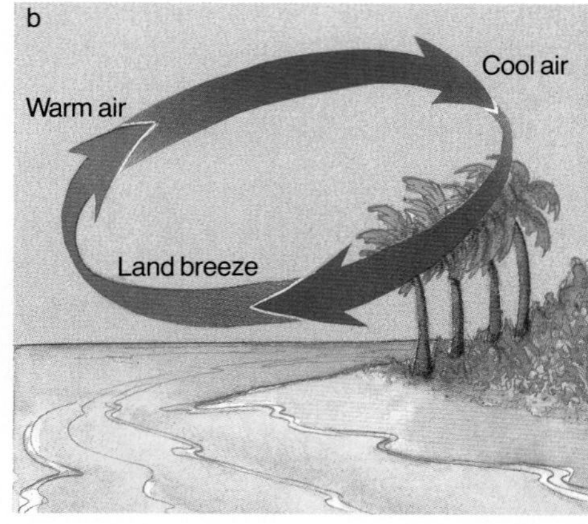

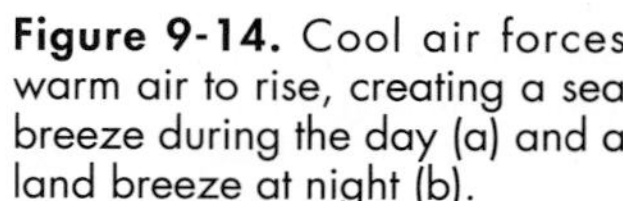

Figure 9-14. Cool air forces warm air to rise, creating a sea breeze during the day (a) and a land breeze at night (b).

At night, the land cools much more rapidly than the ocean water. Air over the land becomes cooler than the air over the ocean. The cool, dense air from the land moves out over the water, pushing the warm air over the water upward. Movements of air toward the water are called **land breezes.** Figure 9-14 illustrates sea breezes and land breezes.

SECTION REVIEW

1. Why do latitudes differ in the amount of solar energy they receive?
2. Why would a sailing ship take one route as it traveled from America to Europe and a different route on its return voyage?
3. Explain why a passenger jet that first flies from South Carolina to Arizona uses more fuel and takes longer to complete its journey than when it returns from Arizona to South Carolina.
4. **Apply:** Explain why the direction of the wind changes during a 24-hour period near the beaches of San Diego, California.

Skill Builder

Comparing and Contrasting

Compare and contrast land and sea breezes. If you need help, refer to Comparing and Contrasting in the **Skill Handbook** on page 683.

OPTIONS

PROGRAM RESOURCES

From the **Teacher Resource Package** use:

Concept Mapping, pages 23-24, Air.

Use **Laboratory Manual,** pages 83-84, Air in Motion.

CHAPTER

REVIEW

SUMMARY

9-1: Earth's Atmosphere

1. Nitrogen and oxygen are the two most common gases in Earth's atmosphere.
2. Earth's atmosphere can be divided into layers based on temperature differences, which in turn cause differences in pressures among the layers.
3. Because the gases in Earth's atmosphere have mass, they push against one another creating air pressure.

9-2: Science and Society: The Ozone Layer

1. Exposure to too much ultraviolet radiation can cause cancer and other health problems in living things.
2. When ozone reacts with chlorofluorocarbons, the molecules of ozone break apart, changing the ozone into oxygen.

9-3: Energy from the Sun

1. Some of the sun's energy that reaches Earth escapes back into space, while some of the energy is absorbed by Earth's air, land, and water.
2. Radiation is the transfer of energy by waves. Conduction is the transfer that occurs when molecules bump into one another. Convection is the transfer of heat due to density differences in the air.

9-4: Movement of Air

1. Earth's surface is curved, thus not all areas receive the same amount of solar radiation.
2. The Coriolis effect is due to Earth's rotation. Land and sea breezes are due to convection currents that form where land areas are next to bodies of water.
3. The doldrums are the windless zone at the equator. The trade winds lie between the equator and 30° north or south of the equator. The prevailing westerlies blow between 30° and 60° north and south of the equator. The polar easterlies blow near the poles.

KEY SCIENCE WORDS

a. **chlorofluorocarbons**
b. **conduction**
c. **convection**
d. **Coriolis effect**
e. **doldrums**
f. **ionosphere**
g. **jet streams**
h. **land breezes**
i. **ozone layer**
j. **polar easterlies**
k. **prevailing westerlies**
l. **radiation**
m. **sea breezes**
n. **trade winds**
o. **troposphere**
p. **ultraviolet radiation**

UNDERSTANDING VOCABULARY

Match each phrase with the correct term from the list of Key Science Words.

1. layer of atmosphere closest to Earth
2. absorbs ultraviolet radiation
3. transfer of energy by waves
4. transfer of heat that occurs due to density differences in air
5. air that turns from its original path experiences this
6. occurs when cold air over water moves inland
7. windless zone at the equator
8. are used by ships sailing from Europe
9. blow in opposite directions from the trade winds
10. winds that blow near the poles

OPTIONS

ASSESSMENT

To assess student understanding of material in this chapter, use the resources listed.

COOPERATIVE LEARNING
Consider using cooperative learning in the THINK AND WRITE CRITICALLY, APPLY, and MORE SKILL BUILDERS sections of the Chapter Review.

PROGRAM RESOURCES

From the **Teacher Resource Package** use:
Chapter Review, pages 21-22.
Chapter and Unit Tests, pages 62-63, Chapter Test.

CHAPTER

REVIEW

SUMMARY

Have students read the summary statements to review the major concepts of the chapter.

UNDERSTANDING VOCABULARY

1. o
2. i
3. l
4. c
5. d
6. m
7. e
8. n
9. k
10. j

CHAPTER
REVIEW

CHECKING CONCEPTS

1. d
2. c
3. d
4. c
5. a
6. b
7. b
8. a
9. c
10. b

UNDERSTANDING CONCEPTS

11. troposphere
12. Chlorofluorocarbons
13. conduction
14. equator
15. doldrums

THINK AND WRITE CRITICALLY

16. Both are layers of Earth's atmosphere. The troposphere marks the lower limit and the thermosphere the upper limit of the atmosphere. Most of the substances that make up air are contained in the troposphere due to greater atmospheric pressures there.

17. These compounds destroy ozone molecules when the two substances come into contact. Banning their use will help to reduce the destruction of Earth's ozone layer.

18. The transfer of energy via radiation does not require matter; whereas in conduction, energy is transferred only when two objects are in direct contact.

19. Air is warmed by direct rays from the sun at the equator and thus will rise. Air cools near the poles because these areas receive slanted solar radiation.

20. Because they blow in different directions, ships use the prevailing westerlies to travel to Europe and take advantage of the trade winds on courses from Europe to the Americas.

CHAPTER
REVIEW

CHECKING CONCEPTS

Choose the word or phrase that completes the sentence.

1. ______ is the most abundant gas in the air.
a. Oxygen **c.** Argon
b. Water vapor **d.** None of these

2. Smog is a mixture of compounds of sulfur, nitrogen, and ______.
a. water vapor **c.** oxygen
b. carbon **d.** argon

3. The ______ is the uppermost layer of the atmosphere.
a. troposphere **c.** mesosphere
b. stratosphere **d.** thermosphere

4. The coldest layer of air is the ______.
a. troposphere **c.** mesosphere
b. stratosphere **d.** thermosphere

5. ______ protects living things from too much ultraviolet radiation.
a. Ozone **c.** Nitrogen
b. Oxygen **d.** Argon

6. ______ is the transfer of energy from a warmer object to a cooler object.
a. Absorption **c.** Radiation
b. Heat **d.** Convection

7. Air in contact with hot surfaces is heated by ______.
a. absorption **c.** radiation
b. conduction **d.** convection

8. Differences in ______ cause wind.
a. pressure **c.** radiation
b. conduction **d.** convection

9. Movement of air toward water is a ______.
a. sea breeze **c.** land breeze
b. doldrum **d.** prevailing wind

10. ______ are near the top of the troposphere.
a. Doldrums **c.** Polar easterlies
b. Jet streams **d.** Trade winds

UNDERSTANDING CONCEPTS

Complete each sentence.

11. Air pressure is greatest in the ______.

12. ______ may be adding to the increase in health hazards by destroying ozone molecules.

13. When objects are in contact, energy is transferred by ______.

14. The ______ receives more radiation from the sun than the poles.

15. The ______ is an area that sailors avoid because air there is moving vertically.

THINK AND WRITE CRITICALLY

16. Compare and contrast the troposphere and the thermosphere.

17. Why have some countries banned the use of chlorofluorocarbons in manufacturing?

18. How does radiation differ from conduction?

19. Explain why air rises at the equator and sinks near the poles.

20. Why do ships take one route from Europe to the Americas and a different route on the return voyage?

APPLY

21. Why are there few or no clouds in the stratosphere?

22. It is thought that life could not exist on land until the ozone layer formed, about 2 billion years ago. Why did life on land require an ozone layer?

23. Explain how a pan of soup on a stove is heated by conduction and convection.

24. Why do land breezes occur during the night and sea breezes during the day?

APPLY

21. There is little or no water vapor from which the clouds could form.

22. The ozone layer prevents harmful ultraviolet radiation from reaching Earth's surface. Early organisms had the oceans in which they lived to protect them from excessive UV.

23. The pan is heated by conduction from the stove. As the temperature of the soup increases, the cooler, denser soup at the top of the pan sinks and pushes up the hotter soup from the bottom of the pan. Energy is then transferred via convection.

25. How would a southward-moving air mass appear to move to an observer at 30° south latitude?

MORE SKILL BUILDERS

If you need help, refer to the Skill Handbook.

1. **Concept Mapping:** Make a cycle concept map that explains how air moves to form a convection current.
2. **Making and Using Graphs:** Does air pressure increase more rapidly at high or low altitudes? Why doesn't the air pressure drop to zero on the graph? At what altitude would it drop to zero?

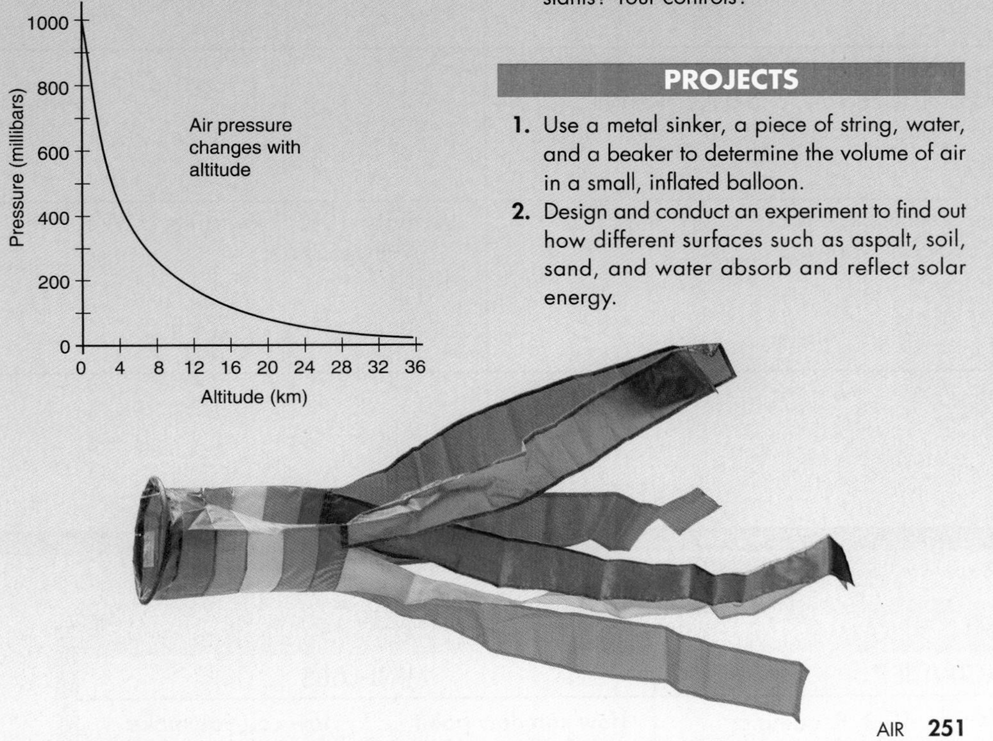

3. **Observing and Inferring:** Suppose you measured the air temperature one meter above the ground on a sunny afternoon and again one hour after sunset. You observed that your second reading was lower than the first. What can you infer from this?
4. **Hypothesizing:** Trees use carbon dioxide to photosynthesize. Carbon dioxide in the atmosphere blocks radiation from Earth's surface from escaping to space. Hypothesize how the temperature on Earth would change if many trees were cut down.
5. **Using Variables, Constants, and Controls:** Describe how you could compare the abilities of soil and water to absorb and release heat. What are your variables? Your constants? Your controls?

PROJECTS

1. Use a metal sinker, a piece of string, water, and a beaker to determine the volume of air in a small, inflated balloon.
2. Design and conduct an experiment to find out how different surfaces such as aspalt, soil, sand, and water absorb and reflect solar energy.

24. During the day, land heats up faster than water. Air above the land becomes less dense than air over water. The air rises and is replaced by cooler air. This causes a sea breeze. At night, air above water is warmer. Being less dense, it rises, and a cool breeze comes from the land.

25. It would appear to be deflected to the right or eastward.

MORE SKILL BUILDERS

1. Concept Mapping:
One possible solution is shown below.

2. Making and Using Graphs: Air pressure increases more rapidly at low altitudes. Air pressure can drop to zero only if no molecules of air are present. At 36 km above Earth's surface (the greatest altitude represented by the graph), molecules are still abundant. The air pressure would drop to zero outside of Earth's atmosphere, effectively at approximately 700 km.

3. Observing and Inferring: During the afternoon, the ground heated up and released its energy into the overlying air. After sunset, the ground was no longer receiving radiant energy and had given up much of its heat to the air above it during the day.

4. Hypothesizing: When trees photosynthesize, they use carbon dioxide. Thus, the amount of this gas would be reduced. When forests are destroyed, photosynthesis stops and CO_2 is released into the atmosphere causing an increase in the temperature of Earth's atmosphere.

5. Using Variables, Constants, and Controls: Students might suggest using plastic boxes with identical amounts of soil and water, a light source, and thermometers. The soil and water are the variables. Constants include identical thermometers and boxes, identical positioning of the thermometers, centering of the light source above the boxes, and the reading of the thermometers at the same time. Boxes of soil and water to which nothing is done are the controls.

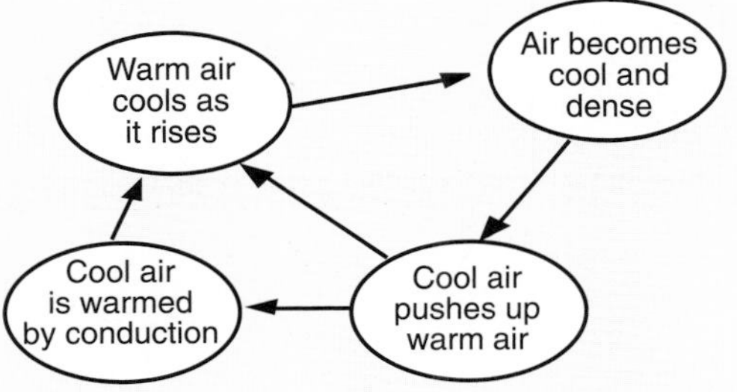

CHAPTER

10 Weather and Climate

CHAPTER SECTION	OBJECTIVES	ACTIVITIES
10-1 What Is Weather? (3 days)	1. **Explain** the role of water vapor in the atmosphere and how it affects weather. 2. **Compare** the origins of rain, hail, sleet, and snow. 3. **Describe** how clouds form.	**MINI-Lab:** *How can dew point be determined?* p. 257 **MINI-Lab:** *How can you make fog?* p. 259 **Activity 10-1:** *Relative Humidity,* p. 261
10-2 Weather Patterns (2 days)	1. **Describe** the weather associated with fronts and high and low pressure areas. 2. **Explain** how low pressure systems form at fronts. 3. **Relate** thunderstorms to tornadoes.	
10-3 Forecasting and Climate (1 day)	1. **Explain** how weather maps are made. 2. **Contrast** tropical, temperate, and polar climates. 3. **Explain** how large bodies of water and mountains affect climate.	
10-4 Can We Slow Down Global Warming? Science & Society (1 day)	1. **Describe** the greenhouse effect. 2. **List** causes of global warming.	**Activity 10-2:** *Reading a Weather Map,* p. 276
Chapter Review		

ACTIVITY MATERIALS

FIND OUT	ACTIVITIES		MINI-LABS	
Page 253 2-liter plastic bottles (2) dishwashing soap water tape	**10-1 Relative Humidity, p. 261** identical Celsius thermometers (2) piece of gauze, 2 cm^2 tape string cardboard beaker of water	**10-2 Reading a Weather Map, p. 276** hand lens Appendix K	**How can dew point be determined? p. 257** shiny metal can or cup thermometer water crushed ice	**How can you make fog? p. 259** hot water bottle ice cube

CHAPTER FEATURES	TEACHER RESOURCE PACKAGE	OTHER RESOURCES
Problem Solving: *Where's the Water?* p. 259 **Skill Builder:** *Concept Mapping,* p. 260	**Ability Level Worksheets** ◆ ***Study Guide,*** p. 42 ● ***Reinforcement,*** p. 42 ▲ ***Enrichment,*** p. 42 **MINI-Lab Worksheet,** pp. 92-93 **Activity Worksheet,** pp. 86-87 **Concept Mapping,** pp. 25-26 **Transparency Masters,** pp. 33-34	**Color Transparency 17,** Cloud Types **Lab Manual:** *Clouds,* p. 85
Technology: *Tailing a Tornado,* p. 267 **Skill Builder:** *Recognizing Cause and Effect,* p. 269	**Ability Level Worksheets** ◆ ***Study Guide,*** p. 43 ● ***Reinforcement,*** p. 43 ▲ ***Enrichment,*** p. 43 **Cross-Curricular Connections,** p. 14 **Transparency Masters,** pp. 35-38	**Color Transparency 18,** Air Masses **Color Transparency 19,** Types of Fronts **Lab Manual:** *Hurricanes,* p. 87
Skill Builder: *Comparing and Contrasting,* p. 273	**Ability Level Worksheets** ◆ ***Study Guide,*** p. 44 ● ***Reinforcement,*** p. 44 ▲ ***Enrichment,*** p. 44 **Critical Thinking/Problem Solving,** p. 16	**Lab Manual:** *Weather Forecasting,* p. 91 **Lab Manual:** *Radiant Energy and Climate,* p. 93
You Decide! p. 275	**Ability Level Worksheets** ◆ ***Study Guide,*** p. 45 ● ***Reinforcement,*** p. 45 ▲ ***Enrichment,*** p. 45 **Activity Worksheet,** pp. 88-89 **Science and Society,** p. 14	
Summary Key Science Words Understanding Vocabulary Checking Concepts Understanding Concepts Think & Write Critically Apply More Skill Builders Projects	**Chapter Review,** pp. 23-24 **Chapter Test,** pp. 66-69	**Chapter Review Software** **Test Bank**

◆ **Basic** ● **Average** ▲ **Advanced**

ADDITIONAL MATERIALS

SOFTWARE	AUDIOVISUAL	BOOKS/MAGAZINES
Weather and Climate, Queue. *Weather Forecasting,* Queue. *Earth and Environment Investigations: Weather Academy,* Focus. *Water and Weather,* Focus.	*Formation of Raindrops,* film, UEVA. *Inconsistent Air,* film, CRM/McGraw-Hill. *Snow,* film, BFA. *Tornado,* film, National Weather Service. *Weather Forecasting,* film, EBEC. *What Makes Clouds,* film, EBEC. *Urban Impact on Weather and Climate,* video, LCA. *Hurricane Hugo,* laserdisc, Floyd Design/Turner Ed. Services. *Interactive Science Series: Weather,* laserdisc, Health Edutech, Inc.	Elliot, George. *Weather Forecasting: Rules, Techniques, and Procedures.* Boston, MA: American Press, 1988. Fairbridge, Rhodes W. and John E. Oliver. *Encyclopedia of Climatology.* NY: Van Nostrand Reinhold, 1986. Lydolph, Paul E. *Weather and Climate.* Lanham, MD: Rowman and Littlefield Publishers, Inc., 1985.

CHAPTER

10

WEATHER AND CLIMATE

THEME DEVELOPMENT: Evolution, scale, and structure are the themes of this chapter. The structures of clouds and how they evolve are presented, beginning with a discussion of condensation. This is followed by discussions of the evolution, scale, and structure of fronts, pressure systems, and severe weather conditions.

CHAPTER OVERVIEW

- **Section 10-1:** This section presents some of the factors that determine weather and explains how clouds and precipitation evolve.
- **Section 10-2:** The evolution, and scale and structure of fronts, pressure systems, and severe weather are discussed.
- **Section 10-3:** Weather map symbols are defined and weather forecasting is explained. Reasons for climatic differences also are examined.
- **Section 10-4: Science and Society:** The greenhouse effect is described. The You Decide feature asks students how people can reduce global warming without affecting the world's economy.

CHAPTER VOCABULARY

weather	hurricane
relative humidity	meteorologist
saturated	station model
dew point	isotherm
fog	isobar
precipitation	temperate zones
air mass	greenhouse effect
front	deforestation
tornado	

CHAPTER

10 Weather and Climate

252

OPTIONS

For Your Gifted Students

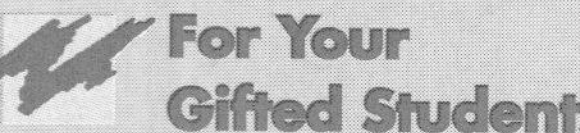

Cooperative Learning: Students can work as Paired Partners to make board games using weather map symbols. Have students label some of the spaces on the board with a weather phenomenon and a short description or fact about it. For example, a space could be labeled: "Hurricane—Blow back 2 spaces." Then have students make cards on which weather map symbols appear on one side. The other side should have a verbal explanation of the symbol. Students could take turns drawing cards. Correct responses will allow students to move ahead the number of spaces the roll of a die indicates.

A tornado is one type of severe weather that you will learn about in this chapter. Most weather conditions, however, are not destructive. How does a tornado move and what forces make it destructive?

FIND OUT!

Do this simple activity to find out more about tornadoes.

Obtain two 2-liter plastic bottles. Fill one about ¾ full of water and add one drop of dishwashing soap. Tape the mouth of the empty bottle to the mouth of the bottle with water in it. Make sure the tape has secured the bottles together. Now, flip the bottles so the one with the water is on top, and move the top bottle in a circular motion. What is forming in the bottle? How is this model of a tornado similar to a real tornado?

Gearing Up

Previewing the Chapter

Use this outline to help you focus on important ideas in this chapter.

Previewing Science Skills

- ▶ In the **Skill Builders,** you will make a concept map, recognize cause and effect, and compare and contrast.
- ▶ In the **Activities,** you will observe, infer, measure, predict, and read a scientific diagram.
- ▶ In the **MINI-Labs,** you will make a model, and observe and infer.

What's next?

You know that weather affects you every day. Luckily, severe weather such as a tornado doesn't occur very often. But weather does constantly change. In this chapter, you'll learn about weather and about the factors that determine our weather.

INTRODUCING THE CHAPTER

Use the Find Out activity to introduce students to one kind of severe weather. Inform students that they will be learning more about weather as they read this chapter.

FIND OUT!

Preparation: Several days before you begin this chapter, have each student bring in a clean, 2-liter plastic bottle.

Materials: two 2-liter plastic bottles for every pair of students, dishwashing soap, heavy tape

Cooperative Learning: Have students work as Paired Partners to do this activity. One person can hold the bottles together while the other tapes them.

Teaching Tips

▶ A spiral funnel of soapy water will form in the top bottle and drop down into the bottom bottle.

▶ This model of a tornado is similar to a real tornado in that both are turbulent, spiral-shaped, and rotate.

Gearing Up

Have students study the Gearing Up feature to familiarize themselves with the chapter. Discuss the relationships of the topics in the outline.

What's Next?

Before beginning the first section, make sure students understand the connection between the Find Out activity and the topics to follow.

For Your Mainstreamed Students

Have students work together to make mobiles of different weather-related phenomena including precipitation types, cloud types, frontal systems, types of storms, or weather systems. Students should categorize each phenomenon and group their pictures, collected from magazines or taken by the students themselves, accordingly. For example, a mobile that shows cloud types could be constructed to include the kind of weather associated with each type of cloud. Or, such a mobile could be constructed to show the different altitudes at which different clouds form.

SECTION 10-1

PREPARATION

SECTION BACKGROUND

▶ Although there are only four basic types of clouds—nimbus, stratus, cumulus, and cirrus—many clouds are combinations of these types. For example, puffy rain clouds are cumulonimbus clouds.

▶ In addition to being classified by shape, clouds can be classified by altitude.

▶ Hail is produced only in cumulonimbus clouds where strong updrafts and supercooled water exist. Rain freezes as it is tossed upward into the cloud. Each time the ice is caught in an updraft and then falls again, a new layer is added to the hailstone.

PREPLANNING

▶ To prepare for the Mini-Lab on page 257, obtain shiny metal containers and thermometers.

▶ To prepare for Activity 10-1, obtain Celsius thermometers, gauze, tape, string, cardboard, and beakers.

1 MOTIVATE

▶ Have students list and discuss various kinds of weather they have experienced. Responses might include tornadoes, hurricanes, and blizzards, as well as rain, thunderstorms, and snow.

▶ Discuss with students direct and indirect ways that the weather affects their lives. One indirect effect is consumers' having to pay more at the market for fruits and vegetables when an agricultural region experiences a very wet growing season as with corn, or a very cold season as with citrus fruits.

10-1 What Is Weather?

New Science Words

weather
relative humidity
saturated
dew point
fog
precipitation

Objectives

- ▶ **Explain the role of water vapor in the atmosphere and how it affects weather.**
- ▶ **Compare the origins of rain, hail, sleet, and snow.**
- ▶ **Describe how clouds form.**

Factors of Weather

What's one of the very first things you want to know every morning when you get up? You probably ask, "What's the weather going to be like today?" You depend on information about the weather for a variety of reasons. You need to decide what to wear to school, and you need to plan after-school activities if they're outdoors.

1 Although you probably use the word *weather* every day, can you really explain what it is? **Weather** refers to the present state of the atmosphere and describes the current conditions. Some of the important factors that determine the present state of the atmosphere are air pressure, wind, temperature, and the amount of moisture in the air.

What are some factors that determine weather?

In Chapter 7, you learned how water moves around the hydrosphere in the water cycle. With the sun providing the energy, water evaporates into the atmosphere. There, it forms clouds and eventually falls back to Earth.

Figure 10-1. The weather influences what you do and what clothes you wear.

OPTIONS

Meeting Different Ability Levels

For Section 10-1, use the following **Teacher Resource Masters** depending upon individual students' needs.

◆ **Study Guide Master** for all students.

● **Reinforcement Master** for students of average and above average ability levels.

▲ **Enrichment Master** for above average students.

Additional Teacher Resource Package masters are listed in the OPTIONS box throughout the section. The additional masters are appropriate for all students.

◆ STUDY GUIDE 42

NAME ______ DATE ______ CLASS ______

STUDY GUIDE — Chapter 10

What Is Weather? — Text Pages 254–260

In the word search puzzle, find and circle the word that completes each sentence. Write the word on the line.

1. The present state of the atmosphere is the **weather**.
2. **Humidity** is the amount of water vapor in the air.
3. Air is **saturated** when it is holding all the moisture it can at a certain temperature.
4. The temperature at which air is saturated and condensation begins is the **dew** point.
5. **Relative** humidity is the amount of water vapor in air compared to the amount of water vapor air can hold at a certain temperature.
6. A **psychrometer** is an instrument that measures relative humidity.
7. When millions of tiny drops of water around dust particles form from condensed humid air, a **cloud** forms.
8. A stratus cloud that forms near the ground is **fog**.
9. Water droplets that become too heavy to remain suspended in the air fall out of the clouds as **precipitation**.
10. **Hail** forms when water drops freeze in layers around small nuclei of ice.
11. Water drops that fall when the temperature is above freezing fall as **rain**.
12. Water drops that fall when the temperature is below freezing fall as **snow**.
13. When snow passes through warm air, melts, and refreezes near the ground, it becomes **sleet**.

T S A T U R A T E D F Q Y M B
B N O P S Y C H R O M E T E R
Y O W Q L N W G A V H R L F I
A W P R E C I P I T A T I O N
J D B C E I T C N U I L N G A
R E L A T I V E X C L O U D C
K W U B L H U M I D I T Y U V
Y J W E A T H E R G M R O M A

42

The water cycle forms the basis of our weather. But the sun does more than just evaporate water. It also heats air, causing it to rise and form the winds that you read about in Chapter 9. The interaction of air, water, and the sun cause our weather.

Humidity

You know from studying the water cycle that the sun evaporates water into the atmosphere. How can air hold water? Air is somewhat like a sponge. A sponge has holes in it that allow it to hold water. Air molecules in the atmosphere have spaces between them too. Like a sponge holds water, the atmosphere holds water vapor molecules. The amount of water vapor in the air is humidity. You've 2 probably heard this term used before. People often comment on the high humidity on hot summer days when the air seems damp and sticky. The amount of water vapor in the air varies from day to day. What factors cause it to change?

The amount of water vapor that air can hold depends on the temperature of the air. At cooler temperatures, air and water vapor molecules are moving slowly. This slow movement makes it easier for the water vapor molecules to join together (condense). At warmer temperatures, air and water vapor molecules are moving quickly. Water vapor molecules can't join together easily. Condensation doesn't occur easily, so this air can hold more water vapor than air with cooler temperatures.

Did You Know?

Arica, Chile, is the driest place on Earth. During one 14-year period, no rain fell at all. During a 59-year period, the average annual rainfall was 0.76 millimeters.

What does the amount of water vapor that air can hold depend on?

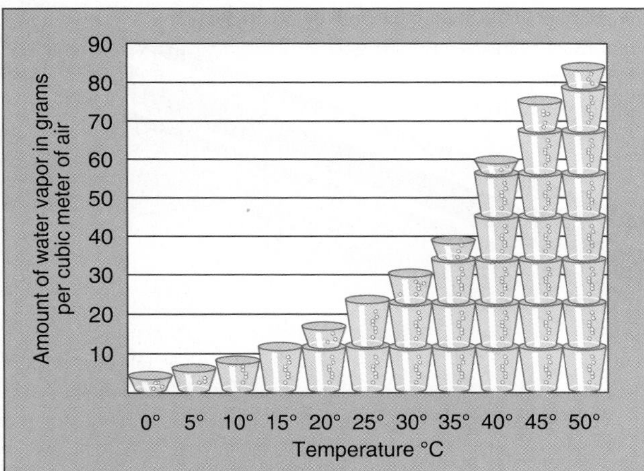

Figure 10-2. This chart shows that the amount of water vapor that air can hold increases with an increase in temperature.

TYING TO PREVIOUS KNOWLEDGE: Students learned about the water cycle in Section 7-1. Have them review the processes shown in Figure 7-2 on page 173.

OBJECTIVES AND SCIENCE WORDS: Have students review the objectives and science words to become familiar with this section.

2 TEACH

Key Concepts are highlighted.

CONCEPT DEVELOPMENT

▶ After students have read pages 254, 255, and 256, ask these questions. **What causes weather?** *The interaction of air, water, and the sun causes weather.* **How can air be compared to a sponge?** *A sponge has holes that allow it to hold liquids. Air molecules also have spaces among them, which can hold water.* **Describe the effect temperature has on the ability of air to hold moisture.** *The warmer the air, the more water vapor it can hold.*

▶ Explain that water vapor is the single most important component of the air in terms of weather and climate.

▶ Make sure students realize that water vapor is a gas and its amount varies from place to place.

● REINFORCEMENT 42

NAME ____________ DATE ________ CLASS ________

REINFORCEMENT Chapter 10

What Is Weather? Text Pages 254–260

Answer the questions and fill in the chart.

1. How does temperature affect humidity? **The warmer the temperature, the more water vapor the air can hold.**
2. Why can't cold air hold much water vapor? **Air and water vapor molecules move slowly, which makes it easier for the water vapor molecules to condense.**
3. Complete the chart below about the types of clouds in Figures 1–4.

FIGURE 1 FIGURE 2 FIGURE 3 FIGURE 4

	Figure 1	Figure 2	Figure 3	Figure 4
Type	cirrus	stratus	cumulus	cumulonimbus
Description	feathery	layered	puffy	towering
Weather	fair	light rain or snow	fair	thunderstorms

4. How do clouds form? **Clouds form when humid air is cooled to its dew point and condenses. The water vapor forms tiny drops of water around dust particles in the atmosphere. Millions of these water drops suspended together form clouds.**

Match the terms in Column I with their descriptions in Column II. Write the letter of the correct description in the blank at the left.

Column I
b 5. snow
a 6. rain
d 7. sleet
c 8. hail

Column II
a. Water drops that fall when the temperature is above freezing
b. Water drops that fall when the temperature is below freezing and become solid
c. Water drops that freeze in layers around small nuclei of ice during thunderstorms
d. Snow that falls through a layer of warm air, melts, and refreezes near the ground

42

▲ ENRICHMENT 42

NAME ____________ DATE ________ CLASS ________

ENRICHMENT Chapter 10

What Is Weather? Text Pages 254–260

RELATING CLOUDS TO WEATHER

Materials
- camera
  CAUTION: Do not aim the camera directly at the sun. Damage could occur to the eyes if direct sunlight is observed.
- roll of film
- pencil and paper

Procedure
1. Take photographs of the sky during the day for seven days.
2. Record the weather conditions and time of day when each photograph is taken.
3. Watch or listen to a nightly weather report and briefly record what conditions existed that day.
4. Make a table of your data.
5. Use your textbook, cloud charts, and weather forecasts to identify the type or types of clouds in each photograph.
6. Look up the weather conditions that each cloud type in your photographs should have associated with it. Compare this information with your observations.

Analyze
1. List the types of clouds you observed and the weather conditions you noted that were associated with each type. Not all types may have been observed. **cumulus—fair weather, partly sunny; cirrus—fair weather but forecast calls for rain; stratus—light rain, gray skies; nimbus—steady rain**
2. Write a description of each cloud type you observed. **cumulus—billowy, looks like big white pillows; cirrus—thin, white, feathery; stratus—low, gray, steady thick cover; nimbus—dark gray with irregular edges**
3. Do you notice any pattern to the clouds observed and the weather experienced? Explain. **Yes, the darker, heavier clouds are associated with drizzle, rain, and snow.**

Conclude and Apply
4. What occurs when a stratus cloud forms close to the ground? **fog**
5. Did you observe fog? What were the temperature and moisture conditions? **Fog occurs when warm, very moist layers of air flow across a cold surface or**

42

CONCEPT DEVELOPMENT

▶ Make a concentrated solution of cobalt chloride and water. Have students use paintbrushes to apply the solution to several sheets of white paper. When the solution dries, the precipitate can be used as an indicator of moisture in the air. Have students place these papers in different rooms around the school building, as well as outside. Have students record the colors of their papers and discuss what may be causing the relative humidity to vary. Pink indicates a high relative humidity; blue a low relative humidity.

▶ Have a volunteer explain the relationship between saturation and dew point. Be certain students understand these concepts because they are the basis for cloud formation and precipitation.

MINI QUIZ

Use the Mini Quiz to check students' recall of chapter content.

1. **_____ is the present state of the atmosphere.** *Weather*
2. **_____ is the amount of water vapor in the air.** *Humidity*
3. **_____ is the amount of water vapor in air, compared to the total amount of water vapor it has room for at a particular temperature.** *Relative humidity*
4. **_____ air has 100 percent relative humidity.** *Saturated*
5. **The _____ is the temperature at which air is saturated and condensation takes place.** *dew point*

CROSS CURRICULUM

▶ Mathematics: Have students work the following problem. At 20°C, a cubic meter of air can hold a total of 12 grams of water vapor. If only 4 grams are present, what is the relative humidity? *(4g ÷ 12g) × 100% = 33%*

Figure 10-3. Condensation forms on a glass when the air next to it is cooled to its dew point.

What will happen to water vapor added to air that is already saturated?

For example, air can hold a maximum of 22 grams of water vapor at 25°C. On the other hand, the same air cooled down to 15°C can only hold about 13 grams of water vapor. This is how temperature affects humidity.

Have you ever heard a weather forecaster speak of rel-
3 ative humidity? **Relative humidity** is a measure of the
amount of water vapor in air, compared to the total amount of water vapor it has room for at a particular temperature. It is stated as a percent. If you hear the weather forecaster say that the relative humidity is 50 percent, that means that the air on that day is holding only 50 percent of the water vapor it is capable of holding. Weather forecasters measure humidity because change in humidity often indicates a change in weather. Meteorologists use a psychrometer (si KRAH muh tur) as seen in Figure 10-4 to measure relative humidity. You'll use a homemade psychrometer in Activity 10-1 to measure the relative humidity of your classroom.

When air is holding all of the moisture it possibly can
4 at a particular temperature, it's said to be **saturated**
(SACH uh rayt id). Saturated air has 100 percent relative humidity. Any more water vapor will condense back to a liquid or freeze depending on its temperature. The temperature at which air is saturated and condensation
5 takes place is the **dew point.**

You've probably experienced the water droplets that form on the outside of a glass of ice water. Why does this occur? The cold glass cools the air next to it. When the air reaches its dew point, the water vapor condenses and forms water droplets on the glass. Dew on grass in the early morning forms

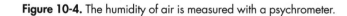

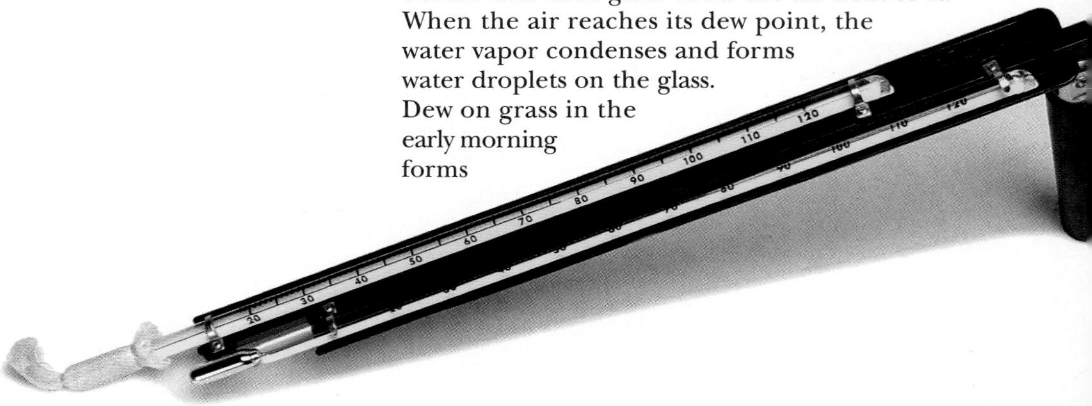

Figure 10-4. The humidity of air is measured with a psychrometer.

OPTIONS

INQUIRY QUESTIONS

▶ **Suppose the computer room and the science room, which are both the same size, have the same humidity, but the computer room is colder. Which room has the higher relative humidity?** *Being colder, the air in the computer room has a lower total capacity to hold water than the air in the science room. Since they both have the same humidity, the water in the air in the computer room represents a greater percentage of the air's capacity. Thus, the computer room has a greater relative humidity.*

the same way. When air near the ground is cooled to its dew point, water vapor condenses and forms droplets on the grass.

Clouds and Precipitation

Have you ever wondered what clouds are made of? Would you believe that clouds are made of millions of tiny drops of water? These drops of water are so small that they are suspended in the air. Why are there clouds in the sky? Clouds form as humid air is cooled to its dew point and condenses. The condensing water vapor forms tiny drops of water around dust particles in the atmosphere. When millions of these drops form together, a cloud forms.

MINI-Lab

How can dew point be determined?

Partially fill a shiny metal container, such as a cup or can, with room temperature water. While slowly stirring the water with a thermometer, carefully add small amounts of ice. Note the exact temperature at which a thin film of moisture first begins to form on the outside of the metal can. Repeat the procedure two more times, making sure that the outside of the can is dry and the water begins at room temperature each time. The average of the three temperature readings at which the moisture begins to appear is the dew point temperature of the air around the container. What factors determine the dew point temperature? Will a change in air temperature cause the dew point temperature to change also? Explain.

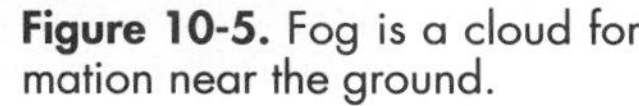

Figure 10-5. Fog is a cloud formation near the ground.

You've probably seen many different types of clouds. They vary in shape and in the altitude at which they form in the atmosphere. Some clouds stack up vertically reaching high into the sky, while others are low and flat. Some dense clouds bring rain or snow, while other thin clouds appear on mostly sunny days. In Table 10-1 you'll find the major types of clouds, a description of each, and the type of weather associated with each.

Some stratus clouds form right next to the ground. Air that is cooled to its dew point near the ground condenses and forms a stratus cloud called **fog.** This also occurs when warm, moist layers flow across a cold surface.

What type of cloud is fog?

CONCEPT DEVELOPMENT

▶ Have students recall from Chapter 6 that wind can carry dust particles high into the air. It is around these particles that condensing water droplets cluster to form clouds.

▶ **How does fog form?** *Air near the ground is cooled to its dew point and condenses to form a low-lying stratus cloud.*

MINI-Lab

Materials: shiny metal can or cup, thermometer, water, crushed ice

Teaching Tips

Cooperative Learning: Have Paired Partners perform this activity.

▶ Stress that the ice must be added very slowly to the water. If this is not done, the water temperature may fall so rapidly that students will be unable to determine the temperature at which the moisture first begins to form on the side of the container.

▶ Advise students not to leave the thermometers resting against the side of the container. Also, students should avoid striking the side of the container with the bulb of the thermometer to avoid breakage.

▶ **Answers:** The dew point is determined by the actual moisture content of the air at any given time. A change in air temperature will not directly affect the dew point temperature. Dew point will only change if the amount of moisture in the air increases or decreases.

INQUIRY QUESTIONS

▶ **Describe the evolution of a cloud.** *Humid air is cooled to its dew point and condenses around dust particles in the atmosphere. Clouds form when millions of these drops collect.*

▶ **Fog is fairly common along some coastlines in the morning. It "burns off" in the late morning or early afternoon. Explain.** *In the morning, the moisture-laden air is cool and the water vapor condenses to form clouds. When the sunlight heats the air, the air molecules move apart, the relative humidity drops, and the clouds disappear.*

PROGRAM RESOURCES

From the **Teacher Resource Package** use:

Activity Worksheets, page 92, Mini-Lab: How can dew point be determined?

CONCEPT DEVELOPMENT

▶ Have students contrast the altitudes and shapes of the following cloud types: nimbostratus, altostratus, and cirrostratus.

CHECK FOR UNDERSTANDING

Have students classify today's clouds. Ask them to use Table 10-1 to determine the approximate height of the clouds and to forecast tomorrow's weather.

RETEACH

Cooperative Learning: Have Paired Partners observe clouds for three consecutive days. Have them use Table 10-1 to identify the clouds observed. Also have them record the weather each day. At the end of the three days, have them compare and contrast their observations with the data in Table 10-1. Have students note any discrepancies between their observations and the information in the table.

EXTENSION

For students who have mastered this section, use the **Reinforcement** and **Enrichment** masters or other OPTIONS provided.

Table 10-1

CLOUD TYPES

VERTICAL CLOUDS 500 to 18 000 meters	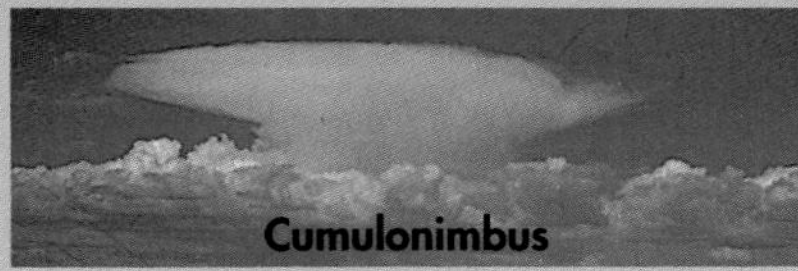 **Cumulonimbus** • Towering clouds, may spread out at top to form an anvil shape • Associated with thunderstorms, heavy rain, hail	 **Cumulus** • Dense, billowy clouds • Associated with fair weather, but may produce precipitation if vertical development is great	
HIGH CLOUDS above 6000 meters	 **Cirrostratus** • Veil-like clouds, may cause halos around the moon or sun • Associated with fair weather, may indicate approaching storm	 **Cirrocumulus** • Thin, white clouds, may look like ripples, waves, or rounded masses • Associated with fair weather, but may indicate approaching storm	 **Cirrus** • Thin, white, feathery clouds of ice crystals • Associated with fair weather, may indicate approaching storms
MIDDLE CLOUDS 2000 to 6000 meters	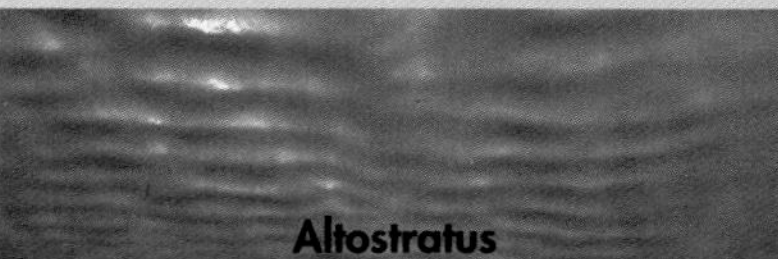 **Altostratus** • Gray fibrous clouds; sun or moon appears as a "bright" spot • May produce light, continuous precipitation	 **Altocumulus** • Light gray clouds in patches or rolls • Often precede rain or thunderstorms	
LOW CLOUDS below 2000 meters	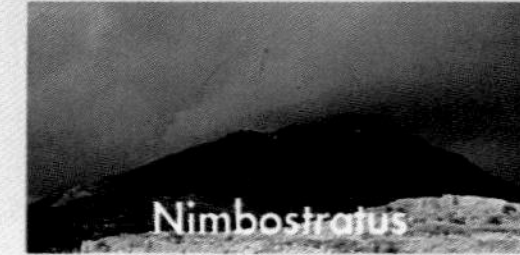 **Nimbostratus** • Thick layer of dark clouds that blocks out the sun • Associated with steady, long precipitation	 **Stratus** • Low layer of gray clouds that may cover the entire sky • Associated with light drizzle	 **Stratocumulus** • Soft gray clouds, may form a continuous layer • Occasionally produce light rain or snow

OPTIONS

INQUIRY QUESTIONS

▶ **What happens to snow that passes through a layer of warm air on its way to the ground?** *It melts to become rain. Or, it may refreeze near the ground and become sleet.*

PROGRAM RESOURCES

From the **Teacher Resource Package** use:
Transparency Masters, pages 33-34, Cloud Types.
Use **Color Transparency** number 17, Cloud Types.
Use **Laboratory Manual** page 85, Clouds.

As long as the water drops remain small, they stay suspended in the air. However, when droplets reach 0.2 millimeters, they're too heavy to remain suspended and fall out of the clouds. Falling water drops form **precipitation.** Precipitation can have many different forms depending on the temperature of the air the water drop falls through. Air temperature determines whether the water droplets form rain, snow, sleet, or hail—the four main types of precipitation. Drops of water that fall in temperatures above freezing fall as rain. Snow forms when the temperature is so cold that water vapor changes directly to a solid—snow. Temperatures in the air must be below freezing for snow to form.

Hail forms when drops of water freeze in layers around a small nucleus of ice. Hail forms in thunderstorms. Hailstones grow larger as they're tossed up and down by rising and falling air currents in the storm. Sleet forms when snow passes through a layer of warm air, melts, and then refreezes near the ground.

MINI-Lab

How can you make fog?

Make fog in a bottle using hot water, a bottle, and an ice cube. Put about 5 centimeters of hot water in the bottom of a tall, slender bottle such as a soft drink bottle. Then place an ice cube so that it rests on the top of the bottle, and observe what happens. Why is fog forming? What is happening to the water vapor that is rising in the bottle?

PROBLEM SOLVING

Where's the Water?

Jason and Kim decided that they would help their father fix spaghetti for dinner, so that he could have time to work in the garden. The sauce was already cooking, and it was time to cook the noodles. Jason filled a large pot 3/4 full with water and turned the burner to the highest temperature setting. After a few minutes of watching the pot, Kim and Jason could see that it was still not boiling. So they decided to watch TV while they were waiting.

They got so interested in the program they were watching, they lost track of the time. All at once, Jason remembered the water on the stove and bolted toward the kitchen. Much to his surprise, the pot was only 1/2 full of boiling water. On the wall above the stove were droplets of water.

After a minute, Jason understood what had happened. He put the noodles in the water and returned to the TV room to explain to Kim what had happened.

Think Critically: What did Jason tell Kim?

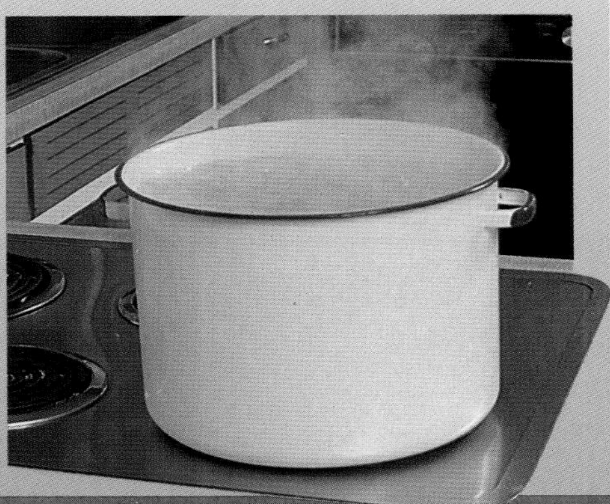

MINI-Lab

Materials: ice cubes, glass bottle, hot water

Teaching Tips

Cooperative Learning: Have Paired Partners perform this activity.

► **CAUTION:** *Do not let the water be heated to the point where it is unsafe for students to handle.*

► **Answers:** Water vapor rising in the bottle is cooled and condenses as it nears the ice cube at the top of the bottle. The condensing water vapor forms fog in the bottle.

CONCEPT DEVELOPMENT

► After students have read this page, ask these questions. **What must happen before precipitation will fall from clouds?** *Droplets must reach 0.2 mm. At that size, they are too massive to remain suspended and will fall as precipitation.* **What determines the kind of precipitation? Explain.** *Temperature determines the type of precipitation. Drops that fall in temperatures above freezing are rain. If the temperature is cold enough for the water vapor to change directly to a solid, the precipitation that falls will be snow.*

TEACHER F.Y.I.

► The largest hailstone ever recorded was found in Coffeyville, Kansas, in 1970. It had a mass of 0.76 kilograms.

PROBLEM SOLVING

Think Critically: The heat had caused some of the water to evaporate. Some of the molecules in the air made contact with the wall and condensation occurred.

ENRICHMENT

► Have students use a video camera to take stop-frame pictures of clouds that are forming. Have them take one picture every 5 minutes for half an hour. Then have them show their tapes to the class at regular speed.

► Have students construct a cloud chamber.

► Have students investigate what is meant by *wind chill.* Have them determine how wind chill is calculated.

PROGRAM RESOURCES

From the **Teacher Resource Package** use:

Activity Worksheets, page 93, Mini-Lab: How can you make fog?

3 CLOSE

▶ Ask questions 1-3 and the **Apply** Question in the Section Review.

FLEX Your Brain

Use the Flex Your Brain activity to have students explore CLOUDS.

SECTION REVIEW ANSWERS

1. Clouds form when air is cooled to its dew point and water vapor condenses around dust particles.

2. Water vapor condenses as temperatures decrease. This causes the movements of water molecules to decrease, which in turn, causes the molecules to join.

3. water vapor in the air and temperature

4. Apply: Molecules in cold air are closer together than those in warmer air. The cold air molecules have fewer spaces in which to trap moisture.

PROGRAM RESOURCES

From the **Teacher Resource Package** use:

Activity Worksheets, page 5, Flex Your Brain.

Concept Mapping, pages 25-26.

Table 10-2

DETERMINING PERCENT RELATIVE HUMIDITY

Dry Bulb Temperature	Dry Bulb Temperature Minus Wet Bulb Temperature, °C									
	1	2	3	4	5	6	7	8	9	10
10°C	88	77	66	55	44	34	24	15	6	
11°C	89	78	67	56	46	36	27	18	9	
12°C	89	78	68	58	48	39	29	21	12	
13°C	89	79	69	59	50	41	32	22	15	7
14°C	90	79	70	60	51	42	34	26	18	10
15°C	90	80	71	61	53	44	36	27	20	13
16°C	90	81	71	63	54	46	38	30	23	15
17°C	90	81	72	64	55	47	40	32	25	18
18°C	91	82	73	65	57	49	41	34	27	20
19°C	91	82	74	65	58	50	43	36	29	22
20°C	91	83	74	67	59	53	46	39	32	26
21°C	91	83	75	67	60	53	46	39	32	26
22°C	92	83	76	68	61	54	47	40	34	28
23°C	92	84	76	69	62	55	48	42	36	30
24°C	92	84	77	69	62	56	49	43	37	31
25°C	92	84	77	70	63	57	50	44	39	33
26°C	92	85	78	71	64	58	51	46	40	34
27°C	92	85	78	71	65	58	52	47	41	36
28°C	93	85	78	72	65	59	53	48	42	37
29°C	93	86	79	72	66	60	54	49	43	38
30°C	93	86	79	73	67	61	55	50	44	39

SECTION REVIEW

1. How do clouds form?
2. When does water vapor in air condense?
3. What two factors determine relative humidity?
4. **Apply:** Explain why cold air can hold less moisture than warm air.

Skill Builder

Concept Mapping

Make a network tree concept map that compares four cloud types. Use these terms: *cirrus, cumulus, stratus, nimbostratus, feathery, fair weather, puffy, layered, precipitation, cloud types, dark,* and *steady precipitation.* If you need help, refer to Concept Mapping in the **Skill Handbook** on pages 688 and 689.

Skill Builder

Possible Solution:

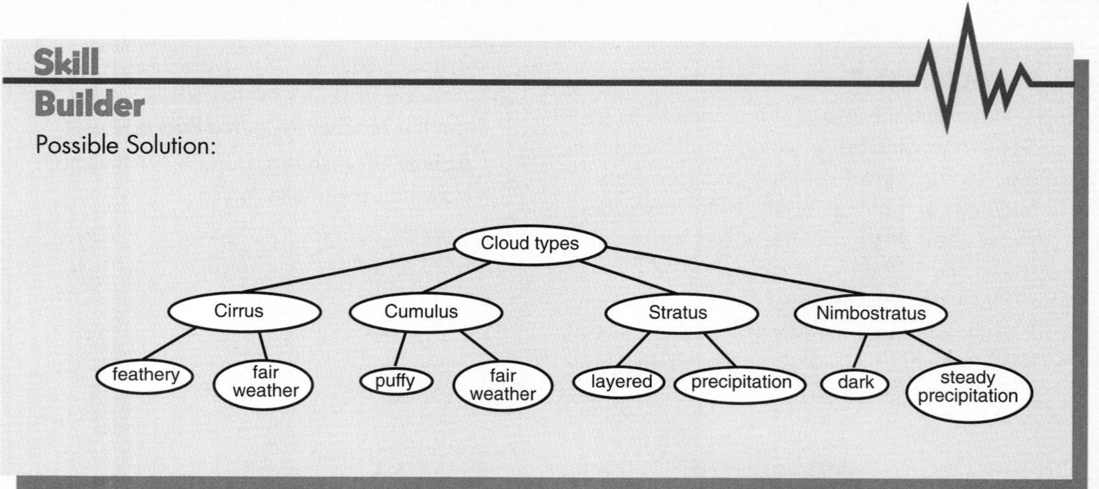

ACTIVITY 10-1
Relative Humidity

Problem: *How is relative humidity determined?*

Materials 

- identical Celsius thermometers (2)
- piece of gauze, 2 cm^2
- tape
- string
- cardboard
- beaker of water

Procedure

1. Attach the gauze to the bulb of one thermometer with string as shown.
2. Tape both thermometers side by side on the cardboard with the bulbs hanging over the edge of one end. You have created a psychrometer.
3. Thoroughly wet the gauze on the thermometer by dipping it into the beaker of water. This is called a wet bulb thermometer.
4. Create air motion across the thermometer bulbs by gently fanning them with a sheet of paper.
5. Wait until the alcohol stops moving in this thermometer and record the temperature.
6. Record the temperature of the dry bulb thermometer.
7. Subtract the wet bulb temperature from the dry bulb temperature.
8. Determine relative humidity using Table 10-2. Find the temperature difference you determined in Step 7 by reading across the top of the table. Keep one finger on this number. Find the dry bulb temperature in the first column of the table. Look across this row until you find the column you marked with your finger. The number at the point where the row and column intersect is the percent relative humidity.
9. Repeat Steps 3-8 at another location inside your school building. Be sure to resoak the wet bulb thermometer at your new test location. Also, wait at least 5 minutes in order to let the thermometers adjust to the new location.
10. Repeat Step 9 at a test site outside of your school building.

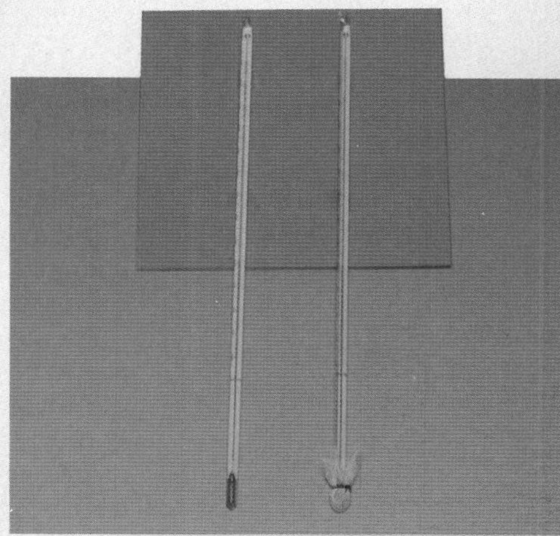

Analyze

1. What was the relative humidity at your three different test sites?

Conclude and Apply

2. Why did the wet bulb thermometer record a temperature lower than that recorded by the dry bulb thermometer?
3. What would be the relative humidity if the wet bulb and dry bulb thermometers recorded the same temperature?
4. How could the relative humidity in your classroom be decreased?
5. Why did the relative humidity vary at your three test sites?
6. How is relative humidity determined?

ACTIVITY 10-1
45 minutes

OBJECTIVE: Determine relative humidity.

PROCESS SKILLS applied in this activity:
▶ **Observing** in Analyze Question 1.
▶ **Inferring** in Conclude and Apply Questions 2, 4, and 6.
▶ **Measuring** in Procedure Steps 5-7.
▶ **Experimenting** in Procedure Steps 1-10.
▶ **Predicting** in Conclude and Apply Question 3.
▶ **Using Numbers** in Procedure Step 8.
▶ **Interpreting Data** in Conclude and Apply Questions 1 and 5.

TEACHING THE ACTIVITY

▶ Calibrate all thermometers ahead of time. You may wish to construct the psychrometer set-ups before class.
▶ For best results in Step 9, have students test an area that you know is likely to have a much different humidity and/or temperature from your classroom. Examples are the gym or the kitchen.

Troubleshooting: The psychrometers will not work if the dry bulb temperature is less than 0°C.

PROGRAM RESOURCES

From the **Teacher Resource Package** use:

Activity Worksheets, page 86-87, Activity 10-1: Relative Humidity.

ANSWERS TO QUESTIONS

1. Answers will vary.
2. The water absorbs some of the heat as it evaporates.
3. 100 percent
4. by increasing the temperature or by using a dehumidifier
5. Three different sites usually have different temperatures and amounts of moisture. Thus, the relative humidities would differ.
6. Relative humidity is determined by finding the temperature difference between a wet bulb and dry bulb thermometer. This difference and the temperature on the dry bulb are used with a relative humidity table to determine the percent relative humidity.

SECTION 10-2

PREPARATION

SECTION BACKGROUND

▶ The stability of an air mass is one factor that determines the weather of an area. Warm, moist air masses are said to be unstable. The warm air at the surface, because it is less dense, will tend to be forced aloft, producing clouds, precipitation, and storms. Cold, dry air masses are stable because cold air is more dense than warmer air and will tend to remain at the surface.

▶ Thunderstorms may form within a moist, warm, unstable air mass without the presence of a front. These storms usually occur in the late afternoon during times of maximum heating.

▶ A constant source of water vapor is essential for the formation of hurricanes. An increase of four or five degrees in tropical air temperature may evaporate thousands of metric tons of moisture and add it to the air over a wide area.

1 MOTIVATE

FLEX Your Brain

Use the Flex Your Brain activity to have students explore AIR MASSES.

▶ Have each student make a list of ways in which severe weather has affected his or her plans for a certain day, his or her personal property, and so on. Pick several students to share these experiences orally.

PROGRAM RESOURCES

From the **Teacher Resource Package** use:

Activity Worksheets, page 5, Flex Your Brain.

Transparency Masters, pages 35-36, Air Masses.

Use **Color Transparency** number 18, Air Masses.

10-2 Weather Patterns

New Science Words

air mass
front
tornado
hurricane

Objectives

- ▶ Describe the weather associated with fronts and high and low pressure areas.
- ▶ Explain how low pressure systems form at fronts.
- ▶ Relate thunderstorms to tornadoes.

Changes in Weather

Why do you ask about the weather in the morning when you get up? Isn't it safe to assume that the weather is the same as it was the day before? Of course not! Weather is always changing because of the constant movement of air and moisture in the atmosphere. These changes are generally related to the development and movement of air masses.

What is an air mass?

An **air mass** is a large body of air that has the same properties as the surface over which it develops. For example, an air mass that develops over land is dry compared to one that develops over water and is moist. Also, an air mass that develops in the tropics is warmer than one that develops at a higher latitude.

Fronts

When you witness a change in the weather from one day to the next, it is due to the movement of air masses.

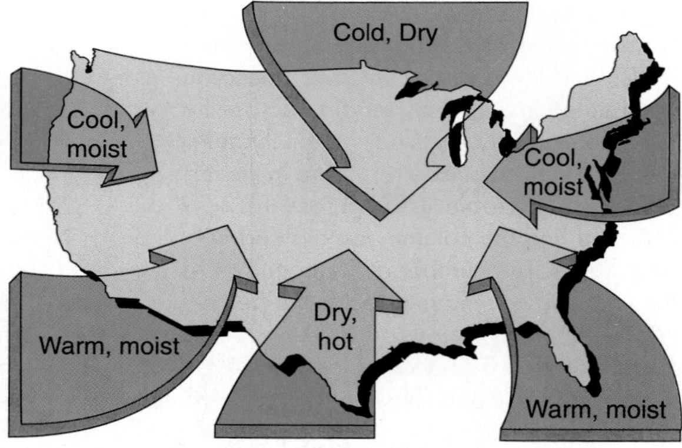

Figure 10-6. These are the six major air masses that affect the United States. Each has the same characteristics of temperature and moisture content as the area over which it forms.

OPTIONS

Meeting Different Ability Levels

For Section 10-2, use the following **Teacher Resource Masters** depending upon individual students' needs.

◆ **Study Guide Master** for all students.

● **Reinforcement Master** for students of average and above average ability levels.

▲ **Enrichment Master** for above average students.

Additional Teacher Resource Package masters are listed in the OPTIONS box throughout the section. The additional masters are appropriate for all students.

◆ STUDY GUIDE 43

NAME ______ DATE ______ CLASS ______

STUDY GUIDE Chapter 10

Weather Patterns Text Pages 262–269

Fill in the sentence outline using information from Section 10–2 in your textbook.

I. Changes in Weather

A. An air mass is **a large body of air that has the same properties as the surface over which it develops.**

B. A front is **the boundary formed when two air masses collide.**

1. A warm front develops when **a warm air mass meets a cold air mass and slides up over it.**
2. A cold front forms when **a cold air mass invades a warm air mass and forces the warm air up rapidly.**
3. A stationary front results when **a warm or cold front stops moving and remains in the same place for several days.**
4. An occluded front results when **two cool air masses merge, forcing the warm air**

II. Pressure Systems

A. High pressure systems generally mean clear weather because **as cold air sinks, it warms and its water vapor evaporates, so there is no moisture to form clouds.**

B. Low pressure systems generally mean cloudy weather because **warm moist air rises, cools, condenses, and forms clouds.**

III. Severe Weather

A. Thunderstorms result from **the rapid upward movement of warm, moist air which cools, condenses, and forms high clouds.**

B. Tornadoes occur in thunderstorms when **warm air is forced upward at great speed, creating low pressure at Earth's surface. Strong winds collide and rotate around the center of the low pressure system. They create a funnel cloud.**

C. Hurricanes are **large, swirling, low pressure systems that form over tropical oceans when opposing winds meet and begin to rotate over warm water**

 43

When an air mass moves, it collides with another air mass, and a boundary forms between the two masses called a **front.** Most changes in weather occur at one of the four types of fronts. 1

A warm front develops when a warm air mass meets a cold air mass. The warm air, because it is less dense, slides up over the cold air. The first sign of this front is the presence of high cirrus clouds that form as rising water vapor condenses. Later, stratus clouds form as the front continues to move. Nimbostratus clouds may develop and produce rain or snow.

A cold front forms when a cold air mass invades a warm air mass. The cold air forces the warm air rapidly aloft along the steep front. Cumulus and cumulonimbus clouds form along the front, producing rain and thunderstorms. 2

A stationary front results when pressure differences cause a warm front or a cold front to stop moving forward. This type of front may remain in the same place for several days. Weather conditions include light winds and precipitation across the entire frontal region.

An occluded front results when two cool air masses merge, forcing the warmer air between them to rise. Strong winds and heavy precipitation may occur in an occluded front.

Precipitation is associated with each type of front. Do you know why? You learned earlier that when air is cooled, its ability to hold water is reduced. All along each of these fronts, warm air is being cooled. The air becomes saturated and water is precipitated.

Figure 10-7. These diagrams show the structure of a cold front, a warm front, and an occluded front.

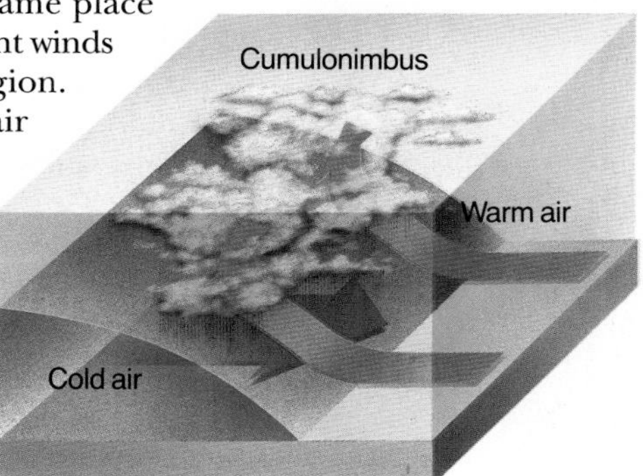

Cold front

Cirrus
Alto stratus
Nimbo stratus
Warm air
Cold air

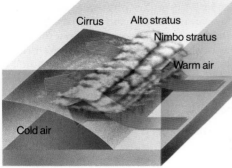

Warm front

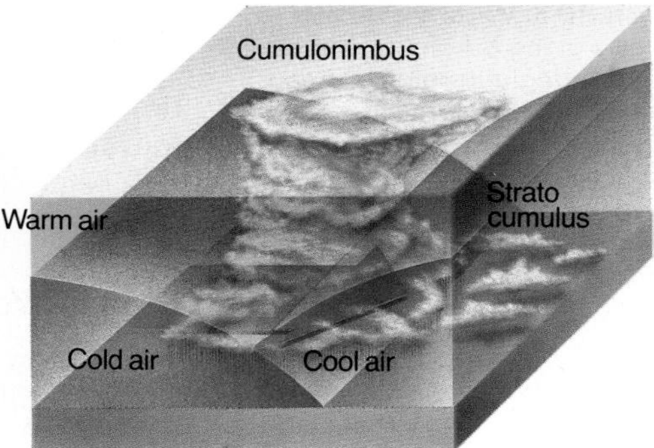

Occluded front

● REINFORCEMENT 43

NAME ______ DATE ______ CLASS ______

REINFORCEMENT — Chapter 10

Weather Patterns — Text Pages 262–269

Use the diagrams to answer the following questions.

Topeka, KS · Kansas City, KS · Indianapolis, IN · Columbus, OH

1. What kinds of clouds form along the front in Figure 1? **cumulus, cumulonimbus**
2. What kind of precipitation might come from these clouds? **heavy rainshowers**
3. What kinds of clouds form along the front in Figure 2? **nimbostratus, stratus, cirrus**
4. What kind of precipitation might come from these clouds? **steady rain or snow**
5. Figure 1 represents a **cold front.**
6. Figure 2 represents a **warm front.**
7. Describe what will happen to the temperature at Columbus, Ohio, when the front passes. **It will rise.**
8. Compare the temperature at Topeka and Kansas City, Kansas. **Topeka is colder than Kansas City.**
9. Fill in the chart about the elements of thunderstorms.

Element of thunderstorms	Caused by
Heavy rain	warm, moist air pushed very high very rapidly that condenses—water drops fall to Earth, colliding with other drops and becoming larger
Strong winds	falling water drops which create a downdraft that spreads across Earth's surface
Lightning	current flowing between regions in the clouds that have positive and negative electrical charges
Thunder	the heating and rapid expansion of the air around a lightning bolt which forms a sound wave
Tornado	warm air forced upward at great speed, creating low pressure at Earth's surface—strong winds at the center of the low pressure collide and rotate, lowering air pressure even more and creating a funnel cloud made of condensed water, dirt, and debris

 43

▲ ENRICHMENT 43

NAME ______ DATE ______ CLASS ______

ENRICHMENT — Chapter 10

Weather Patterns — Text Pages 262–269

READING WEATHER MAPS

Figures 1–4 are weather maps for a 24-hour period. The maps show the position of pressure systems and fronts in the United States every 12 hours, beginning at 12:00 A.M. on Thursday. Examine the maps and think about what is occurring. Then answer the following questions.

FIGURE 1 FIGURE 2 FIGURE 3 FIGURE 4

1. Briefly describe the movement of the high and low pressure systems shown on the maps. **The first high pressure system moved east and off the coast. The second high moved eastward across the United States behind a low and a cold front. This cold front also moved eastward and the low moved along the front from the southwest to the northeast, into the Great Lakes area and on into Canada.**
2. Why do you think the cold front in Figure 1 developed? **The high pressure from Canada is associated with a cold air mass. The front developed along the leading edge of the cold air.**
3. What conditions were necessary for the development of the warm front in Figure 3? **Warm air from the south is associated with a counterclockwise circulation around the low pressure area.**
4. What may be happening to the cold air mass as it moves southward from the Great Plains? **It will become warmer.**
5. Explain what is happening to air along the cold front. **Warm air is forced to rise over the colder air from Canada, forming clouds and precipitation.**

 43

TYING TO PREVIOUS KNOWLEDGE: In Chapter 9, students learned about air pressure. In this section, they will learn how differences in air pressure affect the weather.

OBJECTIVES AND SCIENCE WORDS: Have students review the objectives and science words to become familiar with this section.

2 TEACH

Key Concepts are highlighted.

CONCEPT DEVELOPMENT

▶ Have students examine Figure 10-7 and contrast the cloud types associated with cold, warm, and occluded fronts.

▶ **Demonstration:** Use an aquarium with a glass lid, cold bags of sand or marbles, and a pan of very hot water to make a model of a cold front. Place the pan of water inside the aquarium next to the cold bags. Cover the aquarium with a glass lid. Have students observe what happens. They will notice that condensation occurs on the sides and top of the aquarium, and clouds appear above the cold bags. There is no cloud above the pan because the temperature of the air prevents condensation.

CROSS CURRICULUM

▶ **History/Language Arts:** Have students use dictionaries and other reference books to find out that in the 1940s, the term *front* was used to describe the boundary between two air masses because this boundary was similar to the front along which opposing armies fought.

PROGRAM RESOURCES

From the **Teacher Resource Package** use:

Transparency Masters, pages 37-38, Types of Fronts

Use **Color Transparency** number 19, Types of Fronts

TEACHER F.Y.I.

▶ Because fronts form along low pressure troughs, air pressure drops as a front approaches an area and rises as the front passes the area.

CONCEPT DEVELOPMENT

▶ Ask students the following questions. **What kind of weather is associated with high pressure areas? Why?** *Fair weather occurs because as molecules bump into one another, the air warms. Relative humidity decreases and water vapor evaporates before it can form clouds.* **Why don't pressure systems stay in one place for very long?** *Winds carry them away.*

▶ Have students listen to daily weather reports on the radio and TV.

▶ Using weather maps, encourage students to identify the position and movement of air masses (high pressure areas and low pressure areas). Fronts will be shown as boundaries between two different air masses. The wave cyclone or migrating low will be found on the front and generally will move with the front. Fronts and cyclones are zones of surface convergence. Convergence indicates rising air that is becoming cooler, usually producing clouds and precipitation.

▶ Maritime tropical air often is drawn northward by a low pressure area along the Mississippi Valley. Moist air is heated over land, is forced aloft, and causes thunderstorms throughout the mid-section of the United States.

MINI QUIZ

Use the Mini Quiz to check students' recall of chapter content.

1. **The boundary between two air masses is called a(n) _____.** *front*
2. **A(n) _____ front may remain in the same place for several days.** *stationary*
3. **_____ pressure usually means clear weather.** *High*
4. **Low pressure can form along _____ where warm air meets cold air.** *fronts*
5. **In which direction do low pressure systems swirl in the Northern Hemisphere?** *counterclockwise*

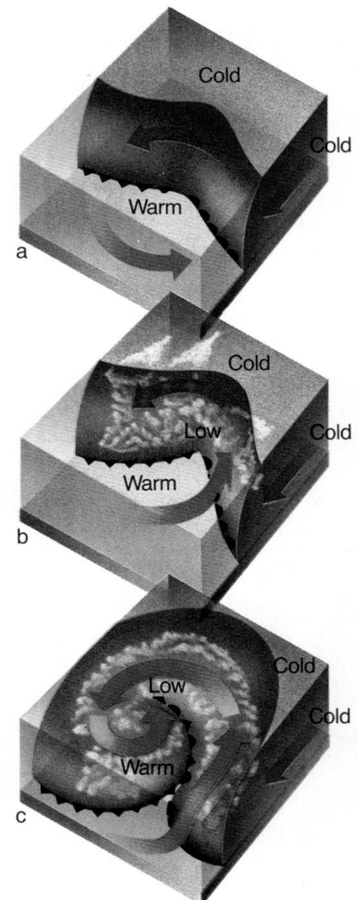

Figure 10-8. When a disturbance occurs along a front (a), the air masses begin to rotate around the disturbance forming a cold front and a warm front, with low pressure at the center (b). Eventually, the cold air forces all of the warm air up, forming an occluded front (c).

Pressure Systems

You've probably heard about low and high pressure systems in weather forecasts. Differences in pressure have
a great effect on the weather. High pressure usually means 3
clear weather and low pressure means cloudy weather.

As you learned in Chapter 9, air molecules have mass and cause air molecules to exert pressure on each other. When air molecules are densely packed, high pressure occurs. Barometers on Earth record high pressure on Earth as a result of cold, dense air that is sinking. As it descends, molecules heat up as more and more of them bump into each other. The warming of the air decreases its relative humidity and water vapor is evaporated. That's why high pressure means good weather. Moisture in the air is evaporated before it can form clouds.

Because of winds in Earth's atmosphere, pressure systems don't usually stay in one place for very long. Sooner or later they move, and another pressure system follows. Barometers record low pressure on Earth as warm, less
dense air rises. One place where low pressure forms is 4
along fronts where warm air meets cold air. These low pressure systems cause most of the weather changes in the United States. Thunderstorms are one result of these low pressure systems.

As stated earlier, different air masses don't mix together when they meet and form a front. Due to the Coriolis
effect, air at this boundary sometimes begins to swirl coun- 5
terclockwise in the northern hemisphere, as seen in Figure 10-8. The rising air in this swirling front forms a low pressure system. As the air in a low pressure system rises, it cools. At a certain point, the air reaches its dew point and condenses, forming clouds. Several different types of precipitation and storms occur in low pressure systems.

After several days, an occluded front evolves from the two swirling air masses in the low pressure system. The warm, moist air is pushed above cold air and the pressure begins to rise, bringing another change in weather.

Severe Weather

You know that weather affects you every day. Usually, you can still go about your business regardless of the weather. If it's raining, you can still go to school, and if it snows a little, you can still get to the store. But some weath-

OPTIONS

INQUIRY QUESTIONS

▶ **Why is stormy weather often associated with fronts?** *There is rapid movement of warm air upward where two air masses meet. The air then becomes saturated with moisture at the front; clouds form; and precipitation begins.*

er conditions prevent you from going about your normal routine. Severe weather is weather conditions that pose danger to humans.

Thunderstorms

Have you ever experienced a thunderstorm? Heavy rain fell, lightning flashed, thunder roared, and maybe hail even fell. What forces cause such extreme weather conditions? Thunderstorms result from the rapid upward movement of warm, moist air. They can occur inside warm, moist air masses and at fronts. As the warm, moist air moves upward, it cools, condenses, and forms cumulonimbus clouds that can reach heights of 10 km. As the rising air reaches its dew point, water droplets and ice form and begin falling the long distance through the clouds toward Earth's surface. As the droplets fall, they collide with other droplets and become larger. The falling droplets create a downdraft of air that spreads out at Earth's surface and causes strong winds associated with thunderstorms.

Thunder and lightning are also associated with thunderstorms. During the rapid uplift of air, electric charges build up in the clouds. Some places in the clouds have a positive electrical charge and some have a negative electrical charge. Lightning occurs when current flows between regions of opposite electrical charge. Bolts of lightning can leap from cloud to cloud and from clouds to Earth.

Did You Know?

One of the largest hailstones ever found fell in Kansas in 1970. The hailstone had a circumference of 44 centimeters.

What causes lightning?

Figure 10-9. A thunderstorm may include heavy rain, strong winds, thunder, lightning, and hail.

REVEALING MISCONCEPTIONS

▶ Ask students if lightning ever travels from Earth's surface to clouds. They are likely to say "No." Explain that in less than 1/10 of a second, a single lightning discharge goes back and forth many times between a cloud and the ground. Although these discharges usually begin in clouds, sometimes they begin on Earth's surface.

▶ Ask students to explain why stormy weather is often associated with fronts. Students should realize that at the boundary where two air masses meet, there is rapid movement of cold air downward and warm air upward. This movement causes winds. The cold air mass becomes saturated with moisture at the front, clouds form, and precipitation begins.

▶ Fronts form at the margins of low pressure systems. Since fronts form along low pressure troughs, air pressure drops as a front approaches an area. Pressure rises as the front passes the area. Winds near Earth's surface always shift clockwise in the Northern Hemisphere as a front passes.

INQUIRY QUESTIONS

▶ **Why do you think hail is common during thunderstorms?** *Thunderstorms result from rapid, upward movements of warm, moist air. Rain freezes as the drops are caught in the updrafts and carried to high altitudes. When these ice granules fall through the clouds, they collect droplets of water. Eventually, the ice balls fall as hail.*

PROGRAM RESOURCES

From the **Teacher Resource Package** use:

Cross-Curricular Connections, page 14, Myths and Weather.

CONCEPT DEVELOPMENT

▶ Explain that thunder and lightning are both waves. Light waves travel faster than sound waves, which is why thunder is heard after the lightning is seen.

▶ Have students research the effects that thunderstorms have on economic issues in your area.

▶ Thunderstorms may form within a moist, warm, unstable air mass without the presence of a front. These storms usually occur in the late afternoon during times of maximum heating.

▶ Explain to students that a thunderstorm has a life cycle consisting of three stages. The initial stage is called the *cumulus* stage and lasts for about 15 minutes. The cumulus stage is the developing stage where strong updrafts are present. The *mature* stage begins as rain falls from the base of the clouds. The falling rain will produce a downdraft that spreads along the ground. The mature stage is the most intense period. Lightning, turbulence, and hail are most severe at this time. The downdrafts finally cut off the updrafts and the cumulonimbus cloud can no longer develop. The *dissipating* stage begins. Precipitation and turbulence cease as the cloud evaporates.

What causes thunder?

Thunder results from the rapid heating of the air around a bolt of lightning. Lightning can reach temperatures of about 28 000°C. That's more than five times the temperature of the surface of the sun! This extreme heat causes the air around the lightning to expand rapidly, forming a sound wave we hear as thunder.

Thunderstorms can cause a lot of damage. The rain sometimes causes flooding, and the lightning can strike objects and set them on fire. Strong winds generated by thunderstorms can also cause damage. If a thunderstorm has winds traveling faster than 80 kilometers per hour and hail more than two centimeters in diameter, it is classified as a severe thunderstorm. Hail can make dents in cars and the siding on houses. Even though the rain from thunderstorms helps crops grow, hail can flatten and destroy a crop in a matter of minutes.

Tornadoes

Some of the most severe thunderstorms produce tornadoes. A **tornado** is a violent, whirling wind that moves in a narrow path over land. In very severe thunderstorms, warm air is forced upward at great speed, causing very low pressure at Earth's surface. Strong winds approaching the center of the low pressure system collide from

Figure 10-10. The diagram on the left shows how wind forms funnel clouds like the one on the right.

OPTIONS

INQUIRY QUESTIONS

▶ **What intensity requirements must a storm have before it can be classified as a severe storm?** *Winds faster than 80 km/hr and hail greater than 2 cm in diameter.*

▶ **What causes the sound we hear as thunder?** *The extreme heat of lightning causes the air around the lightning to expand rapidly, causing a sound wave we hear as thunder.*

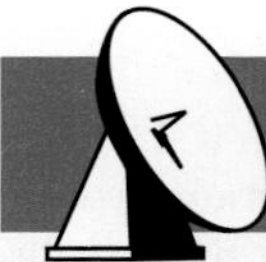

TECHNOLOGY

Tailing a Tornado

A tornado can develop in less than an hour and can destroy property and kill people within a matter of minutes.

Next Generation Weather Radar, or NEXRAD, is a system of radar stations that uses Doppler radar to track severe weather such as tornadoes. Doppler radar sends out radio waves toward the storms. The waves reflect off of the storm clouds and are recorded at the radar station. The shift in frequency of the reflected signals allows meteorologists to determine the position, strength, and wind speed of the storm. Doppler radar helps scientists to detect tornadoes before they touch down.

Think Critically: Suppose a tornado were moving toward your town at 100 km/h. If Doppler radar spotted the storm 160 km from your town, how much time would you have to prepare for the storm?

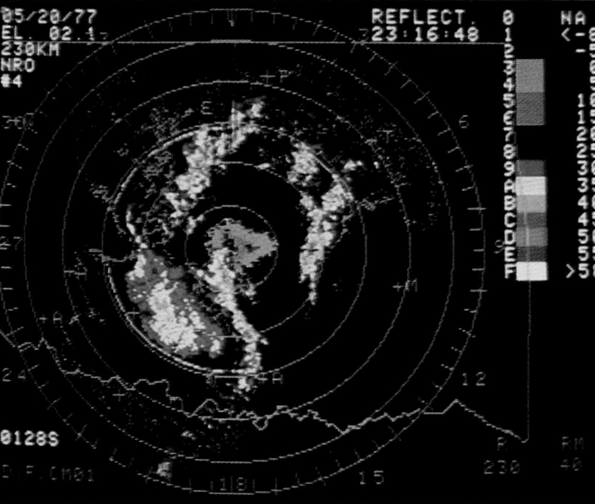

different directions and begin to rotate violently. When this happens, the air pressure inside drops rapidly, and a funnel cloud appears at the base of the cloud. Water vapor condenses in the funnel as it picks up dirt and debris from the ground. This gives a funnel its dark gray or black color.

Why are tornadoes usually dark gray or black?

When tornado funnels touch the ground, buildings and trees are ripped apart by the destructive winds that can reach up to 500 kilometers per hour. The pressure in the center of a tornado is so low that when it passes over buildings, the buildings actually explode because their inside pressure is higher than the tornado's pressure. The updraft in the center of a tornado can be so strong, it can lift animals, cars, and even houses into the air and move them. Even though tornadoes average only 200 meters in diameter, and last for a period of a few minutes, they are one of the most destructive types of storms.

INQUIRY QUESTIONS

▶ **In which direction do tornadoes rotate in the Northern Hemisphere? Explain.** *They rotate in a counterclockwise direction. Tornadoes are low pressure systems, and lows rotate counterclockwise in the Northern Hemisphere.*

▶ **Some tornadoes are white or transparent. Explain.** *Such tornadoes can occur if dirt and debris have not been picked up by the funnel.*

TECHNOLOGY

▶ Inform students that signals reflected from storms have different frequencies. The frequencies appear on the Doppler radar screen as different colors. Green indicates winds coming toward the station, red indicates winds moving away from the station. When red and green signals appear close together, rotation is occurring.

▶ For more information, see "Next-generation Radar Passes Milestone," *Business & Commercial Aviation,* August 1988, p. 37 or "Eye on the Storm," *Scientific American*, August 1987, p. 22.

Think Critically:

100 km/1 h = 160 km/? h

? h = 160 km/100 km × 1 h

? h = 1.6 h or 1 h and 36 min

CONCEPT DEVELOPMENT

▶ Show the movie *Countdown to Survival* by Screenscope, Inc. It emphasizes precautions to take during tornado watches and warnings.

▶ Discuss with students why all watch and warning advisories should be taken seriously.

▶ Review with students tornado drill procedures for your school.

TEACHER F.Y.I.

▶ Many tornadoes in the United States occur in a region called "Tornado Alley." This region extends from northern Texas through Oklahoma, Kansas, and Missouri. In these areas, cool air masses from the west collide with warm, moist air masses from the Gulf of Mexico. As many as 300 tornadoes touch down each year throughout "Tornado Alley."

CONCEPT DEVELOPMENT

►**Describe the evolution of a hurricane.** *A hurricane forms when two opposing winds meet and begin to swirl over tropical oceans, usually between 5° and 20° north latitude. Around the middle of the low pressure area, warm, moist air is forced aloft. As this air rises, it cools and condenses. The storm then becomes a large, swirling, low pressure system.* **What provides the energy for a hurricane?** *Moisture provides the energy for hurricanes.* **What happens to the strength of a hurricane as it moves over land?** *Since its supply of warm, moist air is gone, the storm loses its power.*

CHECK FOR UNDERSTANDING

Have students compare and contrast tornadoes and hurricanes.

RETEACH

Cooperative Learning: Provide students with the boldfaced terms listed below and have Paired Partners contrast tornadoes and hurricanes in reference to the boldfaced terms.

Relative size

Origin

Type of pressure system

Damage

EXTENSION

For students who have mastered this section, use the **Reinforcement** and **Enrichment** masters or other OPTIONS provided.

Science and READING

Go to the library and get a book on weather experiments. Read about how you can make a model hurricane. You may want to consider the project for class. You might also find information about a model hurricane in an encyclopedia.

Hurricanes

The largest and most powerful severe storm is the hurricane. A **hurricane** is a large, swirling, low pressure system that forms over tropical oceans. A storm must have winds of at least 120 km/hour to be called a hurricane.

Hurricanes are similar to low pressure systems on land, but are much larger. They form over tropical oceans where two opposing winds meet and begin to swirl. For example, in the North Atlantic the southeast trade winds and the northeast trade winds sometimes meet. A low pressure area develops in the middle of the swirl and begins rotating counterclockwise in the northern hemisphere. This usually happens between 5° and 20° north latitude where the water is quite warm. Around the middle of the low pressure area, warm, moist air is forced up. As it rises to higher elevations, it cools and moisture condenses.

As long as a hurricane is over water, the warm, moist air will rise and provide energy for the storm. When a hurricane reaches land, however, its supply of warm, moist air is gone and the storm loses power.

A hurricane can create a lot of damage when it reaches land. High winds, tornadoes, heavy rains, high waves, and floods occur. As a result, crops are destroyed, buildings are demolished, and people and other animals are

Figure 10-11. In this hurricane cross section, the red arrows indicate rising warm, moist air forming cumulus and cumulonimbus clouds in bands around the eye. The blue arrows indicate cool, dry air sinking in the eye and between the cloud bands. The purple arrows indicate the circular motion of the spiral cloud bands.

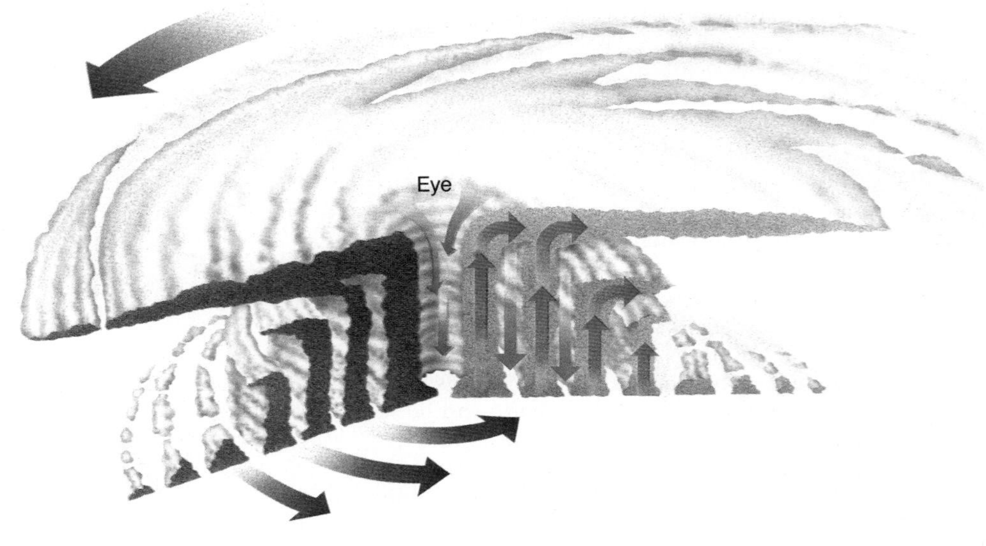

OPTIONS

INQUIRY QUESTIONS

►**Why don't hurricanes form directly over the equator?** *The upward motion of air at the equator as well as a small Coriolis effect don't favor the development of such storms.*

PROGRAM RESOURCES

Use **Laboratory Manual** page 87, Hurricanes

Figure 10-12. Hurricanes can be very destructive.

killed. In 1989, Hurricane Hugo hit the east coast of the United States, killing several people and causing about six billion dollars in damage.

You can see how changes in weather affect your life. The interaction of air and water vapor cause constant change in the atmosphere. Air masses meet and fronts form, causing changes in weather. Severe weather can affect human lives and property.

SECTION REVIEW

1. How can a low pressure system form at a front?
2. What weather is associated with a cold front?
3. Why do high pressure areas usually have clear skies?
4. Explain how a tornado evolves from a thunderstorm.
5. **Apply:** What would happen to a balloon in a tornado? Would it expand or contract? Why?

Recognizing Cause and Effect

Skill Builder

Use your knowledge of weather to answer the following questions. If you need help, refer to Recognizing Cause and Effect in the **Skill Handbook** on page 683.

1. What effect does a warm, dry air mass have on the area over which it forms?
2. What causes a cold front? What effect does a cold front produce?
3. Describe the cause and effect of an occluded front that might form over your city.

3 CLOSE

▶ Ask questions 1-4 and the **Apply** Question in the Section Review.

▶ If you live in a region where hurricanes or tornadoes occur, have students investigate the frequency of these storms for the past ten years.

SECTION REVIEW ANSWERS

1. It can form when a disturbance along a front causes the two air masses to begin to rotate. Low pressure forms at the center as warm air is forced up.

2. cumulus and cumulonimbus clouds, rain, and thunderstorms

3. Air molecules bump into one another and produce heat. This causes water vapor to evaporate rather than to condense to form clouds.

4. In a thunderstorm, warm air is forced quickly aloft, creating a very low pressure area. Strong winds are then able to flow into the center of the low pressure area and begin to rotate. This causes the air pressure to drop rapidly. A tornado then appears at the base of the cloud.

5. Apply: It would expand. Air inside the balloon exerts a greater pressure than the outside air.

Skill Builder

1. A warm, dry air mass will produce fair weather.

2. A cold front forms when a cold air mass invades a warm air mass. Rain showers and thunderstorms result when a cold front passes over an area.

3. An occluded front brings high winds and heavy precipitation to an area.

ENRICHMENT

▶ Have students research how air masses are classified.

▶ Have students collect magazine photos and use them to compare and contrast severe weather phenomena such as blizzards, tornadoes, and hurricanes.

SECTION 10-3

PREPARATION

SECTION BACKGROUND

► In addition to surface weather maps, meteorologists use upper air charts that show the movement of air at various altitudes.

► Satellites take photographs of Earth's atmosphere and send the data to ground stations by microwave transmissions. At night, the satellites photograph infrared waves, which allow determination of the temperature differences between cloudy and clear areas. Satellite photos are very important to weather forecasters because the data they provide about cloud movements enable the forecasters to locate low pressure areas and fronts.

1 MOTIVATE

► Invite a meteorologist to visit the class and talk about weather forecasting.

Cooperative Learning: Have Science Investigation groups examine actual weather maps from the local weather bureau. Ask students to infer the meanings of some of the symbols used on these maps.

STUDENT TEXT QUESTION

► Page 270, paragraph 1: **But what weather concerns do you have in your own climate?** *Answers will vary with your location. Students' answers might include floods, blizzards, tornadoes, severe thunderstorms, sleet, or hail.*

PROGRAM RESOURCES

From the **Teacher Resource Package** use:

Critical Thinking/Problem Solving, page 16, Weather Forecasting Folklore.

Use **Laboratory Manual** page 91, Weather Forecasting.

10-3 Forecasting and Climate

New Science Words

meteorologist
station model
isotherm
isobar
temperate zones

Objectives

- ► **Explain how weather maps are made.**
- ► **Contrast tropical, temperate, and polar climates.**
- ► **Explain how large bodies of water and mountains affect climate.**

Forecasting the Weather

You can easily tell what current weather conditions are by simply making observations. You can feel the temperature and you can see if clouds are in the sky. You also have a general idea of the weather because you are familiar with the climate you live in. For example, if you live in Florida, you probably won't have to worry about snow in the forecast. But what weather concerns do you have in your own climate?

1 A **meteorologist** is a person who studies the weather. Meteorologists make measurements of temperature, air pressure, winds, humidity, and precipitation. In addition to these, radar, computers, and instruments in balloons are also used to gather data. Meteorologists make observations to include on weather maps. They use weather maps to make weather forecasts, and they warn people of severe weather.

Figure 10-13. A station model shows the weather conditions at one specific location.

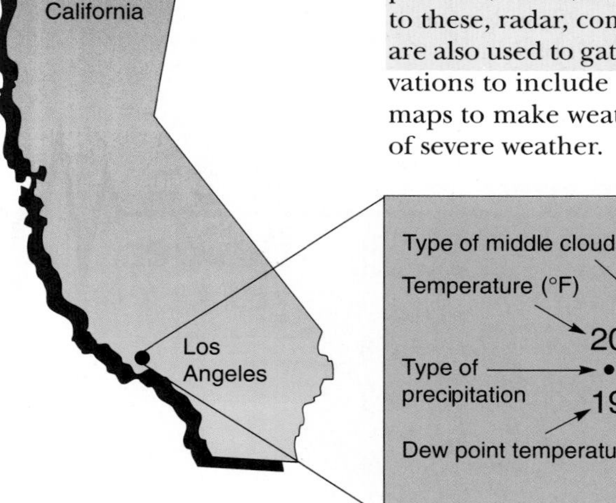

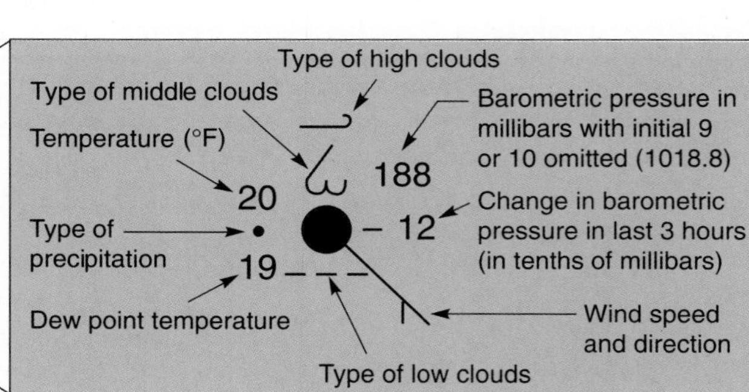

OPTIONS

Meeting Different Ability Levels

For Section 10-3, use the following **Teacher Resource Masters** depending upon individual students' needs.

◆ **Study Guide Master** for all students.

● **Reinforcement Master** for students of average and above average ability levels.

▲ **Enrichment Master** for above average students.

Additional Teacher Resource Package masters are listed in the OPTIONS box throughout the section. The additional masters are appropriate for all students.

◆ STUDY GUIDE 44

NAME ____ DATE ____ CLASS ____

STUDY GUIDE — Chapter 10

Forecasting and Climate — Text Pages 270–273

In the blank at the left, write the letter of the term in Column II that matches each definition in Column I.

	Column I	Column II
i	1. Advisory to prepare for severe weather	a. climate
b	2. Person who studies the weather	b. meteorologist
a	3. Average of all weather conditions of an area over a 30-year period	c. isobar
e	4. Weather information collected by a meteorologist at a specific location	d. isotherm
d	5. Line connecting points of equal temperature on a weather map	e. station model
f	6. Regions on Earth that have cold winters, hot summers, and mild springs and falls	f. temperate zones
j	7. Advisory that severe weather conditions exist	g. polar zones
h	8. Regions on Earth that have hot temperatures all year	h. tropical zones
c	9. Line connecting points of equal atmospheric pressure on a weather map	i. watch
g	10. Regions on Earth extending from the poles to 66 1/2° north and south latitudes	j. warning

Answer the following questions on the lines provided.

11. What do you do if a watch is issued? If a warning is issued? **With a watch, you prepare for bad weather and make plans for where you will go if conditions get worse. With a warning, severe weather exists in your area and you should take immediate action by taking shelter or going to high ground.**

12. How do meteorologists gather weather information? **They measure temperature, air pressure, wind speed and direction, humidity, and precipitation. They include data gathered by radar, computers, and balloons.**

13. What can isobars tell you about wind speed? **Isobars that are close together on a weather map mean that there are great pressure differences in a small area and the winds will be strong. Isobars that are farther apart mean that there is less difference in pressure and the winds will be gentler.**

44

Because storms like hurricanes, tornadoes, blizzards, and thunderstorms can be very dangerous, meteorologists at the National Weather Service issue advisories when 2
severe weather has been observed, or when the conditions are such that severe weather could occur. When a watch is issued, you should prepare for severe weather. Watches are issued for severe thunderstorms, tornadoes, floods, blizzards, and hurricanes. During a watch, stay tuned to a radio or television station that is reporting weather updates. When a warning is issued, severe weather conditions exist, and you should take immediate action. Take shelter during a severe thunderstorm warning. During a tornado warning, go to the basement or a room in the middle of the house away from windows.

How do you suppose the National Weather Service knows when to issue weather advisories? It depends on two sources for its information: meteorologists from around the world and satellites.

Once meteorologists have made their measurements in their specific location, they communicate their findings to the National Weather Service. The Weather Service uses this information to make weather maps that are used to warn of severe weather and to forecast the weather.

Weather maps for large areas show the information collected by meteorologists in specific locations. This information is expressed using combined symbols, form- 3
ing a **station model.** Figure 10-13 shows a station model and the information it contains.

Besides station models, there are also lines on weather maps that indicate atmospheric pressure and temperature. A line that connects points of equal temperature is 4
called an **isotherm.** *Iso* means "same" and *therm* means "temperature." You've probably seen isotherms on weather maps on TV. An **isobar** is a line drawn to connect points of equal atmospheric pressure. Isotherms and isobars are like the contour lines you learned about in Chapter 8. But instead of connecting points of equal elevation, they connect locations of equal temperature or pressure.

Isobars indicate the locations of highs and lows on a map. These areas are drawn as circles with an *H* or an *L* in the middle. You can tell how fast the wind is blowing by looking at how close the isobars are to one another. When isobars are close together, there's a great pressure difference over a small area. That means there are strong winds. If isobars are spread apart, there's less of a difference in pressure, and winds are more gentle.

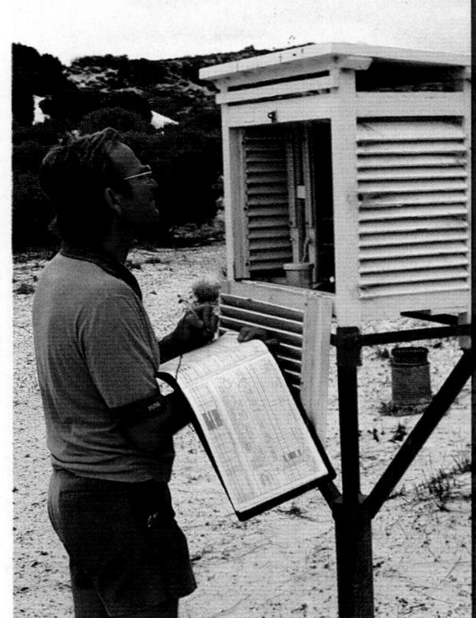

Figure 10-14. This person is collecting data, such as temperature and atmospheric pressure, for a weather forecast.

How are isobars and isotherms similar to, yet different from contour lines?

● REINFORCEMENT 44

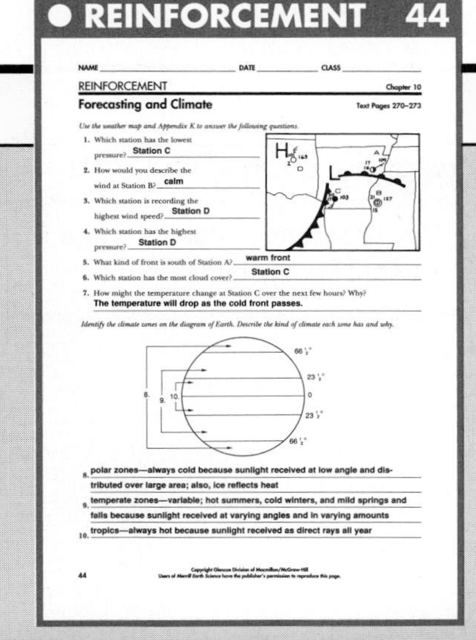

NAME ______ DATE ______ CLASS ______

REINFORCEMENT — Chapter 10

Forecasting and Climate — Text Pages 270–273

Use the weather map and Appendix K to answer the following questions.

1. Which station has the lowest pressure? **Station C**
2. How would you describe the wind at Station B? **calm**
3. Which station is recording the highest wind speed? **Station D**
4. Which station has the highest pressure? **Station D**
5. What kind of front is south of Station A? **warm front**
6. Which station has the most cloud cover? **Station C**
7. How might the temperature change at Station C over the next few hours? Why? **The temperature will drop as the cold front passes.**

Identify the climate zones on the diagram of Earth. Describe the kind of climate each zone has and why.

8. **polar zones—always cold because sunlight received at low angle and distributed over large area; also, ice reflects heat**
9. **temperate zones—variable; hot summers, cold winters, and mild springs and falls because sunlight received at varying angles and in varying amounts**
10. **tropics—always hot because sunlight received as direct rays all year**

44

▲ ENRICHMENT 44

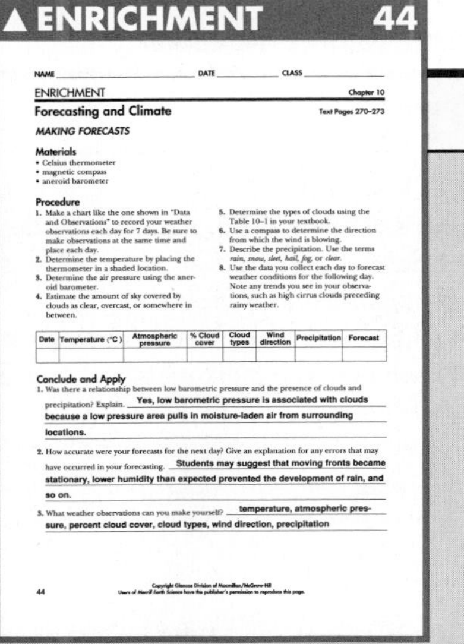

NAME ______ DATE ______ CLASS ______

ENRICHMENT — Chapter 10

Forecasting and Climate — Text Pages 270–273

MAKING FORECASTS

Materials
- Celsius thermometer
- magnetic compass
- aneroid barometer

Procedure
1. Make a chart like the one shown in "Data and Observations" to record your weather observations each day for 7 days. Be sure to make observations at the same time and place each day.
2. Determine the temperature by placing the thermometer in a shaded location.
3. Determine the air pressure using the aneroid barometer.
4. Estimate the amount of sky covered by clouds as clear, overcast, or somewhere in between.
5. Determine the types of clouds using the Table 10–1 in your textbook.
6. Use a compass to determine the direction from which the wind is blowing.
7. Describe the precipitation. Use the terms *rain, snow, sleet, hail, fog,* or *clear.*
8. Use the data you collect each day to forecast weather conditions for the following day. Note any trends you see in your observations, such as high cirrus clouds preceding rainy weather.

Date	Temperature (°C)	Atmospheric pressure	% Cloud cover	Cloud types	Wind direction	Precipitation	Forecast

Conclude and Apply
1. Was there a relationship between low barometric pressure and the presence of clouds and precipitation? Explain. **Yes, low barometric pressure is associated with clouds because a low pressure area pulls in moisture-laden air from surrounding locations.**
2. How accurate were your forecasts for the next day? Give an explanation for any errors that may have occurred in your forecasting. **Students may suggest that moving fronts became stationary, lower humidity than expected prevented the development of rain, and so on.**
3. What weather observations can you make yourself? **temperature, atmospheric pressure, percent cloud cover, cloud types, wind direction, precipitation**

44

TYING TO PREVIOUS KNOWLEDGE: Have students recall from Chapter 8 the function of map legends. Explain that station models, isotherms, and isobars on weather maps serve the same purpose as legends do on maps.

OBJECTIVES AND SCIENCE WORDS: Have students review the objectives and science words to become familiar with this section.

2 TEACH

Key Concepts are highlighted.

CONCEPT DEVELOPMENT

▶ Have students take turns listening to daily weather reports on the radio or TV and then report this information to their peers.

CHECK FOR UNDERSTANDING

Use the Mini Quiz to check for understanding.

MINI QUIZ

Use the Mini Quiz to check students' recall of chapter content.

1. **A(n) ____ is a person who studies weather.** *meteorologist*
2. **The ____ issues advisories when severe weather has been observed.** *National Weather Service*
3. **A(n) ____ contains symbols that show the weather conditions of a specific location.** *station model*
4. **A(n) ____ is a line on a weather map that connects points of equal temperature.** *isotherm*

RETEACH

Using local daily weather maps, have students identify isotherms, and the positions of high and low pressure areas and fronts.

EXTENSION

For students who have mastered this section, use the **Reinforcement** and **Enrichment** masters or other OPTIONS provided.

CONCEPT DEVELOPMENT

▶ After students have read about climates, ask these questions. **Which areas of the world are the warmest? Why?** *The tropics are the warmest because these areas receive the most direct rays of sunlight.* **What is the effect of a large body of water on the climate of the nearby coastal areas?** *The coastal areas are warmer in the winter and cooler in the summer than inland areas.*

Climate

You know that weather conditions vary from day to day in the area where you live. If you live in Montana, you know that you can expect snow in the winter. But what's the weather like in other places around the world like Australia or Greenland? The climate there might be quite different from the one you live in now. As you recall from Chapter 5, climate is the average of all weather conditions of an area over a long period of time. These conditions include the average temperatures, air pressure, humidity, and days of sunshine for a period of 30 years. Greenland is generally cold and damp, whereas much of Australia is hot and dry.

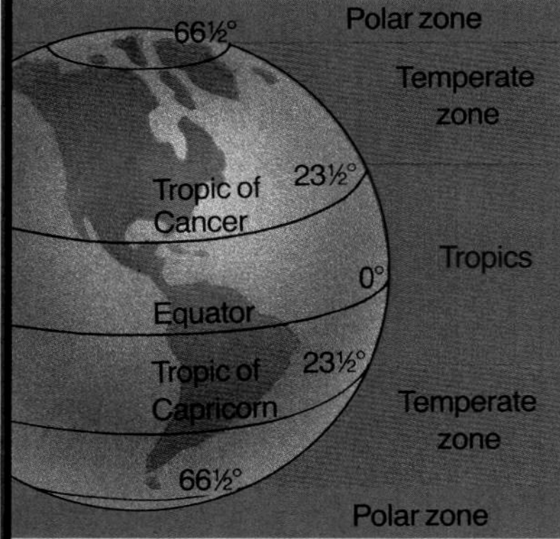

Figure 10-15. Climate zones are determined by the amount of solar energy received at different parts of Earth. The northern boundary of the tropics is called the Tropic of Cancer, and the southern boundary is called the Tropic of Capricorn.

Meteorologists classify climates in several different ways. One way is by the average yearly temperature of different regions. As you learned in Chapter 9, the amount of solar energy received at a particular location on Earth depends on the angle at which the sunlight strikes Earth.

Areas in the tropics (23-1/2° north latitude to 23-1/2° south latitude) receive the most direct rays. Year-round temperatures in these areas are always hot, except at high elevations.

The polar zones extend from the poles to 66-1/2° north and south latitudes. Solar energy hits these regions at a low angle and is distributed over a large area. Also, some of the heat is lost when it's reflected by the polar ice. Therefore, the polar regions are never very warm.

Between the tropics and the polar zones are the **temperate zones.** Those of us living in the continental United States live in a temperate zone. Here, weather generally changes with the seasons. Winters are cold and summers are hot. Spring and fall usually have mild temperatures.

Actually, climates are more complex than the three general divisions of polar, temperate, and tropical. Within each zone, a number of factors affect weather patterns. As you already know, large bodies of water influence the weather. Coastal areas are warmer in the winter and cooler in summer than inland areas. Mountains, too, influence the climate. They act as barriers over which winds must flow. On the side of a mountain facing the wind, air rises, cools, and drops its moisture as precipitation. On the other side of the mountain, the air descends, heats up, and dries out the land. Deserts are common on this side of a mountain.

EcoTip

Save energy this winter. During cold weather, close doors and turn off vents to unused rooms that don't need heating.

OPTIONS

INQUIRY QUESTIONS

▶ **Draw a station model that shows the day's weather data.** *Answers will vary. Refer students to Appendix K for assistance.*

▶ **With all the technology available to meteorologists, why do you think weather forecasts aren't always accurate?** *Weather is constantly evolving. Sometimes the variables that affect weather change much more quickly than expected or much more slowly than predicted.*

PROGRAM RESOURCES

Use **Laboratory Manual** page 93, Radiant Energy and Climate.

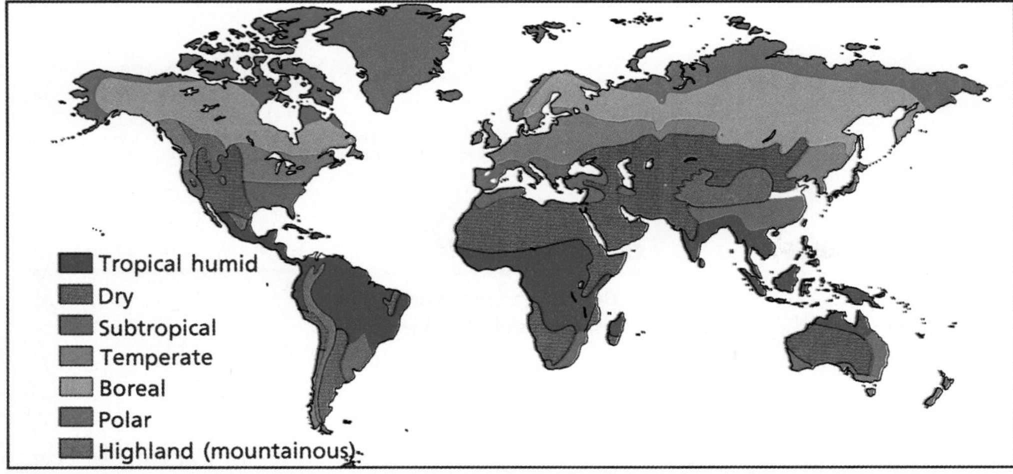

Figure 10-16. This world climate map is based on the average temperature, rainfall, and other measurements over a period of 30 years.

Even though some weather patterns are predictable because of known factors of climate, some weather events are hard to predict. As you've learned in this chapter, weather is constantly changing. Sometimes the conditions that affect weather are unpredictable and can change very quickly. The next time you see a weather report for the United States, look at the weather in a different climate than your own. Imagine how your day would be different with that weather forecast.

SECTION REVIEW

1. How are weather maps made?
2. What are differences between tropical and temperate climates?
3. How do mountains affect climate?
4. **Apply:** Use Appendix K to analyze the station model—Figure 10-13 on page 270. What is the temperature, type of clouds, wind speed and direction, and the type of precipitation at that location?

Comparing and Contrasting — Skill Builder

Contrast Earth's three climate zones. If you need help, refer to Comparing and Contrasting in the **Skill Handbook** on page 683.

3 CLOSE

▶ Ask questions 1-3 and the **Apply** Question in the Section Review.

▶ Have students find some folklore related to weather forecasting. Examples include: "Ring around the moon means rain," and "Red sky in morning, sailors take warning, red sky at night, sailors' delight." Discuss the findings.

SECTION REVIEW ANSWERS

1. Weather maps are made by combining weather information such as: types of clouds, temperature, type of precipitation, wind speed and direction, percentage of cloud cover, and barometric pressure, among others.

2. Tropical climates receive the most direct solar rays. Year-round temperatures are always hot, except at high elevations. Temperate climates experience changes of seasons. Winters are cold, summers are hot, and spring and fall are usually mild.

3. On the side of a mountain facing the wind, air rises, cools, and drops its moisture. On the other side, the air descends, heats, and dries the land.

4. Apply: temperature: 20°C; clouds: cirrus, altostratus, and altocumulus; wind speed: 3-7 knots; wind direction: southeast; precipitation: snow

Skill Builder

The tropics receive the most direct rays from the sun and therefore, areas with tropical climates are always hot. The polar zones receive solar energy at very low angles and thus are never very warm. The temperate zones generally have cold winters and hot summers, with spring and fall being mild seasons.

ENRICHMENT

▶ Have students interview a meteorologist to find out about processes involved with long-range forecasting.

▶ Have students find out how weather forecasting has been improved since the implementation of weather satellites.

▶ Have interested students research the studies that have been made to correlate sunspot activity with climate and weather.

SECTION 10-4

PREPARATION

SECTION BACKGROUND

► Carbon dioxide and water vapor in Earth's atmosphere are transparent to ultraviolet light and visible light, but they absorb infrared radiation. When infrared radiation is absorbed, the atmosphere becomes heated. Some of this heat is radiated back to Earth's surface.

1 MOTIVATE

► **Demonstration:** Obtain two empty, identical aquariums. Tape a thermometer to the inside of each aquarium. Place a glass lid over the top of one of the aquariums. Place both aquariums by a sunny window or below a bright light. Have students observe the temperature differences inside the two aquariums. Lead a discussion of the greenhouse effect.

TYING TO PREVIOUS KNOWLEDGE: Have students recall from Chapter 9 that radiation is one type of heat transfer. Explain that certain gases in the atmosphere prevent radiation from escaping Earth's surface, creating the greenhouse effect.

OBJECTIVES AND SCIENCE WORDS: Have students review the objectives and science words to become familiar with this section.

2 TEACH

Key Concepts are highlighted.

CONCEPT DEVELOPMENT

► **What happens to much of the heat radiated from Earth's surface?** *It is reflected back toward Earth by atmospheric gases.*

10-4 Can We Slow Down Global Warming?

New Science Words

greenhouse effect
deforestation

Objectives

- ► **Describe the greenhouse effect.**
- ► **List causes of global warming.**

The Greenhouse Effect

Why does it get hot in a greenhouse?

Do you remember the last sunny day you got into a car that had the windows up? It was really hot inside. Do you know why? When sunlight shines through the car windows, it is absorbed by the seats and other materials inside the car. Some of this energy is then radiated from the seats as heat. Heat radiation cannot pass through glass, so the temperature inside the car got hotter and hotter. This also happens in glass greenhouses. Sunlight penetrates the glass and heat that is reflected by the plants in the greenhouse can't escape back through the glass. This warms the air in greenhouses.

This process of warming also happens to Earth. As you learned in Chapter 9, much of the heat radiated from Earth's surface is reflected back down to Earth by gases in the atmosphere. This causes Earth's atmosphere to warm up. This process by which heat is trapped by gases

Figure 10-17. In the greenhouse effect, heat from the sun is trapped next to Earth's surface by greenhouse gasses from many sources.

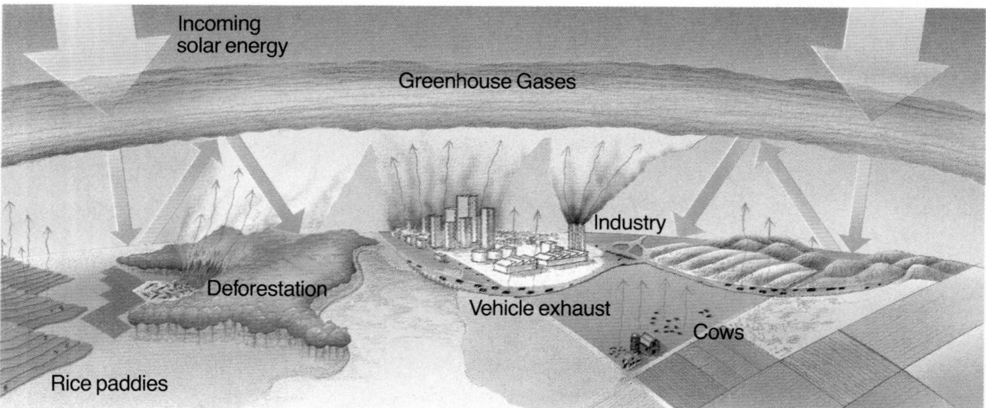

OPTIONS

Meeting Different Ability Levels

For Section 10-4, use the following **Teacher Resource Masters** depending upon individual students' needs.

◆ **Study Guide Master** for all students.

● **Reinforcement Master** for students of average and above average ability levels.

▲ **Enrichment Master** for above average students.

Additional Teacher Resource Package masters are listed in the OPTIONS box throughout the section. The additional masters are appropriate for all students.

◆ STUDY GUIDE 45

NAME ________ DATE ________ CLASS ________

STUDY GUIDE Chapter 10

Can We Slow Down Global Warming? Text Pages 274–275

Write each term in the box after its definition.

global warming	greenhouse effect	deforestation

1. The process by which heat is trapped by gases in Earth's atmosphere **greenhouse effect**
2. The removal of forests **deforestation**
3. A rise in Earth's average temperatures caused by increased amounts of gases in Earth's atmosphere **global warming**

Use the words in the box to fill in the blanks.

risen	gases	Earth	radiated
warm up	sunlight	surface	absorbed
temperature	global warming	greenhouse effect	

Why does a closed car get so hot on a sunny day? **Sunlight** shining through the car's windows is **absorbed** by the objects and materials in the car. Then some of this energy is **radiated** back from the objects and materials in the form of heat. But this heat cannot pass back out through the glass windows. The **temperature** inside the car rises. This process of warming takes place in glass greenhouses, and it also happens to **Earth**. Much of the heat radiated from Earth's **surface** does not go out into space; it is reflected back down to Earth by **gases** in the atmosphere. This reflected heat causes the atmosphere to **warm up**. The process by which heat is trapped and reflected by gases in Earth's atmosphere is known as the **greenhouse effect**. As a result, average temperatures on Earth have **risen** 0.5°C in the last hundred years. This temperature increase is known as **global warming**.

45

in Earth's atmosphere is called the greenhouse effect. Some of the gases that increase the **greenhouse effect** are carbon dioxide, water vapor, methane, nitrous oxide, and chlorofluorocarbons.

Global Warming

During this century, average temperatures on Earth have risen 0.5°C. Although you may think this is a very small temperature change, it indicates that Earth is warming. Some people blame human activities during the past 150 years for contributing to global warming.

One cause of this global warming is the burning of natural gas, petroleum, and coal to get energy. When these fuels are burned, carbon dioxide is released into the atmosphere. Carbon dioxide is one of the main gases that increases the greenhouse effect.

Another cause of global warming is deforestation. **Deforestation** is the removal of forests. Forests around the world are being cleared so that people can use the land for mining, drilling for oil, raising cattle, roads and buildings.

What does deforestation have to do with global warming? There are two problems created when trees are removed. First of all, trees take in carbon dioxide naturally as they grow. When trees are removed, the carbon dioxide they would have removed from the atmosphere is left to cause problems. Secondly, many of the trees that are removed are burned. This burning produces carbon dioxide that goes into the atmosphere.

Figure 10-18. Deforestation contributes to global warming.

Why does deforestation contribute to global warming?

SECTION REVIEW

1. What is the greenhouse effect?
2. How do human activities contribute to global warming?

You Decide!

As more regions of the world become industrialized, the amounts of greenhouse gases added to the atmosphere will increase. Global warming will cause the ice caps to melt, sea level to rise, and rainfall patterns to change. Regulations to reduce greenhouse gases will raise the prices of goods and put some companies out of business. What do you think? How can we reduce global warming without affecting prices and companies?

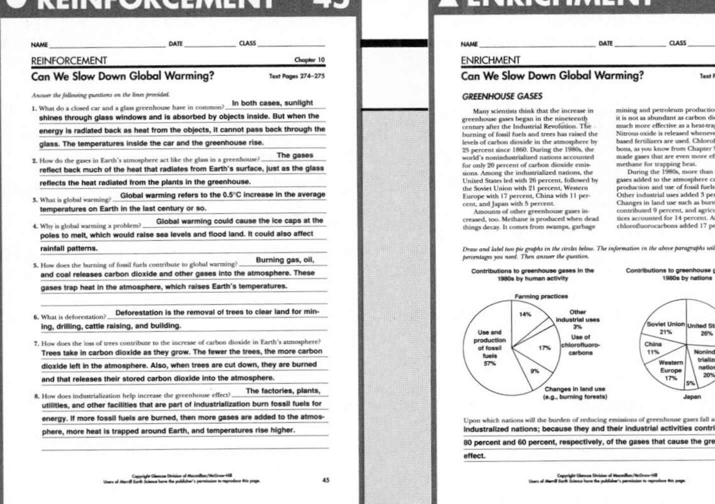

● REINFORCEMENT 45

NAME ______ DATE ______ CLASS ______

REINFORCEMENT — Chapter 10

Can We Slow Down Global Warming? Text Pages 274–275

Answer the following questions on the lines provided.

1. What do a closed car and a glass greenhouse have in common? **In both cases, sunlight shines through glass windows and is absorbed by objects inside. But when the energy is radiated back as heat from the objects, it cannot pass back through the glass. The temperatures inside the car and the greenhouse rise.**
2. How do the gases in Earth's atmosphere act like the glass in a greenhouse? **The gases reflect back much of the heat that radiates from Earth's surface, just as the glass reflects the heat radiated from the plants in the greenhouse.**
3. What is global warming? **Global warming refers to the 0.5°C increase in the average temperatures on Earth in the last century or so.**
4. Why is global warming a problem? **Global warming could cause the ice caps at the poles to melt, which would raise sea levels and flood land. It could also affect rainfall patterns.**
5. How does the burning of fossil fuels contribute to global warming? **Burning gas, oil, and coal releases carbon dioxide and other gases into the atmosphere. These gases trap heat in the atmosphere, which raises Earth's temperatures.**
6. What is deforestation? **Deforestation is the removal of trees to clear land for mining, drilling, cattle raising, and building.**
7. How does the loss of trees contribute to the increase of carbon dioxide in Earth's atmosphere? **Trees take in carbon dioxide as they grow. The fewer the trees, the more carbon dioxide left in the atmosphere. Also, when trees are cut down, they are burned and that releases their stored carbon dioxide into the atmosphere.**
8. How does industrialization help increase the greenhouse effect? **The factories, plants, utilities, and other facilities that are part of industrialization burn fossil fuels for energy. If more fossil fuels are burned, then more gases are added to the atmosphere, more heat is trapped around Earth, and temperatures rise higher.**

45

▲ ENRICHMENT 45

NAME ______ DATE ______ CLASS ______

ENRICHMENT — Chapter 10

Can We Slow Down Global Warming? Text Pages 274–275

GREENHOUSE GASES

Many scientists think that the increase in greenhouse gases began in the nineteenth century after the Industrial Revolution. The burning of fossil fuels and trees has raised the levels of carbon dioxide in the atmosphere by 25 percent since 1860. During the 1980s, the world's nonindustrialized nations accounted for only 20 percent of carbon dioxide emissions. Among the industrialized nations, the United States led with 26 percent, followed by the Soviet Union with 21 percent, Western Europe with 17 percent, China with 11 percent, and Japan with 5 percent.

Amounts of other greenhouse gases increased, too. Methane is produced when dead things decay. It comes from swamps, garbage mining and petroleum production. Although it is not as abundant as carbon dioxide, it is much more effective as a heat-trapping gas. Nitrous oxide is released whenever nitrogen-based fertilizers are used. Chlorofluorocarbons, as you know from Chapter 9, are human-made gases that are even more effective than methane for trapping heat.

During the 1980s, more than half of the gases added to the atmosphere came from the production and use of fossil fuels for energy. Other industrial uses added 3 percent. Changes in land use such as burning forests contributed 9 percent, and agricultural practices accounted for 14 percent. Activities using chlorofluorocarbons added 17 percent.

Draw and label two pie graphs in the circles below. The information in the above paragraphs will give you the percentages you need. Then answer the question.

Upon which nations will the burden of reducing emissions of greenhouse gases fall and why? **Industralized nations; because they and their industrial activities contribute about 80 percent and 60 percent, respectively, of the gases that cause the greenhouse effect.**

45

CHECK FOR UNDERSTANDING

Ask students to explain how the greenhouse effect causes global warming.

RETEACH

Cooperative Learning: Have Study Buddies explain the relationships among *radiation, the greenhouse effect, global warming,* and *deforestation.*

EXTENSION

For students who have mastered this section, use the **Reinforcement** and **Enrichment** masters or other OPTIONS provided.

3 CLOSE

▶ Ask questions 1-2 in the Section Review.

▶ Organize a tree planting session.

SECTION REVIEW ANSWERS

1. the trapping of heat within Earth's atmosphere because of the presence of certain gases like carbon dioxide, water vapor, methane, and nitrous oxide

2. Burning fossil fuels and trees releases stored carbon dioxide into the atmosphere. Deforestation removes trees that would normally reduce the amount of atmospheric carbon dioxide. The use of CFCs also contributes to global warming.

YOU DECIDE!

SCIENCE & SOCIETY

Students may know that by planting trees, conserving fossil fuels, and recycling, global warming can be reduced. Research can be done to discover ways to remove greenhouse gases from the air, to develop alternative energy sources, and to use substances to replace certain greenhouse gases. However, make sure students realize that these activities will create new companies even though others may disappear.

PROGRAM RESOURCES

From the **Teacher Resource Package** use:

Science and Society, page 14, The Global Warming Debate.

ACTIVITY 10-2
45 minutes

OBJECTIVE: Interpret weather map symbols and measurements.

PROCESS SKILLS applied in this activity:
▶ **Interpreting Data** in Analyze Questions 1-4.
▶ **Using Numbers** in Analyze Questions 1 and 2.
▶ **Predicting** in Analyze Question 4 and Conclude and Apply Questions 5 and 6.
▶ **Inferring** in Conclude and Apply Questions 7 and 8.

TEACHING THE ACTIVITY

▶ Some students will need to review the locations of the states and major U.S. cities prior to performing this activity. Having a map of the United States posted in the classroom will be helpful.
▶ Students may wish to use hand lenses to read the small details on the map.
▶ If an opaque projector is available, project the weather map on a screen.

PROGRAM RESOURCES

From the **Teacher Resource Package** use:

Activity Worksheets, pages 88-89, Activity 10-2: Reading a Weather Map.

ACTIVITY 10-2
Reading a Weather Map

Problem: *How do you read a weather map?*

Materials
- hand lens
- Appendix K

Procedure
Use the information provided in the questions below and Appendix K to learn how to read a weather map.

Analyze
1. Find the station models on the map for Tucson, Arizona, and Albuquerque, New Mexico. Find the dew point, cloud coverage, pressure, and temperature at each location.
2. After reviewing information about the spacing of isobars and wind speed in Section 10-3, determine whether the wind would be stronger at Roswell, New Mexico, or at Fort Worth, Texas. Record your answer. What is one other way to tell the wind speed at these locations?
3. Determine the type of front near Key West, Florida. Record your answer.
4. The triangles or half circles on the weather front symbol are on the side of the line that indicates the direction the front is going. Determine the direction that the cold front, located over Colorado and Kansas, is going. Record your answer.

Conclude and Apply
5. Locate the pressure system over Winslow, Arizona. After reviewing Section 10-3, describe what would happen to the weather of Wichita, Kansas, if this pressure system should move there.
6. The prevailing westerlies are the winds responsible for the movement of weather across the United States and Canada. Based on this, would you expect Charleston, South Carolina, to continue to have clear skies? Explain your answer.
7. The line on the station model that indicates wind speed shows from which direction the wind is coming, and the wind is named accordingly. What is the name of the wind at Jackson, Mississippi?

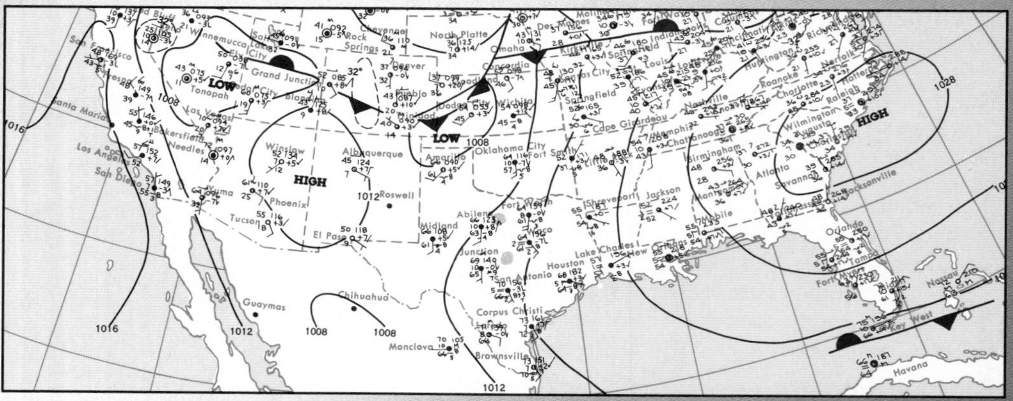

ANSWERS TO QUESTIONS

1. Tucson: dew point 18, no cloud cover, barometric pressure 1011.6 mb, 55°F; Albuquerque: dew point 7, one tenth or less cloud cover, barometric pressure 1012.4 mb, 45°F
2. stronger at Fort Worth because the isobars are closer together; wind speed may also be determined by the number of "feathers" on the line showing wind direction
3. stationary front
4. southeast
5. The skies would clear and there would be fair weather.
6. No, a cold front and low pressure area over Oklahoma are moving toward Charleston.
7. southeast

CHAPTER

REVIEW

SUMMARY

10-1: What Is Weather?

1. Water vapor forms most clouds and the precipitation that falls from them. Water vapor also determines the relative humidity at a given time.

2. Rain, hail, sleet, and snow are types of precipitation that fall from clouds. The state of the precipitation depends on air temperature.

3. Clouds form when air is cooled to its dew point and water vapor condenses around dust.

10-2: Weather Patterns

1. Warm fronts may produce rain or snow. Cold fronts produce rain showers and thunderstorms. A stationary front produces slow winds and precipitation. Occluded fronts are associated with high winds and heavy precipitation. Clear skies and fair weather are due to high pressure areas, whereas low pressure areas are stormy.

2. Low pressure systems form when air at a front begins to swirl, rises and cools, and forms clouds.

3. Tornadoes are small, intense, whirling wind storms that can result from extreme conditions of strong winds and low pressure in thunderstorms.

10-3: Forecasting and Climate

1. Weather maps are made using information collected by meteorologists in their local areas.

2. Areas in the tropics receive the most direct solar rays and thus are hot all year round. Polar regions receive solar energy at low angles and are cold most of the year. Temperate regions usually have four seasons that include hot summers, cold winters, and mild falls and springs.

3. Coastal areas are warmer in the winter and cooler in the summer than inland areas. Mountains tend to also affect climate by making land on the side facing the wind cool and wet and the land on the opposite side of the mountain hot and dry.

10-4: Science and Society: Can We Slow Down Global Warming?

1. Much of the energy radiated from Earth's surface is absorbed and reflected back toward Earth by gases in the atmosphere. This trapping of heat is called the greenhouse effect.

2. The burning of fossil fuels and deforestation contribute to global warming.

KEY SCIENCE WORDS

a. **air mass**
b. **deforestation**
c. **dew point**
d. **fog**
e. **front**
f. **greenhouse effect**
g. **hurricane**
h. **isobar**
i. **isotherm**
j. **meteorologist**
k. **precipitation**
l. **relative humidity**
m. **saturated**
n. **station model**
o. **temperate zones**
p. **tornado**
q. **weather**

UNDERSTANDING VOCABULARY

Match each phrase with the correct term from the list of Key Science Words.

1. temperature at which condensation occurs
2. falling water droplets
3. air that can't hold any more water vapor
4. boundary between air masses
5. violent swirling storm moving in a narrow path
6. large, swirling tropical storm
7. person who studies the weather
8. symbols on a weather map describing weather
9. line on a weather map that indicates points of equal pressure
10. stratus cloud next to the ground

OPTIONS

ASSESSMENT

To assess student understanding of material in this chapter, use the resources listed.

COOPERATIVE LEARNING
Consider using cooperative learning in the THINK AND WRITE CRITICALLY, APPLY, and MORE SKILL BUILDERS sections of the Chapter Review.

PROGRAM RESOURCES

From the **Teacher Resource Package** use:

Chapter Review, pages 23-24.

Chapter and Unit Tests, pages 66-69, Chapter Test.

CHAPTER

REVIEW

SUMMARY

Have students read the summary statements to review the major concepts of the chapter.

UNDERSTANDING VOCABULARY

1. c
2. k
3. m
4. e
5. p
6. g
7. j
8. n
9. h
10. d

CHAPTER
REVIEW

CHECKING CONCEPTS

1. d
2. c
3. a
4. d
5. b
6. d
7. d
8. d
9. b
10. d

UNDERSTANDING CONCEPTS

11. saturated or cooled
12. polar zone
13. air mass
14. tropical
15. station model

THINK AND WRITE CRITICALLY

16. In warm air, gas molecules are farther apart, thus more spaces are available for water vapor molecules. In cool air, the gas molecules are closer together making less space available to water vapor molecules. Thus, warm air is more humid than cool air.

17. The air mass would be cold because of the latitude of Canada. It would also be relatively dry because of its forming over land.

18. Isobars connect points of equal pressure. The distance between adjacent lines indicates pressure differences. When the spacing is small, there's a great difference over a small area. When lines are far apart, pressure changes are small and winds are gentle.

19. Areas in the tropics receive the most direct solar rays, thus they are the warmest climate zones.

20. The sun provides the energy for the water cycle. The heat from the sun causes water to evaporate into the air. Eventually, the water condenses to form clouds. Water falls from clouds as rain, snow, sleet, or hail.

CHAPTER
REVIEW

CHECKING CONCEPTS

Choose the word or phrase that completes the sentence.

1. Weather depends on ______.
   - **a.** air temperature **c.** air pressure
   - **b.** amount of moisture **d.** all of these
2. Cool air can hold ______water vapor as an identical amount of warm air.
   - **a.** the same **c.** less
   - **b.** more **d.** almost the same
3. Air condenses at its ______.
   - **a.** dew point **c.** front
   - **b.** station model **d.** temperate zone
4. ______ forms when water vapor changes directly into a solid.
   - **a.** Rain **c.** Sleet
   - **b.** Hail **d.** Snow
5. ______ clouds are low, layered clouds that may produce precipitation.
   - **a.** Cirrus **c.** Cumulus
   - **b.** Stratus **d.** Nimbus
6. A(n) ______ front forms when two cool air masses merge.
   - **a.** warm **c.** stationary
   - **b.** cold **d.** occluded
7. Tornadoes are destructive because they ____.
   - **a.** have high winds **c.** cause updrafts
   - **b.** have low pressures **d.** all of these
8. A ______ is issued when severe weather conditions exist and immediate action should be taken.
   - **a.** front **c.** station model
   - **b.** watch **d.** warning
9. The poles receive______solar energy.
   - **a.** the most direct **c.** no
   - **b.** the least direct **d.** a lot of
10. The burning of coal releases ____ into the air.
    - **a.** oxygen **c.** methane
    - **b.** nitrous oxide **d.** carbon dioxide

UNDERSTANDING CONCEPTS

Complete each sentence.

11. Water vapor will condense from air when it is ______.
12. The climate region north of 66-1/2° latitude is the ______.
13. A large body of air that has the same properties as the area over which it formed is a(n) ______.
14. Places near the equator have ____ climates.
15. A(n) ______ contains weather information for one local area.

THINK AND WRITE CRITICALLY

16. Explain how temperature affects humidity.
17. Describe the characteristics of an air mass that forms over central Canada in December.
18. What are isobars and how are they used to describe weather conditions?
19. Why do tropical areas have the warmest climates?
20. Describe how water and the sun interact to cause our weather.

APPLY

21. If you hear a weather observation that there is 79 percent relative humidity, what does that mean?
22. What weather conditions would very tall, thick clouds indicate?
23. Why doesn't hail form if rain falls through a freezing layer of air?
24. Why don't hurricanes form in polar regions?
25. If a barometer showed that the air pressure was dropping, what general weather prediction could you make?

MORE SKILL BUILDERS

If you need help, refer to the Skill Handbook.

1. **Comparing and Contrasting:** Compare and contrast tornadoes and hurricanes.
2. **Interpreting Scientific Illustrations:** Describe the weather conditions shown on the station model below.

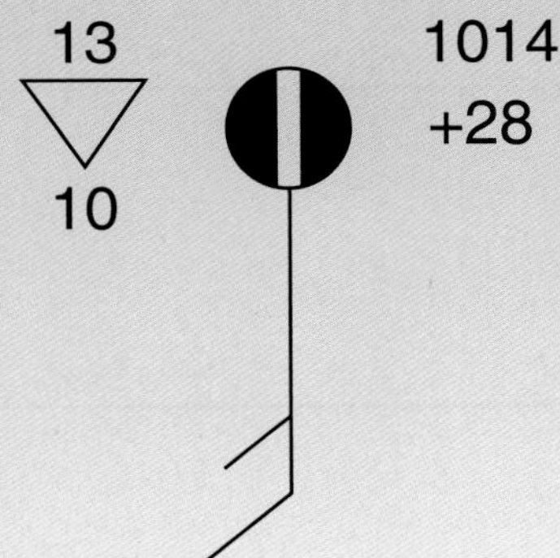

3. **Observing and Inferring:** After letting your cold iced tea sit outside on a hot day, you observe that water droplets have formed on the outside of the glass. What can you infer?
4. **Making and Using Tables:** Use the cloud descriptions in Table 10-1 to describe the weather at your location today. Then try to predict tomorrow's weather.
5. **Hypothesizing:** You observe that a weather map of the United States shows a cold front and a low pressure system to the west of where you live. Hypothesize what the weather in your area will be like in a day or two.

PROJECTS

1. Design and construct an anemometer and a rain gauge. Use them for one week. Compare the accuracy of your instruments with reported data from radio or TV weather reports.
2. Use reference books to compare and contrast the climates of each of the seven continents. Summarize your findings in a table.

APPLY

21. The air is holding only 79 percent of the water vapor it is capable of holding at that temperature.
22. Towering clouds are associated with thunderstorms, heavy rain, and hail.
23. Hail only forms in cumulonimbus clouds where strong updrafts and supercooled water exist. As rain is tossed into higher levels of the cloud, it freezes. New layers of ice are added as the drops are tossed vertically within the cloud.
24. Hurricanes need a constant source of water vapor to form. Then as long as a hurricane is over water, the warm moist air will rise and provide energy for the storm. These conditions don't exist in polar regions.
25. Air pressure drops as a front approaches an area. Stormy weather is often associated with fronts.

MORE SKILL BUILDERS

1. Comparing and Contrasting: Both are forms of severe weather that form when warm air is forced quickly aloft. Both have high winds that are very destructive. A tornado, however, moves in a narrow path over land. A hurricane forms over tropical oceans. Hurricanes last much longer than tornadoes and are usually more destructive.
2. Interpreting Scientific Illustrations: Sky is overcast with openings. Barometric pressure is 1014 mb; it has increased 28 mb in the last 3 hours. Temperature is 13°C and there are showers. Winds are from the SW at 13-17 knots. Dew point temperature is 10°C.
3. Observing and Inferring: The air outside the glass cooled as it came in contact with the glass. As it cooled, it reached its dew point and condensed to form water droplets on the glass.
4. Making and Using Tables: Answers will vary, but students should be able to identify the clouds present and predict what kind of weather will occur based on the types of clouds observed.
5. Hypothesizing: Students should be able to hypothesize that since weather in the U.S. generally travels from west to east, the cold front and the low pressure system are likely to bring cooler temperatures and stormy weather to your area.

CHAPTER

11 Ocean Water

CHAPTER SECTION	OBJECTIVES	ACTIVITIES
11-1 Origin and Composition of Ocean Water (2 days)	1. **Learn** the origin of water in Earth's oceans. 2. **Explain** how dissolved salts and other substances get into seawater. 3. **Describe** the composition of seawater.	**Activity 11-1:** *Desalination,* p. 286
11-2 Ocean Currents (2 days)	1. **Determine** how surface currents are influenced by winds, the Coriolis effect, and continents. 2. **Explain** why waters off the western coasts of continents are usually colder than waters off the eastern coasts of continents. 3. **Describe** how density currents cause ocean water below the surface to circulate.	**MINI-Lab:** *How can you make a density current model?* p. 291
11-3 Ocean Waves and Tides (3 days)	1. **Describe** the parts of a wave. 2. **Differentiate** between the movement of water particles in a wave and the movement of wave energy. 3. **Describe** how waves are created by the energy of wind and the gravitational force of the moon and sun.	**MINI-Lab:** *How do waves move?* p. 294 **Activity 11-2:** *Air Motion and Waves,* p. 297
11-4 Tapping Tidal Energy Science & Society (1 day)	1. **Explain** why Nova Scotia's Bay of Fundy is a good place to build a tidal power plant. 2. **Relate** how a tidal dam converts energy from tides into electricity. 3. **Consider** the consequences of building a power plant at the Bay of Fundy.	
Chapter Review		

ACTIVITY MATERIALS

FIND OUT	ACTIVITIES		MINI-LABS	
Page 281 dishpans toothpicks food coloring ice cubes	**11-1 Desalination, p. 286** pan balance table salt water 500-mL beakers (2) 1000-mL flask 1-hole rubber stopper rubber tubing hot plate cardboard ice shallow pan glass tubing bent at right angle glycerine	towel scissors washers goggles **11-2 Air Motion and Waves, p. 297** white paper electric fan (3-speed) light source clock or watch clear plastic shoe or storage box ring stand water metric ruler, protractor	**How can you make a density current model? p. 291** clear plastic or glass box, or pie plate water food coloring table salt	**How do waves move? p. 294** clear plastic storage box or glass baking dish cork water tape spoon

CHAPTER FEATURES	TEACHER RESOURCE PACKAGE	OTHER RESOURCES
Technology: *Desalting Ocean Water,* p. 285 **Skill Builder:** *Concept Mapping,* p. 285	**Ability Level Worksheets** ◆ ***Study Guide,*** p. 46 ● ***Reinforcement,*** p. 46 ▲ ***Enrichment,*** p. 46 **Activity Worksheet,** pp. 95-96 **Critical Thinking/Problem Solving,** p. 17 **Concept Mapping,** pp. 27-28	**Lab Manual:** *Salt Concentration in Ocean Water,* p. 95 **Lab Manual:** *Fresh Water From Ocean Water,* p. 97 **Lab Manual:** *Floating in Fresh Water and in Ocean Water,* p. 101
Problem Solving: *Testing the Water,* p. 290 **Skill Builder:** *Classifying,* p. 291	**Ability Level Worksheets** ◆ ***Study Guide,*** p. 47 ● ***Reinforcement,*** p. 47 ▲ ***Enrichment,*** p. 47 **MINI-Lab Worksheet,** p. 101 **Cross-Curricular Connections,** p. 15 **Transparency Masters,** pp. 39-40	**Color Transparency 20,** Ocean Currents **Lab Manual:** *Density Currents,* p. 99
Skill Builder: *Comparing and Contrasting,* p. 296	**Ability Level Worksheets** ◆ ***Study Guide,*** p. 48 ● ***Reinforcement,*** p. 48 ▲ ***Enrichment,*** p. 48 **MINI-Lab Worksheet,** p. 102 **Activity Worksheet,** pp. 97-98 **Transparency Masters,** pp. 41-42	**Color Transparency 21,** *Spring/Neap Tides*
You Decide! p. 300	**Ability Level Worksheets** ◆ ***Study Guide,*** p. 49 ● ***Reinforcement,*** p. 49 ▲ ***Enrichment,*** p. 49 **Science and Society,** p. 15	
Summary Key Science Words Understanding Vocabulary Checking Concepts Understanding Concepts Think & Write Critically Apply More Skill Builders Projects	**Chapter Review,** pp. 25-26 **Chapter Test,** pp. 70-73	**Chapter Review Software** **Test Bank**

◆ **Basic** ● **Average** ▲ **Advanced**

ADDITIONAL MATERIALS

SOFTWARE	AUDIOVISUAL	BOOKS/MAGAZINES
The Oceans, Aquarius. *Oceanography,* Picture File, Datatech Software Systems.	*Currents,* film, Time-Life. *The Earth: Coastlines,* film, Coronet. *Ocean Currents,* film, CRM Films. *Waves on Water,* film, EBEC. *The Earth: Oceans,* filmstrip, Singer Media Corp.	Bascom, Willard. *Waves and Beaches: The Dynamics of the Ocean Surface.* rev. & updated ed. NY: Doubleday and Company, Inc., 1988. Ingmanson, Dale E. and William J. Wallace. *Oceanography: An Introduction.* 4th ed. Belmont, CA: Wadsworth Publishing Company, 1989. Moore, Chris. *Oceans.* NY: Penguin Books, 1988.

CHAPTER

11 OCEAN WATER

THEME DEVELOPMENT: Energy is the theme of this chapter. Students will learn that wind provides the energy for surface currents; density currents affect deep water circulation; and wind and the gravitational forces of the sun and moon supply the energy for waves.

CHAPTER OVERVIEW

- **Section 11-1:** This section explains the importance of oceans to all lifeforms on Earth. The origin and composition of oceans are also discussed.
- **Section 11-2:** The influence of winds, the Coriolis effect, and continents on surface currents is presented. The effect of density on deep water circulation is also discussed.
- **Section 11-3:** Ocean waves are examined in terms of wave characteristics, the movement of energy through the waves, and the effect of wind and gravity on waves.
- **Section 11-4: Science and Society:** The advantages and disadvantages of tapping tides for energy are presented. The You Decide feature asks students to determine whether or not a tidal dam should be built at the Bay of Fundy.

CHAPTER VOCABULARY

basins	wave height
salinity	wavelength
surface current	breaker
density current	tides
upwelling	tidal range
crest	turbine
trough	salt marsh

CHAPTER

11 Ocean Water

280

OPTIONS

For Your Gifted Students

Have students find out about the different currents found in Earth's oceans. Then have them make a mural of the oceans, showing the different currents, which should be color coded as either warm or cold currents. Have students discuss which currents cover the most area and which currents are the longest.

Windsurfing looks like a lot of fun, doesn't it! But what makes this sport possible? This windsurfer is making use of wind and waves, two aspects of the ocean environment that you will study in this chapter. How do the mighty forces of ocean waves, currents, and tides work? How are currents formed in the ocean?

FIND OUT!

Do this simple activity to discover how currents work.

Fill a large beaker with warm water. You could also use a pan of water instead of a beaker. Gently add a drop of food coloring at the center. Now carefully float an ice cube at the center. After a minute, what happens to the food coloring? Add two drops of food coloring directly on the ice cube to help you see what is happening. You have just made a density current.

Gearing Up

Previewing the Chapter

Use this outline to help you focus on important ideas in this chapter.

Previewing Science Skills

- ▶ In the **Skill Builders,** you will make a concept map, classify, and compare and contrast.
- ▶ In the **Activities,** you will observe, interpret data, experiment, and hypothesize.
- ▶ In the **MINI-Labs,** you will experiment and make a model.

What's next?

Now that you've made your own and currents, you'll learn how these things happen in Earth's oceans. You'll also learn about the tides and why the oceans are salty.

INTRODUCING THE CHAPTER

Use the Find Out activity to introduce students to currents. Inform students that they will be learning more about ocean circulation as they read the chapter.

FIND OUT!

Preparation: Obtain the following materials for each group of students: a large beaker or dishpan, food coloring, and an ice cube.

Materials: large beaker or dishpan, food coloring, and ice cubes

Cooperative Learning: Have Science Investigation groups perform this activity.

▶ **Answers to Questions:** The water cooled by the ice cube sinks. The food coloring allows you to see the movement of the water.

Gearing Up

Have students study the Gearing Up feature to familiarize themselves with the chapter. Discuss the relationships of the topics in the outline.

What's Next?

Before beginning the first section, make sure students understand the connection between the Find Out activity and the topics to follow.

For Your Mainstreamed Students

Have groups of students make puzzles of the oceans and landmasses of the world by transferring a map of the world onto cardboard and cutting it into pieces. Groups should exchange puzzles and compete to see which group puts the puzzle together the fastest and correctly names the oceans.

SECTION 11-1

PREPARATION

SECTION BACKGROUND

▶ Oceanography is an interrelated study of every aspect of ocean systems and environments.

▶ Chemical oceanography is the study of the chemical properties of seawater and the causes, effects, and changes in ocean chemistry.

▶ Physical oceanography is primarily concerned with energy transmission through ocean water. It deals with wave formation and movement, currents, and tides.

PREPLANNING

▶ To prepare for the Activity 11-1, obtain the materials listed on page 286.

1 MOTIVATE

▶ Ask students to describe what Earth would be like without its oceans. They will probably say that it would be dry. After more thought, they may describe Earth as having no life as we know it. Finally, students should realize that the weather patterns would be quite different without oceans.

▶ Obtain and show the movie *This Land* by Shell Oil Company. The film shows how the ocean basins and sea level have changed throughout geologic time.

11-1 Origin and Composition of Ocean Water

New Science Words

basins
salinity

Objectives

- ▶ Learn the origin of the water in Earth's oceans.
- ▶ Explain how dissolved salts and other substances get into seawater.
- ▶ Describe the composition of seawater.

The Ocean and You

You probably think the ocean doesn't affect you unless you live on a coastline. But actually, the ocean is influencing you right now, no matter where you live. If it is raining or snowing today, most of that water came from the ocean. If today is sunny, it is partly due to weather systems that developed over the ocean. If you eat fish today, it most likely will have come from the ocean.

Oceans also affect the prices charged for clothing, cars, and gasoline. The price includes the cost of shipping those materials across a great barrier, the ocean. If you live near a stream or river that is polluted, that pollution eventually will travel to the ocean. The ocean greatly affects your life.

Figure 11-1. We get some of our oil from rock under the oceans and some of our food from the oceans.

OPTIONS

Meeting Different Ability Levels

For Section 11-1, use the following **Teacher Resource Masters** depending upon individual students' needs.

◆ **Study Guide Master** for all students.

● **Reinforcement Master** for students of average and above average ability levels.

▲ **Enrichment Master** for above average students.

Additional Teacher Resource Package masters are listed in the OPTIONS box throughout the section. The additional masters are appropriate for all students.

◆ STUDY GUIDE 46

NAME ________ DATE ________ CLASS ________

STUDY GUIDE — Chapter 11

Origin and Composition of Ocean Water — Text Pages 282-285

Use the words and phrases in the boxes to fill in the blanks in each section.

basins	halite	silica	volcanoes
calcium	oceans	sodium	water vapor
chlorine	precipitation		

Billions of years ago, **volcanoes** were more active than they are today. As a result, **water vapor** was released into the atmosphere where it condensed and became **precipitation**. The water filled Earth's low areas, or **basins**, and formed **oceans**.

Earth's oceans contain many substances besides water. Some of these substances are elements, such as **calcium**, **silica**, and **sodium**. The two most common elements in ocean water, **chlorine** and sodium, combine to form a salt called **halite**.

bones	fresh	rivers	shells
calcium	groundwater	rocks and minerals	silica
desalination	plants	salinity	volcanoes

The measure of the amount of solids dissolved in seawater is called **salinity**. This measure has been about the same for thousands of years. Why is this true? Substances that are added constantly are being used at the same rate. Some substances are added by **groundwater** that slowly dissolves elements from **rocks and minerals**. Other elements are dissolved and carried to the oceans by flowing **rivers**. Gases, such as chlorine, are added by erupting **volcanoes**. Because there are so many sea **plants** and animals, **calcium** and silica are removed very quickly from seawater. Calcium and **silica** are used by small marine animals to build **bones** and **shells**. In addition, people in some parts of the world remove salt from seawater to obtain **fresh** water for drinking and cooking. This process is called **desalination**.

46

Origin and Composition of Oceans

In the first billion years after Earth was formed, its surface was much more volcanically active than it is today. As you'll learn in Chapter 15, volcanoes not only spew lava and ash, but give off water vapor as well. About 4 billion years ago, this water vapor began to accumulate in Earth's early atmosphere. It eventually cooled enough to condense. Precipitation began to fall onto Earth. Earth's oceans were formed over millions of years as this water filled low areas on Earth called **basins.**

Where did the water come from that formed the oceans?

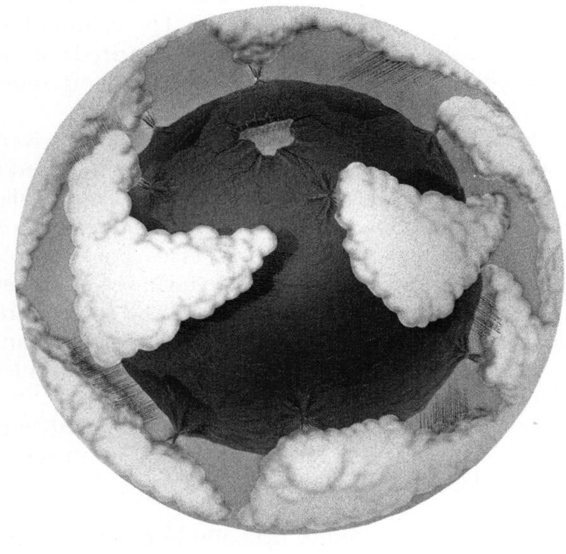

Figure 11-2. Earth's oceans formed from water vapor originally released in the atmosphere by volcanoes.

You learned in Chapter 7 that drinking water is becoming scarce in some states and countries. If Earth's surface is 70 percent ocean, why can't we use this water?

Taste water from the ocean, and you can immediately tell that it is different from the water you drink. It tastes salty. Oceanographers have learned that the ocean contains many dissolved elements, including sodium, chlorine, silica, and calcium.

Where do these elements come from? One source is groundwater, which very slowly dissolves elements such as calcium from rocks and minerals. The calcium is then carried by rivers into the ocean. Another source is volcanoes that erupt, releasing gases into the ocean.

What is one source of the dissolved elements found in ocean water?

● REINFORCEMENT 46

NAME ______ DATE ______ CLASS ______

REINFORCEMENT — Chapter 11

Origin and Composition of Ocean Water — Text Pages 282–285

Complete the following outline.

Oceans

I. What is an ocean?
  A. Contains water
    1. From **volcanic eruption**
    2. From **precipitation**
  B. Fills low areas, or **basins**
  C. Contains elements
    1. Carried from **rivers**
    2. Carried from **groundwater**

II. How do oceans affect us?
  A. Affect atmosphere
    1. **Weather**
    2. Climate
  B. Provide fish and other **food**
  C. Form **barriers** between continents

On the map below, the world's oceans are numbered. Write the correct number next to the name of each ocean in the list.

3 Arctic Ocean
2 Atlantic Ocean
1 Indian Ocean
4 Pacific Ocean

75°N 30° 0 30° 75°S
60°W 90° 120° 150° 180° 150° 120° 90° 60° 30° 0° 30° 60°E

46

▲ ENRICHMENT 46

NAME ______ DATE ______ CLASS ______

ENRICHMENT — Chapter 11

Origin and Composition of Ocean Water — Text Pages 282–285

COMPOSITION OF OCEAN WATER

An average ocean water sample of one kilogram in mass contains about 35 grams of dissolved salts. Four kinds of ions make up 97 percent of the dissolved salts. Of those four kinds, sodium ions and chlorine ions (called chloride ions) make up the largest percentage of the 35 grams. The relative amounts of the four kinds of ions are shown in the table below. Each value represents the percentage of the ions present. Use the table to answer the questions.

Ion	Percent (%) of total salts
Chloride (Cl)	55.0
Sodium (Na)	30.6
Sulfate (So_4)	7.7
Magnesium (Mg)	3.7

1. Calculate how many grams of chloride ions are present in 50 grams of ocean salts. Show your work. **55% × 50 g = 0.55 × 50 g = 27.5 g of chloride ions**
2. How many grams of magnesium ions are present in 50 grams of ocean salts? **3.7% × 50 g = 0.037 × 50 g = 1.8 g of magnesium ions**
3. Suppose you collect 1000 kilograms of sea salt by evaporating ocean water. How much of the 1000 kilograms is sulfate? **7.7% × 1000 kg = 0.077 × 1000 kg = 77 kg of sulfate ions**
4. If you wanted to collect 245 grams of sea salt, how many kilograms of ocean water would you need? **245 grams ÷ 35 g/kg = 7 kg**
5. Suppose the ice cap at the North Pole melted. How might this change the salt content in a kilogram in mass of ocean water? **It would lower the salt content since much more water is added but not any additional salt.**

46

TYING TO PREVIOUS KNOWLEDGE: Have students recall from Chapters 5, 6, and 7 that running water weathers, erodes, and dissolves sediments. Remind students that if these sediments are carried by rivers, they may eventually reach the oceans.

OBJECTIVES AND SCIENCE WORDS: Have students review the objectives and science words to become familiar with this section.

2 TEACH

Key Concepts are highlighted.

CONCEPT DEVELOPMENT

▶ Review the parts and processes of Earth's water cycle. Be sure to emphasize that the ocean is an integral part of this cycle.

▶ After students have read pages 282 and 283, ask a volunteer to define *sea level.* Then pose these questions to the class. **Sea level during the last ice age was 200 meters lower than it is today. Why?** *Much of the water became part of the glaciers, lowering sea level.* **What will happen to sea level if global warming continues?** *Sea level will rise as the ice caps melt.*

STUDENT TEXT QUESTION

▶ Page 283, paragraph 2: **If Earth's surface is 70 percent ocean, why can't we use this water?** *The water is too salty; drinking it would make people and other animals sick.*

CROSS CURRICULUM

▶ **Health:** Have students do some research to find out that many drugs to treat human disorders and diseases are being made from marine organisms. The substances in these organisms were once dissolved in the salt water.

CONCEPT DEVELOPMENT

► **How do sodium and chlorine atoms get into seawater?** *Sodium enters with river water. Chlorine is added by volcanoes.*

► Stress that salinity is a measure of dissolved solids in the oceans. Not all substances in the ocean are salts.

CHECK FOR UNDERSTANDING

Use the Mini Quiz to check for understanding.

MINI QUIZ

Use the Mini Quiz to check students' recall of chapter content.

1. **When sodium and ____ combine in seawater, they form a salt called halite.** *chlorine*
2. **____ percent of the salt in seawater is made of sodium and chlorine.** *Ninety*
3. **____ is a measure of the dissolved solids in seawater.** *Salinity*
4. **____ is used by some marine animals to form their bones.** *Calcium*
5. **Calcium and ____ are used by some marine animals to form shells.** *silica*

RETEACH

Give each student a seashell to examine. Ask students to write paragraphs explaining where the calcium in their shells originated. Students should explain that the calcium was dissolved from rocks and minerals and then carried by rivers into the ocean, where the animals removed it to make their shells.

EXTENSION

For students who have mastered this section, use the **Reinforcement** and **Enrichment** masters or other OPTIONS provided.

The two most abundant dissolved elements are sodium and chlorine. Sodium is dissolved in river water that flows into the ocean. Chlorine gas is added by volcanoes.
1 When sodium and chlorine atoms combine in the seawater, they form a salt called halite. You may recall from Chapter 3 that halite is the salt you use to season food. In the ocean, halite remains dissolved in the seawater. It's this compound, and a few similar compounds, that
2 make ocean water taste salty. Nearly 90 percent of the salt in seawater is made of sodium and chlorine.

Every 1000 L of ocean water contains about 35 L of
3 dissolved salts, or 3.5 percent. **Salinity** is a measure of the amount of solids dissolved in seawater. The salinity of the ocean has stayed about the same for hundreds of millions of years. This tells us that the ocean's composition is in balance.

Although substances are added constantly by rivers, volcanoes, and the atmosphere, they are being used at the same rate by plants and animals, or are forming solids on the ocean bottom. Sea animals and plants use the dissolved substances in their life processes. For example,
4 some marine animals use calcium to form bones. Others
5 use silica and calcium to form shells. Even some plants have silica shells. Because there are so many sea plants and animals, calcium and silica are removed very quickly from seawater.

Now you know where the ocean came from and what it contains. Next we'll see how the ocean is constantly stirred by currents.

EcoTip

Be a beachcomber! Pick up trash at the beach and recycle it.

Why does the salinity of ocean water stay balanced?

Figure 11-3. Ocean water contains about 3.5 percent salts, as shown at the left. The main elements that make up the salts in ocean water are shown at the right.

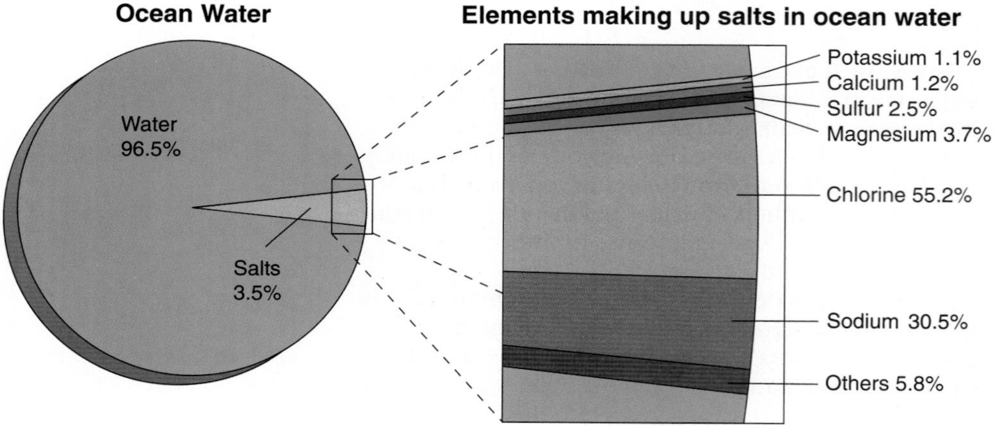

OPTIONS

ENRICHMENT

► Have students compare and contrast the composition of river water with the composition of seawater.

► Have students find out how either a Nansen bottle or salinometer work. Then have them work in groups to build working models of these instruments.

PROGRAM RESOURCES

From the **Teacher Resource Package** use:

Critical Thinking/Problem Solving, page 17, Expensive Water.

Concept Mapping, pages 27-28.

Use **Laboratory Manual** page 95, Salt Concentration in Ocean Water; page 97, Fresh Water from Ocean Water; and page 101, Floating in Fresh Water and Ocean Water.

TECHNOLOGY

Desalting Ocean Water

In some areas that have little fresh water, salt is removed from ocean water. Saudi Arabia, which borders the Red Sea and the Persian Gulf, for example, makes fresh water from salt water using a desalination system.

Desalting ocean water can be done in several ways. In one method, salt water is boiled and the steam is piped into a container where it cools. As the steam forms, the salts are left behind and fresh water is produced.

In another method, permeable membranes and an electric current are used to separate the salt from the water. Membranes that allow positive ions to pass through are placed between membranes that allow only negative ions to pass. The electric current is then used to further separate the ions to produce fresh water.

In a third method of desalination, ocean water is frozen. The salt crystals are separated from the ice crystals by washing the salt from the ice with fresh water. The ice is then melted to produce fresh water.

Think Critically: Why wouldn't desalination be a good way to get fresh water for use in the center of a continent?

SECTION REVIEW

1. How do scientists think Earth's oceans formed?
2. Why does ocean water taste salty?
3. What are three ways that dissolved substances get into seawater? Give an example of each.
4. **Apply:** Why does the salinity of Earth's oceans remain balanced?

Concept Mapping

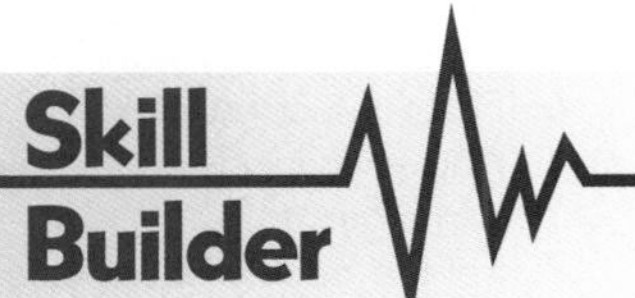

Make a cycle concept map that explains how water from Earth's atmosphere can move to Earth's oceans and back. Use these terms: *evaporates, condenses, falls as precipitation,* and *collects in basins.* If you need help, refer to Concept Mapping in the **Skill Handbook** on pages 688 and 689.

Skill Builder

Possible Solution:

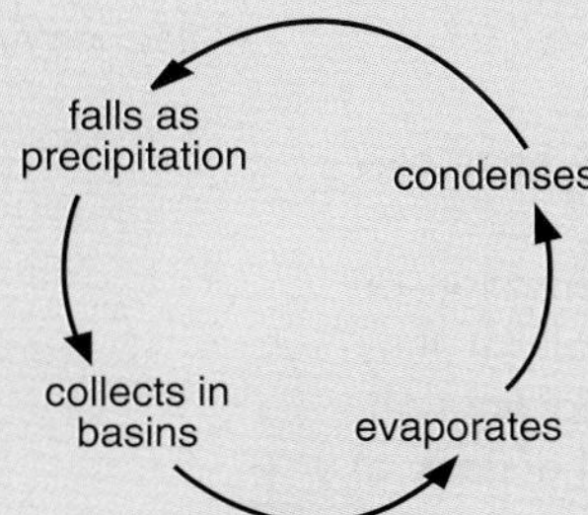

TECHNOLOGY

► For more information, see "Portable and potable [Debouy desalination system]" by J. Widman, *Oceans*, March/April 1984, p. 52.

Think Critically: The interior of a continent would be far from the source of ocean water. It would cost too much to pipe water over long distances.

3 CLOSE

► Ask questions 1-3 and the **Apply** Question in the Section Review.

 **Cooperative Learning:** Provide various water samples to Science Investigation groups. Have the groups use test kits to analyze the chemistry of the water samples.

FLEX Your Brain

Use the Flex Your Brain activity to have students explore SALINITY.

SECTION REVIEW ANSWERS

1. Water vapor from erupting volcanoes began to accumulate, cool, and condense about 4 billion years ago. Precipitation eventually fell and filled deep basins.

2. Salts like halite are dissolved in ocean water.

3. Sources include river water, volcanic water vapor, and the atmosphere. River water provides sodium; volcanic water vapor adds chlorine; and the atmosphere contributes oxygen.

4. Apply: As substances are added to the ocean water, sea animals and plants use these dissolved substances in their life processes. Other substances combine to form solids.

PROGRAM RESOURCES

From the **Teacher Resource Package** use:

Activity Worksheets, page 5, Flex Your Brain.

ACTIVITY 11-1
45 minutes

OBJECTIVE: Produce fresh water from brine by desalination.

PROCESS SKILLS applied in this activity:
▶ **Observing** in Procedure Step 8 and Analyze Question 6.
▶ **Interpreting Data** in Analyze Questions 1-6.
▶ **Experimenting** in Procedure Steps 1-10.
▶ **Formulating Models** in Conclude and Apply Questions 7 and 8.

COOPERATIVE LEARNING Have Science Investigation groups with three or four students per group do this activity.

TEACHING THE ACTIVITY

▶ Have all equipment ready prior to the laboratory day. Be sure that the glass tubing has been cut and bent and fits the holes in the rubber stoppers. Be absolutely sure that all glassware is clean.

▶ Stress that students be careful when inserting the glass tubing into the stopper and the rubber tubing into the glass tubing.

Troubleshooting: Before students begin boiling their solutions, check to see that they have properly assembled the equipment.

PROGRAM RESOURCES

From the **Teacher Resource Package** use:

Activity Worksheets, pages 95-96, Activity 11-1: Desalination.

ACTIVITY 11-1
Desalination

Problem: *How does desalination produce fresh water?*

Materials

- pan balance
- table salt
- water
- 500-mL beakers (2)
- 1000-mL flask
- 1-hole rubber stopper
- rubber tubing
- hot plate
- cardboard
- ice
- shallow pan
- glass tubing bent at right angle
- glycerine
- towel
- scissors
- washers
- goggles

Procedure

1. Dissolve 18 g of table salt in a beaker containing 500 mL of water. Carefully taste the solution. **CAUTION:** *Be sure the glassware is clean.*
2. Put the solution into the flask. Place the flask on the hot plate. Do not turn on the hot plate.
3. Assemble the stopper, glass tubing, and rubber tubing as shown in the photo. To do this, rub a small amount of glycerine on both ends of the glass tubing. Hold the tubing with a towel, and gently slide it into the stopper and rubber tubing.
4. Insert the stopper into the flask. Make sure the glass tubing is above the surface of the solution.
5. Use the scissors to cut a small hole in the piece of cardboard. Insert the free end of the rubber tubing through the hole. Be sure to keep the tubing away from the hot plate.
6. Place the cardboard over a clean beaker. Add several washers to the cardboard to hold it in place.
7. Set the beaker in a shallow pan filled with ice.
8. Turn on the hot plate. Bring the solution to a boil. Observe what happens in the flask and in the beaker.
9. Continue boiling until the solution is almost, but not quite, boiled away.
10. Turn off the hot plate and let the water in the beaker cool.

Analyze

1. What happened to the water in the flask as you boiled the solution?
2. What happened inside the beaker? Explain your answer.
3. Taste the water in the beaker. Is it salty?
4. What remains in the flask?
5. Is the combined water in the flask and in the beaker the same volume you placed in the flask at the beginning of the activity? Explain.
6. Examine the sides of the flask and describe what you see.

Conclude and Apply

7. How might the desalination process be used to extract minerals from seawater?
8. How does desalination produce fresh water?

ANSWERS TO QUESTIONS

1. The volume of water decreased.
2. Water began to fill the beaker as the water vapor condensed.
3. no
4. concentrated salt water
5. It's almost the same. Some may have condensed in the tubing.
6. Some students will note condensation on the sides of their flasks, especially if they have not boiled the solution long enough. Others will note salt crystals on the sides of the flask.
7. Minerals are left behind when the water is removed.
8. Fresh water is evaporated from the saline water, leaving behind salts.

Ocean Currents

11-2

Objectives

- Determine how surface currents are influenced by winds, the Coriolis effect, and continents.
- Explain why waters off the western coasts of continents are usually colder than waters off the eastern coasts of continents.
- Describe how density currents cause ocean water below the surface to circulate.

New Science Words

surface current
density current
upwelling

Surface Currents

When you stir chocolate flavoring into milk, or stir a pot of soup, you make currents with the spoon. The currents are what does the mixing. In the ocean, currents move water from place to place. There are two kinds of currents—surface currents and density currents.

In the late 1760s, the American colonies depended on sailing ships to carry mail back and forth between America and England. But a constant complaint was that it took the mail two weeks longer to travel from England to America than it did to travel the other direction. The Deputy Postmaster General of the colonies, Benjamin Franklin, decided to investigate.

Figure 11-4. Benjamin Franklin completed this map of the Gulf Stream in about 1770.

SECTION 11-2

PREPARATION

SECTION BACKGROUND

- Oceans can be divided into three layers based on temperature. Heat in the surface layer is evenly distributed because of the mixing by waves and the turbulence by currents. The depth of this layer averages 200 to 300 meters below the surface. Below the surface layer is the thermocline, where the temperature is about 5°C. Below the thermocline, temperature decreases slightly to about 1°C.

PREPLANNING

- To prepare for the Mini-Lab, obtain the materials listed on page 291 for each group of students.

1 MOTIVATE

- **Demonstration:** Have a few volunteers help you perform this activity in front of the class. Fill three beakers with 1000 mL of water and label the beakers A, B, and C. Don't put any salt into beaker A. Mix 20 grams of salt into beaker B and 40 grams of salt into beaker C. Explain that the salinity of the water in beaker B is 2 percent and in beaker C it's 4 percent. Then, use a hydrometer to determine the density of the water in each beaker. Have all students make a graph and plot salinity, in percent, on the horizontal axis and density, in g/mL, on the vertical axis. Students will see that there is a direct relationship between salinity and density. Ask students what would happen if more salt were added to beaker C. They should conclude that the density would increase.

FLEX Your Brain

Use the Flex Your Brain activity to have students explore CURRENTS.

INQUIRY QUESTIONS

- **Is the Japan Current colder or warmer than the California Current? Explain your answer.** *The Japan Current is warmer because it originates at the equator. The California Current originates at higher latitudes.*
- **Explain why the North Equatorial Current rotates clockwise, and the South Equatorial Current rotates counterclockwise.** *The Coriolis effect creates these differences.*
- **A *gyre* refers to the circular pattern of water that occurs in each of the major ocean basins. Which currents make up the gyre in the north Pacific Ocean?** *the Japan Current, California Current, and North Equatorial Current*

PROGRAM RESOURCES

From the **Teacher Resource Package** use:

Activity Worksheets, page 5; Flex Your Brain.

TYING TO PREVIOUS KNOWLEDGE: Give students a few moments to compare wind patterns shown in Figure 9-13 on page 247, with major ocean surface currents shown in Figure 11-5. Students should note that water and wind follow similar paths until the continents deflect ocean currents.

OBJECTIVES AND SCIENCE WORDS: Have students review the objectives and science words to become familiar with this section.

2 TEACH

Key Concepts are highlighted.

CONCEPT DEVELOPMENT

▶ **Explain how wind creates surface currents.** *Friction between the wind-blown air and the water surface causes the water to move.*

CROSS CURRICULUM

▶ **Social Studies:** Have students study how the positions of currents affected ancient trade routes. Have them research the discovery of the Gulf Stream by Benjamin Franklin.

Franklin learned that a strong current flowed in the ocean from America toward England. On their way to England, the ships would travel with the current and it added to their speed. However, when the ships traveled the opposite direction, back toward America, they ran against the current and lost speed. This is what made them two weeks late on the trip back from England. Franklin had a cousin named Timothy Folger who was a ship captain. It was actually Folger who told Franklin about the Gulf Stream, and led to the map on page 287.

The current was only 100 km wide, so with a good map, ships could avoid the current on their way to America. To help them, Franklin drew the first map of the current.
1 He called it the Gulf Stream because it flowed out of the Gulf of Mexico.

The Gulf Stream is still flowing. It is one of several surface currents in Earth's oceans seen in Figure 11-5. It's
2 called a **surface current** because it affects only the upper few hundred meters of seawater. Most surface currents are caused by winds. Friction between the windblown air and the water surface causes the water to move. For

Did You Know?

The Gulf Stream, called "a river in the ocean," is bigger than any river on land. It is 800 m deep, flows at an average of 6.5 km/hr, and transports 1000 times as much water as the Mississippi River.

Figure 11-5. This diagram shows the major surface currents of Earth's oceans.

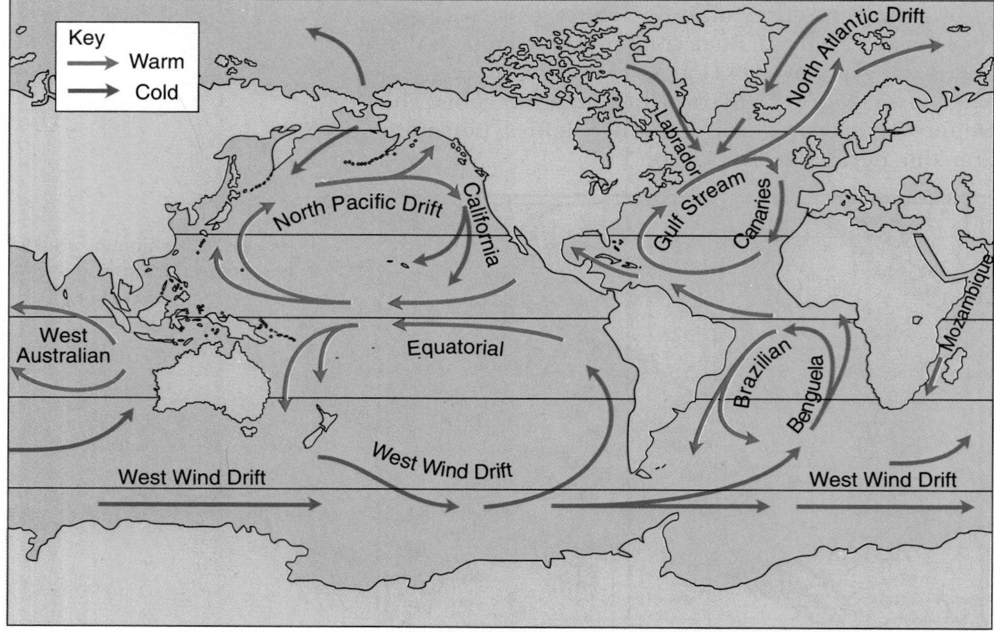

OPTIONS

Meeting Different Ability Levels

For Section 11-2, use the following **Teacher Resource Masters** depending upon individual students' needs.

◆ **Study Guide Master** for all students.

● **Reinforcement Master** for students of average and above average ability levels.

▲ **Enrichment Master** for above average students.

Additional Teacher Resource Package masters are listed in the OPTIONS box throughout the section. The additional masters are appropriate for all students.

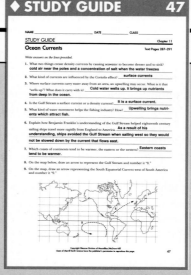

◆ STUDY GUIDE 47

NAME ______ DATE ______ CLASS ______

STUDY GUIDE — Chapter 11

Ocean Currents — Text Pages 287–291

Write answers on the lines provided.

1. What two things create density currents by causing seawater to become denser and to sink? **cold air near the poles and a concentration of salt when the water freezes**
2. What kind of currents are influenced by the Coriolis effect? **surface currents**
3. Where surface currents carry water away from an area, an upwelling may occur. What is it that "wells up"? What does it carry with it? **Cold water wells up. It brings up nutrients from deep in the ocean.**
4. Is the Gulf Stream a surface current or a density current? **It is a surface current.**
5. What kind of water movement helps the fishing industry? How? **Upwelling brings nutrients which attract fish.**
6. Explain how Benjamin Franklin's understanding of the Gulf Stream helped eighteenth century sailing ships travel more rapidly from England to America. **As a result of his understanding, ships avoided the Gulf Stream when sailing west so they would not be slowed down by the current that flows east.**
7. Which coasts of continents tend to be warmer, the eastern or the western? **Eastern coasts tend to be warmer.**
8. On the map below, draw an arrow to represent the Gulf Stream and number it "8."
9. On the map, draw an arrow representing the South Equatorial Current west of South America and number it "9."

example, surface currents in the tropics are pushed by the energy of the trade winds, which you learned about in Chapter 9.

Surface ocean currents, just like surface winds, are influenced by the Coriolis effect, which you also learned about in Chapter 9. The Coriolis
3 effect causes most currents north of the equator to move in a clockwise direction, as the Gulf Stream does. Most currents south of the equator always move in a counterclockwise direction.

Another factor that controls currents is the continents that deflect currents. For example, in the Pacific Ocean, currents moving toward the west are deflected northward by Asia and southward by Australia. These currents then move eastward until they meet North and South America, which deflect them toward the equator.

In Figure 11-5, note that many currents on the western coasts of continents are cold, whereas cur-
4 rents on the eastern coasts are warm. The reason is that currents on the western coasts generally originate far from the equator, in the cooler latitudes. Currents on the eastern coasts originate near the equator.

Surface currents are important because they affect the climate of places they pass by. Iceland is on the Arctic Circle, so you would expect it to have a very frigid climate. But the Gulf Stream flows past Iceland. The current's warm water heats the surrounding air. Because of the Gulf Stream, Iceland has a surprisingly mild climate. If you lived near a seacoast, how do you think the warm or cold currents off your coastline would affect your climate?

00:19 CHAN 3,4 TEMP

RSMAS

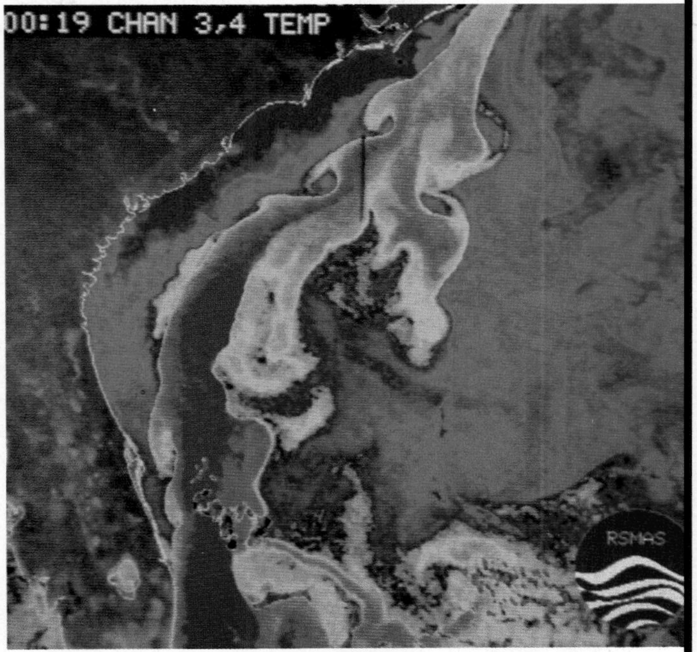

Figure 11-6. Ocean temperature data collected by a satellite were used to make this surface temperature image of the Atlantic Ocean. The warm Gulf Stream waters appear orange and red, and cooler water appears blue and green.

Density Currents

Some currents aren't caused by winds. A **density current** occurs when denser seawater moves toward an area of less dense seawater.

STUDENT TEXT QUESTION

▶ Page 289, paragraph 4: **If you lived near a seacoast, how do you think the warm or cold currents off your coastline would affect your climate?** *Warm currents warm the air while cool currents tend to cool overlying air.*

CONCEPT DEVELOPMENT

▶ **Why are currents on the western coasts of continents cold, and those on the eastern coasts warm?** *The temperatures of the currents depend on where they originate. Those on the western coasts originate in higher latitudes than those on the eastern coasts, which originate near the equator.*

MINI QUIZ

Use the Mini Quiz to check students' recall of chapter content.

1. **Who named the Gulf Stream?** *Benjamin Franklin*
2. **A(n) ____ current affects only the upper few hundred meters of seawater.** *surface*
3. **Most surface ocean currents move in a(n) ____ direction in the Northern Hemisphere.** *clockwise*
4. **Currents on the eastern continental coasts are ____ than currents on the western coasts.** *warmer*

● REINFORCEMENT 47

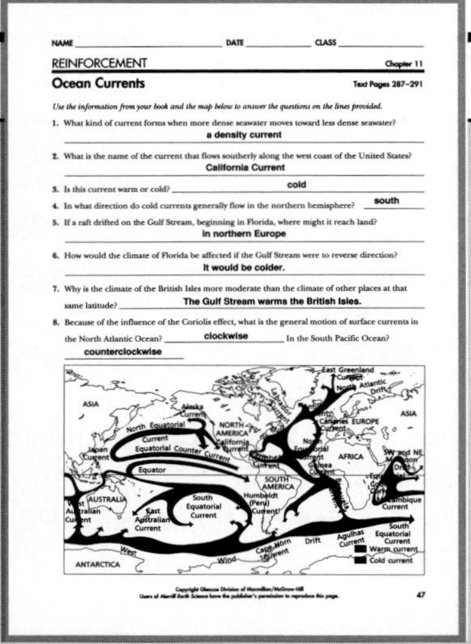

NAME ____ DATE ____ CLASS ____

REINFORCEMENT — Chapter 11

Ocean Currents — Text Pages 287–291

Use the information from your book and the map below to answer the questions on the lines provided.

1. What kind of current forms when more dense seawater moves toward less dense seawater? **a density current**
2. What is the name of the current that flows southerly along the west coast of the United States? **California Current**
3. Is this current warm or cold? **cold**
4. In what direction do cold currents generally flow in the northern hemisphere? **south**
5. If a raft drifted on the Gulf Stream, beginning in Florida, where might it reach land? **In northern Europe**
6. How would the climate of Florida be affected if the Gulf Stream were to reverse direction? **It would be colder.**
7. Why is the climate of the British Isles more moderate than the climate of other places at that same latitude? **The Gulf Stream warms the British Isles.**
8. Because of the influence of the Coriolis effect, what is the general motion of surface currents in the North Atlantic Ocean? **clockwise** In the South Pacific Ocean? **counterclockwise**

47

▲ ENRICHMENT 47

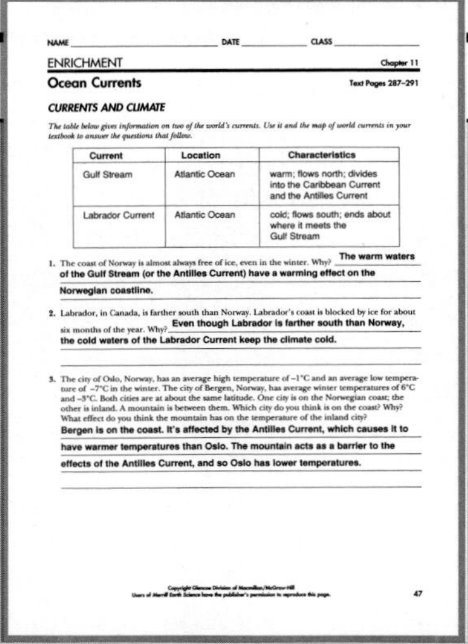

NAME ____ DATE ____ CLASS ____

ENRICHMENT — Chapter 11

Ocean Currents — Text Pages 287–291

CURRENTS AND CLIMATE

The table below gives information on two of the world's currents. Use it and the map of world currents in your textbook to answer the questions that follow.

Current	Location	Characteristics
Gulf Stream	Atlantic Ocean	warm; flows north; divides into the Caribbean Current and the Antilles Current
Labrador Current	Atlantic Ocean	cold; flows south; ends about where it meets the Gulf Stream

1. The coast of Norway is almost always free of ice, even in the winter. Why? **The warm waters of the Gulf Stream (or the Antilles Current) have a warming effect on the Norwegian coastline.**
2. Labrador, in Canada, is farther south than Norway. Labrador's coast is blocked by ice for about six months of the year. Why? **Even though Labrador is farther south than Norway, the cold waters of the Labrador Current keep the climate cold.**
3. The city of Oslo, Norway, has an average high temperature of –1°C and an average low temperature of –7°C in the winter. The city of Bergen, Norway, has average winter temperatures of 6°C and –3°C. Both cities are at about the same latitude. One city is on the Norwegian coast; the other is inland. A mountain is between them. Which city do you think is on the coast? Why? What effect do you think the mountain has on the temperature of the inland city? **Bergen is on the coast. It's affected by the Antilles Current, which causes it to have warmer temperatures than Oslo. The mountain acts as a barrier to the effects of the Antilles Current, and so Oslo has lower temperatures.**

47

CHECK FOR UNDERSTANDING

Ask students to explain why density currents develop in areas where surface waters are very saline.

RETEACH

Demonstration: Fill two Erlenmeyer flasks with water. Add 5 drops of food coloring to one flask. Insert a stopper holding two glass tubes into the other flask, and invert it over the one containing the coloring. Repeat the procedure with two more flasks, but add 35 g of salt to the top flask before putting in the stopper and inverting the flask. Have students observe changes that occur in the sets of flasks. The colored water will not move in the first set of flasks because there is no current. However, in the second setup, the colored water will move up into the top flask. Ask students to explain this movement. Students should conclude that in the second set of flasks, a density current is created as the salty, denser water moves down and the less dense water in the bottom flask moves up.

EXTENSION

For students who have mastered this section, use the **Reinforcement** and **Enrichment** masters or other OPTIONS provided.

PROBLEM SOLVING

Think Critically: The hot water that was added was less dense than the cold water already in the tub. Thus, the hot water remained on top of the colder, denser water.

As you learned in Chapter 2, dense materials sink below less dense materials. In the ocean, denser water around the North Pole and the South Pole sinks and travels along the ocean floor toward the equator. At the same time, less dense water at the equator rises and moves toward the poles along the surface. These two events form a continuous cycle that circulates ocean water.

What is one reason that cold ocean water is more dense than warm ocean water?

What can make seawater denser and sink? The cold air near the poles chills the water, causing its molecules to be less active and closer together. This decreases the volume of the water and makes it denser, so it sinks. Also, the cold climate freezes some of the water. This concentrates the salts in the remaining unfrozen water, which increases its mass, makes it denser, and causes it to sink. Once this happens, the colder, saltier, denser water moves as a mass along the ocean bottom.

You made a density current in the Find Out activity at the beginning of this chapter. As the ice cube melted, its cold water was denser than the warm water in the pan, so the cold water sank to the bottom. This created a density current which moved the food coloring.

PROBLEM SOLVING

Testing the Water

Parul decided that her dog, Grover, needed a bath. She got a metal washtub and began filling it with water from the garden hose. She filled it three-fourths full. When she tested the temperature with her hand, she thought it was just too cold to put Grover into. So, she decided to heat some water on the stove and add that to the washtub. She did this, then retested the water. To her surprise, the surface of the water was very hot, but the bottom three-fourths of the water was still quite cold.

Think Critically: Why wasn't all the water in the tub the same warm temperature?

OPTIONS

INQUIRY QUESTIONS

▶ **Along the eastern shores of oceans, winds blow surface water out from shore. This water is then replaced by cold deep water. Where would you expect this type of upwelling to occur?** *along the coasts of California, Peru, and western Africa*

PROGRAM RESOURCES

From the **Teacher Resource Package** use:

Cross-Curricular Connections, page 15, Classification System.

Transparency Masters, pages 39-40, Ocean Currents.

Use **Color Transparency** number 20, Ocean Currents.

Use **Laboratory Manual** page 99, Density Currents.

At the same time these deep density currents are flowing toward the equator, water at the equator is heated by the sun. It flows on the surface toward the poles to replace the cold water heading toward the equator in the deep ocean. As this heated water leaves the area near the equator, water below it rises, warms, and continues the density current cycle.

In some places, cold water from the deep ocean rises all the way to the surface. This occurs where strong wind-driven surface currents carry water away from an area. An **upwelling** occurs when cold water from deep in the oceans rises to the surface in an area. Upwellings bring high concentrations of nutrients to the surface. This water contains nutrients from organisms that died and sank to the bottom. Because of these nutrients, upwellings are usually good fishing areas. The coasts of Oregon, Washington, and Peru have good fishing because of upwellings.

Our knowledge has come a long way since Benjamin Franklin investigated the Gulf Stream. Today we can track the positions of currents by satellite. We use this information to help ships navigate and to help fishing fleets locate upwellings.

MINI-Lab

How can you make a density current model?

Fill a clear plastic storage box or a glass pie plate or baking dish with water at room temperature. Mix several teaspoons of table salt into a glass of water of the same temperature as the water in the container. Add a few drops of food coloring to the saltwater solution and pour it very gently and slowly into the clear water in the large container. Describe what happens. What conditions in large bodies of water, such as lakes or the ocean, all can create currents caused by density differences?

SECTION REVIEW

1. How does the energy from wind affect the behavior of surface currents?
2. What does the Coriolis effect do to surface currents in the Northern Hemisphere?
3. How do density currents affect the circulation of water in deep parts of the oceans?
4. What type of current is the Gulf Stream?
5. **Apply:** The latitudes of San Diego, California, and Charleston, South Carolina, are exactly the same. However, the average yearly water temperature in the ocean off Charleston is much higher than the water temperature off San Diego. Explain why.

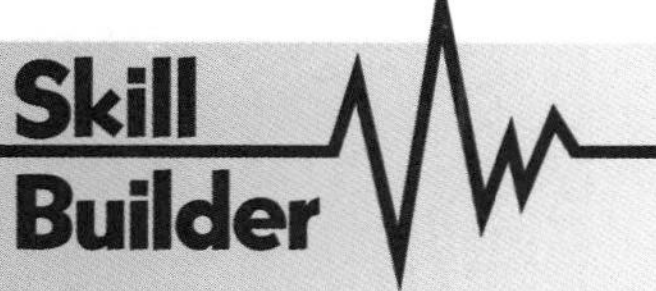

☑ Classifying

How would an ocean current that forms at a depth of one kilometer be classified? If you need help, refer to Classifying in the **Skill Handbook** on page 680.

MINI-Lab

Materials: clear, plastic or glass box or pie plate; water; food coloring; table salt

Teaching Tips

Cooperative Learning: Have Paired Partners do this activity.

Observations and Answers: The colored salt water sinks to the bottom and spreads out toward the sides of the container. Significant density differences are created in large bodies of water through high rates of evaporation of surface water and by exposure to the extreme temperatures that commonly exist at both high and low latitudes.

3 CLOSE

▶Ask questions 1-3 and the **Apply** Question in the Section Review.

Use the Flex Your Brain activity to have students explore UPWELLINGS.

SECTION REVIEW ANSWERS

1. Friction between windblown air and surface water creates currents.
2. It causes the currents to move in a clockwise direction.
3. Cold water at the poles sinks and moves along the ocean bottom toward the equator. At the equator, warm surface water moves toward the poles. The cooler water near the equator then rises, warms, becomes less dense, and replaces the equatorial water.
4. Apply: The water off Charleston originates at the equator. The water off San Diego originates near Alaska.

Skill Builder

Surface currents form only in the upper few hundred meters of the ocean. Thus, a current forming below these depths would be classified as a density current.

ENRICHMENT

▶Have students find out how one of the following hydrologic instruments works: drift bottle, neutrally buoyant float, swallow float, or suspended-drop current meter. Have them work in cooperative groups to build working models.

▶Have students report on the economic significance of upwellings, such as the effects on crops grown or on resort areas.

▶Have students determine why the Sargasso Sea has become polluted.

PROGRAM RESOURCES

From the **Teacher Resource Package** use:

Activity Worksheets, page 101, Mini-Lab: How can you make a density current model?

Activity Worksheets, page 5, Flex Your Brain.

SECTION 11-3

PREPARATION

SECTION BACKGROUND

▶ A breaker forms when the depth of the water is equal to one-half the wavelength of the wave.

▶ The longer wind blows, the higher the waves mount until they reach a maximum height for a given wind velocity. For a given wind velocity, waves tend to be higher on large bodies of water than shallower bodies. This is because waves on the larger bodies can develop without interference from shallow water.

▶ Storm waves have longer wavelengths than normal waves. Thus, their erosional effects on the basin bottom extend relatively far from shore.

PREPLANNING

▶ To prepare for Activity 11-2, obtain the following materials for each Science Investigation group: ring stand, 3-speed electric fan, light source, metric ruler, protractor, and a clear plastic shoe or storage box.

1 MOTIVATE

FLEX Your Brain

Use the Flex Your Brain activity to have students explore WAVES.

▶ A visit to an ocean shore, a flowing river, or a lake will enable students to see how wind affects waves.

CROSS CURRICULUM

▶ **Physical Science:** Have students find out that wave characteristics are the same whether the waves are light waves, earthquake waves, sound waves, or water waves.

PROGRAM RESOURCES

From the **Teacher Resource Package** use:

Activity Worksheets, page 5, Flex Your Brain.

11-3 Ocean Waves and Tides

New Science Words

crest
trough
wave height
wavelength
breaker
tides
tidal range

Objectives

- ▶ Describe the parts of a wave.
- ▶ Differentiate between the movement of water particles in a wave and the movement of wave energy.
- ▶ Describe how waves are created by the energy of wind and the gravitational force of the moon and sun.

Waves

If you've been to the seashore, you have watched the waves roll in. If not, you have seen pictures of waves on TV. Waves are caused by winds, earthquakes, and the gravitational force of the moon and sun. You'll find out about waves caused by earthquakes in Chapter 14. But first, what are waves?

What are waves?

Waves are movements in which water alternately rises and falls. Several terms are used to describe waves. As
1 shown in Figure 11-7, the **crest** is the highest point of the wave. The **trough** is the lowest point. **Wave height** is the
2 vertical distance between crest and trough. **Wavelength** is the horizontal distance between the crests of two successive waves or the troughs of two successive waves.

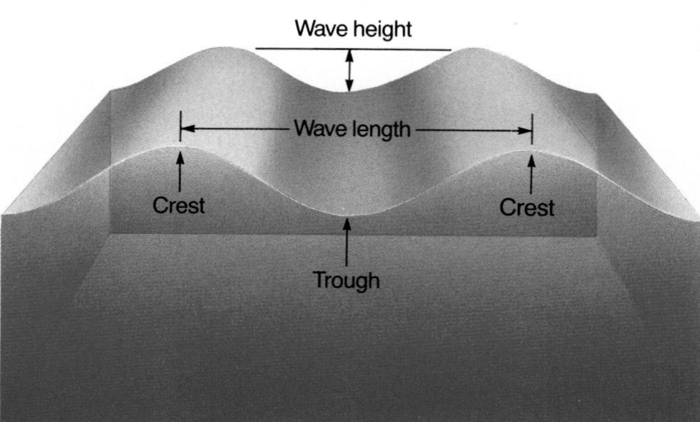

Figure 11-7. Parts of a Wave.

OPTIONS

Meeting Different Ability Levels

For Section 11-3, use the following **Teacher Resource Masters** depending upon individual students' needs.

◆ **Study Guide Master** for all students.

● **Reinforcement Master** for students of average and above average ability levels.

▲ **Enrichment Master** for above average students.

Additional Teacher Resource Package masters are listed in the OPTIONS box throughout the section. The additional masters are appropriate for all students.

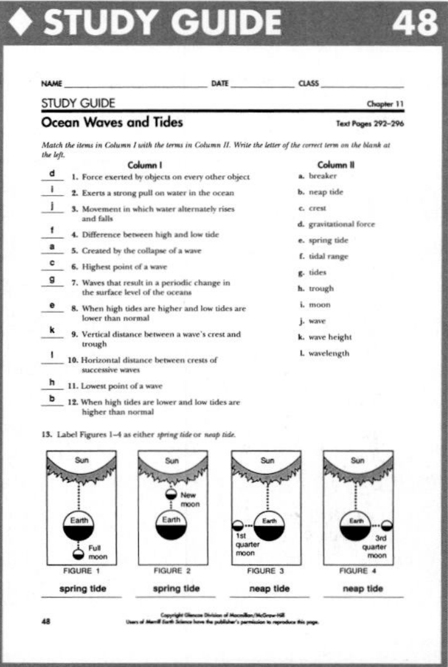
◆ STUDY GUIDE 48

NAME ______ DATE ______ CLASS ______

STUDY GUIDE — Chapter 11

Ocean Waves and Tides — Text Pages 292–296

Match the items in Column I with the terms in Column II. Write the letter of the correct term on the blank at the left.

Column I	Column II
d 1. Force exerted by objects on every other object	a. breaker
i 2. Exerts a strong pull on water in the ocean	b. neap tide
j 3. Movement in which water alternately rises and falls	c. crest
f 4. Difference between high and low tide	d. gravitational force
a 5. Created by the collapse of a wave	e. spring tide
c 6. Highest point of a wave	f. tidal range
g 7. Waves that result in a periodic change in the surface level of the oceans	g. tides
e 8. When high tides are higher and low tides are lower than normal	h. trough
k 9. Vertical distance between a wave's crest and trough	i. moon
l 10. Horizontal distance between crests of successive waves	j. wave
h 11. Lowest point of a wave	k. wave height
b 12. When high tides are lower and low tides are higher than normal	l. wavelength

13. Label Figures 1–4 as either *spring tide* or *neap tide.*

Sun, Earth, Full moon — FIGURE 1: spring tide
Sun, New moon, Earth — FIGURE 2: spring tide
Sun, 1st quarter moon, Earth — FIGURE 3: neap tide
Sun, Earth, 3rd quarter moon — FIGURE 4: neap tide

48

When you watch a wave, it looks like the water moves forward. But it doesn't. The water actually stays in about the same place. An object floating on water will rise and fall as a wave passes, but the object will not move otherwise. Each particle of water in a wave moves around in a circle. Energy moves forward while water particles remain 3
in the same place.

When waves move into a shallow area, water at the bottom of a wave is slowed down by friction with the ocean 4
bottom. This causes them to change shape. As they slow, their crests and troughs become closer together. Their wave heights also increase. The waves continue to grow higher as the water depth decreases. The tops of waves move faster than the bottoms, so when a wave becomes tall enough, it collapses, creating a **breaker.** Then, as the crest falls, the water tumbles over on itself. After a wave breaks onto shore, gravity pulls the water back into the sea.

Now let's look at two very different types of waves: (1) the common sea waves caused by the wind and (2) the long waves of the tides.

Why do waves slow down in shallow water?

Figure 11-8. In water, individual particles of water move in circles as a wave passes, as seen in diagram (a) below. Energy in waves is transferred like falling dominoes (b). Like water particles, individual dominoes remain near where they were standing as they fall and transfer energy.

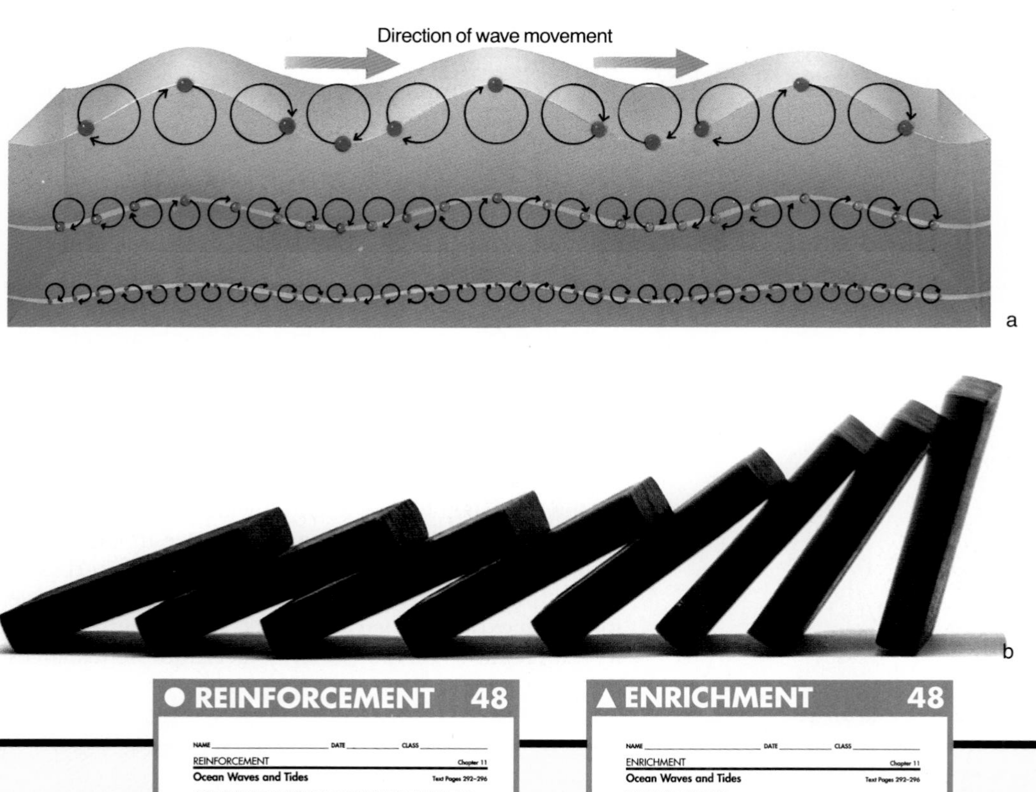

● REINFORCEMENT 48

NAME ____________ DATE ________ CLASS ________

REINFORCEMENT — Chapter 11

Ocean Waves and Tides — Text Pages 292–296

On the graph, plot each data point for high tide. Connect these data points with a red pencil. Plot each data point for low tide. Connect these data points with a blue pencil. Then answer the questions.

Data Table

Date in January	Height of high tide (meters)	Height of low tide (meters)
1	1.4	0.5
2	1.5	0.4
3	1.7	0.2
4	1.8	–0.1
5	2.1	–0.3
6	2.2	–0.5
7	2.3	–0.6
8	2.3	–0.6
9	2.3	–0.6
10	2.1	–0.5
11	1.9	–0.2
12	1.6	–0.1
13	1.6	0.2
14	1.6	0.4
15	1.6	0.4

Tide (meters) — Date in January

1. On which days was the tidal range greatest?
January 7, 8, 9

2. On which day was the tidal range the lowest?
January 1

48

▲ ENRICHMENT 48

NAME ____________ DATE ________ CLASS ________

ENRICHMENT — Chapter 11

Ocean Waves and Tides — Text Pages 292–296

CALCULATING WAVE SPEED

The speed of waves can be easily calculated if you have some basic information. To calculate the speed of a wave, you need to know two things: the wavelength and the wave *period.* A wave period is the time it takes for two consecutive wave crests to pass the same place (or point). For example, if a wave crest passed a rock and 8 seconds later the very next wave crest passed the same rock, the period would be 8 seconds.

Scientists have determined that wave speed is equal to the wavelength divided by the period of the wave. That means that once you know the wavelength and the wave period, you can find the wave speed, using this formula:

$$\text{Wave speed (m/s)} = \frac{\text{Wavelength (m)}}{\text{Periods (s)}}$$

Notice that wavelength is measured in meters (m) and wave period is measured in seconds (s). Use the formula to help you complete the table below. Show all of your work in the space provided.

Wavelength (m/s)	Period (s)	Wave speed (m/s)
24	8	**3**
165	10	**16.5**
48	8	**6**
112	4	**28**
172	10	**17.2**
15.4	2	**7.7**
196.5	15	**13.12**

48

TYING TO PREVIOUS KNOWLEDGE: In order to explain particle motion in a wave, use the analogy of spectators in a stadium or arena. Often, fans successively stand up and sit down in a precise order that imitates wave motion. The result is a "wave" across the stadium or arena.

OBJECTIVES AND SCIENCE WORDS: Have students review the objectives and science words to become familiar with this section.

2 TEACH

Key Concepts are highlighted.

CONCEPT DEVELOPMENT

▶ **Demonstration:** Use a wave demonstration spring to show how energy is transferred through a wave. Tie a piece of ribbon to the middle of the spring. Have two students create a wave while another student holds the ribbon. Have the class note that the ribbon does not move with the wave, but energy moves through the ribbon.

▶ Take students to a shallow stream or lake and have them measure wavelengths and wave heights.

▶ **What happens to the wavelength and wave height as a wave moves into shallow water?** *Wavelength decreases; wave height increases.*

▶ **Contrast the movement of particles in a wave with the movement of energy through a water wave.** *The particles move around in circles while the energy moves forward through the wave.*

CONCEPT DEVELOPMENT

▶ **What causes tides?** *the gravitational attraction among the moon, sun, and Earth*

TEACHER F.Y.I.

▶ An average wave is 3.7 meters high, but the maximum wave height actually measured on the open ocean was 42.4 meters.

CHECK FOR UNDERSTANDING

Use the Mini Quiz to check for understanding.

MINI QUIZ

Use the Mini Quiz to check students' recall of chapter content.

1. **The high point of a wave is the _____.** *crest*
2. **The _____ is the horizontal distance between the crests of two successive waves.** *wavelength*
3. **_____ moves forward in a wave while particles in the wave remain in the same place.** *Energy*
4. **When a wave moves into shallow areas, water at the bottom of the wave is slowed down due to _____ against the ocean bottom.** *friction*

RETEACH

Use a wave demonstration spring to show the following characteristics of waves: crest, trough, wave height, and wavelength.

EXTENSION

For students who have mastered this section, use the **Reinforcement** and **Enrichment** masters or other OPTIONS provided.

MINI-Lab

Materials: clear plastic storage box or glass dish, cork, tape, water, spoon

Teaching Tips

Cooperative Learning: Have Paired Partners perform this activity.

Observations and Answers: The cork doesn't move from the position in the dish, except for the vertical motion created by the passing waves.

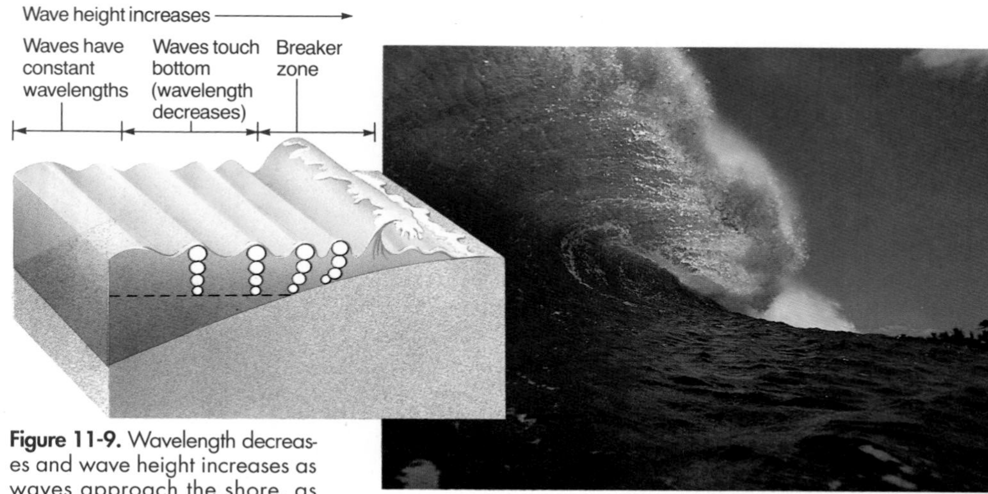

Figure 11-9. Wavelength decreases and wave height increases as waves approach the shore, as shown in diagram at left. This leads to breakers.

MINI-Lab

How do waves move?

Fill a clear plastic storage box or a glass baking dish with water. Float a cork in the middle of the container. Use tape to mark the approximate location of the cork along the top and bottom of the container. Use a spoon to gently make waves in the container. What is happening to the cork while you are making waves? Does the cork move from its original position? Explain.

Waves Caused by Wind

When wind blows across a body of water, friction causes the water to be moved along with the wind. If the speed is great enough, the water begins to pile up, forming a wave. As the wind continues to blow, the wave increases in height.

Waves stop forming when the wind stops blowing. But, once set in motion, waves continue moving for long distances. Waves you might see at a seashore originated many kilometers away. The height of waves depends on the speed of the wind, the distance over which the wind blows, and the length of time the wind blows.

Tides

Besides the waves caused by wind, waves also are created by the gravitational force of the moon, the sun, and Earth. These long waves that result in a periodic change in the surface level of the oceans are called **tides.** Along most seashores, tides make the sea level slowly rise and fall by a few meters twice a day. The **tidal range** is the difference between high tide and low tide.

You learned about gravitational force in Chapter 6 when you learned that gravity causes loose materials to move down a slope. Gravitational force is an attractive force that exists between all objects. The strength of gravity is affected by the masses of objects and the distances

OPTIONS

INQUIRY QUESTIONS

▶ **If high tide is 2.0 meters above average sea level and low tide is 0.5 meters below average sea level, what is the tidal range?** *2.5 meters*

PROGRAM RESOURCES

From the **Teacher Resource Package** use:

Activity Worksheets, page 102, Mini-Lab: How do waves move?

between them. The bigger the objects and the closer they are to one another, the greater the gravitational attraction between them.

The moon and Earth are relatively close together in space, so the moon's gravity exerts a strong pull on Earth. The gravitational force of the moon is stronger on the side of Earth that is facing the moon. The moon's gravity pulls on water particles in the ocean and causes the water to bulge on the side toward the moon and on the side opposite the moon.

These bulges of water on both sides of Earth actually are waves that we call high tides. When high tides form, water is drawn away from the areas between the bulges, creating low tides at those places.

As Earth rotates, different locations on Earth's surface pass through the high and low positions. Many coastal locations, such as the Atlantic and Pacific Coasts of the United States, experience two high tides and two low tides each day. Ocean basins vary in size and shape, so some coastal locations, such as many along the Gulf of Mexico, have only one high and one low tide each day.

The sun also affects tides. The sun can strengthen or weaken the moon's effects. When the moon, Earth, and sun are lined up, high tides are higher and low tides are lower than normal. These are called spring tides. When the sun, Earth, and moon form a right angle, high tides

Did You Know?

On September 23, 1987, volunteers picked up almost a million kilograms of garbage from United States beaches in just 3 hours.

Figure 11-10. The difference between high and low tide is easily seen at Mt. Saint Michel off the northwestern coast of France.

CONCEPT DEVELOPMENT

▶ If your school is located near an ocean, have students determine the times of low and high tides. Then have students record the position of the moon each day and relate it to the high and low tides. It may be possible to obtain tidal information from coastal weather stations or Navy or Coast Guard installations if you do not live near a seacoast.

REVEALING MISCONCEPTIONS

▶ Ask students to guess the wavelength of tides. Most will not realize that the average wavelength is 10 000 km. Superimposed on tide waves are swells, chop, surf, and ripples.

PROGRAM RESOURCES

From the **Teacher Resource Package** use:

Transparency Masters, pages 41-42, Spring/Neap Tides.

Use **Color Transparency** number 21, Spring/Neap Tides.

INQUIRY QUESTIONS

▶ **Why don't all ocean beaches have two high tides and two low tides each day?** *The size and shape of an ocean basin determine the number of tides.*

▶ **Why does the tidal range vary during a given month?** *When the moon, Earth, and sun are lined up, the high tides are at their maximums and low tides are at their lowest; high tides are lower and low tides are higher when the sun, Earth, and moon form a right angle.*

▶ **Contrast the tidal ranges during spring and neap tides.** *Tidal range is highest during spring tides and lowest during neap tides.*

3 CLOSE

▶ Ask questions 1-3 and the **Apply** Question in the Section Review.

FLEX Your Brain

Use the Flex Your Brain activity to have students explore TIDES.

▶ Have students do Activity 11-2 on page 297.

SECTION REVIEW ANSWERS

1. Wavelength is the distance between two crests or two troughs of adjacent waves. Wave height is the vertical distance between the crest and the trough of the same wave.

2. The wave particles do not move. It is energy that moves through the wave.

3. Wind coming in contact with the water creates friction, causing the water to be pushed into waves.

4. Apply: The moon would have to be directly on the other side of Earth. The moon's gravitational attraction causes the water particles in the ocean to bulge both on the side of Earth toward the moon and on the side opposite the moon.

Skill Builder

Both affect tides due to their gravitational attraction for each other and Earth. The effect of the moon is greater, however, because it is closer to Earth than the sun.

Figure 11-11. When the sun, moon, and Earth are aligned, spring tides occur. When the sun, moon, and Earth form a right angle, neap tides occur.

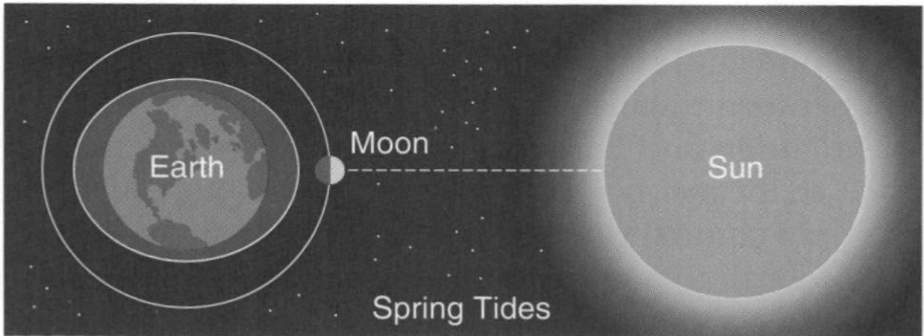

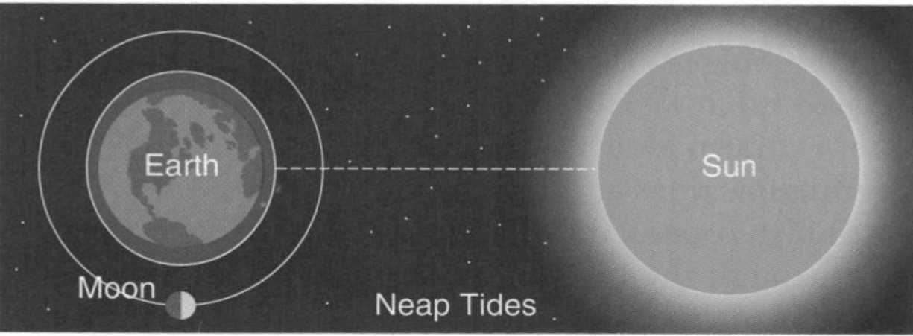

What are neap tides?

are lower and low tides are higher than normal. These are called neap tides.

In this section, you've learned how the energy of the wind and gravity causes waves. Now when you go to the beach, you'll understand the various movements of the water. In the next lesson, you'll see a valuable way that people use the energy of waves.

SECTION REVIEW

1. What do the terms *wavelength* and *wave height* mean?
2. One day at the ocean, you spot a large wave about 200 meters from shore. A few seconds later, the wave breaks on the beach. Why is the breaker composed of different water than the wave was made of when you first saw it?
3. How does wind cause waves?
4. **Apply:** You're walking along a beach on a clear night and you notice that the tide is really high, but the moon is nowhere in sight. Where must the moon be? Why?

Skill Builder

Comparing and Contrasting

Compare and contrast the effects of the sun and moon on Earth's tides. If you need help, refer to Comparing and Contrasting in the **Skill Handbook** on page 683.

OPTIONS

ENRICHMENT

▶ Have students find out about tsunamis and why they cause so much destruction.

▶ Have students research wave-driven turbines.

▶ Have students design and execute experiments that model wave erosion.

PROGRAM RESOURCES

From the **Teacher Resource Package** use:

Activity Worksheets, page 5, Flex Your Brain.

ACTIVITY 11-2
Air Motion and Waves

Problem: *What is the effect of wind on waves?*

Materials  

- white paper
- electric fan (3-speed)
- light source
- clock or watch
- clear plastic shoe or storage box
- ring stand
- water
- metric ruler
- protractor

Procedure

1. Place the light source on the ring stand. Position the plastic box on top of the paper under the ring stand.
2. Arrange the light source so that it shines directly on the box.
3. Pour water into the box to almost fill it.
4. Place the fan at one end of the box as shown in the photo. Start it on slow. **CAUTION:** *Do not allow any part of the fan or cord to come in contact with the water.*
5. After three minutes, measure the height of the waves caused by the fan. Record your observations in a table similar to the one shown. Observe the shadows of the waves on the white paper through the plastic box.
6. After five minutes, measure the waves and record your observations in your table.
7. Repeat Steps 4 to 6 with the fan on medium, and then with the fan on high.
8. Turn off the fan and observe what happens.

Data and Observations Sample Data

Fan Speed	Time	Wave height	Observations
Low	3 min.	2 mm	
	5 min.	3 mm	
Medium	3 min.	3.5 mm	
	5 min.	4.5 mm	Some waves
High	3 min.	5 mm	crest over edge
	5 min.	5.5 mm	of box.

Analyze

1. From your data sheet, is the wave height affected by the length of time that the wind blows? Explain.
2. Is the height of the waves affected by the force (velocity) of the wind? Explain.
3. How does an increase in fan speed affect the pattern of the shadows of waves on the white paper?
4. What caused shadows to appear on the paper below the plastic storage box?
5. What was the effect when you turned off the fan?

Conclude and Apply

6. What three factors cause the wave height to vary in the oceans?
7. Where does the energy that generates waves come from? How could this energy be used to reduce Earth's dependence on its decreasing supply of fossil fuels?

ACTIVITY 11-2
30-35 minutes

OBJECTIVE: Describe the effect that wind has on waves.

PROCESS SKILLS applied in this activity:
- ▶ **Observing** in Procedure Steps 5-8.
- ▶ **Experimenting** in Procedure Steps 1-8.
- ▶ **Determining Cause and Effect** in Analyze Questions 1-5 and Conclude and Apply Question 6.
- ▶ **Defining Operationally** in Conclude and Apply Question 7.
- ▶ **Interpreting Data** in Analyze Questions 1-5.
- ▶ **Hypothesizing** in Conclude and Apply Question 7.
- ▶ **Formulating Models** in Conclude and Apply Question 7.

COOPERATIVE LEARNING Form Science Investigation groups with four students per group and have each group complete the activity.

TEACHING THE ACTIVITY

▶ If a sufficient number of table model 3-speed fans cannot be obtained, the activity can be done by placing three or four student setups on the floor in front of a large, floor model fan that operates at several speeds.

▶ Either an overhead or filmstrip projector works well in place of the recommended light source and ring stand setup.

▶ If necessary, have students review the skill, Determining Cause and Effect, in the **Skill Handbook** on page 683.

PROGRAM RESOURCES

From the **Teacher Resource Package** use:

Activity Worksheets, pages 97-98, Activity 11-2: Air Motion and Waves.

ANSWERS TO QUESTIONS

1. Yes, the longer the wind blows, the higher the wave.
2. Yes, the stronger the wind, the higher the wave.
3. The shadows are closer together and are more easily seen when the fan speed is increased.
4. The light shines onto the waves and shadows are cast onto the paper.
5. When the fan was turned off, the waves disappeared.
6. The time that the wind blows, the velocity of the wind, and the distance over which the wind blows cause wave height to vary.
7. The sun provides energy that causes wind. Wind causes waves. Solar energy could be used to heat buildings. It can also be used to power solar cells.

SECTION 11-4

PREPARATION

SECTION BACKGROUND

► In energy plants that depend on tides, turbines change the energy from the tides into mechanical energy. Then, generators change the mechanical energy into electricity.

► In the tidal power station located on the River Rance in France, a computer continuously controls the pitch of the turbine blades to match the changing direction of the tides.

1 MOTIVATE

FLEX Your Brain

Use the Flex Your Brain activity to have students explore TIDAL POWER.

► Show students pictures of the Bay of Fundy during low and high tide. Then help them locate this bay on a map.

TYING TO PREVIOUS KNOWLEDGE: In Chapters 6 and 7, students learned that the energy of moving water is great enough to weather and erode sediments. In this section, students will learn how people use turbines to capture the energy of moving water.

OBJECTIVES AND SCIENCE WORDS: Have students review the objectives and science words to become familiar with this section.

Science and WRITING

If necessary, review with students the correct format of a business letter. You may wish to have students write one letter to avoid receiving duplicate materials.

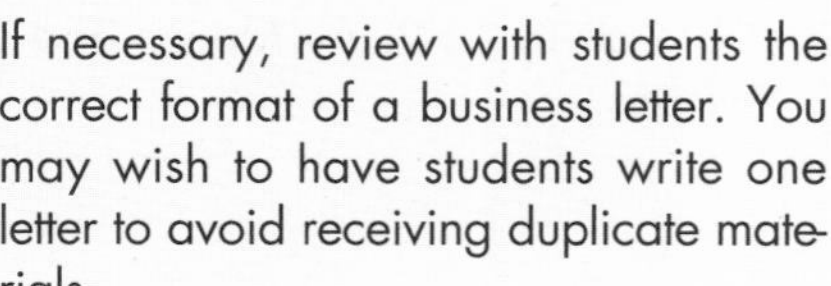

PROGRAM RESOURCES

From the **Teacher Resource Package** use:

Activity Worksheets, page 5, Flex Your Brain.

11-4 Tapping Tidal Energy

New Science Words

turbine
salt marsh

Objectives

- ► Explain why Nova Scotia's Bay of Fundy is a good place to build a tidal power plant.
- ► Relate how a tidal dam converts energy from tides into electricity.
- ► Consider the consequences of building a power plant at the Bay of Fundy.

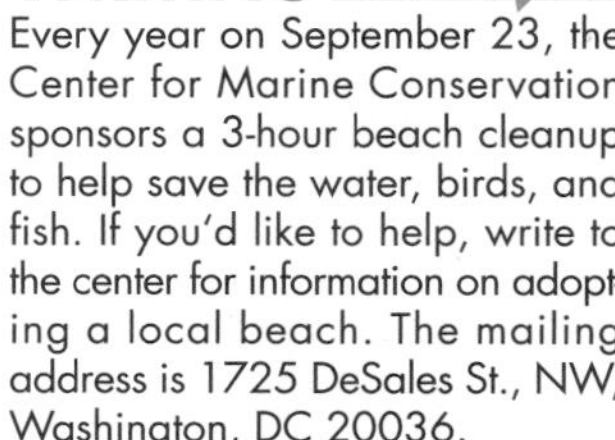

Science and WRITING

Every year on September 23, the Center for Marine Conservation sponsors a 3-hour beach cleanup to help save the water, birds, and fish. If you'd like to help, write to the center for information on adopting a local beach. The mailing address is 1725 DeSales St., NW, Washington, DC 20036.

Tidal Power

Imagine having a constant supply of nonpolluting energy that you could use to generate electricity. You wouldn't be burning fossil fuels or polluting the air. You wouldn't be worried about running out of electricity for heat, air conditioning, and appliances. In areas where there is a large difference between the water level of high and low tide, tides can be used to generate electricity.

Electric power generating plants that use tidal energy already have been built in France, Russia, and China. The Bay of Fundy in Nova Scotia is a perfect location for tapping energy from tides because the tidal range there reaches 16 m, the greatest on Earth. At the Bay of

Figure 11-12. This is the LaRance Tidal Power Plant at Saint Malo, France.

OPTIONS

Meeting Different Ability Levels

For Section 11-4, use the following **Teacher Resource Masters** depending upon individual students' needs.

◆ **Study Guide Master** for all students.

● **Reinforcement Master** for students of average and above average ability levels.

▲ **Enrichment Master** for above average students.

Additional Teacher Resource Package masters are listed in the OPTIONS box throughout the section. The additional masters are appropriate for all students.

◆ STUDY GUIDE 49

NAME ________ DATE ________ CLASS ________

STUDY GUIDE — Chapter 11

Tapping Tidal Energy — Text Pages 298–300

Answer the following questions on the lines provided.

1. Where have electric power generating plants that use tidal energy been built? **France, Russia, China**
2. In what country is the next tidal power plant planned? **Canada**
3. Average tidal ranges throughout the world are between 0.5 and 3 meters. Explain why the Bay of Fundy is a better than average place to build a tidal power plant. **Tidal range in the Bay of Fundy reaches 16 meters, the greatest on Earth. Therefore the outgoing tide would have great energy.**
4. What will hold back the water after the Bay of Fundy tide has come in? **Dam gates will be closed.**
5. What will the outgoing water pass over as it leaves the dam? **It will pass over turbines.**
6. What will the Bay of Fundy power plant produce? **electricity**
7. List advantages of the Bay of Fundy power plant. **The plant will not pollute, will produce a great supply of inexpensive electricity, will not use fossil fuels, will provide jobs.**
8. List disadvantages of the Bay of Fundy power plant. **Turbines will destroy fish. Tides on the Atlantic coast will be affected, resulting in flooded lowlands, destruction of salt marshes and habitats, and contamination of wells.**
9. What bad effect might the Bay of Fundy power plant have on jobs? **At high tide, some farmlands and towns will be flooded. At low tide, some Boston harbor channels will become too shallow to use.**

 49

Fundy, the water moves through a narrow opening into a funnel-shaped bay. The power of the incoming tide has been calculated to have more force than 8000 freight locomotives or 25 000 000 horses. At high tide, the water is kept in the bay by the force of the incoming tide. Then, at low tide it flushes out of the bay.

The Canadian government is building a dam at this site. It will have large gates to let water enter the bay at high tide. Then the gates will be closed, and water will be stored behind the dam. As the tide goes out, the dammed water will pass over turbines in the dam. A **turbine** is similar to a fan blade. When the water pushes the blades, the turbine spins. The spinning turbine turns a generator to produce electricity.

When this power plant is completed, it will provide electrical power to cities in Canada and the United States. Because there will be no expenses of buying fuel, pollution control, or waste disposal, the cost of the power will be relatively low. New jobs will also be created.

Figure 11-13. This diagram shows the basic concept of a tidal dam power plant. As the tide rises, it flows into the bay and becomes trapped by the dam (b). Then as the tide goes down, the water is released through the dam (c) and spins the turbine generator to make electricity.

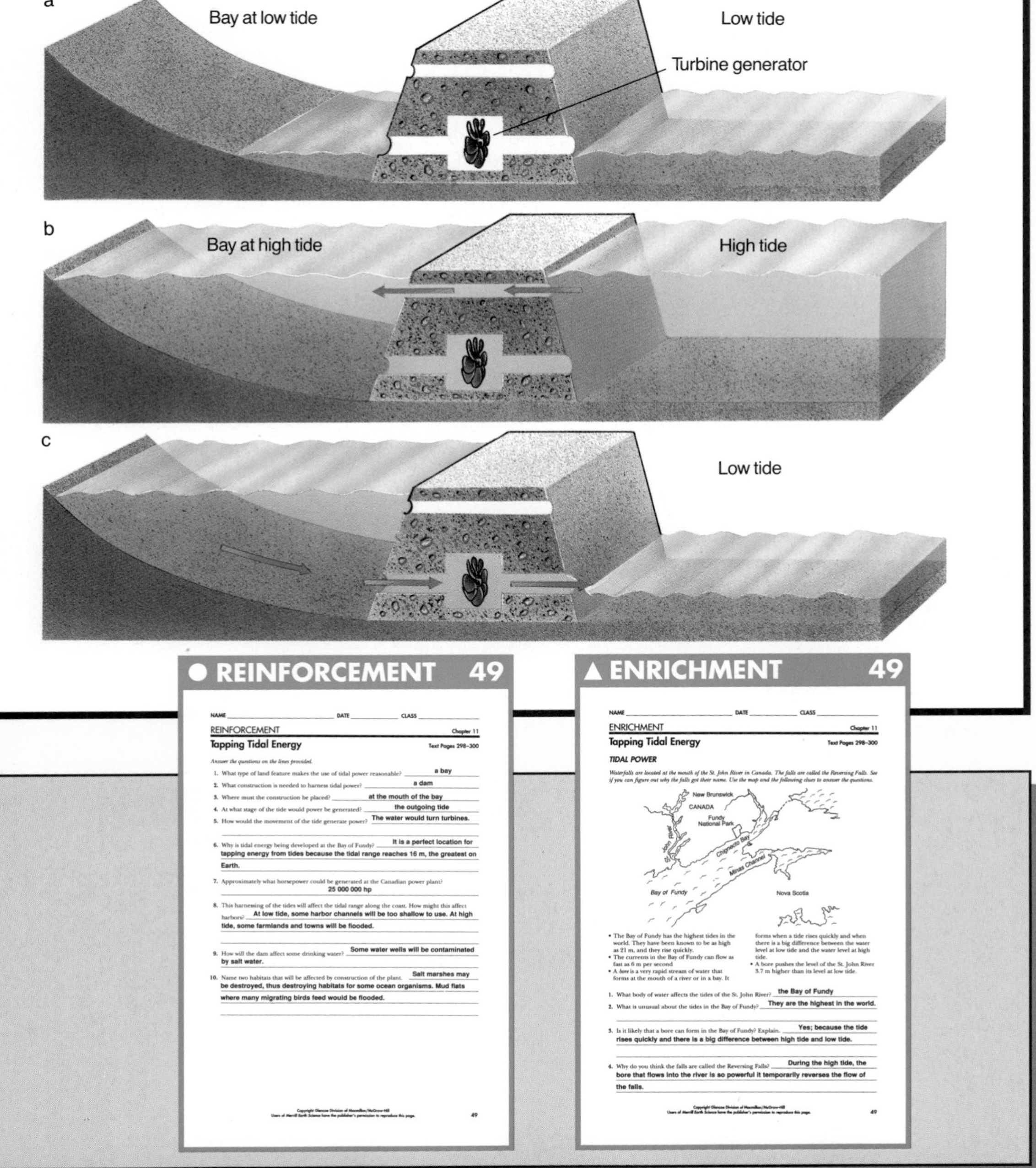

● REINFORCEMENT 49

NAME ______ DATE ______ CLASS ______

REINFORCEMENT Chapter 11

Tapping Tidal Energy Text Pages 298–300

Answer the questions on the lines provided.

1. What type of land feature makes the use of tidal power reasonable? **a bay**
2. What construction is needed to harness tidal power? **a dam**
3. Where must the construction be placed? **at the mouth of the bay**
4. At what stage of the tide would power be generated? **the outgoing tide**
5. How would the movement of the tide generate power? **The water would turn turbines.**
6. Why is tidal energy being developed at the Bay of Fundy? **It is a perfect location for tapping energy from tides because the tidal range reaches 16 m, the greatest on Earth.**
7. Approximately what horsepower could be generated at the Canadian power plant? **25 000 000 hp**
8. This harnessing of the tides will affect the tidal range along the coast. How might this affect harbors? **At low tide, some harbor channels will be too shallow to use. At high tide, some farmlands and towns will be flooded.**
9. How will the dam affect some drinking water? **Some water wells will be contaminated by salt water.**
10. Name two habitats that will be affected by construction of the plant. **Salt marshes may be destroyed, thus destroying habitats for some ocean organisms. Mud flats where many migrating birds feed would be flooded.**

 49

▲ ENRICHMENT 49

NAME ______ DATE ______ CLASS ______

ENRICHMENT Chapter 11

Tapping Tidal Energy Text Pages 298–300

TIDAL POWER

Waterfalls are located at the mouth of the St. John River in Canada. The falls are called the Reversing Falls. See if you can figure out why the falls got their name. Use the map and the following clues to answer the questions.

- The Bay of Fundy has the highest tides in the world. They have been known to be as high as 21 m, and they rise quickly.
- The currents in the Bay of Fundy can flow as fast as 6 m per second
- A *bore* is a very rapid stream of water that forms at the mouth of a river or in a bay. It forms when a tide rises quickly and when there is a big difference between the water level at low tide and the water level at high tide.
- A bore pushes the level of the St. John River 3.7 m higher than its level at low tide.

1. What body of water affects the tides of the St. John River? **the Bay of Fundy**
2. What is unusual about the tides in the Bay of Fundy? **They are the highest in the world.**
3. Is it likely that a bore can form in the Bay of Fundy? Explain. **Yes; because the tide rises quickly and there is a big difference between high tide and low tide.**
4. Why do you think the falls are called the Reversing Falls? **During the high tide, the bore that flows into the river is so powerful it temporarily reverses the flow of the falls.**

 49

2 TEACH

Key Concepts are highlighted.

CONCEPT DEVELOPMENT

▶ Stress to students that tidal power plants are not built along most coastal areas because their usefulness is limited to those few locations in the world that experience tremendous tidal ranges.

▶ After students have read pages 298 and 299, ask these questions. **Why will the cost of electrical power be relatively low from a tidal power plant at the Bay of Fundy?** *There are no expenses for buying fuel, pollution control, or waste disposal.* **What will be the purpose of the large gates that will be built at the dam at the Bay of Fundy?** *They will open to allow water to enter the bay at high tide and close to store water behind the dam.*

CHECK FOR UNDERSTANDING

▶ Ask questions 1 and 2 in the Section Review.

▶ In a class discussion, ask students to explain the advantages and disadvantages of tapping tidal power.

RETEACH

Cooperative Learning: Using the Study Buddy strategy, have students make a chart showing the pros and cons of building tidal power plants.

EXTENSION

For students who have mastered this section, use the **Reinforcement** and **Enrichment** masters or other OPTIONS provided.

Science and READING

Asimov gives us a comparison of Earth's size at a scale we can understand. If Earth were the size of a billiard ball, the oceans would be an unnoticeable film of dampness.

3 CLOSE

FLEX Your Brain

Use the Flex Your Brain activity to have students explore SALT MARSHES.

▶ Have a power plant engineer come to class to discuss how electricity is generated in your area.

SECTION REVIEW ANSWERS

1. It experiences the greatest tidal range in the world. There is a vast amount of energy in these tides.

2. When water is released from the dam, it pushes down over the turbines. The energy of the falling water makes the blades on the turbines spin. The energy of the spinning turbines allows generators to produce electricity.

YOU DECIDE!

Some students will say the benefits outweigh the problems. Because tidal power provides clean fuel, pollution in the area will be reduced and there will be no waste disposal problems. Another benefit is that new jobs will be created. Other students will argue that the destruction of human property and animal and plant habitats makes the building of this dam a bad idea.

Figure 11-14. Some salt marshes like this one will be flooded if a tidal power plant is built at the Bay of Fundy.

However, this dam will create some problems. Shores as far south as Boston, Massachusetts, 600 km away, will have greater tidal ranges than they do now. At low tide, some Boston harbor channels will become too shallow to use. At high tide, some farmlands and towns will be flooded. Water wells will become contaminated with salt water, and valuable salt-marsh habitats will be ruined. A **salt marsh** is the breeding ground of many ocean organisms. If these habitats are destroyed, these organisms will die.

Environmentalists fear that other problems will be created at the dam site. Many fish will be killed by the dam's turbines. Also, the mud flats at the Bay of Fundy, where many migrating birds feed on mud shrimp, will be flooded by the water retained behind the dam. The birds may not be able to find a substitute food source, and could starve to death.

Science and READING

In Isaac Asimov's *New Guide to Science,* he gives a great perspective on the oceans. Report to the class some of the interesting statistics he cites.

SECTION REVIEW

1. Why was the Bay of Fundy picked as a site to build a tidal power plant?
2. How does a tidal dam convert energy from tides into electricity?

You Decide!

When we make changes in our environment, we must consider the consequences. This certainly is the case with the building of a tidal dam at the Bay of Fundy. Consider the benefits and problems involved with the building of this dam. Do you think this tidal dam should be built?

OPTIONS

ENRICHMENT

▶ Have students investigate the similarities of tidal dams and dams built on rivers.

▶ Have students find out about the tidal dams that have been built in France, the U.S.S.R., and China.

▶ Have students work in small groups to make models of tidal power plants.

PROGRAM RESOURCES

From the **Teacher Resource Package** use:

Activity Worksheets, page 5, Flex Your Brain.

Science and Society, page 15, Salt Marshes.

CHAPTER

REVIEW

SUMMARY

11-1: Origin and Composition of Ocean Water

1. Water that fills Earth's oceans started as water vapor released from volcanoes. The water vapor condensed, and rain fell, forming the oceans over millions of years.

2. Groundwater and rivers weather rocks and cause some elements to dissolve. The dissolved elements are carried by rivers to the oceans. Volcanoes also add elements to seawater.

3. Nearly 90 percent of the salt in seawater is halite. Ocean water also contains calcium, silica, and many other substances.

11-2: Ocean Currents

1. Friction between air and the ocean's surface causes surface currents. Surface currents are affected by the Coriolis effect. Currents are also deflected by landmasses.

2. Currents off western coasts originate far from the equator and are cooler than currents on eastern coasts, which begin near the equator.

3. Differences in temperatures and densities between water masses in the ocean set up circulation patterns called density currents.

11-3: Ocean Waves and Tides

1. The crest is the highest point of a wave. The trough is the lowest point. Wave height is the vertical distance between crest and trough. Wavelength is the horizontal distance between two successive wave crests or troughs.

2. Particles of water in ocean waves move in circles, whereas the energy transmitted by the wave moves forward.

3. Wind can cause water to pile up and form waves. Waves called tides are due to the attraction among Earth, the moon, and the sun.

11-4: Science and Society: Tapping Tidal Energy

1. The Bay of Fundy is a good place for tapping tidal energy from tides.

2. A tidal dam has gates that are opened and closed to let water in and out of a bay. The water passes over turbines, which turn generators.

3. Energy from tides is essentially nonpolluting but can cause problems in tidal ranges at other locations. Flooding, contamination of freshwater wells, and damage to habitats are also drawbacks to using energy from tides.

KEY SCIENCE WORDS

a. **basins**
b. **breaker**
c. **crest**
d. **density current**
e. **salinity**
f. **salt marsh**
g. **surface current**
h. **tidal range**
i. **tides**
j. **trough**
k. **turbine**
l. **upwelling**
m. **wave height**
n. **wavelength**

UNDERSTANDING VOCABULARY

Match each phrase with the correct term from the list of Key Science Words.

1. low area that collects water
2. nutrient-rich water that comes to surface
3. a current at or near the surface
4. the lowest point of a wave
5. vertical distance between crests and troughs
6. horizontal difference between crests
7. the highest part of a wave
8. difference between high and low tide
9. spun by falling water to generate electricity
10. breeding place of many sea organisms

OPTIONS

ASSESSMENT

To assess student understanding of material in this chapter, use the resources listed.

COOPERATIVE LEARNING
Consider using cooperative learning in the THINK AND WRITE CRITICALLY, APPLY, and MORE SKILL BUILDERS sections of the Chapter Review.

PROGRAM RESOURCES

From the **Teacher Resource Package** use:

Chapter Review, pages 25-26.

Chapter and Unit Tests, pages 70-73, Chapter Test.

CHAPTER

REVIEW

SUMMARY

Have students read the summary statements to review the major concepts of the chapter.

UNDERSTANDING VOCABULARY

1. a
2. l
3. g
4. j
5. m
6. n
7. c
8. h
9. k
10. f

CHAPTER

REVIEW

CHECKING CONCEPTS

1. b
2. d
3. d
4. d
5. c
6. b
7. d
8. d
9. a
10. d

UNDERSTANDING CONCEPTS

11. basins
12. surface
13. Wavelength
14. gravity
15. Spring

THINK AND WRITE CRITICALLY

16. High tides are bulges of water on either side of Earth due to gravitational attraction among Earth, the sun, and the moon. Spring tides are tides that occur when Earth, the sun, and the moon are lined up. High tides are higher than normal during spring tides.

17. Both move ocean water from place to place. Surface currents are caused by the wind and affect only the upper few hundred meters of seawater. Density currents, on the other hand, occur due to density differences deep in the ocean.

18. Cold water sinks, forcing warmer water to rise. These movements create density currents in the oceans.

19. The crests come together, causing the wave to get taller. Eventually, the top of the wave moves faster than the bottom, which causes the wave to become lopsided.

20. Warm currents will tend to warm overlying air while cold currents will tend to cool the air in the area.

CHAPTER

REVIEW

CHECKING CONCEPTS

Choose the word or phrase that completes the sentence.

1. Water in Earth's oceans came from _______.
   a. salt marshes **c.** basins
   b. volcanoes **d.** surface currents
2. Calcium is carried into the ocean by _______.
   a. rivers **c.** volcanoes
   b. groundwater **d.** all of these
3. _______ is the most common ocean compound.
   a. Oxygen **c.** Silica
   b. Calcium **d.** None of these
4. Most surface currents are caused by _______.
   a. density differences **c.** temperature
   b. the Gulf Stream **d.** wind
5. The highest point on a wave is the _______.
   a. wave height **c.** crest
   b. trough **d.** wavelength
6. Ocean _______ are movements in which water alternately rises and falls.
   a. currents **c.** crests
   b. waves **d.** none of these
7. As waves move into shallow areas, _______.
   a. they slow down
   b. crests and troughs come together
   c. wave height increases
   d. all of these
8. Tides are due to _______ gravitational force.
   a. Earth's **c.** the sun's
   b. the moon's **d.** all of these
9. Tidal power plants use energy from _______.
   a. Earth's oceans **c.** the sun
   b. salt marshes **d.** floods
10. Tidal power plants have _______.
    a. no fuel expenses
    b. no waste to get rid of
    c. no pollution
    d. all of these

UNDERSTANDING CONCEPTS

Complete each sentence.

11. The depressions that hold ocean water are called _______.
12. The Coriolis effect causes _______ currents to be deflected.
13. _______ is the distance between two successive wave crests.
14. The force of _______ causes tides.
15. _______ tides occur when the sun, Earth, and the moon are lined up.

THINK AND WRITE CRITICALLY

16. How are spring tides different from high tides?
17. Compare and contrast surface and density currents.
18. Describe the effects of temperature on density currents.
19. What happens to a wave when it enters shallow water?
20. How can surface currents affect climate?

APPLY

21. Describe the position of the moon and sun if a low tide is higher than normal.
22. Halite makes up 90 percent of the salt in ocean water. How much halite is found in 1000 L of ocean water?
23. Why is ocean water low in silica and calcium?
24. A deep-water wave is one in which the depth is greater than one-half the wavelength. Would a wave with a 10-m wavelength in 8 m of water be a deep-water wave? Explain.
25. How can a tidal power plant in the Bay of Fundy prevent flooding in the area?

MORE SKILL BUILDERS

If you need help, refer to the Skill Handbook.

1. **Recognizing Cause and Effect:** What causes an upwelling?
2. **Comparing and Contrasting:** Compare and contrast wave height and wavelength.
3. **Graphing:** Plot the data provided in the table below on a sheet of graph paper. Label the vertical axis "Tide in Meters" and use a scale running upward from −0.6 m to 2.4 m. The horizontal axis should show days 1 to 30. Plot each data point for high tide and connect with a red pencil. Connect each data point for low tide with a blue pencil. Describe any pattern that you observe in the graphed data.
4. **Outlining:** Make an outline that discusses the pros and cons of tidal power.
5. **Interpreting Data:** Based on the information in this chapter, is there more sodium or calcium in the oceans? Explain your answer.

PROJECTS

1. Design an experiment to test the density of water at different temperatures. Make a table to record your observations and measurements.
2. Design a way to desalinate salt water without using a heat source.

Day	Height of high tide (meters)	Height of low tide (meters)	Day	Height of high tide (meters)	Height of low tide (meters)
1	1.4	0.5	16	1.6	0.2
2	1.5	0.4	17	1.7	0.1
3	1.7	0.2	18	1.7	−0.1
4	1.8	−0.1	19	1.8	−0.2
5	2.1	−0.3	20	1.9	−0.2
6	2.2	−0.5	21	1.9	−0.2
7	2.3	−0.6	22	1.9	−0.2
8	2.3	−0.6	23	1.9	−0.2
9	2.3	−0.6	24	1.8	−0.2
10	2.1	−0.5	25	1.7	−0.1
11	1.9	−0.2	26	1.6	0.0
12	1.6	−0.1	27	1.4	0.1
13	1.6	0.2	28	1.3	0.3
14	1.6	0.4	29	1.5	0.4
15	1.6	0.4	30	1.5	0.5

APPLY

21. Low tides are higher than normal when the sun, moon, and Earth form a right angle.
22. Every 1000 L contains 35 L of dissolved solids. Thus, 0.90 × 35 L = 31.5 L of halite in each 1000 L of saltwater.
23. Many marine organisms use these elements in their life processes, thus removing them from the ocean.
24. Yes, the depth is greater than 5 m; thus the wave is a deep-water wave.
25. Because the flow of water will be controlled by dams, less flooding is likely to occur in some areas if the power plant is constructed. However, other areas will experience more flooding.

MORE SKILL BUILDERS

1. Recognizing Cause and Effect: Overlying water is carried away from an area by wind. This removal of water allows underlying cold water to rise to the surface.
2. Comparing and Contrasting: Both are distances between points on a wave. Wave height is the vertical distance between a crest and trough. Wavelength is the horizontal distance between two successive crests or troughs.
3. Graphing: Students have made a graph that shows tidal range for a beach during one month. Students should observe that when high tides were highest, low tides were lowest. When high tides were lowest, low tides were usually highest. The graph shows small tidal range to great tidal range, to small, to great.
4. Outlining: Students' responses will vary but should at least include the points discussed in Section 11-4. Some students may be able to add other points to their outlines.
5. Interpreting Data: Because sodium isn't used by marine organisms as much as calcium is, there's more sodium in Earth's oceans.

CHAPTER

12 Exploring Oceans

CHAPTER SECTION	OBJECTIVES	ACTIVITIES
12-1 Shorelines (2 days)	1. **Describe** three forces that affect all shore zones. 2. **Contrast** steep shore zones and flat shore zones. 3. **List** some origins of sand.	**Activity 12-1:** *Beach Sand,* p. 311
12-2 The Seafloor (3 days)	1. **Differentiate** among the continental shelf, the continental slope, and the abyssal plain. 2. **Describe** rift zones, mid-ocean ridges, and ocean trenches.	**MINI-Lab:** *How can you model the ocean floor?* p. 314 **Activity 12-2:** *Ocean-Floor Profile,* p. 315
12-3 Life in the Ocean (2 days)	1. **List** six things that the ocean provides for organisms. 2. **Describe** the relationship between photosynthesis and respiration. 3. **List** the key characteristics of plankton, nekton, and benthos.	**MINI-Lab:** *What does plankton look like.* p. 319
12-4 Pollution and Marine Life Science & Society (1 day)	1. **List** seven human activities that pollute the ocean. 2. **Explain** how ocean pollution affects the entire world. 3. **Determine** how we can live on this planet without destroying its oceans.	
Chapter Review		

ACTIVITY MATERIALS

FIND OUT	ACTIVITIES		MINI-LABS	
Page 305 2-liter plastic bottle with cap water eye dropper	**12-1 Beach Sand, p. 311** 3 different types of beach sand stereomicroscope magnet	**12-2 Ocean-Floor Profile, p. 315** graph paper blue and brown pencils	**How can you model the ocean floor? p. 314** clay or plaster of paris newspaper Figures 12-7 and 12-8 paint (optional)	**What does plankton look like? p. 319** ocean or lake water containing microscopic organisms stereomicroscope glass depression slides eye droppers foraminifera, radiolaria, and/or diatoms

CHAPTER FEATURES	TEACHER RESOURCE PACKAGE	OTHER RESOURCES
Skill Builder: *Concept Mapping,* p. 310	**Ability Level Worksheets** ◆ ***Study Guide,*** p. 50 ● ***Reinforcement,*** p. 50 ▲ ***Enrichment,*** p. 50 **Activity Worksheet,** pp. 104-105 **Transparency Masters,** pp. 43-44	**Color Transparency 22,** Beach Landforms **Lab Manual:** *Waves, Currents, and Coastal Features,* p. 103 **Lab Manual:** *Profile of a Coastline,* p. 107
Skill Builder: *Comparing and Contrasting,* p. 314	**Ability Level Worksheets** ◆ ***Study Guide,*** p. 51 ● ***Reinforcement,*** p. 51 ▲ ***Enrichment,*** p. 51 **MINI-Lab Worksheet,** p. 110 **Activity Worksheet,** pp. 106-107 **Science and Society,** p. 16 **Transparency Masters,** pp. 45-48	**Color Transparency 23,** Atoll Formation **Color Transparency 24,** Ocean Floor Features
Technology: *Submersibles,* p. 317 **Skill Builder:** *Using Variables, Constants, and Controls,* p. 321	**Ability Level Worksheets** ◆ ***Study Guide,*** p. 52 ● ***Reinforcement,*** p. 52 ▲ ***Enrichment,*** p. 52 **MINI-Lab Worksheet,** p. 111 **Concept Mapping,** pp. 29-30 **Critical Thinking/Problem Solving,** p. 18	**Lab Manual:** *Ocean Life,* p. 111
Problem Solving: *Washed Ashore,* p. 323 **You Decide!** p. 324	**Ability Level Worksheets** ◆ ***Study Guide,*** p. 53 ● ***Reinforcement,*** p. 53 ▲ ***Enrichment,*** p. 53 **Cross-Curricular Connections,** p. 16 **Transparency Masters,** pp. 49-50	**Color Transparency 25,** Ocean Pollution
Summary Key Science Words Understanding Vocabulary Checking Concepts Understanding Concepts Think & Write Critically Apply More Skill Builders Projects	**Chapter Review,** pp. 27-28 **Chapter Test,** pp. 74-77 **Unit Test,** pp. 78-79	**Chapter Review Software** **Test Bank**

◆ **Basic** ● **Average** ▲ **Advanced**

ADDITIONAL MATERIALS

SOFTWARE	AUDIOVISUAL	BOOKS/MAGAZINES
Shore Features, CDL. *Shore Line Features,* American Peripherals.	*Challenge of the Oceans,* film, CRM Films. *Deep Sea Drilling Project,* film, Sterling Educational Films. *Earth Beneath the Sea,* film, CRM films. *Oceanography: A Voyage to Discovery,* film, Universal Education and Visual Arts. *The Beach: A River of Sand,* film, EBEC.	Cox, Vic. *Ocean Life: Beneath the Crystal Seas.* NY: BDD Promotional Book Company, Inc., 1990. Seibold, E. and W. Burger. *The Sea Floor: An Introduction to Marine Biology.* NY: Springer-Verlag New York, Inc., 1982. Thurman, Harold V. *Essentials of Oceanography.* 3rd ed. Columbus, OH: Merrill Publishing Co., 1990.

CHAPTER

12

EXPLORING OCEANS

THEME DEVELOPMENT: Scale and structure and systems and interactions are the themes of this chapter. The scale and structure of shore zones and ocean floor topography are presented. The systems and interactions themes include discussions of the interdependency of plankton, nekton, and benthos, and ways humans pollute oceans.

CHAPTER OVERVIEW

- **Section 12-1:** This section discusses forces that affect shore zones and contrasts features of steep and flat shore zones.
- **Section 12-2:** The scale, structure, and origin of ocean bottom features are described.
- **Section 12-3:** The interactions among plankton, nekton, and benthos are presented.
- **Section 12-4: Science and Society:** Some of the human activities that pollute oceans are discussed. The You Decide feature asks students to think of ways that people can maintain their lifestyles without polluting Earth's oceans.

CHAPTER VOCABULARY

shore zone
longshore current
beaches
barrier islands
continental shelf
continental slope
abyssal plain
rift zone
mid-ocean ridges
ocean trench
photosynthesis
respiration
chemosynthesis
plankton
nekton
benthos
reef
pollution
thermal pollution

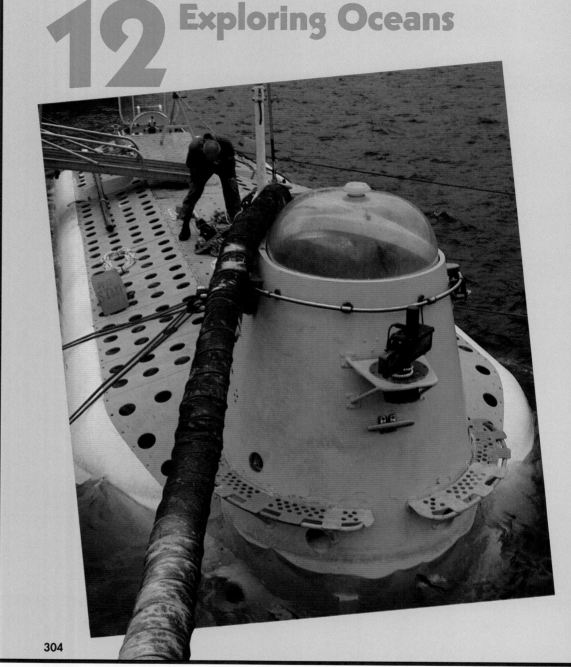

CHAPTER 12

Exploring Oceans

OPTIONS

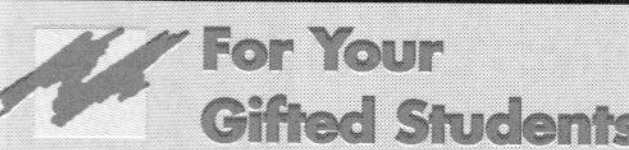

Have students research oil spills that occurred over the last 10 years. They can draw a map of the world and show the areas that have encountered oil spills. Students can make a graph showing the tonnes of oil spilled each year for the 10-year period.

The deep oceans have been a mystery for many years. Submarines called submersibles now allow humans to venture and observe deep into the ocean. How can submersibles dive and rise in the oceans?

FIND OUT!

Do this simple activity to find out how submersibles work.

Fill a 2-liter plastic bottle with water. Draw water into an eye dropper so that there is a small amount of air in the bulb of the dropper. Place the dropper in the plastic bottle. The bulb should be up and the dropper should float in the bottle. Now seal the bottle with its cap. By squeezing on the sides of the bottle, you can cause the dropper to "dive" to the bottom. By squeezing the sides of the bottle, you have compressed the tiny air bubble inside the bulb of the dropper. This decreased the volume of the air and let just enough water into the dropper to make it sink.

Gearing Up

Previewing the Chapter

Use this outline to help you focus on important ideas in this chapter.

Previewing Science Skills

- ▶ In the **Skill Builders**, you will make a concept map, compare and contrast, and use variables, constants, and controls.
- ▶ In the **Activities**, you will observe, classify, measure, infer, predict, use numbers, and hypothesize.
- ▶ In the **MINI-Labs**, you will observe and make a model.

What's next?

In this chapter, you'll first look at seashores and how the waves carve them. Then you'll discover that there are mountains and trenches on the seafloor much larger than ones on Earth's land masses. Finally, you'll meet the plants and creatures that live in the ocean and learn how they are threatened by pollution.

INTRODUCING THE CHAPTER

Use the Find Out activity to introduce students to how submersibles work. Inform students that in the Technology feature, they will be learning more about submersibles and how they can be used to explore ocean features such as ocean bottom structures, oceanic organisms, and ocean pollution.

FIND OUT!

Preparation: Several days before you begin this chapter, have each student bring in a clean, empty, 2-liter plastic bottle with a cap.

Materials: 2-liter plastic bottle with cap, eye dropper, and water for each student

Teaching Tips

▶ Make students aware that there will be a very delicate balance between floating and sinking for the eye dropper. It may take several tries to get the eye dropper to dive.

Gearing Up

Have students study the Gearing Up feature to familiarize themselves with the chapter. Discuss the relationships of the topics in the outline.

What's Next?

Before beginning the first section, make sure students understand the connection between the Find Out activity and the topics to follow.

For Your Mainstreamed Students

Have students make a mural showing a cross section of the ocean from the shore to mid ocean. They should show the diverse life that occurs both from ocean floor to surface and from shore to mid ocean.

SECTION 12-1

PREPARATION

SECTION BACKGROUND

▶ The movement of material along a shoreline is directly related to the velocity of the wind.

▶ Textural terms used to describe sediments are based on size, not composition. Below is a chart of sediment sizes.

Sediment Type	Diameter (mm)
sand	1/16 - 2
granules	2 - 4
pebbles	4 - 64
cobbles	64 - 256

▶ The Atlantic and Gulf Coasts of North America and the coasts of Holland and Poland are noted for their extensive barrier island beaches. Atlantic City, NJ, and Galveston, TX, are built on barrier islands.

PREPLANNING

▶ To prepare for Activity 12-1, obtain the following materials for each Science Investigation team: three different types of beach sand, a stereomicroscope, and a magnet.

1 MOTIVATE

▶ Obtain photographs or slides of various kinds of coastlines. Have students describe what they think may have caused the coastline features shown in each photograph.

FLEX Your Brain

Use the Flex Your Brain activity to have students explore SHORELINES.

PROGRAM RESOURCES

From the **Teacher Resource Package** use:

Activity Worksheets, page 5, Flex Your Brain.

12-1 Shorelines

New Science Words

shore zone
longshore current
beaches
barrier islands

Objectives

- ▶ Describe three forces that affect all shore zones.
- ▶ Contrast steep shore zones and flat shore zones.
- ▶ List some origins of sand.

Shore Zones

Picture yourself sitting on a beautiful white sand beach. Palm trees sway in the breeze above your head, and small children play in the quiet waves lapping at the water's edge. It's hard to imagine a place more peaceful than this shore. Now picture yourself sitting along another shore. You're on a high cliff, overlooking waves crashing onto huge boulders below.

What determines a shore zone?

Both of these settings are shore zones. A **shore zone** is the land area between the water's edge at high tide and the water's edge at low tide. You learned in Chapter 11 that tidal range is the difference in height between high and low tides, a few meters in most places. This produces a shore zone that often is hundreds of meters wide.

The two shore zones we just described are very different. Why are they so different? Both are subjected to the same forces. Both experience the same surface waves, tides, and currents. These cause both shore zones to con-

Figure 12-1. Waves cause shore zones to constantly change.

OPTIONS

Meeting Different Ability Levels

For Section 12-1, use the following **Teacher Resource Masters** depending upon individual students' needs.

◆ **Study Guide Master** for all students.

● **Reinforcement Master** for students of average and above average ability levels.

▲ **Enrichment Master** for above average students.

Additional Teacher Resource Package masters are listed in the OPTIONS box throughout the section. The additional masters are appropriate for all students.

◆ STUDY GUIDE 50

NAME ______ DATE ______ CLASS ______

STUDY GUIDE Chapter 12

Shorelines Text Pages 306–310

Each numbered list below gives some characteristics of one of the shoreline features in the box. Write the name of each shoreline feature above the correct list.

shore zone	flat shore zone	longshore current
steep shore zone	barrier islands	

1. steep shore zone
   - rocks
   - cliffs
   - caves
2. longshore current
   - colliding waves
   - running water
   - parallel to shore
3. shore zone
   - high tide
   - low tide
   - water's edge
4. barrier islands
   - sand deposits
   - separated from mainland
   - dunes
5. flat shore zone
   - beaches
   - sediment deposits
   - sands

*A **cause** is something that makes something happen. An **effect** is what happens. Write the part of the statement that is the cause and the part that is the effect on the lines provided.*

1. Shore zones change constantly because they experience the forces of tides, waves, and currents.
   effect: Shore zones change constantly.
   cause: Tides, waves, and currents are forces on shore zones.
2. When constant wave motion bumps sand grains together, the corners of the sand become rounded.
   effect: The corners of the sand become rounded.
   cause: Constant wave motion bumps sand grains together.
3. The more energy a longshore current has, the more it will erode shore zone sediments.
   effect: More shore zone sediments will be eroded.
   cause: A longshore current has extra energy.
4. Beaches have sand-sized particles because waves break rocks and seashells down.
   effect: Beaches have sand-sized particles.
   cause: Waves break rocks and seashells down.

50

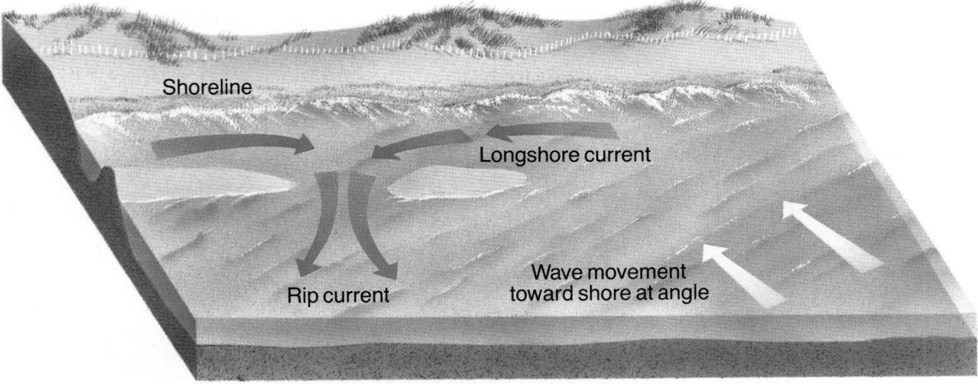

Figure 12-2. Waves approaching the shoreline at an angle cause a longshore current. Rip currents form where longshore currents meet and flow in a swift, narrow current out to sea.

stantly change. Sometimes you can see these changes from hour to hour. We'll look at why these shore zones are different, but first, let's learn about the forces that carve shores.

Along all shore zones, surface waves constantly move sediments. These waves move sediments back and forth across the shore zone. The waves shape shore zones by eroding them and by depositing sediments. The tides also shape shore zones. Every day they raise and lower 1
the place on the shore zone where surface waves erode and deposit sediment.

Waves usually collide with a shore at slight angles. This creates a **longshore current** of water that runs parallel to the shore. Longshore currents carry many metric tons of loose sediments and act like rivers of sand in the ocean. 2
What do you suppose happens if a longshore current isn't carrying all of the sand it has the energy to carry? It will use this extra energy to erode more shore zone sediments.

You've seen the forces that affect all shore zones. Now we'll look at the differences that make one shore a flat, sandy beach and another shore a steep, rocky cliff.

Steep Shore Zones

Along steep shore zones, rocks and cliffs are the most 3
common features. Waves scour the rocks to form hollows or notches. Over time, these enlarge and become caves. Rock fragments broken from the cliffs are ground up by the endless motion of waves. These fragments act like the sand on sandpaper.

TYING TO PREVIOUS KNOWLEDGE: Many students have visited shore zones. Others, who have not had this opportunity, have probably seen them on television. Have students recall the shore zone structures they have seen.

OBJECTIVES AND SCIENCE WORDS: Have students review the objectives and science words to become familiar with this section.

2 TEACH

Key Concepts are highlighted.

CONCEPT DEVELOPMENT

▶ If possible, take students to an ocean coastline to observe the effects of the longshore current.

▶ After students have read pages 306 and 307, ask the following questions. **How are caves created along steep shore zones?** *Waves scour the rocks to form hollows. Eventually, these hollows enlarge to become caves.* **What determines the direction of flow of a longshore current?** *The direction depends on the direction of the waves striking the beach. For example, if the waves are striking from the north, the longshore current will flow to the south.* **What causes shore zones to change?** *Waves, tides, and longshore currents cause sediments to be eroded from some areas and deposited in others.*

● REINFORCEMENT 50

NAME ______ DATE ______ CLASS ______

REINFORCEMENT — Chapter 12

Shorelines — Text Pages 306–310

For each item, write every other letter, beginning with the first letter, on line a. Next, beginning with the second letter, write every other letter on line b. Add spaces between words in a and b. Then on line c, write an explanation of the relationship between the terms in lines a and b.

1. SSTHEOERPEFZLOANTE
   a. steep flat
   b. shore zone
   c. There are two types of shore zones—steep and flat. Cliffs and caves are characteristic of steep shore zones, and beaches are features of flat shore zones.
2. NBOATRORNIAEMRAIISNLLAANNDDS
   a. not on a mainland
   b. barrier islands
   c. Barrier islands are sand deposits that parallel the shore but are separated from the mainland.
3. PLAORNAGLSLHEOLRSETCHUERSRHEONRTE
   a. parallels the shore
   b. longshore current
   c. Waves colliding with a shore at slight angles create a longshore current of water that runs parallel to the shore.
4. SBEEDAICMHEENST
   a. sediment
   b. beaches
   c. Beaches are deposits of sediment that parallel the shore and extend out under the water.
5. TSIUDREFSACCUERWRAEVNETSS
   a. tides, currents
   b. surface waves
   c. All shore zones are subjected to the forces of tides, currents, and surface waves.

50

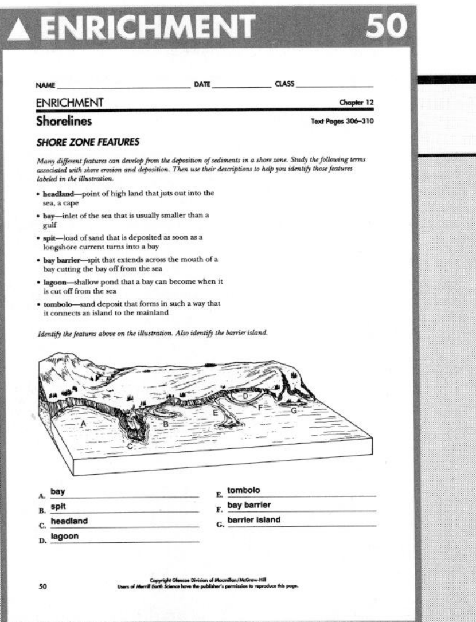

▲ ENRICHMENT 50

NAME ______ DATE ______ CLASS ______

ENRICHMENT — Chapter 12

Shorelines — Text Pages 306–310

SHORE ZONE FEATURES

Many different features can develop from the deposition of sediments in a shore zone. Study the following terms associated with shore erosion and deposition. Then use their descriptions to help you identify those features labeled in the illustration.

- **headland**—point of high land that juts out into the sea, a cape
- **bay**—inlet of the sea that is usually smaller than a gulf
- **spit**—load of sand that is deposited as soon as a longshore current turns into a bay
- **bay barrier**—spit that extends across the mouth of a bay cutting the bay off from the sea
- **lagoon**—shallow pond that a bay can become when it is cut off from the sea
- **tombolo**—sand deposit that forms in such a way that it connects an island to the mainland

Identify the features above on the illustration. Also identify the barrier island.

A. bay
B. spit
C. headland
D. lagoon
E. tombolo
F. bay barrier
G. barrier island

50

CONCEPT DEVELOPMENT

▶ **What is a beach?** *A beach is a deposit that is parallel to a shore.*

▶ Whether sand grains are rounded or angular depends upon time and the weathering processes to which they are exposed. Obtain some angular sand grains and some beach sand. Have students observe the samples and determine that beach sand grains are well rounded.

▶ To help students understand the dynamic nature of a beach area, show films featuring beach environments.

CONCEPT DEVELOPMENT

▶ Explain that a severe storm can drastically change a coastline in a short period of time. Obtain some "before" and "after" photos of areas struck by Hurricane Hugo to stress this concept.

CROSS CURRICULUM

▶ **Economics:** Many coastal cities depend on tourism to help the local economy. When beaches disappear because of erosion, tourists do not visit. For this reason, many cities have spent a lot of money to preserve their beaches. Have students research the costs involved in dredging and building sea walls.

Softer rocks are eroded away before harder rocks, leaving islands of harder rocks. This takes many years, but remember that the ocean never sleeps. In your lifetime, more than 200 million waves will crash onto any shore.

The rock fragments produced by eroding waves are sediment. When steep shore zones are being eroded away, where do you think the sediment goes? Waves carry it away and deposit it where water is quieter. If you want to go to a beach, you probably won't find one where the shore zone is steep.

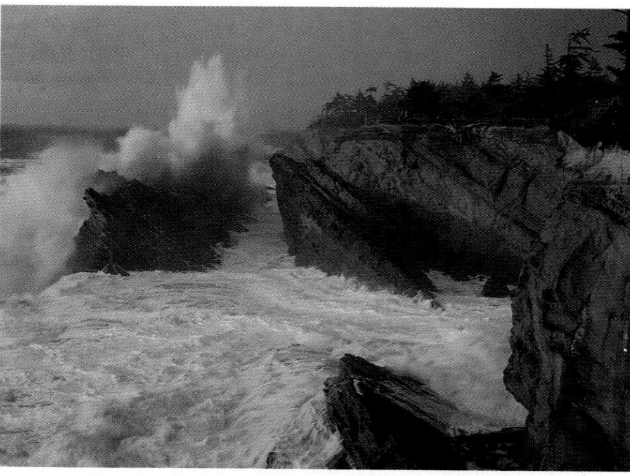

Figure 12-3. A steep, rocky shore zone.

Flat Shore Zones

Flat shore zones are quite different from steep shore zones. Beaches are the main feature here. **Beaches** are deposits of sediment that run parallel to the shore. They extend inland as far as the tides and waves are able to deposit sediment. Beaches also extend out under the water to a depth of 9 to 40 m below the water surface.

What defines the area of a beach?

Beaches are made of different materials. Some are made of rock fragments from the shore zone, and others consist of seashell fragments. These fragments range from pebbles large enough to fill your hand to fine sand. Sand grains are 1/16 to 2 mm in diameter. Why do most beaches have sand-size particles? This is because waves break rocks and seashells down to sand-size particles. The constant wave motion bumps sand grains together and, in the process, rounds their corners.

OPTIONS

INQUIRY QUESTIONS

▶ **How did Galveston Island form?** *Galveston is a barrier island that formed as hurricanes added sediment to underwater sand ridges. This caused the ridges to rise above sea level and become a barrier island.*

PROGRAM RESOURCES

From the **Teacher Resource Package** use:

Transparency Masters, pages 43-44, Beach Landforms.

Use **Color Transparency** number 22, Beach Landforms.

Use **Laboratory Manual** page 103, Waves, Currents and Coastal Features; and page 107, Profile of a Coastline.

Figure 12-4. Sand varies in size and composition. This sand is made of shell fragments.

4 What kinds of materials do you think are in most beach sands? Most are made of resistant minerals such as quartz. However, sands in some places are composed of other things. For example, Hawaii's black sands are made of basalt, and green sands are made of the mineral olivine. Jamaica's white sands are made of coral and shell fragments.

Sand constantly is carried down beaches by longshore currents. When a longshore current loses velocity, it drops its load of sediment to form structures that you can see in Figure 12-5. Sand is also moved by storms and the wind. Thus, beaches are fragile, temporary features that are easily damaged by storms and human activities such as construction.

How does sediment get deposited to form barrier islands?

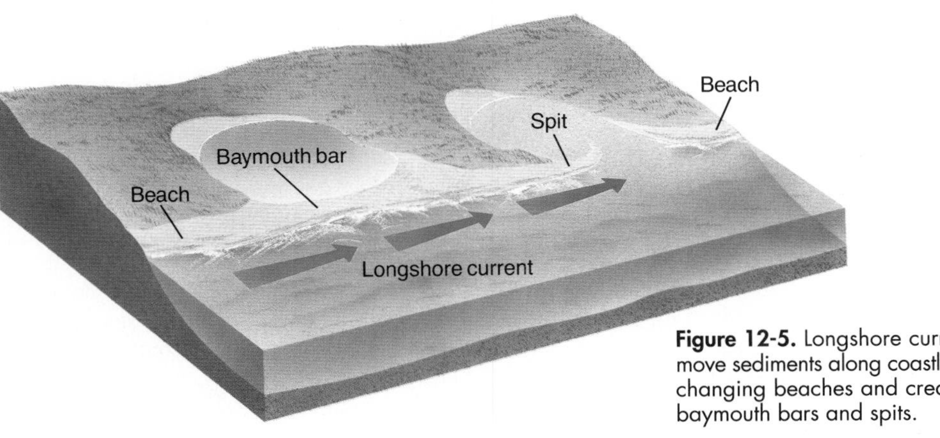

Figure 12-5. Longshore currents move sediments along coastlines, changing beaches and creating baymouth bars and spits.

CHECK FOR UNDERSTANDING

Use the Mini Quiz to check for understanding.

MINI QUIZ

Use the Mini Quiz to check students' recall of chapter content.

1. **____ raise and lower the place on the shore zone where surface waves erode and deposit sediment every day.** *Tides*
2. **____ currents are "rivers of sand" along an ocean shoreline.** *Longshore*
3. **Rocks, cliffs, and caves are common features along _____ shore zones.** *steep*
4. **The most common mineral found in beach sand is _____ .** *quartz*

RETEACH

Show students the same photographs or slides from the Motivate activity on page 306. Have students identify and give reasons for each erosional feature shown in each photograph.

EXTENSION

For students who have mastered this section, use the **Reinforcement** and **Enrichment** masters or other OPTIONS provided.

ENRICHMENT

▶ Have students research how the shape and composition of beach sand differ on the dune, berm, and foreshore of a beach. If possible, have students examine sands from these three locations on the same beach. They will observe that the wind and water have sorted the samples.

▶ Have students research the successfulness of building jetties, floating objects offshore, or burying large plastic tubes of sand on beaches to prevent erosion.

3 CLOSE

► Use an atlas map of the U.S. to show students barrier islands along the coasts of the Carolinas, Georgia, Florida, and Texas.
► Ask questions 1-3 and the **Apply** Question in the Section Review.

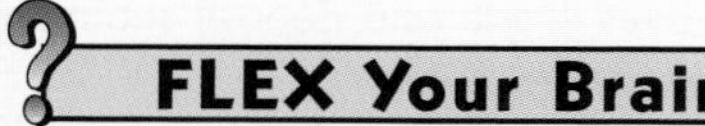

Use the Flex Your Brain activity to have students explore BEACH EROSION.
► Have students do Activity 12-1 on page 311.

SECTION REVIEW ANSWERS

1. waves, tides, and longshore currents
2. Most features of steep shore zones are formed as a result of the erosion of soft materials. The more resistant rocks are left behind to form cliffs and caves. Most features of flat shore zones are created by deposition. Beaches are common along flat shore zones.
3. Sand is resistant sediment eroded from the shore zone rocks, coral and shell fragments, or deposited by rivers that flow to the ocean.
4. Apply: Waves and currents continually change a shore zone. On steep coasts, rock fragments are carried away by waves and deposited elsewhere. Also, many beaches are made of fragments that are too large to be classified as sand.

Skill Builder

Possible Solution:

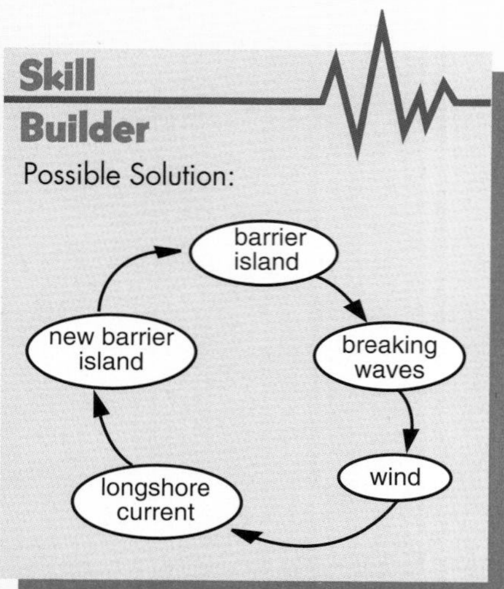

Figure 12-6. The size and shape of barrier islands constantly change due to wave action.

How does a barrier island remain above sea level?

Barrier islands are sand deposits that parallel the shore but are separated from the mainland. North America's Atlantic Coast and the Gulf of Mexico have many barrier islands. These islands start as underwater sand ridges, formed by breaking waves. Hurricanes and storms add sediment to them, raising some to sea level. Once a barrier island is exposed, the wind blows its loose sand into dunes, keeping the island above sea level. As with all seashore features, barrier islands are temporary, lasting from a few years to a few centuries.

Shore zones of all types change constantly due to erosion and deposits from waves, tides, and longshore currents. Storms can alter a shore zone in only minutes. Our beautiful beaches are fragile, temporary features.

SECTION REVIEW

1. What three forces affect all shore zones?
2. Contrast the features you'd find in a steep shore zone with the features you'd find in a flat shore zone.
3. List some origins of sand.
4. **Apply:** Why is there no sand on many of the world's shorelines?

Concept Mapping

Make a cycle concept map that discusses how the sand from a barrier island that is currently in place can become a barrier island 100 years from now. Use these terms: *barrier island, breaking waves, wind, longshore currents,* and *new barrier island.* If you need help, refer to Concept Mapping in the **Skill Handbook** on page 688.

OPTIONS

PROGRAM RESOURCES

From the **Teacher Resource Package** use:

Activity Worksheets, page 5, Flex Your Brain.

ACTIVITY 12-1
Beach Sand

Problem: *What are some characteristics of beach sand?*

Materials
- 3 samples of different types of beach sand
- stereomicroscope
- magnet

Procedure
1. Use the stereomicroscope to examine the sand samples. Copy the data table and record your observations of each sample.
2. Describe the color of each sample.
3. Describe the average roundness of the grains in each sample.
4. Place sand grains from one of your samples in the middle of the circle of the sand gauge shown below the table. Use the upper half of the circle for dark-colored particles, and the bottom half of the circle for light-colored particles. Determine the average size of the grains.
5. Repeat Steps 2-4 for the other two samples.
6. Pour a small amount of sand from one sample into your hand. Describe its texture as "smooth," "rough," or "sharp." Repeat for the other two samples.
7. Describe the luster of the grains as "shiny" or "dull."
8. Determine if a magnet will attract grains in any of the samples.
9. Try to identify the types of fragments that make up your samples. Record the compositions in a table like the one shown.

Analyze
1. Were the grains of a particular sample generally the same size? Explain.
2. Were they generally the same shape?

Conclude and Apply
3. What are some characteristics of beach sand?
4. Why are there differences in the characteristics of different sand samples?

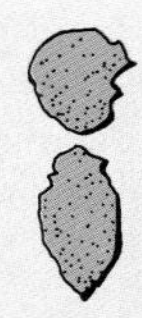

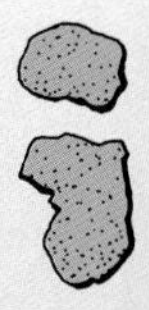

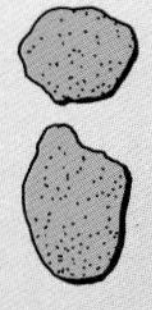

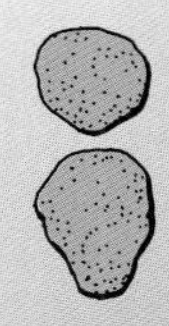

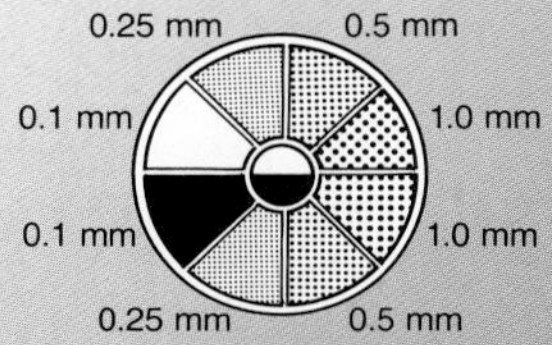

Data and Observations

Sample Data

Sample	Color	Roundness	Grain Size	Texture	Luster	Composition
1	white	rounded	1 mm	smooth	shiny	Quartz
2						
3						

ANSWERS TO QUESTIONS
1. Usually, the grains will have been sorted by size.
2. If the sand is made of only one type of material, the grains will generally be the same shape. However, if the sand is a mixture of materials, the shapes may be quite varied.
3. color, roundness, grain size, texture, luster, and composition
4. The length of time exposed to weathering, the parent material, and erosion by wind and/or water determine the characteristics of sand in a given location.

ACTIVITY 12-1
25-30 minutes

OBJECTIVE: Differentiate among three kinds of beach sand.

PROCESS SKILLS applied in this activity:
▶ **Observing** in Procedure Steps 1-9.
▶ **Interpreting Data** in Analyze Questions 1 and 2 and Conclude and Apply Questions 3 and 4.
▶ **Measuring** in Procedure Step 4.
▶ **Inferring** in Procedure Steps 2, 3, 6, 7, and 8.
▶ **Communicating** in Procedure Steps 1-9.

COOPERATIVE LEARNING Form Science Investigation groups of three students per group to execute this activity.

TEACHING THE ACTIVITY
▶ If local beach sand is available, use it. Because of sorting by the wind and water, sand composition can be quite varied even at different locations of the same beach.
▶ Samples of beach sands may also be obtained from scientific supply distributors.
Alternate Materials: If stereomicroscopes are not available, monocular microscopes with top illumination will work. Hand lenses may be preferable, however.
Troubleshooting: Advise students to be careful not to mix the sand samples. They will need to examine only a small quantity of sand. When they are finished with a sample, they should dispose of it, not try to put it back into the original container.

PROGRAM RESOURCES
From the **Teacher Resource Package** use:
Activity Worksheets, pages 104-105, Activity 12-1: Beach Sand.

PREPARATION

SECTION BACKGROUND

▶ When the last ice age was at its peak, sea level was 110 meters lower than it is today. Many of the structures on the continental shelf were at or above sea level.

▶ Continental slopes drop off at an average rate of 70 meters for every kilometer of horizontal distance. The slopes mark the boundary between continental crust and oceanic crust.

1 MOTIVATE

▶ Ask each student to write a paragraph that begins with: "Many landforms were revealed the day that the oceans suddenly disappeared. I saw..." This activity will lead to a discussion of topographic features of ocean basins.

▶ Have students examine bathymetric maps of the Pacific, Atlantic, and Indian Ocean basins. Have them describe the features they see. These maps are available from scientific catalog companies and from the National Geographic Society.

TEACHER F.Y.I.

▶ Three percent of the water-covered Earth is continental shelf. Continental shelves average 68 km wide and 55-64 m deep.

TYING TO PREVIOUS KNOWLEDGE: Have students recall from Chapter 8 that the major landforms on the continents are plains, plateaus, and mountains. Ask students to compare and contrast the topography of the ocean bottom with the topography of the continents.

12-2 The Seafloor

New Science Words

continental shelf
continental slope
abyssal plain
rift zone
mid-ocean ridges
ocean trench

Objectives

- ▶ **Differentiate among the continental shelf, the continental slope, and the abyssal plain.**
- ▶ **Describe rift zones, mid-ocean ridges, and ocean trenches.**

Continental Shelf, Slope, and Abyssal Plain

Where can you find the biggest mountains, the deepest valleys, and the flattest plains on Earth? They are at the bottom of the ocean. But the mountains, valleys, and plains there are different from those on the continents.

What is the ocean floor called closest to the shoreline?

1 Beyond every shoreline, out under the ocean, extends a flat part of the continent called the **continental shelf.** Along some coasts the continental shelf is wide. For example, on North America's East Coast and Gulf Coast, it's 100-200 km wide. But on coasts where mountains are close to shore, as in California, the shelf is 10-30 km wide. The continental shelf slopes gently out into the ocean. But at the end of the shelf, it dips steeply, forming the **continental slope.**

Think of a large swimming pool. It is much like an ocean basin. The side of the pool is like the continental slope, and the bottom of the pool is the seafloor. The

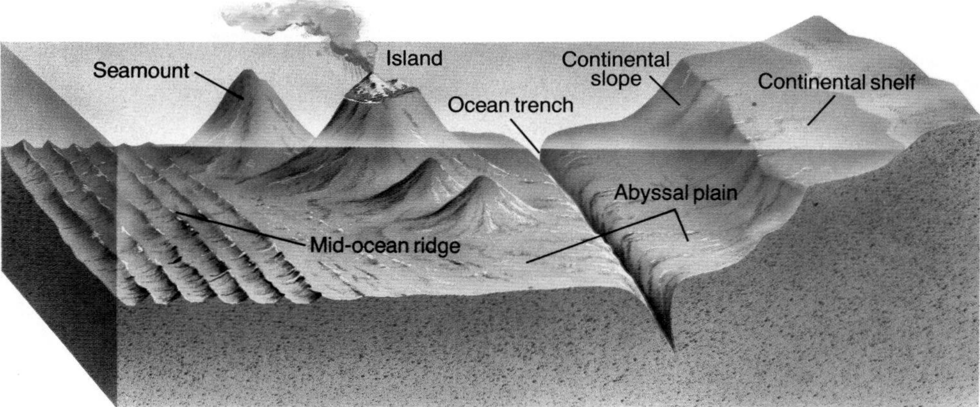

Figure 12-7. This illustration shows some of the features of the ocean floor.

OPTIONS

Meeting Different Ability Levels

For Section 12-2, use the following **Teacher Resource Masters** depending upon individual students' needs.

◆ **Study Guide Master** for all students.

● **Reinforcement Master** for students of average and above average ability levels.

▲ **Enrichment Master** for above average students.

Additional Teacher Resource Package masters are listed in the OPTIONS box throughout the section. The additional masters are appropriate for all students.

◆ STUDY GUIDE 51

NAME ______ DATE ______ CLASS ______

STUDY GUIDE — Chapter 12

The Seafloor — Text Pages 312–314

Write the term that matches each description below on the spaces provided. Then complete Item 9.

1. S [E] A M O U N T
2. A B Y S S A L P [L] A I N
3. C [O] N T I N E N T A L S L O P E
4. I S L [A] N D
5. C O N T I N E N T A L [S] H E L F
6. R I [F] T Z O N E
7. O C E A N T [R] E N C H
8. M I D-[O] C E A N R I D G E S

1. Volcano formed underwater that does not rise above sea level
2. Flat seafloor in the deep ocean formed when deposits of sediment filled valleys
3. Steeply-dipping area at the end of the continental shelf
4. Volcano formed underwater that rises above sea level
5. Gently-sloping part of the continent that extends underwater
6. System of cracks that form where the seafloor is spreading apart
7. Deep ocean valley that forms when one part of the seafloor is pushed beneath another part
8. Underwater mountain chains that form when forces within Earth cause the seafloor to spread apart at rifts and then to buckle
9. Write the letters in the boxes on the lines provided. Then unscramble the letters to complete the sentence that follows.

E L O A S F R O

All of the features identified in this activity are part of the seafloor.

51

seafloor is where you find the flattest areas on Earth. This is because currents deposit sediments from the continental shelves and slopes onto the bottom. These deposits fill in valleys, creating a flat seafloor in the deep ocean called an **abyssal** (a BIHS uhl) **plain.** 

Figure 12-8. This map shows that ocean basins have mountains, valleys, and plains.

Rifts, Ridges, and Trenches

Study the ocean floor map shown in Figure 12-8. Down the middle of some oceans, you can see a system of cracks in the seafloor. These cracks form a **rift zone,** where the seafloor is spreading apart. One rift zone extends southward from Iceland through the center of the Atlantic Ocean. From these cracks, hot lava oozes from Earth's interior. This lava is quickly chilled by the seawater and becomes solid rock, forming new seafloor.

Alongside rift zones you can see underwater mountain ❸ chains called **mid-ocean ridges.** They form because forces within Earth spread the seafloor apart at rifts, causing the seafloor to buckle. Along the mid-ocean ridges you'll find volcanoes. They build up mountains underwater, just as they do on land. A volcano forms an island if it rises above sea level. If it doesn't break the surface, it's called a seamount. The rift zone extending southward from Iceland runs through the Mid-Atlantic Ridge, which is 500 to 5000 km wide and 65 000 km long.

Did You Know?

Until 1977 only five percent of the ocean floor had been charted. NASA's Seasat measured the other 95 percent in only three months in 1978.

● REINFORCEMENT 51

NAME ______ DATE ______ CLASS ______

REINFORCEMENT Chapter 12

The Seafloor Text Pages 312-314

Define or describe each of the following terms.

1. continental shelf **a gently sloping part of the continent that extends out under the water along coastlines**
2. abyssal plain **the broad, flat ocean floor created when deposits fill in valleys**
3. mid-ocean ridge **underwater mountain ranges formed from the buckled seafloor alongside rift zones**
4. continental slope **steeply slanting part of the ocean floor at the end of the continental shelf**
5. seamount **volcano-shaped underwater mountain that does not extend above the surface of the water**
6. ocean trench **long, deep underwater valleys formed when one part of the seafloor is pushed beneath another part of the seafloor**

Use the numbers of the terms above to label this diagram of the ocean floor.

Sea level
1 Continent 4 2 5 3 2 6 Continent

Circle the term in parentheses that best completes each statement.

7. Mid-ocean ridges form because forces within Earth spread the seafloor apart at (rift zones, abyssal plains), causing the seafloor to buckle.
8. Many ocean (plains, trenches) are longer and deeper than valleys on the continents.
9. The flat seafloor in the deep ocean is called the (continental shelf, abyssal plain).
10. At (rift zones, ocean trenches), lava becomes solid rock to form new seafloor.
11. The gently sloping part of a continent that extends underwater is the (continental slope, continetal shelf)
12. A volcano that rises above the ocean's surface is (an island, a seamount).

 51

▲ ENRICHMENT 51

NAME ______ DATE ______ CLASS ______

ENRICHMENT Chapter 12

The Seafloor Text Pages 312-314

FINDING OCEAN DEPTH

Use the information, table, and graph to answer the questions.

Oceanographers know, with sonar, how fast sound waves travel in water. Thus they know how far the waves travel during their round trip to the surface. Half this distance is the depth of the ocean at that spot. The formula used to find the ocean floor depth is

$$D = \frac{1}{2} t \times v$$

In the formula, D stands for depth, t for time between sending and receiving, and v for the velocity or speed of sound in water. The speed of sound in water is 1524 meters per second.

The table below gives you some sonar sounding data. Calculate the ocean floor depth for each sounding. Then plot these depths on the graph below. Smoothly connect the depth points and you will have a cross-sectional map of the South Atlantic Ocean floor. (Note: These data are rounded approximations.)

Station	Time for signal to return (s)	Depth (m)	Station	Time for signal to return (s)	Depth (m)
1	6.0	4572			
2	5.2	3962	6	2.4	1829
3	4.0	3048	7	4.0	3048
4	2.4	1829	8	5.2	3962
5	3.2	2438	9	6.0	4572

Station 1 2 3 4 5 6 7 8 9
Depth (m) 0 (Sea level) 2000 4000 6000
West ← 3000 km → East

1. From what point do oceanographers measure depth? **sea level**
2. At which station(s) is the ocean deepest? **Stations 1 and 9**
3. At which station(s) is the ocean the most shallow? **Stations 4 and 6**
4. What large ocean floor feature is evident in the cross-sectional map? **mid-ocean ridge**

 51

OBJECTIVES AND SCIENCE WORDS: Have students review the objectives and science words to become familiar with this section.

2 TEACH

Key Concepts are highlighted.

CONCEPT DEVELOPMENT

▶ Obtain bathymetric maps and refer to them frequently throughout the remainder of this section. Have students contrast the width of the continental shelf off the east coast of the United States with that off the west coast.

CROSS CURRICULUM

▶ **Social Studies:** Inform students that there are many valuable mineral deposits on the ocean floor. Ask: **Who owns these deposits?** Students should realize that this question is a topic of international law. Have them research the United Nations Law of the Sea conference that began in 1958.

CHECK FOR UNDERSTANDING

Use the Mini Quiz to check for understanding.

MINI QUIZ

Use the Mini Quiz to check students' recall of chapter content.

❶ **The flat part of the continent that extends out from the continent under ocean water is the _____ .** *continental shelf*

❷ **_____ are the flattest areas on Earth.** *Abyssal plains*

❸ **Alongside rift zones are mountain chains called _____ .** *mid-ocean ridges*

RETEACH

Repeat the Motivate activity on page 312. Ask students to describe the scenery along the ocean basin from New York to Africa.

EXTENSION

For students who have mastered this section, use the **Reinforcement** and **Enrichment** masters or other OPTIONS provided.

MINI-Lab

Materials: clay, plaster of paris, newspaper, Figures 12-7 and 12-8

Teaching Tips

▶Tell students that they shouldn't be concerned with scale in their models, but they should be concentrating on placement of features.

Answer to Question

Beach, continental shelf, continental slope

3 CLOSE

▶ Have students do Activity 12-2.

FLEX Your Brain

Use the Flex Your Brain activity to have students explore SEAFLOOR TOPOGRAPHY.

▶ Ask questions 1-2 and the **Apply** Question in the Section Review.

SECTION REVIEW ANSWERS

1. The shelf is a flat, wide extension of a continent. The slope is a very steep extension of the shelf.

2. At rift zones, hot lava oozes from Earth's interior and cools to form new seafloor.

3. Apply: Seamounts are completely below sea level. The "tops" of volcanic islands are above sea level.

Skill Builder

The continental shelf is a flat, wide extension of a continent. The continental slope is the steep slope at the boundary between the continental shelf and the ocean basin floor. Well beyond the slope is the flat part of the ocean called the abyssal plain.

Figure 12-9. If Earth's tallest mountain, Mt. Everest, was set in the bottom of the Marianas Trench, it would still be covered with more than 2000 meters of water.

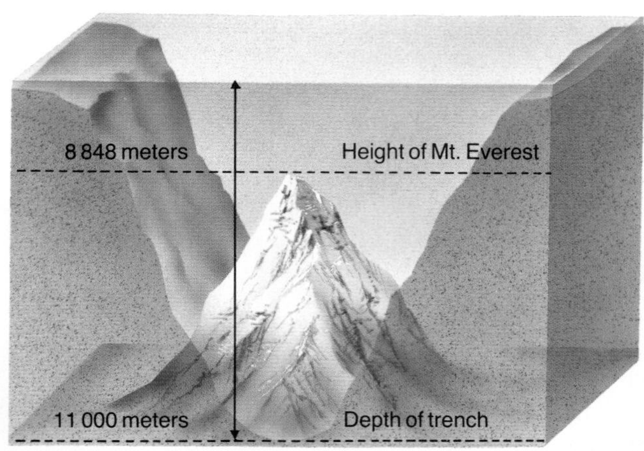

MINI-Lab

How can you model the ocean floor?

Use clay, or plaster of paris and newspaper, to make a model of coastal features and the ocean floor. Use Figures 12-7 and 12-8 as examples and label all of the features. You could also make the model realistic by painting it. What are the features located close to the shorelines?

While forces spread the seafloor apart at rift zones, in other places these forces are shoving pieces of the seafloor against each other. Where one piece of seafloor is pushed beneath another one, a deep **ocean trench** may form. Many oceanic trenches are longer and deeper than any valley you can see on the continents. For example, the Marianas Trench is the Pacific Ocean's deepest place, almost 11 km deep. By contrast, the Grand Canyon is about 1.6 km deep.

You'll learn more about these features of the seafloor in Chapter 13 when you study plate tectonics. Plate tectonics explains how many of the features on land and underwater are formed.

SECTION REVIEW

1. How do the continental shelf and the continental slope differ?
2. What happens at a rift zone?
3. **Apply:** What's the difference between an island and a seamount?

Skill Builder — ☑ Comparing and Contrasting

Compare and contrast the continental shelf, the continental slope, and the abyssal plain. If you need help, refer to Comparing and Contrasting in the **Skill Handbook** on page 683.

OPTIONS

PROGRAM RESOURCES

From the **Teacher Resource Package** use:

Science and Society, page 16, The Chunnel.

Activity Worksheets, Mini-Lab: How can you model the ocean floor? p. 110.

Transparency Masters, pages 45-46, Atoll Formation; and pages 47-48, Ocean Floor Features.

Use **Color Transparency** number 23, Atoll Formation; and number 24, Ocean Floor Features.

INQUIRY QUESTIONS

▶**Have the ocean basins always been in the same locations as they are today? Explain.** *No, the locations of oceans have changed throughout geologic time because of rifting and other forces, and climatic changes.*

▶**Is the Atlantic Ocean getting bigger or smaller? Explain.** *Rifting is occurring in the Atlantic Ocean. The seafloor is spreading, and thus the basin is getting wider.*

ACTIVITY 12-2
Ocean-Floor Profile

Problem: *How can you make a profile of the ocean floor?*

Materials
- graph paper

Procedure
1. Set up a graph as shown.
2. Examine the data listed in the data table. This information was collected at 29 oceanographic locations in the Atlantic Ocean. Each station was along the 39° north latitude line from New Jersey to Portugal.
3. Plot each data point listed on the table. Then connect the points with a smooth line.

Analyze
1. What ocean-floor structures occur between 160 and 1050 km from the coast of New Jersey? Between 2000 and 4500 km? Between 5300 and 5600 km?
2. You have constructed a profile of the ocean floor along the 39°N latitude line. If a profile is drawn to represent an accurate scale model of a feature, both the horizontal and vertical scales of the profile will be the same. What is the vertical scale of your profile? What is the horizontal scale?
3. Does the profile you have drawn give an accurate picture of the ocean floor? Explain.

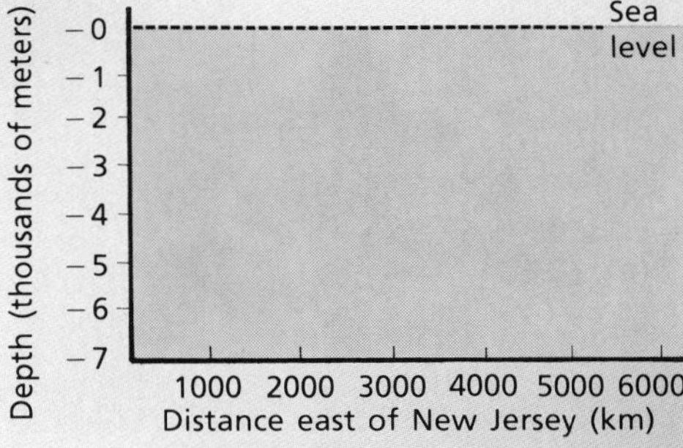

Data and Observations

Station Number	Distance from New Jersey (km)	Depth to Ocean Floor (m)
1	0	0
2	160	165
3	200	1800
4	500	3500
5	800	4600
6	1050	5450
7	1450	5100
8	1800	5300
9	2000	5600
10	2300	4750
11	2400	3500
12	2600	3100
13	3000	4300
14	3200	3900
15	3450	3400
16	3550	2100
17	3600	1330
18	3700	1275
19	3950	1000
20	4000	0
21	4100	1800
22	4350	3650
23	4500	5100
24	5000	5000
25	5300	4200
26	5450	1800
27	5500	920
28	5600	180
29	5650	0

ACTIVITY 12-2
30-40 minutes

OBJECTIVE: Make and **analyze** a profile map of the ocean floor.

PROCESS SKILLS applied in this activity:
▶ **Communicating** in Procedure Steps 1 and 3.
▶ **Inferring** in Analyze Question 3.
▶ **Using Numbers** in Procedure Steps 1 and 3 and Analyze Questions 1 and 2.
▶ **Interpreting Data** in Analyze Questions 1-3.

TEACHING THE ACTIVITY

Troubleshooting: Be sure that students realize that the graph is set up in a form that is different from what they may be used to. Usually, zero is at the bottom of the vertical axis. However, on this graph, it is at the top of the vertical axis. Students may become confused and reverse the data as they begin to plot the points. By walking around the room and checking student progress, many problems can be eliminated.

PROGRAM RESOURCES

From the **Teacher Resource Package** use:

Activity Worksheets, pages 106-107, Activity 12-2: Ocean-Floor Profile.

ANSWERS TO QUESTIONS

1. A continental slope occurs between 160 and 1050 km. The mid-Atlantic Ridge and a rift valley occur between 2000 and 4500 km from New Jersey. A continental slope lies between 5300 and 5600 km from New Jersey.

2. The vertical scale is 1 unit = 1000 meters. The horizontal scale is 1 unit = 1000 kilometers.

3. No, the profile has tremendous vertical exaggeration. To make an accurate profile, the vertical and horizontal scales must be the same.

SECTION 12-3

PREPARATION

SECTION BACKGROUND

▶ Factors such as temperature, light, nutrients, oxygen, substrate, and pollution limit where particular marine organisms can live.

▶ Ninety percent of marine species live on continental shelves, around islands, or on rises less than 200 meters below sea level.

▶ Corals grow best in shallow water where sunlight reaches the reef because corals often exist symbiotically with algae, which need the sunlight to photosynthesize. The algae are dietetic supplements to the coral and rid the coral of some wastes. The algae benefit because they are provided with protected places to live.

PREPLANNING

▶ To prepare for the Mini-Lab, obtain marine or freshwater plankton and microscopes.

1 MOTIVATE

▶ Maintain a saltwater aquarium in the classroom. If this is not possible, take students to a pet store where they can observe various kinds of marine organisms.

▶ Tell students that some scientists predict future societies will live in oceanic cities. Ask students to list drawbacks of such cities. Students may discuss the inability of people to breathe underwater and problems involved with waves and currents, the rough terrain, and the pressure of the overlying water. Ask students how marine organisms are able to survive under these conditions.

12-3 Life in the Ocean

New Science Words

photosynthesis
respiration
chemosynthesis
plankton
nekton
benthos
reef

Objectives

▶ List six things that the ocean provides for organisms.
▶ Describe the relationship between photosynthesis and respiration.
▶ List the key characteristics of plankton, nekton, and benthos.

Life Processes in the Ocean

What would it be like to be a sea creature? In some ways life would be easier than on land. This is because the ocean provides many things that organisms need to survive. You've experienced one of these things if you've gone swimming. Did you feel lighter in the water? This feeling was created because your density is less than water's density, making you buoyant. Buoyancy (BOY un see) allows for easy movement. Therefore, organisms in the ocean use less energy in moving around than you do.

What makes you buoyant?

Seawater also protects against sudden temperature changes. Temperature changes very slowly in the ocean. Marine organisms don't experience the stresses you feel when the air temperature suddenly changes.

1 Water is a basic compound used in all life processes. The tissues of most plants and animals are mostly water. Organisms that live in the ocean have no problem finding water!

Figure 12-10. These life-forms live at shorelines and are sometimes exposed during low tide.

OPTIONS

Meeting Different Ability Levels

For Section 12-3, use the following **Teacher Resource Masters** depending upon individual students' needs.

◆ **Study Guide Master** for all students.

● **Reinforcement Master** for students of average and above average ability levels.

▲ **Enrichment Master** for above average students.

Additional Teacher Resource Package masters are listed in the OPTIONS box throughout the section. The additional masters are appropriate for all students.

◆ STUDY GUIDE 52

NAME ______ DATE ______ CLASS ______

STUDY GUIDE — Chapter 12

Life in the Ocean — Text Pages 316–321

Find the term for each clue in the puzzle and circle it. The terms may read across or down. Then write the term after the clue.

1. Group of ocean life that includes larger animals that swim **nekton**
2. Gas used in the process of photosynthesis **carbon dioxide**
3. Used with sunlight and carbon dioxide by plants in photosynthesis **nutrients**
4. Colony of corals **reef**
5. Needed in photosynthesis but not in chemosynthesis **sunlight**
6. Example of an animal plankton **jellyfish**
7. Process of taking in oxygen and expelling carbon dioxide **respiration**
8. Process by which plants produce food and oxygen **photosynthesis**
9. Animal in the nekton group that roams the entire ocean **whale**
10. Benthos that creates a hard calcium outer covering **coral**
11. Food-chain process that takes place in the rift zones and does not require sunlight **chemosynthesis**
12. Example of plant plankton **diatoms**
13. Group made up of drifting plants and animals **plankton**
14. Gas used in respiration and released in photosynthesis **oxygen**
15. Group made up of organisms that live on the ocean floor **benthos**
16. Examples of nekton such as seals and whales **turtles**

O C A R B O N D I O X I D E
P H O T O S Y N T H E S I S
T R E S P I R A T I O N N U
U C E A W R E E F N L O E N
R I F E H C O R A L A X K L
T N D I A T O M S D L Y T I
L I F P L A N K T O N G O G
E E P B E N T H O S R E N H
S O J E L L Y F I S H N C T
C H E M O S Y N T H E S I S
E S N U T R I E N T S S E S

52

The ocean provides the liquid in which male and female reproductive cells can join. In the ocean, many organisms have external fertilization. This means that the male and female reproductive cells unite outside of the bodies of the parents. The reproductive cells are released by both parents, float to the surface of the water, and unite to form new individuals.

How does ocean water help organisms with their external fertilization?

Another way that ocean water helps organisms is in getting rid of wastes. Their wastes dissolve in seawater and are then used as nutrients by other organisms. Seawater also contains other important nutrients and gases that organisms need. Let's see why these materials are so important.

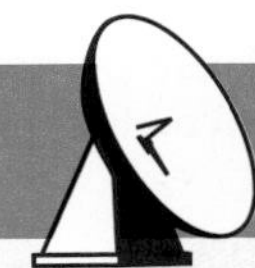

TECHNOLOGY

Submersibles

Submersibles are small submarines that enable scientists to study parts of the ocean that are too deep and dangerous for divers. One of the most famous submersibles, *Alvin*, was used to discover the wreck of the *Titanic* in 1985. *Alvin* is equipped with cameras and a manipulator arm. New submersibles called ROVs (Remotely Operated Vehicles) or minirovers are smaller, less expensive to operate, and have many of the same capabilities as *Alvin*. ROVs can stay underwater for any length of time because they have no crew. They are remotely controlled by a scientist on board a ship. Some are connected to the ship on the surface with a cable. Scientists communicate with the ROV by sending signals through the cable. Other ROVs are not attached to the ship and are controlled by radio signals. ROVs have lights, a video camera, and manipulator arms.

Minirovers have a variety of uses. One ROV was dropped through an eight-foot hole in the Arctic ice to explore ice formations. Other ROVs are being used to study sea life and to inspect ship hulls and pipelines.

Think Critically: What advantages does an ROV have over a submersible with a crew?

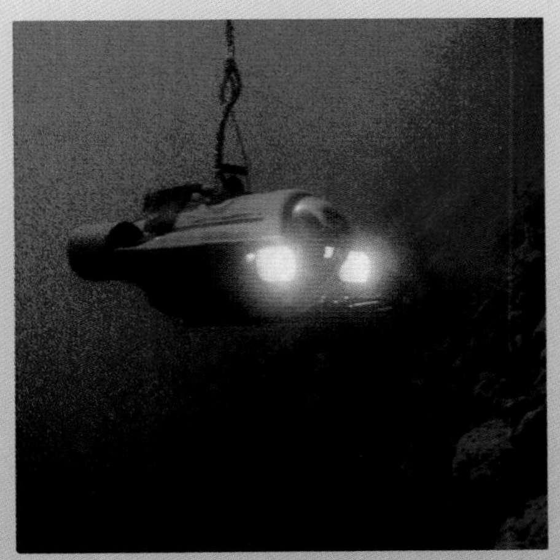

TYING TO PREVIOUS KNOWLEDGE: Students learned in Chapter 9 that water absorbs and releases energy much more slowly than land. Explain that this is why marine organisms experience less stress from temperature changes than do terrestrial organisms.

OBJECTIVES AND SCIENCE WORDS: Have students review the objectives and science words to become familiar with this section.

2 TEACH

Key Concepts are highlighted.

CONCEPT DEVELOPMENT

▶**What happens to the wastes of organisms that live in the oceans?** *The wastes dissolve in seawater and are then used as nutrients by other organisms.*

CROSS CURRICULUM

▶**Language Arts:** Suggest that students read a book, short story, or poem about the oceans. Suggestions include Jules Verne's *Twenty Thousand Leagues Under the Sea* and Ernest Hemingway's *The Old Man and the Sea*.

TECHNOLOGY

▶For more information see *National Geographic*, February, 1990, pages 30-37.

▶**Think Critically:** ROVs are less expensive, can stay under water longer, and don't put humans in as much danger as crewed submersibles.

● REINFORCEMENT 52

NAME ____ DATE ____ CLASS ____

REINFORCEMENT — Chapter 12

Life in the Ocean — Text Pages 316–321

For each item, explain what the terms have in common with one another.

1. buoyancy, constant temperatures, water **These are three of the six things that the ocean provides for organisms.**
2. fish, turtles, whales **These are three different types of nekton in the sea.**
3. carbon dioxide, nutrients, sunlight **These are all used by plants to make food in the process of photosynthesis.**
4. bottom-dwelling fish, snails, corals **These are all types of benthos found in the ocean.**
5. plankton, nekton, benthos **These are the forms of life that inhabit the ocean.**
6. photosynthesis, respiration, chemosynthesis **These are all food-chain processes that support life in the ocean.**
7. jellyfish, diatoms, eggs **These are all part of the plankton life in the ocean.**
8. method of reproduction, method of expelling wastes, nutrients **These are three of the six things the ocean provides sea organisms.**

Rewrite each statement to make it true.

9. Energy is transferred through the food chain from plant-eating animals to plants to animal-eating animals. **Energy is transferred through the food chain from plants to plant-eating animals to animal-eating animals.**
10. One-celled diatoms are plankton from the animal kingdom. **One-celled diatoms are plankton from the plant kingdom.**
11. In respiration, bacteria produce food and oxygen by using dissolved sulfur compounds. **In chemosynthesis, bacteria produce food and oxygen by using sulfur compounds.**
12. Sea urchin capsules cement together to form a reef. **Coral capsules cement together to form a reef.**
13. During the process of photosynthesis, carbon dioxide is released. **During the process of photosynthesis, oxygen is released.**

52

▲ ENRICHMENT 52

NAME ____ DATE ____ CLASS ____

ENRICHMENT — Chapter 12

Life in the Ocean — Text Pages 316–321

PRESERVING THE COASTAL ENVIRONMENT

Read the information and then answer the questions.

For over 50 years, the federal government has been involved in preserving United States coastlines. The government first became involved in coastal preservation through the National Park Service. In 1937, it established the first national seashore at Cape Hatteras in North Carolina. Since that time, the government has set up many other national seashores. It also has passed a number of laws that have made it a guardian of the coastlines.

In 1972, the government passed the Coastal Zone Management Act (CZMA). This act was designed to help protect the coast and the life it supports. The work of the CMZA is accomplished through the cooperative efforts of the government, industry, environmental groups, and citizens. The CZMA programs are managed by the Office of Ocean and Coastal Resource Management under the Department of Commerce.

The act is intended to help balance the demand for using coastal resources with the need to preserve the coasts and the life they support. The act was the first time the federal government became involved in management of land it did not itself own. Coastal states are not required to participate in CMZA programs. They voluntarily join in the programs. To obtain federal money from CMZA, however, the states must have written plans for coastal management.

Through the program, public access to beaches have been made possible. Assistance has been given to help rebuild city waterfronts and create sanctuaries—places where vegetation and wildlife are protected. Coastal sanctuaries protect ocean plant and animal species. Since 1972, other programs have been established as part of the CMZA. One such program is the National Estuarine Sanctuary Program. This program helps states manage estuaries. An estuary is a region where the freshwater flow of a river or swamp meets the sea. The program has set up sanctuaries such as Rookery Bay in Florida. This sanctuary was set up to help preserve swamps of mangrove trees that grow along the Florida coast.

The work of the CMZA continues as it tries to balance the need to preserve the coastal environments with the need for using coastal resources.

1. Why do you think it is important to provide a place where plants are protected? **Answers will vary. Students might mention that plants are food for certain animals, and without the plants, the animals will die.**
2. Drilling for offshore oil can lead to oil leakage that could harm sea plants and animals. Do you think the CMZA should work to suspend offshore drilling for this reason? **Student opinions will vary, but students should consider the need to meet fuel demands as well as the advantages of preserving coastal life in presenting their opinions.**

52

CONCEPT DEVELOPMENT

▶ **Compare and contrast photosynthesis and chemosynthesis.** *Both result in the production of food and oxygen. These processes differ in the raw materials used and the organisms performing the process. During photosynthesis, plants use nutrients, carbon dioxide, and sunlight. During chemosynthesis, bacteria use sulfur compounds.*

▶ Make a list of various kinds of seafood. Have each student select a particular animal or plant from the list and write a brief profile describing its appearance, its habitat, its source of food or nutrients, and its importance in marine food chains.

REVEALING MISCONCEPTIONS

▶ When considering the importance of plants for food, most people think about land plants. Actually, 85 percent of the food products of all plants is produced by marine plants.

Photosynthesis and Respiration

One of the important dissolved gases in seawater is carbon dioxide. Plants use carbon dioxide, nutrients in the water, and sunlight to produce food and oxygen. The food and oxygen are then available to other organisms. The process plants use to make food is called **photosynthesis** (foh toh SIHN thuh sihs). *Photo* refers to light; *synthesis* means to make.

All organisms, including you, perform a process called
2 respiration. During **respiration,** oxygen is combined with food so that the energy in food can be used. The process produces water and carbon dioxide, which plants use in photosynthesis.

How does respiration help photosynthesis?

3 Throughout the ocean, energy is transferred through food chains. Energy moves in this order: from plants, to plant-eating animals, to animal-eating animals. In these food chains, sunlight is very important because plants can perform photosynthesis only in the presence of light.

Chemosynthesis

Another type of food chain in the ocean does not depend on sunlight, however. This food chain depends on bacteria performing a process called **chemosynthesis** (kee moh SIHN thuh sihs). *Chemo* means chemical. This process takes place in rift zones where hot lava oozes from the crust. In these areas, bacteria produce food and oxygen by using dissolved sulfur compounds that escape from the lava. Organisms then feed on the bacteria.

Figure 12-11. Sulfur compounds escaping from a "black smoker" deep sea vent, at left, provide the energy for chemosynthesis. Tube worms, at right, feed on bacteria at the vents.

OPTIONS

PROGRAM RESOURCES

From the **Teacher Resource Package** use:

Critical Thinking/Problem Solving, page 18, Migrations and Mysteries.

Concept Mapping, pages 29-30.

Use **Laboratory Manual** page 111, Ocean Life.

Ocean Life

More animals and plants live in the ocean than anywhere else. Some simply drift with the surface currents. Others swim through the water on their own power or crawl over the sediments. Still others are permanently attached to the ocean bottom.

Plankton

Imagine what it would be like to drift in the currents all of your life. Drifting plants and animals are called **plankton.** You can see most plankton only with a microscope. One plant plankton is the diatom (DI uh tahm). Diatoms are one-celled, yellow-green algae. Although diatoms are tiny, they're very important as the main food for many sea animals.

Examples of animal plankton include eggs, very young fish, jellyfish and crabs, and tiny adults of some organisms. Most animal plankton depend on surface currents to move them, but some can swim.

4

MINI-Lab

What does plankton look like?

Use a microscope to examine examples of ocean or freshwater plankton. If you live near the ocean or a large lake, collect samples of the water, place one or two drops on the microscope slide, and observe with light coming through the sample from beneath. Describe what you see. Your teacher may be able to supply you with samples of the remains of plankton that lived in ancient oceans many years ago. If so, observe these with the microscope also. How do these compare to the examples of modern plankton that you observed?

Nekton

Larger animals that swim are called **nekton** (NEK tuhn). Examples are fish, turtles, whales, and seals. Nekton can move from one depth and place to another. Some prefer cold water, whereas others like warm regions. Some, like whales, roam the entire ocean. Many nekton come to the surface at night to feed on plankton, while others remain in deeper parts of the ocean where sunlight does not reach.

How are nekton different from plankton?

Figure 12-12. Swimming animals are nekton.

CONCEPT DEVELOPMENT

▶ Obtain artwork, photos, or slides showing the different types of organisms that inhabit the oceans at various depths. Have students compare and contrast the conditions found at each depth that make it a suitable habitat.

MINI-Lab

Materials: ocean or lake water containing microscopic organisms; stereomicroscope; glass depression slides; eye droppers; foraminifera, radiolaria, and/or diatoms

Teaching Tips

▶ Microfossils may be obtained from scientific supply companies.

▶ To enhance the number of plankton in a sample, collect the sample several days before doing this activity and allow a handful of vegetation such as grass or brush to "soak" in the water. Leave the storage container uncovered during this time.

▶ Examine the microorganisms in the samples for type and abundance before students complete this activity.

▶ Live plankton in water is best observed with the light source coming from beneath the sample. Microfossils are best observed with a stereomicroscope using top illumination.

▶ **Answer:** Answers will vary depending on the sample of water, but descriptions should accurately depict the variety of microorganisms present. Because microfossils are the remains of the plankton of ancient oceans, students should be able to detect some similarities.

INQUIRY QUESTIONS

▶ **A fish is considered plankton at one stage of its life and nekton at another stage. Explain.** *When it is still inside an egg or is a young hatchling, it drifts with the surface currents and can be considered plankton. When it matures, a fish can move from one depth and place to another and is considered nekton.*

PROGRAM RESOURCES

From the **Teacher Resource Package** use:

Activity Worksheets, page 111, Mini-Lab: What does plankton look like?

Science and MATH

The blue whale can consume 8 million grams of krill in a day, can grow up to 3000 centimeters long, and can have a mass of 200 000 kilograms.

CHECK FOR UNDERSTANDING

Use the Mini Quiz to check for understanding.

MINI QUIZ

Use the Mini Quiz to check students' recall of chapter content.

1. **_____ is the basic substance used in all life processes.** *Water*
2. **When organisms perform _____, oxygen is combined with food, and water and carbon dioxide are produced.** *respiration*
3. **Throughout the ocean, energy is transferred through _____ .** *food chains*
4. **Organisms that drift in the currents are _____ .** *plankton*
5. **Animals that live on the ocean bottom are _____ .** *benthos*

RETEACH

Cooperative Learning: Have each student write the names of three marine organisms, each on a separate small index card. Collect and mix the cards. Divide the class into five Numbered Heads Together teams. Each team will compete against the other and try to identify the organisms as plant or animal, and then as plankton, nekton, or benthos. For example, an adult fish is both nekton and animal. Kelp can be classified as both a plant and a benthos. Explain that the first team member to raise his or her hand with an answer will be recognized. If the answer is incorrect, the team loses one point. The team that scores the most points wins.

EXTENSION

For students who have mastered this section, use the **Reinforcement** and **Enrichment** masters or other OPTIONS provided.

How is the viperfish specially adapted to deep water?

Some of these deep-dwelling creatures have special light-generating organs for attracting live food. The angler fish dangles a luminous lure over its forehead. When small animals bite at the lure, the angler fish swallows them whole. The viperfish has luminous organs in its mouth. It swims with its mouth open, and small organisms swim right into the viperfish's mouth.

Bottom-Dwellers

Plants and animals also live on the seafloor. In fact, many live on the sunlit continental shelf. In shallow water, forests of kelp grow. Kelp is a large brown algae that likes cool water near shore. A special organ holds each kelp plant to the bottom, and gas-filled organs on its stems keep the plant upright in the water. Did you know that kelp is the fastest growing plant in the world? It can grow up to 0.6 m each day and reach lengths of 60 m.

Science and MATH

Blue whales can consume more than 8 tonnes of krill a day. They can grow up to 30 meters in length and can have a mass up to 200 tonnes. Use Appendix A and B on pages 662 and 663 to answer the following questions. How many **grams** of krill can a blue whale consume in one day? How many **centimeters** long can a blue whale become? What can a blue whale's mass get up to in **kilograms**?

5 Many animals called **benthos** (BEN thohs) live on the ocean bottom. Benthos include corals, snails, clams, sea urchins, and bottom-dwelling fish. How do you suppose these animals get food? Many of them eat the partially decomposed matter that sinks to the ocean bottom. Some prey on other benthos, eating them whole. Others are permanently attached to the bottom and filter food particles from water currents. Still others have specialized organs that sting prey that comes near. An attached benthos that stings its prey is coral. Let's learn more about this fascinating animal.

Figure 12-13. This angler fish is adapted to living in the deep ocean.

OPTIONS

INQUIRY QUESTIONS

▶ **Why do you think that many sea creatures live around coral reefs?** *The holes in the reef provide protection against predators for many organisms. Also, there are so many creatures present, because food is plentiful.*

Figure 12-14. Coral reefs are found in warm water near the equator.

Corals live in warm waters close to the equator. Each coral animal builds a hard, boxlike capsule around its body from the calcium it removes from seawater. Each capsule is cemented to others to form a colony called a **reef.** As a coral reef forms, other benthos and nekton begin living on it.

If you could swim quietly through a coral reef, you'd see many ocean organisms interacting. Fish, crabs, sea urchins, and many others congregate in reefs. Nutrients, food, carbon dioxide, and oxygen are cycled among these organisms, although you can't actually see this happening. Plankton, nekton, and benthos all depend on each other for survival, not only in coral reefs, but throughout the entire ocean. It's been this way for millions of years.

SECTION REVIEW

1. What six things does the ocean provide for organisms?
2. Describe the relationship between photosynthesis and respiration.
3. List the key characteristics of plankton, nekton, and benthos.
4. How do benthos get food?
5. **Apply:** In walking along a beach, you find many seashells. Are they the shells of plankton, nekton, or benthos? How can you tell?

Using Variables, Constants, and Controls — Skill Builder

Describe how you can test the effects of salinity on marine organisms. If you need help, refer to Using Variables, Constants, and Controls in the **Skill Handbook** on page 686.

3 CLOSE

▶ Ask questions 1-4 and the **Apply** Question in the Section Review.

FLEX Your Brain

Use the Flex Your Brain activity to have students explore BENTHOS.

SECTION REVIEW ANSWERS

1. buoyancy, protection against sudden temperature changes, a medium for reproduction, moisture, a way to get rid of wastes, and provides nutrients and dissolved gases

2. The products of photosynthesis are the raw materials for respiration, and vice versa. Together, these two processes recycle many substances necessary for life.

3. Plankton drifts in surface currents. Nekton can move from one depth and place to another. Benthos live on the bottom.

4. Many eat partially decomposed matter that sinks to the bottom of the body of water. Others eat other benthos, filter food particles from currents, or have specialized organs that sting prey as they pass by.

5. Apply: They are shells of benthos. If shells are so large that they can be seen without a microscope, they are too large to be plankton. Most seashells are made by animals such as snails or clams.

Skill Builder

Students could obtain several marine algae such as kelp. Three salt solutions could be made using marine salt. One solution would have to approximate the salinity of actual ocean water. Water temperature and the amount and kind of light the organisms are exposed to must be kept constant. Fresh water could be used as a control.

ENRICHMENT

▶ Have students report on well-known reefs such as the Bahaman platform or the Great Barrier Reef of Australia. Have them discuss the conditions that led to the formation of the reefs.

▶ Have students research and then report on several commercial fishing areas of the world. Have them speculate as to why these areas are limited geographically as well as restricted within certain water depths.

PROGRAM RESOURCES

From the **Teacher Resource Package** use:

Activity Worksheets, page 5, Flex Your Brain.

SECTION 12-4

PREPARATION

SECTION BACKGROUND

▶ According to Jacques-Yves Cousteau, more than 40 percent of the world's ocean creatures have been destroyed by pollution and overfishing.

▶ In one survey, 86 percent of the trash observed floating in the northern Pacific Ocean was plastic. For more information on plastics in the ocean, write to the Center for Environmental Education, 1725 DeSales Street NW, Washington, DC 20036. Request the publication entitled *A Citizen's Guide to Plastics in the Ocean: More Than a Litter Problem.*

▶ Oil clogs the breathing and feeding mechanisms of filter-feeding organisms. It can also cause equilibrium problems and skin cancers in fish and ruin chemical transmissions used in mating.

1 MOTIVATE

▶ Show students photos of polluted areas or a movie about water pollution.

▶ **Demonstration:** In order to show students how an oil spill affects organisms, create an oil slick in a pan of water. Dip an object such as a feather into the pan to show how animals can become coated with oil.

PROGRAM RESOURCES

From the **Teacher Resource Package** use:

Cross-Curricular Connections, page 16, Writing Letters.

Transparency Masters, pages 49-50, Sources of Ocean Pollution.

Use **Color Transparency** number 25, Sources of Ocean Pollution.

12-4 Pollution and Marine Life

New Science Words

pollution
thermal pollution

Objectives

- ▶ List seven human activities that pollute the ocean.
- ▶ Explain how ocean pollution affects the entire world.
- ▶ Determine how we can live on this planet without destroying its oceans.

Ocean Pollution

How would you feel if someone came into your bedroom while you were asleep, spilled oil on your carpet, littered your room with plastic bags, cans, bottles, and newspapers, sprayed bug killer all over, scattered sand, and then poured hot water all over you? Organisms in the ocean experience these very things when people pollute seawater.

Pollution occurs whenever harmful substances are introduced into an environment. Most ocean pollution caused by humans is concentrated along the coasts of continents. Let's see what some of the pollutants are.

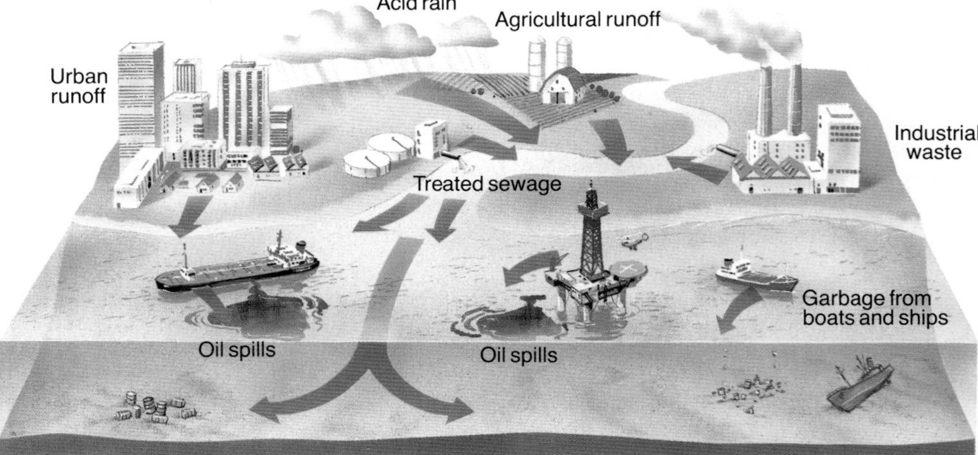

Figure 12-15. Ocean pollution has many sources.

OPTIONS

Meeting Different Ability Levels

For Section 12-4, use the following **Teacher Resource Masters** depending upon individual students' needs.

◆ **Study Guide Master** for all students.

● **Reinforcement Master** for students of average and above average ability levels.

▲ **Enrichment Master** for above average students.

Additional Teacher Resource Package masters are listed in the OPTIONS box throughout the section. The additional masters are appropriate for all students.

◆ **STUDY GUIDE 53**

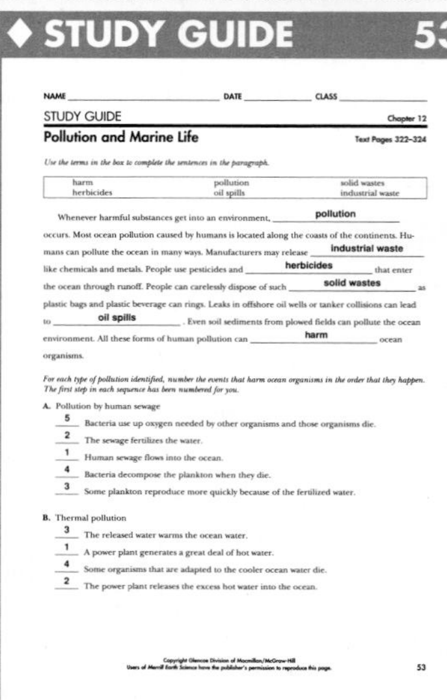

NAME ____________ DATE ________ CLASS ________

STUDY GUIDE — Chapter 12

Pollution and Marine Life — Text Pages 322-324

Use the terms in the box to complete the sentences in the paragraph.

harm	pollution	solid wastes
herbicides	oil spills	industrial waste

Whenever harmful substances get into an environment, **pollution** occurs. Most ocean pollution caused by humans is located along the coasts of the continents. Humans can pollute the ocean in many ways. Manufacturers may release **industrial waste** like chemicals and metals. People use pesticides and **herbicides** that enter the ocean through runoff. People can carelessly dispose of such **solid wastes** as plastic bags and plastic beverage can rings. Leaks in offshore oil wells or tanker collisions can lead to **oil spills**. Even soil sediments from plowed fields can pollute the ocean environment. All these forms of human pollution can **harm** ocean organisms.

For each type of pollution identified, number the events that harm ocean organisms in the order that they happen. The first step in each sequence has been numbered for you.

A. Pollution by human sewage

5 Bacteria use up oxygen needed by other organisms and those organisms die.
2 The sewage fertilizes the water.
1 Human sewage flows into the ocean.
4 Bacteria decompose the plankton when they die.
3 Some plankton reproduce more quickly because of the fertilized water.

B. Thermal pollution

3 The released water warms the ocean water.
1 A power plant generates a great deal of hot water.
4 Some organisms that are adapted to the cooler ocean water die.
2 The power plant releases the excess hot water into the ocean.

53

Industrial wastes sometimes get into seawater. Often, these contain concentrations of metals and chemicals that harm organisms. Solid wastes, such as plastic bags and fishing line left lying on beaches, can entangle animals. Medical waste such as needles, plastic tubing, and bags are a threat to both humans and animals.

Pesticides (insect killers) and herbicides (weed killers) used in farming reach the ocean as runoff. They become concentrated in the tissues of marine organisms.

Crop fertilizers and human sewage create a different kind of problem. They fertilize the water. This causes some types of plant plankton to reproduce very rapidly. When these plants die, they're decomposed by huge numbers of bacteria. The problem is that the bacteria use up much of the oxygen in the water during respiration. Therefore, other organisms such as fish can't get the oxygen they need, and they die.

Oil spills also pollute the ocean. You've heard in the news about major oil spills caused by tanker collisions, and leaks at offshore oil wells. Another source of oil pollution is oil mixed with wastewater that's pumped out of ships. In addition to these sources, oil discarded from cars and industries is sometimes dumped into groundwater and streams. It, too, eventually reaches the ocean.

Did You Know?

In one of the worst oil spills in history, the Exxon *Valdez* dumped 38 million liters of oil over 1000 sq km, an area more than twice as large as the state of Rhode Island.

How does an abundance of bacteria cause other life-forms to die?

PROBLEM SOLVING

Washed Ashore

A chemical plant and a nuclear power plant are both located along Barney Beach. The chemical plant produces electricity by burning coal. The nuclear power plant generates power using nuclear fission, a process that produces vast amounts of energy. The chemical plant is located about 20 kilometers north of Hometown. The nuclear power plant is about 10 kilometers south of the city. Recently, many of the fish along the beaches in the area were washed ashore. Many of the organisms in the shallow waters have also died as a result of thermal pollution.

Think Critically: What do you think is the source of the pollution? Explain.

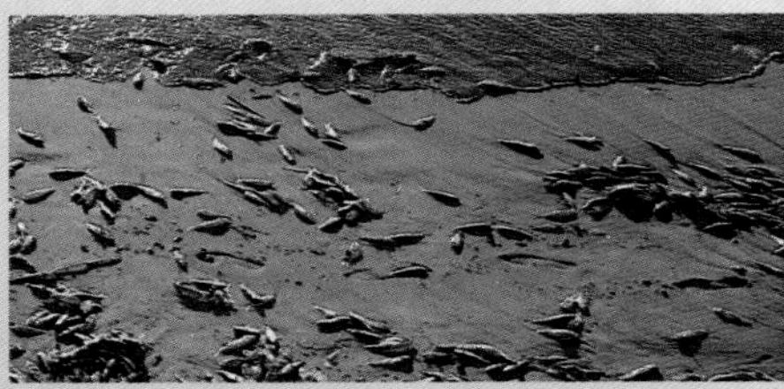

● REINFORCEMENT 53

NAME ____________ DATE ________ CLASS ________

REINFORCEMENT — Chapter 12

Pollution and Marine Life — Text Pages 322–324

In each of the following situations, identify the kind of pollutant involved and what the hazard may be to marine life.

1. **Situation A:** Aware of their need to protect the environment, picnickers on the New Jersey shore clean up their own trash and that left by others. Unfortunately, they missed a plastic ring that held a six-pack of soft drinks together.
   The plastic ring is solid waste that a fish or shore bird could become entangled in.
2. **Situation B:** A power plant releases hot water it has generated into the ocean.
   The hot water is an example of thermal pollution that can kill organisms adapted to cooler water.
3. **Situation C:** A mechanic changes the oil in a car and dumps the old oil down the drain in the garage.
   The oil is an example of oil pollution that may eventually reach the ocean and cause death to sea animals.
4. **Situation D:** Everyday a manufacturer releases waste water into the nearby river. In this water are chemicals used in the manufacturing process.
   The chemicals are examples of industrial waste that can get into seawater and harm the organisms living there.

Explain why each of the following statements is false.

5. Huge amounts of silt accumulating in coastal areas cannot harm sealife. **Great amounts of silt can cause filter-feeding benthos such as oysters and clams to clog up and die.**
6. The destruction of plant plankton by pollution will not affect other forms of life on Earth.
   Plant plankton produces about 70 percent of Earth's oxygen supply. Destroying it could lead to the death of other organisms as well because of the reduced oxygen supply.
7. The use of herbicides by a farmer who doesn't live near the coast will have no chance of hurting the ocean. **The herbicides can end up in the ocean through runoff and could become concentrated in the tissues of sea organisms.**
8. Only oil spills can lead to oil pollution of the sea. **Oil mixed with waste water and oil dumped into streams are also sources of oil pollution.**

 53

▲ ENRICHMENT 53

NAME ____________ DATE ________ CLASS ________

ENRICHMENT — Chapter 12

Pollution and Marine Life — Text Pages 322–324

HOW DO HERBICIDES AFFECT PLANT LIFE IN WATER?

Materials

- dish pan or aquarium
- stirring spoon
- teaspoon
- plant that grows in water
- water
- a commercial weed killer

Procedure

1. Fill the dish pan or aquarium with water.
2. Place the vegetation in the water.
3. Put the dish pan (or aquarium) in a place where it will get plenty of light.
4. Every day for five days, add one teaspoon of weed killer to the water and stir it around. **CAUTION:** *Weed killer is a poison and should be handled carefully. Wash your hands after handling the weed killer.*
5. Observe and record what happens to the plant.
6. After five days, discontinue adding weed killer to the water.
7. After a week observe and record what has happened to the plant.

Data and Observations

Effect of weed killer on water plants	
Day 1	
Day 2	
Day 3	
Day 4	
Day 5	
Week later	

Analyze

1. Does the weed killer have any effect on the plant? **Students should note that the weed killer is causing the plant to die.**
2. Is the plant healthier or sicker a week later? **The plant has been absorbing the weed killer for a longer period of time and should appear less healthy.**

Conclude and Apply

3. Based on your observations, what effect do you think weed killer has on plant life in water?
   Students should note that the weed killer can harm the ocean plants.
4. Can the use of herbicides on land affect ocean life? **Students should note that herbicides can affect ocean life.**

 53

TYING TO PREVIOUS KNOWLEDGE: Have students recall from Chapter 7 that water that does not soak into the ground becomes runoff. Runoff carries with it pesticides, herbicides, fertilizers, and oil from farms, homes, and industries. Eventually, these pollutants get into the ocean.

OBJECTIVES AND SCIENCE WORDS: Have students review the objectives and science words to become familiar with this section.

2 TEACH

Key Concepts are highlighted.

CONCEPT DEVELOPMENT

Cooperative Learning: Stress that ocean pollution is an international problem. Form Problem Solving teams and have students discuss who should pay for the cleanup of ocean pollution.

TEACHER F.Y.I.

▶ In July 1988, beaches from New Jersey to Long Island, New York, were covered with plastic tampon applicators, balls of sewage 5 cm in diameter, drug paraphernalia, and even medical debris, including vials of blood contaminated with AIDS and hepatitis B viruses.

PROBLEM SOLVING

Think Critically: Either factory can be causing the pollution. However, stress that other sources, such as the city itself, may be contributing to the pollution. Some students may suggest that other sources of pollution, in addition to the thermal pollution, are causing some of the deaths.

CHECK FOR UNDERSTANDING

Lead a discussion about why ocean pollution is so harmful to marine organisms.

RETEACH

Obtain articles on the Exxon *Valdez* spill into Prince William Sound. Have students summarize the information presented in the articles.

EXTENSION

For students who have mastered this section, use the **Reinforcement** and **Enrichment** masters or other OPTIONS provided.

3 CLOSE

FLEX Your Brain

Use the Flex Your Brain activity to have students explore OCEAN POLLUTION.

Cooperative Learning: Use the Numbered Heads Together strategy to have students develop a list of ways ocean pollution can be stopped.

▶ Ask questions 1-2 in the Section Review.

SECTION REVIEW ANSWERS

1. disposing of industrial wastes; leaving solid wastes at the beach; using pesticides, herbicides, and fertilizers; dumping untreated sewage; transporting oil; releasing hot water into the ocean; adding sediments; filling in salt marshes

2. Ocean pollution destroys food chains and thus affects Earth's oxygen supply. Also, because all oceans are interconnected, their pollution is a worldwide problem.

YOU DECIDE!

People must not use the oceans as dumping grounds. People must be made aware that what they dump onto the ground eventually gets into the oceans. There need to be stricter laws and enforcement of laws concerning where people are allowed to build.

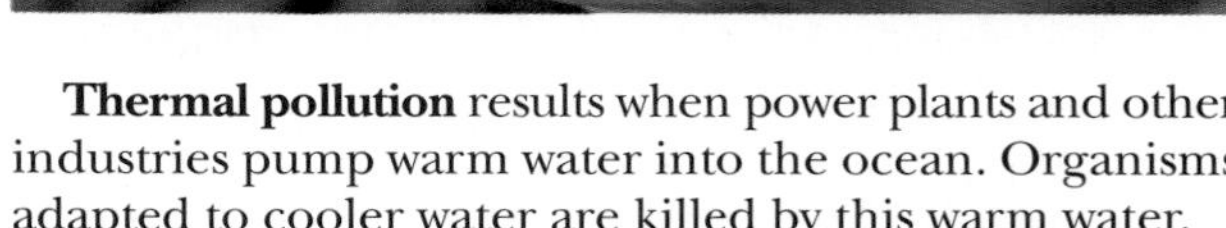

Figure 12-16. Pollution kills marine animals.

Science and READING

In this chapter, several types of water pollution are mentioned, but there is much more to learn about the cause of each of them. Go to the library and read about one specific type of pollution and its causes.

Thermal pollution results when power plants and other industries pump warm water into the ocean. Organisms adapted to cooler water are killed by this warm water.

Did you realize that even natural sediments such as silt and clay can pollute? Human activities such as agriculture, deforestation, and construction tear up the soil. Rain washes the soil into streams and eventually into the ocean. This causes huge amounts of silt to accumulate in some coastal areas. Filter-feeding benthos such as oysters and clams become clogged up and die. Also, when saltwater marshes are filled for land development, marine habitats are destroyed.

When the ocean becomes polluted, it isn't just the resident animals and plants that are affected. Food chains are disrupted and Earth's oxygen supply is affected. Many organisms on Earth depend on the oxygen produced by plant plankton. If the plankton dies, so will many organisms on Earth.

SECTION REVIEW

1. List seven human activities that pollute the ocean.
2. How does pollution of the ocean affect the entire world?

SCIENCE & SOCIETY

You Decide!

In this section, you learned how many human activities are severely polluting our ocean. However, many of these activities are part of the systems that provide your food, home, energy, transportation, and recreation. As Earth's population increases, the problem can only grow worse. How can we maintain our quality of life without destroying life in the ocean? What are your ideas?

OPTIONS

INQUIRY QUESTIONS

▶ **Most ocean pollution caused by humans is concentrated along the coasts of continents. Explain.** *Rivers flowing into the ocean can carry pollutants to these areas. The people who visit beach areas often leave their litter behind. Also, there are large numbers of oil tankers near shore.*

▶ **Along some coasts, "red tides" have become very common. The water is red because of the many algae that reproduce in the sewage-rich water. Besides the red color, what other things would you be likely to see during a red tide? Why?** *There would probably be dead fish and other dead animals seen because during a red tide, the water lacks the oxygen needed by most aquatic organisms for survival.*

PROGRAM RESOURCES

From the **Teacher Resource Package** use:

Activity Worksheets, page 5, Flex Your Brain.

CHAPTER

REVIEW

SUMMARY

12-1: Shorelines

1. Shore zones are subjected to waves, tides, and currents.
2. Rocks and cliffs are common along steep shore zones, whereas sandy beaches are found near flat shore zones.
3. Sand forms when rocks, coral, and seashells are broken into small particles by wave action.

12-2: The Seafloor

1. The continental shelf is a gently sloping part of the continent that extends out under the water along coastlines. The continental slope is the steeply sloping part of the ocean floor extending beyond the continental shelf. The continental slope extends down to the ocean floor.
2. Rift zones are cracks that form where seafloor is spreading apart. Along rift zones, mid-ocean ridges form from buckled seafloor. Ocean trenches form where seafloor is forced under another section of seafloor.

12-3: Life in the Ocean

1. Buoyancy, constant temperatures, water, nutrients, and a method of reproduction are provided to marine organisms by their habitat.
2. Photosynthesis and respiration are two processes that complement one another to recycle nutrients and gases needed by living things.
3. Plankton are microscopic plants and animals that drift in ocean currents. Nekton are marine organisms that swim. Benthos are plants and animals that live on the ocean floor.

12-4: Science and Society: Pollution and Marine Life

1. Industrial, solid, and medical wastes; pesticides, herbicides, and fertilizers; and oil spills and hot water all pollute Earth's ocean.
2. Because all Earth's oceans are interconnected, ocean pollution is a worldwide problem.
3. Careful disposal of wastes, limited usage of agricultural chemicals, and careful construction are only a few ways to reduce ocean pollution.

KEY SCIENCE WORDS

a. **abyssal plain**
b. **barrier islands**
c. **beaches**
d. **benthos**
e. **chemosynthesis**
f. **continental shelf**
g. **continental slope**
h. **longshore current**
i. **mid-ocean ridges**
j. **nekton**
k. **ocean trench**
l. **photosynthesis**
m. **plankton**
n. **pollution**
o. **reef**
p. **respiration**
q. **rift zone**
r. **shore zone**
s. **thermal pollution**

UNDERSTANDING VOCABULARY

Match each phrase with the correct term from the list of Key Science Words.

1. water that flows parallel to the shore
2. any kinds of sediments that are deposited parallel to a shore
3. steep seafloor beyond the continental shelf
4. mountains formed where seafloor is spreading apart
5. plant process that produces oxygen
6. drifting marine plants and animals
7. animals that live on the ocean floor
8. colony made of many coral
9. occurs whenever harmful substances are introduced to the environment
10. when hot water is added to a body of water

OPTIONS

ASSESSMENT

To assess student understanding of material in this chapter, use the resources listed.

COOPERATIVE LEARNING Consider using cooperative learning in the THINK AND WRITE CRITICALLY, APPLY, and MORE SKILL BUILDERS sections of the Chapter Review.

PROGRAM RESOURCES

From the **Teacher Resource Package** use:

Chapter Review, pages 27-28.

Chapter and Unit Tests, pages 74-77, Chapter Test.

CHAPTER

REVIEW

SUMMARY

Have students read the summary statements to review the major concepts of the chapter.

UNDERSTANDING VOCABULARY

1. h
2. c
3. g
4. i
5. l
6. m
7. d
8. o
9. n
10. s

CHAPTER
REVIEW

CHECKING CONCEPTS

1. d
2. c
3. d
4. a
5. d
6. d
7. b
8. b
9. a
10. c

UNDERSTANDING CONCEPTS

11. shore zones
12. rift zones
13. abyssal plain
14. buoyancy
15. thermal pollution

THINK AND WRITE CRITICALLY

16. Erosion and deposition by waves, tides, and currents cause the shoreline to always change—thus, the need for frequent remapping.

17. Both are underwater extensions of the continents. The shelf is closer to shore than the slope, and the slope is much steeper than the shelf.

18. Most organisms are found in the shallower waters due to the penetration of sunlight. Plants need sunlight to produce food, thus most plants are found in the shallow waters. Certain animals rely on the plants for food.

19. Earth's oceans are interconnected, making pollution a worldwide problem.

20. Pesticides and herbicides can reach the ocean in runoff. If they become concentrated in tissues of marine organisms, the organisms may die. Fertilizers can cause depletion of oxygen and result in many deaths.

CHAPTER
REVIEW

CHECKING CONCEPTS

Choose the word or phrase that completes the sentence.

1. Longshore currents ______.
   a. flow parallel to shore
   b. carry loose sediments
   c. erode shores
   d. all of these

2. Beaches are most common along ______.
   a. steep shore zones **c.** flat shore zones
   b. abyssal plains **d.** rift zones

3. Beach sands are moved by ______.
   a. longshore currents **c.** wind
   b. storms **d.** all of these

4. ______ are formed along rift zones.
   a. Mid-ocean ridges **c.** Continental slopes
   b. Oceanic trenches **d.** None of these

5. Organisms that live on the surface are called ______.
   a. nekton **c.** benthos
   b. fish **d.** plankton

6. The ocean provides organisms with ______.
   a. nutrients **c.** a constant temperature
   b. water **d.** all of these

7. Certain bacteria in the ocean perform ______ to provide food for other organisms.
   a. photosynthesis **c.** respiration
   b. chemosynthesis **d.** rifting

8. Ocean swimmers are ______.
   a. benthos **c.** kelp
   b. nekton **d.** coral

9. Most human-made ocean pollution ______.
   a. is near shore **c.** is thermal pollution
   b. is solid waste **d.** harms only plants

10. Fertilizers cause some ______ to reproduce rapidly, resulting in the lack of oxygen.
   a. benthos **c.** plant plankton
   b. animal plankton **d.** coral

UNDERSTANDING CONCEPTS

Complete each sentence.

11. Waves, currents, and tides constantly change ______.

12. New ocean crust forms at ______.

13. The ocean basin is flattest at the ______.

14. The force that allows organisms to "float" in the ocean is called ______.

15. If hot water from manufacturing processes isn't cooled before it leaves the plant, it can cause ______ in a body of water.

THINK AND WRITE CRITICALLY

16. Explain why shorelines are constantly being changed.

17. Compare and contrast the continental shelf with the continental slope.

18. Where would you expect to find the most marine organisms—closer to continents or in deeper waters? Explain.

19. Why is pollution an international problem?

20. Discuss how agricultural chemicals can kill marine organisms.

APPLY

21. A stack is an island of rock along certain shores. Along what kind of shorelines would you find stacks? Explain.
22. Describe an ocean food chain.
23. The distance to the ocean bottom can be calculated using the equation: $D = (1/2 \text{ time} \times v)$, where D is the depth, and v is the velocity of a sound wave. If the velocity is 1500 m/s, what is the depth of the ocean if the wave takes 8 seconds to get back to the ship?
24. Would you expect to find coral reefs growing around the bases of volcanoes off the coast of Alaska? Explain your answer.
25. Some oil spills in the ocean are natural. Where does the oil come from?

MORE SKILL BUILDERS

If you need help, refer to the Skill Handbook.

1. **Inferring:** What is the most common rock on Hawaii?
2. **Comparing and Contrasting:** Compare and contrast mid-ocean ridges and trenches.
3. **Measuring in SI:** If a certain kelp grows at a steady rate of 0.6 m/day, how long would it take to reach a height of 60 m?
4. **Classifying:** Classify each of the following sea creatures according to how they move: shrimp, dolphins, and sea lions.
5. **Concept Mapping:** Make an events chain concept map that describes how crop fertilizers can harm marine fish.

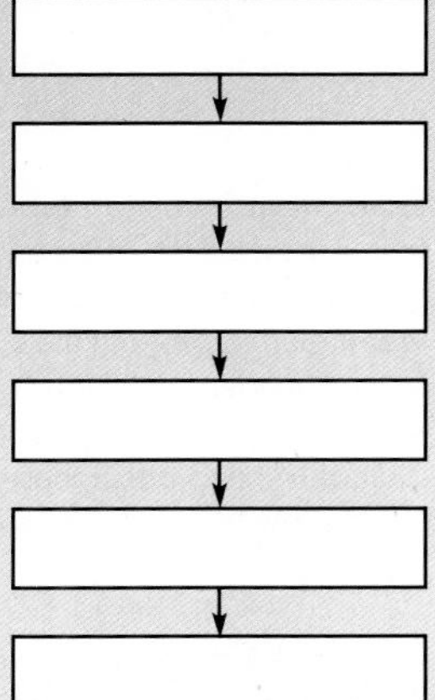

PROJECTS

1. Use a stream table and wooden blocks to make and observe the effects of longshore currents on a coastline.
2. Research the oil spill that occurred in Prince William Sound, Alaska. Then, design a method to clean up an oil spill from a sandy beach. Keep in mind that detergents may cause additional harm to the environment.

APPLY

21. A remnant like a stack would be found along steep, rocky shorelines. Storm waves scour notches at the height of wave action, resulting in stacks.

22. Many ocean food chains depend upon plants, which produce their own food. The next link in such a food chain includes animals that eat plants. These organisms, in turn, are eaten by meat-eating animals. Energy is transferred through all levels of a food chain.

23. $D = (1/2)\ 8\ \text{s} \times 1500\ \text{m/s} = 6000\ \text{m}$

24. No, the waters in the region are too cold for corals, which need warm, tropical waters in which to live.

25. Oil forms when dead marine organisms are buried under sediments for millions of years. The trapped oil can escape through cracks in the seafloor to produce natural oil spills.

MORE SKILL BUILDERS

1. Inferring: The igneous rock basalt, which is eroded to form the black sand beaches, is the most common rock on the island.

2. Comparing and Contrasting: Both are seafloor features. Ridges are mountains, whereas trenches are deep valleys. Crust moves apart near ridges and it collides near trenches.

3. Measuring in SI: 60 m/0.6 m = 100 days

4. Classifying: Shrimp can be benthos, nekton, or plankton. Dolphins and sea lions are nekton.

5. Concept Mapping:

Possible Solution:

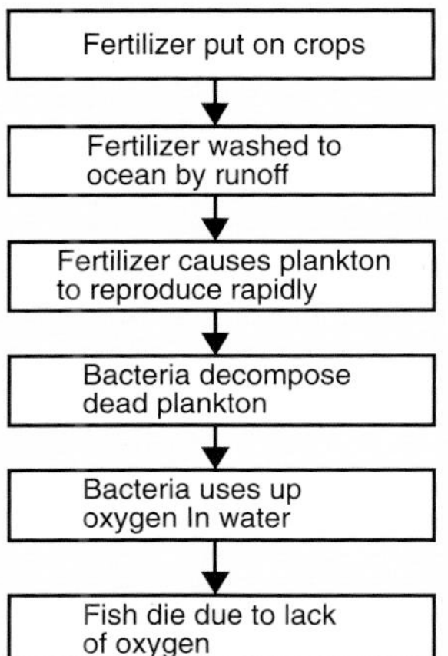
Fertilizer put on crops
Fertilizer washed to ocean by runoff
Fertilizer causes plankton to reproduce rapidly
Bacteria decompose dead plankton
Bacteria uses up oxygen In water
Fish die due to lack of oxygen

UNIT 4
GLOBAL CONNECTIONS

Objective

In this unit ending feature, the unit topic, "Earth's Air and Water," is extended into other disciplines. Students will see how the study of the atmosphere, weather, and Earth's oceans enhance understanding within other disciplines.

Teaching Tips

► Tell students to keep in mind while they are reading this feature the connection between the air and the oceans and how these affect the lives of all living things on the planet.

Motivate

Cooperative Learning: Assign one Connection to each group of students. Have each group research to find out more about the geographic location of the Connection—its climate, culture, flora, and fauna.

Wrap-Up

After students have reviewed all the boxes on these pages, ask them to form a hypothesis about how latitude affects climate.

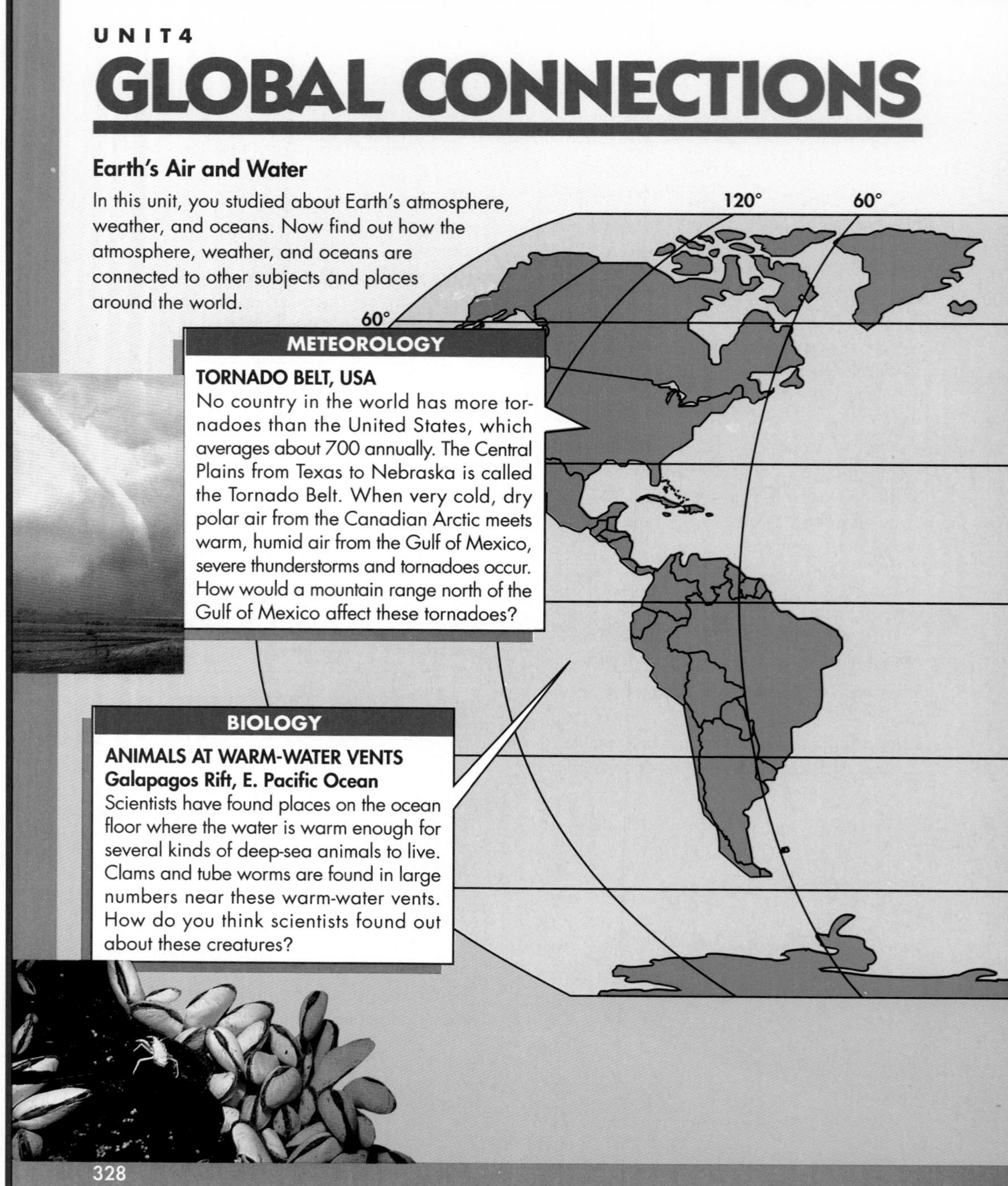
UNIT 4

GLOBAL CONNECTIONS

Earth's Air and Water

In this unit, you studied about Earth's atmosphere, weather, and oceans. Now find out how the atmosphere, weather, and oceans are connected to other subjects and places around the world.

METEOROLOGY

TORNADO BELT, USA

No country in the world has more tornadoes than the United States, which averages about 700 annually. The Central Plains from Texas to Nebraska is called the Tornado Belt. When very cold, dry polar air from the Canadian Arctic meets warm, humid air from the Gulf of Mexico, severe thunderstorms and tornadoes occur. How would a mountain range north of the Gulf of Mexico affect these tornadoes?

BIOLOGY

ANIMALS AT WARM-WATER VENTS
Galapagos Rift, E. Pacific Ocean

Scientists have found places on the ocean floor where the water is warm enough for several kinds of deep-sea animals to live. Clams and tube worms are found in large numbers near these warm-water vents. How do you think scientists found out about these creatures?

328

BIOLOGY

Background: Scientists studying the warm-water vents did not expect to find organisms living on the ocean floor. They knew photosynthesis could not possibly take place so far beneath the surface. Without photosynthesis, they reasoned, there would be no food chains on the deep ocean floor.

Discussion: Discuss why photosynthesis could not take place on the deep ocean floor. Mention that without photosynthesis there can be no plant-based food chains. Students may be surprised to learn that large numbers of bacteria can serve as food for animals. The bacteria that feed on the chemicals present at the warm-water vents are consumed by the clams and other animals present there. Tube worms were also found in large numbers at the vents, but they had no structure by which they could feed on the bacteria there. Scientists discovered colonies of bacteria as parts of the tube worms' body. The tube worms supply bacteria with sulfur and carbon dioxide, while the bacteria enrich the tube worms' blood with needed carbon compounds. Ask students to draw a deep ocean-floor food chain.

Answer to Question: Some scientists went down in submersibles and saw the organisms living near the warm-water vents.

Extension: Have students draw pictures of the warm-water vents and the life-forms associated with them.

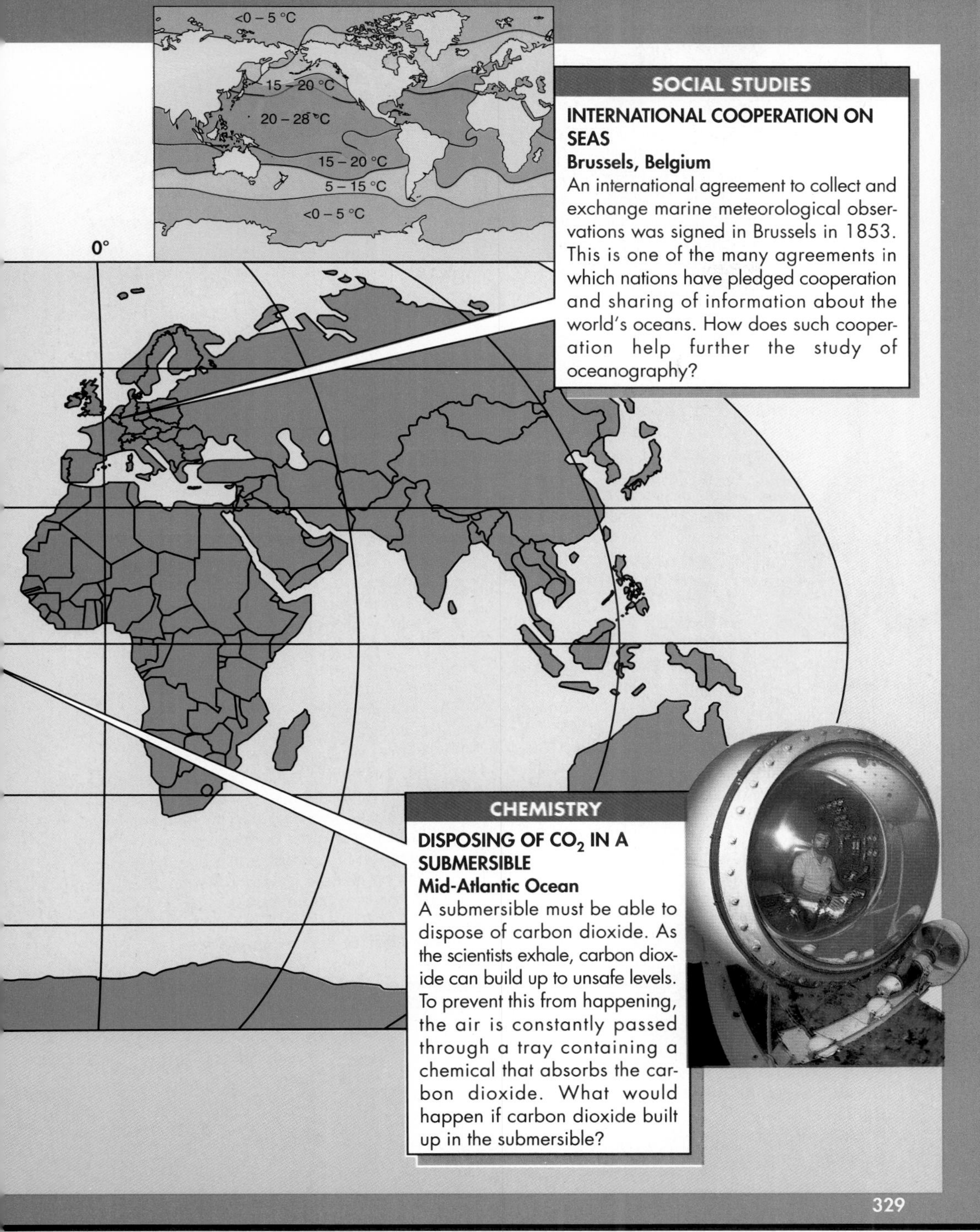

SOCIAL STUDIES

INTERNATIONAL COOPERATION ON SEAS
Brussels, Belgium
An international agreement to collect and exchange marine meteorological observations was signed in Brussels in 1853. This is one of the many agreements in which nations have pledged cooperation and sharing of information about the world's oceans. How does such cooperation help further the study of oceanography?

CHEMISTRY

DISPOSING OF CO_2 IN A SUBMERSIBLE
Mid-Atlantic Ocean
A submersible must be able to dispose of carbon dioxide. As the scientists exhale, carbon dioxide can build up to unsafe levels. To prevent this from happening, the air is constantly passed through a tray containing a chemical that absorbs the carbon dioxide. What would happen if carbon dioxide built up in the submersible?

329

CHEMISTRY

Background: The most important feature of a submersible is its life-support system. Cylinders feed oxygen into the cabin at a controlled rate, and the air is circulated by fans. As the air passes over a tray of lithium hydroxide, carbon dioxide is removed from the air. The "fresh" air is recirculated.
Discussion: Discuss the use of lithium hydroxide in removing carbon dioxide from the air. Tell students that this substance is also used by astronauts during spacewalks. The chemical is contained in a cartridge in the portable oxygen system of the extravehicular spacesuit.
Answer to Question: Carbon dioxide is denser than air and would cut off the scientists' oxygen supply if it were allowed to build up in the submersible.
Extension: Have students compare the atomic mass of a molecule of carbon dioxide to the atomic mass of a molecule of oxygen.

SOCIAL STUDIES

Background: *Physical Geography of the Sea,* written by an American naval officer, Matthew Fontaine Maury in 1855, provided the scientific community with a broad accurate picture of the main systems of oceanic circulation.
Discussion: Discuss the importance of international cooperation, especially on a topic of such importance to the whole world as the ocean. Point out that the size of the ocean makes the study by one nation, acting alone, prohibitive because of the cost and time involved. Since the 1950s international expeditions of several ships were undertaken. All the nations involved shared the information gathered.
Answer to Question: International cooperation has increased the total store of information about the oceans because time and money is spent finding new information instead of repeating what one nation has already discovered.
Extension: Have students draw a map of ocean water circulation.

METEOROLOGY

Background: The contrasting air masses that generate tornadoes are most likely to meet in the Central Plains of the United States. There are no landforms on either side of the Central Plains to interrupt the flow of cold air from the Arctic or the warm air from the Gulf of Mexico.
Discussion: Discuss with students the conditions that favor the Tornado Belt. Mention that although tornadoes may occur during every month of the year, April through June is the period of greatest frequency. Discuss that although warm air travels north from the Gulf States after June, there is little cold air traveling south from the Arctic at this time. Have students explain, using a map, why tornadoes are not frequent in other parts of the country.
Answer to Question: If there were a mountain range across the southeastern part of the United States, there probably would not be tornadoes in the Central Plains. The moist, humid tropical air from the Gulf of Mexico would be forced to rise when it reached the mountains. This would cause it to become cooler and to lose its moisture. The conditions for a tornado would not be present.
Extension: Have students color a map of the United States to show areas where most tornadoes occur during a specific period of time.

OCEANOGRAPHER

Background: Some oceanographers study waves, currents, and tides. Others study the chemicals in seawater. Biological oceanographers study marine organisms and their environments. Still others are concerned with the landforms on the ocean floor.

Related Career	Education
Biological Oceanographer	college
Deep-sea Diver	high school
Oil-rig Technician	associate degree

Career Issue: Some studies of the ocean floor reveal the presence of oil offshore. Many people think that oil companies should not drill for oil in the ocean where there is a chance that oil will leak and cause damage to wildlife. If the amount of oil in the world is not sufficient, do you think oil companies should drill for oil in the ocean?

What do you think? Have students compile a list of specialized careers in the field of oceanography and briefly describe each.

METEOROLOGICAL TECHNICIAN

Background: Many meteorological technicians assist meteorologists as weather observers. Besides measuring weather conditions, they help prepare weather data that is used in making weather reports.

Related Career	Education
Meteorologist	college
Weather Broadcaster	college
Hurricane Hunter	college

Career Issue: Hurricane hunters take their lives in their hands as they fly into a hurricane's eye. However, they can locate a hurricane and accurately pinpoint the direction the storm is taking. This helps prevent a hurricane's hitting an area without ample warning.

What do you think? Lead a discussion about the duties of a meteorological technician in preparations for a weather report.

CAREERS

OCEANOGRAPHER

An *oceanographer* is a geologist who studies Earth's surface beneath the oceans. Some oceanographers use sound waves to explore the ocean floor. Instruments plot each measurement on a chart. All the measurements together produce an accurate picture of the ocean floor over which the ship is traveling. Oceanographers also study the composition and temperature of ocean water all over the world. They have found all the known substances in Earth's crust in ocean water. They study the constant exchange of gases between the ocean and the atmosphere. Their studies show that the amount of carbon dioxide in the atmosphere is increasing.

Oceanographers require a college degree. A student interested in becoming an oceanographer should take courses in chemistry, physics, and languages such as German and Russian.

For Additional Information

Contact the Scripps Institution of Oceanography, La Jolla, CA 92093.

METEOROLOGICAL TECHNICIAN

A *meteorological technician* assists a meteorologist in collecting information about the weather and climate. Technicians use instruments such as thermometers, barometers, and hygrometers to measure different conditions of the atmosphere. They collect data on the wind, temperature, precipitation, air pressure, and other atmospheric conditions. They also assist in measuring chemical substances in the atmosphere, such as carbon dioxide and ozone. The information that meteorological technicians gather helps in making weather forecasts.

Most meteorological technicians have at least an associate degree from a community college in meteorology. A student planning to become a meteorological technician should take courses in mathematics and physics.

For Additional Information

Contact the American Meteorological Society, 45 Beacon Street, Boston, MA 02108.

UNIT READINGS

▶Barton, Robert. *The Oceans.* New York: Facts on File, Inc., 1980.

▶Jones, Philip D. and Tom, M.L. "Global Warming Trends." *Scientific American,* August 1990, pp. 84-91.

▶White, Robert. "The Great Climate Debate." *Scientific American,* July 1990, pp. 36-43.

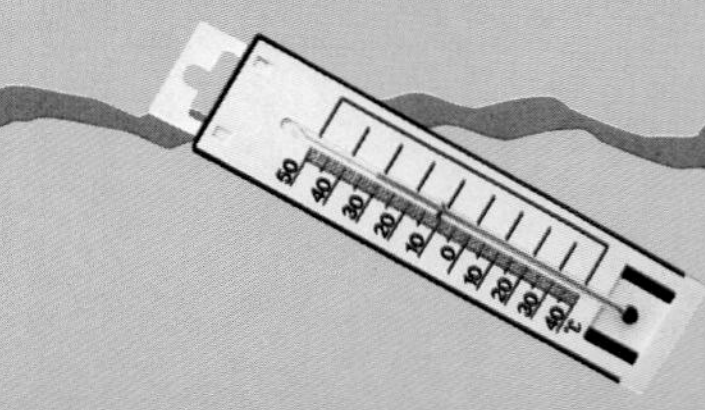

UNIT READINGS

Background

▶ *The Oceans* is a beautifully illustrated book about the oceans.

▶ "Global Warming Trends" discusses the fact that the global temperature has increased by half a degree Celsius in the past century.

▶ "The Great Climate Debate" urges that if changes occurring in our atmosphere are likely to cause consequences, we must understand the problems and promote policies to remedy them.

More Readings

1. Revekin, A. "Energy Watch: Tapping the sea." *Discover,* July, 1989, p. 40. A new machine that will tap the energy of the sun-warmed surface of the ocean is under development.
2. Ross, Philip. "Lorenz's Butterfly: Weather Forecasters Grapple with the Limits of Accuracy." *Scientific American,* September, 1990, p. 42. Local meteorologists can now predict 36 hours ahead with 95 percent reliability versus an 80 percent batting average just 20 years ago.

In Times of Silver Rain

by Langston Hughes

In this unit, you studied how rain forms and its effect on the environment. You've explored rain from the viewpoint of an earth scientist. Now read how one poet, Langston Hughes, described rain.

In time of silver rain
The earth
Puts forth new life again,
Green grasses grow
And flowers lift their heads,
And over the plain
The wonder spreads
  Of life,
  Of life,
  Of life!

In time of silver rain
The butterflies
Lift silken wings
To catch a rainbow cry,
And trees put forth
New leaves to sing
In joy beneath the sky
As down the roadway
Passing boys and girls
Go singing, too.
In time of silver rain
  When spring
  And life
  Are new.

Most people would agree that rain is of vital importance. Without it, Earth would be parched, food supplies would dwindle, and water would be extremely scarce. This is the practical side of rain.

To a poet such as Langston Hughes, rain is filled with beautiful images to inspire poetry. His image of "silver rain" evokes the idea of a shimmering cascade of raindrops—each like a silvered mirror reflecting the effect of rain on the plants growing on the plain.

What do you think the poet means by the phrase in the second stanza "To catch a rainbow cry?" How do you think Langston Hughes feels about rain?

In Your Own Words

▶What images does rain evoke for you? Write a poem or an essay that reveals how you feel when it rains.

Source: Raoul Abdul, ed. *The Magic of Black Poetry,* 1972.

Biography: Langston Hughes (1902-1967) was an American poet, short-story writer, playwright, and writer of humorous sketches of African-American culture. He was born in Joplin, Missouri, and attended Columbia University. In 1960, Langston Hughes was awarded the coveted Spingarn Medal. This medal is bestowed annually to the African-American who, according to the board, reached the highest achievement in his or her field. Hughes contributed to a large extent to the movement known as the Harlem Renaissance—a prolific period for African-American literature in the 1920s. The works of Langston Hughes and several contemporary African-American writers became appreciated by readers of all ethnic groups.

TEACHING STRATEGY

▶Ask students to share their poems or essays about rain.

▶Have students share with the group an experience they have had involving rain. Challenge the others in the group to be aware of the images elicited during the telling of the experience. Have them share these images with the group.

▶Ask students to discuss how people's images of rain might change depending on whether they live in a place that receives four centimeters rain annually or in an area where they receive 400 centimeters of rain with prospects of floods.

Cooperative Learning: Using the Paired Partner strategy, have students prepare one description of rain as written by a poet and another as written by an earth scientist.

▶Tell students that Langston Hughes, writing in *The Nation* magazine in 1926, urged artists to write from their own experiences and not to imitate writers from other ethnic backgrounds. Discuss how this may have affected African-American literature.

Classics

▶Bailey, Herbert S., Jr. "The Voyage of the Challenger." *Scientific American,* May, 1953. This article provides a concise account of the famed *Challenger* voyage and many illustrations, including that of the dredging and sounding apparatus.

▶Tannehill, Ivan Ray. *Hurricane Hunters.* New York. Dodd, Mead, and Co., 1955. This book provides vivid descriptions of the heroic flights of the early hurricane hunters.

Other Works

▶Other works by Langston Hughes: "Winter Moon" and "Night" *The Magic of Black Poetry* New York: Dodd, Mead & Company, 1972.

UNIT

5

CHANGE AND EARTH'S INTERNAL PROCESSES

In Unit 5, students are introduced to the theory of plate tectonics. The major concept of the unit is the relationship of plate tectonics to the occurrence of earthquakes and volcanoes.

CONTENTS

ADVANCE PREPARATION

Activities

▶ **Activity 13-1, page 347,** requires small magnetic compasses and bar magnets from a scientific supply house.

Audiovisuals

▶ **Section 13-4, page 348:** Arrange to show the video "Planet Earth—The Living Machine," The Annenberg/CPB Project.

▶ **Section 14-2, page 366:** Arrange to show the video "Earthquake!" NOVA (WGBH Educational Foundation).

▶ **Section 15-1, page 388:** Arrange to show the video "Volcano!" NOVA (WGBH Educational Foundation).

Field Trips and Speakers

▶ Arrange for a geologist to visit class to discuss plate tectonics.

▶ Arrange to take your class to a rock exposure that demonstrates faulting.

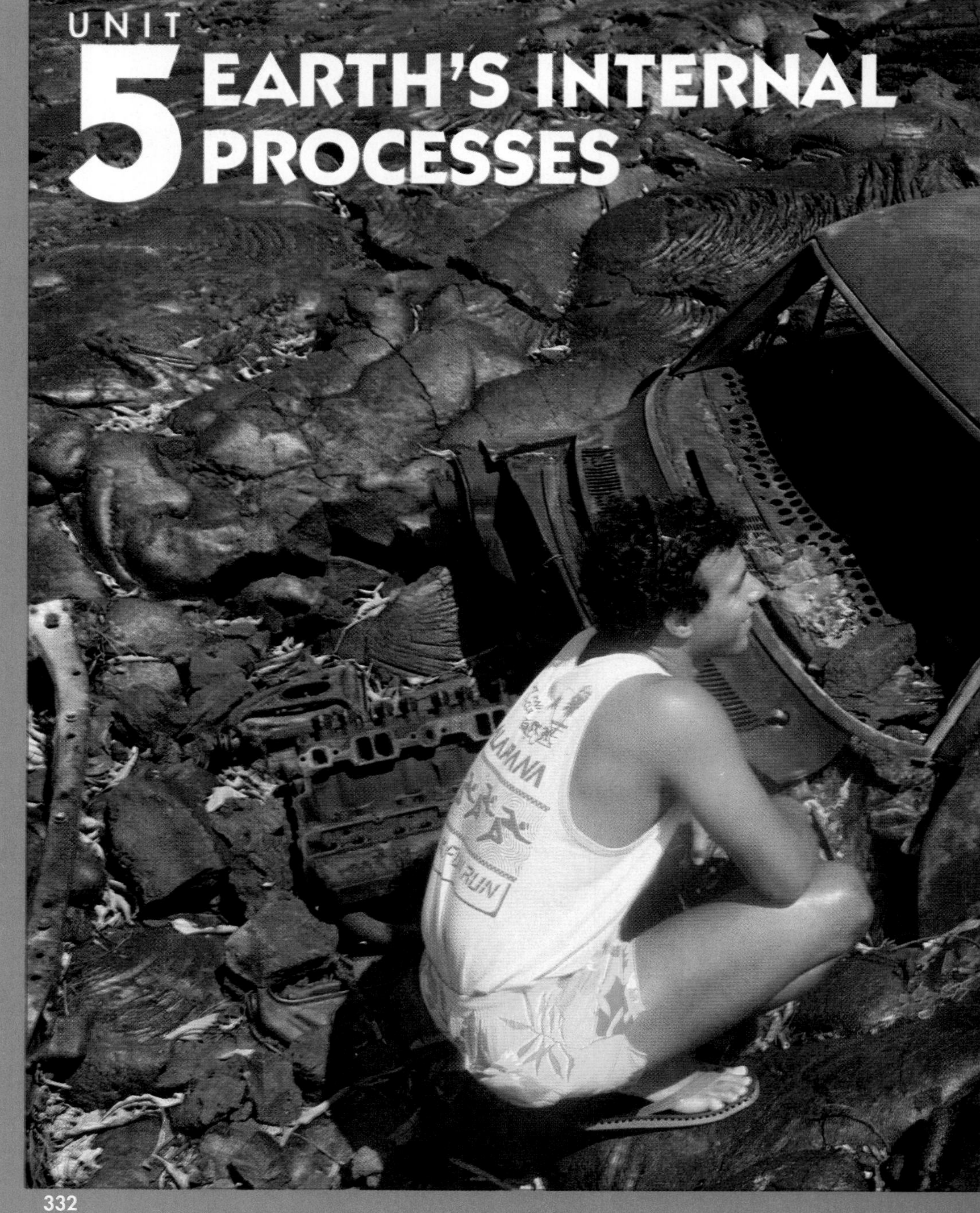

332

OPTIONS

Cross Curriculum

▶ Have students locate Armenia in the former Soviet Union, San Francisco in the United States, and Iran on a map of the world. Discuss how the destructive earthquakes that occurred in these locations in recent years affected the lives of people who live there.

▶ Have students report on the work of Alfred Wegener.

▶ Have students compare the convection currents that are thought to power the movement of Earth's plates to convection currents used in boiling soup.

Science at Home

▶ Have students consider how they would change their homes to make them more earthquake safe. How could objects in the home be made more secure in case an earthquake occurred?

Cooperative Learning: Have groups of students monitor the newspapers, news magazines, and television news for stories about volcanic eruptions around the world.

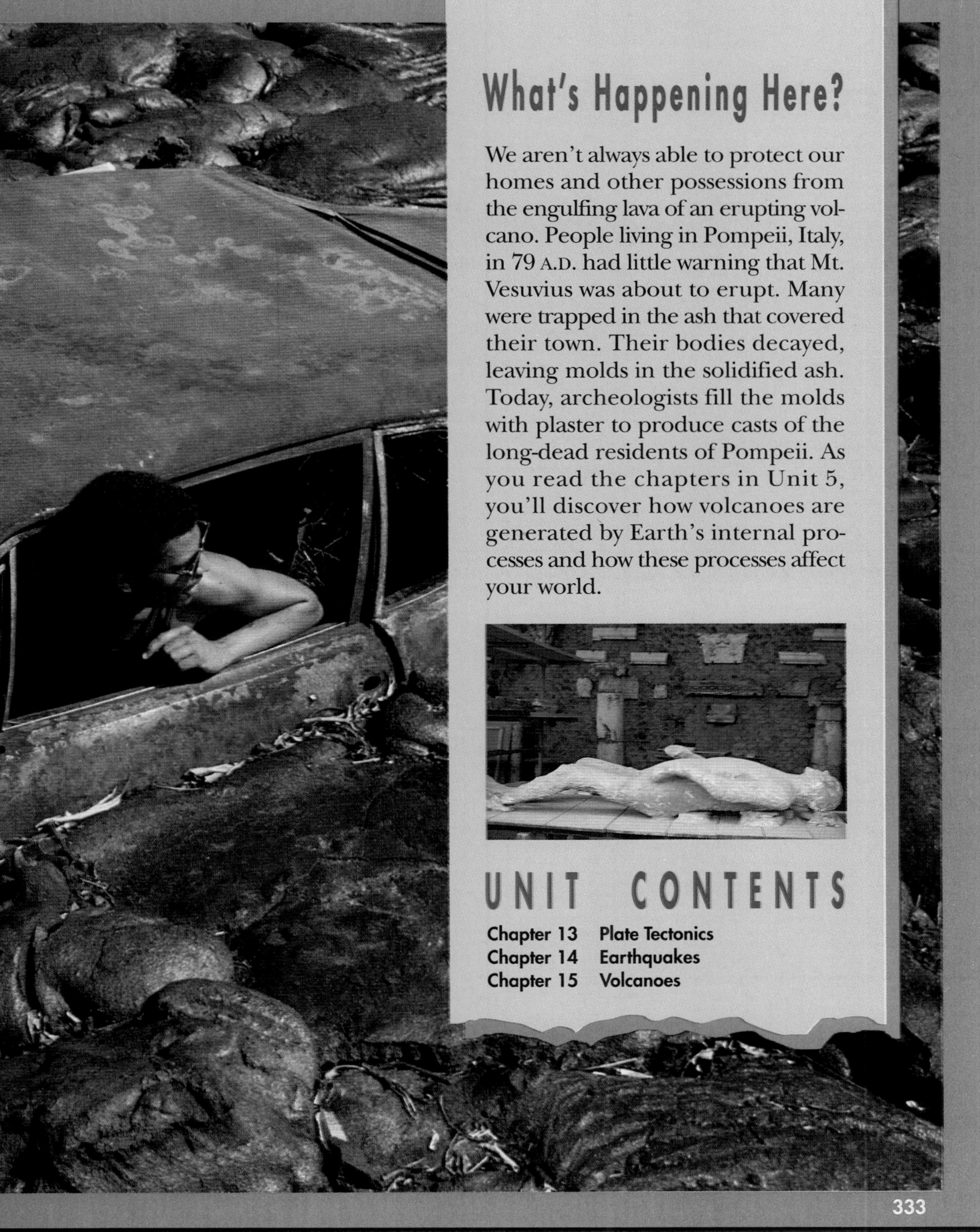

What's Happening Here?

We aren't always able to protect our homes and other possessions from the engulfing lava of an erupting volcano. People living in Pompeii, Italy, in 79 A.D. had little warning that Mt. Vesuvius was about to erupt. Many were trapped in the ash that covered their town. Their bodies decayed, leaving molds in the solidified ash. Today, archeologists fill the molds with plaster to produce casts of the long-dead residents of Pompeii. As you read the chapters in Unit 5, you'll discover how volcanoes are generated by Earth's internal processes and how these processes affect your world.

UNIT CONTENTS

333

INTRODUCING THE UNIT

What's Happening Here?

▶ Have students look at the photos and read the text. Ask them to tell you what's happening here. Point out to students that in this unit they will be studying the theory of plate tectonics and how it relates to earthquakes and volcanoes.

▶ **Background:** The lava of Mauna Loa is low in silica content. The low concentration of silica in the lava causes it to flow very slowly. Although it can prove very destructive to villages in its path, people and many animals can usually walk away from the slowly moving lava.

Previewing the Chapters

▶ Some students may be surprised that earthquakes and volcanoes are related. To preview the unit and to reveal misconceptions, have students compare and contrast Figures 14-1 (page 361) and 15-3 (page 391).

▶ Have students search through the figures and tables in Chapter 13 for evidence supporting continental drift.

▶ After reviewing the figures on pages 362 and 363, have students describe the relative motion of rock layers on opposite sides of normal, reverse, and strike-slip faults.

Tying to Previous Knowledge

▶ Ask students to recall television stories or magazine articles that demonstrated the damage done by earthquakes. Have students speculate on how they think most lives are lost during an earthquake.

▶ Have students list the areas of the United States most susceptible to volcanic activity.

▶ Ask students to look at a globe of Earth and to hypothesize how the continents may have once fit together.

▶ Use the **Inquiry Questions** in the OPTIONS box below to investigate with students the relationship of plate tectonics, earthquakes, and volcanoes.

Multicultural Awareness

Have students collect photographs and articles of volcanoes and earthquakes from around the world. Have students make a collage of the photographs and discuss the cultural effects each volcano or earthquake might have had on the people living there.

Inquiry Questions

Use the following questions to focus an investigation of the relationships of plate tectonics, earthquakes, and volcanoes.

1. Where do most earthquakes and volcanoes occur?
2. How does the location of most earthquakes relate to tectonic plate boundaries?
3. Why is the chain of volcanic islands called Hawaii located in the middle of the Pacific Ocean tectonic plate?

CHAPTER

13 Plate Tectonics

CHAPTER SECTION	OBJECTIVES	ACTIVITIES
13-1 Structure of Earth (1 day)	1. **Diagram** Earth's structure. 2. **Describe** each layer inside Earth.	**MINI-Lab:** *Is it solid or liquid?* p. 339
13-2 Science and New Ideas Science & Society (1 day)	1. **Explain** the idea of continental drift. 2. **Recognize** that new ideas require careful consideration.	
13-3 Evidence for Continental Drift (3 days)	1. **Discuss** four pieces of evidence for the idea of continental drift. 2. **Describe** sea-floor spreading. 3. **Relate** how age and magnetic clues confirm sea-floor spreading.	**Activity 13-1:** *Sea-floor Spreading,* p. 347
13-4 Theory of Plate Tectonics (3 days)	1. **Compare** and **contrast** divergent, convergent, and transform plate boundaries. 2. **Describe** how convection currents might be the cause of plate tectonics.	**MINI-Lab:** *How do convection currents form?* p. 353 **Activity 13-2:** *Rates of Sea-floor Spreading,* p. 354
Chapter Review		

ACTIVITY MATERIALS

FIND OUT	ACTIVITIES		MINI-LABS	
Page 335 scissors thin white paper	**13-1 Sea-floor Spreading, p. 347** metric ruler paper tape small magnetic compasses (2) bar magnets pen or marker	**13-2 Rates of Sea-floor Spreading, p. 354** metric ruler pencil	**Is it solid or liquid? p. 339** taffy or silicon putty textbook hammer safety goggles	**How do convection currents form? p. 353** food coloring water thermal mitts metal saucepan hot plate

CHAPTER FEATURES	TEACHER RESOURCE PACKAGE	OTHER RESOURCES
Technology: *A New Picture of Earth's Interior,* p. 338 **Skill Builder:** *Outlining,* p. 339	**Ability Level Worksheets** ◆ ***Study Guide,*** p.54 ● ***Reinforcement,*** p. 54 ▲ ***Enrichment,*** p. 57 **MINI-Lab Worksheet,** p. 119 **Cross-Curricular Connections,** p. 17 **Transparency Masters,** pp. 51-52	**Color Transparency 26,** Earth Layers
You Decide! p. 341	**Ability Level Worksheets** ◆ ***Study Guide,*** p. 55 ● ***Reinforcement,*** p. 55 ▲ ***Enrichment,*** p. 54 **Science and Society,** p. 17	
Problem Solving: *A Perfect Fit?* p. 344 **Skill Builder:** *Concept Mapping,* p. 346	**Ability Level Worksheets** ◆ ***Study Guide,*** p. 56 ● ***Reinforcement,*** p. 56 ▲ ***Enrichment,*** p. 55 **Activity Worksheet,** pp. 113-114 **Critical Thinking/Problem Solving,** p. 19 **Technology,** pp. 13-14	**Lab Manual:** *Continental Drift,* p. 113
Skill Builder: *Recognizing Cause and Effect,* p. 353	**Ability Level Worksheets** ◆ ***Study Guide,*** p. 57 ● ***Reinforcement,*** p. 57 ▲ ***Enrichment,*** p. 56 **Concept Mapping,** pp. 31-32 **Transparency Masters,** pp. 53-58 **MINI-Lab Worksheet,** p. 120 **Activity Worksheet,** pp. 115-116	**Color Transparency 27,** Oceanic-Continental Convergence **Color Transparency 28,** Oceanic-Oceanic Convergence **Color Transparency 29,** Continental-Continental Convergence
Summary Key Science Words Understanding Vocabulary Checking Concepts Understanding Concepts Think & Write Critically Apply More Skill Builders Projects	**Chapter Review,** pp. 29-30 **Chapter Test,** pp. 89-92	**Chapter Review Software** **Test Bank**

◆ **Basic** ● **Average** ▲ **Advanced**

ADDITIONAL MATERIALS

SOFTWARE	AUDIOVISUAL	BOOKS/MAGAZINES
Geology Picture File, Datatech Software Systems, Inc. *Mountains and Crystal Movements,* D.C. Heath. *Forces in the Earth,* Queue. *Shaping the Earth's Surface,* Focus.	*Continental Drift,* film, Universal Education and Visual Arts. *The Drifting of the Continents,* film, BBC-TV through Time-Life Films. *Famous Boundary of Creation: Mid-Atlantic Ridge,* NOAA. *Earth: The Geology of an Ever-Changing Planet,* video, Focus. *Our Dynamic Earth,* film, NGS.	Condie, Kent C. *Plate Tectonics and Crustal Evolution.* Elmsford, NY: Pergamon Press Inc., 1989. Tarbuck, Edward J. and Frederick K. Lutgens. *The Earth: An Introduction to Physical Geology.* 3rd Ed. Columbus, OH: Merrill Publishing Company, 1990. Windley, Brain F. *The Evolving Continents.* 2nd Ed. NY: John Wiley & Sons, Inc., 1984.

CHAPTER

13

PLATE TECTONICS

THEME DEVELOPMENT: The transfer of energy in Earth's interior sets up massive convection currents in the mantle. These cells are thought to be the driving force that causes the movements of Earth's plates.

CHAPTER OVERVIEW

- **Section 13-1:** This section describes Earth's inner core, outer core, mantle, and crust.
- **Section 13-2: Science and Society:** This section discusses how science discoveries can be met with opposition, even from other scientists. Continental drift is briefly presented as a case study. The You Decide feature asks students to consider how to evaluate new ideas.
- **Section 13-3:** This section describes some of the evidence that supports continental drift. An explanation of sea-floor spreading also is presented.
- **Section 13-4:** Plate tectonics is explained in terms of divergent, convergent, and transform plate boundaries.

CHAPTER VOCABULARY

inner core
outer core
mantle
crust
continental drift
Pangaea
sea-floor spreading
magnetometer
plate tectonics
plates
lithosphere
asthenosphere
divergent boundary
convergent boundary
subduction zone
transform fault
convection current

CHAPTER

13 Plate Tectonics

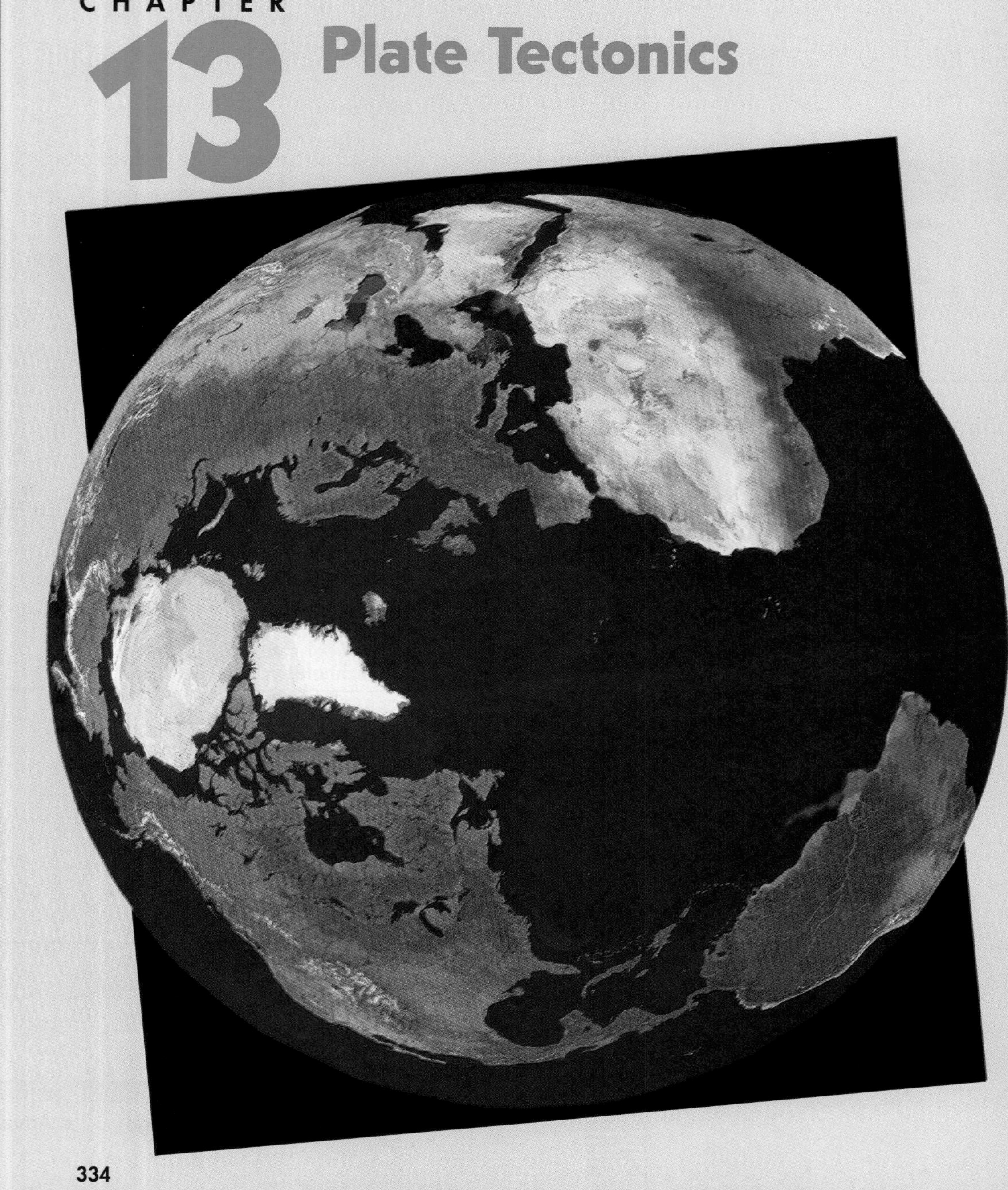

334

OPTIONS

For Your Gifted Students

Have students reduce the outlines of the continents they traced for the Find Out activity so they fit into a circle with a diameter of 10 cm. Students will need to make 12 copies of each continent and cut them all out. Next, have students cut three sheets of $8^1/2 \times 11$ paper into quarters and construct a circle with a 10-cm diameter on each piece. Have students use reference books and arrange the continents on each circle to show a progression, from the formation of Pangaea, to the present, and beyond. Instruct students to place the pages from past to future and staple to form a flip book. Finally, have students speculate what climate, culture, travel, and so on, would have been like if the continents had remained together as Pangaea.

This photo of Earth is unique because the clouds have been removed using a computer. You can see the shapes of the continents just like on a map. Are their shapes related?

FIND OUT!

Do this simple activity to find out how the shapes of the continents are related.

Using thin white paper, trace the outline of the continents using the world map on page 668—Appendix F. Carefully cut each continent out of the paper you traced them on. Using the shapes of the continents as you would pieces of a puzzle, try fitting all continents together into one landmass. Did some continents fit together better than others? Did the shapes of the continents enable you to guess how continents once may have fit together?

Gearing Up

Previewing the Chapter

Use this outline to help you focus on important ideas in this chapter.

Previewing Science Skills

- ▶ In the **Skill Builders,** you will outline, make a concept map, and recognize cause and effect.
- ▶ In the **Activities,** you will analyze and interpret data, make a model, observe, and infer.
- ▶ In the **MINI-Labs,** you will experiment, compare and contrast, observe, and record observations.

What's next?

You've seen that the shapes of the continents can be used to determine if they all fit together at one time in the past. Now you will learn how this and other evidence enabled scientists to draw maps of what ancient Earth may have been like. You will also learn that sections of Earth's crust and mantle move in relation to one another, causing earthquakes, volcanoes, and mountain building.

INTRODUCING THE CHAPTER

Use the Find Out activity to introduce students to continental drift. Briefly explain that the concept of continental drift states that Earth's continents have changed positions over time.

FIND OUT!

Preparation: Obtain scissors for each student in the class.

Materials: scissors, thin white paper

Teaching Tips

▶ Explain that it is not necessary that the continents' outlines be perfect since students are trying to match only the general shapes.

▶ Have students compare their results with other students' results. Discuss differences and similarities.

Gearing Up

Have students study the Gearing Up feature to familiarize themselves with the chapter. Discuss the relationships of the topics in the outline.

What's Next?

Before beginning the first section, make sure students understand the connection between the Find Out activity and the topics to follow.

For Your Mainstreamed Students

▶ Have students place a piece of long, plastic tubing into the neck of a strong balloon and secure the tube so no air can escape the balloon. Have them place the balloon at the bottom of an aquarium tank, with the tubing extending over the top. Add a layer of moist sand and then a layer of dry sand, each about 2 mm deep. Alternate layers several times. Have a student blow up the balloon slowly until the sand begins to crack to simulate an earthquake.

▶ Gifted students may take this simulation one step further. Have those students build a model city on the top of the sand. A student can videotape the "earthquake" and students can prepare a documentary showing how the quake affected the "city."

SECTION 13-1

PREPARATION

SECTION BACKGROUND

▶ Earth's crust is separated from the mantle by a boundary called the Mohorovicić discontinuity, or Moho for short.

▶ Below the Moho, to a depth of about 2900 km, is the mantle. The boundary between the mantle and the outer core is thought to have vast relief of alternating mountains and valleys through which liquid iron flows. The liquid outer core extends to a depth of about 5100 km. A solid inner core underlies the liquid outer core.

▶ Bodies of hot, upwelling material about 2900 km below Earth's surface are associated with "hot spots" in Earth's crust.

PREPLANNING

▶ Obtain some taffy or silicon putty for use in the Mini-Lab on page 339.

1 MOTIVATE

▶ Cut a peach and its pit in half lengthwise and have students observe the layers of the peach. Explain that Earth's layers can be compared to those of the peach.

▶ **Demonstration:** Use a mixture of water and cornstarch to demonstrate how some materials, like Earth's upper mantle, can exhibit characteristics of different states of matter. Mix water into the cornstarch until a very pasty mixture is attained. Have a volunteer demonstrate that the material flows when tilted, but crumbles when he or she drags a finger across it. Compare this material to certain mantle rocks that have characteristics of both liquids and solids.

13-1 Structure of Earth

New Science Words

inner core
outer core
mantle
crust

Objectives

▶ Diagram Earth's structure.
▶ Describe each layer inside Earth.

Structure of Earth

What does soil evolve from?

When you go into school in the morning, what are you walking on? You probably walk on a sidewalk built on top of the soil. You learned in Chapter 5 how soil evolves from weathered rock that lies under the soil. But what lies beneath that? Is the whole interior of Earth solid rock?

1 Earth's interior is made mostly of rock, but it's not all solid. These different forms of rock form four main layers inside Earth. A peach cut in half can be used as a model showing the layers of Earth's interior.

The innermost layer of a peach is the seed inside the pit. Around the seed is a rough oval shaped pit with a very irregular surface. Above the pit is the thick, juicy part of the peach that tastes so good. The outermost layer of a peach is the fuzzy skin. This layer is very thin in comparison to the whole peach. Earth has a similar layered arrangement of different forms of rock.

2 At the very center of Earth is its **inner core.** The inner core is solid and is composed of very dense iron and nickel. Pressure from the layers above the inner core causes the iron and nickel to be solid. This layer can be compared to the seed inside the pit of a peach.

2300 km
1170 km to center
Inner Core
Outer Core

OPTIONS

Meeting Different Ability Levels

For Section 13-1, use the following **Teacher Resource Masters** depending upon individual students' needs.

◆ **Study Guide Master** for all students.

● **Reinforcement Master** for students of average and above average ability levels.

▲ **Enrichment Master** for above average students.

Additional Teacher Resource Package masters are listed in the OPTIONS box throughout the section. The additional masters are appropriate for all students.

◆ **STUDY GUIDE 54**

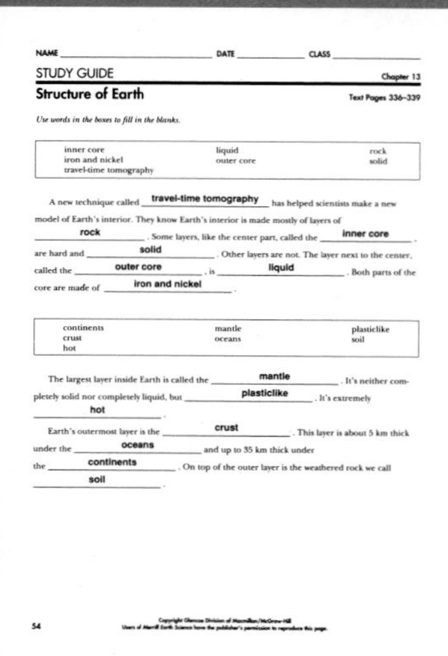

NAME ____ DATE ____ CLASS ____

STUDY GUIDE — Chapter 13

Structure of Earth — Text Pages 336–339

Use words in the boxes to fill in the blanks.

inner core	liquid	rock
iron and nickel	outer core	solid
travel-time tomography		

A new technique called **travel-time tomography** has helped scientists make a new model of Earth's interior. They know Earth's interior is made mostly of layers of **rock**. Some layers, like the center part, called the **inner core**, are hard and **solid**. Other layers are not. The layer next to the center, called the **outer core**, is **liquid**. Both parts of the core are made of **iron and nickel**.

continents	mantle	plasticlike
crust	oceans	soil
hot		

The largest layer inside Earth is called the **mantle**. It's neither completely solid nor completely liquid, but **plasticlike**. It's extremely **hot**.

Earth's outermost layer is the **crust**. This layer is about 5 km thick under the **oceans** and up to 35 km thick under the **continents**. On top of the outer layer is the weathered rock we call **soil**.

54

Above the solid inner core lies the liquid **outer core.** Like the inner core, the outer core is also made of iron and nickel. This layer can be compared to the pit of a peach that covers the seed.

Is the outer core solid or liquid?

3 The **mantle** is the largest layer inside Earth, lying directly above the outer core. It is made mostly of silicon, oxygen, magnesium, and iron. The rock material in the upper mantle is described as "plasticlike." It has characteristics of a solid, but also flows like a liquid when under pressure. Some kinds of hard taffy have this plasticlike characteristic. The taffy can be pulled apart slowly, but if you hit it on the edge of a table it would break. This layer can be compared to the juicy, thickest part of the peach that you eat.

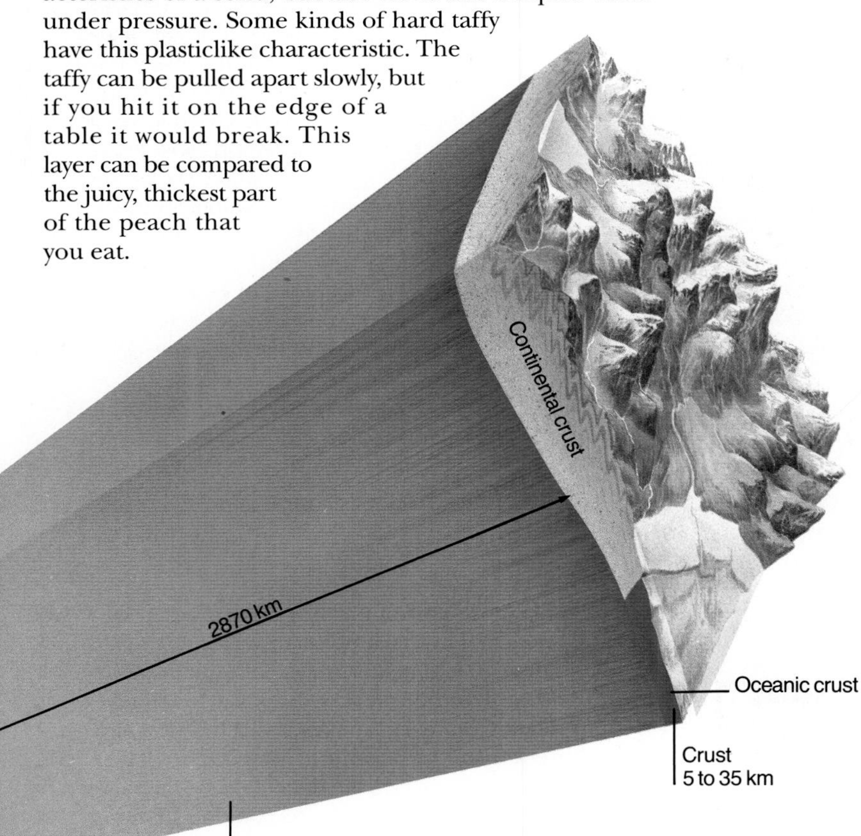

Figure 13-1. This wedge shows the layers inside Earth from the inner core. The inner core, outer core, and mantle are shown at the correct scale, but the crust is shown much thicker than it actually is.

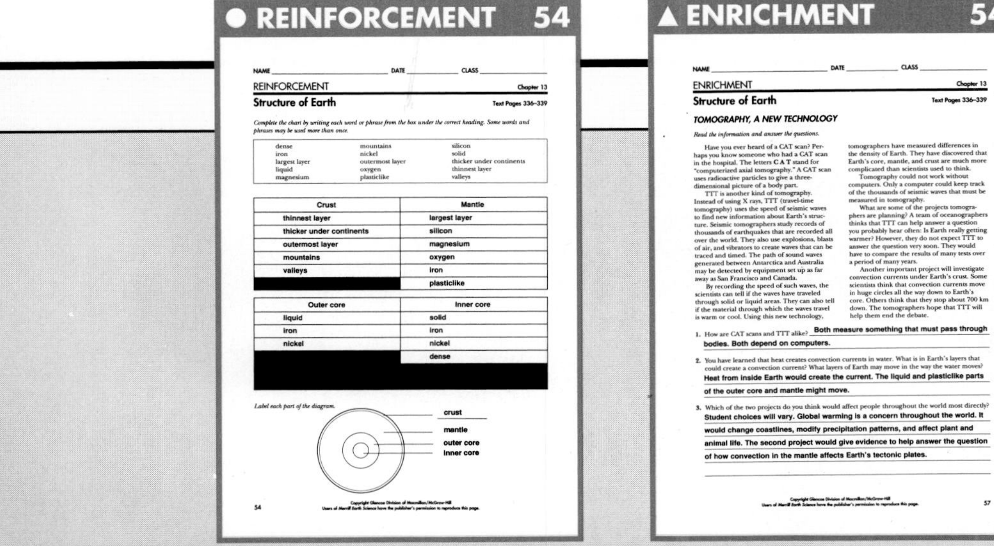

● REINFORCEMENT 54

NAME ______ DATE ______ CLASS ______

REINFORCEMENT — Chapter 13

Structure of Earth — Text Pages 336–339

Complete the chart by writing each word or phrase from the box under the correct heading. Some words and phrases may be used more than once.

dense	mountains	silicon
iron	nickel	solid
largest layer	outermost layer	thicker under continents
liquid	oxygen	thinnest layer
magnesium	plasticlike	valleys

Crust	Mantle
thinnest layer	largest layer
thicker under continents	silicon
outermost layer	magnesium
mountains	oxygen
valleys	iron
	plasticlike

Outer core	Inner core
liquid	solid
iron	iron
nickel	nickel
	dense

Label each part of the diagram.

crust
mantle
outer core
inner core

54

▲ ENRICHMENT 54

NAME ______ DATE ______ CLASS ______

ENRICHMENT — Chapter 13

Structure of Earth — Text Pages 336–339

TOMOGRAPHY, A NEW TECHNOLOGY

Read the information and answer the questions.

Have you ever heard of a CAT scan? Perhaps you know someone who had a CAT scan in the hospital. The letters **C A T** stand for "computerized axial tomography." A CAT scan uses radioactive particles to give a three-dimensional picture of a body part.

TTT is another kind of tomography. Instead of using X rays, TTT (travel-time tomography) uses the speed of seismic waves to find new information about Earth's structure. Seismic tomographers study records of thousands of earthquakes that are recorded all over the world. They also use explosions, blasts of air, and vibrators to create waves that can be traced and timed. The path of sound waves generated between Antarctica and Australia may be detected by equipment set up as far away as San Francisco and Canada.

By recording the speed of such waves, the scientists can tell if the waves have traveled through solid or liquid areas. They can also tell if the material through which the waves travel is warm or cool. Using this new technology, tomographers have measured differences in the density of Earth. They have discovered that Earth's core, mantle, and crust are much more complicated than scientists used to think.

Tomography could not work without computers. Only a computer could keep track of the thousands of seismic waves that must be measured in tomography.

What are some of the projects tomographers are planning? A team of oceanographers thinks that TTT can help answer a question you probably hear often: Is Earth really getting warmer? However, they do not expect TTT to answer the question very soon. They would have to compare the results of many tests over a period of many years.

Another important project will investigate convection currents under Earth's crust. Some scientists think that convection currents move in huge circles all the way down to Earth's core. Others think that they stop about 700 km down. The tomographers hope that TTT will help them end the debate.

1. How are CAT scans and TTT alike? **Both measure something that must pass through bodies. Both depend on computers.**
2. You have learned that heat creates convection currents in water. What is in Earth's layers that could create a convection current? What layers of Earth may move in the way the water moves? **Heat from inside Earth would create the current. The liquid and plasticlike parts of the outer core and mantle might move.**
3. Which of the two projects do you think would affect people throughout the world most directly? **Student choices will vary. Global warming is a concern throughout the world. It would change coastlines, modify precipitation patterns, and affect plant and animal life. The second project would give evidence to help answer the question of how convection in the mantle affects Earth's tectonic plates.**

57

TYING TO PREVIOUS KNOWLEDGE: Have students recall from Chapter 4 how igneous rocks form. Remind students that most of Earth's crust is composed of igneous rocks.

OBJECTIVES AND SCIENCE WORDS: Have students review the objectives and science words to become familiar with this section.

REVEALING MISCONCEPTIONS

▶ Some students think that Earth is a solid sphere. Describe how increased temperatures and pressures can cause rocks to melt. Explain that Earth's outer core is liquid due to the temperatures and pressures at this depth.

2 TEACH

Key Concepts are highlighted.

CONCEPT DEVELOPMENT

Cooperative Learning: Form Expert Teams of five students per team. Each of four students is to be responsible for researching one of the four main layers of Earth's structure. The fifth student is responsible for compiling all information discovered by each expert.

▶ Have students practice sequencing skills by stating Earth's layers from the outside in and then from the inside out.

▶ Hand out samples of granite and basalt and allow students to observe the differences between rocks that make up Earth's continental crust and those that compose ocean crust.

PROGRAM RESOURCES

From the **Teacher Resource Package** use:

Transparency Masters, pages 51-52, Earth Layers.

Cross Curricular Connections, page 17, Calculating Earth Size.

Use **Color Tranparency** number 26, Earth Layers.

TECHNOLOGY

Think Critically: Old models showed concentric layers of Earth that resembled an onion's layers. New models show the relief present at the various Earth boundaries.

CROSS CURRICULUM

▶**Language Arts:** Have students do research to write a brief report about the work of *Glomar Challenger.*

CHECK FOR UNDERSTANDING

Use the Mini Quiz to check for understanding.

MINI QUIZ

Use the Mini Quiz to check students' recall of chapter content.

1. **Earth can be divided into _____ main layers.** *four*
2. **The _____ lies at Earth's center.** *inner core*
3. **What is the thickest part of Earth?** *the mantle*

RETEACH

Cooperative Learning: Using the Paired Partners strategy, have students make four flash cards each showing a sketch of Earth's structure. Have the students color a different layer on each card. On the reverse of the card, have students write the name of the colored layer and some facts about it. Partners can then test each other using the flash cards.

EXTENSION

For students who have mastered this section, use the **Reinforcement** and **Enrichment** masters or other OPTIONS provided.

TECHNOLOGY

A New Picture of Earth's Interior

What does the interior of Earth look like? Since the early 1900s, scientists have been using earthquakes to create models of the structure of Earth's interior. When an earthquake occurs, it generates an energy wave that travels through Earth. By measuring the speed of the wave, scientists constructed a model of Earth's interior that was like an onion. They thought Earth's interior was made of separate layers like an onion's.

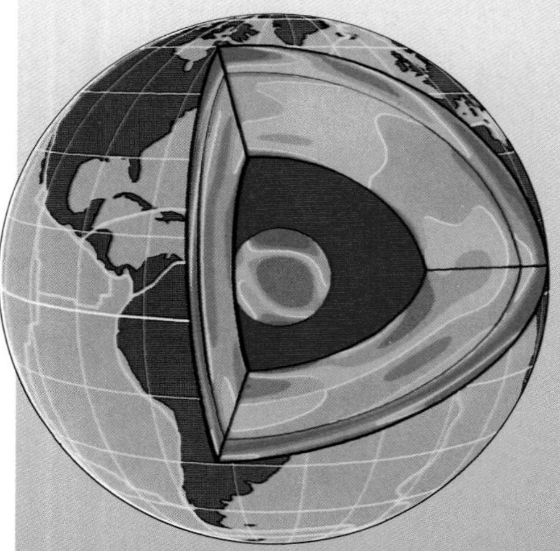

Using a new technique called travel-time tomography (TTT), scientists have made a new model of Earth's interior. TTT uses new technology in which a computer combines data from thousands of earthquakes around the world. The models from the computer have shown hot blobs of mantle material rising from the core-mantel boundary in some places and cooler blobs sinking from the upper mantle in other places.

Think Critically: How is this new model using travel-time tomography different from the old model of Earth's interior?

Did You Know?

The temperature at the center of Earth is about 6600 degrees C, or 1100 degrees hotter than the surface of the sun.

The outermost layer of Earth is the **crust,** similar to the skin of a peach. The crust of Earth varies in thickness. It is greater than 70 kilometers in some mountainous regions and less than five kilometers thick under the oceanic regions. Data from earthquakes indicated that the crust was different from the oceanic crust. Until the late 1960s, scientists had only earthquake data to determine the composition of oceanic crust. Scientists couldn't be sure about the composition of the oceanic crust because it was under up to three kilometers of water and hundreds of meters of sediments. The deep-sea drilling ship *Glomar Challenger* made the recovery of actual ocean floor samples possible. The rock samples proved to be basaltic, as the earthquake data had indicated. Features such as mountains and valleys are part of the crust.

OPTIONS

ENRICHMENT

▶Have students use modeling clay to construct a cut-away model of Earth's structure. Encourage students to show as much detail about Earth's interior as possible. Provide students with the dimensions of Earth's layers so they can make their models to scale.

Figure 13-2. The deep-sea drilling ship *Glomar Challenger* was used to obtain the first samples of oceanic crust.

When you use a peach as a model, you can see that the crust that we live on is very thin in comparison to the other layers inside Earth. Even in Figure 13-1, the thickness of the crust is exaggerated so it can be seen easily. The *Glomar Challenger* couldn't even drill through the crust where it is the thinnest. As you read on, you'll see that unlike the skin of a peach, Earth's crust is always changing and moving.

MINI-Lab

Is it solid or liquid?

Use hard taffy or silicon putty to model the rock in the mantle. Apply differing amounts of force to change its shape. Apply this force in different directions and at different rates. Describe how the taffy or putty reacts when a steady force is applied over several seconds. What happens to the taffy or putty when a greater force is applied rapidly? Describe how the taffy or putty reacts to the different forces. In what ways might the taffy or putty and rock material in Earth's mantle be similar? What causes material in the Earth's mantle to display properties similar to those of the putty and taffy?

SECTION REVIEW

1. Why is the inner core solid?
2. Which part of Earth is comparable to the skin on a peach?
3. Why can the mantle be compared to taffy?
4. **Apply:** Explain why a peach is a good model of Earth's interior.

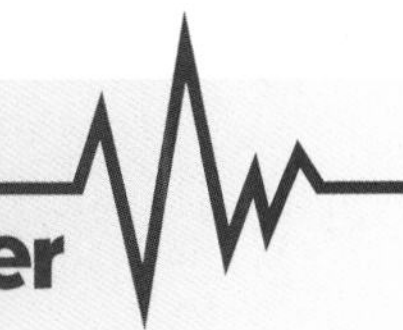

Skill Builder

Outlining

Make an outline that shows the characteristics of each layer of Earth and answer the question below. If you need help, refer to Outlining in the **Skill Handbook** on page 681.

1. What is the inner core composed of?
2. What is the outer core composed of?
3. What is the mantle composed of?

MINI-Lab

Materials: taffy or silicon putty, textbooks, hammer, safety goggles

Teaching Tips

► Have students put the putty or taffy under their textbooks for several minutes. They should discover that the materials "flowed" due to the increased pressure and temperature.

► **Answers:** Both the silicon putty and rocks will bend and flow without breaking if exposed to heat and pressure over a long time period. Pressure over a short time will cause the material to break. Rock in Earth's mantle, when subjected to high pressure and heat over time, will display physical properties similar to those of the silicon putty.

3 CLOSE

► Ask questions 1 and 2 and the **Apply** Question in the Section Review.

FLEX Your Brain

Use the Flex Your Brain activity to have students explore EARTH'S STRUCTURE.

SECTION REVIEW ANSWERS

1. Pressure from overlying rocks causes the inner core to be solid.

2. the crust

3. It is solid but also plasticlike. It will flow under pressure but break if sudden force is applied.

4. Apply: The thickness of each part of the peach is comparable to each layer of Earth.

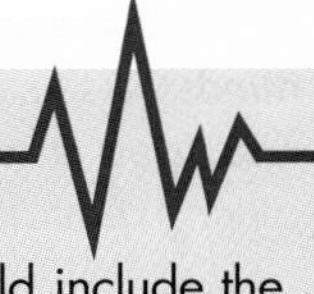

Skill Builder

Students' outlines should include the thickness and composition of each layer. The crust is the thinnest layer of Earth.

1. iron and nickel
2. iron and nickel
3. silicon, oxygen, magnesium, iron

INQUIRY QUESTIONS

► **How do the densities of rocks that make up Earth's crust compare to the densities of rocks of the mantle?** *Crustal rocks have lower densities than mantle rocks.*

► **Samples of rock from the continental crust are easy to obtain, but how can scientists obtain samples of oceanic crust?** *Scientists can use ships equipped with drill pipes to obtain samples of the ocean floor.*

PROGRAM RESOURCES

From the **Teacher Resource Package** use:

Activity Worksheets, page 5, Flex Your Brain.

Activity Worksheets, page 119, Mini-Lab: Is it solid or liquid?

SECTION 13-2

PREPARATION

SECTION BACKGROUND

▶ About 200 million years ago, Pangaea covered about 40 percent of Earth's surface, while a large ocean, Panthalassa, covered the rest of the planet. Pangaea broke up to form Laurasia and Gondwanaland, which were separated by the Tethys Sea.

1 MOTIVATE

FLEX Your Brain

Use the Flex Your Brain activity to have students explore CONTINENTAL DRIFT.

TYING TO PREVIOUS KNOWLEDGE: Have students recall from Chapter 1 the difference between a hypothesis and a theory.

OBJECTIVES AND SCIENCE WORDS: Have students review the objectives and science words to become familiar with this section.

2 TEACH

Key Concepts are highlighted.

CONCEPT DEVELOPMENT

▶ Have students relate the Find Out activity to continental drift. Then ask: **Why did many people close their minds to the idea of continental drift?** *The idea was so different from any other explanations of that time.*

PROGRAM RESOURCES

From the **Teacher Resource Package** use:

Activity Worksheets page 5, Flex Your Brain.

Science and Society, page 17, Examining New Ideas.

13-2 Science and New Ideas

New Science Words

continental drift
Pangaea

Objectives

▶ Explain the idea of continental drift.
▶ Recognize that new ideas require careful consideration.

Are New Ideas Sometimes Laughed At?

When you look at a map of Earth's surface, one thing is very obvious. The edges of some continents look as if they would fit together like a puzzle. In the early 1800s, as accurate maps of Earth's surface were first being developed, others also noticed this fact.

What is continental drift?

Alfred Wegener thought that the fit of the continents wasn't just a coincidence. He believed that all the continents were joined together in the past, and in 1915, proposed the idea of continental drift. **Continental drift** states that continents have moved horizontally to their current locations. Wegener believed that all continents were once connected as one large landmass that broke apart about 200 million years ago. When the continents broke apart, they drifted to their present positions. He called this large landmass **Pangaea** (pan JEE uh), which means "all Earth."

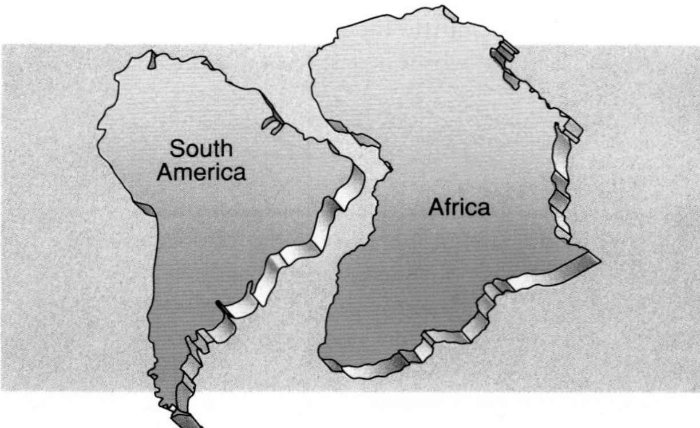

Figure 13-3. The coastlines of South America and Africa look like they would fit together as puzzle pieces.

OPTIONS

Meeting Different Ability Levels

For Section 13-2, use the following **Teacher Resource Masters** depending upon individual students' needs.

◆ **Study Guide Master** for all students.

● **Reinforcement Master** for students of average and above average ability levels.

▲ **Enrichment Master** for above average students.

Additional Teacher Resource Package masters are listed in the OPTIONS box throughout the section. The additional masters are appropriate for all students.

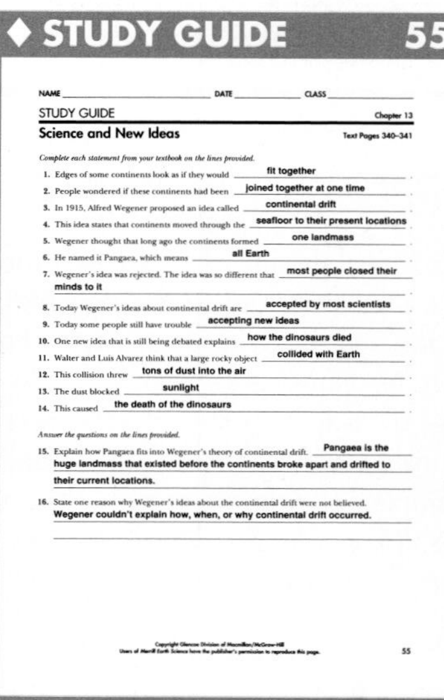

◆ STUDY GUIDE 55

NAME ______ DATE ______ CLASS ______

STUDY GUIDE Chapter 13

Science and New Ideas Text Pages 340–341

Complete each statement from your textbook on the lines provided.

1. Edges of some continents look as if they would **fit together**.
2. People wondered if these continents had been **joined together at one time**.
3. In 1915, Alfred Wegener proposed an idea called **continental drift**.
4. This idea states that continents moved through the **seafloor to their present locations**.
5. Wegener thought that long ago the continents formed **one landmass**.
6. He named it Pangaea, which means **all Earth**.
7. Wegener's idea was rejected. The idea was so different that **most people closed their minds to it**.
8. Today Wegener's ideas about continental drift are **accepted by most scientists**.
9. Today some people still have trouble **accepting new ideas**.
10. One new idea that is still being debated explains **how the dinosaurs died**.
11. Walter and Luis Alvarez think that a large rocky object **collided with Earth**.
12. This collision threw **tons of dust into the air**.
13. The dust blocked **sunlight**.
14. This caused **the death of the dinosaurs**.

Answer the questions on the lines provided.

15. Explain how Pangaea fits into Wegener's theory of continental drift. **Pangaea is the huge landmass that existed before the continents broke apart and drifted to their current locations.**
16. State one reason why Wegener's ideas about the continental drift were not believed. **Wegener couldn't explain how, when, or why continental drift occurred.**

55

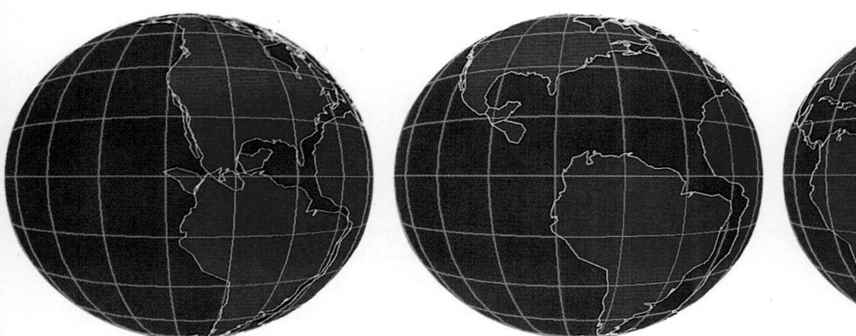

Figure 13-4. These computer models show the probable course that continents have taken. On the far left is their position 200 million years ago, in the middle is their position 100 million years ago, and at right is their current position.

Although the basic idea of continental drift is now widely accepted, it wasn't always that way. Wegener couldn't explain how, when, or why these changes in the position of the continents had taken place. Because other scientists at that time could not provide these explanations either, Wegener's idea of continental drift was rejected. The idea was so different that most people closed their minds to it. In fact, some people laughed and made fun of Wegener's idea. Today, some people are having similar experiences with their new ideas.

One topic that is currently being debated is how the dinosaurs died. Walter and Luis Alvarez have proposed that a large rocky object from space collided with Earth. The collision threw tons of dust into the atmosphere. Sunlight was blocked for several years, eventually causing the death of the dinosaurs.

SECTION REVIEW

1. Explain how Pangaea fits into Wegener's idea of continental drift.
2. State one reason why Wegener's ideas about continental drift were not believed.

You Decide!

SCIENCE & SOCIETY

Because the idea proposed by Walter and Luis Alvarez is so different, many scientists have rejected it completely. What do you think about this issue? Would you accept their idea as a way that the dinosaurs might have been killed? How can you decide which new ideas to reject and which ones to accept?

● REINFORCEMENT 55

NAME ______ DATE ______ CLASS ______

REINFORCEMENT — Chapter 13

Science and New Ideas — Text Pages 340–341

Find the mistakes in the statements below. Rewrite each statement correctly on the lines provided.

1. About 200 million years ago a scientist named Luis Alvarez stated that all continents were once connected. **In 1915 a scientist named Alfred Wegener stated that all continents were once connected.**
2. The continents formed a large landmass which broke apart in 1915. **The continents formed a large landmass which broke apart about 200 million years ago.**
3. Wegener developed his theory after noticing that the edges of some continents seemed to fit together—South America and Pangaea, for example. **Wegener developed his theory after noticing that the edges of some continents seemed to fit together — South America and Africa, for example.**
4. He called his theory drift continental. **He called his theory continental drift.**
5. He named the landmass Africa. **He named the landmass Pangaea.**
6. At first, the theory was widely accepted. **At first, the theory was rejected.**
7. It is now rejected by most scientists. **It's now accepted by most scientists.**
8. Scientists are now discussing the question of when dinosaurs lived. **Scientists are now discussing the question of how dinosaurs died.**
9. Walter and Luis Alvarez have suggested that a large dusty object collided with Earth. **Walter and Luis Alvarez have suggested that a large rocky object collided with Earth.**
10. Sunlight was brighter for several years, causing the death of the dinosaurs. **Sunlight was blocked for several years, causing the death of the dinosaurs.**
11. New ideas are sometimes so different that most people readily accept them. **New ideas are sometimes so different that most people close their minds to them.**

55

▲ ENRICHMENT 55

NAME ______ DATE ______ CLASS ______

ENRICHMENT — Chapter 13

Science and New Ideas — Text Pages 340–341

THE METEORITE THEORY

Use the information below to answer the questions.

You know from your reading of the text that Luis and Walter Alvarez proposed that a large rocky object from space collided with Earth, producing tons of dust that blocked out the sun. This darkening of the atmosphere, they suggested, lasted for several years and caused the death of the dinosaurs and other living things.

On what evidence did the Alvarezes base their proposal? They discovered that rocks in many parts of the world show traces of a thin layer of iridium. They established that these rocks date back to the end of the Cretaceous period, the time when the dinosaurs became extinct. They know that iridium is very rare on Earth, but is present in large quantities in meteorites. Their studies indicate that the colliding meteor was almost 10 km in diameter and that such a meteor would have had a tremendous impact. It would scatter an enormous cloud of debris into the sky. Luis and Walter Alvarez think the cloud would have been so large that the sun would have been dimmed for years. This would cause a cold period—a "long winter." Plants would not grow and temperatures would drop. This would bring about the extinction of many animals.

Many scientists today are not convinced that Luis and Walter Alvarez have developed a realistic theory. No crater has been found, and surely a meteor nearly 10 km in diameter would have left some mark of its impact. In addition, recent studies seem to show that the extinction of many species of animals did not happen all at once. A dolphinlike animal known as the icthyosaur, once thought to have died out at the time of the dinosaurs, is now known to have become extinct millions of years earlier.

If a meteor did not strike Earth, where did the deposits of iridium come from? Some scientists claim that these deposits could be due to increased volcanic activity. It seems that the mystery of the extinction of dinosaurs is still not solved.

1. List the FACTS that support the proposal suggested by Luis and Walter Alvarez.
Dinosaurs and other species are extinct. Iridium can be found in rock layers of the period under study. Iridium is rare on Earth, but common in meteorites. A long winter would destroy some food sources and, therefore, some animals.
2. List the CONCLUSIONS drawn from these facts by Luis and Walter Alvarez.
Iridium is present in quantities because of a collision between Earth and a meteor. The meteor's impact caused a dust cloud that lasted for years. The cloud blotted out the sun. Plants and animals died.
3. List REASONS that some scientists doubt the conclusions of Luis and Walter Alvarez.
There's no crater to show a meteor collision. Iridium could have come from volcanic activity. Animals previously thought to have become extinct at the same time may actually have died out at different times.

54

The computer models shown in Figure 13-4 were generated on a micro computer with *Time-Machine™ Earth* software from Sageware Corporation, 1282 Garner Ave., Schenectady, NY 12309. (518) 377-1052.

CHECK FOR UNDERSTANDING

Lead a discussion that helps students conclude that scientific discoveries should be studied carefully with an open mind before rejection or acceptance.

RETEACH

Show students recent photographs of Mars and radar images of Venus. Ask students to study the photos and accept or reject the hypothesis that there was or is tectonic activity on both planets.

EXTENSION

For students who have mastered this section, use the **Reinforcement** and **Enrichment** masters or other OPTIONS provided.

CONCEPT DEVELOPMENT

▶ Have students research the recent work by Walter and Luis Alvarez concerning dinosaur extinction.

3 CLOSE

▶ Ask questions 1 and 2 in the Section Review.

▶ Have students relate examples from their everyday lives during which they experienced difficulty in convincing others of new ideas.

SECTION REVIEW ANSWERS

1. Pangaea was a supercontinent that broke apart over time. The basis for continental drift is that all continents were once connected and have gradually drifted apart.

2. Wegener could not explain how, when, or why the continents drifted.

YOU DECIDE!

Use the suggestions listed in the Close section above to help students answer these questions.

SECTION 13-3

PREPARATION

SECTION BACKGROUND

▶ Fossils of *Lystrosaurus*, a small reptile that lived about 200 million years ago, have been found in South Africa, Antarctica, and India.

▶ Certain species of green turtles swim from South America to the Ascension Island in the mid-Atlantic to lay their eggs. The turtles may have started this trip when continents were much closer. As the seafloor spread, the instinctive trip became longer.

▶ Wegener's idea of continental drift was rejected mainly because he suggested that the continents plowed through oceanic crust. Sir Harold Jeffries had shown that oceanic crust was too rigid for this to occur, regardless of the mechanism.

▶ Paleomagnetism is the study of the magnetic properties of ancient rocks.

PREPLANNING

▶ To prepare for Activity 13-1, obtain two small magnetic compasses, one bar magnet, and a metric ruler for each group of students.

PROGRAM RESOURCES

From the **Teacher Resource Package** use:

Critical Thinking/Problem Solving, page 19, Pangaea's Climate.

13-3 Evidence for Continental Drift

New Science Words

sea-floor spreading
magnetometer

Objectives

- ▶ Discuss four pieces of evidence for the idea of continental drift.
- ▶ Describe sea-floor spreading.
- ▶ Relate how age and magnetic clues confirm sea-floor spreading.

Early Evidence

Since Wegener's death in 1930, much of his basic idea that the continents drift has been accepted as fact. But the evidence he had at that time to support his idea wasn't enough to convince many. Wegener's early evidence has since been joined by other important proofs. Let's explore both Wegener's clues and some newer ones.

Fossil and Climate Clues

Besides the puzzle-like fit of the continents, other clues were found in fossils. Fossils of the reptile *Mesosaurus* have been found in South America and Africa. This swimming reptile lived in fresh water and on land. How could fossils of the *Mesosaurus* be found so far apart? It's very unlikely that it could have swum between the continents. Wegener thought this reptile lived on both continents when the continents were connected.

Another fossil that helps support continental drift is *Glossopteris*. This fossil fern was found in Africa, Australia, India, South America, and later in Antarctica. Finding this fern in so many areas with widely different climates led Wegener to believe all of these areas were once connected and had a similar climate.

Fossils of warm weather plants were found in Greenland, which has a cold climate. Wegener believed Greenland drifted through the ocean floor from a warmer to a colder climate. He also found glacial clues. Glacial deposits and grooved bedrock found in southern areas of South America, Africa, India, and Australia

Figure 13-5. Alfred Wegener

OPTIONS

Meeting Different Ability Levels

For Section 13-3, use the following **Teacher Resource Masters** depending upon individual students' needs.

◆ **Study Guide Master** for all students.

● **Reinforcement Master** for students of average and above average ability levels.

▲ **Enrichment Master** for above average students.

Additional Teacher Resource Package masters are listed in the OPTIONS box throughout the section. The additional masters are appropriate for all students.

◆ STUDY GUIDE 56

NAME ______ DATE ______ CLASS ______

STUDY GUIDE — Chapter 13

Evidence for Continental Drift — Text Pages 342–347

Use the words and phrases in the boxes to complete each part of the outline.

Climate clues, Fossil clues, Glaciers, Plants, Rock clues

Evidence for continental drift

I. Early evidence
  A. Puzzlelike fit of continents
  B. Fossil clues
    1. Mesosaurus
    2. Glossopteris
    3. Plants
  C. Climate clues
    1. Glaciers
    2. Glacial deposits
  D. Rock clues

Magnetic evidence, Age evidence, Older rock farther from mid-ocean ridge, Reversal of magnetic alignment of rocks, Ocean rock newer than continental rock

II. Later evidence: sea-floor spreading
  A. Age evidence
    1. *Glomar Challenger* research
      a. Newer rock near mid-ocean ridge
      b. Older rock farther from mid-ocean ridge
      c. Ocean rock newer than continental rock
  B. Magnetic evidence
    1. Known reversal of Earth's magnetic field
    2. Reversal of magnetic alignment of rocks

56

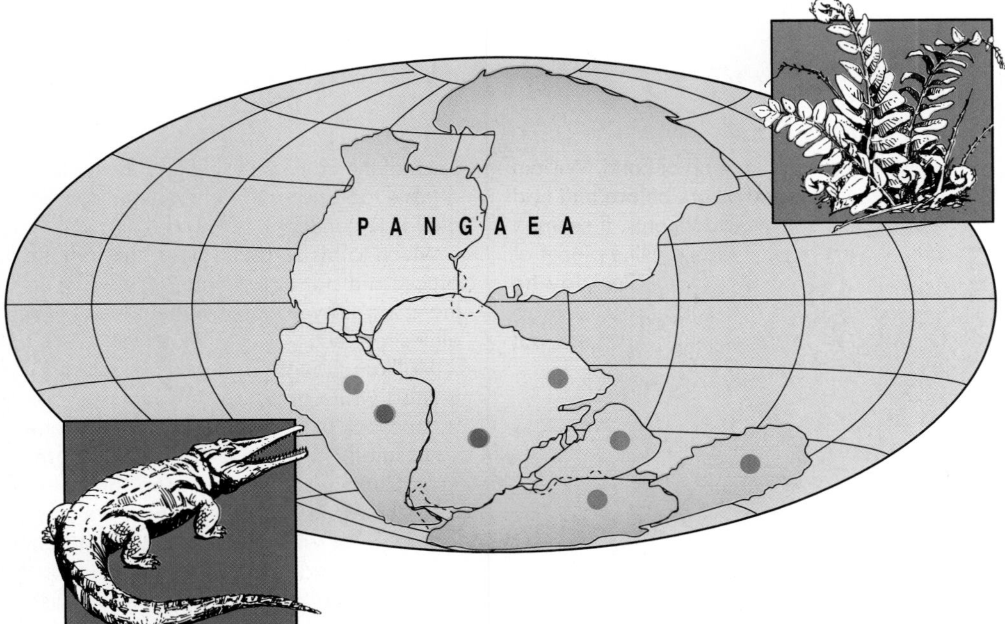

Figure 13-6. *Glossopteris* and *Mesosaurus* lived in many areas of Pangaea. Their fossils are now found on separate continents that have since drifted apart.

indicated that these continents were once covered with glaciers. How could you explain why glacial deposits were found in these areas where no glaciers exist today? Wegener thought that these continents were all connected and covered with ice near Earth's South Pole at one time.

Rock Clues

If the continents were connected at one time, then wouldn't rocks that make up the continents be the same? Yes, similar rock structures are found on different continents. Parts of the Appalachian Mountains of the eastern United States are similar to those found in Greenland and western Europe. If you were to travel to South America and western Africa, you would find rock structures that are very similar. If the continents were connected when the rock structures formed, you would expect them to be the same.

Why are matching rock structures evidence for continental drift?

Rock, fossil, and climate clues were the main points of evidence for continental drift. Later, after Wegener's death, more clues were found and new ideas related to continental drift were discovered.

1 MOTIVATE

FLEX Your Brain

Use the Flex Your Brain activity to have students explore CONTINENTAL DRIFT.

Cooperative Learning: Obtain some plant and animal fossils and place them around the room before class begins. Place identical fossils in at least three widely separated areas of the room. Form Problem Solving teams and have each team list the fossils found at each location. Have students discuss why identical fossils were found at widely separated locations.

TYING TO PREVIOUS KNOWLEDGE: Have students recall how magma forms. Have students discuss how rising magma affects the overlying crust. Ask students what might happen if magma flowed onto the ocean floor.

OBJECTIVES AND SCIENCE WORDS: Have students review the objectives and science words to become familiar with this section.

2 TEACH

Key Concepts are highlighted.

CONCEPT DEVELOPMENT

▶ If possible, obtain a tectonic globe that enables you to move the continents as you teach this section and Section 13-4.

PROGRAM RESOURCES

From the **Teacher Resource Package** use:

Activity Worksheets, page 5, Flex Your Brain.

● REINFORCEMENT 56

NAME ______ DATE ______ CLASS ______

REINFORCEMENT — Chapter 13

Evidence for Continental Drift — Text Pages 342–346

Match the items in Column I with the terms or phrases in Column II. Write the letter of the correct term or phrase in the blank at the left.

	Column I	Column II
l	1. Reptile fossil found in South America and Africa	a. Alfred Wegener
h	2. Fern fossil found in Africa, Australia, India, South America, and Antarctica	b. Appalachians
p	3. Clues that support continental drift	c. away from the mid-ocean ridge
b	4. Mountains similar to those in Greenland and western Europe	d. basalt
m	5. An underwater mountain range	e. continental drift
a	6. Scientist who suggested theory of continental drift	f. glacial deposits
i	7. Scientist who suggested theory of sea-floor spreading	g. *Glomar Challenger*
n	8. Material that rises to surface at mid-ocean ridge	h. *Glossopteris*
c	9. Direction in which ocean floor moves	i. Harry Hess
s	10. Place where the seafloor is forced down into the mantle	j. magnetic
g	11. Research ship	k. magnetometer
t	12. Age of oldest seafloor rocks	l. *Mesosaurus*
r	13. Age of oldest continental rocks	m. mid-ocean ridge
o	14. Location of youngest seafloor rocks	n. molten material in the mantle
d	15. Rock containing iron	o. nearest to ridge
j	16. Poles that reverse themselves	p. rock, fossil, and climate
k	17. Machine that records magnetic data	q. sea-floor spreading
q	18. Process that forms new seafloor	r. 3 billion years
e	19. Movement of continents	s. trench
f	20. Evidence that Africa was once cold	t. 200 million years

56

▲ ENRICHMENT 56

NAME ______ DATE ______ CLASS ______

ENRICHMENT — Chapter 13

Evidence for Continental Drift — Text Pages 342–346

STUDYING SEA-FLOOR SPREADING ON LAND

Read the information and study the maps to answer the questions that follow.

You know from your textbook how sea-floor spreading changes the ocean floor. You know that magma rises at the mid-ocean ridge and flows away from the ridge. In general, this activity is hidden beneath the ocean's water. But there is a place where sea-floor spreading can be seen on land.

FIGURE 1: Iceland, North America, Pacific Ocean, Africa, South America, Atlantic Ocean. Key: Mid-ocean ridge; • Active volcanoes

FIGURE 2: Iceland. 0 100 km. Key: Active volcanoes; formed from today to 10 000 years ago. Formed 10 000 to 2 000 000 years ago. Formed 2 000 000 to 63 000 000 years ago

1. What is the name of the landmass through which the mid-ocean ridge in the Atlantic Ocean passes? **Iceland**
2. How does the land of Iceland confirm sea-floor spreading? **The island's youngest rock is in the center; the oldest is at the eastern and western edges. This shows that on Iceland, as on the ocean floor, molten magma from the mantle rises at the ridge and spreads outward.**
3. At about what rate does magma (rock) on the eastern side of the ridge on Iceland travel per year (1 km = 1 000 000 cm)? **125 000 000 cm / 63 000 000 yr = about 2 cm per year**
4. Why do you think geologists might find Iceland a useful place to carry on research on seafloor spreading? **Research can be done more easily on land and with less expense. Land research can help confirm the findings of underwater research.**

55

CONCEPT DEVELOPMENT

▶ Obtain a landform map of the world. One source of such a map is *Goode's World Atlas*, published by Rand McNally & Company. Have students note the similarities of landforms on the widely separated continents. Then have them visualize what Wegener's Pangaea may have looked like based on the present-day landform map.

▶ Have students answer the following questions. **Briefly describe the theory of sea-floor spreading.** *Magma rises toward Earth's surface at mid-ocean ridges. The magma turns and flows laterally, carrying ocean floor away from the ridge in both directions.* **What have studies performed by crews on the *Glomar Challenger* discovered about oceanic crust?** *No rocks older than 200 million years have been found. The youngest rocks are located near the mid-ocean ridge.*

PROBLEM SOLVING

Think Critically: On his first try, William cut out the continents as they appear above sea level and found the edges didn't fit together very well. He probably remembered that continents extend below sea level as continental shelves. When William included the continental shelf of each continent, he found that the continental "puzzle pieces" fit together very well.

CROSS CURRICULUM

▶ **History:** Have students research the life and scientific work of Alfred Wegener. Encourage students to read about his work in Greenland and how that research led him to formulate his idea of continental drift.

PROBLEM SOLVING

A Perfect Fit?

While looking at a map of Earth, William noticed what many others before him had suggested about the continents. It seemed that they might all fit together like pieces of a puzzle. One day he took an old map and cut out each of the continents. He laid them all on a table top and tried to fit them into a single large continent.

Much to his surprise, he found that the pieces did not fit together very well. Yet there were several areas where the fit was almost perfect.

William thought about this problem for a short while and had an idea. He took one look at another map and made one small adjustment in his procedure. Cutting another old map, he found that almost all of the pieces would fit together with the one slight change in what he had done.

Think Critically: How do you suppose William solved this problem?

Sea-floor Spreading

What did echo sounding discover about the ocean floor?

Up until the early 1950s, little was known about the ocean floors. Scientists didn't have the technology needed to explore the deep oceans. But echo sounding devices allowed scientists to begin making accurate maps of the ocean floor. Soon, scientists discovered a complex ocean floor that had mountains and valleys just like continents had above water. They also found a system of ridges and valleys extending through the center of the Atlantic and
1 in other oceans around the world. The mid-ocean ridges form an underwater mountain range that extends through the center of much of Earth's oceans. This discovery raised the curiosity of many scientists. What formed these mid-ocean ridges?

In the early 1960s, Princeton scientist Harry Hess suggested an explanation. His now famous and accepted theory is known as **sea-floor spreading.** Hess proposed
2 that molten material in the mantle rises to the surface at a mid-ocean ridge. Then it turns and flows sideways,

OPTIONS

INQUIRY QUESTIONS

▶ **What device enabled scientists to discover more about the topography of the ocean floor in the mid-1950s?** *Echo sounding devices enabled scientists to map the ocean floor.*

▶ **Describe how echo sounding works.** *Sound waves are reflected off an object. The time it takes for the waves to return is measured. Thus, the distance to an object can be determined.*

▶ **How does volcanic activity at mid-ocean ridges support the theory of sea-floor spreading?** *Magma from deep inside Earth rises, cools, and pushes Earth's crust apart, causing the seafloor to separate.*

carrying the seafloor away from the ridge in both directions as seen in Figure 13-7. New seafloor is then created in the middle of the mid-ocean ridge by the rising magma. The seafloor that is carried away from the ridge is forced down into the mantle at the edges of the oceans, forming trenches. Sea-floor spreading was later shown to be true by the two following pieces of evidence.

Age Evidence

In 1968, scientists aboard the research ship *Glomar Challenger* began gathering information about the rocks in the seafloor. The *Challenger* is equipped with a drilling rig that allows scientists to drill into the seafloor to obtain rock samples. The scientists began drilling to study the age of rocks in the seafloor and made a remarkable discovery. They found no rocks older than 200 million years. In contrast, some continental rocks are more than three billion years old. Why were these seafloor rocks so young? 3

What did the *Glomar Challenger* discover about the ocean floor?

Scientists also found that the youngest rocks were located at the mid-ocean ridges. The age of the rocks became increasingly older farther from the ridges on both sides. The evidence for sea-floor spreading was getting stronger.

Magnetic Clues

The final bit of evidence in support of sea-floor spreading came with magnetic clues found in the iron-bearing basalt rock in the ocean floor.

Figure 13-7. As the seafloor spreads apart at a mid-ocean ridge, new seafloor is created. The older seafloor moves away from the ridge in both directions.

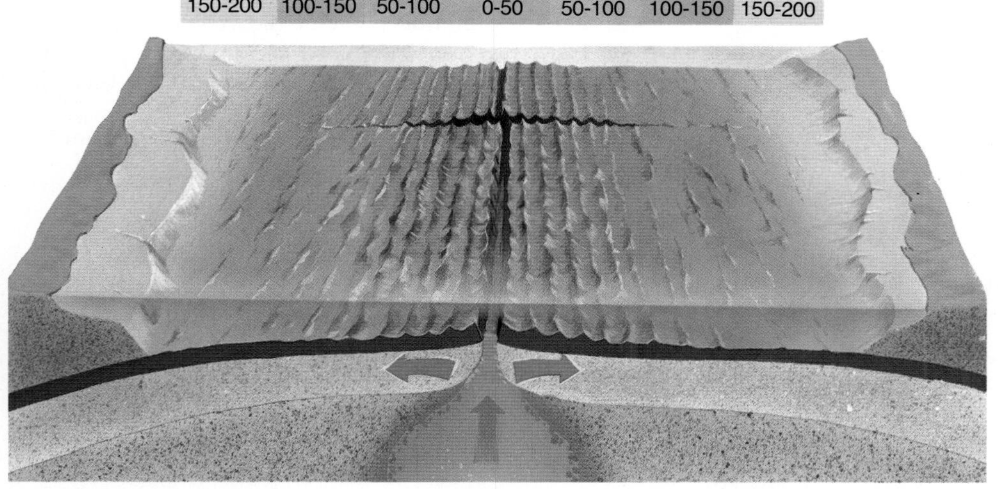

STUDENT TEXT QUESTIONS

▶ Page 345, paragraph 2: **Why were these ocean-floor rocks so young?** *They had formed relatively recently.*

CONCEPT DEVELOPMENT

▶ **Demonstration:** Demonstrate a magnetic field and lines of force by placing iron filings on a stiff piece of cardboard, and placing a large bar magnet below the cardboard. Carefully spray the iron filings with clear lacquer so they retain the alignment. Have students observe the magnetic field produced and the lines of force.

CHECK FOR UNDERSTANDING

Use the Mini Quiz to check for understanding.

MINI QUIZ

Use the Mini Quiz to check students' recall of chapter content.

1. **A(n) ____ is an underwater mountain range.** *mid-ocean ridge*
2. **What happens to magma at a mid-ocean ridge?** *It rises toward Earth's surface.*
3. **How old are the oldest ocean-floor rocks?** *about 200 million years old*

RETEACH

Cooperative Learning: Using the Paired Partner strategy, have students construct 3-dimensional models of rifting at a mid-ocean ridge.

EXTENSION

For students who have mastered this section, use the **Reinforcement** and **Enrichment** masters or other OPTIONS provided.

ENRICHMENT

▶ Have students write reports comparing and contrasting the work of crews aboard the ships *Glomar Challenger* and *JOIDES Resolution*.

▶ Have students find out about the geologic history of Iceland. Have them concentrate on rifting on the island.

PROGRAM RESOURCES

From the **Teacher Resource Package** use:

Technology Worksheet, pages 13-14, Glomar Challenger.

Use **Laboratory Manual** page 113, Continental Drift.

CONCEPT DEVELOPMENT

▶ **How do reversals in Earth's magnetic field affect rocks forming at mid-ocean ridges?** *As magma flows onto the seafloor, minerals containing iron will align with the current magnetic field. When the magnetic field reverses, minerals in the magma cooling at that time will show different alignment.*

3 CLOSE

▶ Ask questions 1-4 and the **Apply** Question in the Section Review.

FLEX Your Brain

Use the Flex Your Brain activity to have students explore SEA-FLOOR SPREADING.

▶ Ask for a volunteer to present a summary of the section as if he or she were informing a classmate who had missed class.

SECTION REVIEW ANSWERS

1. Iron minerals in ocean-floor rocks align with the magnetic field present when the rocks formed. Alternating magnetic bands parallel to mid-ocean ridges have been found and thus support the idea of sea-floor spreading.
2. the puzzle-like fit of the continents
3. Fossils of the same organism have been found in widely separated areas.
4. It is forced down into the mantle at trenches.
5. Apply: Sea-floor spreading states that continents move with the seafloor. Continental drift proposed that the continents plowed through the seafloor.

PROGRAM RESOURCES

From the **Teacher Resource Package** use:

Activity Worksheets, page 5, Flex Your Brain.

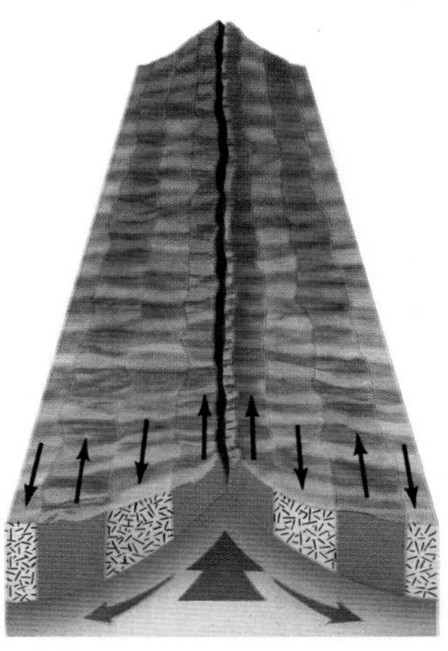

Figure 13-8. Changes in magnetic polarity of the rock on both sides of mid-ocean ridges reflect the past reversals of Earth's magnetic poles. This is evidence for sea-floor spreading.

Scientists know that Earth's magnetic field has reversed itself several times in its past. In other words, the north magnetic pole becomes the south magnetic pole. Iron minerals in rocks such as basalt align themselves according to the magnetic orientation at the time that they form. If Earth's magnetic field is reversed, new iron minerals being formed would reflect that magnetic reversal.

Scientists found that rocks on the ocean floor showed many magnetic reversals. Scientists used a magnetometer to record magnetic data about the rocks in the ocean floor. A **magnetometer** is a sensitive instrument that records magnetic fields. The magnetic alignment of the rocks reversed back and forth in strips parallel to the mid-ocean ridge. These magnetic reversals were found to match with known reversals of Earth's magnetic pole.

This discovery proved that sea-floor spreading was indeed happening. The magnetic reversals showed that new rock was being formed at the mid-ocean ridges.

The ideas of Alfred Wegener and Harry Hess changed the way people think about Earth's crust. Fossil, rock, and climate evidence supporting continental drift is too strong to be discounted. Sea-floor spreading proves that ocean floors change too. You'll see in Section 13-4 how these two ideas are closely related.

SECTION REVIEW

1. How did the magnetic alignment of iron minerals help to prove sea-floor spreading?
2. What continental drift clue did Wegener first use?
3. How were fossils used as clues for continental drift?
4. What eventually happens to seafloor that is carried away from a mid-ocean ridge?
5. **Apply:** How is sea-floor spreading different from continental drift?

Skill Builder — Concept Mapping

Make a concept map that discusses the evidence for continental drift using the following terms and phrases: *continental edges, same fossils, climate, rock structures, on different continents, mountains with similar features, continental ice sheets,* and *puzzle pieces.* If you need help, refer to Concept Mapping in the **Skill Handbook** on page 688.

346

Skill Builder

Possible Solution:

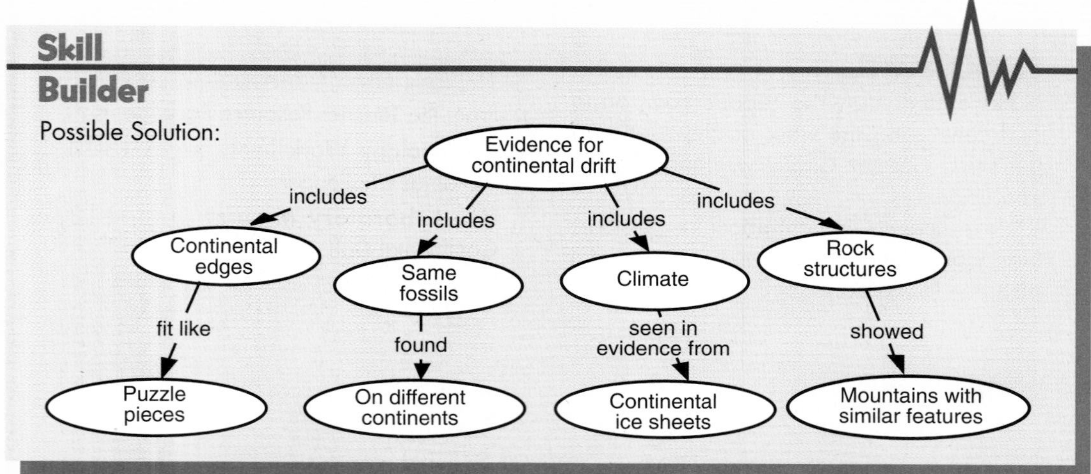

ACTIVITY 13-1
Sea-floor Spreading

Problem: *How does magnetic evidence confirm sea-floor spreading?*

Materials
- metric ruler
- paper
- tape
- small magnetic compasses (2)
- bar magnets
- pen or marker

Procedure
1. Tape several sheets of paper together to produce a strip from 40 to 60 cm in length.
2. Fold the strip of paper and place it between two close desks or piles of books as shown. The paper represents oceanic crust on either side of a mid-ocean ridge.
3. Place the magnets as shown.
4. Place the two compasses next to each other on either side of the space between the desks.
5. Draw a line along each side of the space to represent the edges of the ocean ridge.
6. Beside the line, draw arrows showing the direction the compass needles are pointing.
7. Split the "seafloor" by moving the paper away from the center 3 cm on each side. Reverse the magnets by turning them 180°.

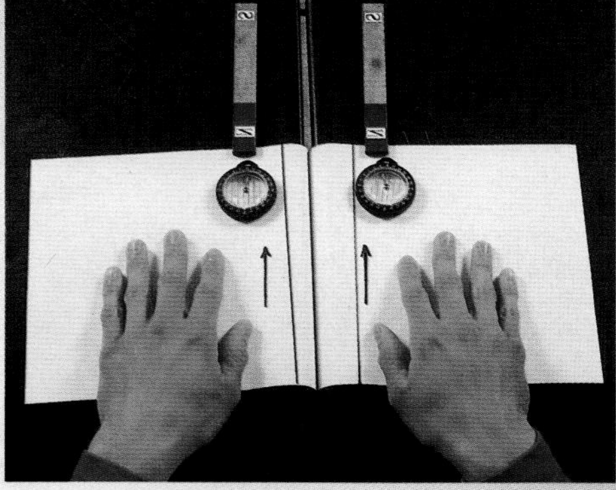

8. Return the compasses to their original positions along the side of the space between the desks. Draw new arrows on the paper to represent the direction that the compass needles are now pointing.
9. Repeat this procedure several times.

Analyze
1. Where are the "oldest" marks on the strip of paper?
2. Compare your completed strip to the patterns in Figure 13-8. What are the similarities and differences?

Conclude and Apply
3. How does this activity compare to the movement of crustal and mantle material?
4. How do the plates move?
5. What is a magnetic reversal?
6. How does this model answer the question of why the ocean basins have younger crustal rocks than the continents?

ACTIVITY 13-1
50 minutes

OBJECTIVE: Describe how plates move during sea-floor spreading.

PROCESS SKILLS applied in this activity:
▶ **Observing** in Procedure Steps 5, 6, and 8.
▶ **Interpreting Data** in Analyze Questions 1 and 2.
▶ **Inferring** in Conclude and Apply Questions 4 and 5.
▶ **Recognizing and Using Spatial Relationships** in Procedure Steps 1-9.
▶ **Formulating Models** in Conclude and Apply Question 3.

TEACHING THE ACTIVITY

▶ Remind students that each time the strip of paper is moved outward, four steps must be completed: (1) the new edges of the ridge must be traced with straight lines; (2) the compasses must be placed back at the edges of the ridge; (3) the magnet must be turned 180°; and (4) new arrows showing how the compasses point must be drawn.

PROGRAM RESOURCES

From the **Teacher Resource Package** use:

Activity Worksheets, pages 113-114, Activity 13-1: Sea-Floor Spreading.

ANSWERS TO QUESTIONS

1. by the edges of the strip
2. The pattern of arrows on the strip should appear similar to the pattern of colors representing the rocks in Figure 13-8. The student-made strips lack the detail of Figure 13-8.
3. It shows how rigid plates move on a partially melted mantle.
4. Earth's plates are transported by convection currents.
5. Earth's magnetic field periodically reverses polarity. That is, the north magnetic pole becomes the south magnetic pole and vice versa.
6. Oceanic crust is younger than continental crust because new crust is constantly being formed at the mid-ocean ridges.

SECTION 13-4

PREPARATION

SECTION BACKGROUND

▶ The Rio Grand Rift, which runs from Colorado through northern New Mexico and into Texas, is concealed under sediment and basalt. The rift is widening due to surrounding plate movements.

▶ Rocks in Alaska's Wrangell Mountains were formed on the floor of the Pacific Ocean, 9600 km away from their present location. These rocks and others in Alaska are thought to have been "scraped off" oceanic plates as the plates were subducted into the asthenosphere.

▶ The Red Sea formed due to divergence along a triple junction, which includes the Great Rift Valley in eastern Africa and the Gulf of Aden.

1 MOTIVATE

▶ Obtain a tectonic globe and have students manipulate the plates into various patterns before beginning this section.

FLEX Your Brain

Use the Flex Your Brain activity to have students explore PLATE TECTONICS.

PROGRAM RESOURCES

From the **Teacher Resource Package** use:

Activity Worksheets, page 5, Flex Your Brain.

13-4 Theory of Plate Tectonics

New Science Words

plate tectonics
plates
lithosphere
asthenosphere
divergent boundary
convergent boundary
subduction zone
transform fault
convection current

Objectives

- ▶ **Compare and contrast divergent, convergent, and transform plate boundaries.**
- ▶ **Describe how convection currents might be the cause of plate tectonics.**

Science and READING

There were many scientists besides Alfred Wegener and Harry Hess who contributed ideas that led to plate tectonics. Some of them include A. L. Du Toit, S. K. Runcorn, Bruce Heezen, Arthur Holmes, J. Tuzo Wilson, Jack Oliver, and Lynn R. Sykes. Get a book on plate tectonics and read about contributions made by these scientists.

Plate Tectonics

With the discovery of sea-floor spreading, scientists began to understand what was happening to Earth's crust and upper mantle. The idea of sea-floor spreading showed that more than just continents were moving as Wegener had thought. It was now evident to scientists that sections of the seafloor and continents move around in relation to one another.

By 1968, scientists had developed a new theory that combined the main ideas of continental drift and sea-floor spreading. The theory of **plate tectonics** states that Earth's crust and upper mantle are broken into sections called **plates.** These plates move around on the mantle.

The continents can be thought of as "rafts" that float and move around on the mantle. Plates are composed

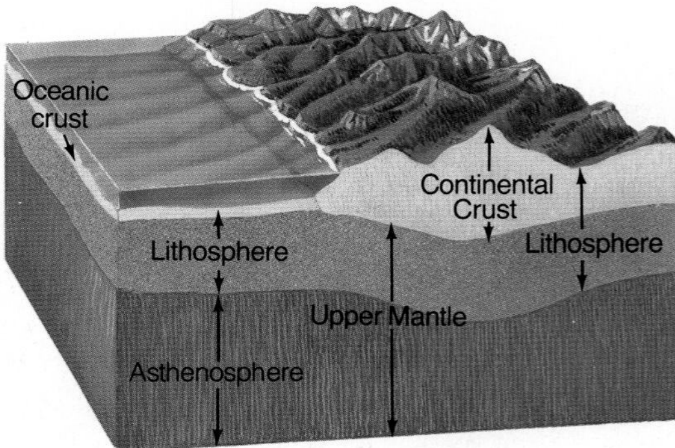

Figure 13-9. The less dense plates of the lithosphere move on the asthenosphere.

OPTIONS

Meeting Different Ability Levels

For Section 13-4, use the following **Teacher Resource Masters** depending upon individual students' needs.

◆ **Study Guide Master** for all students.

● **Reinforcement Master** for students of average and above average ability levels.

▲ **Enrichment Master** for above average students.

Additional Teacher Resource Package masters are listed in the OPTIONS box throughout the section. The additional masters are appropriate for all students.

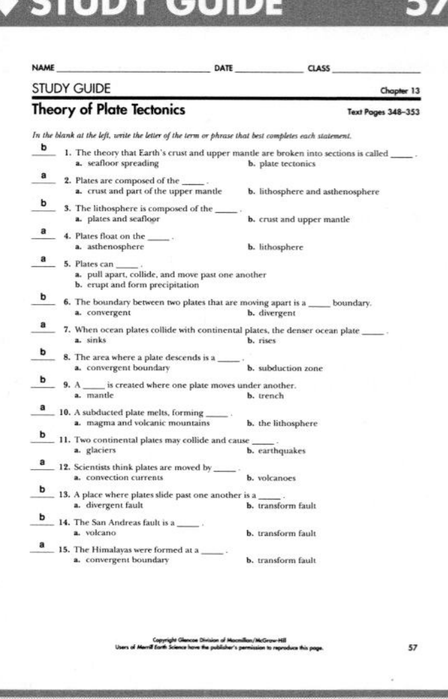

◆ STUDY GUIDE 57

NAME ______ DATE ______ CLASS ______

STUDY GUIDE — Chapter 13

Theory of Plate Tectonics — Text Pages 348–353

In the blank at the left, write the letter of the term or phrase that best completes each statement.

b 1. The theory that Earth's crust and upper mantle are broken into sections is called _____.
a. seafloor spreading b. plate tectonics

a 2. Plates are composed of the _____.
a. crust and part of the upper mantle b. lithosphere and asthenosphere

b 3. The lithosphere is composed of the _____.
a. plates and seafloor b. crust and upper mantle

a 4. Plates float on the _____.
a. asthenosphere b. lithosphere

a 5. Plates can _____.
a. pull apart, collide, and move past one another
b. erupt and form precipitation

b 6. The boundary between two plates that are moving apart is a _____ boundary.
a. convergent b. divergent

a 7. When ocean plates collide with continental plates, the denser ocean plate _____.
a. sinks b. rises

b 8. The area where a plate descends is a _____.
a. convergent boundary b. subduction zone

b 9. A _____ is created where one plate moves under another.
a. mantle b. trench

a 10. A subducted plate melts, forming _____.
a. magma and volcanic mountains b. the lithosphere

b 11. Two continental plates may collide and cause _____.
a. glaciers b. earthquakes

a 12. Scientists think plates are moved by _____.
a. convection currents b. volcanoes

b 13. A place where plates slide past one another is a _____.
a. divergent fault b. transform fault

b 14. The San Andreas fault is a _____.
a. volcano b. transform fault

a 15. The Himalayas were formed at a _____.
a. convergent boundary b. transform fault

57

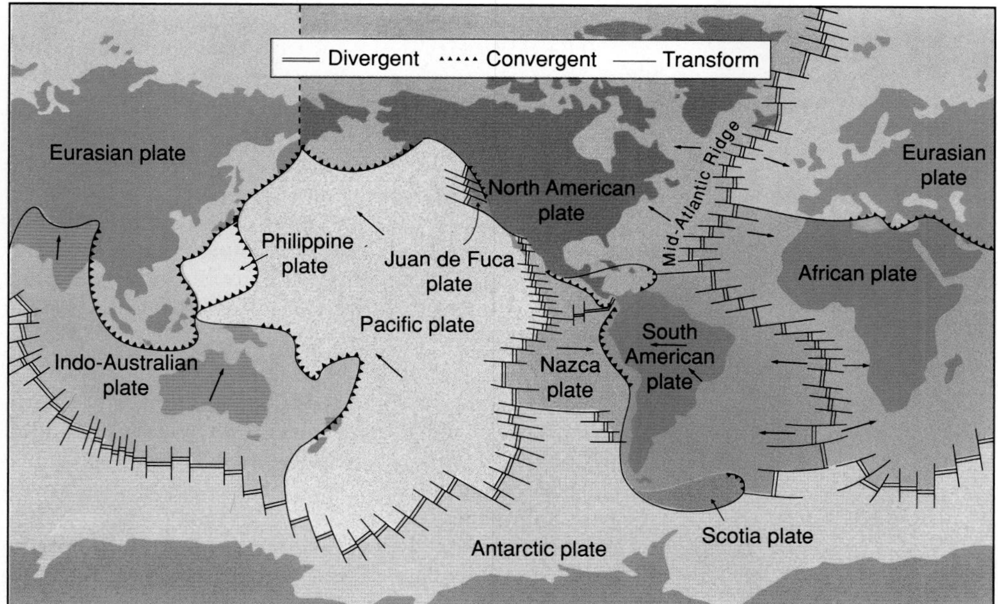

Figure 13-10. This diagram shows the major plates of the lithosphere, their direction of movement, and the type of boundary between them.

of the crust and a part of the upper mantle. These two parts together are called the **lithosphere** (LITH uh sfihr). This rigid layer is about 100 km thick and is less dense than material underneath. This plasticlike layer below the lithosphere is called the **asthenosphere** (as THEN uh sfihr). The less dense plates of the lithosphere "float" and move around on the denser asthenosphere. The interaction of the plates on the asthenosphere is like large flat stones placed in wet cement. You can move the stones around in the cement before it dries.

What happens when plates move? They can interact in three ways. They can move toward each other and collide, they can pull apart, or they can simply move past one another. When the plates interact, the result of their movement is seen at the plate boundaries. Movement along any plate boundary requires that adjustments be made at the other boundaries. Here, mountains are formed, volcanoes erupt, or earthquakes occur. For example, the Pacific Plate moves past the North American Plate, causing earthquakes in California. And it causes volcanoes in Alaska where it collides with the North American Plate. Mountain building, earthquakes, and volcanoes are known as tectonic activities.

What are the three ways in which plates interact?

● REINFORCEMENT 57

NAME ____ DATE ____ CLASS ____

REINFORCEMENT — Chapter 13

Theory of Plate Tectonics — Text Pages 348–353

Use the words in the box to fill in the blanks.

asthenosphere, convection current, lithosphere, plates, plate tectonics

1. The theory of **plate tectonics** states that Earth's crust and upper mantle are broken into sections.
2. These sections, called **plates**, are composed of the crust and a part of the upper mantle.
3. The crust and upper mantle are called the **lithosphere**.
4. Beneath this layer is the plasticlike **asthenosphere**.
5. Many scientists think hot plasticlike rock rises toward the surface, cools, and sinks. This process is called a **convection current**.

Four diagrams are shown in the table below. Explain each diagram to complete the table.

Diagram	Type of boundary and motion at boundary	Diagram	Type of boundary and motion at boundary
6.	divergent boundary; plates move apart	8.	convergent boundary; occurs when two continental plates collide
7.	convergent boundary; an ocean plate sinks under a continental plate or one ocean plate sinks under another ocean plate at a subduction zone	9.	transform fault; occurs when two plates slide past one another

 57

▲ ENRICHMENT 57

NAME ____ DATE ____ CLASS ____

ENRICHMENT — Chapter 13

Theory of Plate Tectonics — Text Pages 348–353

PREDICTING PLATE MOVEMENT

The word *tectonics* comes from the same Greek base word as "architect." Both words deal with building. An architect designs structures. Tectonics is a process by which Earth's structures are built and changed.

1. Cut the map along the boundaries. Move the pieces to show how the plates will move in the next million years, according to the types of boundaries. Tape the pieces in place.
2. In which place(s) did you have to crumple your paper some to account for the various plate movements? **on the Arabian Peninsula along the Arabian Sea.**
3. Compare your new map with those of your classmates. Discuss similarities and account for any differences. **Students should verify that they correctly moved the map to match the type of boundaries.**

Key
Diverging boundary
Converging boundary
Transform fault boundary
Asia
Persian Gulf
Red Sea
Arabian Peninsula
Africa
Gulf of Aden
Arabian Sea

56

TYING TO PREVIOUS KNOWLEDGE: Have students recall some of the recent earthquakes around the world. Have students plot the locations of the quakes on a map. Then, use the map to show students that most earthquakes occur in specific areas.

OBJECTIVES AND SCIENCE WORDS: Have students review the objectives and science words to become familiar with this section.

2 TEACH

Key Concepts are highlighted.

CONCEPT DEVELOPMENT

▶ **Demonstration:** Obtain a piece of flexible foam padding about 8 cm thick. Cut the foam in half to form two "plates." Apply compressional force to demonstrate the folding that occurs when two continental plates converge. Also demonstrate the process of subduction that occurs when an oceanic plate and a continental plate converge.

TEACHER F.Y.I.

▶ The rate at which Earth's plates move is about the same as the rate at which your fingernails grow.

CONCEPT DEVELOPMENT

Cooperative Learning: Show students a topographic map of the ocean floor, which is available from the National Geographic Society. Form Numbered Heads Together groups and have students determine locations on the map where subduction is probably occurring. Have them also locate divergent plate boundaries.

▶ After students have read about divergent and convergent boundaries, pose these questions. **What is a divergent boundary?** *a boundary where two plates move apart from each other* **Name two divergent boundaries.** *the Mid-Atlantic Ridge and the Great Rift Valley* **What happens when an oceanic plate collides with a continental plate?** *The denser oceanic plate sinks under the continental plate.*

EcoTip

Convergent plate boundaries were once suggested as hazardous waste disposal sites. It was thought that wastes dropped into the trenches would be carried into the subduction zone without any harm to the environment. But we know that the subduction process is very slow and that seawater could cause waste containers to leak into the ocean.

Divergent Boundaries

1 The boundary between two plates that are moving apart from one another is called a **divergent boundary.** You learned about divergent boundaries when you read about seafloor spreading. In the Atlantic Ocean, the North American Plate is moving away from the Eurasian and the African plates as seen in Figure 13-10 on page 349. That divergent boundary is called the Mid-Atlantic Ridge. The Great Rift Valley in eastern Africa is another good example of a diverging plate boundary. Here, a valley has formed where two continental plates have separated.

Convergent Boundaries

If new crust is being added at one location, why doesn't Earth's crust keep getting thicker? As new crust is added in one place, it disappears at another. The disappearance of crust can occur where two plates collide at a **convergent boundary.**

2 There are three types of convergent boundaries. When an ocean floor plate collides with a less dense continental plate, the denser ocean plate sinks under the continental plate. The area where an oceanic plate descends into the upper mantle is called a **subduction zone.** Volcanoes occur at subduction zones.

Figure 13-11. As Earth's plates pull apart at some boundaries, they collide at others, forming mountains and volcanoes.

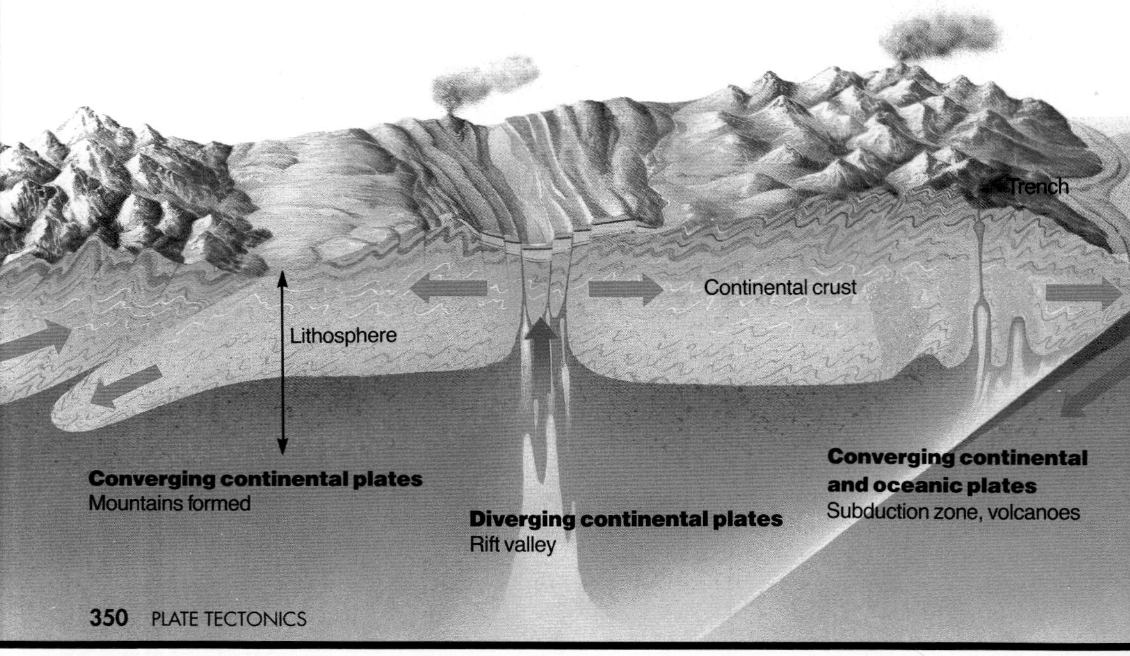

OPTIONS

PROGRAM RESOURCES

From the **Teacher Resource Package** use:

Concept Mapping, pages 31-32.

Transparency Masters, pages 53-54, Oceanic-Continental Convergence; pages 55-56, Oceanic-Oceanic Convergence; pages 57-58, Continental-Continental Convergence.

PROGRAM RESOURCES

Use **Color Transparency** number 27, Oceanic-Continental Convergence; number 28, Oceanic-Oceanic Convergence; number 29, Continental-Continental Convergence.

Figure 13-11 shows how this type of convergent boundary creates a deep-sea trench where one plate is subducting under the other. High temperatures and pressures cause the subducted plate to melt as it descends under the other plate. The newly formed magma rises toward the surface along these plate boundaries, forming volcanic mountains. The Andes Mountains of South America contain many volcanoes. They were formed at the convergent boundary of the Nazca and the South American plates.

The second type of convergent boundary occurs when two ocean plates collide. Like the first type of boundary, when two ocean plates collide, one bends and slides under the other, forming a subduction zone. A deep-sea trench is formed, and the new magma that is produced rises to form an island arc of volcanoes. The islands of Japan are volcanic island arcs formed when two oceanic plates collided.

The third type of convergent boundary occurs when two continental plates collide. Because both of these plates are less dense than the material in the asthenosphere, usually no subduction occurs. The two plates just collide and crumple up, forming mountain ranges. Earthquakes are common at these convergent boundaries. The Himalaya Mountains in Asia were formed when the Indian Plate crashed into the Eurasian Plate.

Did You Know?

The deepest spot in any ocean is the Mariana Trench. Located at the convergent boundary between the Pacific Plate and the Philippine Plate, this deep-sea trench is 11 033 meters deep. It would take the fastest elevator in the Empire State Building more than 30 minutes to reach the bottom.

3 What kinds of plates collided to form the Himalaya Mountains?

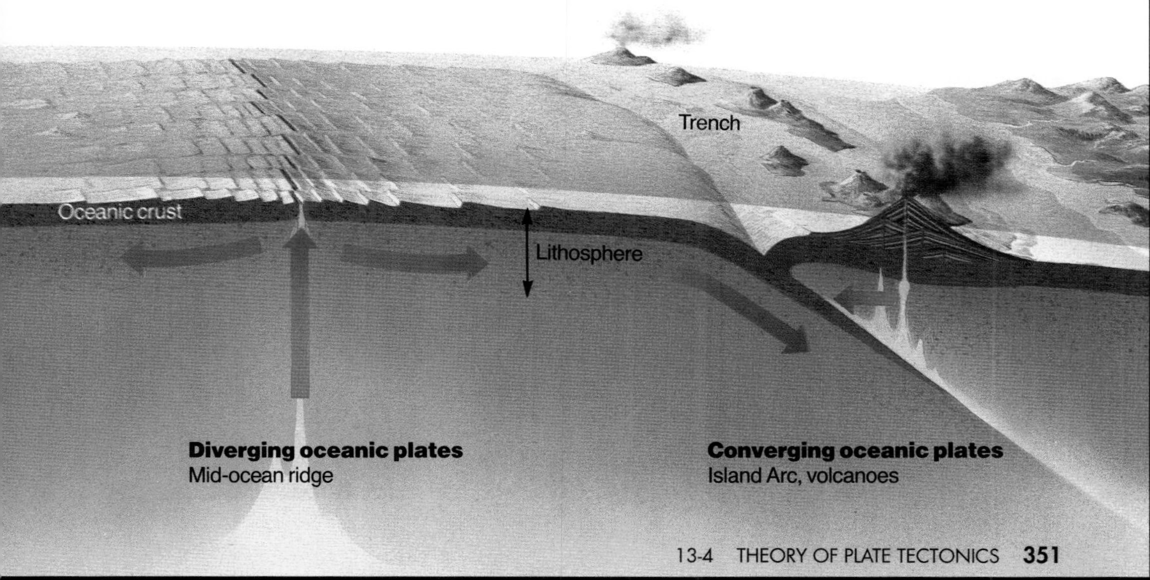

CONCEPT DEVELOPMENT

▶ Have three volunteers illustrate the different types of convergent boundaries on the chalkboard or overhead projector.

▶ Have students use the numbers in Did You Know to compute the speed of the elevator.

$$\frac{11\ 033\ \text{m}}{30\ \text{min}} = 368\ \text{m/min}$$

CROSS CURRICULUM

▶ **Language Arts:** Have students use dictionaries to define the terms *converge* and *diverge.*

MINI QUIZ

Use the Mini Quiz to check students' recall of chapter content.

1. **Boundaries along which plates are moving apart are _____ boundaries.** *divergent*
2. **A(n) _____ forms when an oceanic plate collides with a continental plate.** *subduction zone*
3. **Subduction usually doesn't occur when two _____ plates converge.** *continental*

INQUIRY QUESTIONS

▶ **Why is the Mid-Atlantic Ridge classified as a divergent plate boundary?** *The seafloor is spreading apart at the Mid-Atlantic Ridge.*

▶ **What kinds of landforms result from the collision of two plates?** *Volcanic mountains form when oceanic and continental plates converge. Volcanic island arcs form where two oceanic plates converge. Folded mountain ranges develop when two continental plates converge.*

TEACHER F.Y.I.

▶ Creepmeters, lasers, and geostationary satellites are used to measure plate movement.

▶ The Pacific and North American plates, sliding past each other along the San Andreas fault, each move an average of about 5 cm per year.

REVEALING MISCONCEPTIONS

▶ Ask students to stand perfectly still. Then ask them whether or not they are moving. Explain that Earth movements such as rotation, revolution, and plate movements are not felt by humans. Have students find out the velocities at which each of the processes mentioned occurs.

CHECK FOR UNDERSTANDING

Cooperative Learning: Form four Expert Teams and assign each team one of the following topics to master and present to the class: convergent boundaries, divergent boundaries, transform fault boundaries, and the driving mechanism of plate tectonics.

RETEACH

Using a supermarket conveyor belt as an analogy, explain how Earth's plates move.

EXTENSION

For students who have mastered this section, use the **Reinforcement** and **Enrichment** masters or other OPTIONS provided.

Science and READING

There are myths associated with earthquakes. One of them is that California will break off and fall into the Pacific Ocean someday. Do some reading to see if you can find other myths. Also try to find out what the myths are based on.

Transform Fault Boundaries

The third type of plate boundary is called a **transform fault.** Transform faults occur when two plates slide past one another. This occurs when two plates are moving in opposite directions or in the same direction at different rates. As one plate slides past another, earthquakes occur. The famous San Andreas Fault is a transform fault plate boundary. It has been the site of many earthquakes. The Pacific Plate is sliding past the North American Plate, forming the San Andreas Fault.

Causes of Plate Tectonics

There have been many new discoveries about Earth's crust since Wegener's day. But one question still remains. What causes the plates to move and the seafloor to spread? Scientists now think they have a pretty good idea. They think that plates are moved by the same basic process that is used in heating some buildings. In a forced air heating system, air is warmed in the furnace and a blower forces it into each room of the building. The air rises from the register and releases its heat to surrounding air. The cooler air, which is now denser, sinks to the floor of the room. It returns to the furnace through the cold air return, to be reheated. This entire cycle of heating, rising, cooling, and sinking is called a **convection current.** This same process is thought to be the force behind plate tectonics.

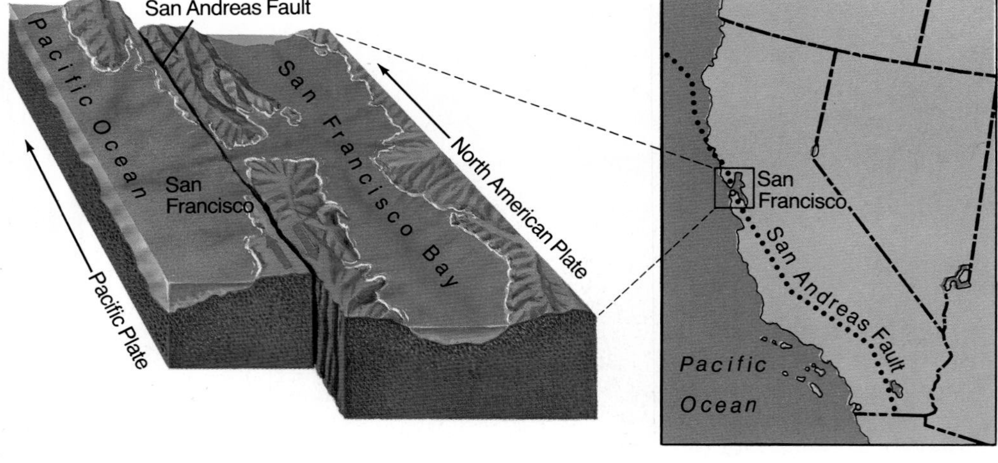

Figure 13-12. The San Andreas Fault forms a transform fault boundary where the Pacific Plate is sliding past the North American Plate.

OPTIONS

INQUIRY QUESTIONS

▶ **Earthquakes are associated with some plate boundaries. Why do you think this is so?** *Much force is involved with plate movements. As plates collide or slide past one another, pressure is released as earthquakes.*

▶ **Describe the driving mechanism of Earth's plates.** *Hot plasticlike material in the asthenosphere rises toward the lithosphere. When the hot material reaches the lithosphere, it moves laterally and carries Earth's plates. As the material cools, it sinks. These huge convection currents in the mantle are the driving force of plate tectonics.*

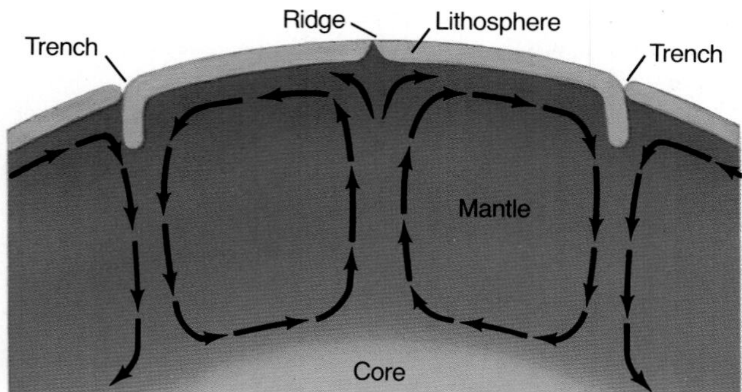

Figure 13-13. Convection currents (see arrows) are the driving force of plate tectonics.

Scientists believe differences in density cause hot plasticlike rock in the asthenosphere to rise toward the surface. When this plasticlike rock reaches Earth's lithosphere, it moves horizontally and carries plates of the lithosphere with it as described earlier. As it cools, the plasticlike rock becomes denser. It then sinks into the mantle, taking overlying crust with it.

These huge convection cells provide the energy to move plates in the lithosphere. Plate tectonics shows how activity inside Earth causes changes on Earth's crust.

MINI-Lab

How do convection currents form?

Fill a metal pan with water to 5 cm from the top. Center the pan on a hot plate and heat. **CAUTION:** *Wear thermal mitts to protect your hands as the pan becomes hot.* Add a few drops of food coloring to the water directly above the hot plate. Watch for currents to form in the water. What do you think causes these currents?

SECTION REVIEW

1. What happens to plates at a transform fault boundary?
2. What type of plate boundary is associated with seafloor spreading?
3. What happens when a denser ocean plate collides with a less dense continental plate?
4. Island arcs form at what type of plate boundary?
5. **Apply:** Looking at Figure 13-10 on page 349 and Appendix F on page 668 if necessary, determine why Iceland could be a dangerous place to live.

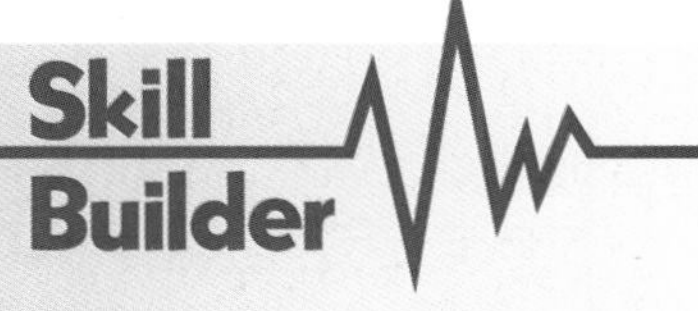

Recognizing Cause and Effect

What causes a divergent boundary to form? What is the effect of collision on the edges of continental plates? Use your knowledge of cause-and-effect relationships to answer the questions. Then, write a cause-and-effect statement explaining the relationship between convection currents and plate movement. If you need help, refer to Recognizing Cause and Effect in the **Skill Handbook** on page 683.

MINI-Lab

Materials: food coloring, water, thermal mitts, metal sauce pan, hot plate

Cooperative Learning: Have students perform this activity as Science Investigation teams.

►**Answer:** The transfer of energy and the resulting density differences cause convection currents.

CONCEPT DEVELOPMENT

► Have students recall other places on Earth where convection currents play a role in circulation. Their responses should include Earth's atmosphere and oceans.

3 CLOSE

► Ask questions 1-4 and the **Apply** Question in the Section Review.

FLEX Your Brain

Use the Flex Your Brain activity to have students explore PLATE BOUNDARIES.

► Ask students to use their hands to demonstrate what happens at plate boundaries.

SECTION REVIEW ANSWERS

1. Plates slide past one another.
2. a divergent boundary
3. The denser plate is subducted under the less dense plate.
4. convergent boundaries
5. Apply: Iceland is a portion of the Mid-Atlantic Ridge, which is a site of volcanic activity.

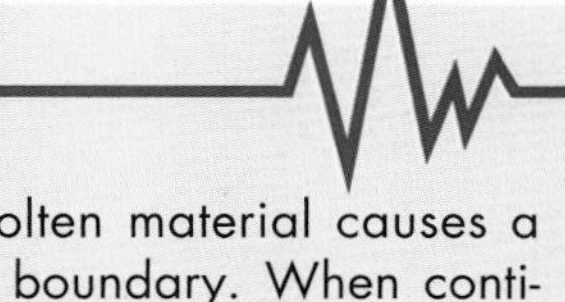

Rising, molten material causes a diverging boundary. When continental plates collide, the pressure causes the edges to buckle and fold, forming mountains. Convection currents in the mantle transfer energy, which causes the overlying plates to move.

ENRICHMENT

► Have students look at Figure 13-10 on page 349. Ask them to draw maps showing where and what kinds of landmasses will be located on Earth's surface in the future.

► Have students compare and contrast continental drift and plate tectonics. Students should emphasize that Wegener's continental drift could not explain how the continents moved, whereas plate tectonics attributes movement to convection currents.

PROGRAM RESOURCES

From the **Teacher Resource Package** use:

Activity Worksheets, page 5, Flex Your Brain.

Activity Worksheets, page 120, Mini-Lab: How do convection currents form?

ACTIVITY 13-2

50-60 minutes

OBJECTIVE: Interpret rock polarity data to **determine** the rate of sea-floor spreading.

PROCESS SKILLS applied in this activity:

▶ **Observing** in Procedure Step 1.

▶ **Inferring** in Analyze Question 2.

▶ **Measuring** in Procedure Steps 2 and 3.

▶ **Using Numbers** in Procedure Steps 2-6, and Conclude and Apply Question 4.

▶ **Interpreting Data** in Analyze Question 1 and Conclude and Apply Questions 3 and 4.

TEACHING THE ACTIVITY

▶ In order to help students understand the information in the figure shown, refer them to Activity 13-1 as well as to the description of magnetic field reversals in Section 13-2. The normal and reversed polarity patterns on the figure shown in the activity are similar to the arrows drawn by the students in Activity 13-1.

Troubleshooting: When calculating the rate of movement in Procedure Step 6, make sure students use the normal polarity average for distance.

▶ The rate of spreading shown by the data in this activity is about 1.2 cm/yr. Divergence at some mid-ocean ridges appears to be taking place at rates of up to 6.0 cm/yr.

PROGRAM RESOURCES

From the **Teacher Resource Package** use:

Activity Worksheets, pages 115-116, Activity 13-2: Rates of Sea-floor Spreading.

ACTIVITY 13-2

Rates of Sea-floor Spreading

Problem: *How can you determine the rate of sea-floor spreading?*

Materials

- metric ruler
- pencil

Procedure

1. Study the magnetic field profile below. You will be working with six major peaks east and west of the Mid-Atlantic Ridge for both normal and reversed polarity.
2. Place the ruler through the first peak west of the main rift. Determine and record the distance in km to the Mid-Atlantic Ridge.
3. Repeat Step 2 for each of the six major peaks east and west of the main rift, for both normal and reversed polarity.
4. Find the average distance from peak to ridge for each pair of corresponding peaks on either side of the ridge. Record these values.
5. Use the normal polarity readings to find the age of the rocks at each average distance.
6. Using normal polarity readings, calculate the rate of movement in cm/year. Use the formula (distance = rate × time) to calculate the rate. You must convert km to cm.

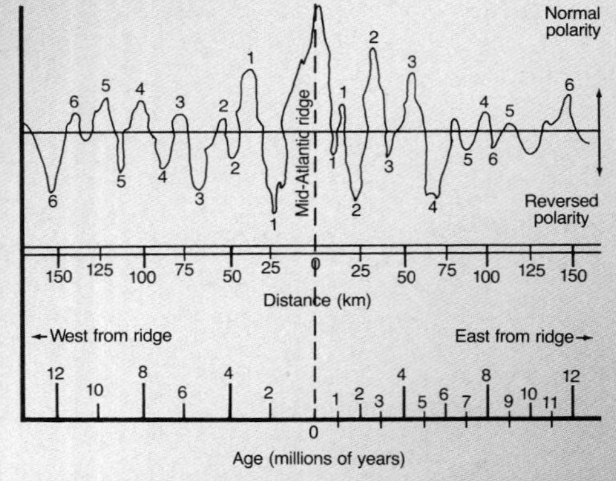

Data and Observations

Sample Data

Peak	1	2	3	4	5	6
Distance west normal polarity	45	65	80	105	120	135
Distance east normal polarity	15	30	55	100	115	150
Average distance	30	47	67	102	117	142
Distance west reversed polarity	25	50	70	95	115	120
Distance east reversed polarity	10	25	45	70	85	100
Average distance	17	37	57	82	100	125
Age from scale (millions of years)	2.5	3.9	5.1	8.1	9.0	11.0
Rate of movement (cm/year)	1.2	1.2	1.3	1.3	1.3	1.3

Analyze

1. Compare the age of the igneous rock found near the mid-ocean ridge to that of the rock found farther away from the ridge.
2. In what way does the information shown in the graph relate to the procedure in Activity 13-1?

Conclude and Apply

3. On your paper, draw a line that would represent the amount of total movement that would occur between a point east of the Mid-Atlantic Ridge and a point west of the ridge in one year.
4. If the distance from a point on the coast of Africa to the Mid-Atlantic Ridge is approximately 2400 km, how long ago was that point in Africa at or near that mid-ocean ridge?

ANSWERS TO QUESTIONS

1. Rocks nearest the ridge are younger than rocks farther from the ridge.

2. The peaks and valleys on the graph correspond to the pattern of reversing arrows on the strip of paper that students constructed in Activity 13-1.

3. The line should be about 1.2 cm long. This is determined by adding the rates of movement on each side of the mid-ocean ridge.

4. Africa should have been in that position about 280 million years ago assuming a relatively constant rate of spreading between the two plates.

CHAPTER

REVIEW

SUMMARY

13-1: Structure of Earth

1. Earth has four main layers: a solid, inner core; a liquid, outer core; the mantle; and the crust.

2. The inner core is solid and is composed of iron and nickel. The outer core is liquid. The upper mantle is plasticlike rock made of silicon, oxygen, magnesium, and iron. The crust is the outermost layer of Earth.

13-2: Science and Society: Science and New Ideas

1. The theory of continental drift states that continents have moved to their present positions on Earth.

2. Some ideas are not taken seriously when first proposed. New ideas should be given careful consideration.

13-3: Evidence for Continental Drift

1. The puzzle-like fit of the continents, fossils, climatic evidence, and similar rock structures support Wegener's idea of continental drift.

2. Sea-floor spreading states that the seafloor is spreading apart at the mid-ocean ridges.

3. Sea-floor spreading is supported by magnetic evidence in rocks and in the age of rocks on the ocean floor.

13-4: Theory of Plate Tectonics

1. Plates move away from each other at divergent boundaries. Plates collide at convergent boundaries. At a transform fault, two plates move horizontally past each other.

2. Hot, plasticlike material from the mantle rises to the lithosphere moves horizontally, cools, and then sinks back into the mantle. The movement of this material sets up convection currents, the driving force of plate tectonics.

KEY SCIENCE WORDS

a. **asthenosphere**
b. **continental drift**
c. **convection current**
d. **convergent boundary**
e. **crust**
f. **divergent boundary**
g. **inner core**
h. **lithosphere**
i. **magnetometer**
j. **mantle**
k. **outer core**
l. **Pangaea**
m. **plates**
n. **plate tectonics**
o. **sea-floor spreading**
p. **subduction zone**
q. **transform fault**

UNDERSTANDING VOCABULARY

Match each phrase with the correct term from the list of Key Science Words.

1. innermost part of Earth
2. Earth's thick, plasticlike layer
3. idea that continents moved to their current positions on Earth
4. large landmass made of all continents
5. Earth's uppermost layer
6. process that forms new seafloor
7. large sections of Earth's crust and upper mantle
8. boundary where plates move apart from each other
9. boundary at which plates collide
10. place where plates slide past one another

CHAPTER

REVIEW

SUMMARY

Have students read the summary statements to review the major concepts of the chapter.

UNDERSTANDING VOCABULARY

1. g
2. j
3. b, n
4. l
5. e
6. o
7. h
8. f
9. d
10. q

OPTIONS

ASSESSMENT

To assess student understanding of material in this chapter, use the resources listed.

COOPERATIVE LEARNING

Consider using cooperative learning in the THINK AND WRITE CRITICALLY, APPLY, and MORE SKILL BUILDERS sections of the Chapter Review.

PROGRAM RESOURCES

From the **Teacher Resource Package** use:

Chapter Review, pages 29-30.

Chapter and Unit Tests, pages 89-92, Chapter Test.

CHAPTER

REVIEW

CHECKING CONCEPTS

1. d	**6.** c
2. d	**7.** d
3. c, a	**8.** b
4. d	**9.** c
5. a	**10.** b

UNDERSTANDING CONCEPTS

11. convection currents
12. crust
13. asthenosphere
14. iron, nickel
15. mid-ocean ridge

THINK AND WRITE CRITICALLY

16. Both propose that the present-day continents have moved over time into their present positions. Continental drift, however, could not provide a mechanism for these movements. The theory of plate tectonics was derived using data from continental drift and sea-floor magnetic studies.

17. Continental drift was met with opposition by certain scientists because the idea was new. Also, because Wegener could not explain how such massive bodies of rock could move, his idea was not taken seriously during his lifetime.

18. A mid-ocean ridge, which is an underground mountain chain, is the point where magma rises to the surface and pushes the old sea floor apart. As the magma cools, new sea floor is formed. This process of ocean floor formation is called sea-floor spreading.

19. All are places where two plates, which are thick slabs of Earth's crust and upper mantle, interact. Divergent boundaries occur where plates move apart from each other. Convergent boundaries form where two plates collide. A transform fault is a boundary in which plates move horizontally past one another.

20. Island arcs form along some convergent plate boundaries. When the two oceanic plates collide, magma forms as the subducted plate melts. The magma rises and forms an island arc of volcanoes.

CHAPTER

REVIEW

CHECKING CONCEPTS

Choose the word or phrase that completes the sentence.

1. Earth's ______ can be compared to the seed of a peach.
a. crust **b.** mantle **c.** outer core **d.** inner core

2. The San Andreas Fault is a ______.
a. divergent boundary
b. subduction zone
c. convergent boundary
d. none of these

3. ______ states that continents moved to their present positions.
a. Subduction
b. Sea-floor spreading
c. Continental drift
d. None of these

4. Evidence supporting continental drift includes ______.
a. fossils **b.** continental margins **c.** rock structures **d.** all of these

5. Evidence from ______ indicates that many continents were near Earth's South Pole.
a. glaciers **b.** mid-ocean ridges **c.** rock structures **d.** plates

6. ______ of iron in rocks confirmed continental drift.
a. Plate movement
b. Subduction
c. Magnetic alignment
d. All of these

7. The theory of ______ states that plates move around on the asthenosphere.
a. continental drift
b. sea-floor spreading
c. subduction
d. none of these

8. The Great Rift Valley is a ______ margin.
a. convergent **b.** divergent **c.** transform fault **d.** lithosphere

9. A ______ forms when a plate slides under another.
a. transform fault **b.** divergent boundary **c.** subduction zone **d.** mid-ocean ridge

10. When two oceanic plates collide, ______ form.
a. folded mountains **b.** island arcs **c.** transform faults **d.** all of these

UNDERSTANDING CONCEPTS

Complete each sentence.

11. Plates move because of ______.
12. Earth's ______ is its thinnest layer.
13. Plates "float" on the ______.
14. Both the inner and the outer core are composed of ______ and ______.
15. Echo sounding led to the discovery of the ______.

THINK AND WRITE CRITICALLY

16. Compare and contrast continental drift and plate tectonics.
17. Why was continental drift initially not accepted by many scientists?
18. Explain the relationship between a mid-ocean ridge and sea-floor spreading.
19. Compare and contrast divergent, convergent, and transform fault boundaries.
20. Explain how island arcs form.

APPLY

21. Why are there few volcanoes in the Himalayas, but many earthquakes?
22. Glacial deposits often form at high latitudes near the poles. Explain why glacial deposits have been found in Africa.
23. How is magnetism used to support the theory of sea-floor spreading?
24. Explain why no volcanoes are forming along the San Andreas Fault.
25. Why wouldn't the fossil of an ocean fish found on two different continents be good evidence of continental drift?

MORE SKILL BUILDERS

If you need help, refer to the Skill Handbook.

1. **Hypothesizing:** Mount St. Helens in the Cascade Mountain Range is a volcano. Use Figure 13-10 on page 349 and Appendix F on page 668 to hypothesize how it may have formed.
2. **Measuring in SI:** Movement along the African Rift Valley is about 2.1 cm per year. If plates continue to move apart at this rate, how large will the rift be (in meters) in 1000 years? 15 500 years?
3. **Outlining:** Outline the major points in Section 13-3.
4. **Comparing and Contrasting:** Compare and contrast the formation of the Andes Mountains and the Himalayas.
5. **Concept Mapping:** Make an events chain concept map that describes sea-floor spreading.

PROJECTS

1. Use modeling clay to construct three-dimensional scale models of each type of plate boundary. Make sure to show the boundaries to a depth of at least a few hundred kilometers. Also show the features that form at each type of boundary.
2. Research the normal and reversed magnetic bands that cover the seafloors. Use the magnetic data to compute the rates of spreading during each magnetic period.

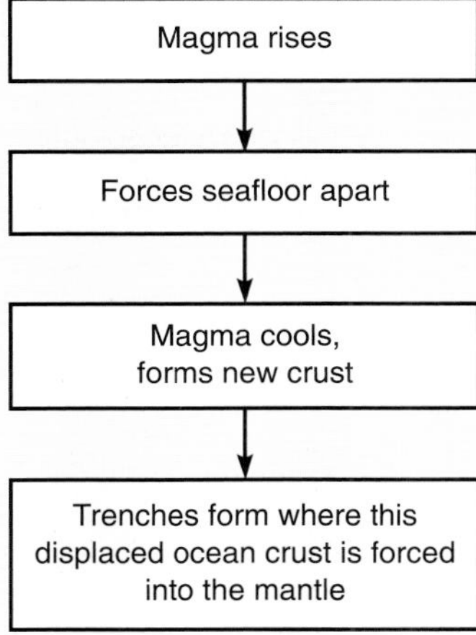

Magma rises
Forces seafloor apart
Magma cools, forms new crust
Trenches form where this displaced ocean crust is forced into the mantle

APPLY

21. Unlike most continent-continent collisions, subduction is occurring as the Indian plate is colliding with the Eurasian plate to form the Himalayas. Because two continental plates are colliding, and the angle of subduction is shallow, there is essentially no volcanism in these mountains.
22. Africa was once located near the South Pole when all the continents were joined as a single landmass.
23. Alternating magnetic bands are symmetric with respect to a mid-ocean ridge.
24. The San Andreas fault is a transform fault boundary. There is no subduction along such plate boundaries; thus there is no volcanism.
25. Fossils of terrestrial organisms are used to support continental drift. Fish are found in oceans, and oceans surround all continents, therefore, most fossil fish aren't good evidence of continental drift.

MORE SKILL BUILDERS

1. Hypothesizing: The volcanoes in the Cascade Range formed when two plates collided at a convergent boundary. The plates were either both oceanic or one was oceanic and the other continental. Volcanoes do not form at the third type of converging boundary—continent-continent.
2. Measuring in SI: 21 m, 325.5 m
3. Outlining: Students' outlines should include all the evidence that supported Wegener's continental drift plus a brief description of sea-floor spreading.
4. Comparing and Contrasting: Both formed as the result of converging plates. The Andes, however, formed as an oceanic plate descended beneath a continental plate. The Himalayas formed as two continental plates collided with one plate subducting beneath the other.
5. Concept Mapping: See left.

CHAPTER

14 Earthquakes

CHAPTER SECTION	OBJECTIVES	ACTIVITIES
14-1 Earthquakes and Plate Tectonics (2 days)	1. **Explain** how earthquakes result from the buildup of stress in Earth's crust. 2. **Contrast** normal, reverse, and strike-slip faults.	**Activity 14-1:** *Earthquake Depths,* p. 365
14-2 Earthquake Information (2 days)	1. **Compare** and **contrast** primary, secondary, and surface waves. 2. **Explain** how an earthquake epicenter is located using seismic wave information. 3. **Describe** how seismic wave studies indicate the structure of Earth's interior.	**MINI-Lab:** *How do you use a travel time graph?* p. 368 **Activity 14-2:** *Locating an Epicenter,* p. 373
14-3 Destruction by Earthquakes (1 day)	1. **Define** *magnitude* and the *Richter Scale.* 2. **List** ways to make your classroom and home more earthquake safe.	
14-4 Living on a Fault Science & Society (1 day)	1. **Recognize** that most loss of life in an earthquake is caused by the destruction of human-made structures. 2. **Decide** who should pay for making structures seismic safe.	**MINI-Lab:** *Should there be a higher tax?* p. 382
Chapter Review		

ACTIVITY MATERIALS

FIND OUT	ACTIVITIES		MINI-LABS	
Page 359 two 10 cm × 5 cm × 1 cm slabs of clay	**14-1 Earthquake Depths, p. 365** graph paper Figures 13-10 and 13-11	**14-2 Locating an Epicenter, p. 373** Figure 14-9 string metric ruler globe paper chalk or water soluble marker	**How do you use a travel time graph? p. 368** Figure 14-9 data table	**Should there be a higher tax? p. 382** none

CHAPTER FEATURES	TEACHER RESOURCE PACKAGE	OTHER RESOURCES
Skill Builder: *Concept Mapping,* p. 364	**Ability Level Worksheets** ◆ ***Study Guide,*** p. 58 ● ***Reinforcement,*** p. 58 ▲ ***Enrichment,*** p. 58 **Activity Worksheet,** pp. 122-123 **Concept Mapping,** pp. 33-34 **Transparency Masters,** pp. 59-60	**Color Transparency 30,** Types of Faults **Lab Manual:** *Earthquakes,* pp. 117-120
Problem Solving: *What's in the Box?* p. 371 **Skill Builder:** *Making and Using Graphs,* p. 372	**Ability Level Worksheets** ◆ ***Study Guide,*** p. 59 ● ***Reinforcement,*** p. 59 ▲ ***Enrichment,*** p. 59 **Activity Worksheet,** pp. 124-125 **MINI-Lab Worksheet,** p. 128 **Transparency Masters,** pp. 61-64	**Color Transparency 31,** Types of Earthquake Waves **Color Transparency 32,** Propagation of Earthquake Waves **Lab Manual:** *Locating an Earthquake,* pp. 121-124
Technology: *Predicting Earthquakes,* p. 376 **Skill Builder:** *Making and Using Tables,* p. 379	**Ability Level Worksheets** ◆ ***Study Guide,*** p. 60 ● ***Reinforcement,*** p. 60 ▲ ***Enrichment,*** p. 60 **Cross-Curricular Connections,** p. 18 **Critical Thinking/Problem Solving,** p. 20	
You Decide! p. 382	**Ability Level Worksheets** ◆ ***Study Guide,*** p. 61 ● ***Reinforcement,*** p. 61 ▲ ***Enrichment,*** p. 61 **Science and Society,** p. 18 **MINI-Lab Worksheet,** p. 129	
Summary Key Science Words Understanding Vocabulary Checking Concepts Understanding Concepts Think & Write Critically Apply More Skill Builders Projects	**Chapter Review,** pp. 31-32 **Chapter Test,** pp. 93-96	**Chapter Review Software** **Test Bank**

◆ **Basic** ● **Average** ▲ **Advanced**

ADDITIONAL MATERIALS

SOFTWARE	AUDIOVISUAL	BOOKS/MAGAZINES
Quakes, MECC. *Earthquakes,* Aquarius. *Earthquakes,* IBM. *The Earthquake Simulator,* Focus.	*Earthquakes: Lesson of a Disaster,* film, EBEC. *The Interior of the Earth,* film, CRM Films. *The San Andreas Fault,* film, EBEC. *Folding,* slide set, NESTA. *Faulting,* slide set, NESTA. *Earth: The Restless Planet,* film, NGS. *The Great Quake of '89,* laserdisc, The Voyager Company. *Predictable Disaster (NOVA),* laserdisc, Image Entertainment.	Bolt, Bruce A. *Earthquakes: Revised and Updated 2nd ed.* NY: Freeman, W.H., & Co., 1980. Foster, Robert J. *General Geology 5th ed.* Westerville, OH: Merrill Publishing Co., 1987.

CHAPTER

14

EARTHQUAKES

THEME DEVELOPMENT: Energy is the theme of this chapter. Energy released during an earthquake as seismic waves should be emphasized as you teach each section.

CHAPTER OVERVIEW

- **Section 14-1:** This section describes the causes of earthquakes. Three types of faults are also defined and described.
- **Section 14-2:** This section presents information that can be obtained from earthquakes. Seismic waves and how they are used to locate an earthquake are discussed. A model of Earth's interior obtained from seismic data is also presented.
- **Section 14-3:** The destruction caused by earthquakes, and methods of measuring earthquake magnitude and destruction are discussed. Earthquake safety also is introduced.
- **Section 14-4: Science and Society:** The advantages of seismic-safe structures are explored. The You Decide feature asks students to consider who should pay for seismic-safe structures.

CHAPTER VOCABULARY

faults
earthquakes
normal fault
reverse fault
strike-slip fault
seismic waves
focus
primary waves
secondary waves
epicenter
surface waves
Moho discontinuity
seismologists
seismograph
magnitude
tsunamis
seismic-safe

CHAPTER

14 Earthquakes

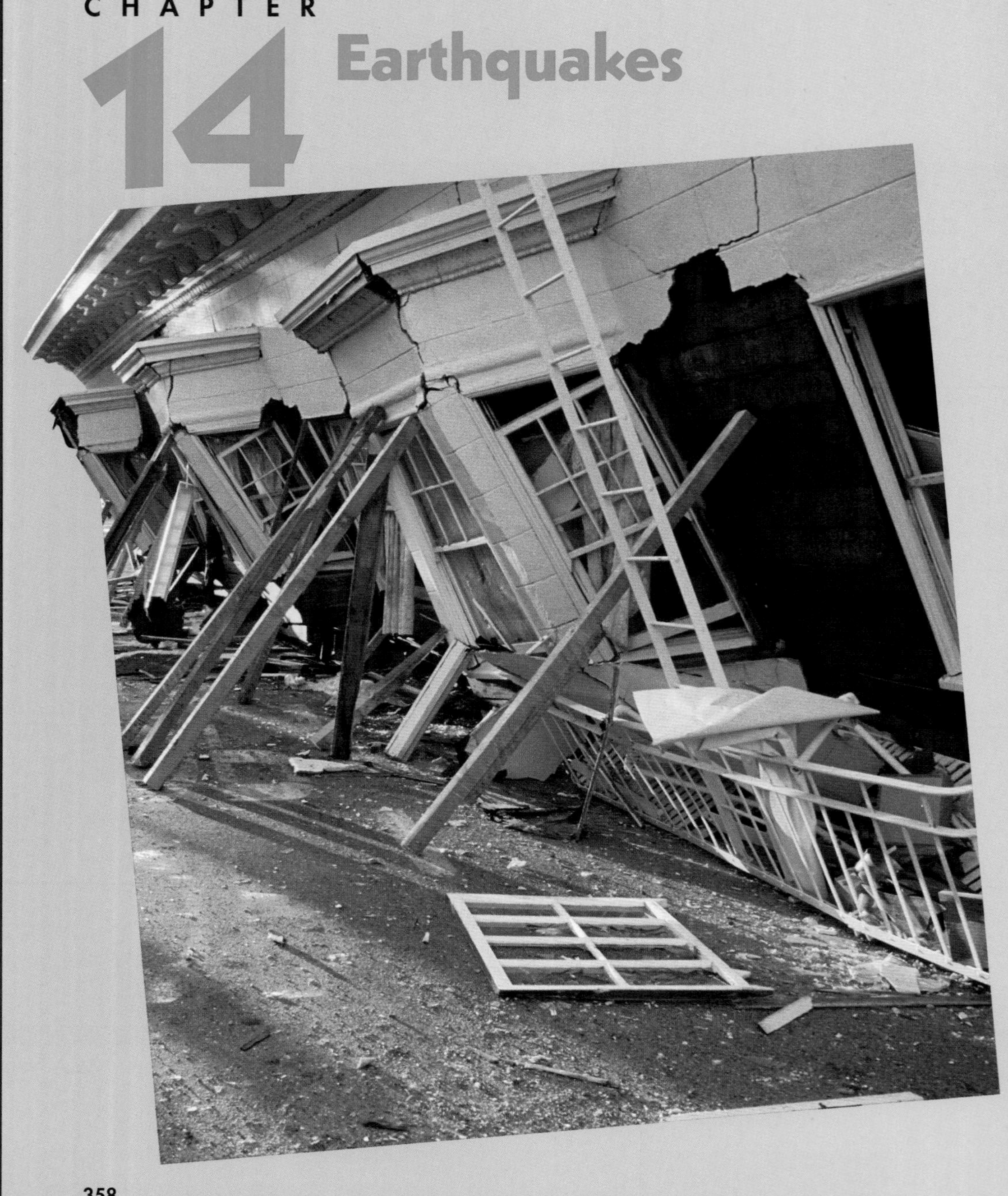

358

OPTIONS

For Your Gifted Students

Have students use toothpicks to design earthquake-resistant buildings and bridges. Have them experiment with shapes and reinforcements. When structures are completed, they can be glued onto posterboard supported by wooden frames. An earthquake can be simulated by applying force to the posterboard. Then have students attach fishing line through the posterboard so that the line freely moves up and down. Have them use spring scales to measure the amount of force applied by lifting or pulling on the line. Structures can be evaluated, compared, and modified.

You may have seen pictures of the October 1989 earthquake that occurred in the San Francisco Bay area. Have you ever thought about what caused this and other earthquakes? As you read this chapter, you will explore how movement and changes in Earth's lithosphere produce earthquakes.

FIND OUT!

Do this simple activity to find out how forces in Earth cause rocks to deform.

Place two pieces of clay flat on a table. Place your hands on opposite ends of one of the pieces of clay. Begin pushing your hands together, compressing the clay. What do you notice about the clay? Draw a picture of the clay on a sheet of paper. Now hold the other piece of clay in your hands. Begin to apply tension by gradually pulling the clay apart. What happens as you pull on the clay? What do you think will happen if you continue to apply tension to the clay? Draw a picture of what you observe.

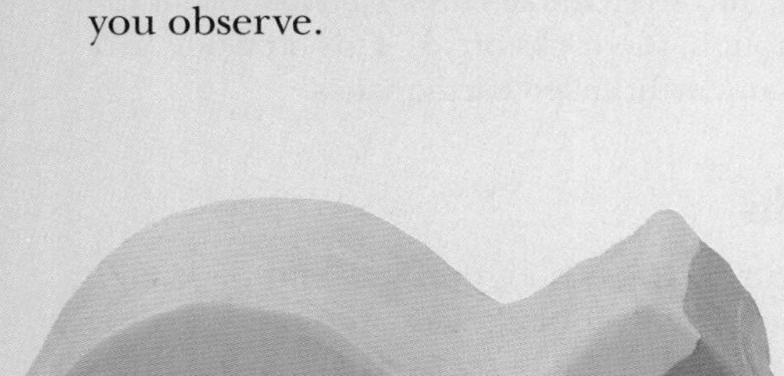

Gearing Up

Previewing the Chapter

Use this outline to help you focus on important ideas in this chapter.

Previewing Science Skills

- In the **Skill Builders,** you will make concept maps, use graphs, and make tables.
- In the **Activities,** you will measure, construct and interpret graphs, analyze data, and draw conclusions.
- In the **MINI-Labs,** you will interpret graphs and apply skills in a role-playing exercise.

What's next?

Now that you've seen how the forces of compression and tension affect a layer of clay, you can relate this to how forces in Earth might affect rock. As you read this chapter, you will learn what causes earthquakes, how their point of origin is located, and what we learn from them.

INTRODUCING THE CHAPTER

Use the Find Out activity to introduce students to forces that cause rocks to deform. Inform students that they will be learning how these forces can cause earthquakes.

FIND OUT!

Preparation: Obtain several kilograms of modeling clay.

Materials: two 10 cm × 5 cm × 1 cm slabs of clay for each group of four students

Cooperative Learning: Form Science Investigation groups of four students per group. Assign one student as the reader; another as the materials handler; and a third as the recorder. The fourth student will perform the activity. The recorder is responsible for the sketches and for writing the answers to the activity questions.

Teaching Tips

- You may wish to have students work with the clay on waxed paper.
- Advise students to gradually apply compression and tension to the slabs of clay.

Gearing Up

Have students study the Gearing Up feature to familiarize themselves with the chapter. Discuss the relationships of the topics in the outline.

What's Next?

Before beginning the first section, make sure students understand the connection between the Find Out activity and the topics to follow.

For Your Mainstreamed Students

Have students conduct research to find out about major earthquakes that have occurred during recorded history. Have them construct timelines of these earthquakes from the earliest to the most recent. The magnitude of each earthquake should be included. Students can also use a world map to mark the locations of these earthquakes. Have students hypothesize why certain areas have more earthquakes than others.

SECTION 14-1

PREPARATION

SECTION BACKGROUND

▶ Relatively large breaks in rocks are fractures. Fractures along which movement occurs are faults.

▶ Whether a rock body bends or breaks depends on the kind and amount of force applied, the rate of application, and the type of rock to which the force is applied.

▶ Compressional forces are applied to rocks at convergent plate boundaries. Tensional forces are applied where plates diverge. Plates sliding past each other generate shear forces.

▶ Compressional and shear forces cause rocks to fold. But if these forces are great or are applied suddenly, breaks can occur. Tensional forces tend to cause fractures.

1 MOTIVATE

▶ Obtain some photographs or articles featuring the Armenian earthquake of 1988 or the Mexico City earthquake of 1985 to share with students. *National Geographic Magazine* is an excellent source for this type of information. Lead a discussion as to why earthquakes are able to cause such destruction.

Cooperative Learning: Form Science Investigation groups with four students per group. Have one student serve as recorder. Have each of the other students apply compression, tension, and shear forces to bars of taffy. Have the recorder draw what happens to each bar of taffy. Have students relate this to what happens to rocks when forces are applied. Ask students what might happen if the force was applied suddenly. Encourage each team to try this.

14-1 Earthquakes and Plate Tectonics

New Science Words

faults
earthquakes
normal fault
reverse fault
strike-slip fault

Objectives

▶ **Explain how earthquakes result from the buildup of stress in Earth's crust.**

▶ **Contrast normal, reverse, and strike-slip faults.**

Did You Know?

The 1989 San Francisco earthquake was caused by the Pacific plate slipping past the North American plate by only 2 m.

Causes of Earthquakes

Think about the last time you used a rubber band to hold a roll of papers together. You knew you could stretch the rubber band only so far before it would break. Rubber bands bend and stretch when force is applied to them. Because they are elastic, they return to their original shape once the force is released.

There is a limit to how far a rubber band will stretch. Once it passes this elastic limit, it breaks. Rocks act in much the same way. Up to a point, applied forces cause rocks to bend and stretch. Once their elastic limit is passed, the rocks break. Rocks break and move along surfaces called **faults**. The rocks on either side of a fault move in different directions.

What produces the forces that cause faults to form? Obviously, something must be causing the rocks to move, otherwise, the rocks would just rest quietly without any stress building up in them. As you know, Earth's crust is in constant motion because of tectonic forces. When plates move, stress is put on rocks. To relieve this stress, the rocks tend to bend, compress, and stretch like rubber bands. But if the force is great enough, the rocks break. This breaking produces vibrations in Earth, called **earthquakes.**

Types of Faults

Compare Figure 14-1 with Figure 13-10 on page 349. You will see that most earthquakes occur along tectonic plate boundaries. In fact, 80 percent of all earthquakes occur along the edges of the Pacific plate.

OPTIONS

Meeting Different Ability Levels

For Section 14-1, use the following **Teacher Resource Masters** depending upon individual students' needs.

◆ **Study Guide Master** for all students.

● **Reinforcement Master** for students of average and above average ability levels.

▲ **Enrichment Master** for above average students.

Additional Teacher Resource Package masters are listed in the OPTIONS box throughout the section. The additional masters are appropriate for all students.

◆ STUDY GUIDE 58

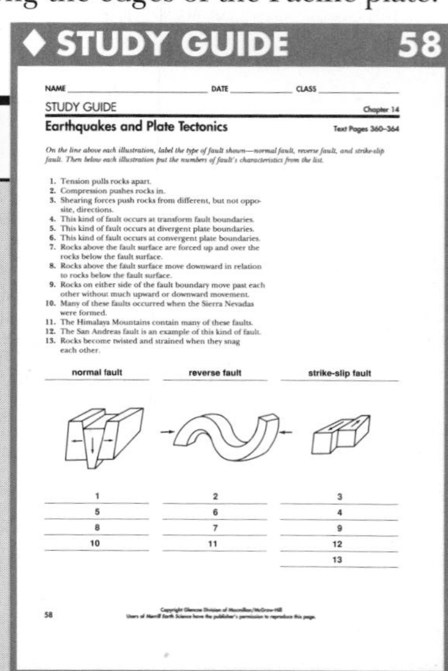

NAME ______ DATE ______ CLASS ______

STUDY GUIDE — Chapter 14

Earthquakes and Plate Tectonics — Text Pages 360-364

On the line above each illustration, label the type of fault shown—normal fault, reverse fault, and strike-slip fault. Then below each illustration put the numbers of fault's characteristics from the list.

1. Tension pulls rocks apart.
2. Compression pushes rocks in.
3. Shearing forces push rocks from different, but not opposite, directions.
4. This kind of fault occurs at transform fault boundaries.
5. This kind of fault occurs at divergent plate boundaries.
6. This kind of fault occurs at convergent plate boundaries.
7. Rocks above the fault surface are forced up and over the rocks below the fault surface.
8. Rocks above the fault surface move downward in relation to rocks below the fault surface.
9. Rocks on either side of the fault boundary move past each other without much upward or downward movement.
10. Many of these faults occurred when the Sierra Nevadas were formed.
11. The Himalaya Mountains contain many of these faults.
12. The San Andreas fault is an example of this kind of fault.
13. Rocks become twisted and strained when they snag each other.

normal fault	reverse fault	strike-slip fault
1	2	3
5	6	4
8	7	9
10	11	12
		13

58

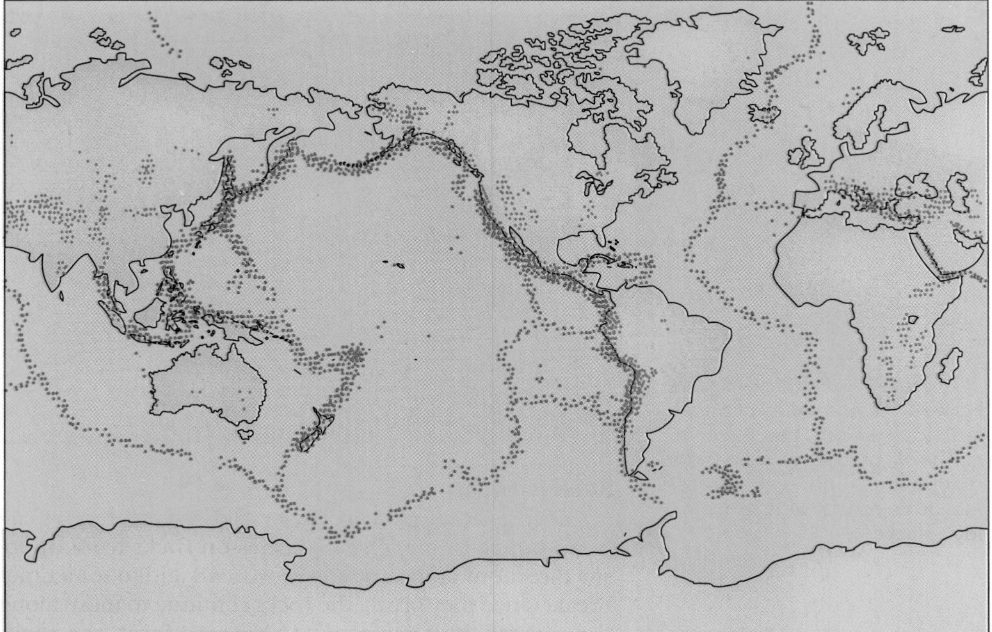

Figure 14-1. The dots represent the epicenters of the major quakes over a ten-year period. Eighty percent of earthquakes occur along the edges of the Pacific plate. This ring of seismic and volcanic activity is called the Pacific Ring of Fire.

Rocks experience several types of forces at the different types of plate boundaries. In the Find Out activity at the beginning of this chapter, you experimented with two of these forces—compression and tension. As you read on, you will discover that rocks also experience a force called shearing. Let's take a look at these three forces and the types of faults they create.

Normal Faults

At divergent plate boundaries, the plates and the rocks that compose them are moving apart. The rocks are subjected to the force of tension. Tension can pull rocks apart and create a **normal fault.** Along a normal fault, rock above the fault surface moves downward in relation to rock below the fault surface. A model of a normal fault is shown in Figure 14-2. 1

Many normal faults occurred during the formation of the Sierra Nevadas. The continental crust was subjected to tension as it spread apart. The resulting mountains are a series of fault blocks.

● REINFORCEMENT 58

NAME ____ DATE ____ CLASS ____

REINFORCEMENT — Chapter 14

Earthquakes and Plate Tectonics — Text Pages 360–364

Write the term that matches each description below on the spaces provided. One letter has been given for each answer.

1. E A R T H Q U A K [E] S
2. T E C T [O] N I C P L A T E S
3. [S] H E A R I N G
4. N O R [M] A L F A U L T
5. [C] O N V E R G E N T P L A T E S
6. D I V E R G E [N] T P L A T E S
7. E L A S T [I] C L I M I T
8. S T R I K E - S L I [P] F A U L T
9. T R A N S F [O] R M F A U L T
10. R E V E [R] S E F A U L T
11. T E N [S] I O N

1. This is the breaking of rocks that causes vibrations in Earth.
2. Most earthquakes occur at the boundaries of these.
3. These forces push on rocks from different, but not opposite, directions.
4. Tension pulls rocks apart and creates this.
5. At these places, rocks are pushed from opposite directions.
6. At these places, plates and the rocks that compose them are moving apart.
7. A bending and stretching rock will break when it reaches this point.
8. Rocks on either side of this move past each other without much upward or downward movement.
9. One of the most famous examples of this boundary is the San Andreas fault in California.
10. Here rocks above this surface are forced up and over rocks below this surface.
11. This force creates a normal fault.

Write the clue letters that were given in the answers.
EOSMCNIPORS

Rearrange the letters to form a word for the force that creates reverse faults.
COMPRESSION

58

▲ ENRICHMENT 58

NAME ____ DATE ____ CLASS ____

ENRICHMENT — Chapter 14

Earthquakes and Plate Tectonics — Text Pages 360–364

WHAT CAUSES EARTHQUAKES?

Long before people understood plate tectonics and the structure of Earth, they experienced earthquakes. They tried to explain what caused them.

Ancient Chinese myths stated that Earth rested on the shoulders of a great ox. Earth's ride on the ox was usually smooth. When the ox shifted the weight of Earth from one shoulder to another, however, the shift caused Earth to quake. The Algonquin of North America believed that Earth rode on the back of a huge tortoise. Earthquakes occurred when the tortoise shifted weight from one leg to another. Japanese mythology explained that the movements of a catfish buried deep in the mud beneath Earth caused earthquakes.

Many people related earthquakes to religion. Early Scandinavian myths said that earthquakes were caused by the god Loki writhing in pain when poison fell on his face. Legends told of Loki killing his brother. As a punishment, a snake dropped poison onto Loki's face. His wife would catch the poison in a bowl before it hit Loki. When the bowl filled, she went to empty it. Then the poison landed on Loki and his writhing caused earthquakes.

Romanian legend noted that Earth rested on pillars of faith, hope, and charity. When people failed to keep one of these virtues, the pillar would weaken and cause earthquakes. Even as late as 1752, the Royal Society of England, a group of respected scientists, noted that "earthquakes only occur when people need chastening."

Aristotle, a Greek philosopher, offered a different explanation for earthquakes. He explained that Earth was filled with deep caverns that sucked up strong winds. When the winds were fanned by fires, they exploded into earthquakes or volcanoes. After Aristotle, many philosophers believed explosions beneath Earth caused earthquakes.

Today scientists accept the relationship between plate tectonics and earthquakes. Advanced scientific study has helped solve the mystery of earthquakes. But they remain as frightening to present-day people as they were to people in the past.

1. Why do you think people have always tried to explain the causes of earthquakes? **Earthquakes are a frightening experience. People usually handle their fears better if they know the cause of them, and thus how to lessen their effects.**
2. If people believed that their actions could cause earthquakes, how might they try to prevent earthquakes? What might they think if an earthquake did occur? **People could try to prevent earthquakes by not commiting wrongful acts. People might accuse others of causing the earthquake if they seem to act in wrongful ways.**
3. Aristotle identified earthquakes as a natural phenomenon. Yet hundreds of years later, the Royal Society of England related earthquakes to human behavior. Why do you think the society did not relate earthquakes to natural phenomena? **Student opinions may vary, but they may conclude that the Royal Society did not have the scientific evidence or technology needed to identify the causes of earthquakes.**

58

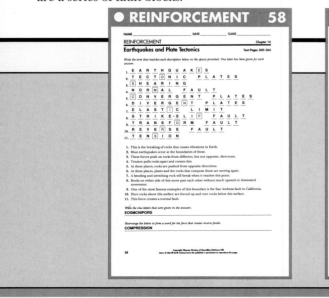

TYING TO PREVIOUS KNOWLEDGE: Have students recall from Chapter 13 the three types of plate boundaries. Explain the kind of force associated with each kind of boundary.

OBJECTIVES AND SCIENCE WORDS: Have students review the objectives and science words to become familiar with this section.

2 TEACH

Key Concepts are highlighted.

CONCEPT DEVELOPMENT

▶ **What is a rock's elastic limit?** *the point at which a rock no longer bends but rather breaks due to applied forces*

▶ Different materials have different elastic limits. Have students bend the materials listed to see what happens once the elastic limit is reached on a piece of stiff cardboard, a plastic drinking straw, a wooden tongue depressor, a thin steel wire, some silicon putty, and a very thin sheet of slate or shale. Have students wear goggles during this activity.

▶ **What is an earthquake?** *strong vibrations due to certain Earth movements*

CONCEPT DEVELOPMENT

▶ **Demonstration:** Contrast the three types of faults by preparing a large, triple-decker peanut butter and jelly sandwich. Cut off the crusts so the individual layers can be seen. Construct a "fault" at about a 30° angle by cutting through the sandwich. Move the separate halves of the sandwich to demonstrate normal, reverse, and strike-slip faults.

FLEX Your Brain

Use the Flex Your Brain activity to have students explore CAUSES OF EARTHQUAKES. Students should discover that Earthquakes can be caused not only by movement along plate boundaries but also by movement of magma during volcanic activity. Some students may also investigate *Earth tides*. Earth tides are the cyclic rising and falling of the surface of the solid earth. They are similar to ocean tides in that they are also the result of the gravitational attraction of the sun and moon. This fluctuation of the solid earth (of up to 20 centimeters) is often suspected to be a cause of some earthquakes.

CROSS CURRICULUM

▶ **Mathematics:** The Sierra Nevadas formed about 10 million years ago. Mt. Whitney is one of the many peaks in the range that stand 4000 m above sea level. Have students compute an average annual rate of uplift.

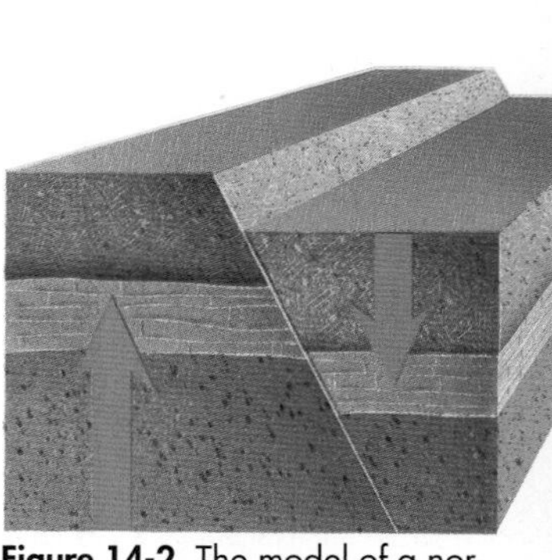

Figure 14-2. The model of a normal fault shows the relative movement of rocks on either side of the fault line. The Sierra Nevadas consist of a series of fault blocks.

Reverse Faults

Compression forces are generated at convergent plate boundaries. Compression pushes on rocks from opposite directions and causes them to bend and to sometimes break. Once they break, the rocks continue to move along the reverse fault surface. At a **reverse fault,** the rocks
2 above the fault surface are forced up and over the rocks below the fault surface.

The Himalaya Mountains of India contain many reverse faults. The continental crusts of India and Asia are still being subjected to compressional forces as two tectonic plates continue to converge.

Figure 14-3. The relative movement of rocks in a reverse fault results from applied pressure. Why do the Himalaya Mountains exhibit so many reverse faults?

OPTIONS

INQUIRY QUESTIONS

▶ **What happens to rocks when compression is gradually applied?** *Gradual pushing from opposite directions tends to make rocks bend or fold.*

▶ **What will happen if compression is applied very quickly to rocks?** *Rocks will bend until their elastic limits are reached. Once this occurs, the rocks will break.*

▶ **How do reverse faults differ from normal faults?** In reverse faults, rocks above the fault surface are forced up and over the rocks below the fault surface. In normal faults, rocks above the fault surface move downward relative to rocks below the fault surface.

▶ **Describe the movement along the San Andreas fault.** *Rocks are moving past each other without much vertical movement.*

▶ **How do shearing forces differ from compressional forces?** *Shearing forces push on rocks from different, but not opposite, directions. Compressional forces push on rocks from directly opposite sides.*

Strike-slip Faults

Recall the transform fault boundaries you studied in Chapter 13. The most famous example of this type of plate boundary is the San Andreas Fault of California. A transform fault, like the San Andreas, is a type of strike-slip fault. At a **strike-slip fault,** rocks on either side of the 3
fault surface are moving past each other without much upward or downward movement. Compare the fault in Figure 14-4 with those on the previous page. How do they differ?

Rocks along strike-slip faults are subjected to shearing forces. Shearing forces push on rocks from different, but not opposite, directions. As the rocks move past each other, their irregular surfaces snag each other, and the

What type of force is generated at a strike-slip fault boundary?

Figure 14-4. There is very little vertical movement along a strike-slip fault such as the San Andreas Fault shown here.

rocks are twisted and strained. Not only are they deformed, but the snagging of the irregular surface hinders the movement of the plates. As tectonic forces keep driving the plates to move, the stress builds up and the rocks reach their elastic limit. They break and an earthquake results.

Earthquakes can be dramatic events. Some have devastating effects, others go almost unnoticed. Regardless of their magnitudes, most earthquakes are the result of plates moving over, under, and around each other. If these plates simply slid smoothly past each other, the

CONCEPT DEVELOPMENT

▶ Have students construct a movable model of a strike-slip fault.

▶ After students have read page 363, ask the following question: **What might happen to the course of a stream that crosses a strike-slip fault?** *The stream's path will be offset as movement occurs along the fault. Often, streams flowing perpendicular to a strike-slip fault make a sharp, right-angle turn along the fault and then flow perpendicular to it again on the other side. Eventually, the stream may abandon its old channel if it becomes severely offset and a new, easier route can be cut.*

TEACHER F.Y.I.

▶ The San Andreas fault is a fault system of many interconnecting faults.

CHECK FOR UNDERSTANDING

Use the Mini Quiz to check for understanding.

MINI QUIZ

Use the Mini Quiz to check students' recall of chapter content.

1. **Which type of force causes a normal fault?** *tension*
2. **Rocks above the fault surface are forced up and over the rocks below the fault surface in a _____ fault.** *reverse*
3. **The _____ fault is a strike-slip fault.** *San Andreas*

RETEACH

Have students use their hands or textbooks to demonstrate the movement that occurs along each of the three kinds of faults.

EXTENSION

For students who have mastered this section, use the **Reinforcement** and **Enrichment** masters or other OPTIONS provided.

ENRICHMENT

▶ Have students compare a map of earthquake belts with a map that shows plate boundaries. Encourage students to relate the type of plate boundary to the depth and strength of earthquakes that occur near it.

▶ Interested students can explore Earth tides and their possible correlation with earthquakes. Earth tides are discussed briefly in the Flex Your Brain feature on page 362.

PROGRAM RESOURCES

From the **Teacher Resource Package** use:
Activity Masters, page 5, Flex Your Brain.
Use **Laboratory Manual,** pages 117-120, Earthquakes.

REVEALING MISCONCEPTIONS

▶ After students compare Figure 14-1 on page 361 with Figure 13-10 on page 349, ask them if your region of the country is susceptible to earthquakes. Then ask students to consider whether earthquakes are limited to plate boundaries. Some students may think that earthquakes only occur near plate boundaries. Explain that although certain areas are more likely to experience an earthquake, earthquakes can occur anywhere.

3 CLOSE

▶ Ask questions 1-4 and the **Apply** Question in the Section Review.

▶ Invite an engineer to visit class to discuss the problems associated with construction near a fault.

SECTION REVIEW ANSWERS

1. Plate movement puts stress on rocks. Rocks can break under such stress and cause earthquakes.

2. shearing, compression

3. The forces that cause the faults are different. Normal faults are caused by tension. Reverse faults are due to compression. Tension allows the rocks above the fault to slide downward as the rocks are pulled apart. Compression forces one block of rocks up and over another.

4. reverse faults

5. Apply: Most earthquakes occur near plate boundaries. If earthquakes have occurred in an area in the past, they will probably occur again, but it cannot be predicted when.

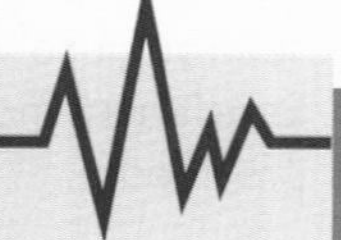

Skill Builder

Possible Solution: Stress causes bending and stretching. The elastic limit is reached, which results in an earthquake.

Figure 14-5. These railroad tracks along Mexico's Pacific coast were twisted during an earthquake. They illustrate the damage that can occur from seismic waves and fault movements.

tension, compression, and shear forces would not build up stress. But in actuality, rocks do experience these forces and stress builds up in them. When rocks break because of the stress, energy is released along the fault surfaces and we observe the effects in the form of earthquakes.

SECTION REVIEW

1. How is plate tectonics related to earthquakes?
2. What type of force is usually generated at strike-slip fault boundaries? What type of force causes reverse faults to form?
3. The surfaces of normal faults and reverse faults look very similar. Why do rocks above the fault surface slide down at a normal fault and up at a reverse fault?
4. The Appalachian Mountains formed when two plates collided. What type of fault do you think is most common in these mountains?
5. **Apply:** Why is it easier to predict where an earthquake will occur than it is to predict when it will occur?

Skill Builder

Concept Mapping

Make a cycle concept map that shows why many earthquakes occur along the San Andreas fault. Use these terms and phrases: *rocks, stress, bend and stretch, elastic limit reached, earthquakes.* If you need help, refer to Concept Mapping in the **Skill Handbook** on pages 688 and 689.

OPTIONS

PROGRAM RESOURCES

From the **Teacher Resource Package** use:
Concept Mapping, pages 33-34.
Transparency Masters, pages 59-60, Types of Faults.
Use **Color Transparency** number 30, Types of Faults.

ACTIVITY 14-1
Earthquake Depths

Problem: *What do earthquakes tell us about plate boundaries?*

Materials
- graph paper
- Figures 13-10 and 13-11

Procedure
1. The data table below shows the depths and locations of earthquake foci near the coast of a continent. Use the table to construct a line graph. Place "Distance from the coast" on the horizontal axis. Begin labeling at the far left with 100 km west. To the right of it should be 0 km then 100 km east, 200 km east, 300 km east, and so on through 700 km east. The coast of the continent is represented by 0 km.
2. Label the vertical axis "Depth below Earth's surface." Label the top of the graph 0 km to represent Earth's surface. Label the bottom of the vertical axis −800 km.
3. Plot the focus depth against the distance and direction from the coast for each earthquake in the table below.

Analyze
1. What is the relationship between distance from the coast to the epicenters and the depth of the earthquake?
2. Is this a converging plate boundary or a strike-slip plate boundary? How do you know?

Conclude and Apply
3. Is the continent located east or west of the plate boundary? How do you know?
4. Why don't earthquakes occur below a depth of 700 km? (HINT: Think about the structure of the asthenosphere compared to the lithosphere.)
5. What do earthquakes tell us about plate boundaries?

Data and Observations

Quake	Focus Depth	Distance of Epicenter from Coast (km)	Quake	Focus Depth	Distance of Epicenter from Coast (km)
A	− 55 km	0	L	− 45 km	95 east
B	− 295 km	100 east	M	− 305 km	495 east
C	− 390 km	455 east	N	− 480 km	285 east
D	− 60 km	75 east	O	− 665 km	545 east
E	− 130 km	255 east	P	− 85 km	90 west
F	− 195 km	65 east	Q	− 525 km	205 east
G	− 695 km	400 east	R	− 85 km	25 west
H	− 20 km	40 west	S	− 445 km	595 east
I	− 505 km	695 east	T	− 635 km	665 east
J	− 520 km	390 east	U	− 55 km	95 west
K	− 385 km	335 east	V	− 70 km	100 west

ACTIVITY 14-1
50 minutes

OBJECTIVE: Utilize earthquake data to **determine** one type of plate boundary.

PROCESS SKILLS applied in this activity:
- ▶ **Inferring** in Conclude and Apply Question 4.
- ▶ **Communicating** in Procedure Steps 1-3.
- ▶ **Using Numbers** in Procedure Steps 1-3.
- ▶ **Interpreting Data** in Analyze Question 1 and Conclude and Apply Questions 3 and 5.
- ▶ **Defining Operationally** in Analyze Question 2.

TEACHING THE ACTIVITY
- ▶ Some students may need to review the differences among the three types of plate boundaries from Chapter 13.
- ▶ Students' graphs should resemble the one shown below:

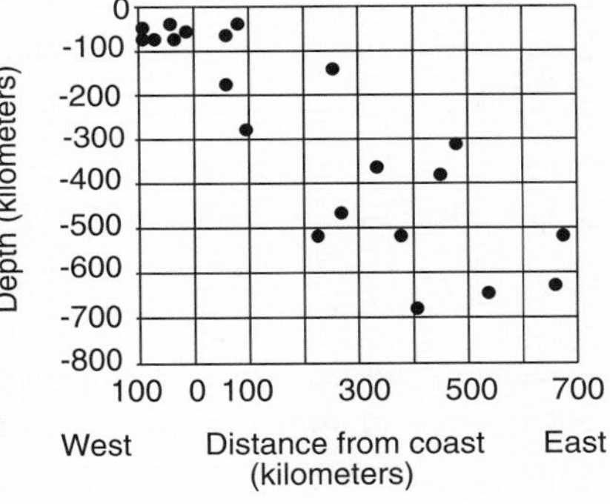

PROGRAM RESOURCES
From the **Teacher Resource Package** use:
Activity Worksheets, pages 122-123, Activity 14-1: Earthquake Depths.

ANSWERS TO QUESTIONS
1. The earthquakes near the coast are shallow quakes. Moving inland, the earthquakes become progressively deeper.
2. Deep earthquakes are associated with subduction zones at converging plate boundaries. It appears that the less dense continental crust is overriding the more dense oceanic crust to its west. The oceanic crust is being subducted into the mantle.
3. Because the plate being subducted from the west appears to be the more dense oceanic crust material, the continent must be located east of the coastline.
4. The tremendous pressure and temperatures at this depth and below reduce the rigidity of solids. Generally, earthquakes occur because of the fracturing of solids. The asthenosphere is mostly molten. Some earthquakes occur in the stenosphere when solid continental crust is forced downward into the asthenosphere. There, it breaks, releasing energy in the form of seismic waves.
5. By mapping the pattern of epicenters and depths, seismologists are able to identify the locations and types of plate boundaries.

SECTION 14-2

PREPARATION

SECTION BACKGROUND

▶ Primary waves are referred to as P-waves, secondary waves as S-waves, and surface waves as L-waves.

▶ Primary waves generated at the focus of an earthquake travel outward through Earth's interior. Sometimes these waves enter Earth's atmosphere and cause the loud noises associated with earthquakes.

▶ The focus of an earthquake can be shallow, intermediate, or deep. Shallow-focus earthquakes occur at divergent plate boundaries and near the edges of converging plates. Intermediate- and deep-focus earthquakes occur along subduction zones.

PREPLANNING

▶ To prepare for Activity 14-2, obtain string, metric rulers, and several globes of Earth.

1 MOTIVATE

▶ **Demonstration:** Place a large, flat pan of water in front of the class. Ask a volunteer to drop a small rock into the water. Have the other students observe the waves that are generated. Explain that the wave movement in the water is similar to the movement of certain types of earthquake waves through Earth's interior.

14-2 Earthquake Information

New Science Words

seismic waves
focus
primary waves
secondary waves
epicenter
surface waves
Moho discontinuity

Objectives

- ▶ Compare and contrast primary, secondary, and surface waves.
- ▶ Explain how an earthquake epicenter is located using seismic wave information.
- ▶ Describe how seismic wave studies indicate the structure of Earth's interior.

Types of Seismic Waves

Have you ever seen a coiled-spring toy? When children play with a coiled-spring toy, they send energy waves through it. **Seismic waves,** generated by an earthquake, are similar to the waves of the toy. Where are seismic waves formed? How do they move through Earth and how can we use the information that they carry? Let's investigate how scientists have answered these questions.

As you have learned, when rocks move along a fault surface, energy is released. The point in Earth's interior where this release occurs is the **focus** of the earthquake. Seismic waves are produced and travel outward from the earthquake focus.

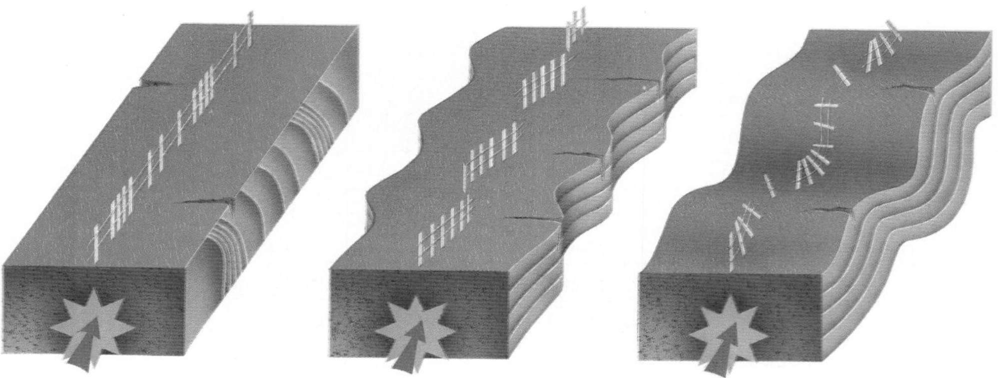

Figure 14-6. Primary waves cause the ground to compress and stretch. Secondary waves cause the ground to move perpendicular to the direction of the wave. Surface waves cause the most damage by creating vertical motion at the surface.

OPTIONS

Meeting Different Ability Levels

For Section 14-2, use the following **Teacher Resource Masters** depending upon individual students' needs.

◆ **Study Guide Master** for all students.

● **Reinforcement Master** for students of average and above average ability levels.

▲ **Enrichment Master** for above average students.

Additional Teacher Resource Package masters are listed in the OPTIONS box throughout the section. The additional masters are appropriate for all students.

◆ STUDY GUIDE 59

NAME ______ DATE ______ CLASS ______

STUDY GUIDE — Chapter 14

Earthquake Information — Text Pages 366–372

Solve the crossword puzzle by using the clues provided.

1 SURFACEWAVES
1 SEISMICWAVES
2 FOCUS
3 PRIMARYWAVES
4 EPICENTER
5 MOHODISCONTINUITY
6 SHADOWZONE
7 SECONDARYWAVES

Across

1. These move by giving particles a circular motion and are generated by energy that travels outward from the epicenter. (2 words)
5. This is the name for the boundary between Earth's crust and the upper mantle. (2 words)
6. Area where no seismic waves are detected (2 words)
7. These move through Earth by causing particles to move at right angles to the waves' direction. (2 words)

Down

1. These are forms of energy that are produced at an earthquake's point of origin and travel outward. (2 words)
2. This is the point in Earth's interior where the energy of an earthquake is released.
3. These cause particles to move back and forth in the same direction the waves are moving. (2 words)
4. This is the point on Earth's surface directly above an earthquake's point of origin.

Identify points A and B on the illustration. One is the epicenter of an earthquake, and one is the focus.

A. epicenter
B. focus

A
B

59

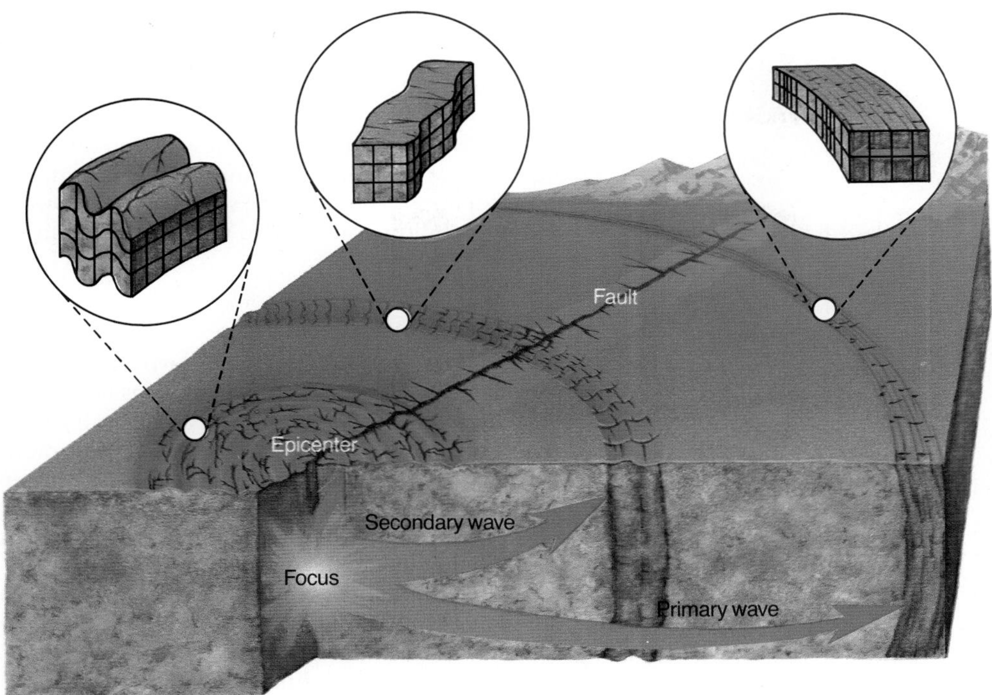

Waves that move through Earth by causing particles in rocks to move back and forth in the same direction the wave is moving are called **primary waves.** If you squeeze one end of a coiled-spring toy and then release it, you cause it to compress and then stretch as the primary wave travels through it. Particles in rocks also compress together and stretch apart, transmitting primary waves through the rock.

Now, if you and a friend stretch the coiled-spring toy between you, and then move one end up and down, a different type of wave will pass through the toy. The spring will move up and down as the wave moves along
it. **Secondary waves** move through Earth by causing par- 1
ticles in rocks to move at right angles to the direction of the wave.

The point on Earth's surface directly above an earthquake's focus is the **epicenter.** Energy that reaches the 2
surface of Earth generates waves that travel outward from the epicenter. These waves, called **surface waves,** move by giving particles a circular motion.

Figure 14-7. Primary and secondary waves travel outward from the focus. Surface waves move outward from the epicenter. The enlarged blocks show how the waves deform rock and soil as they pass by.

How do primary and secondary waves differ?

● REINFORCEMENT 59

NAME ______ DATE ______ CLASS ______

REINFORCEMENT — Chapter 14

Earthquake Information — Text Pages 366–372

The graph below shows travel time in minutes and distance traveled for primary and secondary waves. Primary and secondary waves start at the same time but do not travel at the same speed. Study the graph. Use the graph to help answer the questions that follow.

Travel time (min.) — 2, 4, 6, 8, 10, 12, 14, 16, 18, 20, 22
Secondary wave
Primary wave
Distance traveled (1000 km units) — 0, 1, 2, 3, 4, 5, 6, 7, 8, 9, 10

1. How long does it take for a primary wave to travel 2000 kilometers? **4 minutes**
2. How long does it take for a secondary wave to travel 2000 kilometers? **7 minutes**
3. How far does a secondary wave travel in 10 minutes? **3000 km**
4. How far does a primary wave travel in 10 minutes? **about 6750 km**
5. What happens to the time difference between primary and secondary waves as the distance traveled gets longer? **The time difference increases as the distance traveled increases.**
6. Suppose a primary and secondary wave both traveled a distance of 5000 kilometers before they are picked up by a seismograph. Which wave will arrive first? **primary**
7. How much time lag at 5000 km will there be between these two waves? **7 minutes**
8. Suppose both a primary and secondary wave start together and travel for 5 minutes. Which wave will travel farther? **The primary wave will travel farther.**

 59

▲ ENRICHMENT 59

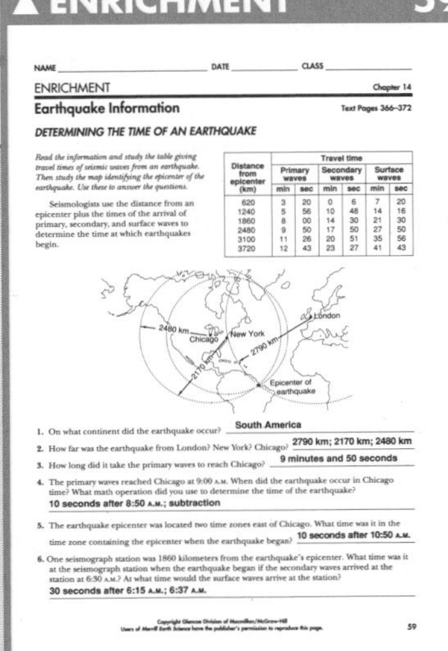

NAME ______ DATE ______ CLASS ______

ENRICHMENT — Chapter 14

Earthquake Information — Text Pages 366–372

DETERMINING THE TIME OF AN EARTHQUAKE

Read the information and study the table giving travel times of seismic waves from an earthquake. Then study the map identifying the epicenter of the earthquake. Use these to answer the questions.

Seismologists use the distance from an epicenter plus the times of the arrival of primary, secondary, and surface waves to determine the time at which earthquakes begin.

Distance from epicenter (km)	Travel time					
	Primary waves		Secondary waves		Surface waves	
	min	sec	min	sec	min	sec
620	3	20	0	6	7	20
1240	5	56	10	48	14	16
1860	8	00	14	30	21	30
2480	9	50	17	50	27	50
3100	11	26	20	51	35	56
3720	12	43	23	27	41	43

1. On what continent did the earthquake occur? **South America**
2. How far was the earthquake from London? New York? Chicago? **2790 km; 2170 km; 2480 km**
3. How long did it take the primary waves to reach Chicago? **9 minutes and 50 seconds**
4. The primary waves reached Chicago at 9:00 A.M. When did the earthquake occur in Chicago time? What math operation did you use to determine the time of the earthquake? **10 seconds after 8:50 A.M.; subtraction**
5. The earthquake epicenter was located two time zones east of Chicago. What time was it in the time zone containing the epicenter when the earthquake began? **10 seconds after 10:50 A.M.**
6. One seismograph station was 1860 kilometers from the earthquake's epicenter. What time was it at the seismograph station when the earthquake began if the secondary waves arrived at the station at 6:30 A.M.? At what time would the surface waves arrive at the station? **30 seconds after 6:15 A.M.; 6:37 A.M.**

 59

TYING TO PREVIOUS KNOWLEDGE: Have students recall from Chapter 13 the model presented of Earth's interior. Ask students to think about how seismic waves are affected by the different parts of Earth's interior.

OBJECTIVES AND SCIENCE WORDS: Have students review the objectives and science words to become familiar with this section.

FLEX Your Brain

Use the Flex Your Brain activity to have students explore DEPTHS OF EARTHQUAKE FOCI. Students may discover that an earthquake focus is shallow, relative to Earth's diameter. Earthquakes originate only in the lithosphere and asthenosphere. Most earthquake foci are less than 700 km deep.

REVEALING MISCONCEPTIONS

▶ Many students think that all earthquakes begin at Earth's surface. Explain that earthquakes originate at the point where rocks break. This can occur near Earth's surface or deep inside Earth's crust or asthenosphere.

▶ Some students may question how rocks can break in the asthenosphere which is composed of molten, fluid material. Explain that solid continental crust is forced downward into the asthenosphere at subduction zones. The solid crust can break and release seismic waves. Refer to Figure 13-11 on page 350 to illustrate this concept.

2 TEACH

Key Concepts are highlighted.

CONCEPT DEVELOPMENT

▶ Obtain a Slinky and demonstrate the movement of matter with each kind of seismic wave as volunteers explain the movement caused by each wave.

▶ Ask students to define *focus* and *epicenter.*

CONCEPT DEVELOPMENT

Cooperative Learning: Form Numbered Heads Together groups and ask the following questions. **What is an earthquake focus?** *the point in Earth's interior where energy is released from rocks* **How do primary, secondary, and surface waves differ?** *Primary waves travel the fastest and cause particles to move back and forth in the same direction as that of wave propogation. Secondary waves are slower than primary waves and cause particles to move at right angles to the direction of the waves. Surface waves are formed at Earth's surface and cause a circular motion of particles.*

MINI-Lab

Distance (km)	Difference in arrival times
1500	2 min, 45 s
2250	3 min, 40 s
3000	4 min, 30 s
4000	5 min, 35 s
7000	8 min, 24 s
9000	10 min, 05 s

▶ **Answer:** The difference in arrival times is a direct but not constant relationship. The difference in times increases with distance to the earthquake.

MINI-Lab

How do you use a travel time graph?

Use Figure 14-9 to determine the difference in arrival times for primary and secondary waves at the distances listed in the data table below. Two examples are provided for you. What happens to the difference in arrival times as the distance from the earthquake increases?

Distance (km)	Difference in arrival time
1500	2 min 45 sec
2250	
3000	
4000	5 min 35 sec
7000	
9000	

If you've ever floated on an innertube in a wave pool, you've experienced this type of wave. The wave lifts you and your innertube, moves you in a circle, and places you back down.

Surface waves cause most of the destruction during an earthquake. Because most buildings are very rigid, they begin to fall apart when surface waves pass. The waves cause one part of the building to move up while another part moves down.

Locating an Epicenter

Primary, secondary, and surface waves don't travel through Earth at the same speed. Primary waves are the
3 fastest; surface waves are the slowest. Can you think of a way this information could be used to determine how far away an earthquake epicenter is? Think of the last time you and two friends rode your bikes to the store. You were fastest so you arrived first. In fact, the longer you rode, the farther ahead of your friends you became.

You'll learn in the next section that seismic waves are measured at seismograph stations. Primary waves arrive first, secondary waves second, and surface waves last. This enables scientists to determine the distance to an earthquake epicenter. The farther apart the waves, the farther away the epicenter is. When epicenters are far from the seismograph station, the primary wave has more time to put distance between it and the secondary and surface waves.

Figure 14-8. This system of lasers monitors the movement along the San Andreas Fault. It's mounted on a hilltop in Parkfield, CA. Lasers bounce off a series of 18 reflectors positioned several kilometers away. Any change in a reflector's position is measured. Movements of less than one millimeter along the fault can be detected.

OPTIONS

INQUIRY QUESTIONS

▶ **Why are surface waves the most destructive seismic waves?** *Surface waves propel particles in circles. Rigid structures crumble when some particles move up while other particles in the structure move down.*

▶ **How can seismic waves be used to measure the distance to an earthquake epicenter?** *Because seismic waves move at different speeds, the difference in their arrival times can be used to measure the distance they've traveled from the earthquake.*

PROGRAM RESOURCES

From the **Teacher Resource Package** use:

Activity Worksheets, page 128, Mini-Lab: How do you use a travel time graph?

Transparency Masters, pages 61-62, Types of Earthquake Waves.

Use **Color Transparency** number 31, Types of Earthquake Waves.

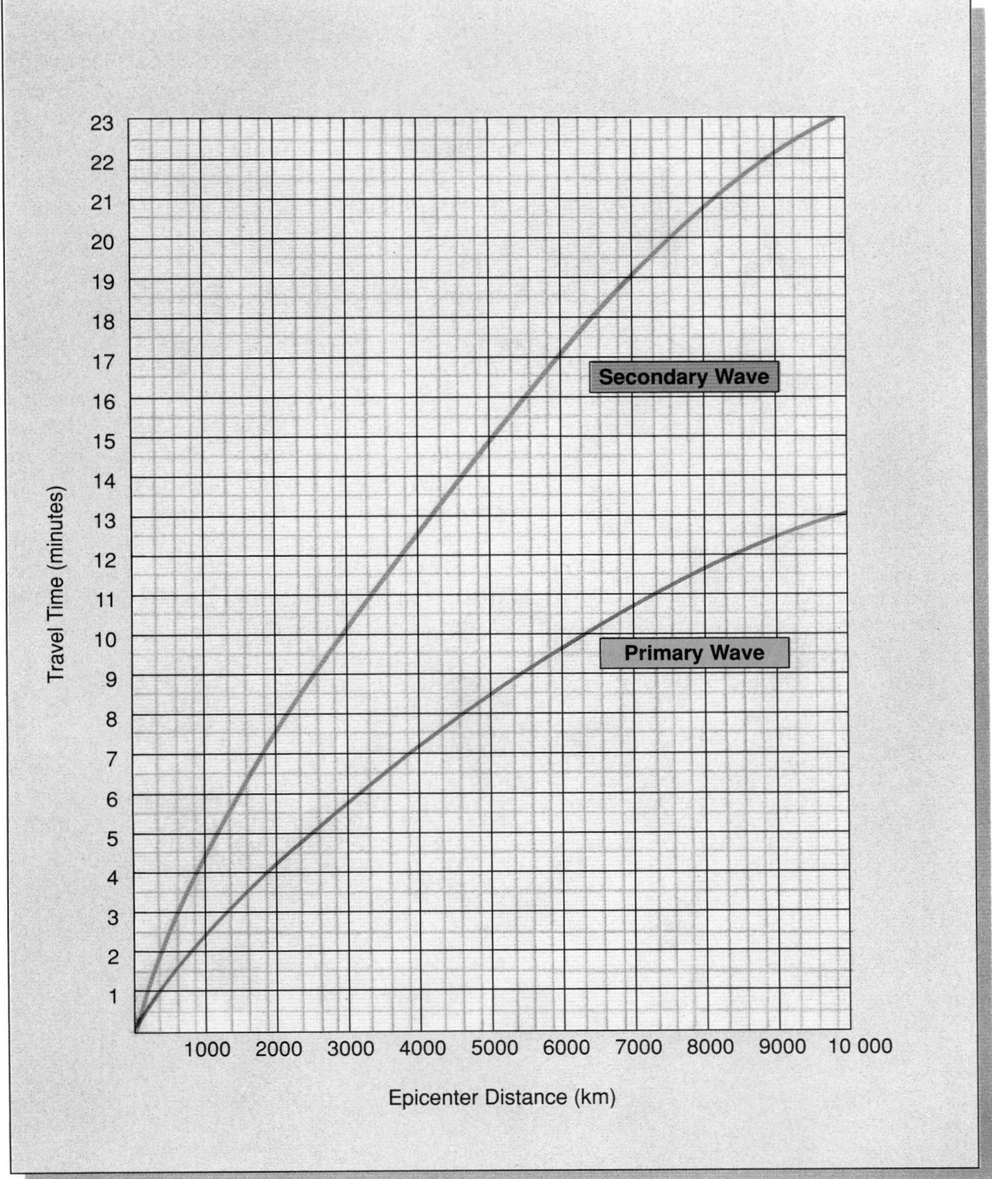

Figure 14-9. This graph shows the distance the primary and secondary waves travel with time. By measuring the difference in arrival times, a seismologist can determine the distance to the epicenter.

CROSS CURRICULUM

► **Language Arts:** Have students research the origin of the word *seismic.* Seismic comes from the Greek term *seismos*, meaning "shock."

TEACHER F.Y.I.

► Primary waves travel at about 6.0 km/s through granitic crust. Secondary waves travel at about 3.5 km/s through the same material while surface waves travel at about 2.0 km/s.

MINI QUIZ

Use the Mini Quiz to check students' recall of chapter content.

1. **Secondary seismic waves cause rock particles to move ____ to the direction of the wave.** *at right angles*
2. **The point on Earth's surface directly above an earthquake focus is the ____ .** *epicenter*
3. **____ waves are the first seismic waves to arrive at a seismic station.** *Primary*

PROGRAM RESOURCES

From the **Teacher Resource Package** use:
Transparency Masters, pages 63-64, Propagation of Earthquake Waves.
Use **Color Transparency** number 32, Propagation of Earthquake Waves.
Use **Laboratory Manual,** pages 121-124, Locating an Earthquake.

STUDENT TEXT QUESTION

▶ Page 370, paragraph 1: **Why is one seismograph station not enough?** *One station will give the distance from, but not the direction to, the epicenter.*

CHECK FOR UNDERSTANDING

Have students write short paragraphs to explain why at least three seismograph stations are needed to locate an earthquake epicenter.

RETEACH

Use a world map, a ruler, a drawing compass, and the data for earthquake "A" on page 373 to demonstrate how an epicenter is located.

EXTENSION

For students who have mastered this section, use the **Reinforcement** and **Enrichment** masters or other OPTIONS provided.

How are seismographs used to locate epicenters?

If seismic wave information is obtained at three seismograph stations, the location of the epicenter can be determined. To locate an epicenter, scientists draw circles around each station on a map. The radius of each circle equals that station's distance from the earthquake epicenter. The point where all three circles intersect is the location of the earthquake epicenter. Why is one seismograph station not enough?

Using Seismic Waves to Map Earth's Interior

In Chapter 13, you learned that Earth is divided into layers. These layers are the crust, upper mantle, lower mantle, outer core, and inner core. Without ever having been there, how do scientists know what Earth's interior is like? Scientists have found that at certain depths, the speed and path of seismic waves change. These changes mark the boundaries of the layers in Earth.

Seismic waves speed up when they reach the bottom of the crust. This boundary between the crust and the upper mantle is called the **Moho discontinuity.** The boundary was discovered by the Yugoslavian scientist,

Figure 14-10. The radius of each circle is equal to the distance to the epicenter from each seismograph station. The intersection of the three circles is the location of the epicenter.

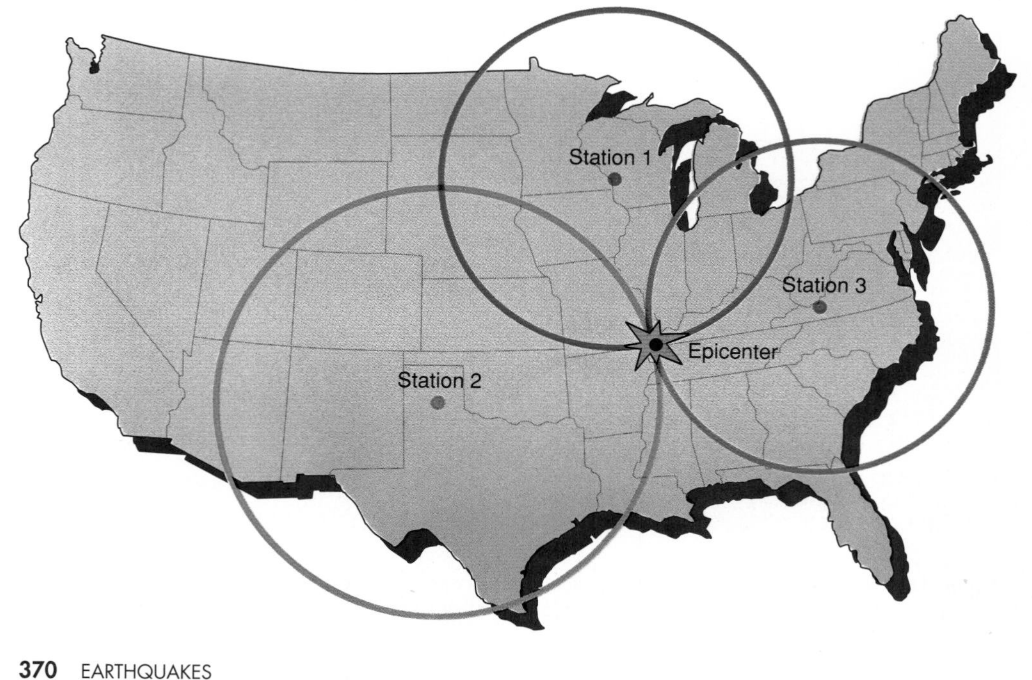

OPTIONS

INQUIRY QUESTIONS

▶ **Will using four seismograph stations make locating an earthquake any more accurate?** *Probably not. Three seismograph stations enable scientists to locate the exact position of an earthquake epicenter. The fourth station may be used to verify the location.*

▶ **What do changes in the speed and direction of seismic waves indicate about Earth's interior?** *Different layers have different densities.*

PROBLEM SOLVING

What's in the Box?

Maria returned home from school one day to find a box, approximately 30 cm × 18 cm × 12 cm, sitting on the kitchen table. Her aunt had come to visit and brought Maria a present. In order for Maria to get the present, she had to be able to tell her aunt at least three facts about it. Maria could do anything she needed to do to the box except open it to look at the gift directly. Of course, Maria would be careful not to damage the gift.

Think Critically: How many facts do you think Maria can learn about the gift? How is Maria's challenge related to earthquakes and mapping Earth's interior?

Andrija Mohorovičić (moh hoh ROH vuh chihch), who inferred that seismic waves speed up because they're passing into a denser layer of the lithosphere.

Primary and secondary waves slow down when they hit the plasticlike asthenosphere and then speed up again as they're transmitted through the solid lower mantle.

There's an area on Earth, between 105° and 140° from the focus, where no waves are detected. This area is called the shadow zone. Secondary waves aren't transmitted through liquid, so they're stopped completely when they hit the liquid outer core. Primary waves are slowed and deflected but not stopped by the liquid outer core. The deflection of the primary waves and the stopping of the secondary waves create the shadow zone. These primary waves again speed up as they travel through the solid inner core.

Why is a shadow zone produced?

The boundaries between layers in Earth not only cause seismic waves to change in speed, but they also cause the waves to bend. Figure 14-11 shows how all of this information has led to the model we now have for Earth's interior.

CONCEPT DEVELOPMENT

▶ Ask students these questions. **What is the shadow zone?** *an area on Earth between 105° and 140° from the focus of an earthquake* **Why are no secondary waves received in this zone?** *Secondary waves can't pass through liquids, so they stop when they hit the liquid outer core.*

PROBLEM SOLVING

Maria can use the size of the box and its heft to learn about the gift. Gently shaking the box could also give clues to its contents. The senses of hearing, touch, and smell are also useful to Maria's determining the box's contents.

Think Critically: Maria's situation is very similar to that of scientists who study Earth's interior. They must make many inferences about Earth's structure based on the behavior of seismic waves.

ENRICHMENT

▶ Have students construct a three-dimensional scale model of Earth's interior that shows the shadow zone.

3 CLOSE

▶ Call on volunteers to describe how particles move when primary, secondary, and surface waves move through objects.

Cooperative Learning: Using the Paired Partner strategy, have students draw models of Earth's structure showing all layers, and how each type of seismic wave is affected as it passes through Earth's interior.

▶ Ask questions 1-3 and the **Apply** Question in the Section Review.

SECTION REVIEW ANSWERS

1. surface waves

2. As the wave passes, the poles would move toward and away from one another.

3. The circles drawn from distances from two stations will intersect in two places, giving two possible epicenter locations. Data from a third station are needed to pinpoint which of those two possible points is the epicenter location.

4. Apply: No secondary waves would be recorded more than 105° from the epicenter. China would likely experience primary waves because it is outside of the shadow zone. Most secondary waves would not reach China because they would have to travel through the liquid outer core. However, some parts of China may receive some secondary waves that were deflected at the core boundary.

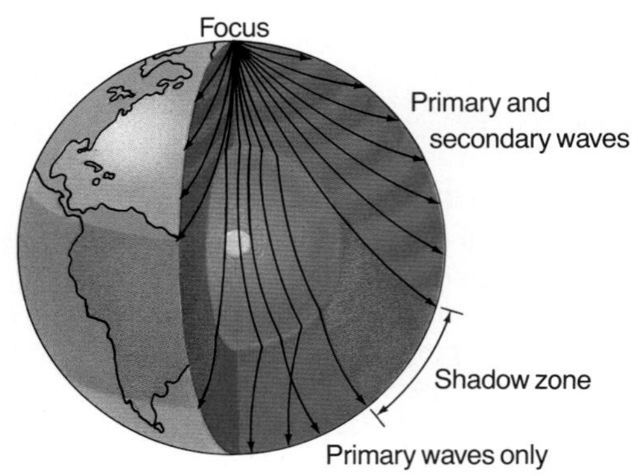

Figure 14-11. Primary waves bend when they contact the outer core, and secondary waves are stopped completely. Primary waves that are transmitted through the outer and inner cores are detected beyond the shadow zone.

SECTION REVIEW

1. Which type of seismic wave does the most damage to property?
2. Draw a diagram of what would happen to a row of evenly spaced utility poles as a primary wave traveled parallel to the row.
3. Why is a seismic record from three locations needed to determine the position of an epicenter?
4. **Apply:** Suppose an earthquake occurs at the San Andreas Fault. What area on Earth would experience no secondary waves? Would China experience primary and secondary waves from the earthquake? Explain your answers.

Skill Builder

Making and Using Graphs

Use the data table below to make a graph of some travel times of earthquake waves. Which line represents primary waves? Which line represents secondary waves? If you need help, refer to Making and Using Graphs in the **Skill Handbook** on page 691.

Distance from earthquake (km)	1 500	2 000	5 000	5 500	8 600	10 000
Time (minutes)	5.0	2.5	14.0	7.0	11.0	23.5

Skill Builder

The P-wave is represented by the points (2000, 2.5), (5500, 7.0), and (8600, 11.0). The points (1500, 5.0), (5000, 14.0), and (10 000, 23.5) represent the slower S-wave. If students have difficulty determining which points should be connected to form a curve, have them first analyze the data table to determine which data pairs correspond to P-waves and which correspond to S-waves. Start out by comparing the arrival times of waves at 1500 km and 2000 km. Clearly, two different waves are needed to account for the indicated arrival times. The P-wave was able to travel 2000 km in less time than it took for the S-wave to travel only 1500 km. The same logic can be applied to the data pairs of (5000, 14.0) and (5500, 7.0). Students can conclude that (8600, 11.0) cannot belong to the wave that travelled only 5000 km in 14.0 minutes.

ACTIVITY 14-2
Locating an Epicenter

Problem: *How are epicenters located?*

Materials
- Figure 14-9
- string
- metric ruler
- globe
- paper
- chalk or water-soluble marker

Procedure
1. Determine the difference in arrival time between the primary and secondary waves at each station for each quake from the data table below.
2. Use Figure 14-9 to determine the distance in kilometers of each seismograph from the epicenter of each earthquake. Record these data in the Data and Observations table. An example has been done for you. The difference in arrival times in Paris for earthquake B is 10.0 minutes. On the graph, the primary and secondary waves are separated along the vertical axis by 10.0 minutes at 9750 km.

Data and Observations

Location of Seismograph	Wave	Wave Arrival Times	
		Earthquake A	Earthquake B
(1) New York	P	2:24:05 PM	1:19:00 PM
	S	2:28:55 PM	1:24:40 PM
(2) Seattle	P	2:24:40 PM	1:14:37 PM
	S	2:30:00 PM	1:16:52 PM
(3) Rio de Janeiro	P	2:29:00 PM	—
	S	2:38:05 PM	—
(4) Paris	P	2:30:15 PM	1:24:05 PM
	S	2:40:29 PM	1:34:05 PM
(5) Tokyo	P	—	1:23:30 PM
	S	—	1:33:05 PM

Data and Observations Sample Data

	Calculated distance from epicenter (km) from each seismograph location				
Quake	(1)	(2)	(3)	(4)	(5)
A	3750	4250	8000	9750	—
B	4500	1250	—	9750	8500

3. Using the string, measure the circumference of the globe. Determine a scale of centimeters of string to kilometers on Earth's surface. (Earth's circumference = 40 000 km.)
4. For each earthquake, A and B, place one end of the string at each seismic station location. Use the chalk or marker to draw a circle with a radius equal to the distance to the epicenter of the quake.
5. Identify the epicenter for each earthquake.

Analyze
1. How is the distance of a seismograph from the earthquake related to the arrival time of the waves?
2. What is the location of the epicenter of each earthquake?
3. How many stations were necessary in order to accurately locate each epicenter?

Conclude and Apply
4. Predict why some seismographs didn't receive secondary waves from some quakes?
5. How are epicenters located?

ACTIVITY 14-2
50-60 minutes

OBJECTIVE: Use an earthquake wave travel time graph to **determine** the location of actual earthquake epicenters.

PROCESS SKILLS applied in this activity:
▶ **Inferring** in Analyze Question 3.
▶ **Using Numbers** in Procedure Steps 1-4.
▶ **Interpreting Data** in Analyze Questions 1 and 2.
▶ **Defining Operationally** in Procedure Step 5 and Conclude and Apply Questions 4 and 5.

TEACHING THE ACTIVITY
▶ Be sure students understand how to use Figure 14-9 before beginning this activity.
▶ **Data and Observations**

Calculated distance to epicenter (km) from each seismograph location					
Quake	(1)	(2)	(3)	(4)	(5)
A	3750	4250	8000	9750	—
B	4500	1250	—	9750	8500

PROGRAM RESOURCES
From the **Teacher Resource Package** use:
Activity Worksheets, pages 124-125, Activity 14-2: Locating an Epicenter.

ANSWERS TO QUESTIONS
1. The difference in arrival time between P- and S-waves increases as the distance of the seismic station to the earthquake increases. This time interval can be used to calculate the distance between the seismograph and the earthquake.
2. A: Mexico City, Mexico; B: San Francisco, California
3. It takes a minimum of three seismic stations to accurately locate the epicenter of an earthquake.
4. Use a globe to demonstrate that these seismic stations are between about 105° and 140° from the epicenters and are, therefore, in the shadow zone.
5. Epicenters are located using the difference between P- and S-wave arrival times from at least three seismic stations.

SECTION 14-3

PREPARATION

SECTION BACKGROUND

▶ The extent of the damage caused by an earthquake depends on the distance to the epicenter, the bedrock of the area struck, local soil types, and the number and type of structures subjected to the quake, among other factors.

▶ During the 1985 earthquake, the soft, unconsolidated sediments underlying Mexico City amplified the vibrations of the earthquake.

▶ The Modified Mercalli Scale is used to measure the intensity or amount of damage done by an earthquake. A rating of I to II is a low intensity quake, while an earthquake measuring XII designates total destruction of the stricken area.

▶ More than one million earthquakes occur every year. Most are not directly observable by humans. However, on the average, 20 earthquakes strong enough to be felt occur each day in California.

1 MOTIVATE

▶ Tape a stiff sheet of paper to the side of a closed shoe box. Have a volunteer slowly draw a straight line from the top of the sheet to the bottom. Then, have the volunteer attempt the same feat as another student bounces a small rubber ball on the top of the box. Use this crude analogy to explain how a seismograph works.

14-3 Destruction by Earthquakes

New Science Words

seismologists
seismograph
magnitude
tsunamis

Objectives

- ▶ Define magnitude and the Richter Scale.
- ▶ List ways to make your classroom and home more earthquake safe.

Measuring Earthquakes

On October 17, 1989, an earthquake shocked the San Francisco Bay area. Surface waves moved through the area in less than 20 seconds, but their effects will be felt for years to come. The quake killed 67 people and damaged billions of dollars of property. In 1988, more than 45 000 people died when an earthquake struck Armenia. More than 50 000 died in the June 1990 earthquake that struck Iran. What determines the amount of damage done by an earthquake, and what can you do to protect yourself from the effects?

Figure 14-12. Most of the damage that resulted during the 1989 San Francisco earthquake was caused by surface waves.

OPTIONS

Meeting Different Ability Levels

For Section 14-3, use the following **Teacher Resource Masters** depending upon individual students' needs.

◆ **Study Guide Master** for all students.

● **Reinforcement Master** for students of average and above average ability levels.

▲ **Enrichment Master** for above average students.

Additional Teacher Resource Package masters are listed in the OPTIONS box throughout the section. The additional masters are appropriate for all students.

◆ STUDY GUIDE 60

NAME ______ DATE ______ CLASS ______

STUDY GUIDE — Chapter 14

Destruction by Earthquakes — Text Pages 374–379

Rewrite each sentence by changing the italicized word or words to make the sentence correct.

1. A *Richter Scale* is an instrument that is used to record primary, secondary, and surface waves of an earthquake. **A seismograph is an instrument that is used to record primary, secondary, and surface waves of an earthquake.**
2. An earthquake's *severity* is the measure of the energy released by the earthquake. **An earthquake's magnitude is the measure of the energy released by the earthquake.**
3. Seismic sea waves are also called *secondary waves*. **Seismic sea waves are also called tsunamis.**
4. A scientist who studies earthquakes is a *seismograph*. **A scientist who studies earthquakes is a seismologist.**
5. Scientists use the *Moho Scale* to measure the magnitude of earthquakes. **Scientists use the Richter Scale to measure the magnitude of earthquakes.**
6. The earthquake in Kansu, China, registered 8.5 on the Richter Scale and released *ten* times more energy than the one in Messina, Italy, that registered 7.5. **The earthquake in Kansu, China, registered 8.5 on the Richter Scale and released thirty times more energy than the one in Messina, Italy, that registered 7.5.**
7. An earthquake that registers between 8.0 and 8.9 on the Richter Scale is likely to happen *about five times* a year. **An earthquake that registers between 8.0 and 8.9 on the Richter Scale is likely to happen less than once a year.**
8. To help make your home earthquake safe, place *heavy objects* on the highest shelves. **To help make your home earthquake safe, place lightweight objects on the highest shelves.**
9. An earthquake with a magnitude of 6.7 would release thirty times more energy than an earthquake with a *magnitude of 7.7*. **An earthquake with a magnitude of 6.7 would release thirty times more energy than an earthquake with a magnitude of 5.7.**
10. In a year, you could expect *about 6000* earthquakes with magnitudes between 1.0 and 3.9. **In a year, you could expect more than 100 000 earthquakes with magnitudes between 1.0 and 3.9.**

60

Scientists who study earthquakes and seismic waves are **seismologists.** They use an instrument called a **seismograph** (1) to record primary, secondary, and surface waves from earthquakes all over the world. As you learned earlier, an earthquake's epicenter can be located by studying the record from three seismograph stations.

One type of seismograph has a drum holding a sheet of paper on a fixed frame. A pendulum with an attached pen is suspended from the frame. When seismic waves occur at the station, the drum vibrates but the pendulum remains at rest. The pen on the pendulum traces a record of the vibrations on a sheet of paper. The height of the lines traced on the paper is a measure of the energy released, or **magnitude** of the earthquake. Seismologists (2) use the Richter (RIHK tur) Scale to describe earthquake magnitudes. The scale describes how much energy is released by the earthquake. Thirty times as much energy

Science and MATH

Calculate the difference in energy released between an earthquake of magnitude 8 and one of magnitude 5.5.

Table 14-1

STRONG EARTHQUAKES			
Year	**Location**	**Richter Value**	**Deaths**
1556	Shensi, China	?	830 000
1737	Calcutta, India	?	300 000
1755	Lisbon, Portugal	8.8	60 000
1811-12	New Madrid, MO	8.3	few
1886	Charleston, SC	?	60
1906	San Francisco, CA	8.3	700
1908	Messina, Italy	7.5	120 000
1920	Kansu, China	8.5	180 000
1923	Tokyo, Japan	8.3	143 000
1939	Concepcion, Chile	8.3	30 000
1960	Southern Chile	8.6	5 700
1964	Prince William Sound, AK	8.5	117
1970	Peru	7.8	66 000
1975	Liaoning Province, China	7.5	few
1976	Tangshan, China	7.6	240 000
1985	Mexico City, Mexico	8.1	7 000
1988	Armenia	6.9	45 000
1989	San Francisco Bay, CA	7.1	67
1990	Iran	7.7	50 000

● REINFORCEMENT 60

NAME ______ DATE ______ CLASS ______

REINFORCEMENT — Chapter 14

Destruction by Earthquakes — Text Pages 374–379

Write the names of the seismograph parts illustrated on the lines provided.

A. frame
B. drum and paper
C. pendulum
D. pen

Use Table 14-1 on page 375 of your text to help you answer the following questions.

1. When and where was the strongest earthquake listed in the table? **1755 in Lisbon, Portugal**
2. How many earthquakes on the chart had a Richter value of 8.3? **four**
3. Where were the earthquakes that had a Richter value of 8.3? **New Madrid, Missouri; San Francisco; Tokyo, Japan; and Concepcion, Chile**
4. Why might so many more people have died in the Tokyo earthquake than in the New Madrid earthquake? **Students might infer that Tokyo was more populated than New Madrid was at the times of the earthquakes.**
5. Which earthquakes were thirty times stronger than the one in Messina, Italy? **earthquakes in Kansu, China, and in Prince William Sound, Alaska**
6. Which earthquake was the one in southern Chile thirty times stronger than? **the one in Tangshan, China**
7. Although the 1975 and 1976 earthquakes in China were only 0.1 Richter values apart, why might so many more people have died in the 1976 earthquake? **Students might infer that fewer people lived in the area of the 1975 earthquake. Note: City was evacuated because of signs of a pending earthquake.**
8. Which earthquakes occurred in North America? **the earthquakes in New Madrid, Missouri; Charleston, South Carolina; San Francisco; Prince William Sound, Alaska; Mexico City; and San Francisco Bay**
9. Which earthquake was thirty times greater than an earthquake registering 7.1 would be? **the 1985 earthquake in Mexico City**

60

▲ ENRICHMENT 60

NAME ______ DATE ______ CLASS ______

ENRICHMENT — Chapter 14

Destruction by Earthquakes — Text Pages 374–379

EARTHQUAKE INTENSITY

In addition to the magnitude of an earthquake, seismologists also try to determine the intensity of an earthquake. Intensity is the damage caused on the surface by an earthquake. In 1902, Italian seismologist Giuseppe Mercalli developed an intensity scale. The scale has since been modified. The scale uses Roman numerals to designate the amount of damage caused by an earthquake.

Study the Modified Mercalli Scale and then answer the questions.

Modified Mercalli Scale of earthquake Intensity

I. Not felt except by a very few under especially favorable circumstances. Birds and animals uneasy. Delicately suspended objects may swing.
II. Felt only by a few persons at rest, especially on upper floors of buildings.
III. Felt noticeably indoors, especially on upper floors of buildings, but many people do not recognize it as an earthquake. Parked cars may rock slightly. Vibrations like the passing of light trucks. Duration of shaking can be estimated.
IV. Felt indoors by many, outdoors by few. If at night, some awakened. Dishes, windows, doors disturbed. Walls creak. Sensation like the passing of heavy trucks. Parked cars rock noticeably.
V. Felt by nearly everyone. Some dishes, windows, etc., broken. A few instances of cracked plaster. Unstable objects overturned. Disturbances of trees, poles, and other tall objects sometimes noticed. Pendulum clocks may stop.
VI. Felt by all. Many frightened and run outdoors. Some heavy furniture moved. Books knocked off shelves, pictures off walls. Small church and school bells ring. A few instances of damaged chimneys. Otherwise damage is slight.
VII. Everybody runs outdoors. Difficult to stand up. Negligible damage in buildings of good design and construction; slight to moderate in well-built ordinary structures; considerable in poorly built or badly designed structures; some chimneys broken.
VIII. Damage slight in specially designed structures; partial collapse in ordinary buildings; great damage to poorly built structures. Panel walls thrown out of frame structures. Chimneys, factory stacks, columns, monuments, and walls fall. Heavy furniture overturned. Some sand and mud ejected from cracks in the ground. Changes in well water.
IX. Damage considerable in specially designed structures; well-designed frame structures thrown out of plumb; partial collapse of substantial buildings. Buildings shifted off foundations, ground cracked. Serious damage to reservoirs and underground pipes. General panic.
X. Some well-built wooden structures destroyed; most masonry and frame structures destroyed. Ground badly cracked. Rails bent slightly. Considerable landslides from river banks and steep slopes. Shifted sand and mud. Water splashed over banks.
XI. Few masonry structures remain standing. Bridges destroyed. Broad fissures in ground. Underground pipelines out of service. Earth slumps and land slips in soft ground. Rails bent severely.
XII. Damage total. Waves seen on ground surfaces. Lines of sight and level distorted. Objects thrown upward into the air.

1. At what intensity is there considerable damage to poorly built buildings? **Level VII**
2. If you are on the first floor in a building, are you likely to feel an intensity II tremor? **Most people on lower floors are unlikely to feel an intensity II tremor.**
3. If the pendulum clock in your home stops during an earthquake, at least what intensity is the earthquake in your area? **at least intensity V**
4. During the Lisbon earthquake in 1755, a second shock wave hit. It caused the river to pull back from its banks and then the water surged forward. What intensity do you think the second shock wave was? **The second shock wave was likely to have been at least a X, because this is the intensity at which water splashes over its banks.**

60

TYING TO PREVIOUS KNOWLEDGE: Have students review the positions of plate boundaries from Chapter 13. Explain that the locations of most earthquake epicenters are at or near plate boundaries.

OBJECTIVES AND SCIENCE WORDS: Have students review the objectives and science words to become familiar with this section.

2 TEACH

Key Concepts are highlighted.

STUDENT TEXT QUESTION

▶ Page 374, paragraph 1: **What determines the amount of damage done by an earthquake, and what can you do to protect yourself from the effects?** *The amount of damage depends on the magnitude of the earthquake, the type of structures in the stricken area, population density, and the type of substrate in the area hit by the quake. Refer students to page 378 regarding earthquake safety.*

CONCEPT DEVELOPMENT

Cooperative Learning: Form Numbered Heads Together groups of four students per group. Have students study Table 14-1 and hypothesize as to why some strong earthquakes caused so much loss of life while others caused very little.

Science and MATH

$8 - 5.5 = 2.5$
$30^{2.5} = 4929.5$

TECHNOLOGY

For more information about the topics covered in the Technology feature, refer to "Wake Up, East and Midwest" by J. Madeleine Nash, *Time*, October 8, 1990, pp. 79-80.

Think Critically: Seismographs only record movements as they happen. They don't "foretell" when movements may occur.

CROSS CURRICULUM

▶ **Social Studies:** Have each student write a report on a particular earthquake. Have students report on how the area and the lives of people in the area struck by the earthquake were changed.

▶ **Language Arts:** Have students use the *Reader's Guide to Periodical Literature* to find and read articles on earthquakes in Armenia (1988), the San Francisco Bay area (1989), and Iran (1990).

TEACHER F.Y.I.

▶ Three of the strongest earthquakes in the United States occurred along the New Madrid fault system centered in Missouri.

TECHNOLOGY

Predicting Earthquakes

In 1990, a climate consultant predicted that a major quake would strike New Madrid, Missouri, on December 3, 1990. A parade scheduled for that date was postponed and businesses announced they would be closed. But most scientists weren't surprised when it didn't strike on the predicted date. Today, seismologists review the earthquake history of a region to predict when one might strike in the future. Scientists hope that a new approach to predicting earthquakes will be more reliable. A series of satellites developed for use in navigation may provide the answer. The satellites emit radio signals that are picked up by radio receivers on Earth's surface. When Earth's crust deforms, by as little as a few centimeters, it can be detected because the radio receivers move along with it.

Think Critically: Both seismographs and satellites detect movement in Earth's crust. Why aren't seismographs very useful for predicting quakes?

is released for every increase of 1.0 on the scale. For example, a magnitude 8.5 earthquake releases about 30 times as much energy as a magnitude 7.5 earthquake. Table 14-2 shows how often earthquakes of the various magnitudes are expected to occur.

Tsunamis

Most earthquake damage happens when surface waves cause buildings, bridges, and roads to collapse. People living near the seashore, however, have another concern. An earthquake under the sea causes abrupt movement of the ocean floor. The movement pushes against the water, generating a powerful wave that travels to the surface. After reaching the surface, the wave can travel thousands of kilometers in all directions.

OPTIONS

INQUIRY QUESTIONS

▶ **Can an earthquake that originates in Alaska cause destruction and devastation on the coast of California? Explain.** *Yes, an Alaskan earthquake can generate tsunamis. If the tsunamis approached California shores, enormous walls of water could engulf cities along the coast.*

▶ **Suppose an earthquake with a magnitude of 3.4 releases 9×10^{13} ergs of energy. How much energy would be released by a quake measuring 4.4?** *$30 \times 9 \times 10^{13}$ ergs = 2.7×10^{15} ergs*

Table 14-2

EARTHQUAKE OCCURRENCES	
Richter Magnitude	**Number Expected per Year**
1.0 to 3.9	> 100 000
4.0 to 4.9	6 200
5.0 to 5.9	800
6.0 to 6.9	120
7.0 to 7.9	20
8.0 to 8.9	< 1

An earthquake wave has a wavelength of several kilometers. Therefore, such a wave stirs a tremendous amount of water in a circular motion as it passes. Far from shore, an earthquake-generated wave is so long that a large ship may ride over it without anyone noticing. But when one of these waves breaks on a shore, it forms a towering crest that can reach 30 meters high.

Ocean waves generated by earthquakes are called seismic sea waves, or **tsunamis** (soo NAHM eez). Tsunamis engulf people and entire towns in huge walls of water, causing great destruction and loss of life. 3

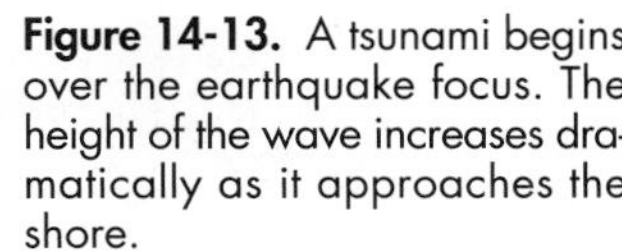

Figure 14-13. A tsunami begins over the earthquake focus. The height of the wave increases dramatically as it approaches the shore.

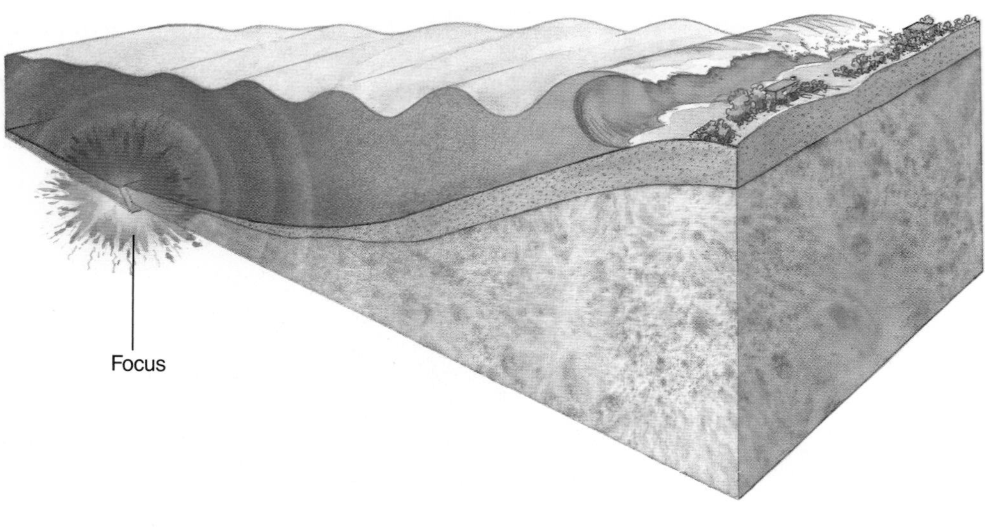

REVEALING MISCONCEPTIONS

▶ Some people inaccurately refer to tsunamis as tidal waves. Explain that tsunamis are not caused by tides but by earthquakes.

MINI QUIZ

Use the Mini Quiz to check students' recall of chapter content.

1. **A(n) _____ is an instrument that records primary, secondary, and surface waves from earthquakes.** *seismograph*
2. **The energy released by an earthquake is its _____ .** *magnitude*
3. **Sea waves caused by earthquakes are _____ .** *tsunamis*

ENRICHMENT

▶ Have students write brief descriptions of the damage done when tsunamis came ashore along the Pacific coast following the Alaskan earthquake of 1964.

▶ Have students investigate the Mexico City earthquake of 1985. Have them determine why less damage occurred near the epicenter than occurred in Mexico City.

PROGRAM RESOURCES

From the **Teacher Resource Package** use:

Critical Thinking/Problem Solving, page 20, Can Earthquakes be Predicted?

Cross-Curricular Connections, page 18, Obtaining Information From Maps.

REVEALING MISCONCEPTIONS

▶ Some students might think it is best to be in the shelter of a building during an earthquake. Show pictures of earthquake destruction and emphasize that most loss of life occurs when buildings, or items within buildings, fall on people. The safest place to be during an earthquake is in the open, away from structures, cliffs, or tall trees.

CONCEPT DEVELOPMENT

Cooperative Learning: Using the Paired Partner strategy, have students draw posters that show one aspect of earthquake safety. Posters can show what to do in preparation for a possible earthquake, what to do during an earthquake, or what precautions to take after an earthquake.

CHECK FOR UNDERSTANDING

After students have read this page, ask questions 1-3 and the **Apply** Question in the Section Review.

RETEACH

Show students pictures of the destruction that occurred during the 1906 earthquake in San Francisco. Ask students to speculate what caused the almost total destruction of the city. Fires were a major factor in the destruction. Fires resulted when gas lines broke.

EXTENSION

For students who have mastered this Section, use the **Reinforcement** and **Enrichment** masters or other OPTIONS provided.

EcoTip

Stored containers of radioactive waste from nuclear power plants may become ruptured during earthquakes. Reduce the production of radioactive waste by conserving energy—turn off lights, stereos, and televisions when not in use.

Earthquake Safety

You've seen the destruction that earthquakes can cause. But, there are ways to minimize the damage and loss of life.

One of the first steps in earthquake safety is to study the earthquake history of a region. If you live in an area that's had earthquakes in the past, you can expect them to occur there in the future. As you know, most earthquakes happen along plate boundaries. Figure 14-1 shows that severe earthquakes can happen in other places. Being prepared is an important step in earthquake safety.

Make your home as earthquake safe as possible. Take heavy objects down from high shelves and place them on lower shelves. To reduce the chance of fire from broken gas lines, see that hot-water heaters and gas appliances are held securely in place. During an earthquake, keep away from windows and avoid anything that could fall on you. Watch for fallen power lines and possible fire hazards. Stay clear of rubble that could contain many sharp edges. In the Science and Society section that follows, you will see how practicing earthquake safety and preparing for an earthquake make a difference in the amount of damage done by an earthquake.

EXTRA EXTRA EXTRA

EXTRA San Francisco Chronicle

The Largest Daily Circulation in Northern California

WEDNESDAY, OCTOBER 18, 1989

415-777-1111 25 CENTS

125th Year No. 236

HUNDREDS DEAD IN HUGE QUAKE

Oakland Freeway Collapses

Bay Bridge Section Fails

Today's Chronicle

OPTIONS

INQUIRY QUESTIONS

▶ **Why do most earthquakes occur along plate boundaries?** *Forces exerted on Earth's rocks at plate boundaries cause rocks to move, bend, and eventually break.*

▶ **Why should you remove heavy objects from high shelves if you live in an earthquake-prone area?** *Heavy objects could fall during an earthquake, causing severe damage or injury.*

▶ **How can broken gas lines contribute to the destruction caused by an earthquake?** *Broken gas lines can leak and possibly start a fire. If water lines are also broken, the fire can't be fought.*

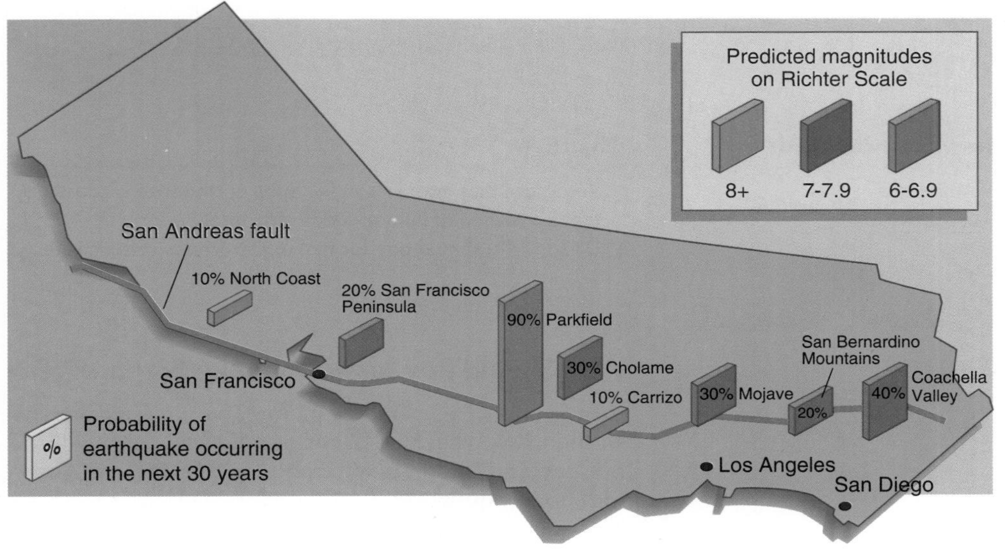

Figure 14-14. The bars on the map show the probabilities that an earthquake of the specified magnitude will strike within the next 30 years. Many residents of California are preparing for the major earthquakes predicted to hit their areas.

SECTION REVIEW

1. How often might you expect a magnitude 6.0 earthquake to occur?
2. What is the magnitude of an earthquake that releases 30 times as much energy as the one that hit Armenia?
3. A friend of yours moves to southern California, near the San Andreas Fault. What can you tell her to help her prepare for an earthquake?
4. **Apply:** Explain why a seismograph wouldn't work if the pen vibrated along with the rest of the machine.

Making and Using Tables

Skill Builder

Use Table 14-1 to answer the following questions.

1. Which earthquake listed resulted in the greatest number of deaths? The fewest?
2. Which quake listed had the highest magnitude?
3. Hypothesize why the 1920 China quake resulted in fewer deaths than the 1976 quake.

If you need help, refer to Making and Using Tables in the **Skill Handbook** on page 690.

3 CLOSE

▶ Obtain a seismogram. Many universities have seismographs. Point out primary, secondary, and surface waves on the seismic wave record.

FLEX Your Brain

Use the Flex Your Brain activity to have students explore TSUNAMIS.

SECTION REVIEW ANSWERS

1. about 120 times/year
2. 7.9
3. You can suggest that her family not place heavy objects on high shelves and check to see that the water heater and gas appliances are well secured. You may also want to advise her to check with local authorities regarding earthquake safety measures.
4. **Apply:** In order for a seismograph to record vibrations, some point within the instrument must remain at rest. Most seismographs consist of a fixed frame that is attached to Earth. A pen records the seismic waves onto paper on a vibrating drum.

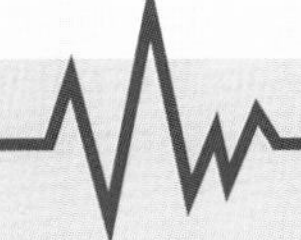

Skill Builder

1. The most deaths occurred during the 1556 China quake. The fewest deaths resulted from the 1886 South Carolina quake.
2. the 1755 Portugal quake
3. Although the 1920 earthquake had a greater magnitude, fewer deaths may have resulted, perhaps due to fewer people living in the Kansu area.

ENRICHMENT

▶ Have students find out if your area is prone to earthquakes. If so, have them develop an earthquake awareness program, which should include a list of tasks to perform to make a house as earthquake-safe as possible.

PROGRAM RESOURCES

From the **Teacher Resource Package** use: **Activity Worksheets**, page 5, Flex Your Brain.

SECTION 14-4

PREPARATION

SECTION BACKGROUND

▶ Following the 1985 Mexico City earthquake, Los Angeles accelerated its seismic-safe program. Owners now have nine years to make buildings seismic-safe or the structures must be torn down.

1 MOTIVATE

FLEX Your Brain

Use the Flex Your Brain activity to have students explore HOME-OWNER'S OR RENTER'S EARTHQUAKE INSURANCE.

▶ **Demonstration:** Make four pillars from building blocks. Gently bump the pillars to show how easy it is to knock them down. Restack the blocks, but secure the blocks within each pillar with rubber bands. Again, gently bump the pillars to demonstrate that they are more resistant to "crumbling."

TYING TO PREVIOUS KNOWLEDGE: Have students think about recent news stories on earthquakes. Relate the amount of damage that occurred to the type of structures within the areas struck by the earthquakes.

OBJECTIVES AND SCIENCE WORDS: Have students review the objectives and science words to become familiar with this section.

14-4 Living on a Fault

New Science Words

seismic-safe

Objectives

- ▶ Recognize that most loss of life in an earthquake is caused by the destruction of human-made structures.
- ▶ Decide who should pay for making structures seismic safe.

Who Should Pay for Earthquake Preparation?

In Section 14-3, you saw pictures of the aftermath of earthquakes. What kind of damage did you see? Buildings, bridges, and highways were cracked and broken. Some were totally destroyed.

1 Most loss of life in an earthquake occurs when people are trapped in and on these crumbling structures. What can be done to reduce loss of life? Who should be responsible for the cost of making structures seismic safe?

Seismic-safe structures are resistant to vibrations that occur during an earthquake. You can see the advantage of seismic safety by watching a young child play with blocks. He or she builds them up and becomes very upset

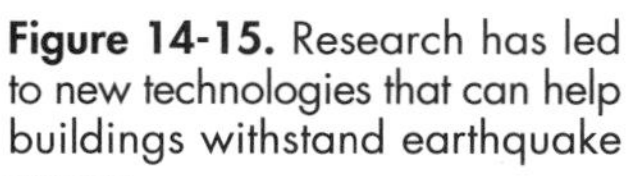

Figure 14-15. Research has led to new technologies that can help buildings withstand earthquake waves.

OPTIONS

Meeting Different Ability Levels

For Section 14-4, use the following **Teacher Resource Masters** depending upon individual students' needs.

◆ **Study Guide Master** for all students.

● **Reinforcement Master** for students of average and above average ability levels.

▲ **Enrichment Master** for above average students.

Additional Teacher Resource Package masters are listed in the OPTIONS box throughout the section. The additional masters are appropriate for all students.

◆ STUDY GUIDE 61

NAME ________ DATE ________ CLASS ________

STUDY GUIDE — Chapter 14

Living on a Fault — Text Pages 380–382

Use the terms in the box to complete the sentences.

seismic-safe	earthquake	magnitudes
building codes	vibrations	crumbling structures
San Francisco Bay	highways	underground pipes

1. An **earthquake** can result in the loss of life and great damage to structures built by people.
2. Most deaths occur when people are trapped in or on **crumbling structures**.
3. Much of the Pacific Coast including the **San Francisco Bay** area is earthquake-prone.
4. As a result, California has enforced strict **building codes** for new construction.
5. The codes have requirements to make new buildings **seismic-safe** structures.
6. Today many high-rise office buildings stand on steel and rubber springs that help the building ride out the **vibrations** caused by earthquakes.
7. **Highways** are being built with reinforcing rods in their cement columns.
8. Lives and property could be saved by replacing old **underground pipes** for gas and water with new ones that will bend during an earthquake.
9. By having seismic-safe structures, the San Francisco Bay area did not experience as much loss of life as other areas that had earthquakes with similar **magnitudes**.

Answer the following questions in complete sentences.

1. What do the San Francisco Bay area, Armenia, and Iran have in common? **All are sites of recent earthquakes.**
2. How are highway pillars with spiral reinforcing rods wrapped around them and buildings standing on steel and rubber springs alike? **Both are structures that are seismic safe.**
3. Why did Interstate 880 collapse during the earthquake in the San Francisco Bay area? **The highway was not seismic safe and could not withstand the earthquake's vibrations.**
4. Why did California enforce stricter building codes? **California is part of an earthquake-prone area. The codes are intended to help make structures seismic safe.**

61

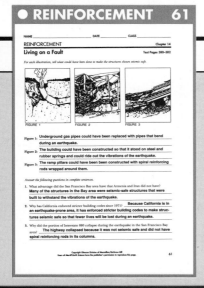

Figure 14-16. Seismic-safe highways are supported by vertical steel rods wrapped with reinforcing rods encased in concrete. The major highway that collapsed in San Francisco in 1989 lacked the seismic-safe construction shown at the right.

when the dog walks by and knocks them down. What do you think would happen if rubber bands were wrapped around the columns of blocks? The block structure would be more resistant to falling. When making seismic-safe
highways, cement pillars have spiral reinforcing rods ②
wrapped around them. These rods act the same as rubber bands do on the blocks.

Will making structures seismic safe reduce the loss of life in an earthquake? Look again at Table 14-1. Notice that earthquakes in Armenia (December 1988), in the San Francisco Bay area (October 1989), and in Iran (June 1990) are all close in magnitude. However, the loss of life in these earthquakes were quite different. Why were so many more lives lost in Armenia and Iran than in the San Francisco Bay area?

The San Francisco Bay area, as well as much of the Pacific Coast, is very susceptible to earthquakes. People living in the California area have been getting ready for big earthquakes for many years. Since 1971, stricter building codes have been enforced and older buildings have been reinforced. In other parts of the world, such seismic-safe structures are rare or don't exist at all.

Today in California, some new buildings are anchored
to flexible, circular moorings made of steel plates filled ③
with alternating layers of rubber and steel. When an

● REINFORCEMENT 61

NAME ________ DATE ________ CLASS ________

REINFORCEMENT — Chapter 14

Living on a Fault — Text Pages 380–382

For each illustration, tell what could have been done to make the structures shown seismic safe.

FIGURE 1 FIGURE 2 FIGURE 3

Figure 1: **Underground gas pipes could have been replaced with pipes that bend during an earthquake.**

Figure 2: **The building could have been constructed so that it stood on steel and rubber springs and could ride out the vibrations of the earthquake.**

Figure 3: **The ramp pillars could have been been constructed with spiral reinforcing rods wrapped around them.**

Answer the following questions in complete sentences.

1. What advantage did the San Francisco Bay area have that Armenia and Iran did not have? **Many of the structures in the Bay area were seismic-safe structures that were built to withstand the vibrations of the earthquake.**
2. Why has California enforced stricter building codes since 1971? **Because California is in an earthquake-prone area, it has enforced stricter building codes to make structures seismic safe so that fewer lives will be lost during an earthquake.**
3. Why did the portion of Interstate 880 collapse during the earthquake in the San Francisco Bay area? **The highway collapsed because it was not seismic safe and did not have spiral reinforcing rods in its columns.**

 61

▲ ENRICHMENT 61

NAME ________ DATE ________ CLASS ________

ENRICHMENT — Chapter 14

Living on a Fault — Text Pages 380–382

AFTERMATH OF EARTHQUAKES

Often it's not an earthquake itself that causes the loss of life or physical destruction. It is the aftermath, or the effects of the earthquake, that cause the loss. The 1923 earthquake in Tokyo resulted in the deaths of about 140 000 people and the destruction of about 300 000 buildings. How could this have happened when only about one percent of the buildings in Tokyo were destroyed by the earthquake? Most Tokyo homes were built of wood and paper. Wood, because of its flexibility, can withstand even many severe earthquakes. But it can't survive fire. Tokyo was destroyed by two fires started from stoves overturned by the earthquake. The fires raged through the paper and wood homes. People tried to flee the raging fires. The narrow streets and wooden bridges were crowded with panicked people. For many, there was no escape. The fires, not the earthquake, claimed most of the lives lost in Tokyo.

Following an earthquake in Niigata, Japan, in 1964, some apartment buildings began to tilt and sink into the ground. The buildings had not been damaged by the earthquake. What happened to them? The apartment buildings were built on water-soaked sandy soil. Following the tremors of the earthquake, the soil became liquefied and acted much like quicksand. The apartment buildings sank into the liquefied soil.

Landslides and tsunamis triggered by earthquakes are two other events that can cause destruction and loss of life. The tsunami triggered by the earthquake in Concepcion, Chile, hit Hilo, Hawaii, fifteen hours after the earthquake. Late at night, a 12-meter wall of water flooded into downtown Hilo. Sixty-one people lost their lives. Sometimes the events triggered by earthquakes result in as much destruction and death as the earthquakes themselves.

1. What advantage do wood buildings have during an earthquake? **The wood buildings are flexible and can withstand even severe earthquake tremors.**
2. In what ways are wood buildings a hazard during earthquakes? **The wood buildings are a fire hazard. Although they may remain standing, they can easily fuel a fire and lead to a disaster.**
3. What lesson do you think could be learned from the disastrous aftermath of the earthquakes **Answers will vary. Students might suggest that streets be widened, that fire-resistant building materials be used, that emergency evacuation plans are needed, that buildings be built on solid foundations.**

 61

2 TEACH

Key Concepts are highlighted.

STUDENT TEXT QUESTIONS

▶ Page 381, paragraph 2: **Will making structures seismic-safe reduce the loss of life in an earthquake?** *Studies indicate that seismic-safe structures would reduce loss of life.* **Why were so many more lives lost in Armenia and Iran than in the San Francisco Bay area?** *Many buildings in Armenia and Iran weren't seismic-safe and fell on people during the earthquakes.*

CHECK FOR UNDERSTANDING

Use the Mini Quiz to check for understanding.

MINI QUIZ

Use the Mini Quiz to check students' recall of chapter content.

① **How does most loss of life occur during an earthquake?** *people being trapped in and on crumbling structures*

② **How are cement pillars on highways made seismic-safe?** *by wrapping spiral reinforcement rods around them*

③ **How have buildings in San Francisco been altered to suit the tectonic activity in the area?** *They've been reinforced or are built on steel and rubber springs.*

RETEACH

Cooperative Learning: Using the Paired Partners strategy, show students pictures of buildings and structures that have experienced earthquakes. Have students try to determine which buildings were probably seismic-safe.

EXTENSION

For students who have mastered this section, use the **Reinforcement** and **Enrichment** masters or other OPTIONS provided.

MINI-Lab

Teaching Tips

▶It is important that students realize two aspects of this issue at the onset: (1) there has not been a major earthquake in this part of the United States for almost a century; and (2) seismologists rate the potential for a major quake during the next 20 years as very high for this geographic region.

▶**Answer:** Since it is unlikely that these students have had much experience with paying their share of local taxes as yet, it might be advisable to have them survey their parents' feelings on the issue beforehand.

3 CLOSE

▶ Invite an architect to visit your class to discuss designs that could be used to make buildings and other structures seismic-safe.

▶ Call on a volunteer to recap the section.

▶ Ask questions 1 and 2 in the Section Review

SECTION REVIEW ANSWERS

1. More structures in San Francisco than in the other two areas are seismic-safe.

2. Funds to make structures seismic-safe may not be available. In some areas of the world, regulations may not exist or be followed when construction is done.

YOU DECIDE!

Students' responses might include that people can't control tectonic processes, thus taxes should be shared by all. Others will argue that many people choose to live in earthquake-prone areas and therefore should be willing to bear the burden of such taxes.

MINI-Lab

Should there be a higher tax?

Work in a group with four other students in this role-playing activity. Each of you will assume the role of either debate moderator, pro-tax citizen, anti-tax citizen, or audience (two players). The debate moderator will control a debate between the pro-tax citizen who favors higher local taxes to pay for new seismic-safe highways and the anti-tax citizen opposed to the tax. The two audience players will each ask at least five questions of the debaters. Your locality is Missouri which has experienced some of the strongest quakes in the United States. Which way would you vote on the tax proposal?

earthquake occurs, the lower portion of the mooring stretches back and forth with the waves. The rubber portions of the moorings absorb most of the wave motion of the quake. The building itself only sways gently. Tests have shown that buildings supported with these moorings should be able to withstand an earthquake measuring up to 8.3 on the Richter scale without major damage.

One structure severely damaged in the San Francisco Bay area earthquake was Interstate Highway 880. The collapsed highway, shown in Figure 14-16, was due to be renovated to make it seismic safe. Built in the 1950s, it didn't have spiral reinforcing rods in its concrete columns. When the surface waves hit, the upper highway went in one direction; the lower one went in the opposite direction. The columns collapsed and the upper highway came crashing down onto the lower one.

Highways and buildings in earthquake-prone areas can be made seismic safe. Lives and property can be saved by replacing underground water and gas pipes with ones that will bend, but not break, during an earthquake. But who should pay for these renovations? In some parts of the United States and of the world, people can afford to build seismic-safe structures. In other cases, people can't even afford food and shelter. In these areas, seismic-safe structures can be constructed only if people outside of the region are willing to help.

SECTION REVIEW

1. Why did more people die in the earthquakes in Armenia and Iran than in San Francisco?
2. What conditions can exist that cause greater loss of life during one earthquake than during another of the same magnitude?

You Decide!

Suppose you are living in an area that's never had a severe earthquake. Would you be willing to pay an earthquake safety tax to help others in other parts of the United States? In other parts of the world? Some people think you should. Others think only those living in the area should pay. What do you think?

OPTIONS

ENRICHMENT

▶ Have groups of students build models of seismic-safe structures. Assign one group to design a test chamber to check each structure for strength and durability during an "earthquake."

PROGRAM RESOURCES

From the **Teacher Resource Package** use:

Activity Worksheets, page 129, Mini-Lab: Should there be a higher tax?

Science and Society, page 18, Earthquakes in Mid-America.

CHAPTER

REVIEW

SUMMARY

14-1: Earthquakes and Plate Tectonics

1. Plate movements put stress on rocks. To a point, the rocks bend and stretch. But if the force is great enough, rocks will break and produce earthquakes.
2. Normal faults form when rocks undergo tension. Compressional forces produce reverse faults. Strike-slip faults result from shearing forces.

14-2: Earthquake Information

1. Primary waves compress and stretch rock particles as the waves move. Secondary waves move by, causing particles in rocks to move at right angles to the direction of the waves. Surface waves move by, giving rock particles a circular motion.
2. By measuring the speeds of seismic waves, scientists are able to locate the epicenter of an earthquake.
3. By observing the speeds and paths of seismic waves, scientists are able to determine the boundaries among Earth's layers.

14-3: Destruction by Earthquakes

1. The magnitude of an earthquake is a measure of the energy released by the quake. The Richter Scale describes how much energy is released by an earthquake.
2. Removing objects from high shelves and securing hot-water heaters and gas appliances are ways to prevent damage due to earthquakes.

14-4: Science and Society: Living on a Fault

1. Most lives lost during an earthquake are due to the destruction of human-made structures.
2. Money for seismic-safe structures might come from people who live in the earthquake-prone area or from people in other parts of the country or the world.

KEY SCIENCE WORDS

a. **earthquakes**
b. **epicenter**
c. **faults**
d. **focus**
e. **magnitude**
f. **Moho discontinuity**
g. **normal fault**
h. **primary waves**
i. **reverse fault**
j. **secondary waves**
k. **seismic-safe**
l. **seismic waves**
m. **seismograph**
n. **seismologists**
o. **strike-slip fault**
p. **surface waves**
q. **tsunamis**

UNDERSTANDING VOCABULARY

Match each phrase with the correct term from the list of Key Science Words.

1. a fault formed due to tension on rocks
2. fault due to shearing forces
3. point where earthquake energy is released
4. point on Earth's surface directly above the origin of an earthquake
5. waves that produce a circular motion of particles
6. boundary between the crust and mantle
7. instrument that records seismic waves
8. measure of energy released by a quake
9. seismic sea waves
10. refers to structures that are resistant to seismic vibrations

CHAPTER

REVIEW

SUMMARY

Have students read the summary statements to review the major concepts of the chapter.

UNDERSTANDING VOCABULARY

1. g
2. o
3. d
4. b
5. p
6. f
7. m
8. e
9. q
10. k

ASSESSMENT

To assess student understanding of material in this chapter, use the resources listed.

COOPERATIVE LEARNING

Consider using cooperative learning in the THINK AND WRITE CRITICALLY, APPLY, and MORE SKILL BUILDERS sections of the Chapter Review.

PROGRAM RESOURCES

From the **Teacher Resource Package** use:
Chapter Review, pages 31-38.
Chapter and Unit Tests, pages 93-96, Chapter Test.

CHAPTER

REVIEW

CHECKING CONCEPTS

1. c	**6.** b
2. a	**7.** b
3. b	**8.** d
4. b	**9.** a
5. a	**10.** c

UNDERSTANDING CONCEPTS

11. elastic limit
12. Primary
13. Strength or magnitude, population of an area
14. seismograph
15. Seismic-safe

THINK AND WRITE CRITICALLY

16. Normal faults are due to tension and the rock above the fault surface moves down relative to the rock below the surface. A reverse fault is due to compressional forces in which rocks above the fault surface move up over rocks below the fault surface.
17. Both are released during an earthquake and both change speeds as they travel through Earth. Unlike primary waves, however, secondary waves do not travel through liquids. Also, primary waves travel back and forth along rock particles. Secondary waves move perpendicular to the rocks through which they travel.
18. Secondary waves cannot travel through liquids and are never observed opposite a quake's epicenter. Primary waves slow down when they reach the outer core. Thus, scientists concluded that the outer core was liquid.
19. An earthquake with a magnitude of 3.0 releases about 900 times as much energy as a quake with a magnitude of 1.0.
20. Fewer seismic-safe structures were in place than today. Also, more people used gas as a source of energy. Toppling buildings caused numerous gas lines to break, which led to fires.

CHAPTER

REVIEW

CHECKING CONCEPTS

Choose the word or phrase that completes the sentence.

1. Most earthquakes occur along ______.
  a. normal faults **c.** plate boundaries
  b. tsunamis **d.** all of these

2. A ______ fault forms when the rock above the fault surface moves down relative to the rock below the fault surface.
  a. normal **c.** reverse
  b. strike-slip **d.** shearing

3. Seismic waves move outward from the ______.
  a. epicenter **c.** Moho discontinuity
  b. focus **d.** tsunami

4. ______ waves stretch and compress rocks.
  a. Surface **c.** Secondary
  b. Primary **d.** All of these

5. ______ waves are the slowest.
  a. Surface **c.** Secondary
  b. Primary **d.** Tsunami

6. At least ______ seismograph stations are needed to locate the epicenter of an earthquake.
  a. two **c.** four
  b. three **d.** five

7. Primary waves ______ when they go through solids.
  a. slow down **c.** stay the same
  b. speed up **d.** quit moving

8. The ______ of a seismograph remains still.
  a. sheet of paper **c.** drum
  b. pen **d.** pendulum

9. An earthquake of magnitude 7.5 has ______ energy than a quake of 6.5.
  a. 30 times more **c.** twice as much
  b. 30 times less **d.** about half as much

10. Most lost lives during a quake are due to ______.
  a. tsunamis **c.** collapse of buildings
  b. primary waves **d.** broken gas lines

UNDERSTANDING CONCEPTS

Complete each sentence.

11. Earthquakes occur when the ______ of rocks is passed.

12. ______ waves cause rock particles to move parallel to the direction of wave movement.

13. ______ and ______ determine the amount of damage an earthquake causes.

14. The height of the lines traced by a(n) ______ is directly related to the amount of energy released.

15. ______ structures, such as highways with reinforcing bands wrapped around their pillars, save lives.

THINK AND WRITE CRITICALLY

16. Contrast normal faults with reverse faults.

17. How are primary and secondary waves alike? How are they different?

18. Explain how seismic records were used to determine that Earth's outer core is liquid.

19. What is the relationship between earthquakes with magnitudes on the Richter Scale of 1.0 and 3.0?

20. In 1906, an earthquake with a magnitude of 8.6 struck San Francisco. Most of the damage done was due to fire. Hypothesize why this is so.

APPLY

21. What kind of faults would you expect to be most common along the mid-Atlantic Ridge? Explain.
22. Where is earthquake damage greater—nearer the focus or nearer the epicenter? Explain.
23. Explain why the pendulum of a seismograph remains at rest.
24. Tsunamis are often called tidal waves. Explain why this is incorrect.
25. Which would probably be more stable during an earthquake—a single-story wood-frame house or a brick building? Explain.

MORE SKILL BUILDERS

If you need help, refer to the Skill Handbook.

1. **Interpreting Scientific Illustrations:** The illustration below is a typical record of earthquake waves made on a seismograph. How many minutes passed between the arrival of the first primary wave and the first secondary wave? The last primary wave and the first surface wave?
2. **Interpreting Scientific Illustrations:** Suppose another seismograph station were located in the shadow zone of the same earthquake from Question 1. How would the record of the seismograph located in the shadow zone compare to the record shown below?
3. **Outlining:** Make an outline of the material presented in Section 14-1.
4. **Measuring in SI:** Use an atlas and metric ruler to answer the following. Primary waves travel at about 6 km/s in continental crust. How long would it take a primary wave to travel from San Francisco, CA to Reno, NV?
5. **Using Variables, Constants, and Controls:** Leah investigated how waves are reflected from curved and flat surfaces using water, a dropper, and flexible cardboard. She filled two flat pans half full of water and produced ripples with water from the dropper. One pan held the flat cardboard; the other the curved piece. What are her variables? What should she keep constant?

PROJECTS

1. Make a simple seismograph. Experiment with different "seismic" sources such as pounding your fist, hammering, and dropping a brick to see how they affect the height of the lines produced on the drum of your device.
2. Research how magnetometers, tiltmeters, and radon detectors are used to help predict the possibility of earthquakes.

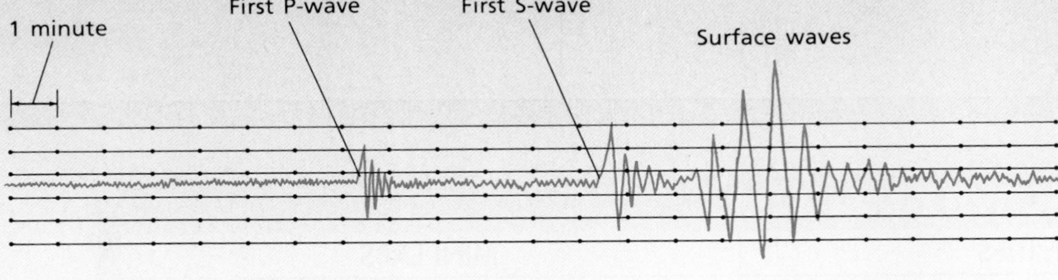

APPLY

21. The mid-Atlantic Ridge is a spreading center or divergent boundary. Tension along the ridge causes normal faults to form.

22. Earthquake damage is greatest near the epicenter because surface waves, which cause most of the destruction of an earthquake, are released at the epicenter. The focus is deep in Earth's crust; little "damage" occurs near it.

23. The pendulum of a seismograph hangs from a fixed frame. Thus, the pendulum acts as a point of reference.

24. Tsunamis are caused by earthquakes that displace the ocean floor. Tides, on the other hand, are caused by the gravitational pull among the sun, moon, and Earth.

25. The single-story wood frame house would be more stable because the wood is able to "give" more than the masonry building when surface waves travel through it.

MORE SKILL BUILDERS

1. Interpreting Scientific Illustrations: about 5 minutes; about 6.5 minutes

2. Interpreting Scientific Illustrations: No waves would be recorded at the seismic station in the shadow zone.

3. Outlining: Students' outlines should compare and contrast the types of faults and the forces that cause each.

4. Measuring in SI: The distance between San Francisco and Reno is about 300 km. Thus, 300 km ÷ 6 km/s = 50 seconds.

5. Using Variables, Constants, and Controls: The only variable should be the shape of the cardboard. All other parameters should remain constant.

CHAPTER

15 Volcanoes

CHAPTER SECTION	OBJECTIVES	ACTIVITIES
15-1 Volcanoes and Plate Tectonics (3 days)	1. **Describe** how volcanoes can affect people. 2. **Describe** conditions that cause volcanoes. 3. **Describe** the relationship between volcanoes and plate tectonics.	**Activity 15-1:** *Locating Active Volcanoes,* p. 393
15-2 Geothermal Energy from Volcanoes Science & Society (1 day)	1. **List** the pros and cons of using geothermal energy to produce electricity. 2. **Form an opinion** as to whether the geothermal energy under the Hawaiian Islands should be used to generate electricity.	**MINI-Lab:** *How are the shapes of volcanic cones different?* p. 399 **Activity 15-2:** *Identifying Types of Volcanoes,* p. 403
15-3 Eruptions and Forms of Volcanoes (3 days)	1. **Relate** the explosiveness of a volcanic eruption to the silica and water vapor content of its lava. 2. **Describe** three forms of volcanoes.	**MINI-Lab:** *What are some properties of volcanic materials?* p. 405
15-4 Volcanic Features (2 days)	1. **Give examples** of intrusive igneous features and how they form. 2. **Explain** how a volcanic neck and a caldera form.	
Chapter Review		

ACTIVITY MATERIALS

FIND OUT	ACTIVITIES		MINI-LABS	
Page 387 baking soda red food coloring safety glasses vinegar modeling clay	**15-1 Locating Active Volcanoes, p. 393** world map (Appendix F) tracing paper Figure 13-10 on page 349	**15-2 Identifying Types of Volcanoes, p. 403** Table 15-1 paper pencil	**How are the shapes of volcanic cones different? p. 399** cereal or sand paper plates (2) protractor plaster of paris	**What are some properties of volcanic materials? p. 405** samples of volcanic ejecta pin dissecting probe microscope

CHAPTER FEATURES	TEACHER RESOURCE PACKAGE	OTHER RESOURCES
Skill Builder: *Concept Mapping,* p. 392	**Ability Level Worksheets** ◆ ***Study Guide,*** p. 62 ● ***Reinforcement,*** p. 62 ▲ ***Enrichment,*** p. 62 **Activity Worksheet,** pp. 131-132 **Cross-Curricular Connections,** p. 19 **Transparency Masters,** pp. 67-68	**Color Transparency 34,** Active Volcanoes/Hot Spots **Lab Manual:** *Volcanic Preservation,* p. 127
You Decide! p. 395	**Ability Level Worksheets** ◆ ***Study Guide,*** p. 63 ● ***Reinforcement,*** p. 63 ▲ ***Enrichment,*** p. 63 **Critical Thinking/Problem Solving,** p. 21 **Science and Society,** p. 19	
Technology: *Volcanic Eruptions,* p. 398 **Problem Solving:** *The Rock Star,* p. 401 **Skill Builder:** *Sequencing,* p. 402	**Ability Level Worksheets** ◆ ***Study Guide,*** p.64 ● ***Reinforcement,*** p. 64 ▲ ***Enrichment,*** p. 64 **Activity Worksheet,** pp. 133-135 **Concept Mapping,** pp. 35-36 **MINI-Lab Worksheet,** p. 139	
Skill Builder: *Comparing and Contrasting,* p. 406	**Ability Level Worksheets** ◆ ***Study Guide,*** p. 65 ● ***Reinforcement,*** p. 65 ▲ ***Enrichment,*** p. 65 **MINI-Lab Worksheet,** p. 140	**Color Transparency 33,** Volcanic Landforms **Lab Manual:** *Effect of Magma on Surrounding Rock,* p. 125
Summary Key Science Words Understanding Vocabulary Checking Concepts Understanding Concepts Think & Write Critically Apply More Skill Builders Projects	**Chapter Review,** pp. 33-34 **Chapter Test,** pp. 97-100 **Unit Test,** pp. 101-102	**Chapter Review Software** **Test Bank**

◆ **Basic** ● **Average** ▲ **Advanced**

ADDITIONAL MATERIALS

SOFTWARE	AUDIOVISUAL	BOOKS/MAGAZINES
Volcanoes, Earthware Computer Services. *Volcanoes,* IBM.	*The Earth and Its Wonders: Volcanoes,* filmstrip/cassette, EBEC. *The Earth: Volcanoes,* film, Coronet/MTI. *Return to Mt. St. Helens,* video, NOVA (PBS). *Volcano,* video, Focus. *Born of Fire (National Geographic)* laserdisc, Image Entertainment. *Volcanoes: Exploring the Restless Earth/Heartbeat of a Volcano,* laserdisc, EBEC.	Bowen, R. *Geothermal Resources.* NY: Elsevier Science Publishing Company, Inc., 1989. Bullard, Fred M. *Volcanoes of the Earth.* 2nd Rev. Ed. Austin, TX: University of Texas Press, 1984. Ollier, Cliff. *Volcanoes.* Cambridge, MA: Basil Blackwell, Inc., 1988.

CHAPTER

15

VOLCANOES

THEME DEVELOPMENT: Energy is the theme of this chapter. The energy involved in the formation of magma, its rising upward through the mantle and finally flowing onto the surface as lava should be focal points of the chapter. The evolution of volcanoes is a secondary chapter theme.

CHAPTER OVERVIEW

- **Section 15-1:** Volcanoes, how they form, and how they can affect people are discussed. The link between volcanism and plate tectonics also is presented.
- **Section 15-2: Science and Society:** Geothermal energy is defined and discussed. The You Decide feature asks students whether geothermal energy should be used to generate electricity in Hawaii.
- **Section 15-3:** Section 15-3 discusses the relationship between lava composition and the explosiveness of a volcano. Three forms of volcanoes are described.
- **Section 15-4:** This section compares and contrasts the mode of formation and other characteristics of several intrusive rock features.

CHAPTER VOCABULARY

volcano
vent
crater
Pacific Ring of Fire
hot spots
geothermal energy
shield volcano
tephra
cinder cone
composite volcano
batholiths
dike
sill
laccolith
volcanic neck
caldera

CHAPTER

15 Volcanoes

386

OPTIONS

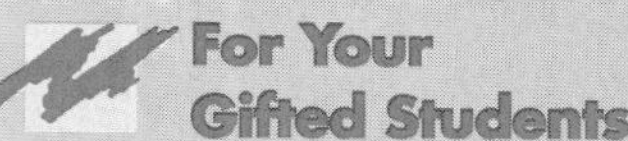

For Your Gifted Students

Have each student write a story about a volcanic eruption as told from the point of view of a human observer, an animal, a plant, someone caught in the vicinity of the erupting volcano, or an inanimate object. The stories should include descriptions of the eruption in detail, from the early stages of development to the aftermath. Encourage creativity but insist on scientific accuracy.

This explosive eruption is ejecting tonnes of volcanic ash into the atmosphere. Volcanoes can be spectacular and dangerous. They also can be useful. How do volcanoes erupt?

FIND OUT!

Do this simple activity to discover how volcanoes erupt.

Use clay to make a small model volcano with a crater at the top. Place a small amount of baking soda and a drop of red food coloring in the crater. After putting on safety goggles to protect your eyes, add approximately 20 mL of vinegar to the baking soda in the crater and observe what happens. Describe how your model eruption is similar to a real volcanic eruption. In what ways is it different?

Gearing Up

Previewing the Chapter

Use this outline to help you focus on important ideas in this chapter.

Previewing Science Skills

- In the **Skill Builders,** you will make a concept map, sequence events, and compare and contrast.
- In the **Activities,** you will hypothesize, measure, observe, predict, classify, infer, and interpret data.
- In the **MINI-Labs,** you will observe and compare and contrast.

What's next?

You've seen that gases and other materials flow out of a volcano as it erupts. Now you'll learn about some famous volcanoes and what caused them to form. You also will learn where on Earth volcanoes occur and how this relates to plate tectonics.

For Your Mainstreamed Students

Have students work in small groups to make clay models of shield volcanoes, cinder cones, and composite volcanoes. Both lava and tephra should be represented.

INTRODUCING THE CHAPTER

Use the Find Out activity to introduce students to volcanic eruptions. Inform students that they will be learning more about volcanoes as they read this chapter.

FIND OUT!

Preparation: Obtain enough modeling clay, baking soda, red food coloring, and vinegar for each Science Investigation team.

Materials: modeling clay, a small box of baking soda, red food coloring, vinegar, and safety goggles

Cooperative Learning: Form Science Investigation groups with four students in each group. Assign the following roles: reader, materials handler, and recorder. The fourth student should perform the activity.

Teaching Tips

- You may wish to have each group place a small metal cup in the crater of the model volcano to hold the baking soda and vinegar.
- Caution students to use only a very small amount of baking soda and one drop of food coloring as instructed.
- Cover the work areas with plastic to contain the materials and keep them off the floor.
- Be certain that all students wear their safety goggles throughout the activity.

Gearing Up

Have students study the Gearing Up feature to familiarize themselves with the chapter. Discuss the relationships of the topics in the outline.

What's Next?

Before beginning the first section, make sure students understand the connection between the Find Out activity and the topics to follow.

SECTION 15-1

PREPARATION

SECTION BACKGROUND

▶ The many geysers and hot springs in Yellowstone National Park suggest that the area overlies a hot spot in the mantle. At least three major volcanic eruptions have occurred in this area during the last two million years. The last eruption occurred about 6000 years ago and ejected nearly 1000 cubic kilometers of volcanic debris that reached as far as present-day Texas and Kansas.

▶ Lava from volcanoes in Hawaii and Iceland is basaltic and originates deep within Earth.

▶ Mount Saint Helens is made of granitic lava, which contains large quantities of silica and water.

1 MOTIVATE

Use the Flex Your Brain activity to have students explore HOW VOLCANOES FORM.

▶ Show the video, "Volcanoes," which is a part of the *NOVA* television program. The film is available from Ambrose Video, 381 Park Avenue South, New York, NY 10016.

Science and READING

Have students use geology or history books rather than encyclopedias to do this assignment.

PROGRAM RESOURCES

From the **Teacher Resource Package** use:

Activity Worksheets, page 5, Flex Your Brain.

15-1 Volcanoes and Plate Tectonics

New Science Words

volcano
vent
crater
Pacific Ring of Fire
hot spots

Objectives

- ▶ Describe how volcanoes can affect people.
- ▶ Describe conditions that cause volcanoes.
- ▶ Describe the relationship between volcanoes and plate tectonics.

Science and READING

The events involving many famous volcanic eruptions around the world have been recorded. Go to the library and read a book about famous eruptions such as the 1902 eruption of Mount Pelée and read how it affected the people there.

Volcanoes and You

If you live near the Pacific Ocean, you may have seen a volcano. If not, you've probably seen pictures of them. A **volcano** is a mountain that forms when layers of lava and volcanic ash erupt and build up. Most of Earth's volcanoes are dormant, which means that they are not currently active, but more than 600 are active. Active volcanoes sometimes spew smoke, steam, ash, cinders, and flows of lava. Here are stories of some famous volcanoes. Read them and notice the fact that all volcanoes are not the same.

In 1902, Mount Pelée (puh LAY) on the Caribbean island of Martinique erupted. A very hot gas cloud from the volcano flowed over a nearby city and killed almost all of the 30 000 people there. One survivor was a prisoner who was protected by the dungeon he was in. In 1980, Mount Saint Helens in Washington State erupted. It was one of the largest recent volcanic eruptions in North America. Geologists warned people to leave the area surrounding the mountain. Most people left, but a few stayed. About 60 were killed as a result of Mount Saint Helens exploding. Heat from the eruption melted snow, which caused flooding in the area also.

For centuries, Kilauea (kee law WAY uh) volcano in Hawaii has been erupting, but not explosively. Every few years lava flows out for a while. The lava covered a town and burned houses in 1990, but no one was hurt because
1 the lava moved slowly. Kilauea is the world's most active volcano.

OPTIONS

Meeting Different Ability Levels

For Section 15-1, use the following **Teacher Resource Masters** depending upon individual students' needs.

◆ **Study Guide Master** for all students.

● **Reinforcement Master** for students of average and above average ability levels.

▲ **Enrichment Master** for above average students.

Additional Teacher Resource Package masters are listed in the OPTIONS box throughout the section. The additional masters are appropriate for all students.

◆ STUDY GUIDE 62

NAME ________ DATE ________ CLASS ________

STUDY GUIDE — Chapter 15

Volcanoes and Plate Tectonics — Text Pages 388–392

Write the term or phrase that matches each definition below. Use the letters in the boxes to answer Item 14.

1. [P] L A T E S
2. [L] A V A
3. C R [A] T E R
4. R I F [T] S
5. A C T I V [E]
6. D O R [M] A N T
7. R I N G [O] F F I R E
8. [V] E N T S
9. D I V [E] R G E N T
10. M A G [M] A
11. C O N V [E] R G E N T
12. V O L C A [N] O
13. H O T S P O [T]

1. Structures in Earth that move on the asthenosphere
2. Magma that flows out onto Earth's surface
3. Opening at the top of a volcano's vent
4. Long, deep cracks formed when plates separate
5. The state of volcanoes currently spewing smoke, ash, steam, cinders, and/or lava
6. The state of volcanoes not currently active
7. Area around Pacific plate where earthquakes and volcanoes are common, the Pacific ____
8. Openings in Earth's crust that allow magma to reach the surface
9. Type of boundary where plates separate
10. Melted rock deep inside Earth
11. Type of boundary where one plate slides under another plate
12. Mountain formed from layers of lava and volcanic ash
13. Area in Earth's mantle hot enough to melt rock into magma and create volcanoes
14. What process helps in the formation of volcanoes? plate movement

62

Figure 15-1. The often-erupting Kilauea volcano in Hawaii destroyed homes with this lava flow.

What Causes Volcanoes?

What happens inside Earth to create volcanoes? Why are some areas of Earth more likely to have volcanoes than others?

You learned in Chapter 4 that rock deep inside Earth melts to form magma and that magma is called lava when it flows out onto Earth's surface. You also learned that heat and pressure cause rock to melt and form magma. Some deep rocks already are molten. Others are hot enough that a small rise in temperature can melt them to form magma.

Magma is less dense than the rock around it, so it very slowly rises toward Earth's surface. You can see this process if you turn a bottle of cold syrup upside down. Watch the less-dense air bubbles push the syrup aside and slowly rise to the top.

Why does magma rise?

After many thousands or even millions of years, some magma reaches Earth's surface and flows out through an opening called a **vent.** As lava flows out, it cools quickly and becomes solid, forming layers of igneous rock around the vent. The opening at the top of a volcano's vent is the **crater.** ❷

● **REINFORCEMENT 62**

NAME _____ DATE _____ CLASS _____

REINFORCEMENT — Chapter 15

Volcanoes and Plate Tectonics — Text Pages 388–392

1. Use the diagram to identify the parts of a volcano.

A. ash, gas
B. crater
C. lava
D. vent
E. magma

2. Identify the three kinds of places where volcanoes can occur. Explain how a volcano can form at each and give an example of a volcano.

(1) convergent plate boundaries—One plate sliding under another plate forms a subduction zone. Magma created in the zone moves to the surface to form volcanoes. An example is Mount Saint Helens in Washington.

(2) divergent plate boundaries—Two plates separate, forming deep cracks or rifts. Magma flows through the rifts and builds up from the seafloor. An example is any volcano in Iceland.

(3) hot spot—Hot area in the mantle melts rock into magma which rises through the crust to form volcanoes. An example is Kilauea in Hawaii.

3. Describe the role of the Pacific Ring of Fire in the formation of volcanoes. Tectonic movement in the area around the Pacific plate where it collides with other plates leads to the formation of volcanoes.

62

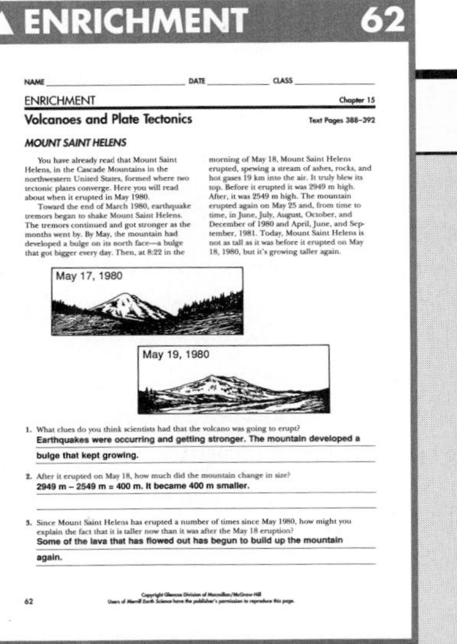

▲ **ENRICHMENT 62**

NAME _____ DATE _____ CLASS _____

ENRICHMENT — Chapter 15

Volcanoes and Plate Tectonics — Text Pages 388–392

MOUNT SAINT HELENS

You have already read that Mount Saint Helens, in the Cascade Mountains in the northwestern United States, formed where two tectonic plates converge. Here you will read about when it erupted in May 1980.

Toward the end of March 1980, earthquake tremors began to shake Mount Saint Helens. The tremors continued and got stronger as the months went by. By May, the mountain had developed a bulge on its north face—a bulge that got bigger every day. Then, at 8:22 in the morning of May 18, Mount Saint Helens erupted, spewing a stream of ashes, rocks, and hot gases 19 km into the air. It truly blew its top. Before it erupted it was 2949 m high. After, it was 2549 m high. The mountain erupted again on May 25 and, from time to time, in June, July, August, October, and December of 1980 and April, June, and September, 1981. Today, Mount Saint Helens is not as tall as it was before it erupted on May 18, 1980, but it's growing taller again.

1. What clues do you think scientists had that the volcano was going to erupt? Earthquakes were occurring and getting stronger. The mountain developed a bulge that kept growing.

2. After it erupted on May 18, how much did the mountain change in size? 2949 m – 2549 m = 400 m. It became 400 m smaller.

3. Since Mount Saint Helens has erupted a number of times since May 1980, how might you explain the fact that it is taller now than it was after the May 18 eruption? Some of the lava that has flowed out has begun to build up the mountain again.

62

TYING TO PREVIOUS KNOWLEDGE: Have students recall from Chapter 13 the types of plate boundaries. Ask for a volunteer to explain that as magma rises toward Earth's surface at divergent boundaries, it is deflected sideways, causing plate movement. The resulting rift is a site of volcanism. Have another volunteer explain the volcanism associated with convergent boundaries.

OBJECTIVES AND SCIENCE WORDS: Have students review the objectives and science words to become familiar with this section.

2 TEACH

Key Concepts are highlighted.

CONCEPT DEVELOPMENT

Cooperative Learning: Have Paired Partners contrast the explosions discussed on page 388 and arrange the three volcanoes from least explosive to most explosive. Kilauea is the least explosive volcano listed while Mount St. Helens is probably the most explosive.

▶ Have students discuss how volcanic activity might affect your geographic locale.

▶ Ask students to hypothesize why some people live so close to volcanoes knowing that eruptions can be so dangerous. Students' responses might include economic reasons, the scenery, the rarity of explosions, among other reasons.

PROGRAM RESOURCES

From the **Teacher Resource Package** use:

Cross-Curricular Connections, page 19, Deadly Eruptions.

Use **Laboratory Manual** page 127, Volcanic Preservation.

CONCEPT DEVELOPMENT

▶ Have volunteers compare and contrast volcanism at divergent and convergent boundaries.

▶ **Demonstration:** Attach an air pump to a balloon neck and then place the balloon under a large piece of denim. As you gradually inflate the balloon, explain that the "bulge" in the cloth represents lava that causes doming on the cloth "volcano." Ask students what will happen if you continue to inflate the balloon. Students should conclude that as the "lava dome" continues to increase in size, there's a good probability that the "volcano" will erupt. Inform them that bulging and earthquakes are often precursors to eruptions as was the case prior to the 1980 Mount Saint Helens' eruption.

REVEALING MISCONCEPTIONS

▶ Some students may think only people living near a volcano are affected when the volcano erupts. Inform them that ash from Mount Saint Helens fell on much of the United States in 1980. Winds are able to carry volcanic debris thousands of kilometers.

TEACHER F.Y.I.

▶ Island arc complexes such as those in Japan and the Aleutian Islands form when two oceanic plates collide and one is forced below the other.

Did You Know?

From 1986 to 1989, the Kilauea volcano produced enough lava to cover a four-lane highway from New York to San Francisco nine meters deep.

Where Do Volcanoes Occur?

Volcanoes form in three kinds of places that are directly related to plate tectonics. You learned about two of these places in Chapter 13 when you studied plate tectonics. Volcanoes occur at divergent plate boundaries, at convergent plate boundaries, and at locations not at plate boundaries called hot spots. There are many examples of volcanoes around the world at the three different types of locations related to plate tectonics. Let's explore Iceland, Hawaii, and Mount Saint Helens.

Divergent Boundaries

Iceland is a large island in the North Atlantic Ocean. It is near the Arctic Circle and has some glaciers. But it also has many volcanoes. Iceland has volcanic activity because it sits on top of the Mid-Atlantic Ridge.

Why is there volcanic activity in Iceland?

You learned in Chapter 13 that the Mid-Atlantic Ridge is a divergent plate boundary. Where plates separate, they
3 form long, deep cracks called rifts. Magma flows from rifts as lava and is instantly cooled by the seawater. As more lava flows, it builds up from the seafloor. Sometimes the volcanoes rise above sea level, forming islands such as Iceland.

Figure 15-2. Volcanic ash covered these buildings in Iceland.

Convergent Boundaries

Mount Saint Helens is not an island. It is one of several volcanoes that make up the Cascade Mountain Range in Oregon and Washington in the northwestern United States. Why are there volcanoes here?

OPTIONS

INQUIRY QUESTIONS

▶ **Explain how volcanoes form at divergent plate boundaries.** *Magma rises because it is less dense than the surrounding rock. A central crack or rift forms as the plates move apart. Some of the magma flows onto Earth's surface as lava to form volcanoes.*

▶ **How do volcanoes with bases on the ocean floor emerge above sea level?** *Seawater quickly cools lava as it flows onto the ocean floor. Successive lava flows accumulate to form volcanoes.*

▶ **Why do few volcanoes form when two continental plates converge?** *Because continental plates have the same densities, neither plate subducts. Folded mountains rather than volcanic mountains form when two continental plates collide.*

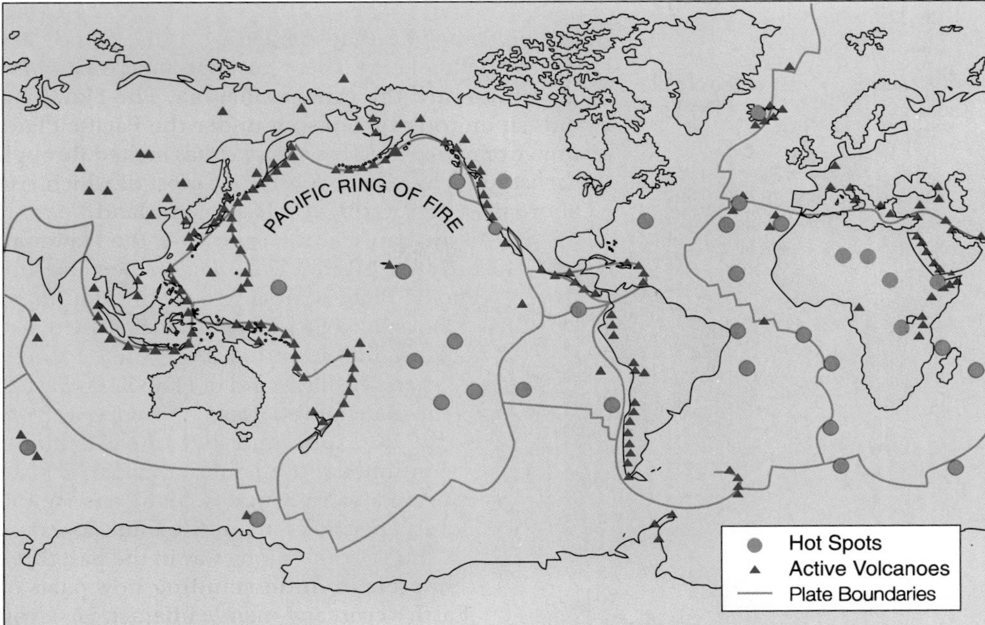

Figure 15-3. This diagram shows the active volcanoes and hot spots around the world. Note their relationship to plate boundaries you learned about in Chapter 13.

Mount Saint Helens and the other volcanic peaks in the Cascade Range formed because of a convergent plate boundary. Here, the Juan de Fuca Plate is converging with the North American Plate. Magma that is created in the subduction zone works its way to the surface, forming the volcanoes of the Cascades.

Such volcanoes have formed all around the Pacific Plate where it collides with other plates. This area around the Pacific Plate where earthquakes and volcanoes are common is called the **Pacific Ring of Fire.** All of the earthquakes and volcanoes in the Pacific Ring of Fire can be attributed to tectonic movement at the boundary of the Pacific Plate. Mount Saint Helens is just one volcano in the Pacific Ring of Fire. Can you list others?

4 What causes volcanic activity around the Pacific Ring of Fire?

Hot Spots

Like Iceland, the Hawaiian Islands also are volcanic islands. But unlike Iceland, they haven't formed at a plate boundary. The Hawaiian Islands are in the middle of the Pacific Plate, far from its edges. What process could be forming them?

STUDENT TEXT QUESTION

▶ Page 391, paragraph 2: **Mount Saint Helens is just one volcano in the Pacific Ring of Fire. Can you list others?** *Mt. Rainier, Mt. Hood, Mt. Jefferson, Crater Lake, and Mt. Shasta are just a few.*

MINI QUIZ

Use the Mini Quiz to check students' recall of chapter content.

1. **What is the world's most active volcano?** *Kilauea*
2. **What is a crater?** *the opening at the top of a volcano*
3. **Lava flows from _____ at divergent boundaries.** *rifts*
4. **What is the Pacific Ring of Fire?** *a belt around the Pacific plate along which earthquakes and volcanoes are common*

CROSS CURRICULUM

▶ **Geography:** Display a map of the world on a bulletin board in the classroom. Have each student in the class locate one active volcano on the map. Then, have each student place a pin with the name of the volcano at the proper position on the map. Have the class as a whole note any patterns.

CHECK FOR UNDERSTANDING

What processes around the Pacific Ocean are causing the volcanic activity? *subduction at convergent plate boundaries*

RETEACH

Draw a cross section of a subduction zone on a transparency. Explain how material from one plate melts due to changes in pressure and temperature as it is subducted. The melted material is less dense than the surrounding material and thus rises toward Earth's surface to form volcanoes.

EXTENSION

For students who have mastered this section, use the **Reinforcement** and **Enrichment** masters or other OPTIONS provided.

ENRICHMENT

▶ Have students find out about the geologic events observed prior to the eruption of Mount Saint Helens in May 1980. Have students contrast the predictability of volcanic eruptions with that of earthquakes.

▶ Have students find out about nuée ardentes and the conditions necessary to produce them.

▶ Have students research to find out what kinds of processes caused the formation of the Columbia Plateau in the northwestern United States.

CONCEPT DEVELOPMENT

► **Why do volcanoes form above hot spots?** *Hot spots generate magma that rises to Earth's surface. When this magma flows onto Earth's surface as lava, volcanoes form.*

3 CLOSE

► Have students use Figure 15-3 to locate the three major volcanic belts on Earth. Have them then classify each area of volcanism as being due to hot spots, divergence, or convergence.

► Ask questions 1-3 and the **Apply** Question in the Section Review.

SECTION REVIEW ANSWERS

1. Lava from volcanoes has covered and destroyed roads and towns. People have been forced to leave their homes, while others have been killed or injured.

2. Magma, being less dense than surrounding material, rises toward Earth's surface. It then flows onto the surface as lava to form volcanoes.

3. Volcanoes form when: lava flows onto Earth's surface at divergent boundaries; one plate subducts under another and the associated magma eventually rises to Earth's surface; or plates move over hot spots in Earth's mantle.

4. Apply: Yes, as the Pacific plate moves over the hot spot presently under Hawaii, new volcanoes will form. One has recently formed off the coast of Hawaii.

Skill Builder

Possible Solution:

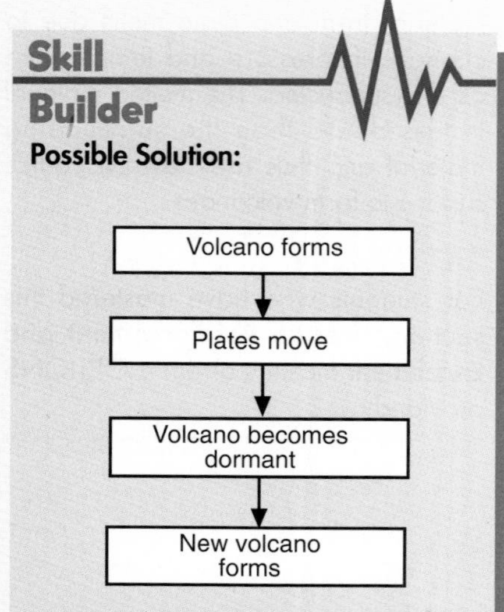

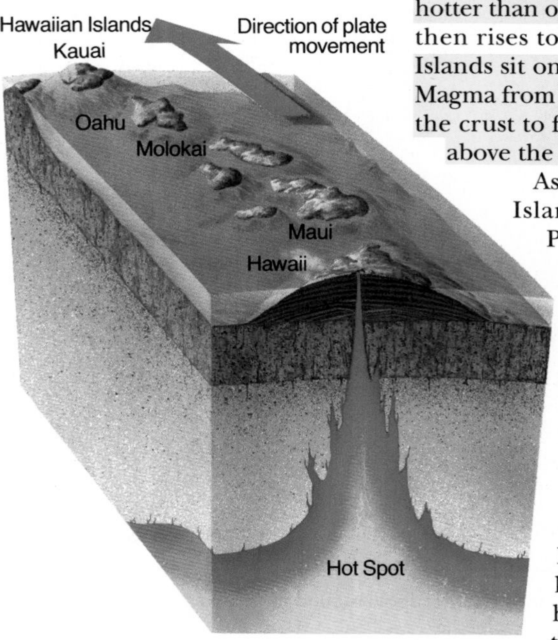

Figure 15-4. The Hawaiian Islands have formed as the Pacific Plate moves over a hot spot.

Geologists believe that some areas in the mantle are hotter than other areas. These **hot spots** melt rock which then rises toward the crust as magma. The Hawaiian Islands sit on top of a hot spot under the Pacific Plate. Magma from deep in Earth's mantle has melted through the crust to form several volcanoes, most of which rise above the water to form an Hawaiian Island.

As you can see in Figure 15-4, the Hawaiian Islands are all in a line. This is because the Pacific Plate is moving over the stationary hot spot. The island of Kauai is the oldest Hawaiian island and was once located where the big island of Hawaii is today. As the plate moved, Kauai moved away from the hot spot and became dormant. Continued movement of the Pacific Plate formed Oahu, Molokai, Maui, and Hawaii over a period of about five million years.

You've come a long way in the past three chapters in understanding how parts of Earth's crust and mantle interact. First, you learned the theory of plate tectonics and how Earth's lithosphere is divided into plates that move on the asthenosphere. Then you learned that these movements cause earthquakes that affect people all over the world. Now you can see that tectonic activity can also lead to the formation of volcanoes at diverging or converging plate boundaries and at hot spots.

SECTION REVIEW

1. How do volcanoes affect people?
2. How does magma deep inside Earth cause volcanoes?
3. How is plate tectonics related to volcanoes?
4. **Apply:** Do you think that any more Hawaiian islands may be created? How could it happen?

Concept Mapping

Make a concept map that shows how the Hawaiian Islands formed over a hot spot. Use these terms and phrases: *volcano forms, plate moves, volcano becomes dormant, new volcano forms.* If you need help, refer to Concept Mapping in the **Skill Handbook** on pages 688 and 689.

OPTIONS

PROGRAM RESOURCES

From the **Teacher Resource Package** use:

Transparency Masters, pages 67-68, Active Volcanoes and Hot Spots.

Use **Color Transparency** number 34, Active Volcanoes and Hot Spots.

ACTIVITY 15-1
Locating Active Volcanoes

Problem: *Where do active volcanoes occur?*

Materials
- world map (Appendix F)
- tracing paper
- Figure 13-10 on page 349

Procedure
1. Use tracing paper to outline the continents on the world map in Appendix F. Include the lines of latitude and longitude on your tracing.
2. Listed at right are the latitudes and longitudes of 20 active volcanoes around the world. Locate them on the world map. Mark and name their locations on your tracing.
3. Compare your tracing to Figure 13-10 in Chapter 13, which shows the major plate boundaries around the world.
4. On a data table like the one shown, list the location of each volcano. Then, place a check in the column that best describes the type of tectonic process (divergent plate boundary, convergent plate boundary, or hot spot) that is causing the volcano in that location.

Analyze
1. Describe the patterns of distribution that the volcanoes form on Earth.
2. From looking at these patterns and the locations of the active volcanoes, is there a relationship between plate tectonics and volcanoes? What is it?

Conclude and Apply
3. Is there a relationship between the locations of the active volcanoes and areas of earthquake activity described in Chapter 14? Explain.

Data and Observations
Sample Data

Volcano	Volcano location	Convergent	Divergent	Hot Spot
# 1	Iceland		X	
# 2	Saudi Arabia		X	
#19	Azores		X	
#20	U.S.S.R.	X		

Volcano	Latitude	Longitude
#1	64° N	19° W
#2	28° N	34° E
#3	43° S	172° E
#4	35° N	136° E
#5	18° S	68° W
#6	25° S	114° W
#7	20° N	155° W
#8	54° N	167° W
#9	16° N	122° E
#10	28° N	17° W
#11	15° N	43° E
#12	6° N	75° W
#13	64° S	158° E
#14	38° S	78° E
#15	21° S	56° E
#16	38° N	26° E
#17	7° S	13° W
#18	2° S	102° E
#19	38° N	30° W
#20	54° N	159° E

ACTIVITY 15-1
50 minutes

OBJECTIVE: Determine relationships among the locations of active volcanoes, earthquakes, and plate boundaries.

PROCESS SKILLS applied in this activity:
- ▶ **Communicating** in Procedure Steps 1-4.
- ▶ **Interpreting Data** in Procedure Step 4, Analyze Questions 1 and 2, and Conclude and Apply Question 3.
- ▶ **Observing** in Procedure Step 3.
- ▶ **Hypothesizing** in Analyze Questions 1 and 2 and Conclude and Apply Question 3.
- ▶ **Measuring** in Procedure Step 2.

COOPERATIVE LEARNING Form two- or three-member Science Investigation groups to do this activity.

TEACHING THE ACTIVITY
▶ You may want to have copies of a complete data table available for each group to use as a worksheet for this activity.

▶ A large poster-size world map, suitable for students to mark or, if mounted on cardboard, to stick map pins into would be very helpful.

▶ Review from Chapter 8 how to determine locations using lines of latitude and longitude.

▶ You may want to show students how to do the activity by doing Volcano #1 with them as an example. This volcano is located near Iceland along the Mid-Atlantic ridge, which is a divergent margin.

ANSWERS TO QUESTIONS
1. Since only 20 of the approximately 600 active volcanoes are plotted, students may not be able to detect a pattern. They may note, however, that more volcanoes appear to be associated with the Pacific Ocean. It would take a number of additional plottings for the actual pattern to become obvious.

2. With the exception of Volcanoes 7, 10, and 15, all of the active volcanoes are located along or very near plate boundaries. Volcanoes 1, 2, 6, 11, 13, 14, 17 and 19 occur on or near rift zones and represent divergent plate boundaries. Volcanoes 3, 4, 5, 8, 9, 11, 16, 18, and 20 occur near subduction zones and represent converging plates.

3. All active volcanoes occur within active earthquake zones, which are also commonly associated with plate boundaries.

PROGRAM RESOURCES
From the **Teacher Resource Package** use:

Activity Worksheets, pages 131-132, Activity 15-1: Locating Active Volcanoes.

SECTION 15-2

PREPARATION

SECTION BACKGROUND

▶The Geysers, the first commercial geothermal energy power plant in the United States, located 144 km north of San Francisco, was built in 1960. By 1986, The Geysers was generating enough electricity to satisfy the needs of San Francisco and Oakland.

1 MOTIVATE

Cooperative Learning: Have Paired Partners do some research that will allow them to draw a cross-sectional diagram showing how geothermal energy is tapped and used to generate electricity.

TYING TO PREVIOUS KNOWLEDGE: Have students discuss the problems caused by the destruction of rain forests. Relate this to potential problems in Hawaii if electricity is generated from geothermal energy.

OBJECTIVES AND SCIENCE WORDS: Have students review the objectives and science words to become familiar with this section.

2 TEACH

Key Concepts are highlighted.

CONCEPT DEVELOPMENT

▶ After students have read this section, ask the following questions. **What will be the source of geothermal energy in Hawaii?** *magma* **How will the magma be used?** *The magma can be used to heat water to produce steam. The steam will, in turn, spin generators to make electricity.*

15-2 Geothermal Energy from Volcanoes

New Science Words

geothermal energy

Objectives

- ▶ List the pros and cons of using geothermal energy to produce electricity.
- ▶ Form an opinion as to whether the geothermal energy under the Hawaiian Islands should be used to generate electricity.

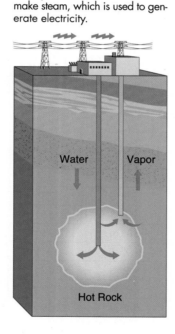

Figure 15-5. Heat from volcanic activity is used to heat water and make steam, which is used to generate electricity.

Electricity from Geothermal Energy?

Because of destructive eruptions like that at Mount Saint Helens, we usually think of igneous activity as destructive. But some people in Hawaii want to use the heat from igneous activity to generate electricity. You learned that Kilauea is the most active volcano on Earth. The magma underneath volcanoes holds tremendous thermal energy. This **geothermal energy** can be used to generate electricity. The heat from magma can be used to heat water and produce steam in a power plant on the surface. The steam is pressurized and then spins generators that make electricity.

Right now, Hawaii depends on oil to generate 87 percent of its electricity. Government officials hope that Hawaii will stop using fossil fuels by the year 2007. They hope to generate all of Hawaii's electricity by using geothermal energy. If this happened, Hawaii could stop burning fossil fuels. This would reduce air pollution, and Hawaii would have to buy less oil. This would also reduce the danger of oil spills from tankers.

Geothermal energy is a proven energy technology. It is used in more than 20 foreign countries including Iceland. Geothermal energy supplies about 5 percent of California's electricity.

But what problems might be caused by using the geothermal energy beneath Kilauea? Some people worry that using geothermal energy might harm the rain forest. To tap the energy, roadways must be cleared, power plants must be built, and drilling rigs must be moved in.

OPTIONS

Meeting Different Ability Levels

For Section 15-2, use the following **Teacher Resource Masters** depending upon individual students' needs.

- ◆ **Study Guide Master** for all students.
- ● **Reinforcement Master** for students of average and above average ability levels.
- ▲ **Enrichment Master** for above average students.

Additional Teacher Resource Package masters are listed in the OPTIONS box throughout the section. The additional masters are appropriate for all students.

◆ STUDY GUIDE 63

NAME ______ DATE ______ CLASS ______

STUDY GUIDE — Chapter 15

Geothermal Energy from Volcanoes — Text Pages 394–395

Answer the following questions on the lines provided.

1. Define geothermal energy. **Heat from magma is used to produce steam that spins generators to make electricity.**

2. Write the following sentences in the proper sequence to show how geothermal energy is used.
   - Hot water produces steam.
   - Generators make electricity.
   - Magma heats water.
   - Steam spins generators.
   - Magma is very hot.

   (1) **Magma is very hot.**
   (2) **Magma heats water.**
   (3) **Hot water produces steam.**
   (4) **Steam spins generators.**
   (5) **Generators make electricity.**

3. Make a list of the advantages and disadvantages of using geothermal energy in Hawaii.

   Advantages
   reduction in use of fossil fuels
   reduction in air pollution
   reduction in need to buy fossil fuels
   reduction in risk of oil spills

   Disadvantages
   destruction of areas of rain forest
   damage to environment from heavy construction
   release of harmful gases from magma

4. Why is Hawaii considering the development of geothermal energy? **Hawaii depends on oil to generate 87 percent of its electricity. By using geothermal energy, Hawaii could stop burning fossil fuels.**

 63

Figure 15-6. These people protested geothermal energy development in Hawaii.

You see why they are concerned. If you have watched a road or a large factory being built, you may have seen the damage to the environment that construction can cause. Another concern is that drilling might release harmful gases from the magma. People who are against the project say that solar energy and wind energy should be used instead of geothermal energy.

Those who favor the project claim that only small areas of rain forest would be cleared. They say harmful gases are not significant, because Kilauea already releases huge amounts of them.

SECTION REVIEW

1. What are two advantages and two disadvantages of using geothermal energy to generate electricity in Hawaii?
2. How will the use of geothermal energy on Hawaii reduce the danger of oil spills from oil tankers in the ocean?

You Decide!

Using geothermal energy from hot magma beneath Hawaii's volcanoes is very controversial. Is damage to rain forests offset by the advantages of geothermal energy? Is it better to destroy some rain forest than to continue releasing pollution into the air from burning fossil fuels? What do you think about geothermal energy use in Hawaii?

● REINFORCEMENT 63

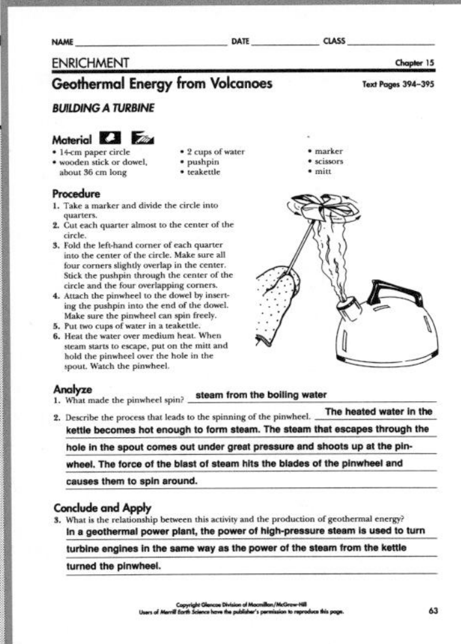

NAME ________ DATE ________ CLASS ________

ENRICHMENT — Chapter 15

Geothermal Energy from Volcanoes — Text Pages 394–395

BUILDING A TURBINE

Material
- 14-cm paper circle
- wooden stick or dowel, about 36 cm long
- 2 cups of water
- pushpin
- teakettle
- marker
- scissors
- mitt

Procedure
1. Take a marker and divide the circle into quarters.
2. Cut each quarter almost to the center of the circle.
3. Fold the left-hand corner of each quarter into the center of the circle. Make sure all four corners slightly overlap in the center. Stick the pushpin through the center of the circle and the four overlapping corners.
4. Attach the pinwheel to the dowel by inserting the pushpin into the end of the dowel. Make sure the pinwheel can spin freely.
5. Put two cups of water in a teakettle.
6. Heat the water over medium heat. When steam starts to escape, put on the mitt and hold the pinwheel over the hole in the spout. Watch the pinwheel.

Analyze
1. What made the pinwheel spin? **steam from the boiling water**
2. Describe the process that leads to the spinning of the pinwheel. **The heated water in the kettle becomes hot enough to form steam. The steam that escapes through the hole in the spout comes out under great pressure and shoots up at the pinwheel. The force of the blast of steam hits the blades of the pinwheel and causes them to spin around.**

Conclude and Apply
3. What is the relationship between this activity and the production of geothermal energy? **In a geothermal power plant, the power of high-pressure steam is used to turn turbine engines in the same way as the power of the steam from the kettle turned the pinwheel.**

 63

▲ ENRICHMENT 63

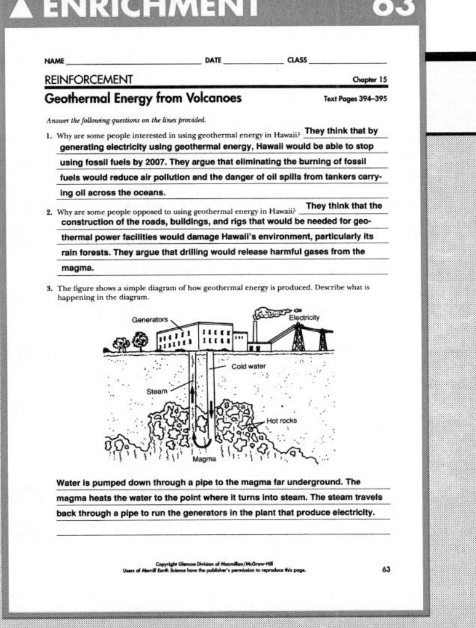

NAME ________ DATE ________ CLASS ________

REINFORCEMENT — Chapter 15

Geothermal Energy from Volcanoes — Text Pages 394–395

Answer the following questions on the lines provided.

1. Why are some people interested in using geothermal energy in Hawaii? **They think that by generating electricity using geothermal energy, Hawaii would be able to stop using fossil fuels by 2007. They argue that eliminating the burning of fossil fuels would reduce air pollution and the danger of oil spills from tankers carrying oil across the oceans.**
2. Why are some people opposed to using geothermal energy in Hawaii? **They think that the construction of the roads, buildings, and rigs that would be needed for geothermal power facilities would damage Hawaii's environment, particularly its rain forests. They argue that drilling would release harmful gases from the magma.**
3. The figure shows a simple diagram of how geothermal energy is produced. Describe what is happening in the diagram.

Water is pumped down through a pipe to the magma far underground. The magma heats the water to the point where it turns into steam. The steam travels back through a pipe to run the generators in the plant that produce electricity.

 63

CHECK FOR UNDERSTANDING

Ask students to describe the damage to the environment a geothermal energy power plant might cause.

RETEACH

Show photographs of different types of damage done by humans to the environment. Ask students to hypothesize how the damage could have been minimized or even eliminated.

EXTENSION

For students who have mastered this section, use the **Reinforcement** and **Enrichment** masters or other OPTIONS provided.

3 CLOSE

▶ Use the questions in the You Decide feature to have students debate whether or not geothermal energy should be tapped in Hawaii.

▶ Ask questions 1-2 in the Section Review.

SECTION REVIEW ANSWERS

1. Advantages include reducing the need for fossil fuels and reducing air pollution. Using this energy could harm the rain forests and produce harmful gases.

2. Hawaii would use less oil and therefore, buy less oil, reducing the risk of oil spills into the surrounding waters.

YOU DECIDE!

Make sure students understand the global consequences of cutting vast numbers of trees. Review the processes of photosynthesis and respiration, if necessary. Make sure students support their opinions with facts.

PROGRAM RESOURCES

From the **Teacher Resource Package** use:

Critical Thinking/Problem Solving, page 21, Hydrothermal Energy.

Science and Society, page 19, Using Geothermal Energy.

SECTION 15-3

PREPARATION

SECTION BACKGROUND

▶ Volcanic domes sometimes form within the crater of a composite volcano. The domes are bulbous masses of hardened granitic lava above and around the volcano's vent.

▶ Composite volcanoes are also known as stratovolcanoes because of the stratified layers of tephra and lava that make up their flanks.

▶ Pahoehoe is a basaltic lava that forms a smooth or ropy-looking surface. Basaltic lava flows with rough, jagged, sharp edges are called aa.

▶ Volcanic ash is any extruded material 2.0 mm or less in diameter. Volcanic bombs are ejected fragments larger than 64 mm in size. Bombs form when lava is thrown through the air and cools rapidly while still in flight.

PREPLANNING

▶ To prepare for the Mini-Lab, obtain cereal, sand, plaster of paris, and paper plates for each pair of students.

15-3 Eruptions and Forms of Volcanoes

New Science Words

shield volcano
tephra
cinder cone
composite volcano

Objectives

- ▶ Relate the explosiveness of a volcanic eruption to the silica and water vapor content of its lava.
- ▶ Describe three forms of volcanoes.

Types of Eruptions

Some volcanic eruptions are explosive and violent, like those from Mount Pelée and Mount Saint Helens. But in others, the lava quietly flows from a vent, as in the Kilauea volcano eruptions. What causes this difference?

There are two important factors that determine whether an eruption will be explosive or quiet. One is the amount of water vapor and other gases that are trapped in the magma. The other factor is whether the magma is basaltic or granitic as you learned about in

OPTIONS

Meeting Different Ability Levels

For Section 15-3, use the following **Teacher Resource Masters** depending upon individual students' needs.

◆ **Study Guide Master** for all students.

● **Reinforcement Master** for students of average and above average ability levels.

▲ **Enrichment Master** for above average students.

Additional Teacher Resource Package masters are listed in the OPTIONS box throughout the section. The additional masters are appropriate for all students.

◆ STUDY GUIDE 64

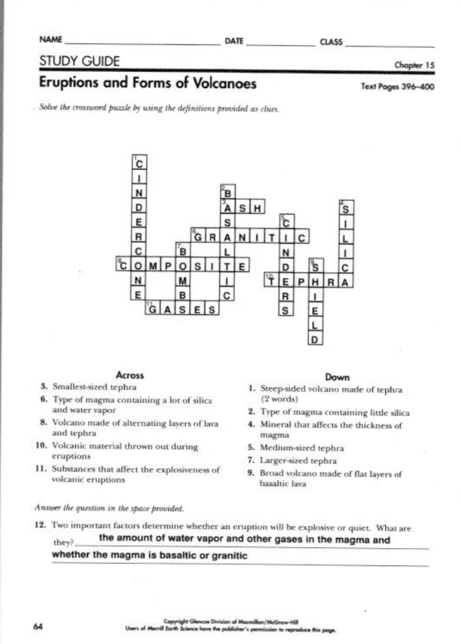

NAME ______ DATE ______ CLASS ______

STUDY GUIDE — Chapter 15

Eruptions and Forms of Volcanoes — Text Pages 396–400

Solve the crossword puzzle by using the definitions provided as clues.

Across
3. Smallest-sized tephra
6. Type of magma containing a lot of silica and water vapor
8. Volcano made of alternating layers of lava and tephra
10. Volcanic material thrown out during eruptions
11. Substances that affect the explosiveness of volcanic eruptions

Down
1. Steep-sided volcano made of tephra (2 words)
2. Type of magma containing little silica
4. Mineral that affects the thickness of magma
5. Medium-sized tephra
7. Larger-sized tephra
9. Broad volcano made of flat layers of basaltic lava

Answer the question in the space provided.

12. Two important factors determine whether an eruption will be explosive or quiet. What are they? **the amount of water vapor and other gases in the magma and whether the magma is basaltic or granitic**

64

Chapter 4. Let's look first at the gas content of the magma.

Have you ever shaken a soft drink container and then quickly opened it? The pressure from the gas in the drink builds up and is released suddenly when you open it, spraying the drink. In the same way, gases such as water vapor and carbon dioxide are trapped in magma by the pressure of the surrounding magma. As the magma nears the surface, the pressure is reduced. This allows the gas to escape the magma. Gas escapes easily from some magma during quiet eruptions. Gas that gets trapped under high pressure eventually escapes, causing explosive eruptions.

What happens if gas cannot escape easily from magma?

The second major factor that affects the type of eruption is the composition of the magma. Basaltic magma contains little silica, is very fluid, and produces quiet, nonexplosive eruptions like those at Kilauea. This type of lava pours from volcanic vents and runs down the side of the volcano. These quiet eruptions form volcanoes over mid-ocean rift zones like Iceland and hot spots like Hawaii. You may have seen on TV that people can walk right up to some lava flows on Kilauea volcano. Because the magma is very fluid when it rises in a vent, trapped gases can escape easily in a nonexplosive manner. Sometimes gas causes lava fountains during quiet eruptions.

Figure 15-7. A calm day in Washington was suddenly interrupted when Mount Saint Helens erupted on May 18, 1980.

● REINFORCEMENT 64

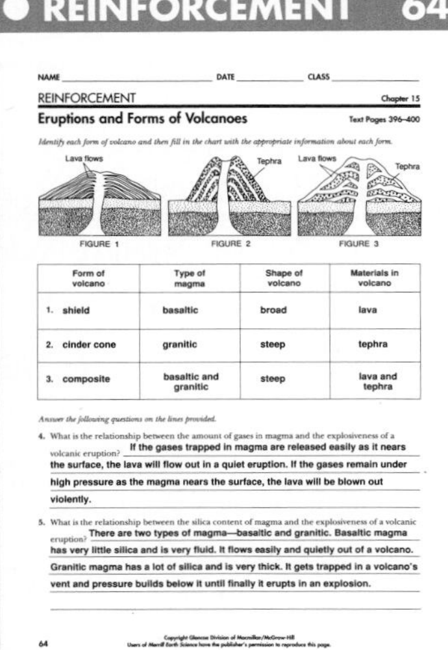

NAME ______ DATE ______ CLASS ______

REINFORCEMENT — Chapter 15

Eruptions and Forms of Volcanoes — Text Pages 396–400

Identify each form of volcano and then fill in the chart with the appropriate information about each form.

Form of volcano	Type of magma	Shape of volcano	Materials in volcano
1. shield	basaltic	broad	lava
2. cinder cone	granitic	steep	tephra
3. composite	basaltic and granitic	steep	lava and tephra

Answer the following questions on the lines provided.

4. What is the relationship between the amount of gases in magma and the explosiveness of a volcanic eruption? **If the gases trapped in magma are released easily as it nears the surface, the lava will flow out in a quiet eruption. If the gases remain under high pressure as the magma nears the surface, the lava will be blown out violently.**

5. What is the relationship between the silica content of magma and the explosiveness of a volcanic eruption? **There are two types of magma—basaltic and granitic. Basaltic magma has very little silica and is very fluid. It flows easily and quietly out of a volcano. Granitic magma has a lot of silica and is very thick. It gets trapped in a volcano's vent and pressure builds below it until finally it erupts in an explosion.**

64

▲ ENRICHMENT 64

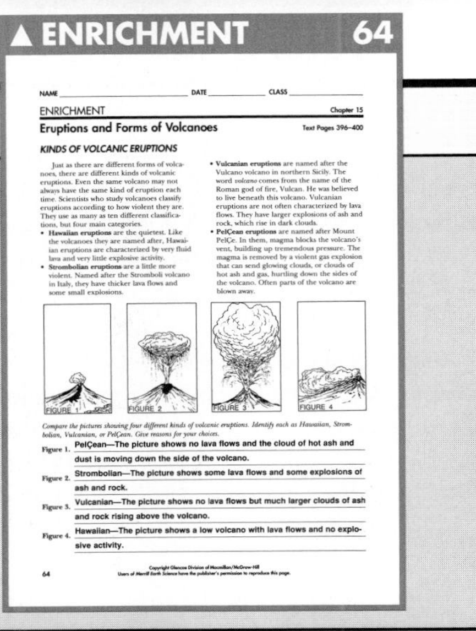

NAME ______ DATE ______ CLASS ______

ENRICHMENT — Chapter 15

Eruptions and Forms of Volcanoes — Text Pages 396–400

KINDS OF VOLCANIC ERUPTIONS

Just as there are different forms of volcanoes, there are different kinds of volcanic eruptions. Even the same volcano may not always have the same kind of eruption each time. Scientists who study volcanoes classify eruptions according to how violent they are. They use as many as ten different classifications, but four main categories.

- **Hawaiian eruptions** are the quietest. Like the volcanoes they are named after, Hawaiian eruptions are characterized by very fluid lava and very little explosive activity.
- **Strombolian eruptions** are a little more violent. Named after the Stromboli volcano in Italy, they have thicker lava flows and some small explosions.
- **Vulcanian eruptions** are named after the Vulcano volcano in northern Sicily. The word *volcano* comes from the name of the Roman god of fire, Vulcan. He was believed to live beneath this volcano. Vulcanian eruptions are not often characterized by lava flows. They have larger explosions of ash and rock, which rise in dark clouds.
- **PelÇean eruptions** are named after Mount PelÇe. In them, magma blocks the volcano's vent, building up tremendous pressure. The magma is removed by a violent gas explosion that can send glowing clouds, or clouds of hot ash and gas, hurtling down the sides of the volcano. Often parts of the volcano are blown away.

Compare the pictures showing four different kinds of volcanic eruptions. Identify each as Hawaiian, Strombolian, Vulcanian, or PelÇean. Give reasons for your choices.

Figure 1. **PelÇean—The picture shows no lava flows and the cloud of hot ash and dust is moving down the side of the volcano.**

Figure 2. **Strombolian—The picture shows some lava flows and some explosions of ash and rock.**

Figure 3. **Vulcanian—The picture shows no lava flows but much larger clouds of ash and rock rising above the volcano.**

Figure 4. **Hawaiian—The picture shows a low volcano with lava flows and no explosive activity.**

64

1 MOTIVATE

FLEX Your Brain

Use the Flex Your Brain activity to have students explore BASALTIC AND GRANITIC MAGMAS.

▶ Have a volunteer or two read his or her story about volcanic eruptions. Refer to the OPTIONS box on page 387.

TYING TO PREVIOUS KNOWLEDGE: Most students have probably opened a warm carbonated beverage only to have it gush from its container. Compare this to volcanic eruptions. Gases in the beverage, along with the relatively warm temperature, cause the liquid to be forced from the container. In a similar way, water vapor and other gases determine the force of a volcanic eruption.

OBJECTIVES AND SCIENCE WORDS: Have students review the objectives and science words to become familiar with this section.

2 TEACH

Key Concepts are highlighted.

CONCEPT DEVELOPMENT

▶ After students have read pages 396 and 397, ask: **What determines the explosiveness of a volcanic eruption?** *the amount of gases trapped in the magma and the composition of the magma*

PROGRAM RESOURCES

From the **Teacher Resource Package** use:

Activity Worksheets, page 5, Flex Your Brain.

CONCEPT DEVELOPMENT

▶**What kinds of eruptions are produced by basaltic lavas?** *nonexplosive, quiet eruptions* **What kinds of eruptions are generated by granitic lavas?** *explosive, violent eruptions*

TECHNOLOGY

For more information, see "Eruption in Colombia" by Bart McDowell, *National Geographic Magazine*, May 1986, pp. 641-653.

Think Critically: Underground movements of huge bodies of magma and vast amounts of gases cause the earthquakes that accompany volcanic eruptions. Using the sensors could perhaps give people time to evacuate the area, if needed.

Why does granitic magma cause explosive eruptions?

Granitic magma, on the other hand, produces explosive, violent eruptions like those at Mount Saint Helens. It often forms in the subduction zones at convergent plate boundaries. 1 Granitic magma, as you learned in Chapter 4, is very thick and contains a lot of silica. Because it is thick, it gets trapped in vents, causing pressure to build up beneath it. When an explosive eruption occurs, the gases expand rapidly, often carrying pieces of lava in the explosion.

Another factor that causes granitic magma to erupt explosively is its high water content. This magma at subduction zones contains a lot of water vapor. This is because of the wet oceanic crust that is carried into the subduction zone. The trapped water vapor in the thick magma causes explosive eruptions. Different types of eruptions form different types of volcanic cones.

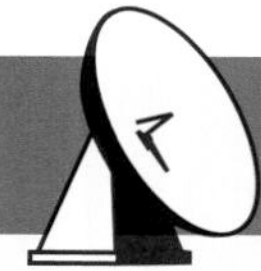

TECHNOLOGY

Volcanic Eruptions

On November 13, 1985, Colombia's volcano Nevado del Ruiz erupted. On that day, nearly 23 000 people lost their lives not from the exploding mountain or from lava flows, but from mudflows. Mudflows are another hazard of volcanoes. Many volcanic peaks have a high enough elevation that they are covered with snow fields and glaciers. The heat from volcanic activity melts this snow and ice during an eruption. This can mean disaster for people living below such a volcano. The melted snow mixes with ash from the eruption and soil from the mountain and flows rapidly downhill as it did in Colombia.

The Japanese have developed mudflow control technology to protect populated areas below active volcanoes. Their technology is designed to slow down mud as it flows down valleys. They have installed concrete and steel damlike structures in valleys where mudflows have occured before. This will give the villagers below time to evacuate the area. The Japanese also use television cameras as earthquake sensors to help them detect eruptions.

Think Critically: Why would earthquake sensors be used to detect volcanic eruptions?

OPTIONS

INQUIRY QUESTIONS

▶**Why does granitic lava erupt so explosively?** *Granitic lava contains a lot of silica, which tends to trap water vapor and other gases. Pressure builds, and when it is finally released, an explosive eruption occurs.*

▶**Where does granitic magma accumulate most of its water?** *At subduction zones, wet oceanic crust and sediments are carried down into the mantle. This water then becomes trapped in the magma that forms.*

PROGRAM RESOURCES

From the **Teacher Resource Package** use:
Concept Mapping, pages 35-36.

Forms of Volcanoes

A volcano's form depends on whether it is the result of a quiet or an explosive eruption and the type of lava it is made of—basaltic or granitic. Volcanoes are of three basic forms—shield volcanoes, cinder cone volcanoes, ❷ or composite volcanoes.

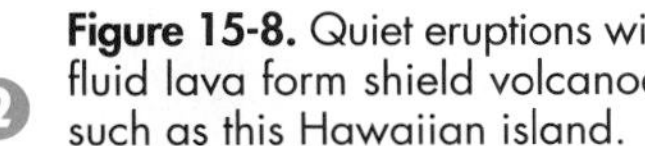

Figure 15-8. Quiet eruptions with fluid lava form shield volcanoes such as this Hawaiian island.

Shield Volcano

Quiet eruptions spread out basaltic lava in flat layers. The buildup of these layers forms a broad volcano with gently sloping sides called a **shield volcano.** Examples of ❸ shield volcanoes are the Hawaiian Islands and volcanoes in rift zones like Iceland.

Cinder Cone Volcano

Explosive eruptions throw lava high into the air. The lava cools and hardens into different sizes of volcanic material called **tephra.** Tephra varies from volcanic ash— ❹ the smallest—to cinders, to larger rocks called bombs.

When tephra falls to the ground, it forms a steep-sided, loosely consolidated **cinder cone** volcano. A Mexican farmer learned about cinder cones one morning when he went to his cornfield. He discovered a long crack in the ground, with ash, cinders, and lava around the opening. In just a few days, a cinder cone several hundred meters high covered his cornfield. It is the volcano named Parícutin (puh REE kuh teen).

MINI-Lab

How are the shapes of volcanic cones different?

Make models of a cinder cone and a shield volcano. First, pour a granulated substance such as a cereal or sand onto one spot on a paper plate, forming a cinder cone volcano. Use a protractor to measure the slope angle of the sides of the volcano. Then mix a batch of plaster of paris and pour it onto one spot on another paper plate, forming a shield volcano. Allow it to dry before measuring the slope angle of the sides. Which type of volcano has steeper sides? Why is this so?

CONCEPT DEVELOPMENT

Cooperative Learning: Have Science Investigation groups use sand, gravel, small rocks, and modeling clay to construct realistic models of the three major forms of volcanoes.

▶Show the video, "The Heat Within," from the series entitled *The Miracle Planet.* The video is available from Resolution Video, 1-800-843-0048.

TEACHER F.Y.I.

▶Mauna Loa in Hawaii is the largest active volcano on Earth. This shield volcano rises more than 9 km above the ocean floor.

REVEALING MISCONCEPTIONS

▶Most students think that volcanic eruptions occur only at the top of the mountain in the previously formed crater. Inform students that the initial eruption of Mount Saint Helens in 1980 occurred on the flank of the mountain as well as at the top. Tremendous amounts of debris were forced laterally from the volcano, knocking down thousands of 60-meter high trees.

MINI-Lab

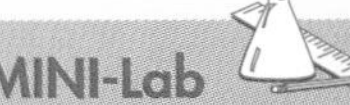

Materials: cereal or sand, plaster of paris, paper plates, and protractors

Teaching Tips

▶Review how to measure angles with a protractor, if necessary.

▶**Answers:** The cinder cone is steeper because it is made of material formed during explosive eruptions. Lava that forms shield volcanoes is ejected with much less force. Thus, shield volcanoes have gently sloping flanks.

INQUIRY QUESTIONS

▶**Just as with volcano Nevado del Ruiz, massive mudflows occurred following the May1980 eruption of Mount Saint Helens. What do you think caused the mudflows around Mount Saint Helens?** *Snowfields and glaciers had developed at high elevations. When Mount Saint Helens erupted, this snow and ice melted and mixed with sediments to form massive mudflows.*

▶**What causes tephra to form?** *When lava is ejected high into the air, it cools and hardens quickly. This material varies in size and is called tephra.*

PROGRAM RESOURCES

From the **Teacher Resource Package** use:

Activity Worksheets, page 139, Mini-Lab: How are the shapes of volcanic cones different?

MINI QUIZ

Use the Mini Quiz to check students' recall of chapter content.

1. **_____ magma is very thick and contains a lot of silica.** *Granitic*
2. **The three forms of volcanoes are _____.** *shield, cinder cone, and composite volcanoes*
3. **_____ volcanoes are broad with gently sloping sides and form from basaltic lava.** *Shield*
4. **Volcanic material ejected high into the air during explosive volcanic eruptions is _____ .** *tephra*
5. **What form of volcano is made of alternating layers of tephra and lava?** *a composite volcano*

CROSS CURRICULUM

▶ **History:** Have students find out about the eruptions of Mount Vesuvius in Italy, in particular, the eruption of A.D. 79 and how it affected Pompeii and Herculaneum. Students' reports should include what has been learned about life in Pompeii since excavation of the city began in the 1800s.

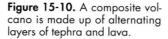

Figure 15-9. A cinder cone volcano is composed of layers of tephra and has steep sides.

Composite Volcano

Some volcanic eruptions can vary between quiet and violent. An explosive period can release gas and ash, forming a tephra layer. Then, the eruption can switch over to a quiet period, erupting lava over the top of the tephra. When this cycle of lava and tephra is repeated over and
5 over in alternating layers, a **composite volcano** is formed. Composite volcanoes are found mostly at convergent plate boundaries, above subduction zones. Mount Saint Helens is an example.

Figure 15-10. A composite volcano is made up of alternating layers of tephra and lava.

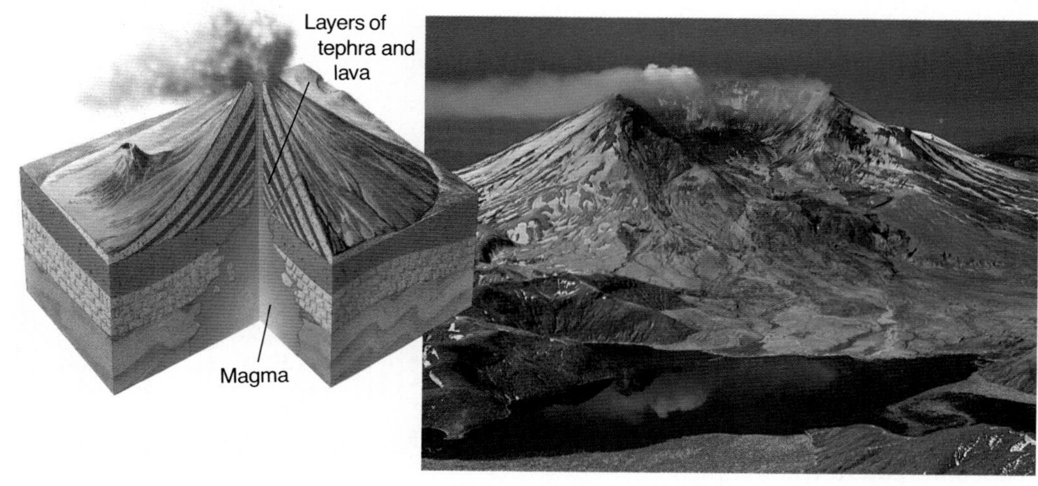

OPTIONS

INQUIRY QUESTIONS

▶ **What is a composite volcano?** *A composite volcano is made of alternating layers of tephra and lava.*

▶ **How does a volcano become dormant?** *Pressure in the magma chamber, which feeds the volcano, may be lowered after an eruption. Magma within a volcano may harden and keep magma from below from rising.*

PROBLEM SOLVING

The Rock Star

Janet is an avid rock and mineral collector. Because her earth science class was studying volcanoes, Janet thought she would trick the class using two igneous rock samples from her collection.

The next day Janet explained to the class that both rock samples were extrusive volcanic rocks. She then asked the class to predict what would happen if she dropped the samples into a glass of water. Most classmates predicted that the rocks would sink. The class watched closely as she dropped the first rock into a glass of water. It sank as predicted. She then dropped the second rock into a glass of water. But, the second rock floated. Why did one rock sink and the other rock float?

Think Critically: Explain how each rock was formed by volcanic activity. What enabled the second rock to float?

As you can see, there are many factors that affect volcanic eruptions and the form of a volcano. Mount Saint Helens was formed as the Juan de Fuca Plate was subducted under the North American Plate. Silica-rich magma rose toward the surface. Successive eruptions of lava and tephra produced the composite volcano that towers above the surrounding landscape. Magma inside the volcano solidified, blocking the opening to the surface. But as the magma continued to rise, it caused the pressure to build up in the volcano. In May of 1980, Mount Saint Helens released the pressure in a series of explosive eruptions as seen in Figure 15-7 on page 397.

What tectonic activity caused Mount Saint Helens to erupt?

The same forces that caused the Mount Saint Helens volcanic activity have also caused other eruptions. In 1991, Mount Unzen in Japan and Mount Pinatubo in the Philipines violently erupted after lying dormant for 300 and over 600 years respectively. The islands of Japan and the Philippines are volcanic island arcs, formed as the Pacific and the Philippine Plates converged with the Eurasian Plate.

CHECK FOR UNDERSTANDING

Ask students to contrast the three forms of volcanoes discussed in the section.

RETEACH

Have students make tables listing the type of lava, the shape, the type of eruption, and an example of each of the three kinds of volcanoes.

EXTENSION

For students who have mastered this section, use the **Reinforcement** and **Enrichment** masters or other OPTIONS provided.

PROBLEM SOLVING

►The rock with the greater density sank; the rock whose density was less than water floated.

Think Critically: The rock that sank was formed as lava cooled quickly. The floating rock formed when lava was explosively thrown out of a volcano. The second rock floated because the gases trapped during its formation made it less dense than water.

ENRICHMENT

► Have students research various recent volcanic eruptions and how they affected people who live and work in the areas stricken.

3 CLOSE

Use the Flex Your Brain activity to have students explore THE THREE FORMS OF VOLCANOES.

▶ Ask questions 1-2 and the **Apply** Question in the Section Review.

SECTION REVIEW ANSWERS

1. The amount of water vapor and other gases contained in the magma and the other kinds of components of the magma determine whether eruptions are quiet or explosive.

2. Shield volcanoes like the Hawaiian Islands have broad, gently sloping sides. Cinder cones are steep-sided volcanoes made of tephra. Parícutin is a cinder cone volcano. Composite volcanoes like Mount Saint Helens contain alternating layers of tephra and solidified lava.

3. Apply: The lava from Krakatoa was probably granitic because of the explosive nature of the eruption.

Skill Builder

1. Subduction zone formed.
2. Silica-rich magma rises.
3. Composite volcano formed.
4. Pressure builds.
5. Erupts in 1980.
6. Magma in volcano solidifies.

Table 15-1

15 SELECTED ERUPTIONS IN HISTORY							
Volcano and Location	Year	Type	Eruptive Force	Magma Content Silica	Magma Content H_2O	Ability of Magma to Flow	Products of Eruption
Etna, Sicily	1669	composite	moderate	high	low	medium	lava, ash
Tambora, Indonesia	1815	cinder	high	high	high	low	cinders, gas
Krakatoa, Indonesia	1883	cinder	high	high	high	low	cinders, gas
Pelée, Martinique	1902	cinder	high	high	high	low	gas, ash
Vesuvius, Italy	1906	composite	moderate	high	low	medium	lava, ash
Lassen, California	1915	composite	moderate	high	low	low	ash, cinders
Mauna Loa, Hawaii	1933	shield	low	low	low	high	lava
Parícutin, Mexico	1943	cinder	moderate	high	low	medium	ash, cinders
Surtsey, Iceland	1963	shield	moderate	low	low	high	lava, ash
Kelut, Indonesia	1966	cinder	high	high	high	low	gas, ash
Arenal, Costa Rica	1968	cinder	high	high	low	low	gas, ash
Helgafell, Iceland	1973	shield	moderate	low	high	medium	gas, ash
Saint Helens, WA	1980	composite	high	high	high	low	gas, ash
Laki, Iceland	1983	shield	moderate	low	low	medium	lava, ash
Kilauea Iki, Hawaii	1989	shield	low	low	low	high	lava

SECTION REVIEW

1. Some volcanic eruptions are quiet and others are violent. What causes this difference?
2. Name and describe the three forms of volcanoes and give examples.
3. **Apply:** In 1883, an island volcano named Krakatoa (krak uh TOH uh) erupted explosively. The island is in Indonesia, in the Pacific Ring of Fire. Which kind of lava did Krakatoa erupt—basaltic or granitic? How do you know?

Skill Builder

☑ Sequencing

Arrange these events of the history of Mount Saint Helens in correct order. If you need help, refer to Sequencing in the **Skill Handbook** on page 680.

Erupts in 1980	Composite volcano formed
Subduction zone formed	Silica-rich magma rises
Pressure builds	Magma in volcano solidifies

OPTIONS

PROGRAM RESOURCES

From the **Teacher Resource Package** use:

Activity Worksheets, page 5, Flex Your Brain.

ACTIVITY 15-2
Identifying Types of Volcanoes

Problem: *How are the properties of magma related to volcano type?*

Materials
- Table 15-1
- paper
- pencil

Procedure
1. Copy the graph shown at right.
2. Using the information from Table 15-1, plot the magma content data for each of the volcanoes listed by writing the name of the basic type of volcano in the appropriate spot on the graph. The data for the 1669 eruption of Mount Etna has already been plotted for you on the diagram.
3. When the plotting of all 15 volcanoes has been completed, analyze the patterns of volcanic types on the diagram to answer the questions.

Data and Observations
Sample Data

Silica content of magma	Water content of magma: low	Water content of magma: high
high	Composite Composite Cinder Cinder Composite	Cinder Cinder Cinder Composite Cinder
low	Shield Shield Shield Shield	Shield

Analyze
1. What relationship appears to exist between the ability of the magma to flow and the eruptive force of the volcano?
2. Which would be more liquid in its properties, a magma that flows easily or one that flows poorly or with difficulty?
3. What relationship appears to exist between the silica or water content of the magma and the nature of the material ejected from the volcano during the eruptions?

Conclude and Apply
4. How is the ability of the magma to flow related to its silica and water content?
5. Which of the two variables (silica or water content) appears to have the greater effect on the eruptive force of the volcano?
6. What relationship appears to exist between the silica and water content of the magma and the type of volcano that is produced?

ACTIVITY 15-2
30-40 minutes

OBJECTIVE: Relate the physical and chemical properties of magma to the nature of the volcanic eruptions and the volcanic form.

PROCESS SKILLS applied in this activity:
▶ **Classifying** in Procedure Step 2.
▶ **Inferring** in Procedure Step 3.
▶ **Communicating** in Procedure Steps 1-3.
▶ **Interpreting Data** in Analyze Questions 1-3 and Conclude and Apply Question 4.
▶ **Hypothesizing** in Conclude and Apply Questions 5 and 6.

COOPERATIVE LEARNING Have Science Investigation groups of two to three students perform this activity.

TEACHING THE ACTIVITY
▶ Enlarge the figure to be used in this activity and distribute copies onto which students are to plot the data given.

PROGRAM RESOURCES

From the **Teacher Resource Package** use:

Activity Worksheets, pages 133-135, Activity 15-2: Identifying Types of Volcanoes.

ANSWERS TO QUESTIONS
1. the greater the ability of the magma to flow, the lower the eruptive force of the volcano, and vice versa
2. a magma that flows easily
3. Volcanoes with magma that is low in silica and water tend to produce lavas that are more fluid. Magma and lava high in silica and water tend to produce cinders, ash, and superheated gases.
4. The ability of a magma or lava to flow is greater when the silica and water contents are low.
5. The silica content seems to have a greater effect than does the water content.
6. Shield volcanoes result from magma with relatively low amounts of silica and water. The lavas from cinder cone volcanoes have relatively high amounts of silica and water. Composite volcanoes appear to eject materials with a range of chemical properties.

SECTION 15-4

PREPARATION

SECTION BACKGROUND

▶ Crater Lake, Oregon, formed about 7000 years ago when a volcano spewed 40 to 50 cubic kilometers of volcanic material into the air. With the magma chamber then partly emptied, 1500 meters of the original 3600-meter cone collapsed. Rainwater has filled the caldera to form a lake.

PREPLANNING

▶ Obtain different types of volcanic ejecta from a scientific supply company for the Mini-Lab on page 405.

1 MOTIVATE

▶ Have students speculate as to what might happen to magma that doesn't reach Earth's surface. Responses may include that it stays molten or can solidify when it reaches a certain depth below the surface.

FLEX Your Brain

Use the Flex Your Brain activity to have students explore INTRUSIVE IGNEOUS ROCK FEATURES.

TYING TO PREVIOUS KNOWLEDGE: Have students recall from Chapter 13 that Earth's mantle is partially molten. Some of this material has risen and cooled to form intrusive igneous rock structures.

OBJECTIVES AND SCIENCE WORDS: Have students review the objectives and science words to become familiar with this section.

15-4 Volcanic Features

New Science Words

batholiths
dike
sill
laccolith
volcanic neck
caldera

Objectives

- ▶ Give examples of intrusive igneous features and how they form.
- ▶ Explain how a volcanic neck and a caldera form.

Intrusive Features

We can observe volcanoes because they are examples of igneous activity on the surface of Earth. But there is far more igneous activity underground because most magma never reaches the surface to form volcanoes. As you learned in Chapter 4, magma that cools underground forms intrusive igneous rock. What forms do intrusive igneous rocks take on? You can look at some of these features in Figure 15-12.

1 The largest intrusive igneous rock bodies are **batholiths.** They can be many hundreds of kilometers wide and long and several kilometers thick. Batholiths form when huge bodies of magma cool underground and stop rising. Not all of them are hidden in Earth, though. Some batholiths have been exposed at Earth's surface by erosion. The

Figure 15-11. Most of the bare rock visible in Yosemite National Park is a batholith that was exposed by erosion.

OPTIONS

Meeting Different Ability Levels

For Section 15-4, use the following **Teacher Resource Masters** depending upon individual students' needs.

◆ **Study Guide Master** for all students.

● **Reinforcement Master** for students of average and above average ability levels.

▲ **Enrichment Master** for above average students.

Additional Teacher Resource Package masters are listed in the OPTIONS box throughout the section. The additional masters are appropriate for all students.

◆ STUDY GUIDE 65

NAME ________ DATE ________ CLASS ________

STUDY GUIDE — Chapter 15

Volcanic Features — Text Pages 404–406

In the blank at the left, write the letter of the term or phrase that correctly completes each statement.

a 1. Masses of magma that cool underground and form the largest igneous rock bodies are called _____.
a. batholiths b. laccoliths

b 2. Ship Rock in New Mexico is an example of a _____.
a. laccolith b. volcanic neck

a 3. Most igneous activity takes place _____.
a. underground b. above ground

b 4. Magma that squeezes into a horizontal crack and hardens forms a _____.
a. dike b. sill

b 5. When the top of a volcano collapses into the vent, a _____ is formed.
a. crater b. caldera

b 6. A dome of rock pushed up by a magma sill is a _____.
a. batholith b. laccolith

a 7. Volcanic features that can sometimes be seen above ground are _____.
a. volcanic necks and batholiths b. dikes and sills

a 8. Magma that squeezes into a vertical crack and hardens forms a _____.
a. dike b. sill

b 9. Crater Lake in Oregon is an example of a _____.
a. dike b. caldera

b 10. When erosion wears away the outside of a volcano, sometimes a solid magma core called a _____ is left exposed.
a. cinder cone b. volcanic neck

a 11. The granite domes in Yosemite National Park in California are part of a _____.
a. batholith b. sill

b 12. Volcanoes are examples of igneous activity _____.
a. underground b. above ground

b 13. Magma that cools underground forms _____ igneous rock.
a. extrusive b. intrusive

a 14. The difference between dikes and sills is the _____ of their formation.
a. direction b. size

65

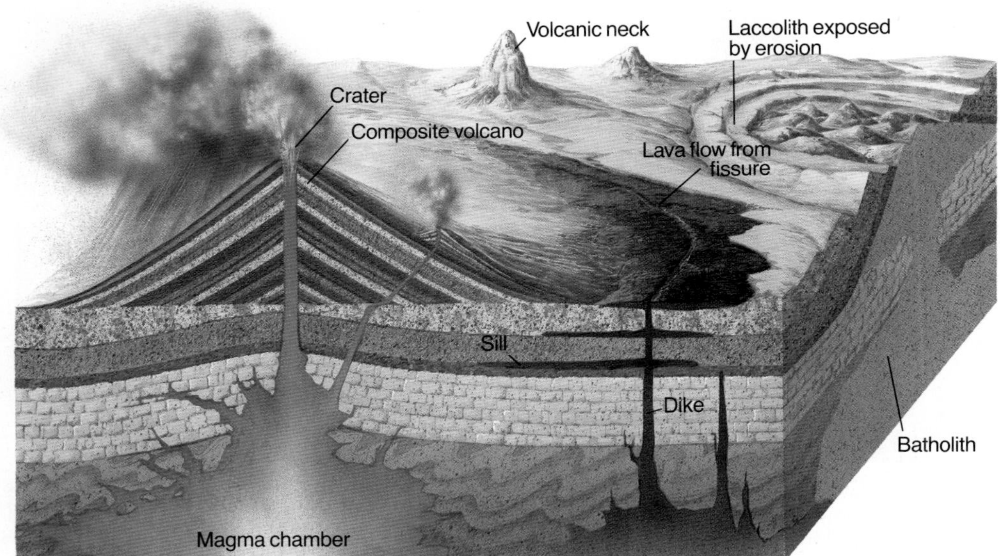

Figure 15-12. This diagram shows intrusive and other features associated with volcanic activity.

granite domes of Yosemite National Park, as seen in Figure 15-11, are exposed parts of a huge batholith that extends much of the length of California.

Magma sometimes squeezes into cracks in rock below the surface. This is like squeezing toothpaste into the spaces between your teeth. Magma that is squeezed into a vertical crack and hardens is called a **dike.** Magma that is squeezed into a horizontal crack and hardens is called a **sill.** You can remember the difference between a dike and a sill because a sill forms horizontally like a windowsill. Dikes and sills run from a few meters to hundreds of meters long. Some magma that forms a sill may continue to push the rock layers upward. This forms a dome of rock called a **laccolith.**

Other Features

When a volcano stops erupting, the magma hardens inside the vent. Erosion begins to wear away the volcano. The cone is much softer than the solid igneous rock in the vent. So, the cone erodes away first, leaving behind the solid igneous core as a **volcanic neck.** Ship Rock, New Mexico, is a volcanic neck. It is just one of many volcanic necks in the southwest United States.

2

MINI-Lab

What are some properties of volcanic materials?

If your teacher is able to provide you with some products of volcanic eruptions, take the time to observe their physical properties closely. Use a pin or dissecting probe to scratch away particles of volcanic rock. Rub these particles, volcanic ash, and beach sand from volcanic areas slowly between your fingers. Observe the volcanic material brightly illuminated under a microscope. Describe what you see and feel. What physical properties of these materials might be used to identify them as having a volcanic origin?

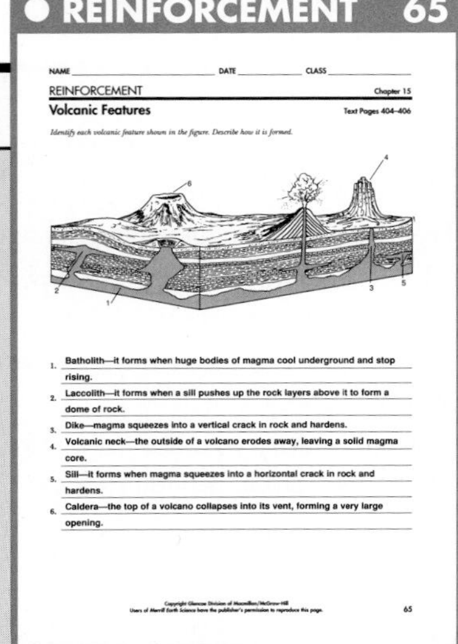

● REINFORCEMENT 65

NAME ______ DATE ______ CLASS ______

REINFORCEMENT — Chapter 15

Volcanic Features — Text Pages 404–406

Identify each volcanic feature shown in the figure. Describe how it is formed.

1. Batholith—it forms when huge bodies of magma cool underground and stop rising.
2. Laccolith—it forms when a sill pushes up the rock layers above it to form a dome of rock.
3. Dike—magma squeezes into a vertical crack in rock and hardens.
4. Volcanic neck—the outside of a volcano erodes away, leaving a solid magma core.
5. Sill—it forms when magma squeezes into a horizontal crack in rock and hardens.
6. Caldera—the top of a volcano collapses into its vent, forming a very large opening.

 65

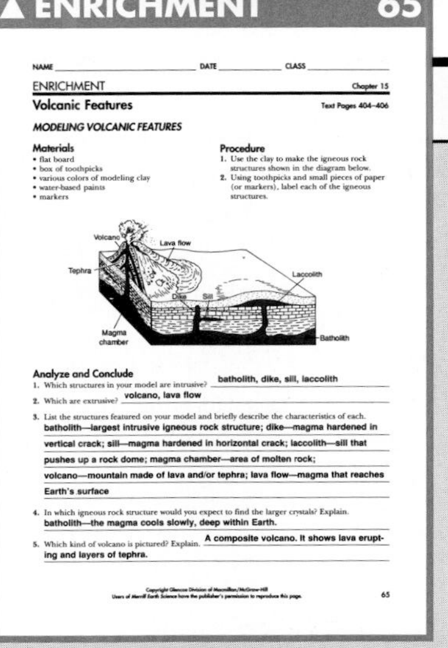

▲ ENRICHMENT 65

NAME ______ DATE ______ CLASS ______

ENRICHMENT — Chapter 15

Volcanic Features — Text Pages 404–406

MODELING VOLCANIC FEATURES

Materials
- flat board
- box of toothpicks
- various colors of modeling clay
- water-based paints
- markers

Procedure
1. Use the clay to make the igneous rock structures shown in the diagram below.
2. Using toothpicks and small pieces of paper (or markers), label each of the igneous structures.

Analyze and Conclude
1. Which structures in your model are intrusive? batholith, dike, sill, laccolith
2. Which are extrusive? volcano, lava flow
3. List the structures featured on your model and briefly describe the characteristics of each. batholith—largest intrusive igneous rock structure; dike—magma hardened in vertical crack; sill—magma hardened in horizontal crack; laccolith—sill that pushes up a rock dome; magma chamber—area of molten rock; volcano—mountain made of lava and/or tephra; lava flow—magma that reaches Earth's surface
4. In which igneous rock structure would you expect to find the larger crystals? Explain. batholith—the magma cools slowly, deep within Earth.
5. Which kind of volcano is pictured? Explain. A composite volcano. It shows lava erupting and layers of tephra.

 65

2 TEACH

Key Concepts are highlighted.

CONCEPT DEVELOPMENT

▶ Have students study Figure 15-12. Ask for volunteers to describe, in their own words, the shape and geometric relationships to the surrounding rocks of each of the intrusive igneous rock features.

MINI-Lab

Materials: volcanic material such as pumice, volcanic ash, scoria, obsidian, aa, pahoehoe, and/or volcanic beach sand; pin or dissecting probe; microscope

Teaching Tips

▶ **CAUTION:** *Volcanic material, especially volcanic ash, is extremely abrasive. Have students handle the materials with care. Students should wash their hands thoroughly after completing this activity.*

▶ Volcanic material is glassy. Volcanic ash appears sharp and jagged under magnification. Volcanic beach sand resembles tiny beads of glass under magnification.

▶ **Answers:** Volcanic products commonly exhibit many properties of glass, especially under magnification.

CROSS CURRICULUM

▶**History:** Have students report on the historical significance of each of the people carved on Mount Rushmore in the Black Hills of South Dakota.

PROGRAM RESOURCES

From the **Teacher Resource Package** use:

Activity Worksheets, page 5, Flex Your Brain.

Activity Worksheets, page 140, Mini-Lab: What are some properties of volcanic materials?

CHECK FOR UNDERSTANDING

Use the Mini Quiz to check for understanding.

MINI QUIZ

Use the Mini Quiz to check students' recall of chapter content.

1. **The largest intrusive igneous rock bodies are _____ .** *batholiths*
2. **Magma that squeezes into horizontal cracks forms a _____ .** *sill*
3. **A(n) _____ forms when the top of a volcano collapses.** *caldera*

RETEACH

Make and use flash cards of the intrusive rock features.

EXTENSION

For students who have mastered this section, use the **Reinforcement** and **Enrichment** masters.

3 CLOSE

▶ Ask questions 1-3 and the **Apply** Question in the Section Review.

Cooperative Learning: Have Paired Partners do the Skill Builder on this page.

SECTION REVIEW ANSWERS

1. A dike forms when magma cuts across preexisting rocks. A sill is parallel to existing rocks.

2. A caldera forms when the top of a volcano collapses into the magma chamber. A crater is the opening.

3. A volcanic neck forms as magma hardens in the vent of the volcano. As a volcano is eroded, the neck remains.

4. Apply: The features formed when magma cooled underground. Erosion later exposed the dome.

Skill Builder

All are intrusive igneous features. Dikes and sills are tabular. Laccoliths are domed. Dikes and sills are smaller than batholiths and laccoliths.

Figure 15-13. Crater Lake (right), formed when the top of the volcano collapsed, forming a caldera as shown in the sequence (left).

Sometimes after an eruption, the top of a volcano collapses down into the vent. This produces a very large
3 opening called a **caldera** (kal DARE uh). You studied the topography of a caldera in Chapter 8. Crater Lake in Oregon is a caldera that is now a lake.

Chapter 15 has shown one way that Earth's surface is continually built up and worn down. The surface is built up by volcanoes. Igneous rock is also formed when magma hardens below ground. Eventually, the processes of erosion wear down the rock, exposing batholiths and forming volcanic necks. Plate tectonics ensures that the processes that cause volcanoes will continue.

SECTION REVIEW

1. What is the difference between a dike and a sill?
2. What's the difference between a caldera and a crater?
3. What is a volcanic neck and how does it form?
4. **Apply:** Why are the dome features of Yosemite National Park actually intrusive volcanic features when they are exposed at the surface in the park?

☑ Comparing and Contrasting

Compare and contrast dikes, sills, batholiths, and laccoliths. If you need help, refer to Comparing and Contrasting in the **Skill Handbook** on page 683.

OPTIONS

ENRICHMENT

▶ Have students do research to find out when and how the Sierra Nevada batholith formed and what the estimated size of the complex is thought to be.

▶ Have students find out how the volcanic neck and related dikes at Ship Rock, New Mexico, formed.

PROGRAM RESOURCES

From the **Teacher Resource Package** use:

Transparency Masters, page 65-66, Volcanic Landforms.

Use **Color Transparency** number 33, Volcanic Landforms.

Use **Laboratory Manual** page 125, Effect of Magma on Surrounding Rock.

CHAPTER

REVIEW

SUMMARY

15-1: Volcanoes and Plate Tectonics

1. Volcanoes can be dangerous to people, causing deaths and destroying property.
2. Rocks in the mantle melt to form magma, which rises and eventually reaches Earth's surface. When the magma flows through vents, it becomes lava and forms volcanoes.
3. Volcanoes along rift zones form when magma from the rift flows to the seafloor. The lava builds up from the seafloor to form a volcanic island. Volcanoes over hot spots form when the rising magma breaks through the crust and forms a mountain. Volcanoes also form when an ocean plate is subducted under a continental plate. Here, the ocean plate melts to form volcanic mountains.

15-2: Science and Society: Geothermal Energy from Volcanoes

1. Geothermal energy can reduce the dependence on oil and thus reduce air pollution and the risk of oil spills. Developing geothermal energy in Hawaii would destroy some of the rain forests. Also, drilling might release harmful gases into the air.
2. You may think geothermal energy should be developed on Hawaii, or you may think it would be too environmentally harmful.

15-3: Eruptions and Forms of Volcanoes

1. Basaltic lavas, because they are thin and flow easily, produce quiet eruptions. Silica-rich lavas are thick and stiff, and thus produce very violent eruptions. Water vapor in magma adds to its explosiveness.
2. Shield volcanoes are mountains made of basaltic lava and have gently sloping sides. Cinder cones are steep-sided and are made of tephra. Composite volcanoes, made of silica-rich basalt and tephra, are steep-sided mountains.

15-4: Volcanic Features

1. Batholiths, dikes, sills, and laccoliths form when magma solidifies underground.
2. A caldera forms when the top of a volcano collapses, forming a very large depression.

KEY SCIENCE WORDS

a. **batholiths**
b. **caldera**
c. **cinder cone**
d. **composite volcano**
e. **crater**
f. **dike**
g. **geothermal energy**
h. **hot spots**
i. **laccolith**
j. **Pacific Ring of Fire**
k. **shield volcano**
l. **sill**
m. **tephra**
n. **vent**
o. **volcanic neck**
p. **volcano**

UNDERSTANDING VOCABULARY

Match each phrase with the correct term from the list of Key Science Words.

1. mountain made of lava and/or volcanic ash
2. large depression formed by the collapse of a volcano
3. solid magma core of a volcano
4. volcano with gently sloping sides
5. ash and cinders thrown from a volcano
6. steep-sided volcano of lava and tephra
7. the largest igneous intrusion
8. an opening through which lava flows
9. a horizontal igneous intrusion
10. energy that comes from magma

OPTIONS

ASSESSMENT

To assess student understanding of material in this chapter, use the resources listed.

COOPERATIVE LEARNING

Consider using cooperative learning in the THINK AND WRITE CRITICALLY, APPLY, and MORE SKILL BUILDERS sections of the Chapter Review.

PROGRAM RESOURCES

From the **Teacher Resource Package** use:
Chapter Review, pages 33-34.
Chapter and Unit Tests, pages 97-102, Chapter Test.

CHAPTER

REVIEW

SUMMARY

Have students read the summary statements to review the major concepts of the chapter.

UNDERSTANDING VOCABULARY

1. p
2. b
3. o
4. k
5. m
6. d
7. a
8. n
9. l
10. g

CHAPTER

REVIEW

CHECKING CONCEPTS

1. d
2. b
3. a
4. d
5. c
6. a
7. b
8. b
9. d
10. d

UNDERSTANDING CONCEPTS

11. lava
12. vents
13. dormant
14. hot spot
15. Geothermal energy

THINK AND WRITE CRITICALLY

16. Volcanoes differ in size and shape mainly due to the composition of the lava that forms them. Volcanoes also differ depending upon where they form.

17. Lava flowing from rifts cools instantly when it comes in contact with seawater. The basaltic lava builds up to form shield volcanoes. Volcanoes that form along subduction zones are composite volcanoes made of layers of silica-rich lava and tephra.

18. Both form when magma reaches Earth's surface. Basaltic lava is very fluid. Granitic lava, on the other hand, is very thick and stiff.

19. Answers will vary slightly. A typical response might be: Lava flows onto Earth's surface through the vent of a volcano. The opening at the top of a volcano's vent is the crater. If a crater is very large, it is a caldera.

20. Geothermal energy is energy derived from hot areas deep within Earth. The heat produced can convert water to steam, which can be used to generate electricity.

CHAPTER

REVIEW

CHECKING CONCEPTS

Choose the word or phrase that completes the sentence.

1. Volcanoes form near _______.
- **a.** diverging plates
- **b.** hot spots
- **c.** converging plates
- **d.** all of these

2. Hawaii is made of volcanoes due to _______.
- **a.** diverging plates
- **b.** a hot spot
- **c.** converging plates
- **d.** all of these

3. Lavas ______ produce violent volcanic eruptions.
- **a.** rich in silica
- **b.** that are fluid
- **c.** made of basalt
- **d.** none of these

4. Magma rich in silica produces ______ eruptions.
- **a.** flowing
- **b.** caldera
- **c.** quiet
- **d.** explosive

5. A _______ is made of tephra.
- **a.** shield volcano
- **b.** caldera
- **c.** cinder cone
- **d.** composite volcano

6. Kilauea is a _______.
- **a.** shield volcano
- **b.** composite volcano
- **c.** cinder cone
- **d.** rift zone

7. Magma that squeezes into a vertical crack then hardens is a _______.
- **a.** sill
- **b.** dike
- **c.** volcanic neck
- **d.** batholith

8. A _______ is a dome-shaped igneous intrusion body.
- **a.** dike
- **b.** laccolith
- **c.** sill
- **d.** none of these

9. Geothermal energy comes from _______.
- **a.** fossil fuels
- **b.** electricity
- **c.** the sun
- **d.** magma

10. Using geothermal energy in Hawaii might _______.
- **a.** release volcanic gases
- **b.** replace fossil fuels
- **c.** harm forests
- **d.** all of these

UNDERSTANDING CONCEPTS

Complete each sentence.

11. Magma that reaches Earth's surface is called _______.

12. Openings in Earth's crust through which lava flows to form volcanoes are _______.

13. A volcano that is not currently active is _______.

14. If a volcano doesn't form at a plate boundary, it forms over a(n) _______.

15. _______ could be used in Hawaii to convert water into steam, which would be used to generate electricity.

THINK AND WRITE CRITICALLY

16. Why do volcanoes differ in shape?

17. Contrast volcanoes that form along rift zones with those that form along subduction zones.

18. Compare and contrast basaltic lava with granitic lava.

19. Explain how these terms are related: vent, caldera, and crater.

20. What is geothermal energy?

APPLY

21. Explain how glaciers and volcanoes can exist on Iceland.
22. What kind of eruption is produced when basaltic lava flows from a volcano? Explain.
23. How are volcanoes related to earthquakes?
24. A mountain called Misti is a volcano in Peru. Peru is on the western border of South America. How might this volcano have formed?
25. In addition to Iceland and Hawaii, where else on Earth do you think could people use geothermal energy?

MORE SKILL BUILDERS

If you need help, refer to the Skill Handbook.

1. **Concept Mapping:** Make a network tree concept map that compares quiet eruptions to explosive eruptions. Use the following words and phrases: *type of eruption, high silica, quiet, flows easily, granitic, explosive, non-flowing, cinder cone, Parícutin, Hawaii, shield, low silica, basaltic.*

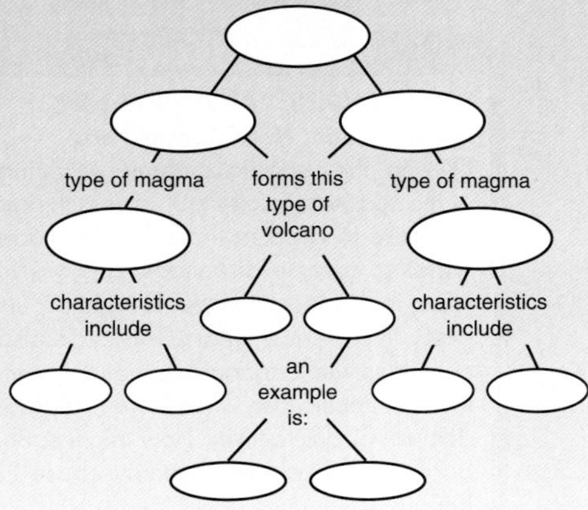

2. **Observing and Inferring:** A volcano violently erupted in Indonesia in 1883. What can you infer about the magma's composition? If people saw the eruption, what were they able to observe about the flow of the lava?
3. **Comparing and Contrasting:** Compare and contrast batholiths and laccoliths.
4. **Classifying:** Mount Fuji is a volcano in Japan. Its steep sides are made of layers of silica-rich lava and ash. Classify Mount Fuji.
5. **Measuring in SI:** The base of the volcano Mauna Loa is about 5000 meters below sea level. The total height of the volcano is 9560 m. What percentage of the volcano is above sea level? Below sea level?

PROJECTS

1. Use reference books to prepare a short report explaining the relationship between plate tectonics and volcanoes. Make a simple map of the world that shows plate boundaries and the locations of major volcanoes.
2. Find out how the eruption of Mount Saint Helens affected plants and animals in the area. Find photos that show what the area looked like shortly after the eruption and what it looks like now. How long did it take the area to "recover" from the eruption?

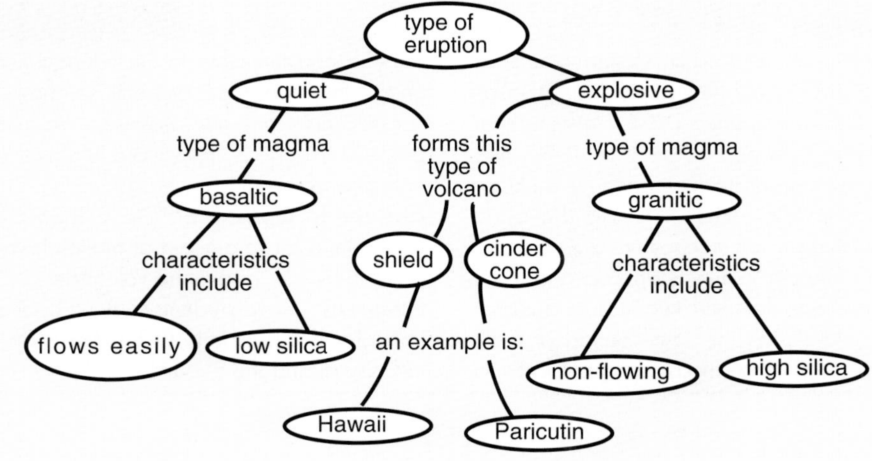

APPLY

21. Students should recall from Chapter 6 that glaciers form at high elevations and high latitudes. Iceland is at a relatively high latitude. The Mid-Atlantic Ridge, on the other hand, is a plate tectonic feature on the ocean bottom. Because glaciers and volcanoes are caused by different processes, there is no reason why they can't coexist.

22. Basaltic lava, unlike silica-rich lava, is very fluid. Because it flows easily, relatively mild eruptions are produced by basaltic-lava volcanoes.

23. Volcanoes along rifts zones and subduction zones form when Earth's plates either move apart or collide. The enormous forces produced by plate movements can produce earthquakes.

24. Students should be able to infer that the volcano, like those in the Cascades, formed as the result of subduction. Displaying a map of North and South America might be helpful in answering this question. Referring students to a map of plate boundaries would also be useful.

25. Areas with volcanic activity such as Italy, Mexico, New Zealand, and Japan, to name a few, are able to make use of geothermal energy.

MORE SKILL BUILDERS

1. Concept Mapping:
Possible solution: See below left.

2. Observing and Inferring: The eruption was violent, thus the amounts of silica and water vapor were high. Such lava is stiff and thick, and if people did observe the flow, they would have seen it flow slowly.

3. Comparing and Contrasting: Both are intrusive igneous rock structures that form when magma cools deep within Earth. Batholiths are much larger, though, than laccoliths. Laccoliths are domed.

4. Classifying: Mount Fuji is a composite volcano.

5. Measuring in SI: Of the total height, 4560 m is above sea level. Thus, about 48% is above sea level and 52% is below sea level.

UNIT 5
GLOBAL CONNECTIONS

Objective

In this unit ending feature, the unit topic is extended into other disciplines. Students will see how the plate tectonic model has led to a better understanding of phenomena observed in many disciplines.

Motivate

Cooperative Learning: Assign one Connection to each group of students. Using the Expert Teams strategy, have each group research to find out more about the geographic location of the Connection—its climate, culture, and ecological issues.

Wrap-Up

Ask students to form a hypothesis about how plate tectonics has affected the fauna of Australia.

PHYSICS

Background: Earthquake vibrations usually weaken as they spread away from the epicenter. At first, scientists thought the soft natural sediments and landfill materials underlying many damaged structures had amplified the seismic waves. However, they noticed that seismic stations located on hard rock also shook harder than normal for a magnitude 7.1 quake.

Discussion: Discuss that reflection plays a role in many phenomena. Reflection of sound waves is used by oceanographers to produce contour maps of the surface of the ocean floor. Reflection of seismic waves is used by geologists to determine the structure of Earth's interior. Discuss how the reflection of seismic waves during the San Francisco earthquake appears to have increased the shock waves.

Answer to Question: Reflection of seismic waves is used by geologists to determine the structure of Earth's interior.

Extension: Have students draw Earth's interior showing the Moho discontinuity and how seismic waves might reflect from it.

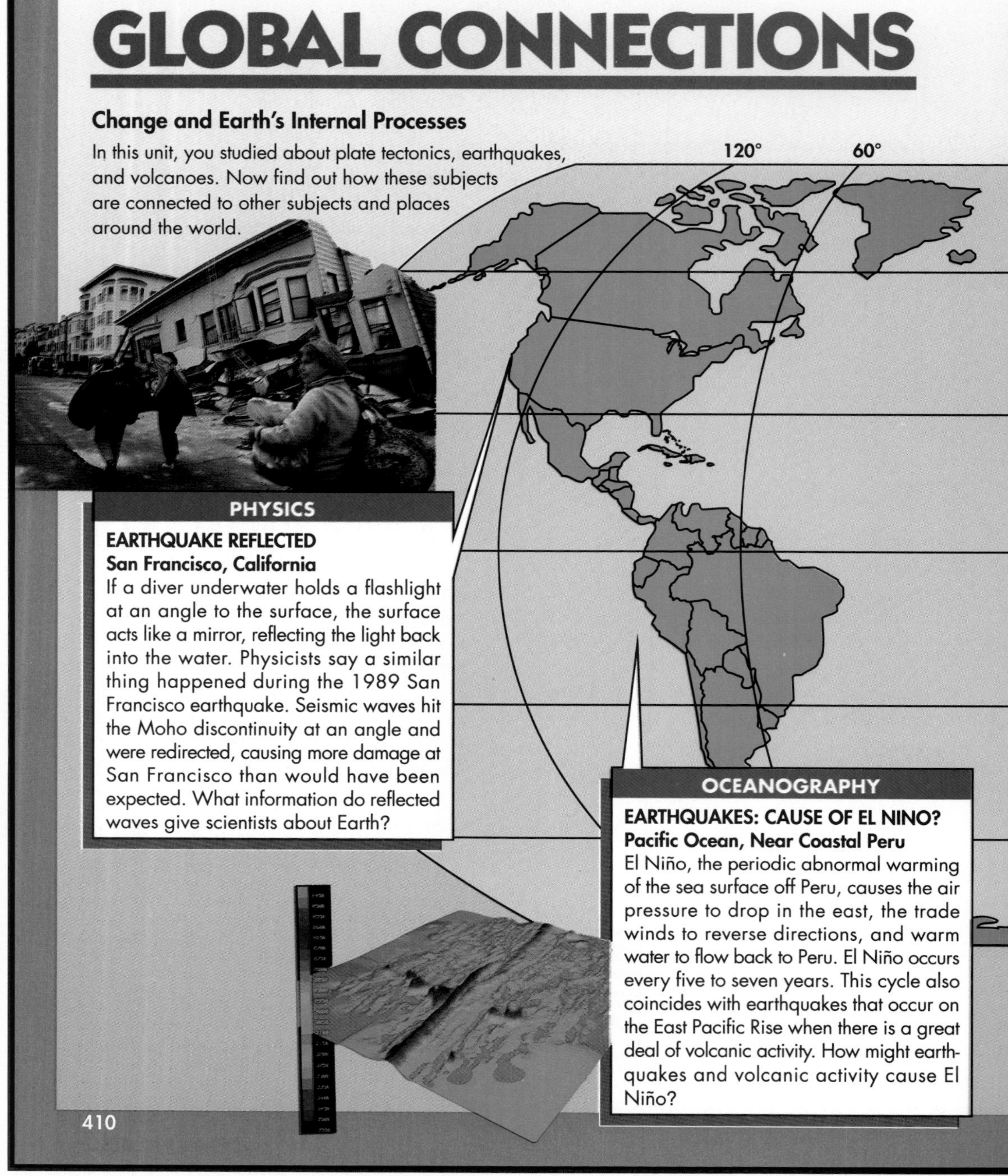

UNIT 5
GLOBAL CONNECTIONS
Change and Earth's Internal Processes
In this unit, you studied about plate tectonics, earthquakes, and volcanoes. Now find out how these subjects are connected to other subjects and places around the world.
120°
60°
PHYSICS
EARTHQUAKE REFLECTED
San Francisco, California
If a diver underwater holds a flashlight at an angle to the surface, the surface acts like a mirror, reflecting the light back into the water. Physicists say a similar thing happened during the 1989 San Francisco earthquake. Seismic waves hit the Moho discontinuity at an angle and were redirected, causing more damage at San Francisco than would have been expected. What information do reflected waves give scientists about Earth?
OCEANOGRAPHY
EARTHQUAKES: CAUSE OF EL NINO?
Pacific Ocean, Near Coastal Peru
El Niño, the periodic abnormal warming of the sea surface off Peru, causes the air pressure to drop in the east, the trade winds to reverse directions, and warm water to flow back to Peru. El Niño occurs every five to seven years. This cycle also coincides with earthquakes that occur on the East Pacific Rise when there is a great deal of volcanic activity. How might earthquakes and volcanic activity cause El Niño?
410

OCEANOGRAPHY

Background: Daniel Walker, a seismologist at the University of Hawaii, has studied earthquakes at the East Pacific Rise since 1964. He found that every El Niño between 1964 and 1987 has been accompanied or just preceded by a cluster of intensive earthquakes. He says the odds against this being a coincidence are 300 to 1.

Discussion: Discuss Walker's approach in forming his hypothesis. He had two sets of data for the same area during the same period of time. One set consisted of the measurements related to El Niño and the other to the earthquakes occurring in the area. Have students see how Walker came to his conclusion. Ask what he must do to prove his theory. (Gather more information about both phenomena.)

Answer to Question: The volcanic activity pours out a large amount of molten lava, which heats the water above the volcanoes.

Extension: Have students write a brief description of what happens to the Peruvian fishing industry during the El Niño.

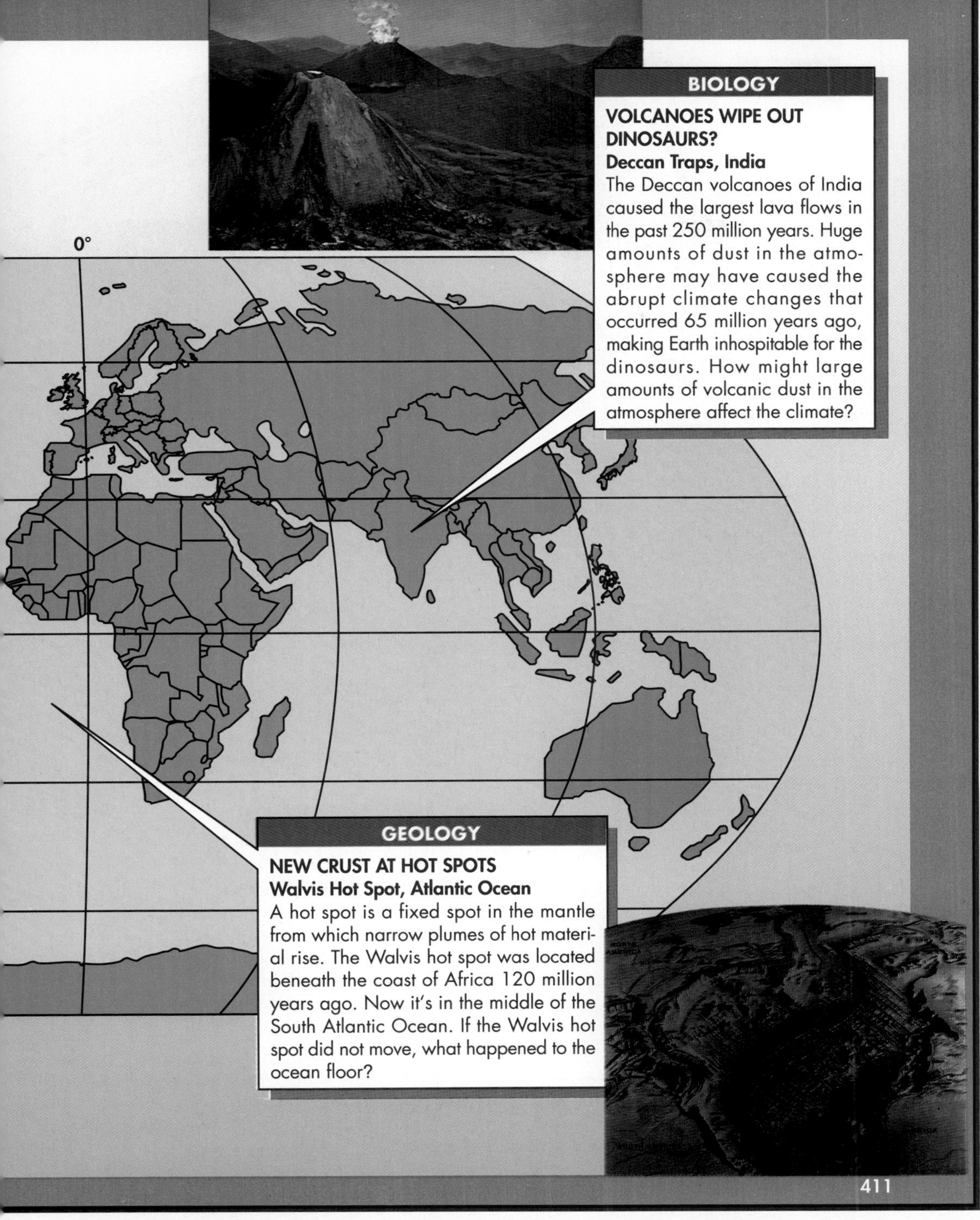

BIOLOGY
VOLCANOES WIPE OUT DINOSAURS?
Deccan Traps, India
The Deccan volcanoes of India caused the largest lava flows in the past 250 million years. Huge amounts of dust in the atmosphere may have caused the abrupt climate changes that occurred 65 million years ago, making Earth inhospitable for the dinosaurs. How might large amounts of volcanic dust in the atmosphere affect the climate?
0°
GEOLOGY
NEW CRUST AT HOT SPOTS
Walvis Hot Spot, Atlantic Ocean
A hot spot is a fixed spot in the mantle from which narrow plumes of hot material rise. The Walvis hot spot was located beneath the coast of Africa 120 million years ago. Now it's in the middle of the South Atlantic Ocean. If the Walvis hot spot did not move, what happened to the ocean floor?
411

GEOLOGY

Background: The South Atlantic began to open between South America and Africa about 125 million years ago. It seemed that a zipper holding the two continents together opened up over a period of 5 million years. Actually, it was caused by decompression over the Walvis hot spot, which released massive amounts of lava onto Africa and South America. As this lava added to Earth's crust, Africa and South America drifted farther apart.

Discussion: Discuss the fact that geologists can trace the growth of Earth's crust by locating the igneous layer which is typical of a volcanic margin that lies between the African and South American coast. Discuss that locating the hot spot is done by measuring the amount of melt and the mantle temperature.

Answer to Question: As Earth's crust grew from the lava flowing from volcanoes above the hot spot, Africa and South America moved farther apart.

Extension: Have students trace South America and Africa on paper, cut them out, and bring them together like pieces of a puzzle.

BIOLOGY

Background: Two theories compete to explain the catastrophic climate change that occurred 65 million years ago and culminated in the extinction of the dinosaurs and many other organisms. One theory states that an asteroid impact was the cause, and proponents of the theory point to a layer of iridium that appears in Earth's crust dating to this time. Iridium is rare in Earth's crust but is relatively abundant in other parts of the solar system. Those who argue for a volcanic cause claim that iridium is also emitted from volcanoes, such as the Kilauea volcano in Hawaii. Secondly, they present evidence that the extinction of the dinosaurs occurred over a period of hundreds of thousands of years. This period is comparable to the duration of Deccan volcanism. Likewise, the iridium layer seems to have been laid down over a similar period of years.

Discussion: This is an excellent opportunity to introduce students to a conflict that has produced excellent research among scientists. Discuss the merits of both theories. Ask students to discuss which theory they think has more merit.

Answer to Question: Huge amounts of volcanic dust circling Earth would cut down on the sunlight and reduce the amount of photosynthesis.

Extension: Have students make a pie graph of gases emitted by volcanoes. Gases are composed of 70% H_2O, 15% CO_2, 5% each of nitrogen and sulfur compounds, and 5% other gases.

SEISMOLOGIST

Background: Seismologists provide information about what is happening at the major faults. This information helps people and local governments prepare for emergencies. Information about earthquakes is also useful in establishing building codes.

Related Career	Education
Fire Fighter	high school
Emergency Worker	high school
Building Inspector	college

Career Issue: Some people feel that seismologists should not try to predict when an earthquake will happen, because up until now they have had little success in pinpointing the exact time of earthquakes. Others feel that people who live in earthquake-prone areas should always be prepared for the possibility of an earthquake and that periodic predictions keep them alert.

What do you think? Have students try to draw a straight line while a classmate gently bumps them. Relate this to seismograms.

GEOPHYSICAL TECHNICIAN

Background: Oil companies, weather bureaus, harbor information bureaus, earthquake watch centers, oceanographic institutes, and volcano watch centers all have need of geophysical technicians to read instruments and collect data.

Related Career	Education
geophysicist	college
oil geophysicist	college
volcanologist	college

Career Issue: Some parts of the country have all sorts of instruments in place to study the slightest movement of Earth's crust. Other parts of the country that may also be prone to earthquakes have no such elaborate array of instruments.

What do you think? Have students discuss whether expensive seismic instruments should be located in all areas of the country.

CAREERS

SEISMOLOGIST

A *seismologist* studies the seismic waves produced by earthquakes. To record seismic waves, they use an instrument called a seismograph. Seismologists also try to predict when an earthquake will occur. To do this, they may study radon measurements in certain wells, which change at the time of an earthquake.

Seismologists require a college degree in geology, with an emphasis on seismology. Many seismologists have an advanced degree.

For Additional Information

Contact the American Geological Institute, 4220 King Street, Alexandria, VA 22302.

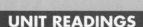

GEOPHYSICAL TECHNICIAN

A *geophysical technician* assists a geophysicist by collecting data from seismic waves. The data may be used to locate oil and natural gas. Geophysical technicians may also collect meteorological data or oceanographic data. They may be involved in any field related to the study of Earth or other planets.

Geophysical technicians require an associate degree in geophysics or a related field.

For Additional Information

Contact the Society of Exploration Geophysicists, P.O. Box 70240, Tulsa, OK 74170.

UNIT READINGS

▶Erickson, Jon. *Volcanoes and Earthquakes*. Blue Ridge Summit, Pennsylvania: Tab Books, Inc., 1988.

▶Weiner, Jonathan. *Planet Earth*. New York: Bantam Books, Inc., 1986, pp. 5-49.

▶White, Robert S. and Dan P. McKenzie. "Volcanism at Rifts." *Scientific American*, July 1989, pp. 62-71.

412

UNIT READINGS

Background

▶ *Volcanoes and Earthquakes* is a well-illustrated book that contains an excellent coverage of both topics in its title.

▶ *Planet Earth* contains extensive background on the theories of continental drift and sea-floor spreading.

▶ "Volcanism at Rifts" provides a clear explanation of the effect of volcanoes on sea-floor spreading

More Readings

1. Ritchie, David. *Superquake*. New York: Crown Publishers, Inc., 1988. This book discusses why earthquakes occur and why the West Coast is ripe for disaster.
2. Stein, Ross S. and Robert S. Yeats. "Hidden Earthquakes." *Scientific American*, June, 1989, pp. 48-57. This article shows that earthquakes can take place not only at faults that cut Earth's surface, but also on hidden faults under folds in the terrain.

SCIENCE & ART

Mount Fuji: Woodcuts by Hokusai

Mount Fuji is the highest mountain in Japan, located on the island of Honshu about 97 kilometers west of Tokyo. An inactive volcano crater is located at its summit.

Because Mount Fuji is a sacred mountain to many, thousands of Japanese pilgrims climb it every year. It is no wonder that artists have featured the mountain in many works of art. The great artist Katsushika Hokusai made woodcuts showing thirty-six different views of Mount Fuji. Beautiful ink prints were made using the woodcuts.

The prints were made from one block of wood. The artist drew a design on paper in ink, which was then glued onto a block of hardwood. Then, a carver cut away the wood between the lines of the drawing. The design itself was left on the block. A printer then applied a water-based ink to the block, which was then transferred to absorbent paper. The block could be used to make many prints.

Hokusai critiqued his own work in the following translation by Richard Lane, which shows the artist's humility and sense of humor.

"From the age of fifty I produced a number of designs, yet of all I drew prior to the age of seventy there is truly nothing of any great note. At the age of seventy-three, I finally came to understand somewhat the nature of birds, animals, insects, fishes—the vital nature of grasses and trees. Therefore, at eighty I shall have made great progress, at ninety I shall have penetrated even further the deeper meaning of things, and at one hundred I shall have become truly marvelous, and at one hundred and ten, each dot, each line shall surely possess a life of its own." (Unfortunately, Hokusai lived to be only eighty-nine!)

After Hokusai's death in 1849, some of his prints were shown in other parts of the world. Artists outside of Japan, including James A. M. Whistler of the United States, Edgar Degas, Paul Gauguin, and Henri de Toulouse-Lautrec of France, and Vincent van Gogh of the Netherlands were all influenced by the work of Hokusai.

Write

▶ Look up information about the artists that were influenced by Hokusai. What characteristics of Hokusai do you think most influenced artists of the West? Write an essay supporting your view.

Source: *Masterpieces of Fifty Centuries: The Metropolitan Museum of Art.* p. 302.

Biography: Katushika Hokusai (1760-1849) was born in what is now Tokyo. He is famous for his woodcuts of Japanese landscapes. Most of his work was produced after the age of 60. Although his woodcuts were popular worldwide, Hokusai spent most of his life in poverty.

TEACHING STRATEGY

▶ Ask students what they like best about the woodcut by Hokusai.

Cooperative Learning: Using the Paired Partner strategy, have groups of students discuss the advantage of a woodcut print over a painting. Students will no doubt see that many prints can be made from the original without having to repaint the picture. More people worldwide can see the work of the artist from the prints.

▶ Ask students why they think Mount Fuji was chosen by Hokusai as the subject of thirty-six woodcuts.

▶ Have students write an essay or a poem describing the beauty of Mount Fuji.

Other Works

▶ Other Japanese woodcuts include: Hokusai, Katushika. "Ono Waterfall." British Museum, London. Hiroshige, Ando. "Night Rain at Karasaki." Metropolitan Museum of Art. Kuniyoshi, Utagawa. "Tsunami." Victoria and Albert Museum, London.

Classics

▶ Wegener, Alfred. *The Origin of the Continents and the Oceans.* 1915. Translated by John Biram 1929. Reprint New York: Dover Publications, 1966. The book tells how the idea of continental drift first occurred to Wegener.

▶ Wilson, J. Tuzo. "Evidence from Islands on the Spreading of Ocean Floors." *Nature,* February 9, 1963, pp. 536-538. Wilson built upon Harry Hess's ideas on sea-floor spreading by providing evidence to substantiate the theory.

UNIT

CHANGE AND EARTH'S HISTORY

In Unit 6, students are introduced to the record of Earth's past. The unit is organized by evolutionary changes in Earth's life and geologic structures, with chapters on clues to Earth's past and the geologic time scale.

CONTENTS

ADVANCE PREPARATION

Activities

▶ **Activity 16-2, page 440,** requires shoe boxes with lids. Have your students bring them from home.

▶ **Activity 17-1, page 456,** requires a deck of playing cards.

▶ **Activity 17-2, page 468,** requires adding machine tape.

Audiovisuals

▶ **Section 16-1, page 418:** Arrange to show the filmstrip/cassette program "Fossils: Evidence of Life," Educational Dimensions.

▶ Other videos available on this subject include, "The Hunt for China's Dinosaurs," "The Case of the Flying Dinosaur," and "T. rex Exposed," NOVA (WGBH Educational Foundation).

Field Trips and Speakers

▶ Arrange for a fossil collector to visit your class.

▶ Arrange to take your class to a local museum or rock exposure that contains fossils.

UNIT

6 CHANGE AND EARTH'S HISTORY

414

OPTIONS

Cross Curriculum

▶ Ask students to list the titles of any stories they have read about dinosaurs.

▶ Have students research works of art that have been made from the ivory of protected or endangered species.

▶ Have students compare and contrast animals that lived during the most recent ice age with present-day animals.

▶ Have students write papers on whether they think humans should work to save endangered organisms from extinction.

Science at Home

▶ Have students study rock exposures near their homes for evidence of fossils in the rocks. Students may also bring in fossils they have collected, or others have collected for them, from other locations. Have students share their fossils with the class.

Cooperative Learning: Have groups of three students form Science Investigation teams to speculate on what might have caused the extinction of the dinosaurs, the woolly mammoth, or other organisms students may have read about.

What's Happening Here?

When people think of extinctions, they often think of life-forms that lived long ago. Humans, however, are causing the extinction of many present-day life-forms. Although hunting elephants for their ivory tusks is illegal in many African countries, poachers continue to kill the large animals. Elephants are becoming an endangered species because their ivory is valued for carvings and jewelry. In Unit 6, you'll learn more about extinctions and how the fossil record indicates when extinctions occurred throughout Earth's past. You will also learn more about how people may affect the rate of extinctions.

UNIT CONTENTS

INTRODUCING THE UNIT

What's Happening Here?

▶ Have students look at the photos and read the text. Ask them to tell you what's happening here. Point out to students that in this unit they will be studying how geologists have been able to date Earth's rocks by studying the fossils left by ancient life. They will also learn of other ways in which Earth's age has been determined. The evolution of life from early forms to more complex forms will also be presented.

▶ **Background:** The total population of African elephants numbers around 650 000. At the present rate at which they are killed for their tusks, about 90 000 per year, African elephants could become extinct in just a few years.

Previewing the Chapters

Cooperative Learning: Using the Paired Partners strategy, have students study the figures in Section 16-1 for examples of how fossils form. Have partners devise a simple demonstration that shows one of these processes. Encourage each team to share their idea with other partner teams.

▶ Direct students to Figure 17-4 on page 450. Ask students to explain why one moth has a survival advantage over the other moth in the photo on the left in Figure 17-4. Is the same moth at an advantage or disadvantage in the photo on the right?

Tying to Previous Knowledge

▶ Lead students in a discussion of recent visits to the zoo where they might have observed animals that are listed as endangered species.

▶ Ask students if they have ever dug a hole in their yard and found leaves, bones, or other items buried in the soil. Have students compare this to processes that cause fossils to form.

▶ Ask students to speculate on what type of trace fossils (evidence of animal activity) humans of the future may find in rocks that are being formed at this time.

▶ Use the **Inquiry Questions** in the OPTIONS box below to investigate with students conditions that might cause entire species to become extinct.

Multicultural Awareness

Have students research why the buffalo almost became extinct when the western region of the United States was settled by pioneers. Native Americans had co-existed with the buffalo for centuries. They killed buffalo to use their meat, bones, hide, and other body parts. However, they did so at a rate that allowed the buffalo to reproduce and replenish their numbers. How did the culture of the pioneers differ from the culture of the Native Americans? How might that have led to the near extinction?

Inquiry Questions

Use the following questions to focus a discussion on what conditions might cause entire species to become extinct.

1. Why did the horse evolve from a small animal that grazed on shrubs, to a larger, animal that grazed on grasslands?
2. If a species does not adapt to a changing environment, what might happen to it?
3. If the seas become warmer, and one type of organism dies off because of the change in temperature, what will happen to organisms that relied on the first type for food?

CHAPTER

16 Clues to Earth's Past

CHAPTER SECTION	OBJECTIVES	ACTIVITIES
16-1 Fossils (1 day)	1. **List** the conditions necessary for fossils to form. 2. **Describe** processes of fossil formation. 3. **Explain** how fossil correlation is used to determine rock ages.	**MINI-Lab:** *What type of fossils might we leave for future generations?* p. 419
16-2 Extinction of Dinosaurs Science & Society (2 days)	1. **Discuss** the meteorite-impact theory of dinosaur extinction. 2. **Describe** several theories on why dinosaurs became extinct.	**Activity 16-1:** *Determining Relative Ages,* p. 429
16-3 Relative Ages of Rocks (2 days)	1. **Describe** several methods used to date rock layers relative to other rock layers. 2. **Interpret** gaps in the rock record. 3. **Give** an example of how rock layers may be correlated with other rock layers.	
16-4 Absolute Ages of Rocks (2 days)	1. **Identify** how absolute dating differs from relative dating. 2. **Describe** how the half-lives of isotopes are used to determine a rock's age.	**MINI-Lab:** *What are some of the relative and absolute dates of events in Earth's history?* p. 437 **Activity 16-2:** *Radioactive Decay,* p. 440
Chapter Review		

ACTIVITY MATERIALS

FIND OUT	ACTIVITIES		MINI-LABS	
Page 417 milk carton plaster of paris leaf, shell, or bone petroleum jelly	**16-1 Determining Relative Ages, p. 429** none	**16-2 Radioactive Decay, p. 440** shoe box w/lid paper clips pennies (100) brass fasteners (100) graph paper colored pencils (2)	**What type of fossils might we leave for future generations? p. 419** paper pencil	**What are some of the relative and absolute dates of events in Earth's history? p. 437** adding machine tape meterstick pencil

CHAPTER FEATURES	TEACHER RESOURCE PACKAGE	OTHER RESOURCES
Technology: *Recovering Fossils,* p. 424 **Skill Builder:** *Concept Mapping,* p. 425	**Ability Level Worksheets** ♦ ***Study Guide,*** p. 66 ● ***Reinforcement,*** p. 66 ▲ ***Enrichment,*** p. 66 **MINI-Lab Worksheet,** p. 148 **Critical Thinking/Problem Solving,** p. 22 **Concept Mapping,** pp. 37-38 **Technology,** pp. 15-16	**Lab Manual:** *Carbon Impressions,* pp. 133-134
You Decide! p. 428	**Ability Level Worksheets** ♦ ***Study Guide,*** p. 67 ● ***Reinforcement,*** p. 67 ▲ ***Enrichment,*** p. 67 **Activity Worksheet,** pp. 142-143 **Cross-Curricular Connections,** p. 20 **Science and Society,** p. 20	
Problem Solving: *Closing the Gap,* p. 434 **Skill Builder:** *Interpreting Data,* p. 435	**Ability Level Worksheets** ♦ ***Study Guide,*** p. 68 ● ***Reinforcement,*** p. 68 ▲ ***Enrichment,*** p. 68 **Transparency Masters,** pp. 69-72	**Lab Manual:** *Law of Superposition,* pp. 129-132 **Color Transparency 35,** Rock Relationships **Color Transparency 36,** Dating Rock Layers with Fossils
Skill Builder: *Making and Using Tables,* p. 439	**Ability Level Worksheets** ♦ ***Study Guide,*** p. 69 ● ***Reinforcement,*** p. 69 ▲ ***Enrichment,*** p. 69 **MINI-Lab Worksheet,** p. 149 **Activity Worksheet,** pp. 144-145	
Summary Key Science Words Understanding Vocabulary Checking Concepts Understanding Concepts Think & Write Critically Apply More Skill Builders Projects	**Chapter Review,** pp. 35-36 **Chapter Test,** pp. 110-113	**Chapter Review Software** **Test Bank**

♦ **Basic** ● **Average** ▲ **Advanced**

ADDITIONAL MATERIALS

SOFTWARE	AUDIOVISUAL	BOOKS/MAGAZINES
Stratigraphy, Aquarius, Inc. *Dating and Geologic Time,* D.C. Heath.	*Fossils: Clues from Prehistoric Times,* film, Coronet/MTI. *History: Layer on Layer,* film, CRM Films. *Reflections on Time,* film, EBEC. *How Fossils are Formed,* filmstrip, Time-Life. *Fossils and the Relative Ages of Rocks,* filmstrip, Time-Life. *Succession on Lava,* film, EBEC. *Fossils: Evidence of Life,* video, Focus.	Fenton, Carroll L. and Mildred A. Fenton. *Fossil Book: A Record of Prehistoric Life.* rev. ed. NY: Doubleday, 1989. Lane, Gary N. *Life of the Past.* Westerville, OH: Merrill Publishing Co., 1986. Windley, Brian F. *The Early History of the Earth: Based on the Proceeding of NATO Advanced Study Institute Held at the University of Leicester, April 5-11, 1975.* Ann Arbor, MI: Books on Demand, 1975.

CHAPTER 16

CLUES TO EARTH'S PAST

THEME DEVELOPMENT: The evolution of life-forms throughout geologic time as shown by the fossil record should be a major focus of your teaching the chapter. The changes in life-forms on Earth can be used to obtain relative ages of rocks and date certain geologic events.

CHAPTER OVERVIEW

- **Section 16-1:** This section describes fossils and the conditions needed for them to form. Using fossils as indicators of age and ancient environments concludes the section.
- **Section 16-2: Science and Society:** Theories explaining why dinosaurs became extinct are explored. The You Decide feature asks students whether changes in our environment could lead to the extinction of humans.
- **Section 16-3:** This section explains how relative ages of rocks are determined. Methods used to correlate rocks are also described.
- **Section 16-4:** Section 16-4 contrasts absolute and relative dating. The process of radioactive decay is also described.

CHAPTER VOCABULARY

fossils
petrified remains
carbonaceous film
mold
cast
index fossils
extinct
law of superposition
relative dating
unconformities
absolute dating
radioactive decay
half-life
radiometric dating
uniformitarianism

CHAPTER 16 Clues to Earth's Past

416

OPTIONS

For Your Gifted Students

Have students imagine they are fossils. Have them write their autobiographies and describe what they have seen and experienced. The stories should also include how the organism died and became a fossil. Encourage creativity but insist on scientific accuracy.

These remains of a crinoid are a fossil. Crinoids are still living in today's oceans, but we have fossils of ancient crinoids dating back more than 450 million years. How do such fossils form? What evidence of past life do we have?

FIND OUT!

Do this simple activity to see how some fossils are formed.

Cut the top off of a small milk carton and add enough plaster of Paris to fill it halfway. Mix enough water with the plaster of Paris so that it's smooth and thick. Coat a leaf, shell, or bone with petroleum jelly. Press it into the plaster of Paris. Allow the plaster of Paris to dry at least 24 hours and then remove the leaf, shell, or bone. Compare the shapes of the objects with the imprints they left in the plaster. Look at the imprints made by others in your class. Can you determine, from the imprints alone, what type of objects made them? How do you think imprints of once-living organisms are made in nature?

Gearing Up

Previewing the Chapter

Use this outline to help you focus on important ideas in this chapter.

Previewing Science Skills

- ▶ In the **Skill Builders,** you will make concept maps, interpret data, and use tables.
- ▶ In the **Activities,** you will interpret illustrations, analyze data, and draw conclusions.
- ▶ In the **MINI-Labs,** you will apply previous knowledge and make inferences.

What's next?

Now that you've seen how imprints of plant and animal remains can be made in plaster of Paris, you can relate this to the formation of fossils in Earth's rocks. As you read this chapter, you'll learn about different types of fossils and how they form. You will also learn how fossils and other evidence are used to measure the age of a rock.

INTRODUCING THE CHAPTER

Use the Find Out activity to introduce students to one method of fossil formation. Inform students they will be learning more about fossils and how they form as they study the chapter.

FIND OUT!

Preparation: Have students bring in small, clean, empty milk cartons; leaves; shells; or clean meat bones. Obtain a package of plaster of Paris and a container of petroleum jelly.

Materials: one small milk carton for each student; enough plaster of Paris to fill each carton half full; water; petroleum jelly; and leaves, shells, or bones

Teaching Tips

▶ Have students cover their desks or tables with newspaper to facilitate cleanup.

▶ Mix up the plaster of Paris a few days before students do this activity. Then tell them approximately how much water is needed to achieve a smooth, thick mixture.

▶ Have each student make an imprint of each of the three items. Then have students compare and contrast the detail of each of their "fossils."

Gearing Up

Have students study the Gearing Up feature to familiarize themselves with the chapter. Discuss the relationships of the topics in the outline.

What's Next?

Before beginning the first section, make sure students understand the connection between the Find Out activity and the topics to follow.

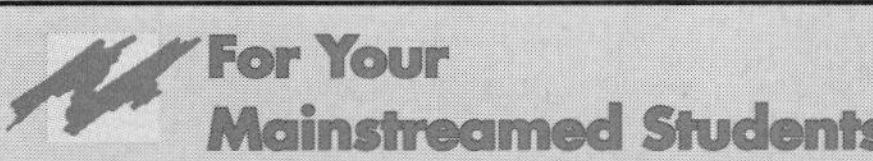

For Your Mainstreamed Students

Have students make dinosaur dioramas depicting Earth's topography and plant life present during that time. Students can work in small groups. Explain that some research will have to be done before beginning the activity.

SECTION 16-1

PREPARATION

SECTION BACKGROUND

▶ Scientists think that certain reptiles swallowed stones to aid in digestion. When the organism died and decayed, the polished stones, called gastroliths, were left behind. Gastroliths and fossilized fecal materials, or coprolites, are trace fossils.

▶ Facies fossils are the remains of organisms that were restricted to a stratigraphic facies or were adapted to living in a restricted environment. Facies fossils enable paleontologists to reconstruct models depicting ancient climates.

PREPLANNING

▶ Obtain fossils described in this section for students to observe.

1 MOTIVATE

FLEX Your Brain

Use the Flex Your Brain activity to have students explore TYRANNOSAURUS REX or STEGOSAURUS.

▶ Obtain examples of each type of fossil described in this section. Allow students time to explore the differences and similarities of each type.

PROGRAM RESOURCES

From the **Teacher Resource Package** use:

Activity Worksheets, page 5, Flex Your Brain.

Activity Worksheets, page 148, Mini-Lab: What type of fossils might we leave for future generations?

16-1 Fossils

New Science Words

fossils
petrified remains
carbonaceous film
mold
cast
index fossils

Objectives

▶ List the conditions necessary for fossils to form.
▶ Describe processes of fossil formation.
▶ Explain how fossil correlation is used to determine rock ages.

Traces from Our Past

The dense forest thunders as the *Tyrannosaurus rex* charges forward in pursuit of her evening meal. On the other side of the swamp, a herd of apatosaurs moves slowly and cautiously onward. The adults surround the young to protect them from predators. Soon, night will fall on this prehistoric day, 70 million years ago.

Does this scene sound familiar to you? It's likely that you've read about dinosaurs and other past inhabitants of Earth before. But how do you know they really existed? What evidence do we have of past life on Earth?

Figure 16-1. Scientists and artists can reconstruct what dinosaurs looked like using fossil remains. Pictured here is *Stegosaurus*.

OPTIONS

Meeting Different Ability Levels

For Section 16-1, use the following **Teacher Resource Masters** depending upon individual students' needs.

◆ **Study Guide Master** for all students.

● **Reinforcement Master** for students of average and above average ability levels.

▲ **Enrichment Master** for above average students.

Additional Teacher Resource Package masters are listed in the OPTIONS box throughout the section. The additional masters are appropriate for all students.

◆ STUDY GUIDE 66

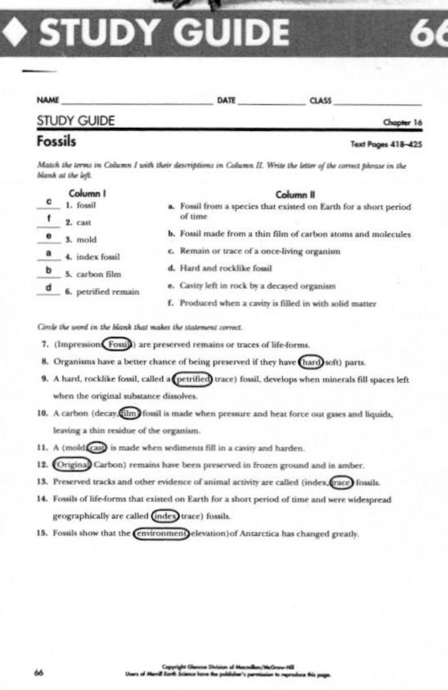

NAME ______ DATE ______ CLASS ______

STUDY GUIDE — Chapter 16

Fossils — Text Pages 418–425

Match the terms in Column I with their descriptions in Column II. Write the letter of the correct phrase in the blank at the left.

Column I	Column II
c 1. fossil	a. Fossil from a species that existed on Earth for a short period of time
f 2. cast	b. Fossil made from a thin film of carbon atoms and molecules
e 3. mold	c. Remain or trace of a once-living organism
a 4. index fossil	d. Hard and rocklike fossil
b 5. carbon film	e. Cavity left in rock by a decayed organism
d 6. petrified remain	f. Produced when a cavity is filled in with solid matter

Circle the word in the blank that makes the statement correct.

7. (Impressions, Fossils) are preserved remains or traces of life-forms.
8. Organisms have a better chance of being preserved if they have (hard, soft) parts.
9. A hard, rocklike fossil, called a (petrified, trace) fossil, develops when minerals fill spaces left when the original substance dissolves.
10. A carbon (decay, film) fossil is made when pressure and heat force out gases and liquids, leaving a thin residue of the organism.
11. A (mold, cast) is made when sediments fill in a cavity and harden.
12. (Original, Carbon) remains have been preserved in frozen ground and in amber.
13. Preserved tracks and other evidence of animal activity are called (index, trace) fossils.
14. Fossils of life-forms that existed on Earth for a short period of time and were widespread geographically are called (index, trace) fossils.
15. Fossils show that the (environment, elevation) of Antarctica has changed greatly.

66

In the Find Out activity, you made imprints of parts of organisms. The imprints were records, or evidence, of life. If they had been evidence of life that once existed, but no longer exists, then they would be fossils. **Fossils** are the remains or traces of once-living organisms. By studying fossils, geologists help solve mysteries of Earth's past. Fossils have helped geologists and biologists determine approximately when life began, when plants and animals first lived on land, and when certain types of organisms, such as the dinosaurs, disappeared. Fossils tell us not only *when* and *where* organisms once lived, but also *how* they lived. 1

How Fossils Form

Usually the remains of dead plants and animals are quickly destroyed. Scavengers eat the dead organisms, or bacteria cause them to decay. If you've ever left a banana on the shelf too long, you've seen this process begin. Compounds in the banana cause it to become soft and moist, and bacteria move in and cause it to quickly decay. What keeps some plants and animals from decaying so they can become fossils?

First of all, to become a fossil the body of a dead organism must be protected from scavengers and bacteria. One way this can occur is when the body is quickly covered by sediments. If a fish dies and sinks to the bottom of a pond, sediments carried into the pond by a stream will rapidly cover the fish. As a result, no animals or bacteria can get to it. Quick burial, however, isn't enough to make a fossil.

Organisms have a better chance of being preserved if they have hard parts such as bones, shells, teeth, or wood. As you know, these hard parts are less likely to be eaten by other organisms and are less likely to weather away. Most fossils that have been found are the hard parts of organisms.

MINI-Lab

What type of fossils might we leave for future generations?

Suppose you are to decide on five items to be placed in a plastic "time capsule." The capsule will be buried in soil so that some future generation might dig it up and learn about their ancestors and how they lived. List the five items you would bury in the plastic container. Keep in mind that they might have to endure the natural weathering and erosion processes if the container is damaged. Explain what you expect the future generation to be able to learn from each item. Can they learn about our average size and weight? Can they learn about the environment we live in? What other things can they learn?

TYING TO PREVIOUS KNOWLEDGE: Have students recall from Chapter 4 how sedimentary rocks are formed. Remind students that sedimentary rocks are generally the only rock type that contains fossils.

OBJECTIVES AND SCIENCE WORDS: Have students review the objectives and science words to become familiar with this section.

2 TEACH

Key Concepts are highlighted.

STUDENT TEXT QUESTION

▶ Page 418, paragraph 2: **What evidence do we have of past life on Earth?** *Fossils are evidence of past life.*

MINI-Lab

Materials: paper and pencil

Teaching Tips

▶Introduce this activity by asking students how we know about ancient individuals and civilizations such as the pharaohs of Egypt or the Aztecs of South America.

Cooperative Learning: Form Problem Solving teams with four or five students per group. Ask for a consensus list from each group. Then write each group's list of five "artifacts" on the chalkboard. Have the class, on a consensus basis, determine the five items to be placed in the time capsule.

▶**Answers:** There are no right or wrong answers for this activity. This kind of group activity is similar to the decision-making process that must be completed for any long-duration time capsule placement or the launching of space capsules intended for travel outside our solar system.

● REINFORCEMENT 66

NAME ______ DATE ______ CLASS ______

REINFORCEMENT — Chapter 16

Fossils — Text Pages 418–425

Write the word "no" in front of statements that do not describe a fossil. Write "fossil" if the statement describes a fossil. After each fossil description, name the type described.

fossil 1. Dinosaur tracks in rocks **trace fossil**

no 2. Bird tracks in snow ______

fossil 3. Dinosaur leg bone containing quartz instead of calcium **petrified remains**

fossil 4. Insect in amber from a pine tree **original remains**

no 5. Oil formed from sea animals of long ago ______

fossil 6. Rocklike wood from a tree that lived millions of years ago **petrified remains**

no 7. Sandstone showing ripple marks from water ______

no 8. Living pine tree more than 4000 years old ______

fossil 9. Thin cavity in a rock showing where a shell had decayed **mold**

fossil 10. Shell-shaped mineral found in rock cavity **cast**

fossil 11. Flesh, fur, and bones of a woolly mammoth preserved in frozen ground **original remains**

no 12. Arrowhead made thousands of years ago ______

fossil 13. Burrows of worms that lived millions of years ago **trace fossil**

fossil 14. Rocklike parts of a species of fish that lived a short time in several parts of the world **index fossil**

fossil 15. Thin layer of carbon from the remains of a plant that lived thousands of years ago **carbon film**

Answer the following questions on the lines provided.

16. What three kinds of information can geologists gather from a study of fossils? **Fossils tell when, where, and how organisms once lived.**

17. What must happen to a dead organism if a fossil is to form? **It must be covered rapidly to keep it from scavengers and bacteria, and it should have hard body parts.**

18. What do you know about a rock layer found on a mountain if you find a seashell fossil in the layer? **The rock layer was once under water.**

66

▲ ENRICHMENT 66

NAME ______ DATE ______ CLASS ______

ENRICHMENT — Chapter 16

Fossils — Text Pages 418–425

COLLECTING FOSSILS

Many people throughout the world have a fascinating hobby. They collect fossils. Some of these collectors want only to find good specimens. Others, taking it more seriously, make an effort to find a wide variety of specimens. They display them with information about the fossils and where they were found.

Collections can be organized into three categories: invertebrates, vertebrates, and plants. Invertebrates are animals that have no backbones. Examples of these are clams, snails, and lobsters. Vertebrates are animals with backbones. Fish, amphibians, reptiles, birds, and mammals have backbones. Plants, the third category, are a common type of fossil.

Invertebrate fossils often found include snails, clams, corals and impressions of sponges. Vertebrate fossils that amateur collectors commonly find include reptiles and fish. Birds are the rarest of the vertebrate fossils. And plant fossils are more common than vertebrates. Collectors often find cone-bearing plants, leaves, and seeds.

A serious fossil collector needs only simple equipment: a small pick to get the rock that contains the fossil, a hand lens, a compass, newspaper to wrap specimens, a pencil, and note-sized paper or cards to record data about each fossil.

A responsible collector will want to take some precautions. First, remember that if you are planning to look for fossils on private land, you must have permission. If you are collecting fossils on public land, you must check to see what laws apply. For example, collecting very small specimens from most public parks is permitted, but that is not the case everywhere. Ask!

1. Why do you think fossils of corals, bryozoans, and other sea creatures are more common than fossils of birds? **Answers may vary. Birds have light, fragile skeletons and no teeth. They're common prey, and predators often consume their bones. Also, there were more sea creatures than birds.**

2. How can you combine the types of fossils listed in your text (petrified, mold, etc.) and the three classes listed in the article? **Each of the three categories can be subdivided into the categories listed in the text. Another solution would be to subdivide each text category into three subcategories.**

3. Plan a chart for a collector to use to record fossil finds.

Sample chart

Fossil	Type of fossil	Where fossil was found	Description of fossil

66

CONCEPT DEVELOPMENT

Cooperative Learning: Form Science Investigation groups with three students per group. Provide students with petrified remains, carbonaceous film, molds, casts, original remains, and trace fossils and have them identify the fossils by their mode of preservation.

Cooperative Learning: Form Expert Teams with five students per group. Each group is to be responsible for one of the five types of fossils discussed in this section.

▶ After students have read pages 420 and 421, pose the questions that follow. **How does a carbonaceous film form?** *As an organism decays, gases and liquids are squeezed from its body by overlying sediments. Heat also drives off the gases and liquids. The carbon atoms and molecules that remain form a fossil of the organism.* **How do molds and casts differ?** *When an organism dies, it may become buried in sediment. As the sediments harden to form rocks, the organism slowly decays. When the organic material is completely gone, an impression or mold of the organism is left in the rock. If sediments later fill the cavity and then harden, a cast of the organism is formed.*

Figure 16-2. Much of the original matter in these petrified plant remains has been replaced by quartz and other minerals.

Petrified Remains

You have some idea of what *Tyrannosaurus rex* looked like because you've seen illustrations of this dinosaur. The artists who draw *Tyrannosaurus rex* base their illustrations on fossils. One type of fossil they use is petrified bone. Perhaps you've seen skeletal remains of dinosaurs towering above you in museums. These bones are usually petrified.

How do petrified remains differ from original remains?

2 **Petrified remains** are hard and rocklike. Some or all of the original materials in the remains have been replaced by minerals. For example, a solution of water and dissolved quartz may flow through the bones of a dead organism. The water dissolves the calcium in the bone and deposits quartz in its place. Quartz is harder than calcium, so the petrified bone is rocklike.

We learn about past life-forms from bones, wood, and other remains that become petrified. But there are also many other types of fossils to consider.

EcoTip

Will the fossils you leave behind pollute the environment? Plastic foam cups and plates last up to 500 years in a landfill. Reduce waste by washing and reusing cups and plates whenever possible.

Carbonaceous Films

The tissues of most organisms are made of compounds that contain carbon. Sometimes the only fossil remains of a dead plant or animal is this carbon. As you know, fossils usually form when a dead organism is buried in sedi-

OPTIONS

ENRICHMENT

▶ Ask students to bring in fossils they might have collected or received from others. Have the class determine the type of fossil and, if possible, the organism that produced each.

▶ Have students research to find out what types of information can be learned about extinct animals from studying gastroliths and coprolites left by the organisms.

ments. When more and more sediments pile up, the organism is subjected to pressure and heat. These conditions force gases and liquids from the body. A thin film of carbon residue is left, forming an outline of the original plant part. This process of chemically changing plant material is called carbonization, and it produces a fossil 3
called a **carbonaceous film.**

In swamps and deltas, large volumes of plant matter accumulate. Over millions of years, these deposits can be completely carbonized, forming the sedimentary rock coal. Coal is more important as a source of fuel than as a fossil because the structure of the original plant is lost when the coal forms.

Molds and Casts

How are molds and casts related?

Think again about the impressions in plaster of Paris you made earlier. In nature, such impressions are made when seashells or other hard parts of organisms fall into soft sediments such as mud and beach sand. The object and sediments are then covered by more sediments. Compaction and cementation turn the sediments into rock. Cracks in the rock let water and air reach the shell or hard part and it then decays, leaving behind a cavity in the rock called a **mold.** Later, other sediments may fill in
the cavity, harden into rock, and produce a **cast** of the 4
original object.

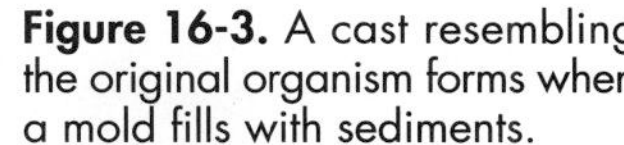

Figure 16-3. A cast resembling the original organism forms when a mold fills with sediments.

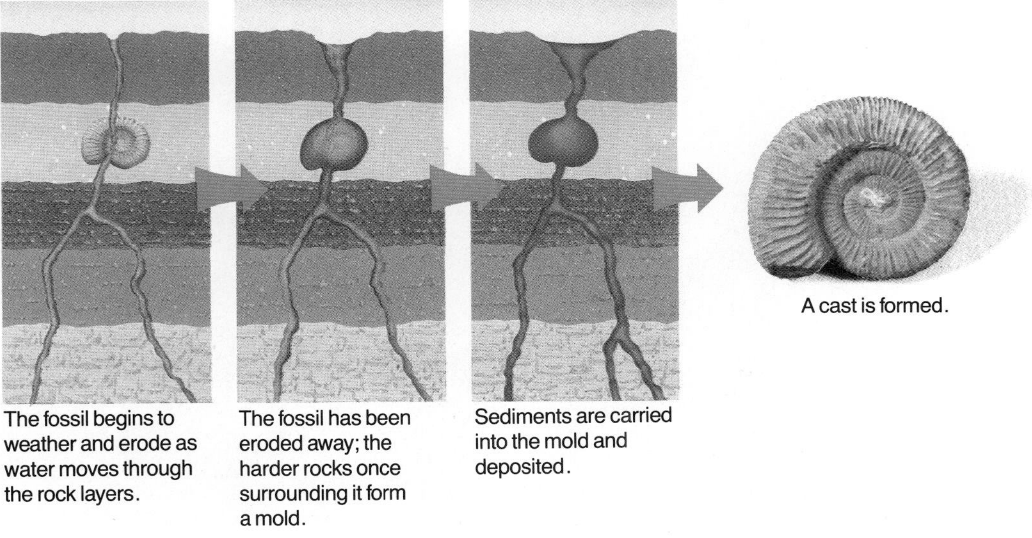
The fossil begins to weather and erode as water moves through the rock layers.
The fossil has been eroded away; the harder rocks once surrounding it form a mold.
Sediments are carried into the mold and deposited.
A cast is formed.

CHECK FOR UNDERSTANDING

Have a volunteer list the sequence of events necessary to form mold and cast fossils.

RETEACH

Cooperative Learning: Form Science Investigation groups with four students per group. Assign the roles of reader, materials handler, "fossil" maker, and recorder. Have students determine which of the following types of sediments would best preserve fossils by pressing shells or bones into mixtures of sand and water; clay and water; and gravel, clay, and water. The recorder should report which mixture of sediments allowed the best imprint to be formed.

EXTENSION

For students who have mastered this section, use the **Reinforcement** and **Enrichment** masters or other OPTIONS provided.

ENRICHMENT

▶ Determine if any students in your class work with ceramics as a hobby. If so, have these students construct an analogy between the molds used in making ceramic statues and those formed in nature. Students may wish to use a statue to demonstate why the internal structure of an organism is not preserved when casts are formed.

PROGRAM RESOURCES

From the **Teacher Resource Package** use:

Technology, pages 15-16, Rotary Oil Rig.

Use **Laboratory Manual,** pages 133-134, Carbon Impressions.

REVEALING MISCONCEPTIONS

▶ Some students might think that fossils form only from ancient life. Ask them what happens to organisms that die and settle to the bottom of a lake or ocean. Explain that these remains are buried quickly by sediments. Once buried, they begin the process of fossilization. In time, they will become fossils.

CONCEPT DEVELOPMENT

▶ Ask students these questions about trace fossils. **How do trace fossils differ from other types of fossils?** *Trace fossils are not formed from body parts. They are evidence of an organism's activity.* **What information about early life-forms can be obtained from the depth and separation of tracks left in sediment?** *The approximate size and mass of the organism that left them can be determined.* **What could you conclude about an organism if you found small, fossilized tracks that were far apart?** *Small tracks indicate a small organism. Therefore, if tracks are far apart, the organism was probably able to move swiftly or run.*

MINI QUIZ

Use the Mini Quiz to check students' recall of chapter content.

1. **_____ are remains or traces of once-living organisms preserved in Earth's rocks.** *Fossils*
2. **When minerals replace the original material of an organism, the fossil that forms is a(n) _____ .** *petrified remain*
3. **A(n) _____ forms when a thin film of carbon is left behind after gases and liquids are removed from an organism.** *carbonaceous film*
4. **Sediment that fills a cavity and hardens forms a(n) _____ of the original organism.** *cast*
5. **_____ fossils are tracks and other evidence of animal activity.** *Trace*

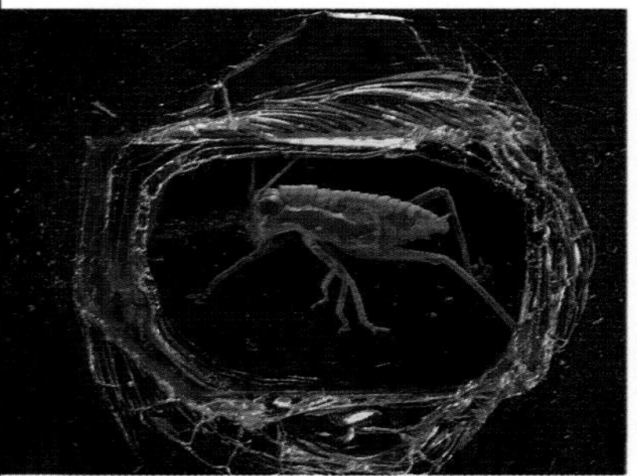

Figure 16-4. This 40 million year old grasshopper was trapped in the sticky resin produced by a plant. Over time, the resin crystallized into amber, preserving the insect inside.

Original Remains

Sometimes the actual organism or parts of organisms are found. Figure 16-4 shows an insect trapped in amber, a crystallized form of the sticky resin produced by some trees. The amber protects the insect's body from decay and petrification. Other organisms, such as woolly mammoths, have been found preserved in frozen ground. Some woolly mammoths have been found with their skin and hair intact.

Trace Fossils

It's not only from body parts that we learn about organisms. We also learn from the tracks and traces they leave behind. Fossilized tracks and other evidence of animal
5 activity are called trace fossils. Perhaps your parents made your handprint or footprint in plaster of Paris when you were born. If so, it's a record that tells something about you. From it, we can guess your approximate size and maybe your weight. Animals walking on Earth long ago have left similar tracks. In some cases, tracks can tell us more about how an organism lived than any other type of fossil.

Figure 16-5. Tracks in solidified mud indicate that adult apatosaurs protected their young by surrounding them as they traveled in herds.

OPTIONS

INQUIRY QUESTIONS

▶ **How does amber protect a trapped insect's body from decay?** *If the amber completely covers the insect's body, it will prevent bacteria, air, and water from reacting with the insect.*

▶ **Why do you think the skin and hair of some woolly mammoths have been found intact?** *These animals lived during the last ice age. When they became trapped within the ice, the low temperatures kept bacteria from developing and reproducing.*

▶ **Why are index fossils useful to earth scientists?** *Because the organisms that formed them existed for short periods of time, the fossils are very good indicators of the ages of the rocks in which they are found.*

From a set of tracks at Davenport Ranch, Texas, we have learned something about the social life of *Apatosaurus*, one of the largest dinosaurs. The tracks were made by a traveling herd. The largest tracks are on the outer edges and the smallest are on the inside. This suggests that the adult apatosaurs surrounded the young as they traveled—probably to protect them from enemies, such as allosaurs. In fact, a nearby set of allosaur tracks indicates that one was stalking the herd, following alongside waiting for a chance to attack.

Other trace fossils include worm holes and burrows made by sea creatures. These, too, tell us something about the life-style of these animals. As you can see, a combination of fossils can tell us a great deal about the individuals that inhabited Earth before us.

List several examples of trace fossils.

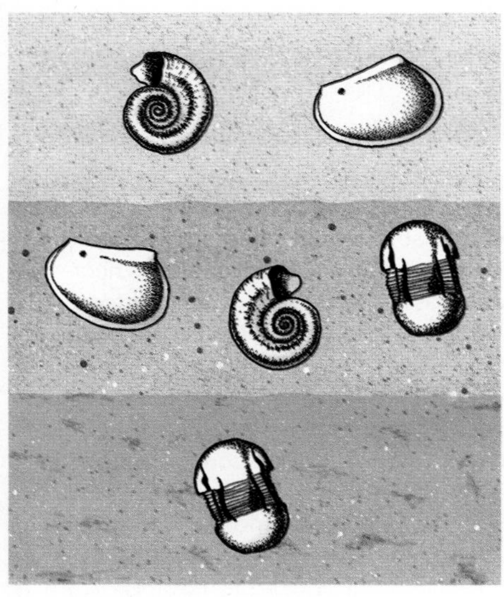

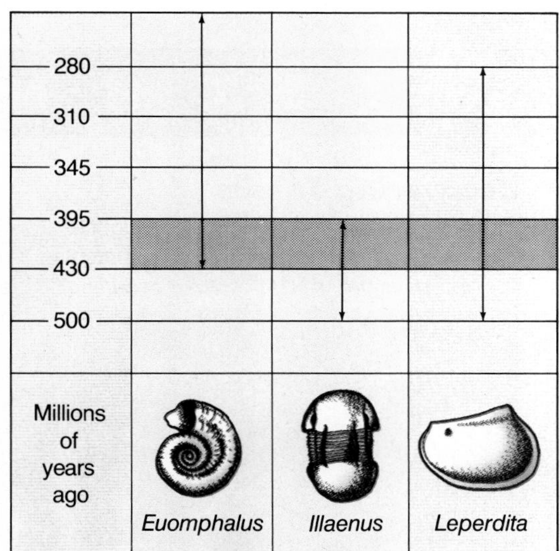

Figure 16-6. The chart on the right shows when each organism inhabited Earth. The middle layer of rock had to be deposited between 430 and 395 million years ago—the only time all three types of organisms in the layer were alive.

Index Fossils

One thing we've learned by studying fossils is that organisms are constantly changing, or evolving. A species inhabits Earth for only a certain period of time before it evolves into a new species or dies out completely. Some species of organisms inhabit Earth for very long periods of time without changing much. Others remain unchanged for only a short time. It's these organisms that produce index fossils.

TEACHER F.Y.I.

▶ Most fossils are found in sedimentary rocks. When sedimentary rocks melt and become igneous rocks, the fossils are destroyed. Fossils contained in rocks that undergo metamorphism are usually altered and unrecognizable.

CONCEPT DEVELOPMENT

▶ Have students read the following article: "Dinosaur Eggs: The Inside Story," pp. 61-67, *Natural History*, December, 1989, by J. R. Horner and D. B. Weishampel. Have students write a brief summary of what the location of the dinosaur nests tells us about these extinct creatures.

ENRICHMENT

▶ Have an interested student research and report on the "Tollund Man." The Tollund Man is the preserved body of a human found in Tollund Fen, Denmark. His remains were spectacularly well preserved in the shallow, oxygen-starved water of the fen. Tollund Man was found with his leather cap still in place on his head. All of his facial hairs and the pores and wrinkles of his skin are easily visible. One of the things that makes this find particularly interesting is that Tollund Man has a rope noose around his neck. Scientists have inferred that he was hanged and then thrown into the fen approximately 2000 years ago.

TEACHER F.Y.I.

▶ Trilobites are excellent index fossils because these marine organisms lived and became extinct during the Paleozoic Era.

TECHNOLOGY

▶ Explain that the processing of fossils at museums varies depending upon how the fossils will be displayed. Students are probably most familiar with free mounts. Steel skeletons are often used to support the large bones of mastodons, dinosaurs, mammoths, and other large animals.

▶ For more information, see "Geology in Milwaukee," *Earth Science*, Winter, 1986, pp. 18-21.

Think Critically: The bones have been buried for millions of years. Exposing them to air, light, and microorganisms makes them fragile.

How do index fossils differ from other fossils?

Index fossils are fossils from species that existed on Earth for short periods of time and were widespread geographically. Scientists use index fossils to determine the age of rock layers. For example, suppose you find a rock layer containing fossils of an organism that lived only between 100 and 145 million years ago. You can conclude that the rock layer must have formed during that time.

Fossils and Ancient Environments

Fossils can also be used to determine what the environment of an area was like long ago. For example, rocks in Antarctica contain fossils of tropical plants. The environment of Antarctica today certainly isn't tropical, but we know that it was when the fossilized plants were living.

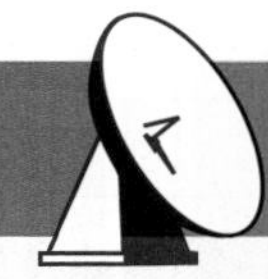

TECHNOLOGY

Recovering Fossils

When scientists locate an area thought to have fossils, large earth-moving equipment or explosives are used to remove overlying rocks and soil. Smaller and smaller tools are then used as the excavation draws nearer to the fossils. In the final phases of fossil recovery, tiny picks and brushes are used to remove soil from the fossils.

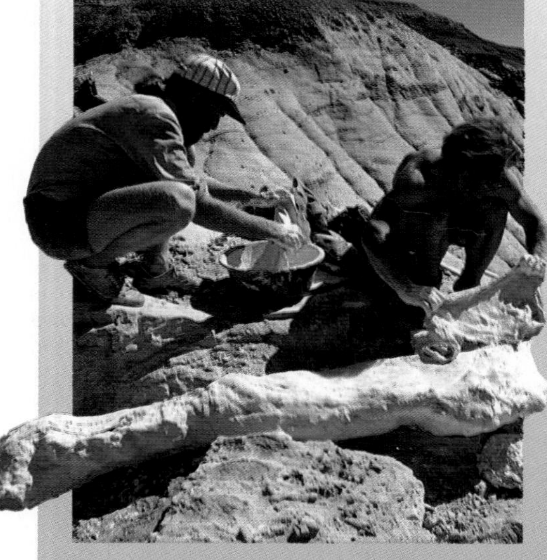

In order for the fossils to be removed or transported, they must be strengthened and protected. Large, brittle bones, such as dinosaur remains, are first covered with a layer of shellac. Then, strips of wet newspaper are molded onto the fossils. Finally, a plaster mixture is used to coat burlap straps, which are then applied to the fossils. This final step produces a kind of cast that protects and supports the fossils. The cast can be made even stronger with wooden sticks. The reinforced fossils are now ready to be transported to a museum, where they will undergo final preparations before being placed on exhibit.

Think Critically: Why are remains such as dinosaur bones so fragile?

OPTIONS

INQUIRY QUESTIONS

▶ **How are certain fossils indicators of ancient environments?** *Some organisms are restricted to a specific environment. The rocks in which fossils of such organisms are found allow scientists to determine the environment that existed when the organisms were alive.*

▶ **If you found fossilized trilobites in bedrock near your school, what could you state about the ancient environment of the area?** *The area must have been covered by a shallow sea at some time in the past because trilobites were marine animals.*

PROGRAM RESOURCES

From the **Teacher Resource Package** use:

Critical Thinking/Problem Solving, page 22, Putting Clues Together.

Concept Mapping, pages 37-38.

How would you explain the presence of fossilized brachiopods, animals that once lived in shallow seas, in the rocks of the midwest United States? The central portion of North America was covered by a shallow sea when the brachiopods were living.

Fossils tell us not only about past life on Earth, but about the history of the rock layers that contain them.

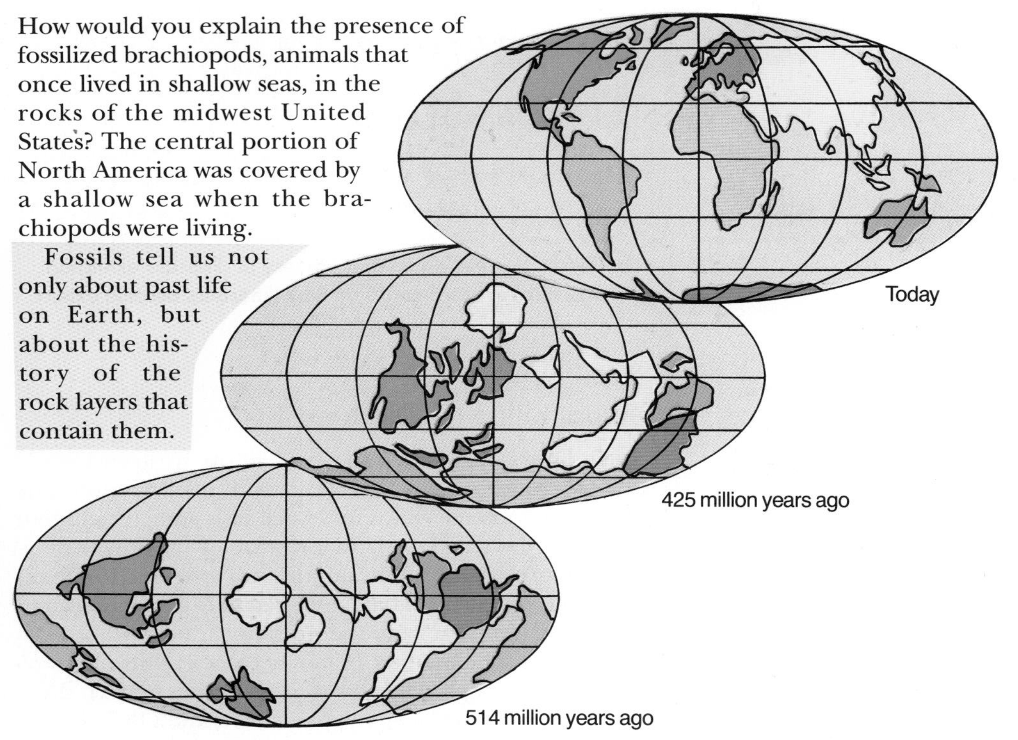

Figure 16-7. The position and environment of Antarctica, shown in red, have changed through time. Fossils found in its rocks indicate Antarctica once had a tropical environment.

SECTION REVIEW

1. What conditions are needed for most fossils to form?
2. What type of fossil forms when the organism decays leaving a cavity in the rock?
3. What can be said about the ages of two widely separated layers of rock that contain the same type of fossil?
4. **Apply:** Why would dinosaur bones be considered useful index fossils?

Concept Mapping

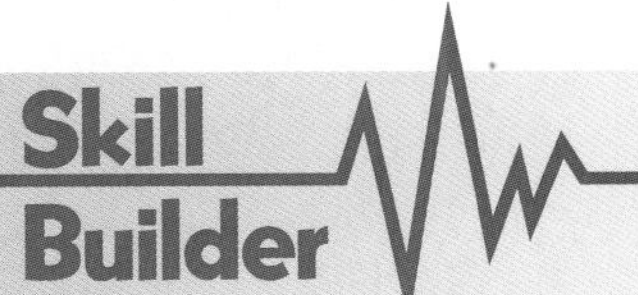

Make a concept map that compares and contrasts petrified remains and original remains. Use these terms and phrases: *original remains, evidence of former life, petrified remains, replaced by minerals,* and *actual parts of organisms.* If you need help, refer to Concept Mapping in the **Skill Handbook** on pages 688 and 689.

3 CLOSE

▶ Ask questions 1-3 and the **Apply** Question in the Section Review.

▶ Invite a fossil collector to visit your class to discuss the kinds of fossils found in your area.

▶ Call on volunteers to present key concepts of the lesson as if he or she were informing a classmate who had been absent.

SECTION REVIEW ANSWERS

1. quick burial and the presence of hard parts

2. a cast

3. Both layers of rock formed during the period of time that the fossil-producing organism lived; the two layers of rock may be similar in age if the organism existed for only a short period of Earth's history.

4. Apply: Dinosaurs lived in many areas of the world during a limited period of time in Earth's past. Dinosaur fossils can be used to determine an age range of the rocks in which they are found.

Skill Builder

Possible Solution:

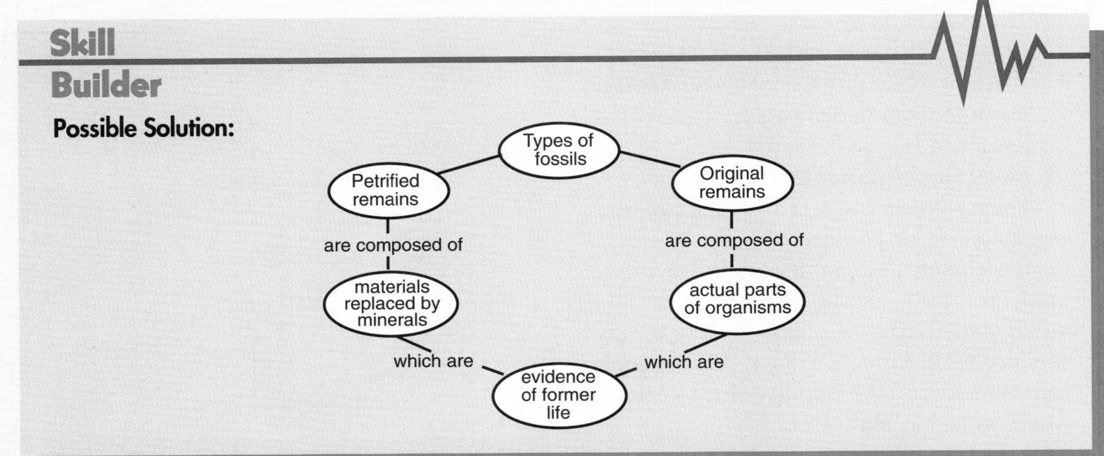

SECTION 16-2

PREPARATION

SECTION BACKGROUND

► Several theories have been proposed to explain the extinction of dinosaurs. One theory proposes that a disease of epidemic proportion swept Earth, causing the extinction. Small mammals may have been able to rob dinosaur nests of their eggs, resulting in fewer dinosaurs. Gradually changing climates also may have led to the extinction of the dinosaurs.

► The fossil record indicates that mass extinctions have occurred on Earth about every 26 million years. Some scientists think this may be due to a companion star, named Nemesis, that orbits our sun. Theories suggest that every 26 million years, Nemesis passes through the Oort Comet Cloud, which surrounds our solar system. Many comets, hurled toward the inner solar system, pass into Earth's atmosphere and cause the extinctions.

1 MOTIVATE

Cooperative Learning: Form Numbered Heads Together groups. Ask students to hypothesize what might happen to life on Earth today if for some reason light from the sun were unable to reach Earth for several years. Students should realize that much of the plant life on Earth would die. Photosynthesizing organisms are the base of all food chains. Plants also produce oxygen. Thus, their demise would affect the survival of most life-forms.

► Have students find out about the largest meat-eating land animal ever to walk on Earth—*Tyrannosaurus rex*.

16-2 Extinction of Dinosaurs

New Science Words

extinct

Objectives

- ► Discuss the meteorite-impact theory of dinosaur extinction.
- ► Describe several theories on why dinosaurs became extinct.

What Killed the Dinosaurs?

In layers of sedimentary rock in the western United States rest the remains of thousands of dinosaurs. The bones tell us that dinosaurs were fast, agile, intelligent animals who ruled the land longer than any other organism before or since. Why are they no longer a dominant life-form on Earth? What happened to the dinosaurs, and what can we learn from their disappearance?

1 The last species of dinosaurs became extinct about 65 million years ago. When a species becomes **extinct,** there are no longer any living members of its kind. Before their extinction, species of dinosaurs had dominated the land

Figure 16-8. Evidence in the rock record indicates a large meteorite may have struck Earth at about the same time the dinosaurs became extinct.

OPTIONS

Meeting Different Ability Levels

For Section 16-2, use the following **Teacher Resource Masters** depending upon individual students' needs.

◆ **Study Guide Master** for all students.

● **Reinforcement Master** for students of average and above average ability levels.

▲ **Enrichment Master** for above average students.

Additional Teacher Resource Package masters are listed in the OPTIONS box throughout the section. The additional masters are appropriate for all students.

◆ STUDY GUIDE 67

NAME ____________ DATE ________ CLASS ________

STUDY GUIDE — Chapter 16

Extinction of the Dinosaurs — Text Pages 426–428

Use the words in the boxes to fill in the blanks.

dominant	mammals	130 million	intelligent

Dinosaurs were abundant on Earth's land for about **130 million** years. These fast, agile, and **intelligent** animals were the **dominant** land animals. Only after the end of their rule did another class of animals, **mammals**, increase.

Alvarez iridium collision	dinosaurs dust theory	extinct meteorite	western 65 million

The remains of **dinosaurs** have been found in the **western** part of the United States. These great animals have been **extinct** for about **65 million** years. Two scientists, Luis and Walter **Alvarez**, have uncovered traces of **iridium** in rock layers. They now think they know why the animals died. Their **theory** is that Earth and a **meteorite** from space had a **collision**. This raised **dust**, which dimmed the sun's light. The meteorite's impact would also account for the iridium deposit.

mineral	photosynthesis	temperature	vocanic activity

The meteorite collision has been rejected by some scientists who think increased **volcanic activity** is a more likely theory. Either event would explain the presence of the rare **mineral** iridium and would have resulted in a dimming of the sun. This would kill plants that depend on the sun for **photosynthesis** and would lower Earth's **temperature**.

67

for 130 million years. Mammals have ruled the land for only the last 65 million years, and humans and their direct ancestors have been around for less than 6 million. The dinosaurs are no longer on Earth, but we learn from them by investigating what caused their extinction.

One theory of dinosaur extinction is that a large meteorite collided with Earth. The collision threw dust and debris into Earth's upper atmosphere. The collision may have also caused large forest fires that would have added smoke to the atmosphere.

If enough dust and smoke were released into Earth's upper atmosphere, the sun would have been completely blocked out. If the sun's energy remained blocked off for a long time, plants couldn't have carried on photosynthesis and would have died. With no food, plant-eating dinosaurs also would have died. With no plant-eating dinosaurs to prey on, meat-eating dinosaurs would have starved as well.

Luis and Walter Alvarez, whom you first learned about in Chapter 13, may have found evidence to support the theory that a meteorite collided with Earth. They found a layer of clay in a column of sedimentary rock that was deposited at about the same time the dinosaurs became extinct. The layer contained small deformed grains of
quartz very much like those found near meteorite craters 2
elsewhere on Earth. But more importantly, the clay layer is rich in the element iridium. Iridium is rare on Earth's surface but found in greater amounts in meteorites.

The iridium in the clay layer may have come from the meteorite when it broke apart on impact. As the dust from the meteorite and the impact crater settled, the Alvarezes believe it formed the clay layer.

Some scientists believe the Alvarez theory is too complex and look for simpler explanations for the dinosaur
extinction. Perhaps the iridium-rich clay layer can be 3
explained by large amounts of volcanic activity. The iridium may have been brought up from deep inside Earth. The volcanic activity could have caused large amounts

Did You Know?

Earth is losing about three species every day. That number is expected to increase as we destroy natural environments such as grasslands, wetlands, and rain forests.

● REINFORCEMENT 67

NAME ______ DATE ______ CLASS ______

REINFORCEMENT — Chapter 16

Extinction of the Dinosaurs — Text Pages 426–428

Answer the following questions on the lines provided.

1. What does the term *extinct* mean? **There are no longer any living members of that species.**
2. What did the remains of dinosaurs found in the western United States tell us? **Dinosaurs were fast, agile, intelligent animals.**
3. Compare the amount of time that dinosaurs lived on Earth to the length of time humanlike ancestors and other mammals have lived on Earth. **Dinosaurs existed for 130 million years. Mammals have lived only the last 65 million years and humanlike animals for the last 3 to 4 million years.**
4. What are two theories regarding the extinction of the dinosaurs? **Theories include (1) a meteorite collided with Earth; (2) there was an unusual amount of volcanic activity.**
5. What evidence supports both leading theories regarding the extinction of dinosaurs? **Scientists have found a layer of clay from the time when dinosaurs became extinct. The clay layer is rich in iridium which is rare on Earth's surface but more abundant in meteorites and magma.**
6. What do the sun's rays have to do with the two leading theories of dinosaur extinction? **Both events would have caused dust and debris to cloud the sun's rays.**
7. How would the activity related to the sun's rays have changed the environment and affected dinosaurs? **Dust and debris blocking the sun's rays would have caused cold and darkness. This, in turn, would have destroyed the dinosaur's food sources and may have prevented reproduction.**
8. What have we learned from dinosaurs' becoming extinct? **We've learned that all organisms are dependent on their environment.**

 67

▲ ENRICHMENT 67

NAME ______ DATE ______ CLASS ______

ENRICHMENT — Chapter 16

Extinction of the Dinosaurs — Text Pages 426–428

DINOSAURS IN ARGENTINA

Use the information below to answer the questions.

You know that geologists study rocks and minerals. Geologists are also interested in fossils, but two other kinds of scientists are specialists in the study of fossils. Paleontologists study life that existed in ancient times, usually through fossils. Evolutionary biologists study the changes in forms of life over long periods of time.

A paleontologist working in Argentina about thirty years ago was led by a local goatherder to the bones of a 230-million-year-old carnivore. He named the animal "herrerasaurus" after the herder, Victorino Herrera, who had taken him to the site. Paul Sereno, an evolutionary biologist from Chicago, and a team of Argentine researchers returned a few years ago to the site where herrerasaurus had been identified. They found more bones and, eventually, a nearly complete skeleton. The skull even included teeth, which are often missing in fossils. The herrerasaurus skull had an extra jaw hinge, like snakes have today. This would enable it to prey on and grasp very large animals. It had serrated teeth to tear tough flesh. It also had claws on its short forelegs. It may have walked on hind legs and used its forelegs to grasp prey.

Since then, Sereno and others have uncovered parts of skeletons of varying sizes. They have determined that an adult herrerasaurus might be 4.6 meters tall and weigh up to 275 kilograms.

Have Sereno and the other searchers found the oldest dinosaur that ever lived? So far, they have the oldest dinosaur to be uncovered. In rocks below the herrerasaurus, Sereno discovered the remains of an animal that existed before dinosaurs. It dates back about 245 million years. Biologists and paleontologists are curious about what more can be found in the region.

1. Locate Argentina on a map and calculate its approximate distance from the western United States where Luis and Walter Alvarez worked. What does the distance between the two places add to the theories that dinosaurs became extinct after Earth collided with a meteorite or that there was a period of great volcanic activity? **Whichever theory is true, the impact of the meteorite or the volcanic activity must have been enormous to cloud the sun over such a great distance.**
2. If Sereno decides to search the area for an older dinosaur than the herrerasaurus, where should he look? Give reasons for your answer. **Since Sereno found remains below the herrerasaurus of an animal that lived before dinosaurs, he should probably search between the two fossils to see if the layers in between contain fossils of a dinosaur older than the herrerasaurus.**

 67

TYING TO PREVIOUS KNOWLEDGE: Have students recall from Chapter 13 that a large landmass called Pangaea once existed on Earth. Explain that as Pangaea separated, changes in global climate occurred. Climatic changes are considered to be one possible cause of dinosaur extinctions.

OBJECTIVES AND SCIENCE WORDS: Have students review the objectives and science words to become familiar with this section.

2 TEACH

Key Concepts are highlighted.

CONCEPT DEVELOPMENT

Use the Flex Your Brain activity to have students explore CAUSES OF ANIMAL AND PLANT EXTINCTIONS.

Cooperative Learning: Form Expert Teams. Assign each group member a different theory on dinosaur extinction. Have students research their assigned topics and present their findings to their original groups.

▶ Compose two debating teams. Have them debate whether or not the extinction of the dinosaurs was caused by meteorite impacts.

▶ Have students use the data in the Did You Know feature on page 427 to calculate how many species have become extinct during their lifetimes .

PROGRAM RESOURCES

From the **Teacher Resource Package** use:

Activity Worksheets, page 5, Flex Your Brain.

Cross-Curricular Connections, page 20, Writing a News Article.

Science and Society, page 20, Extinctions in Modern Times.

CHECK FOR UNDERSTANDING

Use the Mini Quiz to check for understanding.

MINI-QUIZ

Use the Mini Quiz to check students' recall of chapter content.

1. **The last species of dinosaurs became extinct about _____ years ago.** *65 million*
2. **The Alvarez' found a layer of clay containing _____ and _____ that supported a meteorite-impact theory.** *iridium, deformed quartz grains*
3. **High concentrations of iridium in sedimentary layers can be explained by _____ activity as well as by a meteorite impact.** *volcanic*
4. **The rock record indicates that global temperatures _____ about 65 million years ago.** *decreased*

RETEACH

Show students photographs of volcanic eruptions such as the 1980 Mount St. Helens eruption. Ask students what might happen to Earth's atmosphere if many volcanoes erupted at the same time.

EXTENSION

For students who have mastered this section, use the **Reinforcement** and **Enrichment** masters or other OPTIONS provided.

3 CLOSE

► Ask questions 1-3 in the Section Review.

SECTION REVIEW ANSWERS

1. about 65 million years ago

2. An iridium-rich layer of clay was deposited in many areas of the world at about the same time dinosaurs became extinct. Iridium is rare on Earth but more common in meteorites.

3. The iridium may have been deposited as the meteorite broke apart on impact. Extensive volcanic activity could have brought the element to Earth's surface.

Figure 16-9. The dinosaurs were well adapted to their environments. When their environments changed, they perished. Are we headed for the same fate?

of dust to enter Earth's atmosphere. The rock record 4 indicates that global temperatures started to go down about 65 million years ago. Perhaps with colder temperatures, the dinosaurs could not produce offspring and eventually died.

It's difficult to know for sure what caused Earth's environment to change 65 million years ago. But one thing that we have learned from the dinosaurs is that all organisms are dependent on their environment.

SECTION REVIEW

1. How long ago did dinosaurs become extinct?
2. What evidence indicates that a meteorite collided with Earth and may have caused the extinction of the dinosaurs?
3. Discuss two theories that explain how iridium could have gotten into the clay layer deposited about 65 million years ago.

SCIENCE & SOCIETY

You Decide!

Compared to dinosaurs, humans have inhabited Earth for a very short time. As you read in Chapters 9 and 10, we face possible changes in our environment because of the destruction of the ozone, the greenhouse effect, and other pollution. Do we need to worry about disappearing like the dinosaurs did? Is it possible that our environment is changing enough to cause the extinction of our own species?

YOU DECIDE!

►Students' opinions will vary but should be backed by scientific facts. This would be a good time to stress the enormous impact humans have on the planet and how the negative effects could be lessened by recycling and conservation.

ACTIVITY 16-1
Determining Relative Ages

Problem: *How can the relative order of events be determined in layers of rock?*

Procedure

1. Study Figures a and b below. The legend provided will help you interpret the figures.
2. Determine the relative ages of the rock layers, unconformities, igneous dikes, and fault in each figure.
3. Answer the questions in the Analyze and Conclude and Apply sections that follow.

Analyze

Figure A

1. Were any layers of rock deposited after the igneous dike formed? Explain.
2. What type of unconformity is shown? Is it possible that there were originally more layers of rock than are shown here? Explain.
3. What type of fault is shown?
4. Based on the figure alone, do you know whether the shale was deposited before or after the fault occurred? Assume that the layers have not been overturned.
5. Is it possible to determine if the igneous dike formed before or after the fault occurred? Explain.

Figure B

6. What type of fault is shown?
7. Is the igneous dike on the left older or younger than the unconformity nearest the surface? Explain.
8. Are the two igneous dikes shown the same age? How do you know?
9. Which two layers of rock may have been much thicker at one time than they are now?

Conclude and Apply

10. Make a sketch of Figure a. Indicate on it the relative age of each rock layer, igneous dike, fault, and unconformity. For example, the shale layer is the oldest, so mark it with a "1." Mark the next oldest feature with a "2" and so on.
11. Repeat the procedure in Question 10 for Figure b.

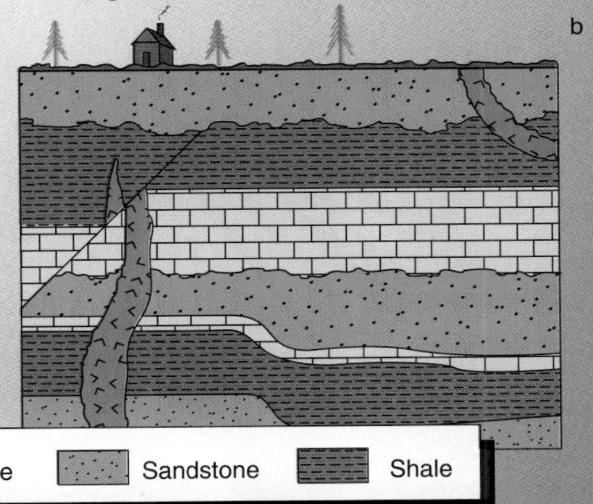

ACTIVITY 16-1
40-45 minutes

OBJECTIVE: Determine the relative order of events by interpreting geologic cross sections.

PROCESS SKILLS applied in this activity:
▶ **Inferring** in Procedure Step 2.
▶ **Interpreting Data** in Analyze Questions 1-9.
▶ **Formulating Models** in Conclude and Apply Questions 10 and 11.
▶ **Recognizing and Using Spatial Relationships** in Analyze Questions 1-9 and Conclude and Apply Questions 10 and 11.

COOPERATIVE LEARNING
Form Science Investigation teams with three or four students per group.

TEACHING THE ACTIVITY

▶ Explain to each group that they are to examine the two cross sections closely and make a number of inferences based on the clues provided and their knowledge of superposition, unconformities, faulting, and intrusive igneous activity. Have each group reach consensus on each of the questions for both cross sections.

▶ Collect written answers from each group. Review the answers to each question with the entire class. Where differences occur, ask representatives of each group to explain how their group arrived at their answer.

PROGRAM RESOURCES

From the **Teacher Resource Package** use:

Activity Worksheets, pages 142-143, Activity 16-1: Determining Relative Ages.

ANSWERS TO QUESTIONS

1. No, since the dike intrudes every layer, it must be the youngest feature.
2. a disconformity; yes, as with any unconformity, other rock could have existed and been eroded
3. a reverse fault
4. Since the shale is older than the overlying layers that have been offset by the fault, it was deposited *before* faulting.
5. No, more data is needed.
6. a normal fault
7. Since the dike is offset by the fault but the unconformity is not, the dike is older.
8. Since the dike on the right intrudes the sandstone and the dike that has been offset by the fault is older than the sandstone, the two dikes formed at different times.
9. The sandstone and shale exhibit disconformities at their upper surfaces. These may indicate erosion.
10. 1) shale, 2) sandstone, 3) limestone, 4) disconformity, 5) sandstone, 6) limestone, 7) fault, 8) igneous intrusion; note that another possible solution is 7) igneous intrusion and 8) fault
11. 1) sandstone, 2) shale, 3) limestone, 4) sandstone, 5) limestone, 6) shale, 7) igneous intrusion (left), 8) fault, 9) disconformity, 10) sandstone, and 11) igneous intrusion (right)

SECTION 16-3

PREPARATION

SECTION BACKGROUND

► The law of faunal succession states that fossil organisms occur in rocks in a definite and determinable order. Thus, rocks formed during a particular interval of geologic time can be recognized by their fossil content.

► A geologic column is a composite diagram that shows the rocks of a given area in the sequence in which they occur.

► Correlation of geologic columns from many locations enables geologists to construct geologic maps. Geologic maps show the relative age, distribution, and structural features of surface rocks.

1 MOTIVATE

► **Demonstration:** Without explaining your actions to the students, place layer upon layer of five different colored clays on top of your desk. Use a knife to carefully cut a "fault" through all the layers. Now place a sixth layer on top of the faulted ones. Ask students to determine the relative ages of the layers and the fault.

16-3 Relative Ages of Rocks

New Science Words

law of superposition
relative dating
unconformities

Objectives

- ► Describe several methods used to date rock layers relative to other rock layers.
- ► Interpret gaps in the rock record.
- ► Give an example of how rock layers may be correlated with other rock layers.

How is the law of superposition used by geologists?

The Law of Superposition

It's a hot summer day in July and you're getting ready to meet your friends at the local park. You put on your helmet and pads and grab your skateboard. But the bearings in one of the wheels are worn, and the wheel isn't spinning freely. You remember reading an article in a skateboarding magazine about how to replace wheels, and you decide to look it up. In your room is a stack of magazines from the past year. You know that the article came out in the January edition, so it must be near the bottom of the pile. As you dig downward, you find the March issue then the February issue. January must be next.

How did you know that the issue of the magazine would be on bottom? To find the older edition under newer ones, you applied the law of superposition.

The **law of superposition** states that in a layer of rock, the oldest rocks are on the bottom and the rocks become progressively younger toward the top. Why is this the case, and is it always true? 1

As you know, sediments are often deposited in layers, forming layers of sedimentary rock. The first layer to form is usually on the bottom. Each additional layer forms on top of the previous one. Unless forces, such as those generated by tectonic activity, overturn the layers, the oldest rocks are found at the bottom. When layers have been overturned, geologists use other clues in the rock layers to determine their original positions.

OPTIONS

Meeting Different Ability Levels

For Section 16-3, use the following **Teacher Resource Masters** depending upon individual students' needs.

◆ **Study Guide Master** for all students.

● **Reinforcement Master** for students of average and above average ability levels.

▲ **Enrichment Master** for above average students.

Additional Teacher Resource Package masters are listed in the OPTIONS box throughout the section. The additional masters are appropriate for all students.

◆ STUDY GUIDE 68

NAME ________ DATE ________ CLASS ________

STUDY GUIDE — Chapter 16

Relative Ages of Rocks — Text Pages 430-435

In the blank at the left, write the letter of the term or phrase that best completes each statement.

b 1. In layers of undisturbed sedimentary rock, the oldest rocks are on the ____. a. top b. bottom

a 2. Sediments deposited in layers form ____ rocks. a. sedimentary b. igneous

a 3. The statement that old rocks are on the bottom in layers of undisturbed rock is called the ____. a. law of superposition b. tectonic theory

b 4. Sometimes layers of rock are overturned by forces generated by ____. a. superposition b. tectonic activity

a 5. Determining the age of rocks by examining their position in a layer is called ____. a. relative dating b. faulting

b 6. Gaps in rock layers are called ____. a. faults b. unconformities

b 7. The type of unconformity in which an erosional surface exists in one of several horizontal layers is called a(n) ____. a. angular unconformity b. disconformity

b 8. Matching of rock layers in two different areas is called ____ the layers. a. concluding b. correlating

a 9. One way to match rock layers that are apart is to see if the same type of ____ are found in both places. a. fossils b. water

b 10. Sometimes rock layers are visible because they have been exposed by ____ cutting through them. a. volcanoes b. streams

a 11. Some unconformities are the result of ____. a. erosion b. volcanoes

12. Number the rock layers according to their relative ages. Label the oldest rock type #1.

A. #6
B. #5
C. #3
D. #2
E. #1
F. #4

68

Relative Dating

Suppose you now want to look for another issue of your skateboarding magazine. You're not sure exactly how old it is; all you know is that it arrived after the January issue. You can find it in the stack by using relative dating.

Relative dating is used in geology to determine the order of events and the relative age of rocks by examining the position of rocks in a sequence. For example, if layers of sedimentary rock have a fault running through them, you know that the layers had to be there first before a fault could form in them. The relative age of the rocks is older than the relative age of the fault.

2 How are relative dating and the law of superposition related?

Relative dating doesn't tell you anything about the exact age of rock layers. You don't know if a layer is 100 million or 10 000 years old, only that it's younger than the layers below it and older than the fault running through it.

Relative dating works well if rocks haven't been folded or overturned by tectonic processes. For example, look at Figure 16-10. Which layer is the oldest? In cases where rock layers have been disturbed, you may have to look for fossils and other clues to date the rocks. If you find a fossil in the top layer that's older than a fossil in a lower layer, you can hypothesize that the layers have been overturned.

Figure 16-10. Starting with layer 1, can you tell if the layers become progressively older or younger? Methods other than using the law of superposition must be used to date overturned or disturbed layers.

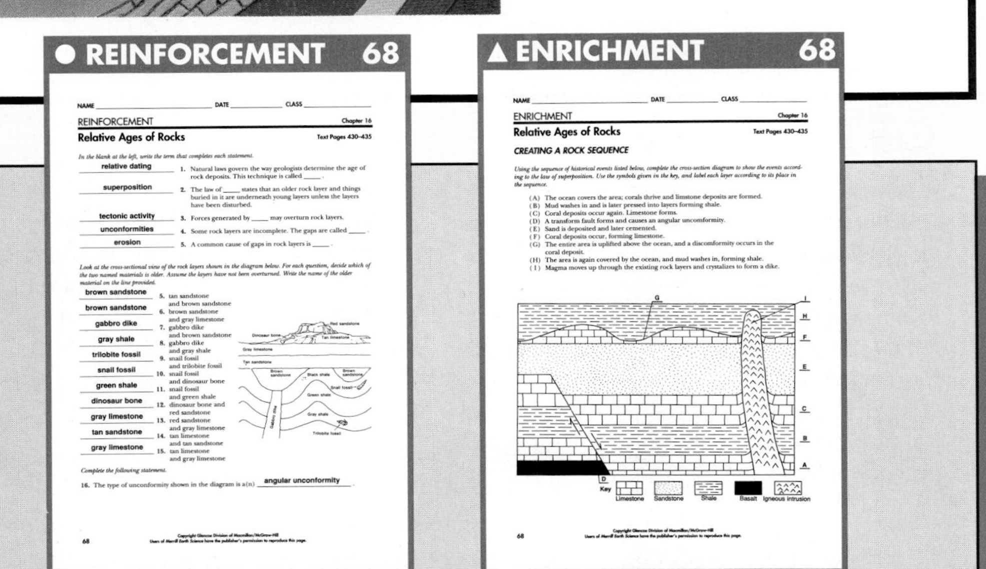

● REINFORCEMENT 68

NAME ______ DATE ______ CLASS ______

REINFORCEMENT — Chapter 16

Relative Ages of Rocks — Text Pages 430–435

In the blank at the left, write the term that completes each statement.

relative dating — 1. Natural laws govern the way geologists determine the age of rock deposits. This technique is called ____ .

superposition — 2. The law of ____ states that an older rock layer and things buried in it are underneath young layers unless the layers have been disturbed.

tectonic activity — 3. Forces generated by ____ may overturn rock layers.

unconformities — 4. Some rock layers are incomplete. The gaps are called ____ .

erosion — 5. A common cause of gaps in rock layers is ____ .

Look at the cross-sectional view of the rock layers shown in the diagram below. For each question, decide which of the two named materials is older. Assume the layers have not been overturned. Write the name of the older material on the line provided.

brown sandstone — 5. tan sandstone and brown sandstone

brown sandstone — 6. brown sandstone and gray limestone

gabbro dike — 7. gabbro dike and brown sandstone

gray shale — 8. gabbro dike and gray shale

trilobite fossil — 9. snail fossil and trilobite fossil

snail fossil — 10. snail fossil and dinosaur bone

green shale — 11. snail fossil and green shale

dinosaur bone — 12. dinosaur bone and red sandstone

gray limestone — 13. red sandstone and gray limestone

tan sandstone — 14. tan limestone and tan sandstone

gray limestone — 15. tan limestone and gray limestone

Complete the following statement.

16. The type of unconformity shown in the diagram is a(n) angular unconformity .

68

▲ ENRICHMENT 68

NAME ______ DATE ______ CLASS ______

ENRICHMENT — Chapter 16

Relative Ages of Rocks — Text Pages 430–435

CREATING A ROCK SEQUENCE

Using the sequence of historical events listed below, complete the cross-section diagram to show the events according to the law of superposition. Use the symbols given in the key, and label each layer according to its place in the sequence.

(A) The ocean covers the area; corals thrive and limstone deposits are formed.
(B) Mud washes in and is later pressed into layers forming shale.
(C) Coral deposits occur again. Limestone forms.
(D) A transform fault forms and causes an angular uncomformity.
(E) Sand is deposited and later cemented.
(F) Coral deposits occur, forming limestone.
(G) The entire area is uplifted above the ocean, and a discomformity occurs in the coral deposit.
(H) The area is again covered by the ocean, and mud washes in, forming shale.
(I) Magma moves up through the existing rock layers and crystalizes to form a dike.

68

TYING TO PREVIOUS KNOWLEDGE: Students experience "superposition" in their everyday lives. Have students relate how sequences of sedimentary rocks are similar to the bricks in a brick house or building. A bricklayer must place the first layer of bricks before he or she can lay another layer on top. The bricks at the base of a building are "older" than those above it.

OBJECTIVES AND SCIENCE WORDS: Have students review the objectives and science words to become familiar with this section.

2 TEACH

Key Concepts are highlighted.

CONCEPT DEVELOPMENT

Cooperative Learning: Using the Paired Partners strategy, have students determine the relative ages of the rocks and features shown in Figure 16-10.

PROGRAM RESOURCES

Use **Laboratory Manual,** pages 129-132, Law of Superposition.

CONCEPT DEVELOPMENT

▶ **Demonstration:** Use a set of books from an encyclopedia to demonstrate unconformities. Construct an angular unconformity by stacking volumes 1, 2, 3, and 4 in numerical order, with volume 1 on the bottom. Tilt the books at an angle and then horizontally place volumes 7 and 8 on top of the tilted books. Demonstrate a disconformity by stacking volumes 1, 2, 3, and 4 in numerical order, with volume 1 on the bottom. Add volumes 7, 8, and 9 to the stack. Explain that the missing volumes in each case create the unconformity.

TEACHER F.Y.I.

▶ Another type of unconformity, called a nonconformity, forms when sedimentary rocks are deposited on older, eroded igneous or metamorphic rocks.

Unconformities

As you have seen, a layer of rock is a record of past events. But some rock records are incomplete—there are layers missing. These gaps in rock layers are called **unconformities.**

Name and describe two types of unconformities.

Unconformities develop when agents of erosion remove existing rock layers. They also form when a period of time passes without any new deposition occurring to form new layers of rock.

3 Figure 16-11 illustrates one way an unconformity can form. Horizontal layers of sedimentary rock are tilted and uplifted above the surface of the water, where agents of erosion and weathering wear them down. Eventually, the tilted layers are again underwater where new sediments are deposited on them in horizontal layers. The rock record records the event as tilted layers of rock meeting horizontal ones. Such an unconformity is called an angular unconformity.

Figure 16-11. An angular unconformity results when horizontal and tilted layers contact each other.

Rocks formed as horizontal layers

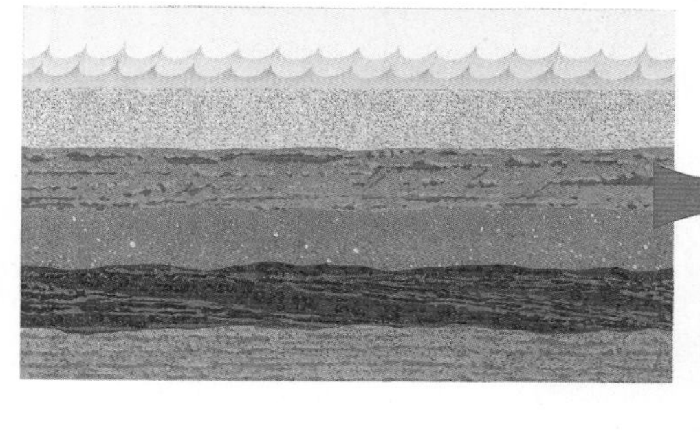

The rock layers are tilted as they're lifted above the water surface

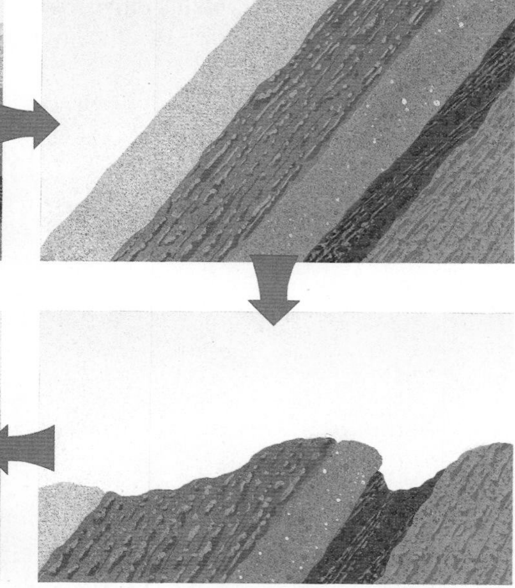

The tilted layers are eroded above the water surface

An angular unconformity results when new horizontal layers form on the tilted layers

OPTIONS

INQUIRY QUESTIONS

▶ **What does an unconformity tell you about the geology of the area?** *At some time in the past, erosion removed some rock and/or time passed without any rock formation.*

▶ **How does an angular unconformity form?** *Horizontal rock layers are uplifted, tilted, and eroded. The surface between these rocks and younger horizontal rocks is an angular unconformity.*

▶ **How might a disconformity form?** Horizontal rock layers are uplifted and eroded. Younger rocks are deposited on this erosional surface to form a disconformity.

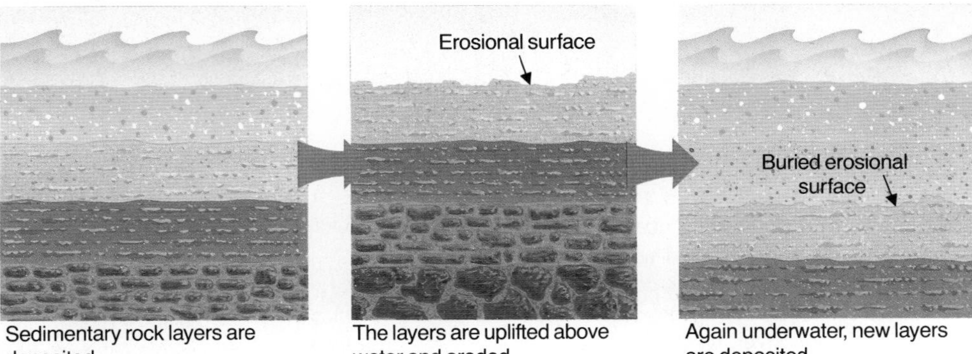
Erosional surface
Buried erosional surface
Sedimentary rock layers are deposited
The layers are uplifted above water and eroded
Again underwater, new layers are deposited

Figure 16-12. The buried erosional surface in the far right illustration is a disconformity.

Suppose you're standing before a great wall of sedimentary rock layers. Here, layers of sandstone, shale, and limestone are stacked neatly on top of each other in horizontal layers. The rock record looks complete, but in actuality, there are layers missing. If you look closely you may find an old erosional surface in one of the layers. This records a time when the rocks were lifted above the water surface and eroded. Then new sedimentary rocks formed above the eroded surface when it was again lowered beneath the water surface. Even though all the layers are horizontal, there's still a gap in the record. This type of unconformity, called a disconformity, is illustrated in Figure 16-12. 4

Correlating Rock Layers

Suppose you're a geologist working in Utah near Canyonlands National Park and Bryce Canyon National Park. You're studying a layer of sandstone in Bryce Canyon. Later, when you visit the Canyonlands, you notice that a layer of sandstone there looks just like the sandstone in Bryce Canyon, 250 kilometers away. Above the sandstone in the Canyonlands is a layer of limestone and then another sandstone layer. You return to Bryce Canyon and find the same sequence—sandstone, limestone, and sandstone. What do you conclude?

It's likely that you're actually looking at the same rocks at the two locations. These rocks are parts of huge deposits that covered this whole area of Utah. The sandstones and limestone you found at the two parks are the exposed surfaces of the same rock layers.

REVEALING MISCONCEPTIONS

▶ Some students may think that geographically diverse sedimentary rocks are different rocks. Although this is sometimes true, explain that during many times in the geologic past, Earth's present-day landmasses were covered by shallow seas. Rocks that span vast geographical areas formed as the seas regressed and transgressed.

MINI QUIZ

Use the Mini Quiz to check students' recall of chapter content.

1. **What is the law of superposition?** *A law that states that in an undisturbed rock sequence, the oldest rocks are at the bottom of the sequence.*
2. **_____ is a technique that determines the ages of rocks as compared to one another.** *Relative dating*
3. **An unconformity between tilted and horizontal rock is a(n) _____ .** *angular unconformity*
4. **A gap between horizontal rock layers is a(n) _____ .** *disconformity*

CROSS CURRICULUM

▶ **Geography:** Obtain state geologic maps of Colorado, Utah, Arizona, and New Mexico. Have students examine the maps and note that when they are arranged geographically, many of the rocks extend across state boundaries. Have students research to find out about the geologic history of this area during the Mesozoic and Cenozoic Eras.

ENRICHMENT

▶ Demonstrate the principles of deposition and superposition discussed in the Section Review **Apply** Question 3. Place an inverted bowl in the bottom of an empty ten-gallon fish aquarium. Add enough water just to cover the bowl. Add colored sand to the water and allow it to settle, forming a layer. This first layer of sand should not completely cover the bowl. Using sand of a different color, add another layer of sediment and allow it to settle. Again, be sure you don't add enough to cover the top of the bowl. Continue adding layers of sand (using alternating colors) until the bowl is finally covered after approximately five depositional layers. Have students note that the layers did not arch upward or follow the contour of the dome. Instead, they formed horizontal layers around the dome. Relate this demonstration to the **Apply** question. Have a volunteer explain how the bowl differs from the igneous intrusion described in the question.

PROBLEM SOLVING

Schist and gneiss are at the base of each column. At least three unconformities occur in the Westwater column; at least two are shown in the Green River column. Unconformities exist between gray sandstone and red shale, between red shale and red sandstone, and between green shale and schist or gneiss.

Think Critically: Deposition of rocks in the Green River area was interrupted by periods of erosion and/or nondeposition as shown by the unconformities. There are several hypotheses that could explain why rocks are missing from the Westwater column. The rocks could have been deposited and later eroded. Or, the beds may never have been deposited in the area.

CHECK FOR UNDERSTANDING

Use the Problem Solving activity above to check for understanding.

RETEACH

Use an overhead projector and a transparency to reconstruct the geologic columns in the Problem Solving activity. Start at the bottom of each column and explain the geologic processes involved as you move upward through the rock layers.

EXTENSION

For students who have mastered this section, use the **Reinforcement** and **Enrichment** masters or other OPTIONS provided.

PROBLEM SOLVING

Closing the Gap

Lana and Geoff spent part of their summer vacation on a field trip through Colorado and Utah. They observed many rock outcrops and recorded what they saw in notebooks. The geologic column on the left was drawn by Lana from observations made in Green River, Utah. The column on the right was made by Geoff from the data he collected in Westwater, Colorado. Help them reconstruct the geologic history of the area by answering the following. What type of rock is found at the base of each column? How many unconformities occur in each column? Describe the locations of these unconformities.

Think Critically: Explain the geologic history of the Green River area in terms of erosion and deposition. Why are some formations missing from the Westwater column?

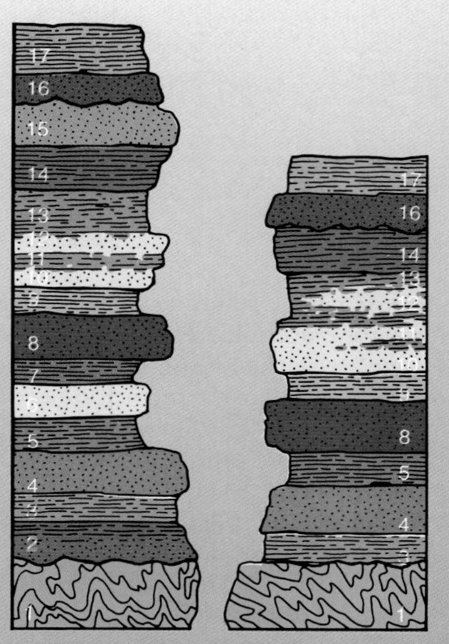

Why is it more difficult to correlate some layers than others?

Geologist match up, or correlate, layers of rocks over great distances. It's not always easy to say that rock exposed in one area is the same rock exposed in another area. Sometimes it's possible to simply walk along the layer for kilometers and prove that it's one continuous formation. In other cases, such as at the Canyonlands and Bryce Canyon, the rock layers are exposed only where rivers have cut down through overlying layers of rock and sediment. How can you prove that the limestone sandwiched between the two sandstones in the Canyonlands is the same limestone at Bryce Canyon? One way is to use fossil evidence. If the same types of fossils are found in both exposures of limestone, it's a good indication that the limestone at each location is the same age, and therefore, one continuous deposit.

OPTIONS

INQUIRY QUESTIONS

▶ **How do geologists correlate rocks?** *Geologists use fossils contained in rocks and the rock type to correlate geographically distant rocks.*

▶ **Suppose you found identical fossils in rocks from widely separated locations. Are you guaranteed the rocks are the same age? Explain.** *No, the fossils may be from an organism that changed little throughout geologic time. Such fossils are not reliable indicators of age.*

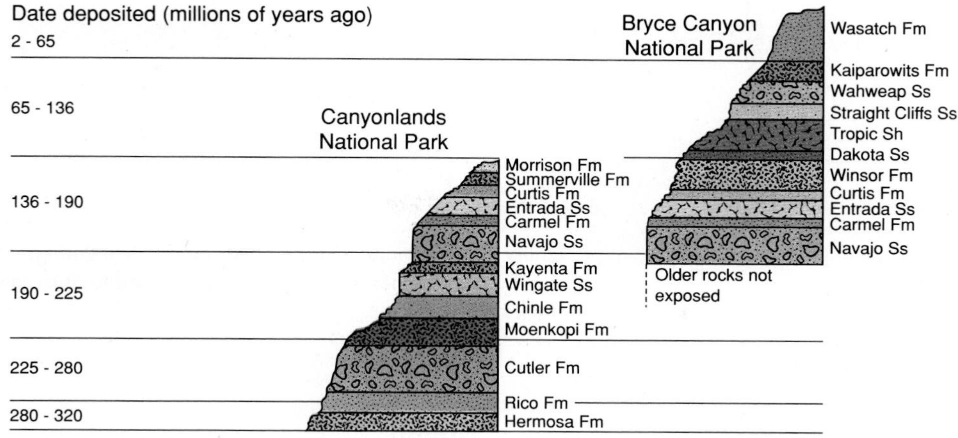

Figure 16-13. The many rock layers, or formations, in Canyonlands and Bryce Canyon have been dated and named. Some formations have been correlated between the two canyons. Which layers are present at both canyons? (NOTE: Fm = formation, Ss = sandstone, Sh = shale.)

Are there other ways to correlate layers of rock? Is there a way to say that two rocks are the same age? Sometimes relative dating isn't enough, and absolute dating must be used. In the next section, you will see how the actual age of rocks can be determined and how we've been able to determine the age of Earth from dating rocks.

SECTION REVIEW

1. Suppose you haven't cleaned out your locker all year. Where would you expect to find papers from the beginning of the year? What principle in geology would you use to find these old papers?
2. Why is it more difficult to recognize a disconformity than an angular unconformity?
3. **Apply:** What is the relative age of an igneous intrusion that is forcing overlying sedimentary rock layers to dome upward?

Interpreting Data — Skill Builder

A geologist finds a series of rocks. The sandstone contains a trilobite that is 400 million years old. The shale contains some graptolites, which are between 550 and 500 million years old. The limestone, which lies under the sandstone, contains fossils that are between 500 and 400 million years old. Which rock bed is oldest? Explain. If you need help, refer to Interpreting Data in the **Skill Handbook** on page 687.

3 CLOSE

▶ Ask questions 1 and 2 and the **Apply** Question in the Section Review.

Cooperative Learning: Copy three related but simple geologic columns from an introductory college-level geology book. Have students work as Paired Partners to correlate the rocks across the three columns.

SECTION REVIEW ANSWERS

1. Older papers would probably be closer to the bottom of the locker than more recent papers. Applying the law of superposition might help in finding the papers.

2. An angular unconformity is a physical boundary in which tilted rocks are overlain by horizontal rocks. In a disconformity, all the rocks are relatively horizontal—the unconformity is a "missing" rock.

3. Apply: The igneous intrusion is younger than the sedimentary rocks being domed upward. Sedimentary layers are almost always deposited horizontally. The layers would not be deposited in a domed, or arched, formation.

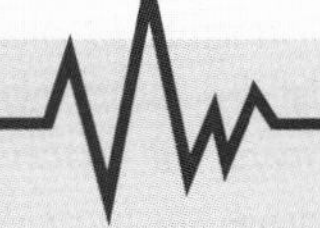

Skill Builder

The shale is the oldest; the sandstone is the youngest.

ENRICHMENT

▶ Provide students with a somewhat complex geologic cross section from an introductory college earth science text. Have them determine the relative ages of the rocks, faults, intrusions, and/or unconformities present.

PROGRAM RESOURCES

From the **Teacher Resource Package** use:

Transparency Masters, pages 69-70, Rock Relationships.

Transparency Masters, pages 71-72, Dating Rock Layers with Fossils.

Use **Color Transparency** number 35, Rock Relationships.

Use **Color Transparency** number 36, Dating Rock Layers with Fossils.

SECTION 16-4

PREPARATION

SECTION BACKGROUND

► Radiometric dating that uses the radioactive isotope carbon-14 is referred to as radiocarbon dating.

► A varve, which is a layer of sediment that is deposited over one year's time, can be used to calculate the absolute age of lake deposits.

PREPLANNING

► To prepare for Activity 16-2, have students bring shoe boxes with lids. For each group, obtain 100 paper clips, 100 pennies, and 100 brass fasteners.

1 MOTIVATE

Cooperative Learning: Form Problem Solving Teams with five students per group. Have students determine the relative ages of the members of their group. Have a recorder from each group list students from youngest to oldest. Then have students list the exact age in years, months, and days for each student in the group. Have students use this analogy to determine the difference between relative and absolute dating methods.

TYING TO PREVIOUS KNOWLEDGE: Have students recall from Chapter 2 that atoms of the same element with different numbers of neutrons are called isotopes. Radioactive isotopes are used in absolute dating.

OBJECTIVES AND SCIENCE WORDS: Have students review the objectives and science words to become familiar with this section.

16-4 Absolute Ages of Rocks

New Science Words

absolute dating
radioactive decay
half-life
radiometric dating
uniformitarianism

Objectives

► Identify how absolute dating differs from relative dating.
► Describe how the half-lives of isotopes are used to determine a rock's age.

Absolute Dating

As you continue to shuffle through your stack of skateboarding magazines looking for articles about wheels and bearings, you decide you need to restack them into a neat pile. By now, they're a jumble and no longer in order of their relative ages. How can you stack them so the oldest are on bottom and the newest on top? Fortunately, magazines have their dates printed on their covers. So, stacking magazines in order is a simple process. Unfortunately for geologists, rocks don't have their ages stamped on them. Or do they?

Contrast absolute and relative dating.

1 **Absolute dating** is a method used by geologists to determine the age, in years, of a rock or other object. Absolute dating is a process that uses the properties of atoms in rocks and other objects to determine their ages.

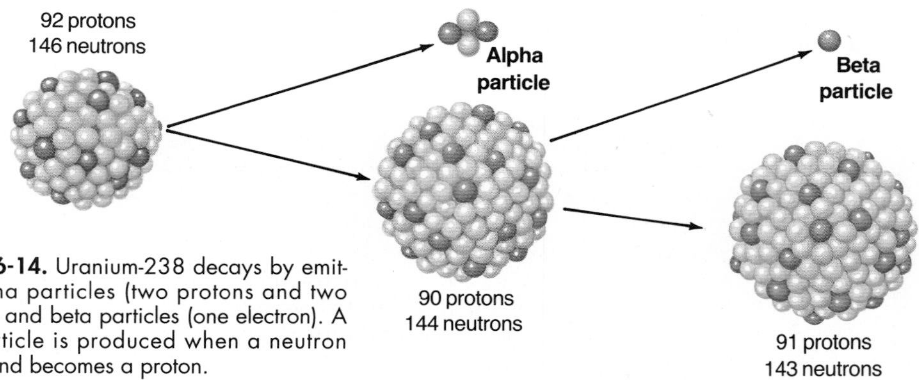

Figure 16-14. Uranium-238 decays by emitting alpha particles (two protons and two neutrons) and beta particles (one electron). A beta particle is produced when a neutron decays and becomes a proton.

OPTIONS

Meeting Different Ability Levels

For Section 16-4, use the following **Teacher Resource Masters** depending upon individual students' needs.

◆ **Study Guide Master** for all students.
● **Reinforcement Master** for students of average and above average ability levels.
▲ **Enrichment Master** for above average students.

Additional Teacher Resource Package masters are listed in the OPTIONS box throughout the section. The additional masters are appropriate for all students.

◆ STUDY GUIDE 69

NAME ____ DATE ____ CLASS ____

STUDY GUIDE — Chapter 16

Absolute Ages of Rocks — Text Pages 436–439

Use the words in the boxes to fill in the blanks.

absolute dating	element	neutrons
age	isotopes	radioactive
atoms	lead-206	uranium-238

Besides relative dating, geologists use another method to determine in years the **age** of rocks and other objects. It's called **absolute dating**. It's a process that uses the properties of the **atoms** in objects.

Elements can have atoms with different numbers of **neutrons** in their nuclei. Some of these **isotopes** undergo a process of **radioactive** decay. When the isotope decays, a new **element** is formed. An example of this decay is the change of the isotope **uranium-238** to **lead-206**.

carbon-14	nitrogen-14	radiometric dating
daughter product	parent material	uniformitarianism
half-life		

Another example of decaying isotopes is the isotope **carbon-14**, which decays to **nitrogen-14**. The original isotope in this process is called the **parent material**. The isotope that results from the decay is the **daughter product**.

Every radioactive parent material has a certain rate at which it decays to its daughter product. This rate is known as its **half-life**.

Calculating the absolute age of a rock is called **radiometric dating**. Long before this was possible, a Scottish scientist estimated that Earth was millions of years old. He used the principle called **uniformitarianism**, which states that Earth's processes occurring today are similar to those that occurred in the past.

69

Radioactive Decay

In Chapter 2, you learned that an element can have atoms with different numbers of neutrons in their nuclei. Some of these isotopes undergo a process called radioactive decay. When an atom of an isotope decays, one of its neutrons breaks down into a proton and and an electron. The electron leaves the atom as a beta particle. The nucleus loses a neutron, but gains a proton. Some isotopes give off two protons and two neutrons in the form of an alpha particle. As you know, when the number of protons in an atom is changed, as it is in **radioactive decay,** a new element is formed. For example, when an atom of the radioactive isotope uranium-238 decays, it eventually ②
forms an atom of lead-206. Lead-206 isn't radioactive, so it doesn't decay any further.

In the case of uranium decaying to lead, uranium-238 is known as the parent material and lead-206 as the daughter product. Another example of a parent material is carbon-14, which decays to its daughter, nitrogen-14. Each radioactive parent material has a certain rate at which it decays to its daughter product. This rate is known as its ③
half-life.

The **half-life** of an isotope is the time it takes for half of the atoms in the isotope to decay. For example, the half-life of carbon-14 is 5730 years. So, it will take 5730 years for half of the carbon-14 atoms in an object to decay to nitrogen-14. You might guess that in another 5730 years, all of the remaining carbon-14 atoms will have decayed to nitrogen-14. However, this is not the case. Only half of the atoms of carbon-14 remaining after the first 5730 years will decay during the second 5730 years. So, after two half-lives, one-fourth of the original carbon-14 atoms still remains. Half of them will decay after another 5730 years. After three half-lives, one-eighth of the original carbon-14 atoms still remains. After many half-lives, such a small amount of the parent material remains that it all decays to its daughter product.

Radiometric Dating

To a geologist, the decay of radioactive isotopes is like a clock ticking away, keeping track of time that's passed since rocks have formed. As time passes, the concentration of parent material in a rock decreases as the

MINI-Lab 

What are some of the relative and absolute dates of events in Earth's history?

Listed below are several events in Earth's history. List them in the relative order in which you think they occurred. Make a time line using the following dates: 4.6 billion years, 3.5 billion years, 1.0 billion years, 630 million years, 410 million years, 360 million years, 210 million years, 65 million years, and 5 million years. Match each event on your list with the absolute date on your time line. Check your time line with your teacher or other reference source.

Events: *Earth forms, first multicellular plants evolve, first plants move onto the land, first mammals evolve, first multicellular animals evolve, dinosaurs become extinct, first animals move onto the land, first human ancestors evolve, formation of oldest known fossils.*

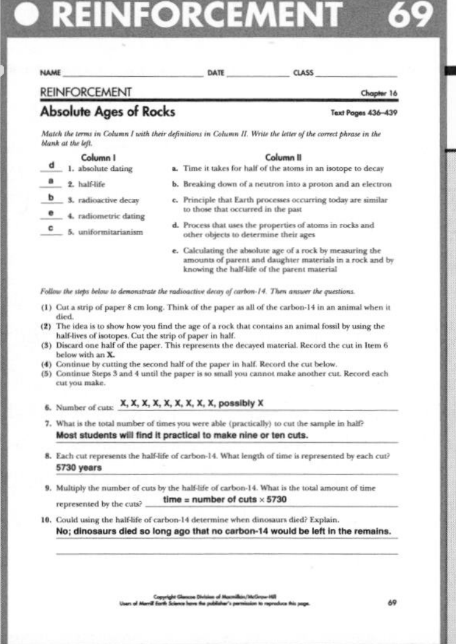

● REINFORCEMENT 69

NAME ______ DATE ______ CLASS ______

REINFORCEMENT Chapter 16

Absolute Ages of Rocks Text Pages 436–439

Match the terms in Column I with their definitions in Column II. Write the letter of the correct phrase in the blank at the left.

Column I	Column II
d 1. absolute dating	a. Time it takes for half of the atoms in an isotope to decay
a 2. half-life	b. Breaking down of a neutron into a proton and an electron
b 3. radioactive decay	c. Principle that Earth processes occurring today are similar to those that occurred in the past
e 4. radiometric dating	d. Process that uses the properties of atoms in rocks and other objects to determine their ages
c 5. uniformitarianism	e. Calculating the absolute age of a rock by measuring the amounts of parent and daughter materials in a rock and by knowing the half-life of the parent material

Follow the steps below to demonstrate the radioactive decay of carbon-14. Then answer the questions.

(1) Cut a strip of paper 8 cm long. Think of the paper as all of the carbon-14 in an animal when it died.
(2) The idea is to show how you find the age of a rock that contains an animal fossil by using the half-lives of isotopes. Cut the strip of paper in half.
(3) Discard one half of the paper. This represents the decayed material. Record the cut in Item 6 below with an X.
(4) Continue by cutting the second half of the paper in half. Record the cut below.
(5) Continue Steps 3 and 4 until the paper is so small you cannot make another cut. Record each cut you make.

6. Number of cuts: X, X, X, X, X, X, X, X, X, possibly X
7. What is the total number of times you were able (practically) to cut the sample in half? Most students will find it practical to make nine or ten cuts.
8. Each cut represents the half-life of carbon-14. What length of time is represented by each cut? 5730 years
9. Multiply the number of cuts by the half-life of carbon-14. What is the total amount of time represented by the cuts? time = number of cuts × 5730
10. Could using the half-life of carbon-14 determine when dinosaurs died? Explain. No; dinosaurs died so long ago that no carbon-14 would be left in the remains.

 69

▲ ENRICHMENT 69

NAME ______ DATE ______ CLASS ______

ENRICHMENT Chapter 16

Absolute Ages of Rocks Text Pages 436–439

CALCULATING HALF-LIVES

You learned in the chapter about the half-lives of carbon-14 and radium. Here is a table of some other isotopes and their half-lives. Use the table to answer the questions that follow.

Isotope	Half-life
Plutonium-238	86 years
Americium-241	433 years
Curium-242	163 days
Berkelium-249	314 days
Californium-249	360 days
Einsteinium-253	20 days
Nobelium-259	1 1/2 hours
Lawrencium-260	180 seconds
Element 103-262	40 seconds

1. If you had a 100-gram sample of plutonium, how much would still remain in 43 years? 75 grams
2. What happened to the part of the plutonium that is no longer there? It changed into another substance.
3. If you had a 5-gram sample of Lawrencium, how much would still remain in 30 minutes? none
4. If you had a 100-gram sample of Einsteinium, how much would you have left after 40 days? 25 grams
5. A rock sample contains 7.5 grams of Californium-249 and 52.5 grams of the product into which the Californium has changed. How old is the rock? 1440 days

 69

2 TEACH

Key Concepts are highlighted.

CONCEPT DEVELOPMENT

Cooperative Learning: Using the Paired Partners strategy, have students compute the age of a rock sample that contains 1/64 of the original carbon-14 isotope. The sample is about 34 380 years old.

MINI-Lab 

Materials: adding machine tape, meterstick, pencil

Teaching Tips

Cooperative Learning: Have Paired Partners do this activity.

►Suggest a scale of 1 millimeter for each 1 million years. This will require a 4.6-meter (or longer) piece of adding machine tape.

►If a different scale is used, have students calculate the length of tape needed before starting their timelines.

►**Answers:**

Event	Years Before Present
Earth forms	4.6 billion
oldest known fossils	3.5 billion
1st multicelled plants	1.0 billion
1st multicelled animals	630 million
1st plants on land	410 million
1st animals on land	360 million
1st mammals	210 million
dinosaurs extinct	65 million
1st human ancestors	5 million

MINI QUIZ

Use the Mini Quiz to check students' recall of chapter content.

① **Which method of dating determines the age of a rock in years?** *absolute dating*

② **What is the daughter element of uranium-238?** *lead-206*

③ **What is the time it takes for half of a radioactive isotope to decay?** *half-life*

TEACHER F.Y.I.

▶ Recent theories suggest the moon formed about 100 million years after Earth. Thus, Earth must be at least as old as the oldest known moon rocks, which are 4.45 billion years. Astronomers assume Earth formed at the same time as most meteorites. The ages of the oldest known meteorites are 4.55 billion years old. Based on this, Earth's age is estimated to be 4.6 billion years.

REVEALING MISCONCEPTIONS

▶ Ask students if a radiometric age can be determined for a conglomerate containing fragments of radioactive materials. Explain that radiometric dating of a conglomerate will give the age of the mineral fragments being dated. The radiometric dating method will determine when the minerals formed, *not* when they were cemented together to form the conglomerate.

CHECK FOR UNDERSTANDING

Ask each student to write a brief paragraph explaining what happens to a radioactive isotope that enables it to be used in radiometric dating.

RETEACH

Ask students to imagine that a sheet of paper represents the amount of parent radioactive isotope in a rock. State that the half-life of the parent isotope is 20 seconds. After 20 seconds, tear the sheet of paper in half. Set one half of the sheet of paper aside, and explain that it represents the daughter isotope. Every 20 seconds, repeat the process with the paper that remains. Ask students to describe what has happened to the amount of parent isotope. Lead students to conclude that at some point, all of the parent isotope will decay.

EXTENSION

For students who have mastered this section, use the **Reinforcement** and **Enrichment** masters or other OPTIONS provided.

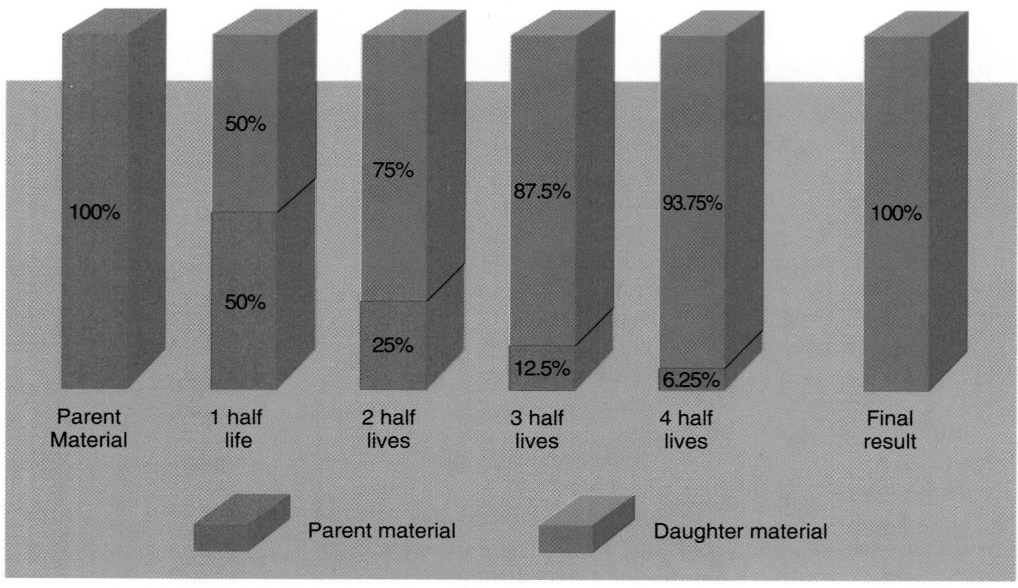

Figure 16-15. After each half-life, one-half the amount of parent material remains. Eventually, such a small amount of the parent material is left that it all decays to daughter material.

concentration of daughter product increases. By measuring the amounts of parent and daughter materials in a rock and by knowing the half-life of the parent, a geologist can calculate the absolute age of the rock. This process is called **radiometric dating.**

A scientist must decide which parent and daughter materials to measure when dating a rock or fossil. If the object to be dated is very old, then an isotope with a long half-life must be used. For example, if a fossil is 1 billion years old, there would be no carbon-14 left to measure. However, the half-life of uranium-238 is 4.5 billion years. Enough of the parent and daughter would still be present to measure.

Carbon-14 is useful for dating fossils up to 75 000 years old. Organisms take in carbon from the environment to build tissues in their bodies. When the organism dies, some of the carbon-14 decays and escapes as nitrogen-14 gas. The amount of carbon-14 remaining can be measured to determine the age of the fossil.

Radiometric dating has been used to date the oldest rocks found on Earth. These rocks are 3.96 billion years old. Scientists have determined that the oldest known fossils are 3.5 billion years old and have estimated the age of Earth at 4.6 billion years.

Did You Know?

The half-life of rubidium-87 is 500 billion years. That's more than ten times the age of Earth.

OPTIONS

INQUIRY QUESTIONS

▶ **Why is radiometric dating often more useful to geologists than relative dating?** *Radiometric dating enables geologists to determine the exact ages of rocks. Relative dating produces a sequence of geologic events based on the relationships among the events.*

▶ **How do geologists use radioactive decay to determine the absolute age of a rock?** *The rate of decay, called the half-life, is the time it takes for half of the parent isotope to decay into the daughter isotope. The rate of decay together with the amounts of parent and daughter isotopes remaining in a rock are used to determine its absolute age.*

PROGRAM RESOURCES

From the **Teacher Resource Package** use:

Activity Worksheets, page 149, Mini-Lab: What are some of the relative and absolute dates of events in Earth's history?

Before radiometric dating was available, many people had estimated the age of Earth to be only a few thousand years old. But in the 1700s, Scottish scientist James Hutton estimated that Earth was much older. He used the principle of **uniformitarianism.** This principle states that Earth processes occurring today are similar to those that occurred in the past. He observed that the processes that changed the rocks and land around him were very slow, and he inferred that they had been just as slow throughout Earth's history. Hutton hypothesized that it took much longer than a few thousand years to form the layers of rock around him and to erode mountains that once towered kilometers high.

Hutton and others concluded that Earth was millions of years old, not thousands. Since their time, geologists have established that Earth is indeed very old. But only by observing the processes occurring around us today have we been able to unlock the mysteries of our past. As you read the next chapter, you will see how observing life on Earth today has allowed us to understand how organisms have evolved through time.

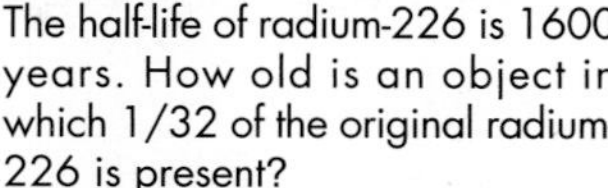

Science and MATH

The half-life of radium-226 is 1600 years. How old is an object in which 1/32 of the original radium-226 is present?

SECTION REVIEW

1. Suppose you discover three layers of rock that have not been overturned. You measure the absolute age of the middle layer to be 120 million years old. What can you say about the ages of the layers above and below it?
2. Suppose you now date an igneous dike running through only the bottom two layers. The dike is cut off by the upper rock layer. The dike is 70 million years old. What can you say about the absolute age of the upper layer?
3. **Apply:** How old would a fossil be if it had only one-eighth of its original carbon-14 remaining?

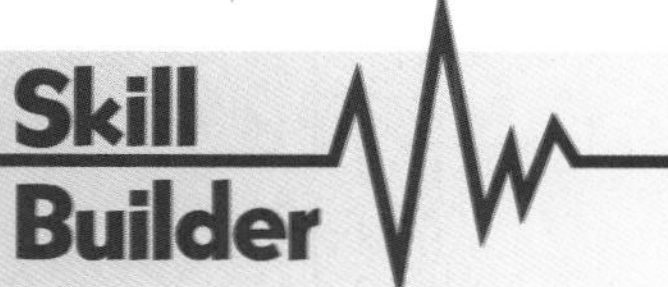

Skill Builder: Making and Using Tables

Make a table that shows the amounts of parent and daughter materials left of a radioactive element after four half-lives if the original parent material had a mass of 100 g. If you need help, refer to Making and Using Tables in the **Skill Handbook** on page 690.

Skill Builder

Possible Solution:

Half-Life	Parent	Daughter
0	100 g	0 g
1	50 g	50 g
2	25 g	75 g
3	12.5 g	87.5 g
4	6.25 g	93.75 g

CROSS CURRICULUM

▶ **Chemistry:** Have students find out the different types of radiation emitted from the isotopes used in radiometric dating.

Science and MATH

After five half-lives, 1/32 of the original isotope remains. Five times 1600 equals 8000 years.

3 CLOSE

Cooperative Learning: Form Science Investigation groups of three students per group. Have each group obtain a beaker containing various amounts—750 mL, 500 mL, 250 mL, and so on—of water. Tell students that the water represents a radioactive isotope. Have students hypothesize how much water would remain in their group's beaker after three half-lives. Then have students remove half of the water for each of three half-lives.

FLEX Your Brain

Use the Flex Your Brain activity to have students explore ABSOLUTE DATING.

▶ Invite a chemistry teacher to discuss the applications of radioactive isotopes.

SECTION REVIEW ANSWERS

1. The top layer is less than 120 million years old; the bottom layer is more than 120 million years old. However, you can't say anything about their absolute ages.

2. The upper layer is younger than 70 million years. At one time, the dike may have extended above the present middle layer into an upper layer that is no longer there. A disconformity may exist between the present middle and upper layers. The disconformity would represent a buried erosional surface that truncated the upper portion of the dike. The present upper layer may have been deposited on top of the erosional surface.

3. Apply: After three half-lives, 1/8 of the original C-14 would remain. Thus, the fossil would be 17 190 years old.

ACTIVITY 16-2
45 minutes

OBJECTIVE: Formulate a model showing how radioactive decay is used to determine the ages of rocks.

PROCESS SKILLS applied in this activity:
▶ **Using Numbers** in Procedure Steps 1-7.
▶ **Interpreting Data** in Analyze Questions 1-3.
▶ **Formulating Models** in Procedure Steps 1-7 and Analyze Question 1.
▶ **Predicting** in Conclude and Apply Question 4.
▶ **Inferring** in Conclude and Apply Question 5.

COOPERATIVE LEARNING
Have Paired Partners perform this activity.

TEACHING THE ACTIVITY

▶ Combine the average data from all student groups. Provide this information so that students can construct graphs in Step 7. Students should graph class data.
▶ To remove all fasteners, students may need to shake the box more than 15 times.
▶ Note that by beginning with 100 objects for the first shake, the number of objects remaining *will* be the percentage of original objects remaining.

PROGRAM RESOURCES

From the **Teacher Resource Package** use:

Activity Worksheets, pages 144-145, Activity 16-2: Radioactive Decay.

ACTIVITY 16-2
Radioactive Decay

Problem: *How can absolute age be determined by radioactive decay?*

Materials
- shoe box with lid
- paper clips (100)
- pennies (100)
- brass fasteners (100)
- graph paper
- colored pencils (2)

Procedure
1. Place 100 pennies into the shoe box with all heads up.
2. Place the lid on the box and shake it one time.
3. Remove the lid. Replace the pennies that are now tails up with paper clips. Record the number of pennies remaining in the box in a data table similar to the one shown.
4. Repeat Steps 2 and 3 until all the pennies have been removed.
5. Remove the paper clips from the box. Put an "X" on one of the shorter sides of the box. Place 100 fasteners in the box.
6. Repeat Steps 2 and 3 until all the fasteners have been removed. Remove only the fasteners that point toward the "X." Be sure to replace them with paper clips.
7. Plot both sets of data on the same graph. Graph the "shake number" on the horizontal axis and the "number of pennies or fasteners remaining" on the vertical axis. Be sure to use a different colored pencil for each set of data.

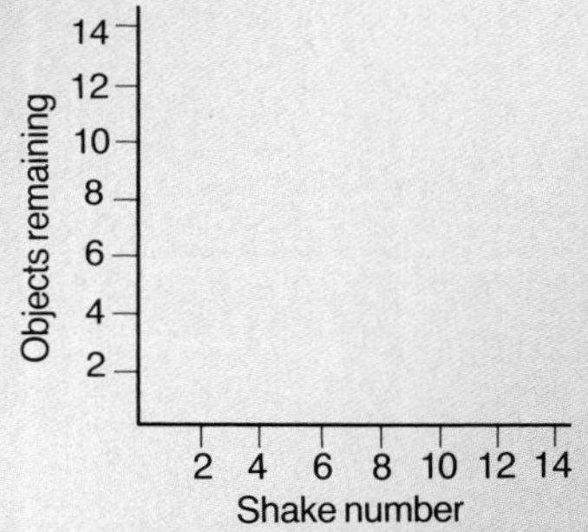

Data and Observations Sample Data

Shake number	Number Remaining	
	Pennies	Fasteners
0	100	100
1	51	83
2	25	69
12	0	7
13	0	5
14	0	4
15	0	2

Analyze
1. In this model of radioactive decay, what do the coins and fasteners represent? The paper clips? The box? Each shake?
2. What was the half-life of the pennies? The fasteners?
3. How does the difference between the two objects affect the half-life? Compare the objects to the differences among radioactive elements.

Conclude and Apply
4. Suppose you could make only one shake in 100 years. How many years would it take to have 25 coins and 75 paper clips remaining? 25 fasteners and 75 paper clips remaining?
5. How can absolute age of rocks be determined?

ANSWERS TO QUESTIONS

1. The coins and fasteners represent radioactive isotopes; paper clips represent the stable daughter products; the box represents the rock in which decay occurs; and each shake represents a time interval.
2. Answers will vary. The number of shakes it takes to have half of each set of objects replaced is one half-life.
3. The two types of objects have different probabilities of landing either heads down or pointing toward the "X." Different elements have different half-lives because their atomic structures differ.
4. Assuming the class average results shown, it would take two half-lives or two shakes for the coins and seven shakes for the fasteners.
5. First determine the percentage of original radioactive material remaining in the rock as compared to the daughter material to which it decays. Then multiply the number of half-lives that have occurred by the length of time required for each half-life.

CHAPTER

REVIEW

SUMMARY

16-1: Fossils

1. In order for fossils to form, hard parts of the dead organisms must be covered quickly.

2. Some fossils form when original materials that made up the organisms are replaced with minerals. Other fossils form when remains are subjected to heat and pressure, leaving only a carbonaceous film behind. Some fossils are the actual remains of once-living organisms. Some fossils are merely the tracks or traces left by former organisms.

3. In nearly all situations, a rock layer can be no older or younger than the age of the fossils embedded in it.

16-2: Science and Society: Extinction of the Dinosaurs

1. The meteorite-impact theory of dinosaur extinction states that a large object from space collided with Earth and caused vast climate changes. Dinosaurs weren't able to adapt and eventually became extinct.

2. Another theory suggests that volcanic activity led to the extinction of the dinosaurs.

16-3: Relative Ages of Rocks

1. The law of superposition states that older rocks lie underneath younger rocks in areas where the rocks haven't been disturbed. Faults are always younger than the rocks they cross-cut. These two concepts can be used to determine relative ages of rocks.

2. Unconformities, or gaps in the rock record, are due to erosion, nondeposition, or both.

3. Fossils and rock types are often helpful when correlating similar rock bodies.

16-4: Absolute Ages of Rocks

1. Relative dating of rocks, unlike absolute dating, doesn't provide an exact age for the rocks.

2. The half-life of a radioactive isotope is the time it takes for half of the atoms in the isotope to decay. Because half-lives are constant, absolute ages of rocks containing radioactive elements can be determined.

KEY SCIENCE WORDS

a. **absolute dating**
b. **carbonaceous film**
c. **cast**
d. **extinct**
e. **fossils**
f. **half-life**
g. **index fossils**
h. **law of superposition**
i. **mold**
j. **petrified remains**
k. **radioactive decay**
l. **radiometric dating**
m. **relative dating**
n. **unconformities**
o. **uniformitarianism**

UNDERSTANDING VOCABULARY

Match each phrase with the correct term from the list of Key Science Words.

1. thin film of carbon preserved as a fossil
2. rocklike fossils made of minerals
3. fossils of species that existed for a short time
4. states that older rocks lie under younger rocks
5. states that natural processes occur today as they did in the past
6. gaps in the rock record
7. method that gives actual rock ages
8. neutrons break down during this process
9. the time it takes for half of the atoms of a radioactive isotope to decay
10. this process measures the amounts of parent and daughter materials to determine age

CHAPTER

REVIEW

SUMMARY

Have students read the summary statements to review the major concepts of the chapter.

UNDERSTANDING VOCABULARY

1. b
2. j
3. g
4. h
5. o
6. n
7. a
8. k
9. f
10. l

ASSESSMENT

To assess student understanding of material in this chapter, use the resources listed.

COOPERATIVE LEARNING

Consider using cooperative learning in the THINK AND WRITE CRITICALLY, APPLY, and MORE SKILL BUILDERS sections of the Chapter Review.

PROGRAM RESOURCES

From the **Teacher Resource Package** use:

Chapter Review, pages 35-36.

Chapter and Unit Tests, pages 110-113, Chapter Test.

CHAPTER

REVIEW

CHECKING CONCEPTS

1. b
2. d
3. c
4. c
5. d
6. d
7. c
8. d
9. d
10. d

UNDERSTANDING CONCEPTS

11. cast
12. uniformitarianism
13. relative
14. radioactive decay
15. half-life

THINK AND WRITE CRITICALLY

16. Absolute dates are the actual number of years that have passed. Relative dates are comparisons of events relative to a given event.

17. Both are evidence of once-living organisms. Molds are cavities left when a shell or bone decays. When sediments fill a cavity and harden, casts are produced.

18. Hutton and others observed that geologic processes were generally very slow. These scientists were able then to conclude that if such processes were similar to those in the past, Earth must be millions not thousands of years old.

19. Iridium is not common on Earth. It is more common in meteorites, however. If a meteorite struck Earth while the dinosaurs lived, the impact could have changed climate conditions enough that dinosaur species weren't able to adapt and eventually became extinct.

20. After one half-life, the parent-to-daughter ratio is 4/8 to 4/8. After two half-lives, the ratio is 2/8 to 6/8. After three half-lives, it is 1/8 to 7/8.

CHAPTER

REVIEW

CHECKING CONCEPTS

Choose the word or phrase that completes the sentence.

1. Remains of organisms in rocks are ______.
   a. half-lives c. unconformities
   b. fossils d. extinctions
2. Fossils may form when dead organisms are ______.
   a. buried quickly
   b. kept from bacteria
   c. made of hard parts
   d. all of these
3. ______ are cavities left in rocks when a shell or bone decays.
   a. Casts c. Molds
   b. Petrified remains d. None of these
4. Dinosaurs lived ______.
   a. about 1000 years ago
   b. about 10 000 years ago
   c. before humans
   d. with humans
5. Extinction of dinosaurs may have been due to ______.
   a. changes in climate
   b. volcanoes
   c. hunting by humans
   d. both a and b
6. A fault can be used to find the ______ age of a group of rocks.
   a. absolute c. index
   b. radiometric d. relative
7. An unconformity between horizontal rock layers is a(n) ______.
   a. angular unconformity c. disconformity
   b. fault d. none of these
8. Rocks can be correlated using ______.
   a. fossils c. absolute ages
   b. rock types d. all of these
9. In one type of radioactive decay, a(n) ______ breaks down.
   a. alpha particle c. beta particle
   b. proton d. neutron
10. Radiometric dating indicates that Earth is ______ years old.
    a. 2000 c. 3.5 billion
    b. 5000 d. 4.6 billion

UNDERSTANDING CONCEPTS

Complete each sentence.

11. In a mold and cast fossil, the ______ might be mistaken for a petrified fossil.
12. Another way to state the principle of ______ is to say "the present is the key to the past."
13. Determining ages of rocks by using a fault that cuts across the rocks is an example of ______ dating.
14. During ______, new elements are formed.
15. The ______ of carbon-14 is 5730 years.

THINK AND WRITE CRITICALLY

16. How do relative and absolute dating methods differ?
17. Compare and contrast fossil molds and casts.
18. Why did James Hutton and others infer that Earth had to be much older than a few thousand years?
19. Explain why a clay layer rich in iridium might explain why the dinosaurs became extinct.
20. How many half-lives have passed in a rock containing 1/8 of the original radioactive material and 7/8 of the daughter product?

APPLY

21. We don't have a complete fossil record of life on Earth. Give some reasons why.
22. Suppose a lava flow were found between two sedimentary rock layers. How could the lava flow be used to date the rocks? (HINT: Most lava contains radioactive isotopes.)
23. Mammals began to evolve on Earth shortly before the dinosaurs became extinct. Suggest a hypothesis explaining how the mammals may have caused the dinosaurs to become extinct.
24. Suppose you're correlating rock layers in the western United States. You find a layer of shale that contains volcanic dust deposits. How can this layer help you in your correlation over a large area?
25. Why is carbon-14 not suitable for dating fossils formed about 2 million years ago?

MORE SKILL BUILDERS

If you need help, refer to the Skill Handbook.

1. **Making and Using Graphs:** Copy and complete the graph below to show the radioactive decay of an element with a half-life of 1 million years.

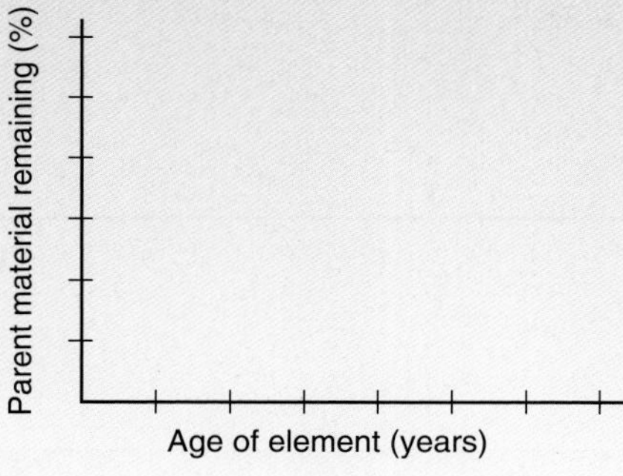

2. **Observing and Inferring:** Suppose you found a rock containing brachiopods. What can you infer about the environment in which the rock formed?
3. **Recognizing Cause and Effect:** Explain why some woolly mammoths have been found intact in frozen ground.
4. **Classifying:** Suppose you were given a set of ten fossils to classify. Make a table to classify each specimen according to the type of fossil it is.
5. **Outlining:** Make an outline of Section 16-1 that discusses the ways in which fossils form.

PROJECTS

1. Start your own fossil collection. Label each find as to type, approximate age, and the place where it was found. Most state geological surveys can provide you with reference material that explains the types of fossils you are apt to find in your area.
2. Find out about other extinctions that occurred at about the same time as the dinosaur extinctions. Were these extinctions caused by the same events that may have killed the dinosaurs?

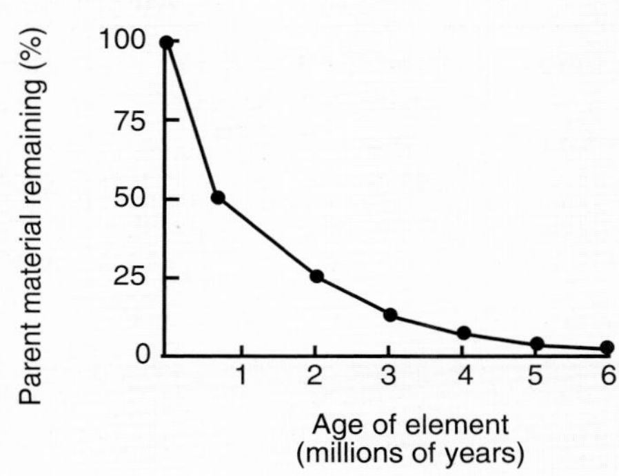

APPLY

21. The fossil record is incomplete because erosion and decay can destroy evidence of life if it's not buried quickly and protected from oxygen and moisture. Deeply buried remains are frequently destroyed by metamorphism.

22. Since the lava contains radioactive elements, an absolute age for the flow can be determined. This age can then be used to determine relative ages for the rocks above and below the flow.

23. Mammals may have raided dinosaur nests for food. Destroying large numbers of dinosaur eggs may have contributed to their extinction.

24. It's likely that any layer of shale containing volcanic dust is part of the same shale deposit. The dust-rich shale can act as a marker.

25. The half-life of carbon-14 is too short. All of the original carbon-14 in a fossil that's 2 million years old would have decayed and escaped as nitrogen gas. There would be no carbon-14 left to measure.

MORE SKILL BUILDERS

1. Making and Using Graphs: Each time unit on the horizontal axis should equal one million years. The decay curve is exponential. See the graph shown below.

2. Observing and Inferring: Brachiopods are marine animals. Thus, the rock formed in an ancient ocean.

3. Recognizing Cause and Effect: The cold temperatures caused the body functions to stop, helping to preserve the entire animal, much like freezing foods helps preserve them.

4. Classifying: One way to classify them is by the process that formed them. Examples of this type of classification could include petrification, mold and cast, preservation in amber, and carbonization. Other classification schemes are possible. Accept any logical answer.

5. Outlining: Answers will vary, but the objectives listed should be among the points included in students' outlines.

CHAPTER

17 Geologic Time

CHAPTER SECTION	OBJECTIVES	ACTIVITIES
17-1 Evolution and Geologic Time (2 days)	1. **Explain** how geologic time is divided into units. 2. **Relate** organic evolution to divisions on the geologic time scale. 3. **Describe** how plate tectonics affects organic evolution.	
17-2 Present-Day Rapid Extinctions Science & Society (2 days)	1. **Recognize** how humans have caused extinctions. 2. **Predict** what might happen to the diversity of life on Earth if land is developed without protection of natural habitats. 3. **Decide** what can be done to stop or slow down the rate of species extinction.	**Activity 17-1:** *Evolution Within a Species,* p. 456
17-3 Early Earth History (1 day)	1. **Identify** dominant life-forms in the Precambrian and Paleozoic Eras. 2. **Draw** conclusions about how organisms adapted to changing environments in the Precambrian and Paleozoic Eras. 3. **Describe** changes in Earth and its life-forms at the end of the Paleozoic Era.	**MINI-Lab:** *How can fossils be used to date rock layers?* p. 459
17-4 Middle and Recent Earth History (2 days)	1. **Compare** and **contrast** dominant life-forms in the Mesozoic and Cenozoic Eras. 2. **Explain** how changes caused by plate tectonics affected the evolution of life during the Mesozoic Era. 3. **Identify** when humans first appeared on Earth.	**MINI-Lab:** *How old is the Atlantic Ocean?* p. 465 **Activity 17-2:** *Geologic Time Line,* p. 468
Chapter Review		

ACTIVITY MATERIALS

FIND OUT	ACTIVITIES		MINI-LABS	
Page 445 green, orange, and blue yarn 3 cm in length (15 pieces of each color) green construction paper tweezers	**17-1 Evolution Within a Species, p. 456** deck of playing cards	**17-2 Geologic Time Line, p. 468** adding machine tape meterstick pencil scissors	**How can fossils be used to date rock layers? p. 459** paper pencil	**How old is the Atlantic Ocean? p. 465** globe or world map meterstick geologic time scale in Figure 17-2

CHAPTER FEATURES	TEACHER RESOURCE PACKAGE	OTHER RESOURCES
Technology: *Embryology,* p. 451 **Skill Builder:** *Recognizing Cause and Effect,* p. 453	**Ability Level Worksheets** ◆ ***Study Guide,*** p. 70 ● ***Reinforcement,*** p. 70 ▲ ***Enrichment,*** p. 70 **Concept Mapping,** pp. 39-40 **Transparency Masters,** pp. 73-74	**Color Transparency 37,** Geological Time Scale **Lab Manual:** *Geologic Time,* pp. 135-138 **Lab Manual:** *Differences in Species,* pp. 139-140
You Decide! p. 455	**Ability Level Worksheets** ◆ ***Study Guide,*** p. 71 ● ***Reinforcement,*** p. 71 ▲ ***Enrichment,*** p. 71 **Activity Worksheet,** pp. 151-152 **Science and Society,** p. 21	
Problem Solving: *Paleozoic Puzzle,* p. 460 **Skill Builder:** *Making and Using Tables,* p. 461	**Ability Level Worksheets** ◆ ***Study Guide,*** p. 72 ● ***Reinforcement,*** p. 72 ▲ ***Enrichment,*** p. 72 **MINI-Lab Worksheet,** p. 157	
Skill Builder: *Sequencing,* p. 467	**Ability Level Worksheets** ◆ ***Study Guide,*** p. 73 ● ***Reinforcement,*** p. 73 ▲ ***Enrichment,*** p. 73 **Activity Worksheet,** pp. 153-154 **MINI-Lab Worksheet,** p. 158 **Transparency Masters,** pp. 75-76 **Critical Thinking/Problem Solving,** p. 23 **Cross-Curricular Connections,** p. 21	**Color Transparency 38,** Human Evolution
Summary Key Science Words Understanding Vocabulary Checking Concepts Understanding Concepts Think & Write Critically Apply More Skill Builders Projects	**Chapter Review,** pp. 37-38 **Chapter Test,** pp. 114-117 **Unit Test 6,** pp. 118-119	**Chapter Review Software** **Test Bank**

◆ **Basic** ● **Average** ▲ **Advanced**

ADDITIONAL MATERIALS

SOFTWARE	AUDIOVISUAL	BOOKS/MAGAZINES
Duration of Epochs/Periods, Micro Learningware. *Types of Animals Present,* Micro Learningware. *Earth's History: The Record in Rocks,* Queue.	*The Legacy of L.S.B. Leakey,* film, NGS. *Message from a Dinosaur,* film, EBEC. *The Earth: Discovering its History,* film, Coronet/MTI. *Age of Mammals,* filmstrip, Time-Life. *Fossils and Prehistoric Environments,* filmstrip, Time-Life. *Up Through the Coal Age,* filmstrip, Time-Life. *Dinosaurs of the Gobi,* video, NOVA (PBS).	Cooper, John D. *A Trip Through Time: Principles of Historical Geology.* Westerville, OH: Merrill Publishing Co., 1984. Stanley, Steven M. *Earth and Life Through Time.* 2nd ed. NY: W.H. Freeman, and Co., 1988. Tarbuch, Edward J. and Frederick K. Lutgens. *Earth: An Introduction to Physical Geology.* 3rd ed. Cols, OH: Merrill Publishing Company, 1990.

CHAPTER

17

GEOLOGIC TIME

THEME DEVELOPMENT: Evolution is the main theme emphasized in this chapter. Organic evolution, as it is used in dividing Earth's history into the geologic time scale, should be a major focus of all sections in this chapter.

CHAPTER OVERVIEW

- **Section 17-1:** This section presents the division of Earth's history into the geologic time scale. Organic evolution within a species and speciation are also introduced.
- **Section 17-2: Science and Society:** The present-day rate of extinction is presented in this section. The You Decide feature challenges students to consider reasons to prevent extinctions.
- **Section 17-3:** Earth history during the Precambrian and Paleozoic Eras is described in this section. Changes in Earth and its life-forms in each of the two eras are presented.
- **Section 17-4:** This section describes changes in Earth and its life-forms during the Mesozoic and Cenozoic Eras.

CHAPTER VOCABULARY

geologic time scale	habitat
eras	Precambrian Era
periods	cyanobacteria
epochs	Paleozoic Era
organic evolution	amphibians
species	reptiles
natural selection	Mesozoic Era
endangered	Cenozoic Era

CHAPTER

17 Geologic Time

OPTIONS

For Your Gifted Students

Have students interview a grandparent or other senior citizen. They should ask what major changes in the world the senior has observed. Changes could be in inventions, transportation, communication, the environment, health, and political and philosophical issues. Students should develop a time line of some of these major events in this person's "era." Can the "era" be divided into "periods" based on certain events or characteristics?

Dinosaurs had to compete with each other and other organisms to survive. They were successful animals because they were well-adapted to their environments.

FIND OUT!

Do this activity to observe how traits determine whether an individual survives in an environment.

Cut green, orange, and blue yarn into 3-cm lengths. You should have 15 pieces of each color when you're done. Place all of the pieces on a sheet of green construction paper. Use a pair of tweezers to pick up as many pieces of yarn as you can in 15 seconds. How many pieces of each color did you pick up? Suppose the construction paper represents green grass, each piece of yarn represents an insect, and your tweezers represent a bird preying on the insects. Would you expect many orange or blue insects to survive over a long period of time? What advantage would the green insects have over the others?

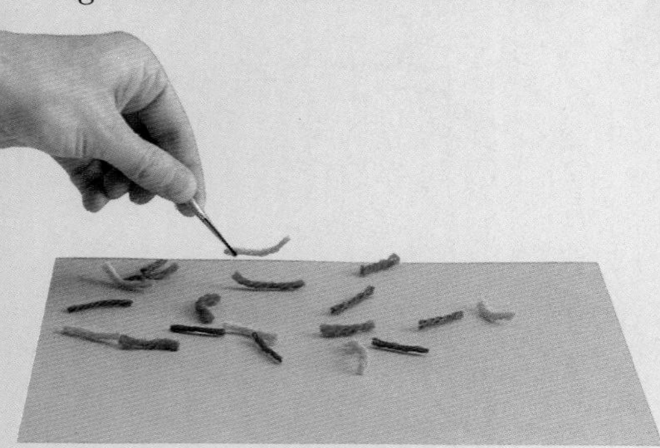

Gearing Up

Previewing the Chapter

Use this outline to help you focus on important ideas in this chapter.

Section 17-1 Evolution and Geologic Time
- The Geologic Time Scale
- Organic Evolution
- The Effect of Plate Tectonics on Earth History

Section 17-2 Science and Society
Present-Day Rapid Extinctions
- Can Humans Slow the Rate of Extinctions?

Section 17-3 Early Earth History
- The Precambrian Era
- The Paleozoic Era

Section 17-4 Middle and Recent Earth History
- The Mesozoic Era
- The Cenozoic Era

Previewing Science Skills

- In the **Skill Builders,** you will recognize cause and effect, make and use tables, and sequence events.
- In the **Activities,** you will measure in SI, hypothesize, formulate models, make mathematical calculations, and make inferences.
- In the **MINI-Labs,** you will measure in SI and make mathematical calculations.

What's next?

In the Find Out activity, you demonstrated that some individuals are better suited to survive in a particular environment. They often survive, reproduce, and pass on their traits while other individuals do not. This is the process of evolution by natural selection, and you'll learn more about it in this chapter.

For Your Mainstreamed Students

Demonstrate to students the relatively short amount of time humans have existed compared to the whole of Earth's history. Have students lie flat on the floor to represent the beginning of Earth. Since the Precambrian Era made up about 88 percent of Earth's history, have students sit up, forming an 80 degree angle with their bodies. The Paleozoic, Mesozoic, and Cenozoic Eras can be represented by moving only ten more degrees until students are sitting in an upright position, forming a 90 degree angle with their bodies.

INTRODUCING THE CHAPTER

Use the Find Out activity to introduce students to the concept of natural selection. Inform students that they will be learning more about evolution and changes in Earth through time.

FIND OUT!

Materials: 15 pieces each of green, orange, and blue yarn cut into 3-cm lengths; a sheet of green construction paper; stopwatch; scissors; and tweezers for each group

Cooperative Learning: Form Science Investigation groups of four students per group. Assign student roles that include a reader, a materials handler, a recorder, and a reporter. Have students perform the activity as a group.

Teaching Tips

- Try to match the color of the green yarn to the color of the green construction paper.
- You may wish to have students perform this activity prior to reading the chapter opener and the questions at the end of the Find Out text. If students know the object of the activity prior to performing the procedure, they may skew the results by intentionally picking up a particular color of yarn. To prevent this, give the students step-by-step instructions orally instead of having them read the instructions from the text.
- Caution students to handle the scissors and tweezers with care.
- Call on the reporters of each group to answer the in-text questions.

Gearing Up

Have students study the Gearing Up feature to familiarize themselves with the chapter. Discuss the relationships of the topics in the outline.

What's Next?

Before beginning the first section, make sure students understand the connection between the Find Out activity and the topics to follow.

SECTION 17-1

PREPARATION

SECTION BACKGROUND

▶In 1799, William Smith, an English surveyor and geologic hobbyist, noted while working on a canal project that rock layers in any local section could be distinguished readily from those above and below by the sorts of fossils they contained. Smith's discovery proved to be a turning point in the development of a geologic time scale.

▶Geologic history is based on the study of sedimentary rocks and their fossils. Although the geologic time scale was originally based on relative dating, absolute dating methods have enabled geologists to determine absolute dates of many rocks and some geologic events.

▶Periods on the geologic time scale are usually named for geographic regions where the rocks of that age were first studied. Rocks of the Pennsylvanian Period are found exposed in Pennsylvania. Rocks of the Mississippian Period are exposed along the Mississippi River. These two periods are sometimes classified together as the Carboniferous Period because of the large concentration of coal present in rocks of this age.

1 MOTIVATE

Cooperative Learning: Form Numbered Heads Together groups with four students per group. Have students list the three most recent eras. Have them identify which organisms evolved, existed, and/or became extinct in each era. Call on a student from each group to present a summary of the information listed by the group.

17-1 Evolution and Geologic Time

New Science Words

geologic time scale
eras
periods
epochs
organic evolution
species
natural selection

Objectives

- ▶ **Explain how geologic time is divided into units.**
- ▶ **Relate organic evolution to divisions on the geologic time scale.**
- ▶ **Describe how plate tectonics affects organic evolution.**

The Geologic Time Scale

It's a rainy day in the prairie lands of the central United States. A herd of horses is roaming toward a local stream where they can find fresh drinking water. Their large, powerful muscles easily carry them across several kilometers of open grassland. Along the way, they occasionally stop to feed on the grass.

The horses are well suited for this environment. Their hoofed feet allow them to run at great speeds to protect themselves from predators. The males use their speed and power to compete with other males for territory and mates. The teeth of the horses allow them to grind up grass.

The characteristics of the horses allow them to survive in the demanding environment in which they live. These same characteristics are what you would use to describe a horse—a large, powerful, hoofed animal with teeth made for grinding up grasses and grains.

Merychippus
Mesohippus
Eohippus
50 Million Years
35 Million Years
20 Million Years

Figure 17-1. As the horse species evolved, horses increased in size. The evolution of single-toed, hoofed feet enabled horses to run faster.

OPTIONS

Meeting Different Ability Levels

For Section 17-1, use the following **Teacher Resource Masters** depending upon individual students' needs.

◆ **Study Guide Master** for all students.

● **Reinforcement Master** for students of average and above average ability levels.

▲ **Enrichment Master** for above average students.

Additional Teacher Resource Package masters are listed in the OPTIONS box throughout the section. The additional masters are appropriate for all students.

◆ STUDY GUIDE 70

NAME ______ DATE ______ CLASS ______

STUDY GUIDE — Chapter 17

Evolution and Geologic Time — Text Pages 446–453

Use the words in the box to fill in the blanks in the statements.

adapted	continents	environment	extinct
epochs	eras	fossils	plate tectonics
geologic time scale	natural selection	organic evolution	periods
species			

1. The division of Earth's history into units makes up the **geologic time scale**.
2. Major divisions of Earth's history are **eras**.
3. Each major division may be divided into **periods**.
4. The Cenozoic Era is divided into **epochs**.
5. Clues to which organisms lived in different eras are found in **fossils**.
6. A gradual change in life-forms over time is **organic evolution**.
7. Each change in Earth created different surroundings for organisms, these surroundings are called their **environment**.
8. A group of organisms that normally reproduce only among themselves is a **species**.
9. After major changes in Earth's environments, species either died out or **adapted**.
10. Species that could not adapt to changes eventually became **extinct**.
11. Organisms with traits that are suited to an environment survive by the process of **natural selection**.
12. At different times in Earth's history, plate tectonics caused collision and separation of **continents**.
13. Many species adapted or became extinct because **plate tectonics** caused their environments to change when the continents collided or separated.

70

Suppose you found a fossil of an animal that was the size of a dog. The animal had four toes on its front feet ❶ and three toes on its hind feet. Its teeth were sharp—well suited for eating shrubs and bushes, but not for grinding grass. Would you classify this as a fossil of a horse? In fact, it may be just that.

At one time in Earth's history, horses were small, they had several toes and no hoofs, and they had teeth much different from the teeth of today's horses. Before that time, there were no animals we would classify as horses. Before that, there weren't even mammals. If you look far back into time, there were no animals and no plants. At one point, there were only the molecules that combine to make life, but not life itself. The appearance and disappearance of types of organisms throughout Earth's history give us markers in time. We can divide up Earth's history into smaller units based on the types of life-forms living during certain periods. The division of Earth's history into smaller units makes up the **geologic time scale.** Some of the divisions in the geologic time scale are also based on geologic changes occurring at the time. ❷

What are the divisions of the geologic time scale based on?

The geologic time scale is a record of Earth's history, starting with Earth's formation about 4.6 billion years ago. Each period of time is named. When fossils and rock layers are dated, scientists can assign them to a specific place on the geologic time scale. As you can see in Figure 17-2, the time scale is divided into subunits.

Equus
Pliohippus
5 Million Years
Today

● REINFORCEMENT 70

NAME ______ DATE ______ CLASS ______

REINFORCEMENT — Chapter 17

Evolution and Geologic Time — Text Pages 446–453

Answer the following questions on the lines provided.

1. What determines the divisions of eras and periods on the geologic time scale? **the types of life-forms and geologic events**
2. Which of the eras on the geologic time scale is divided into both periods and epochs? **Cenozoic Era**
3. How does natural selection affect the kinds of species that will live in an environment that is changing? **Species with traits that are suited to the new environment have a better chance of survival than those that aren't suited.**
4. How does evolution take place within a species? **Animals that survive produce young with the characteristic that enabled the parent to survive.**
5. How has studying embryos of various organisms supported theories of organic evolution? **The embryos share many characteristics of development. Embryos of closely related species show similar features and patterns of development.**
6. What might bring about the evolution of a new species? **Animals that can't survive may move, breed among the isolated group, and evolve into a new species.**
7. How might geologic events, such as the movement of tectonic plates, affect the environment in which species live? **The rearranging of land and sea causes changes in climates.**
8. Why were corals a dominant life-form on Earth during the Silurian Period? **Warm, shallow seas covered much of the globe. Corals are sea animals which thrive in shallow, warm water.**
9. Why are corals no longer a dominant form? **Glaciers began to form; some species of corals couldn't adapt to cooler climates. There are few warm, shallow seas today.**
10. In what epoch, period, and era do you live? **In the Recent Epoch, Quaternary Period, Cenozoic Era**

70

▲ ENRICHMENT 70

NAME ______ DATE ______ CLASS ______

ENRICHMENT — Chapter 17

Evolution and Geologic Time — Text Pages 446–453

THE EARLIEST PRIMATES

Read the following information. Then answer the questions.

Fossils have allowed scientists to trace the evolution of not just the horse, but of many species of animals. From the fossils, scientists have learned a tremendous amount about what earlier forms of these animals looked like. One of the problems, though, in studying fossils is that often not all the fossil skeleton can be found. Therefore, scientists have to draw conclusions about the animal without being able to study the animal's entire structure. This particular problem led to some interesting "reconclusions" about primates in 1990.

Primates are a group of about 200 species of animals that include lemurs, monkeys, apes, and humans. They are grouped together on the basis of similar skeletal and other features. It's believed that they have a common ancestor and developed into separate species over millions of years.

For a long time, paleontologists thought that the oldest primates were the 60-million-year-old creatures they named plesiadapiforms. Plesiadapiform fossils included teeth, jaws, and parts of skulls. From the fossils, scientists concluded that plesiadapiform was a primate. Certainly, its teeth were like those of other primates. They were adapted for grinding, designed for a diet of insects, fruits, and seeds.

In 1990, new plesiadapiform bones were dug up in Wyoming. These included the first complete skull and some parts never found before, fingers and wrists. The paleontologists who studied the finger bones were surprised to find that they did not resemble those of primates. The only living animal with a similar arrangement of finger bones is a small tree-dwelling mammal of the Borneo and Philippine rain forests, called a colugo. The scientists who examined the intact skull identified it as resembling that of the colugo. The conclusion was that plesiadapiforms were not primates, since colugos are not primates.

Other scientists were studying an animal discovered at the foot of the High Atlas mountains in Morocco. Called the Altiatlasius, the creature lived 60 million years ago. The paleontologists found ten tiny teeth similar to those in one of today's smallest primates, the 57-gram mouse lemur of Madagascar.

Another animal, less advanced but much larger than the Altiatlasius, has also been found. Many scientists are calling it an earlier primate. It's a house-cat-sized microsyopid and may have lived more than 60 million years ago. It's identified as an early primate from its bone structure.

1. If the microsyopid is proved to be a primate, what conclusion about primates might be changed? **The conclusion that primates evolved only 60 million years ago.**
2. Why do you think the Altiatlasius was so named? **High Atlas is the name of the mountains where the fossil was found. *Alti* means "high," as in *altitude*. *Atlas* is the second part of the mountain's name.**
3. What does the reading tell you about scientific inquiries? **Answers may vary. An important point is that scientists use new information to change existing theories.**

70

TYING TO PREVIOUS KNOWLEDGE: Many students are familiar with horses as large, grazing, hoofed animals that can carry humans on their backs. Ask students to picture a horse, no larger than a dog, with several toes on its feet. Explain that fossil evidence indicates that present-day horses have evolved from much smaller, multi-toed ancestors.

OBJECTIVES AND SCIENCE WORDS: Have students review the objectives and science words to become familiar with this section.

2 TEACH

Key Concepts are highlighted.

CONCEPT DEVELOPMENT

Cooperative Learning: Using the Paired Partners strategy have students relate subdivisions on the geologic time scale to events in the school year. Have students discuss events that have occurred during the school year. Have them list events from the latest to earliest. Ask students to describe the number of events and the details they can remember from early in the year and compare these to events later in the year. Students should notice that events that have occurred recently are remembered in greater detail. Relate this to the fact that the record of geologic events in recent periods is much more detailed than the record of events from periods long ago.

CONCEPT DEVELOPMENT

▶ Discuss the "Time Ribbon" illustrated in Figure 17-2. Point out that the dates shown under each period or epoch mark the beginning of that division of time. For example, the Cambrian Period began 570 million years ago. This date also marks the end of the Precambrian Era.

Cooperative Learning: Form Numbered Heads Together groups with four students per group. Provide students with geologic maps of your area. Ask students to determine the age of rocks located near the school or their homes. Bring in samples of rock from a local exposure and have students determine what type of rock it is. Inform them of where you obtained the rocks and have them locate the area on their maps. Ask them what age they think the rock samples are. Be sure that the rocks were removed from a rock layer and not just picked up off the ground.

REVEALING MISCONCEPTIONS

▶ Many students will think that scientists have obtained a complete record of Earth's past from fossils contained in the rocks. Explain that very little is known about the first 4 billion years because much of the fossil record has been destroyed. Explain that gaps in the fossil record exist in more recent rocks because of erosion.

CROSS CURRICULUM

▶ **Mathematics:** Have students construct a pie graph representing geologic time. Students should convert the time in each era into a percentage of the total time since Earth's formation, 4.6 billion years ago. The Precambrian Era represents about 88 percent of Earth's history. Eighty-eight percent of 360° is 316°. The Paleozoic Era comprises about 7.5 percent of Earth's history, or 27° on the pie graph. The Mesozoic Era comprises about 3 percent, or 12°, of the graph. The remaining 5° represents the Cenozoic Era, or 1.5 percent of Earth's history. Suggest that students use different colors to emphasize the different eras on their pie graphs. Students' pie graphs should resemble the one shown on page 471 of the Chapter Review.

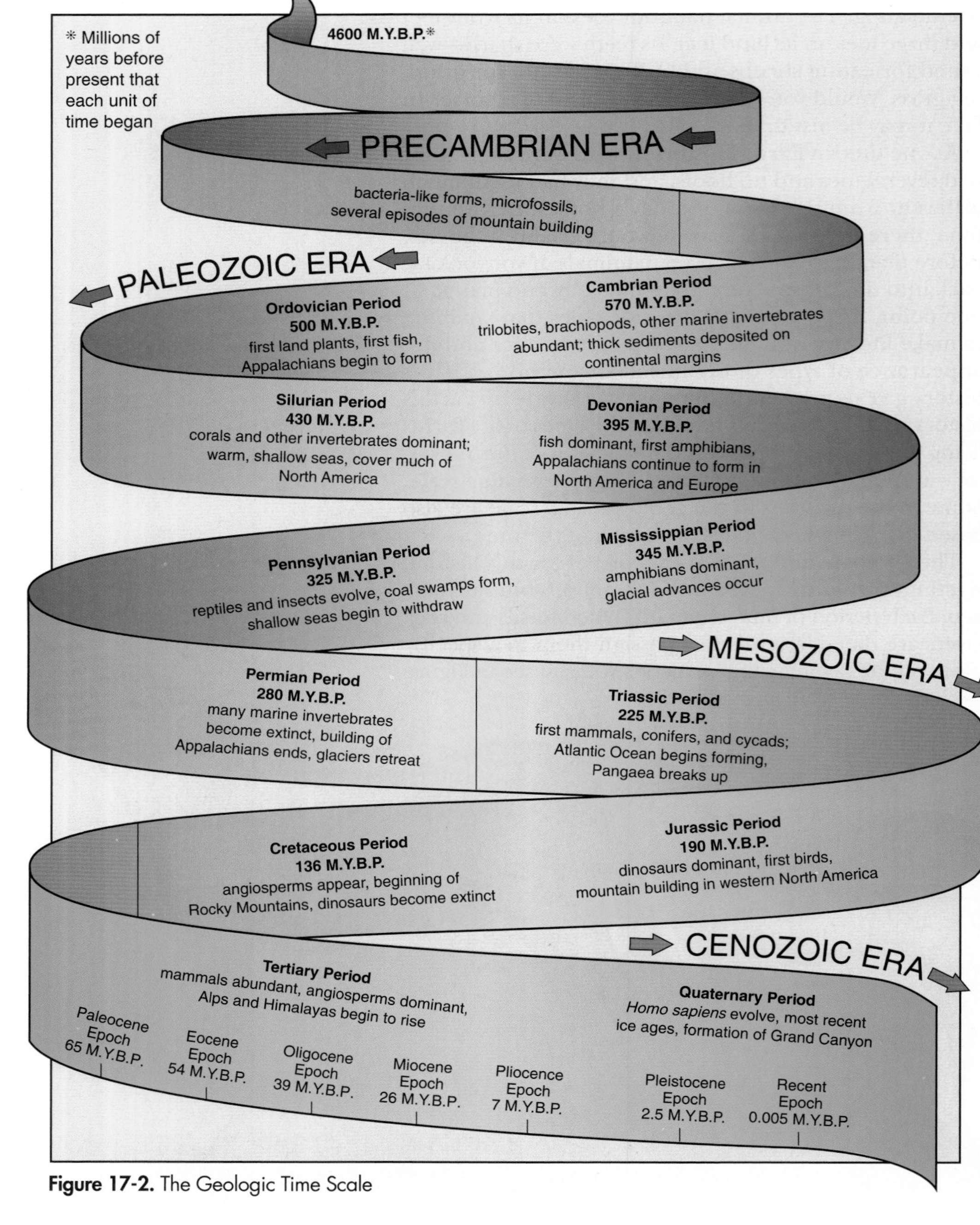

Figure 17-2. The Geologic Time Scale

OPTIONS

INQUIRY QUESTIONS

▶ **What does M.Y.B.P. stand for in figure 17-2?** *millions of years before present*

▶ **When did the Mesozoic Era begin?** *225 million years ago*

▶ **When did the Paleozoic Era begin and end?** *It began 570 million years ago and ended 225 million years ago.*

▶ **Which two periods make up the Cenozoic Era?** *the Tertiary and Quaternary Periods*

▶ **How many epochs make up the Tertiary Period?** *5 epochs*

▶ **How long ago did the epoch in which you live begin?** *The Recent Epoch began 5000 years ago.*

PROGRAM RESOURCES

From the **Teacher Resource Package,** use:

Transparency Masters, pages 73-74, Geologic Time Scale.

Use **Color Transparency** number 37, Geologic Time Scale.

There are three types of subdivisions of geologic time—eras, periods, and epochs. **Eras** are the major subdivision of the geologic time scale. As you can see, the Mesozoic Era began about 225 million years ago and ended with the extinction of the dinosaurs and other organisms about 65 million years ago.

Eras are subdivided into **periods.** Periods are based on the types of life existing at the time and on geologic events, such as mountain building and plate movements, occurring at the time.

Which periods make up the Paleozoic Era?

Periods may be divided into smaller units of time called **epochs.** Figure 17-2 shows that only the Cenozoic Era is broken into epochs. Why would this be true? The fossil record and geologic history is more complete in recent rock layers. As a result, geologists have more markers to divide the time with.

Organic Evolution

Based on the fossil record, organisms appear to have followed an ordered series of changes. This gradual
change in life-forms through time is known as **organic** 3
evolution. Most theories describing the processes of organic evolution state that changes in the environment result in changes in species of organisms.

A **species** is a group of organisms that normally reproduce only among themselves. For example, dogs are a 4
species of animals because they mate and reproduce only with other dogs. Within one species, individual organisms possess certain traits that give them a better chance to survive.

Figure 17-3. In some cases, animals of different species can breed and produce offspring. A horse (a) and a donkey (c) can produce a mule (b). Mules possess characteristics of both horses and donkeys, making them desirable work animals. Mules are sterile—they can't reproduce.

a

b

c

CHECK FOR UNDERSTANDING

Use the Mini Quiz to check for understanding.

MINI QUIZ

Use the Mini Quiz to check students' recall of chapter content.

1. **At one time in Earth's history, horses were the size of a present-day ______, they had several ______ on their feet, and their teeth were suited for eating _______.** *dog, toes, shrubs and bushes*
2. **The geologic time scale is divided into units of time based on ______ and ______.** *the types of life-forms existing during certain times, the geologic changes that have occurred*
3. **What is the gradual change in life-forms through time known as?** *organic evolution*
4. **A(n) _____ is a group of organisms that normally reproduce only among themselves.** *species*
5. **_____ is the process by which organisms with traits that are suited to a certain environment have a better chance of survival than organisms that are not suited.** *Natural selection*

RETEACH

▶ Give students a geologic time scale and have them identify the eras by coloring their headings in with a colored pencil. Have students identify periods and epochs by coloring their headings in with two different colored pencils.

▶ Have students make a network tree concept map of the geologic time scale. Students' maps should show the hierarchy among the divisions of time.

EXTENSION

For students who have mastered this section, use the **Reinforcement** and **Enrichment** masters or other OPTIONS provided.

PROGRAM RESOURCES

From the **Teacher Resource Package,** use:

Concept Mapping, pages 39-40.

Use **Laboratory Manual,** pages 135-138, Geologic Time.

Use **Laboratory Manual,** pages 139-140, Differences in a Species.

TEACHER F.Y.I.

▶ The investigations and observations of Charles Darwin that led to his theory of evolution by natural selection took place during the cruise of the ship *H.M.S. Beagle*. *The Beagle* traveled through islands in the South Pacific Ocean from 1831 through 1833. Some of Darwin's most significant and famous observations were made while visiting the Galapagos Archipelago off the coast of Ecuador.

CONCEPT DEVELOPMENT

Cooperative Learning: Have students study the chart, "The Victims and Survivors," from the article, "Extinctions," by Rick Gore in *National Geographic,* June 1989, pp. 662-699. Using the Paired Partner strategy, have students make pie charts that show the percentage of extinctions that occurred at the end of the Ordovician Period (70 percent of all species), the Devonian Period (70 percent of all invertebrate species), the Permian Period (over 90 percent of all species), and the Cretaceous Period (all dinosaurs and about 70 percent of all other animal species). Have partners quiz each other on which mass extinction was the greatest. The extinction event at the end of the Permian Period is regarded as the greatest.

▶ Have students write a report on how a species of mammal might evolve by natural selection if the climate of an area became much cooler. Inform them that some of the organisms within the species have more fur covering their bodies than most other members of the species do. Their reports should include the idea that organisms with less fur might not be able to survive in the colder climate long enough to reproduce. The organisms with more fur would survive longer and would perhaps pass the trait of thicker fur on to their offspring. As more time passed, more and more members of the species would have the thicker fur until finally almost all members of the species would be thick-furred.

Science and READING

One theory of evolution was proposed by the naturalist Jean Baptiste de Lamarck in the early 19th century. He stated that evolution occurred because an individual organism acquires traits it needs for survival. He explained the long neck of a giraffe by saying that individual giraffes stretched their necks to reach leaves on tall trees. They then passed this trait on to their offspring. Research how his theory has been disproved.

Evolution within a Species

Suppose a species of bird exists on an island. A few of the individuals have a very hard beak, but most have soft beaks. Now suppose most of the food the birds rely on has a hard shell around it. Which of the birds will be better suited, or more fit, to survive? The birds with the harder beaks will be better able to break the hard shell on the food and, therefore, have an advantage over the soft-beaked individuals in the species. Some of the soft-beaked birds may die from lack of food. The hard-beaked birds have a better chance of surviving and producing offspring. Their offspring will inherit the trait of having a hard beak. Gradually the number of hard-beaked birds becomes greater, and the number of soft-beaked birds decreases. The species has evolved so that nearly all of its members have hard beaks.

Because the selection of the hard-beaked birds was a natural process, this process is called natural selection. Charles Darwin, a naturalist who sailed around the world to study wildlife, developed the theory of evolution by natural selection. He proposed that **natural selection** is
5 the process by which organisms with traits that are suited to a certain environment have a better chance of survival than organisms whose traits are not suited to it.

Notice in the example of the birds that individual soft-beaked birds didn't change into hard-beaked birds. A species only evolves a new trait if some members already possess that trait. If no bird in the species had possessed a hard beak, the species would not have been able to evolve into a species of hard-beaked birds. The birds may have been able to survive, if they could find soft food to eat, or they may have died out completely.

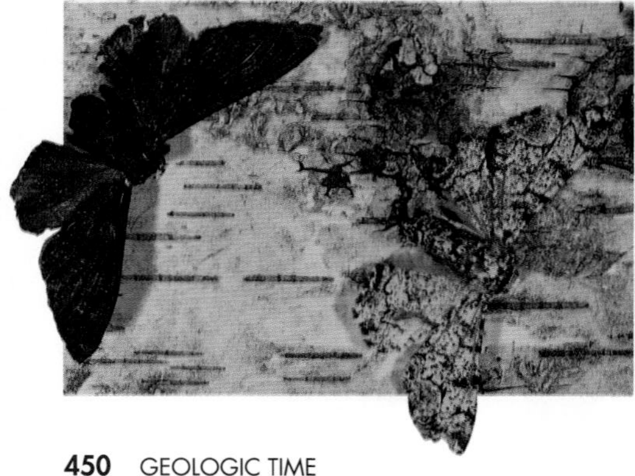

Figure 17-4. Before pollution darkened tree bark, light-colored members of the peppered moth species were abundant. Their light color hid them from birds in search of a meal. When pollution covered the trees, the dark members of the species began to survive and reproduce more often than the lighter members. The evolution of the peppered moths demonstrates how nature selects for certain characteristics.

OPTIONS

INQUIRY QUESTIONS

▶ **How do certain traits develop within a species of animal?** *If a certain trait makes an individual organism better able to survive in a particular environment, that trait will likely be passed on to offspring. Animals without the favorable trait are less likely to survive long enough to have offspring. As time passes, more and more offspring with the favorable trait survive.*

▶ **In the process of natural selection, do individual organisms develop new traits that make them better able to survive? Explain.** *No, individuals do not evolve new traits. If no organisms within a species possess a particular trait, the species will not be able to evolve into a species with that trait.*

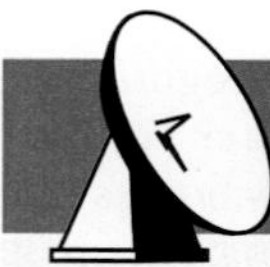

TECHNOLOGY

Embryology

Evidence for evolution has come from studying the embryos of organisms of different species. It's difficult to tell the difference between the embryos of a reptile (left) and a human (right) just by looking at them. The embryos of each of these animals have tails and gill pouches during periods in their development. In fact, at some point during their growth, both of these embryos develop many features that are found in adult fish. Why are fishlike features present in the embryos of reptiles, mammals, and birds?

Because reptiles, mammals, and birds evolved from early fish, they go through the same basic development as fish. As the embryos of these animals develop, they undergo the pattern of changes that their fish ancestors underwent. As they continue to develop, they undergo the changes that have evolved in their species.

By studying the similarities between the embryos of different species, we have discovered clues about which species are most closely related. Those species with similar embryo development probably shared a common ancestor in relatively recent geologic history.

Think Critically: Humans didn't evolve from dinosaurs, yet a human embryo would probably have several features and developmental patterns in common with a dinosaur embryo. Explain why this would be the case.

The Evolution of New Species

Natural selection explains not only how characteristics develop within a species, but also how new species arise. For example, if the soft-beaked birds in our example would have moved to a different part of the island where soft food was available, they may have survived. The soft-beaked birds would continue to reproduce apart from the hard-beaked birds on a different part of the island. Over time, the soft-beaked birds would develop characteristics that were different from those of the hard-beaked birds. At some point, the birds would no longer be breeding with each other. They would have evolved into two different species.

TECHNOLOGY

For more information on evolution and the evidence for the theory of natural selection, see *Hen's Teeth and Horse's* Toes by Stephen J. Gould, George J. McLeod, LTD., Toronto, Canada, 1983.

Think Critically: Humans and dinosaurs share a common ancestor. Both evolved from fish, so dinosaur embryos went through developmental stages similar to those that human embryos undergo today.

CONCEPT DEVELOPMENT

▶ Have students continue their study of the evolving thick-furred organism. Ask them to consider what might happen if thin-furred individuals of the same species continued to live in an area that was relatively warm. Have students explain how this might lead to the evolution of two species. Students should realize that as the two groups continue to live independent of one another, they will gradually diversify more and more. Eventually, they will no longer be able to interbreed even if they once again inhabit the same geographic region.

ENRICHMENT

▶ Have students research the work of early geologists in the construction of the geologic time scale. Scientists the students should research are James Hutton (1726-1797), William "Strata" Smith (1769-1838), and Charles Lyell (1797-1875).

▶ The fossil record indicates that mass extinctions have occurred on Earth about every 26 million years. Have students speculate on what might have caused this to occur. After they have expressed their thoughts, discuss the Nemesis theory. Some scientists think a small, dark companion star, named Nemesis, may orbit our sun once every 26 million years. As Nemesis orbits our sun, it may approach close enough to disturb the Oort comet cloud. This could send a large number of comets toward the inner solar system. Comets colliding with Earth could send great clouds of dust and smoke into the atmosphere, blocking out sunlight for several years. This could cause mass extinctions.

CONCEPT DEVELOPMENT

▶ **Demonstration:** Demonstrate how life-forms change through geologic time by showing pictures or models of the development of the horse through time. Use pictures or models of the leg structure and point out how the multi-toed early horse changed over time. Indicate how the middle toe of each foot became larger and larger until now it has become a single-toe. Demonstrate how the overall size of the horse has changed from the size of a dog to its present size. Relate these changes to adaptations to the changing environment.

CHECK FOR UNDERSTANDING

▶ Ask questions 1-4 and the **Apply** Question in the Section Review.

▶ Ask the following question. **How could species of organisms be affected by plate tectonic activity?** *As plates move across Earth's surface, continents collide and separate many times. As continents collide, mountains are built up that can separate species that normally live together. Also, environments change as oceans deepen and become shallow and as land masses move. The environmental changes result in the evolution of new species and the evolution of traits within species.*

RETEACH

Refer students to Figure 13-11 on page 350. Help students recall how Earth's surface is affected at convergent boundaries. Obtain a piece of flexible foam padding about 8 cm thick. Demonstrate the action of a convergent plate boundary by cutting the foam in half and then applying compressional force. When two continental plates converge, rock layers are bent upward into folds. Relate this to the formation of mountain chains that could have long term effects on life-forms living in the area.

EXTENSION

For students who have mastered this section, use the **Reinforcement** and **Enrichment** masters or other OPTIONS provided.

Think again of the horses discussed at the beginning of this section. Why did they change over time? You have learned that fossil evidence shows that early horses were small, multi-toed animals adapted to grazing on shrubs and bushes. As environments on Earth changed from brushy fields to open grasslands, the horse species became bigger and developed hoofs and complex molars. Over millions of years, horses became adapted to open grasslands by the process of natural selection. As the environment changed, the horse species adapted and survived.

Many species that lived on Earth during its long history couldn't adapt to changing environments. Such species became extinct. What processes on Earth could cause environments to change so much that species must adapt or become extinct?

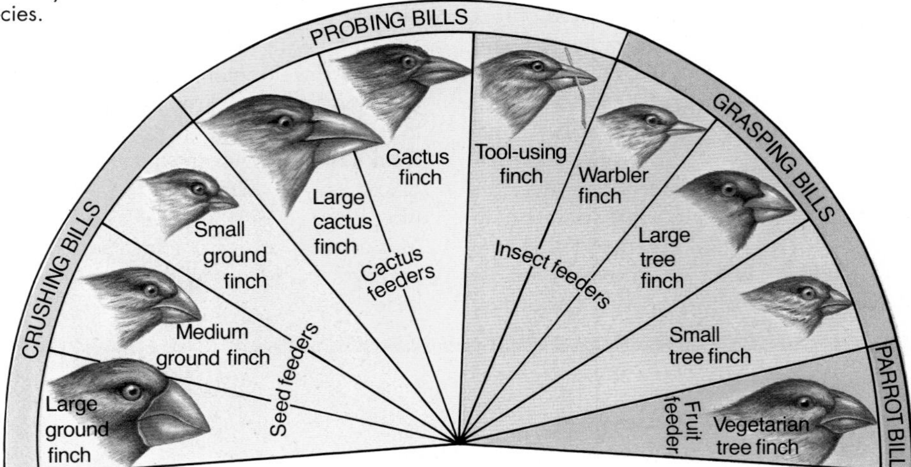

Figure 17-5. These ten species of finches on Isle Santa Cruz in the Galapagos archipelago evolved from one ancestral species. Small groups of the ancestral species became isolated when they began to specialize in the types of food they ate. These groups eventually evolved into different species.

The Effect of Plate Tectonics on Earth History

Plate tectonics is one process that causes changing environments on Earth. As plates on Earth's surface move about, continents collide with and separate from each other many times. Collisions cause mountain building and the draining of seas. Separations cause deeper seas to develop between continents. This rearranging of land and sea causes changes in climates. How might these changes affect organisms?

OPTIONS

INQUIRY QUESTIONS

▶ **Why was the horse able to survive as the environments in which it lived changed?** *Over time, the horse species adapted to the new environment and was able to survive.*

▶ **If a species cannot adapt to changes in its environment, what happens to it?** *The species will become extinct.*

▶ **What processes could cause major changes in the environment?** *Collisions of plates can cause mountains to build up and seas to drain away. Seas between moving continental plates can become deeper or more shallow. Pollution can make it impossible for certain organisms to survive. Changes of this type can cause changes in the climate that might affect organisms.*

▶ **How might changes in the environment cause the extinction of a species?** *If no members of a species possess characteristics suitable to the new environment, the species will not be able to evolve to adapt to the environment.*

If species adapt to the changes, or evolve, they survive. If a species doesn't have individuals with characteristics needed to survive in the changing environment, the species becomes extinct. Look again at Figure 17-2. Note that during the Silurian Period, warm, shallow seas covered much of North America. Corals, which are sea animals, were a dominant life-form on Earth. But as plate tectonic processes changed Earth's surface, climates also changed. Glaciers started to form during the Permian Period. Some species of corals weren't able to adapt to the cooler climate. Thus, corals became less and less abundant. Certain other sea creatures, like the trilobites, couldn't adapt to the changes and eventually became extinct.

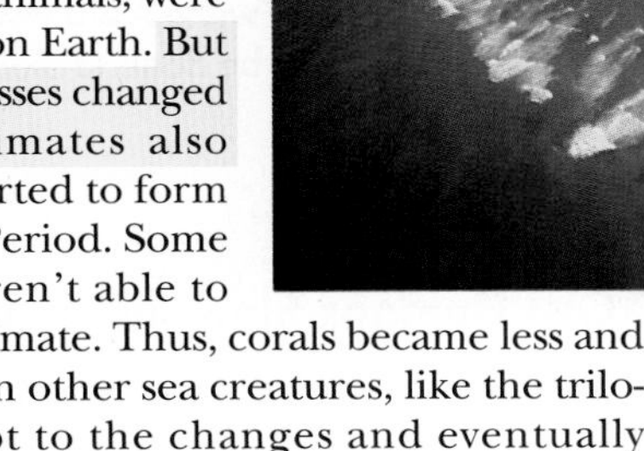

Figure 17-6. During the Silurian Period, most of North America was covered by warm, shallow seas. Coral thrived in this environment.

SECTION REVIEW

1. What are the types of subdivisions of geologic time?
2. What is organic evolution?
3. How does organic evolution relate to the geologic time scale?
4. How does plate tectonics affect organic evolution?
5. **Apply:** Today, the peppered moth species shown in Figure 17-4 has many light-colored individuals. How can this be attributed to recent anti-pollution laws?

Recognizing Cause and Effect

Skill Builder

Answer the questions below. If you need help, refer to Recognizing Cause and Effect in the **Skill Handbook** on page 683.

1. If there had been no horses with fewer than three toes, could the species have evolved into a single-toed, hoofed species? Explain.
2. Is natural selection a cause or effect of organic evolution?
3. How could the evolution of a trait within one species affect the evolution of a trait within another species? Give an example.

3 CLOSE

▶ Invite a biology teacher or senior student into class to discuss the theory of organic evolution.

▶ Call on a student volunteer to read the lesson objectives aloud. Allow students time to covertly remember how each objective was achieved. Ask for a volunteer to present a summary of how plate tectonics might affect organic evolution. Have another student relate organic evolution to the geologic time scale. Elicit help from other students if needed.

SECTION REVIEW ANSWERS

1. eras, periods, and epochs
2. the gradual change of life-forms over time
3. Changes in or massive extinctions of life-forms are used to divide geologic time into units.
4. As landmasses move across Earth, climates on the continents change dramatically. Through natural selection, only those individuals suited to the changes survive and reproduce. They pass their traits to their offspring. Over many generations, the species has evolved so that it is characterized by the traits that enable it to survive in the changed environment.
5. Apply: Anti-pollution laws have resulted in less smog and, therefore, less dark-colored residue on the bark of local trees. The light-colored moths are well camouflaged against the lighter bark. They are suited to survive and reproduce, passing on their light color to their offspring.

Skill Builder

1. Species only change when variations within individuals exist. It's possible that some individuals existed with one middle toe that was large compared to the other smaller side toes. Over time, the large middle toe was selected for and eventually, one large toe evolved.
2. a cause
3. Species are interdependent. Changes within the organisms of an ecosystem affect all aspects of that ecosystem. For example, if a species evolves so that it is no longer available as the primary food source for another species, the predator species must evolve so that it can prey on other sources or become extinct.

SECTION 17-2

1 MOTIVATE

TYING TO PREVIOUS KNOWLEDGE: Help students recall the characteristics of the tropical rain forest biome from their study of life science. Tropical rain forests are found in low-lying regions near the equator.

OBJECTIVES AND SCIENCE WORDS: Have students review the objectives and science words to become familiar with this section.

2 TEACH

Key Concepts are highlighted.

CONCEPT DEVELOPMENT

▶ Discuss the fact that 80 percent of all deforestation of Amazonian rain forests has occurred since 1980.

▶ Have students discuss the significance of the fact that one-quarter of all pharmaceuticals are derived from rain-forest plants. Students should realize that the destruction of a habitat so rich in species has serious philosophical and economic ramifications.

Cooperative Learning: Using the Numbered Heads Together strategy, have students discuss how destruction of habitats might be detrimental to all humans. Have students list reasons to prevent extinctions. Ask one student in each group to present a summary of the group's ideas to the class.

TEACHER F.Y.I.

▶ The National Cancer Institute has identified plants that may be useful in the treatment of cancer. Of those identified, 70 percent are found only in rain forests.

PROGRAM RESOURCES

From the **Teacher Resource Package** use:

Science and Society, page 21, Why Save a Habitat?

17-2 Present-Day Rapid Extinctions

New Science Words

endangered
habitat

Objectives

- ▶ **Recognize how humans have caused extinctions.**
- ▶ **Predict what might happen to the diversity of life on Earth if land is developed without protection of natural habitats.**
- ▶ **Decide what can be done to stop or slow down the rate of species extinction.**

Can Humans Slow the Rate of Extinctions?

For years you've watched and listened to a beautiful species of bird near your home. Now you learn that a new mall is to be built just down the road. The birds live in the trees that need to be cut down to make room for the mall. The mall is important to the community's economy, but the birds are important to the community's environment. What can be done to allow the economic development without destroying the area where the birds live?

You've learned that extinctions have occurred throughout Earth history. They were caused by changes in environments or competition with other species for resources. Some of these extinctions may have been caused by the appearance of early humans. Present-day humans are causing extinctions at a much greater rate.

How do humans cause extinctions? When humans kill organisms faster than they can reproduce, the number of members in their species decreases. Such species can become endangered. A species becomes **endangered** when only a small number of its members are living. If the number of members of a species continues to dwindle, the species can become extinct. A species becomes extinct when no more of its members are living. Once a species is extinct, it will never again exist on our planet.

Humans cause extinctions by hunting, carelessness, and by making changes in the environment. Often, we take over the natural habitats of other species, leaving

Figure 17-7. The dodo bird became extinct approximately 300 years ago.

OPTIONS

Meeting Different Ability Levels

For Section 17-2, use the following **Teacher Resource Masters** depending upon individual students' needs.

◆ **Study Guide Master** for all students.

● **Reinforcement Master** for students of average and above average ability levels.

▲ **Enrichment Master** for above average students.

Additional Teacher Resource Package masters are listed in the OPTIONS box throughout the section. The additional masters are appropriate for all students.

◆ STUDY GUIDE 71

NAME ____________ DATE ________ CLASS ________

STUDY GUIDE — Chapter 17

Present-Day Rapid Extinctions — Text Pages 454–455

Read each statement, and then answer the questions in complete sentences.

1. Throughout Earth's history, species have become extinct. What causes extinction? **Changes in environments or competition with other species for resources causes extinction.**
2. The activities of humans living about 10 000 years ago may have caused some extinctions. How do present-day humans affect animal species? **They are causing extinctions at a greater rate.**
3. How might economic development in a city or suburb affect the habitat of birds that are in the area? **Trees are often cut down to make room for buildings and factories, making conditions more difficult for birds.**
4. Tropical rain forests contain 50 to 80 percent of Earth's species. What has been done to threaten these species? **People have cleared much of these forests for farming, logging, and other industries.**
5. Organisms need a place to live, grow, and interact with each other and their environment. What is such a place called? **Such a place is called a habitat.**
6. Habitats are being destroyed in many places. What may happen to the organisms that live in these habitats? **They may become extinct.**
7. Some species that still exist are endangered. What does *endangered* mean? **A species is endangered when only a small number of its members are living.**
8. Some people want to save habitats by restricting construction and planning projects so habitats are disturbed as little as possible. What are these people trying to slow down? **They are trying to slow down the rate of extinctions.**
9. Some medicines and other products come from various organisms. Why might this be a reason to try to save organisms? **If we don't, we may miss opportunities to invent new medicines that could be derived from the organisms.**

 71

them with no food or space in which to live. Pollution also causes extinctions.

You may have heard about problems caused by the cutting or burning of tropical rain forests. During the past decade, people have cleared much of these forests for farming, logging, and other industries. In doing so, many habitats have been destroyed. A **habitat** is where organisms live, grow, and interact with each other and with the environment. Many species on Earth can live in only one type of habitat. If the habitat is destroyed, so are all members of the species.

The tropical rain forest habitat covers only about seven percent of Earth's surface, but contains 50 to 80 percent of Earth's species. Think of what would happen to these species if the tropical rain forests were destroyed. Nearly all would become extinct.

Several possible solutions have been proposed to slow the rate of extinctions. Governments could restrict construction to allow both development and preservation. Projects could be planned so that habitats are disturbed as little as possible. When clearing land, some could be left in its natural state.

Figure 17-8. This African mountain gorilla makes its home in Rwanda. However, the expansion of human settlements into the habitat of mountain gorillas has led to their endangerment.

SECTION REVIEW

1. List three ways humans cause extinctions.
2. How does developing land reduce the diversity of life on Earth?
3. How might humans work to slow the rate of present-day extinctions?
4. Why is the loss of rain forest habitats of great concern to environmentalists?

You Decide!

Many of the medicines and other products used by people come from organisms. In some cases, the substances in these products are produced in only one species of organism. Some people fear that by causing the disappearance of species before we have even discovered their existence, we will miss opportunities to invent new medicines that could be derived from the organisms. Do you think this is a good enough reason to restrict development so that species aren't eliminated? Are there other reasons to prevent extinctions?

● REINFORCEMENT 71

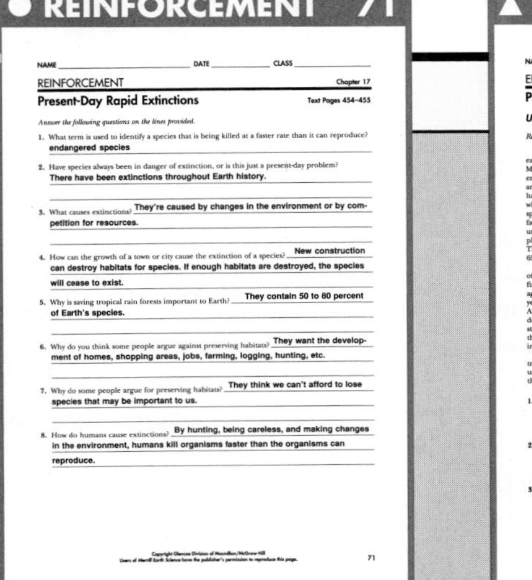

NAME ____________ DATE ________ CLASS ________

REINFORCEMENT — Chapter 17

Present-Day Rapid Extinctions — Text Pages 454–455

Answer the following questions on the lines provided.

1. What term is used to identify a species that is being killed at a faster rate than it can reproduce? **endangered species**
2. Have species always been in danger of extinction, or is this just a present-day problem? **There have been extinctions throughout Earth history.**
3. What causes extinctions? **They're caused by changes in the environment or by competition for resources.**
4. How can the growth of a town or city cause the extinction of a species? **New construction can destroy habitats for species. If enough habitats are destroyed, the species will cease to exist.**
5. Why is saving tropical rain forests important to Earth? **They contain 50 to 80 percent of Earth's species.**
6. Why do you think some people argue against preserving habitats? **They want the development of homes, shopping areas, jobs, farming, logging, hunting, etc.**
7. Why do some people argue for preserving habitats? **They think we can't afford to lose species that may be important to us.**
8. How do humans cause extinctions? **By hunting, being careless, and making changes in the environment, humans kill organisms faster than the organisms can reproduce.**

71

▲ ENRICHMENT 71

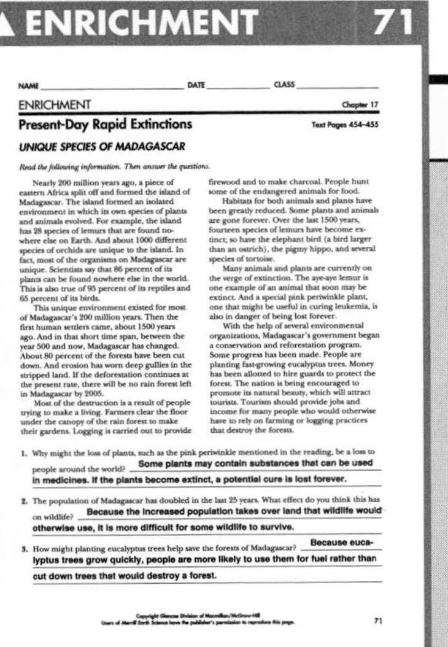

NAME ____________ DATE ________ CLASS ________

ENRICHMENT — Chapter 17

Present-Day Rapid Extinctions — Text Pages 454–455

UNIQUE SPECIES OF MADAGASCAR

Read the following information. Then answer the questions.

Nearly 200 million years ago, a piece of eastern Africa split off and formed the island of Madagascar. The island formed an isolated environment in which its own species of plants and animals evolved. For example, the island has 28 species of lemurs that are found nowhere else on Earth. And about 1000 different species of orchids are unique to the island. In fact, most of the organisms on Madagascar are unique. Scientists say that 86 percent of its plants can be found nowhere else in the world. This is also true of 95 percent of its reptiles and 65 percent of its birds.

This unique environment existed for most of Madagascar's 200 million years. Then the first human settlers came, about 1500 years ago. And in that short time span, between the year 500 and now, Madagascar has changed. About 80 percent of the forests have been cut down. And erosion has worn deep gullies in the stripped land. If the deforestation continues at the present rate, there will be no rain forest left in Madagascar by 2005.

Most of the destruction is a result of people trying to make a living. Farmers clear the floor under the canopy of the rain forest to make their gardens. Logging is carried out to provide firewood and to make charcoal. People hunt some of the endangered animals for food.

Habitats for both animals and plants have been greatly reduced. Some plants and animals are gone forever. Over the last 1500 years, fourteen species of lemurs have become extinct; so have the elephant bird (a bird larger than an ostrich), the pigmy hippo, and several species of tortoise.

Many animals and plants are currently on the verge of extinction. The aye-aye lemur is one example of an animal that soon may be extinct. And a special pink periwinkle plant, one that might be useful in curing leukemia, is also in danger of being lost forever.

With the help of several environmental organizations, Madagascar's government began a conservation and reforestation program. Some progress has been made. People are planting fast-growing eucalyptus trees. Money has been allotted to hire guards to protect the forest. The nation is being encouraged to promote its natural beauty, which will attract tourists. Tourism should provide jobs and income for many people who would otherwise have to rely on farming or logging practices that destroy the forests.

1. Why might the loss of plants, such as the pink periwinkle mentioned in the reading, be a loss to people around the world? **Some plants may contain substances that can be used in medicines. If the plants become extinct, a potential cure is lost forever.**
2. The population of Madagascar has doubled in the last 25 years. What effect do you think this has on wildlife? **Because the increased population takes over land that wildlife would otherwise use, it is more difficult for some wildlife to survive.**
3. How might planting eucalyptus trees help save the forests of Madagascar? **Because eucalyptus trees grow quickly, people are more likely to use them for fuel rather than cut down trees that would destroy a forest.**

71

CONCEPT DEVELOPMENT

▶ For information on rainforest deforestation, have interested students write to the Rainforest Action Network, 301 Broadway, Suite A, San Francisco, CA 94133, or call (415) 398-4404.

CHECK FOR UNDERSTANDING

Ask questions 1-4 in the Section Review.

RETEACH

Show students pictures of the results of deforestation associated with slash and burn farming in South America and Asia. Explain that destruction of rain forests is permanent. Also explain that soil in a tropical rain forest only supports farming for a few years before new areas must be cleared to grow new crops.

EXTENSION

For students who have mastered this section, use the **Reinforcement** and **Enrichment** masters or other OPTIONS provided.

3 CLOSE

▶ Invite a doctor into class to discuss medicines that are derived from other organisms and how the study of medicine would be affected by high extinction rates.

SECTION REVIEW ANSWERS

1. hunting, carelessness, and by making changes in the environment
2. Developing land can destroy habitats for organisms that cannot survive elsewhere. When the habitat is destroyed, the organisms die off.
3. Answers will vary but might include government restrictions on construction to allow both development and preservation.
4. Tropical rain forests contain 50 to 80 percent of Earth's species. The losses are permanent.

YOU DECIDE!

Answers will vary greatly. Discuss all reasonable viewpoints.

ACTIVITY 17-1
30 minutes

OBJECTIVE: Formulate a model showing the role of natural selection in creating variations within a species.

PROCESS SKILLS applied in this activity:
▶ **Formulating Models** in Procedure Steps 1-10.
▶ **Using Numbers** in Procedure Steps 3, 5, 8, and 10.
▶ **Interpreting Data** in Analyze Questions 1 and 5.
▶ **Analyzing** in Analyze Questions 1-2 and in Conclude and Apply Question 4.
▶ **Recognizing Cause and Effect** in Conclude and Apply Questions 4 and 7.
▶ **Communicating** in Conclude and Apply Question 8.

COOPERATIVE LEARNING
Students should work in Science Investigation Teams of three individuals. One student should handle the cards, one should perform the mathematical operations (addition and averaging), and a third student should record the results.

TEACHING THE ACTIVITY

Preparation: Remove the cards that will not be used in this activity prior to class time. This will eliminate Step 1 of the Procedure and reduce the time needed by students to perform the activity.

▶ Inform students that the natural selection process described and modeled in this activity is not unlike that which is thought to have led to the present-day African giraffe.

PROGRAM RESOURCES

From the **Teacher Resource Package** use:

Activity Worksheets, pages 151-152, Activity 17-1: Evolution within a Species.

ACTIVITY 17-1
Evolution within a Species

Problem: *How does a trait evolve within a species?*

Materials
- Deck of playing cards

Procedure
1. Remove all of the Kings, Queens, Jacks, and Aces from a deck of playing cards.
2. Each remaining playing card represents an individual in a population of animals called "varimals." The number on each card represents the height of the individual. For example, the "5 of diamonds" is a varimal that's 5 units tall.
3. Calculate the average height of the population of varimals represented by your cards.
4. Suppose varimals eat grass, shrubs, and leaves from trees. A drought causes many of these plants to die. All that's left are a few tall trees. Only varimals at least 6 units tall can reach the leaves on these trees.
5. All the varimals under 6 units leave the area to seek food elsewhere or die from starvation. Discard all of the cards with a number value less than 6. Calculate the new average height of the population of varimals.
6. Shuffle the deck of remaining cards.
7. Draw two cards at a time. Each pair represents a pair of varimals that will mate and produce offspring.
8. The offspring of each pair reaches a height equal to the average height of his or her parents. Calculate and record the height of each offspring.
9. Now suppose all the varimals under 8 units tall die or migrate because of another shortage of food. Discard all of the parents that are under 8 units tall. On your data table, mark out all of the offspring under 8 units tall.
10. Calculate the new average height of varimals. Include both the parents and offspring in your calculation.

Analyze
1. How did the average height of the population change over time?
2. If you hadn't discarded the shortest varimals in Step 5, would the average height of the population have changed as dramatically? Explain.
3. What trait was selected for in this activity?

Conclude and Apply
4. Why didn't every member of the original population reproduce?
5. If there had been no varimals over 6 units tall in Step 5, what would have happened to the population?
6. Did any individual varimal increase in height because of natural selection? Explain.
7. If there had been no variation in height in the population before the droughts occurred, would the species have been able to evolve into a taller species than it started as?
8. How does this activity demonstrate that traits evolve in species?

ANSWERS TO QUESTIONS

1. The average height increased over time.
2. No. The average would have remained at about 6.
3. height; specifically, the ability to reach food at a distance above the ground
4. Some of the original varimals weren't able to obtain enough food to survive and, therefore, weren't available to reproduce.
5. This particular population of varimals would have become extinct.
6. No, individuals do not evolve inheritable adaptations. Natural selection is the preservation of favorable characteristics that already exist within a species. These characteristics are passed from one generation to the next. Natural selection did play a role in the increased average height of the offspring.
7. Probably not. If all of the individual varimals would have been the same height, no group of individuals would have an advantage in reaching the tall food. In that case, any evolution of the varimal population would have likely occurred from some variation of a trait other than height.
8. By creating the variation of a trait within the varimal population, in this case height, the model demonstrates how the species was able to evolve into one capable of reaching food high above the ground. This process, by which individuals with more favorable traits are able to survive and produce offspring with these same traits, is known as natural selection.

Early Earth History 17-3

Objectives

- Identify dominant life-forms in the Precambrian and Paleozoic Eras.
- Draw conclusions about how organisms adapted to changing environments in the Precambrian and Paleozoic Eras.
- Describe changes in Earth and its life-forms at the end of the Paleozoic Era.

New Science Words

Precambrian Era
cyanobacteria
Paleozoic Era
amphibians
reptiles

The Precambrian Era

Look again at Figure 17-2. Which part of Earth's history is the longest? The **Precambrian** (pree KAM bree un) **Era** makes up about 90 percent of Earth's history. This time lasted from 4.6 billion to about 570 million years ago. Although the Precambrian Era is the longest unit of geologic time, relatively little is known about Earth and the organisms that lived during this time. Why is the fossil record from the Precambrian Era so sparse?

Precambrian rocks have been deeply buried and changed by heat and pressure. They have also been eroded more than more recent rocks. These changes affect

Figure 17-9. Lightning or the sun may have provided the energy necessary to build amino acids out of the simple compounds in Earth's Precambrian atmosphere. Amino acids are the "building blocks of life." These amino acids reacted with each other and combined to form the compounds from which life evolved.

OPTIONS

INQUIRY QUESTIONS

▶ **Why were most life-forms during the Paleozoic Era marine life-forms?** *Warm, shallow seas covered much of Earth's surface.*

▶ **Why are brachiopod fossils considered good indicators of ancient marine environments?** *They were very common during the Paleozoic Era when warm, shallow seas covered much of Earth's surface and are still found today in warm, sea environments.*

▶ **What development enabled animal life to move from the sea onto land?** *Plant life developed on land.*

▶ **Why do scientists think lung fish may have evolved into amphibians?** *Lung fish can breathe air as they travel across land from one body of water to the next.*

▶ **What might have caused the mass extinctions that occurred at the end of the Paleozoic Era?** *The environment changed perhaps as a result of plate tectonics because at this time, all continental plates were coming together.*

SECTION 17-3

PREPARATION

SECTION BACKGROUND

▶ Trilobites are a common fossil from the Cambrian Period. They were probably not active swimmers, but crawled along the bottom scavenging for food. Trilobites were widespread and diverse, which makes them excellent index fossils for the Paleozoic Era.

▶ The Paleozoic Era is subdivided into seven periods. Each period is named for the geographic area where its rocks were first studied.

1 MOTIVATE

TYING TO PREVIOUS KNOWLEDGE: Help students recall the chemical composition and physical properties of ozone discussed in Chapter 9. Remind students that ozone is made of three oxygen atoms (O_3) bonded together. When discussing the production of molecular oxygen (O_2) by cyanobacteria, relate the fact that ozone is produced when energy (such as that supplied by the sun or by lightning) is added to molecular oxygen (O_2).

OBJECTIVES AND SCIENCE WORDS: Have students review the objectives and science words to become familiar with this section.

REVEALING MISCONCEPTIONS

▶ Ask students to hypothesize when sharks appeared on Earth. Many students will consider sharks to be modern-day animals since they are still around. Explain that sharks evolved during the Ordovician Period about 500 million years ago. They are one of the earliest forms of fish to evolve.

2 TEACH

Key Concepts are highlighted.

CROSS CURRICULUM

▶ **Life Science:** Have students research the role cyanobacteria played in transforming Earth's early atmosphere into one containing free molecular oxygen (O_2). Students should discover that cyanobacteria are single-celled, photosynthesizing organisms. Have students explore how the process of photosynthesis generates oxygen. Have students prepare a report on cyanobacteria, including a discussion of the importance of the development of an ozone layer in the upper atmosphere to the development of more complex organisms.

CONCEPT DEVELOPMENT

Cooperative Learning: Form Numbered Heads Together groups with four students per group to answer the following question. **Why was the development of single-celled cyanobacteria so important to the evolution of more complex organisms?** *As they evolved, cyanobacteria helped change Earth's atmosphere. They exchanged oxygen for other atmospheric gases. The amount of oxygen in the atmosphere increased, allowing an ozone layer to develop. The layer shielded Earth's surface from harmful ultraviolet radiation from the sun. Complex life-forms were able to evolve in the changed environment.*

TEACHER F.Y.I.

▶ The Precambrian Era spans some 4 billion, 30 million years, seven times longer than the time spanned by the other three geologic eras together.

not only the rocks but the fossil record as well. Most fossils can't withstand the metamorphic and erosional processes that Precambrian rocks have experienced.

It wasn't until fossilized cyanobacteria, called stromatolites, were found that scientists could begin to unravel Earth's complex history. **Cyanobacteria** are bacteria (1) thought to be one of the earliest forms of life on Earth. Cyanobacteria first appeared on Earth about 3.5 billion years ago. As these organisms evolved, they helped to change Earth's atmosphere. During the few billion years following the appearance of cyanobacteria, oxygen became a major gas in Earth's atmosphere. The ozone layer in the stratosphere also began to develop, shielding Earth from ultraviolet rays. These major changes in the air allowed species of single-celled organisms to evolve into more complex organisms.

What role did cyanobacteria play in the evolution of Earth's atmosphere?

Figure 17-10. Cyanobacteria produce mound-shaped layers of calcium carbonate called *stromatolites*. Stromatolites were common about 2.8 billion years ago and are still being formed by some cyanobacteria today.

Animals without backbones, called invertebrates, developed near the end of the Precambrian. Imprints of jellyfish and marine worms have been found in late Precambrian rocks. Because invertebrates were soft, they weren't easily preserved as fossils. This is another reason the Precambrian fossil record is so sparse.

The Paleozoic Era

In Chapter 16, you discovered that fossils are more likely to form if organisms have hard parts. When organisms developed hard parts, the **Paleozoic** (pay lee uh ZOH ihk) **Era** began. Fossils were more easily preserved.

OPTIONS

Meeting Different Ability Levels

For Section 17-3, use the following **Teacher Resource Masters** depending upon individual students' needs.

◆ **Study Guide Master** for all students.

● **Reinforcement Master** for students of average and above average ability levels.

▲ **Enrichment Master** for above average students.

Additional Teacher Resource Package masters are listed in the OPTIONS box throughout the section. The additional masters are appropriate for all students.

◆ STUDY GUIDE 72

NAME ____________ DATE ________ CLASS ________

STUDY GUIDE — Chapter 17

Early Earth History — Text Pages 457–461

Answer the questions on the lines at the left.

Precambrian Era 1. Which era in the geologic time scale lasted the longest?

Precambrian Era 2. Which era is the oldest era?

cyanobacteria 3. What is thought to be one of the earliest forms of life on Earth?

oxygen; ozone layer 4. What appeared in the atmosphere that allowed more complex organisms to develop?

invertebrates 5. What kind of animals developed near the end of the first era?

Paleozoic Era 6. What name was given to the second of Earth's eras?

warm, shallow seas 7. What covered most of Earth's surface at the beginning of the second era?

fish 8. What familiar marine life-form evolved during this era?

amphibians 9. What type of animal evolved that lived out of water but reproduced in water?

Appalachian Mountains 10. What mountain chain was caused by the collision of the Eurasian or African continental plates with the North American plate?

reptiles 11. What type of animal is thought to have developed after the evolution of an egg that would not dry out on land?

coal 12. The formation of swamps and the decay of swamp vegetation are the basis for what fossil fuel?

Answer the following questions in complete sentences on the lines provided.

13. What happened to all of the continental plates near the end of the Paleozoic Era? **They came together to form Pangaea.**

14. What happened to many land and sea animals at this time? **The land and sea animals became extinct.**

72

Figure 17-11. This model recreates a Paleozoic sea. Trilobites, brachiopods, mollusks, and other organisms were common marine animals of the time.

The Paleozoic Era, or era of ancient life, began about 570 million years ago. Warm, shallow seas covered much of Earth's surface during early Paleozoic time. Because of this, most of the life-forms were marine, meaning they lived in the ocean. Trilobites (TRI luh bites) were very common. Brachiopods (BRAY kee uh pahdz) and crinoids (KRI noyds), which still exist today, were also very common. Although these animals may not be familiar to you, one type of animal you are familiar with—the fish—also evolved during this era.

The Paleozoic Era is broken into seven periods. The beginning of the Ordovician Period is marked by the beginning of the Appalachian Mountain building process. This was probably caused by the collision of the Eurasian or African continental plate with the North American Plate.

The first vertebrates, animals with backbones, developed during the Ordovician Period. Plant life moved from the oceans onto land during the Silurian Period. Fish became dominant in the Devonian Period. By this time plant life had developed on land, and animals began to move onto land as well.

One type of fish evolved a lung that enabled it to survive out of water. This fish had fins that allowed it to move across land. The fact that lung fish could move across the land and breathe air has led scientists to theorize that lung fish evolved into amphibians (am FIHB ee unz). 2 **Amphibians** live on land and breathe air, but must return to water to reproduce. Their eggs must be kept moist in water. They first appeared during the Devonian Period and became the dominant form of vertebrate life on land by the Mississippian Period.

MINI-Lab

How can fossils be used to date rock layers?

Suppose you find a layer of sedimentary rocks containing fossils. You number the layers 1 through 5, from bottom to top. The bottom layer, layer 1, contains fossils C and A. Layer 2 contains fossils A, B, and C. Layer 3 contains fossils A, B, and D. Layer 4 contains fossils B and D. The top layer, layer 5, contains only fossil D. You know the geologic periods during which each type of organism producing the fossils lived. Fossil A lived from the Cambrian through the Devonian Periods. Fossil B lived from the Ordovician through the Pennsylvanian. Fossil C lived from the Cambrian through the Ordovician. Fossil D lived from the Devonian through the Permian. Construct illustrations to help you determine the ages of each rock layer. It's possible to date only two of the layers to one specific period. Which layers are they? Why isn't it possible to determine during which specific period the other layers formed? What is the age or possible ages of each layer?

MINI-Lab

Teaching Tips

▶ Sketch the geologic column described in the Mini-Lab. Label the layers 1 through 5 and indicate which fossils, A through D, are in each layer.

▶ Have students construct a chart like the one shown below. The chart illustrates when each fossil organism, A through D, existed.

▶ For each rock layer, list the periods during which it could have formed based on the fossils within it.

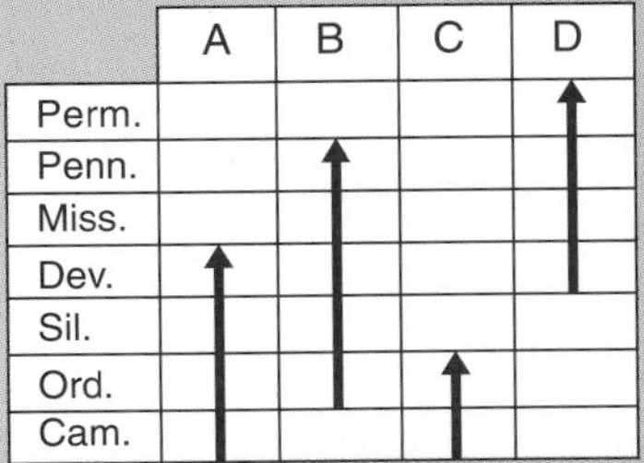

	A	B	C	D
Perm.				
Penn.				
Miss.				
Dev.				
Sil.				
Ord.				
Cam.				

Answers to Questions: The only layer that can be dated to one specific period is Layer 3 since it contains both fossils A and D. The only period of time that both of these fossil organisms existed together was during the Devonian. The apparent absence of a fossil within a layer does not necessarily mean that the organism did not exist at that time, only that it hasn't been found in the particular rock layer. Only the combination of fossils that *are* found can be used for dating the layer. Based on the information provided, Layer 1 could be either of Cambrian or Ordovician age. Layer 2 could be Ordovician, Silurian, or Devonian. Layer 3 must be Devonian. Layer 4 could have formed during the Devonian, Mississippian, or Pennsylvanian periods. Layer 5 could have formed anytime from the beginning of the Devonian through the end of the Permian.

● **REINFORCEMENT 72**

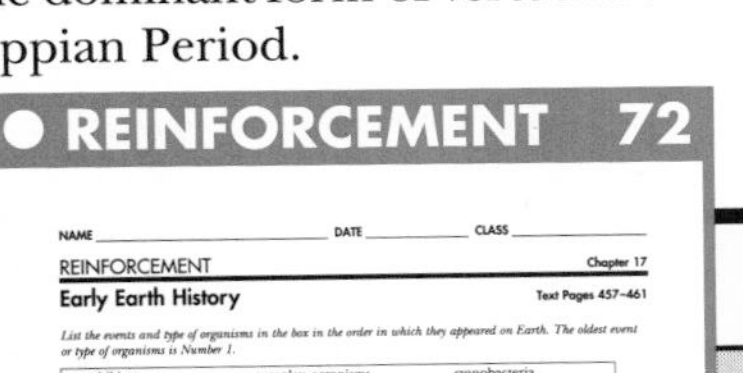

NAME ______ DATE ______ CLASS ______

REINFORCEMENT — Chapter 17

Early Earth History — Text Pages 457–461

List the events and type of organisms in the box in the order in which they appeared on Earth. The oldest event or type of organisms is Number 1.

amphibians	complex organisms	cyanobacteria
fish	invertebrates	organisms with hard parts
shielding of Earth from ultraviolet rays	Pangaea	reptiles
	oxygen and ozone layer	

1. cyanobacteria
2. oxygen and ozone layer
3. shielding of Earth from ultraviolet rays
4. complex organisms
5. invertebrates
6. organisms with hard parts
7. fish
8. amphibians
9. reptiles
10. Pangaea

Answer the following questions on the lines provided.

11. Which of the events in the list occurred in the Precambrian Era? **#1–5** Which occurred in the Paleozoic Era? **#6–10**
12. Why is so little known about the Precambrian Era? **Precambrian rocks have been deeply buried, changed by heat and pressure, and eroded. Many fossils can't withstand these processes.**
13. Why did coal deposits begin to form in the Paleozoic Era? **Swamps formed. When swamp vegetation died, it was deposited in layers, buried, and slowly changed to coal beds.**
14. What might have caused the mass extinctions of many land and sea animals at the end of the Paleozoic Era? **With the forming of Pangaea, oceans and landmasses changed and climates changed from mild and warm to cold and dry.**

72

▲ **ENRICHMENT 72**

NAME ______ DATE ______ CLASS ______

ENRICHMENT — Chapter 17

Early Earth History — Text Pages 457–461

HOW CAN YOU MAKE A "FOSSIL"?

Materials

- paper towels
- heavy books
- baking soda
- stems, leaves, flowers, or other organic material

Procedure

1. Make a stack of 4 or 5 squares of paper toweling.
2. Sprinkle the top paper towel with baking soda.
3. Lay organic material flat on the baking soda.
4. Cover the organic material with a thin layer of baking soda. Then place another 4 or 5 squares of paper toweling over it.
5. Place a pile of heavy books on the paper toweling. Leave the books undisturbed for 2 or 3 days.
6. Remove the books. Carefully remove the upper layers of toweling and gently shake off the top layer of baking soda.

Analyze

1. Describe the "fossil" created by this experiment. Include color, shape, and similarity to the original organic material in your description. **The "fossil" will look much like the original leaves or flowers, but the color will be faded.**
2. Explain why this is not a true fossil. **Fossils are the remains of life-forms preserved in Earth's rocks.**
3. What is the purpose of the baking soda? **The baking soda dries the plant tissue.**
4. What material or action in the formation of true fossils is represented by the books? **The books take the place of the rocks that would exert pressure on the forming fossil.**

Conclude and Apply

5. If the material had been buried in mud, what would eventually have happened to the tissue of the organic matter? **Organic matter would no longer be present. Weathering and activity of microorganisms would have caused it to decay.**
6. How would your experiment differ if you placed a piece of seashell instead of a leaf between the layers of paper toweling? Explain your answer. **The seashell would probably have shown little change since it is hard and contains less moisture than leaves or flowers.**

72

PROBLEM SOLVING

Paleozoic Puzzle

Neila enjoyed finding and collecting fossils. She had investigated many of the rock outcrops in her city and had begun an excellent collection of local fossil types. Her favorite fossil was a particular species of brachiopod known as a *Mucrospirifer*. She identified her fossil using pictures and descriptions from a book on Paleozoic fossils.

While on a trip with her family to visit relatives in another state, Neila found what seemed like the same type of *Mucrospirifer* fossil in a rock formation on her aunt's farm.

Think Critically: What could Neila say about the rocks in which she found both fossils?

EcoTip

Oil forms from the decay of dead plant material. It takes millions of years for it to form. All the oil we use today formed during the time of the dinosaurs. Because oil is a nonrenewable resource, we need to conserve it. Call a garage in your area to find out how you can recycle used motor oil.

Over time, one species of amphibian evolved an egg with a membrane that protected it from drying out. Because of this, the species no longer needed to return to water to reproduce. By the Pennsylvanian Period, some
3 species of amphibians had evolved into reptiles. **Reptiles** do not need to return to water to reproduce. They have a skin composed of hard scales that prevent loss of body fluids. Their skin enables them to survive farther from water. They can survive in the relatively dry climates where amphibians cannot.

Many of the coal deposits mined today in the United States began forming during the Pennsylvanian Period. Inland seas were cut off from the oceans. Swamps similar to those found in the Florida Everglades formed. When the swamp vegetation died, it was deposited in layers and quickly buried. This material later changed to the coal beds of today.

Mass extinctions of many land and sea animals occurred to signal the end of the Paleozoic Era. The cause of these extinctions may have been changes in the environment caused by plate tectonics. Near the end of the Permian Period, all continental plates came together to form the single landmass Pangaea.

PROBLEM SOLVING

Think Critically: Both rock formations formed during the time that the species of *Mucrospirifer* existed. It cannot be concluded from the information given whether the two rock outcrops are part of the same formation. They may have been deposited at different times. For example, if the particular species of *Mucrospirifer* existed for 100 000 years, one formation may have been deposited at the beginning of that 100 000 year period and the other formation near its end.

CHECK FOR UNDERSTANDING

Use the Mini Quiz to check for understanding.

MINI QUIZ

Use the Mini Quiz to check students' recall of chapter content.

1. **Earth's complex history began to unravel once scientists found fossilized ___.** *cyanobacteria*
2. **Once fish developed a lung, it is thought they evolved into ____.** *amphibians*
3. **When some species of amphibians evolved an egg with a membrane that protected it from drying out, they no longer needed to return to water to reproduce. These amphibians evolved into ____.** *reptiles*

RETEACH

Cooperative Learning: Using the Paired Partners strategy, have students list the characteristics of amphibians that make them different from fish and the characteristics of reptiles that make them different from amphibians. Have partners test each other on the differences and search through magazine articles for photographs of amphibians and reptiles.

EXTENSION

For students who have mastered this section, use the **Reinforcement** and **Enrichment** masters or other OPTIONS provided.

OPTIONS

ENRICHMENT

▶ Have students identify the organisms shown in the diorama of the Paleozoic Era in Figure 17-11.

▶ Have students research the Pennsylvanian Period coal swamps, where much of the coal used today was formed. Show students samples of peat, lignite (palm coal), bituminous coal, and anthracite coal. Describe the process that must occur for plant remains to change into coal. Refer students to Chapter 18 for a description of this process.

PROGRAM RESOURCES

From the **Teacher Resource Package** use:

Activity Worksheets, page 157, Mini-Lab: How can fossils be used to date rock layers?

Figure 17-12. Reptile egg shells prevent developing embryos from drying out. Unlike frogs, salamanders, and other amphibians, reptiles can lay their eggs on land. This allows them to survive in relatively dry environments.

The slow, gradual collision of continental plates caused mountain building. Mountain building processes caused seas to drain away, and interior deserts spread over much of the United States and parts of Europe. Climates changed from mild and warm to cold and dry. The areas of oceans and landmasses changed. Many species, especially sea creatures, weren't able to adapt to these and other changes and became extinct.

Why did many sea creatures become extinct at the end of the Cambrian Period?

SECTION REVIEW

1. What major change in life-forms occurred to separate Precambrian time from Paleozoic time?
2. What geologic events occurred at the end of the Paleozoic Era?
3. **Apply:** How might geologic events at the end of the Paleozoic Era have caused the mass extinctions that occurred?

Making and Using Tables

Skill Builder

Use Figure 17-2 to answer these questions about the Paleozoic Era. If you need help, refer to Making and Using Tables in the **Skill Handbook** on page 690.

1. When did the Paleozoic Era begin? When did it end?
2. How long did the Silurian Period last?
3. When did the Appalachian Mountains start to form?
4. When did the first insects appear on Earth?

Skill Builder

1. 570 million years ago; 225 million years ago
2. 35 million years
3. during the Ordovician Period—between 500 million and 430 million years ago
4. during the Pennsylvanian Period—between 280 million and 325 million years ago

3 CLOSE

▶ Have students read the article, "Whale Feet," by James Trefil, *Discover,* May 1991, pp. 45-48. The article discusses fossils of *Basilosaurus* found in the Egyptian desert. The presence of hind legs on this ancestral whale provide a connection to possible theories on whale evolution. The article examines the significance of finding vestigial appendages clearly "designed" for use on land on an aquatic animal. The discoveries reported in this article are significant because they support the theory that ancestors of present-day whales were land mammals that moved to the sea.

▶ Ask questions 1-2 and the **Apply** Question in the Section Review.

SECTION REVIEW ANSWERS

1. The evolution of organisms with hard parts marked the beginning of a new era in Earth's history.
2. Continents once again drifted together, mountains were built as continents collided, and seas drained away creating deserts.
3. Apply: Environments would have changed and many life-forms could not have adapted quickly enough. When Pangaea formed, life-forms that were separated were now together. These life-forms now competed for food. This could have caused changes in the life-forms and could have led to the extinction of some organisms. The extinction of one species may cause the extinction of other species as well. For example, some animals depend on one type of plant as their primary food source. If the plant disappears, the species of animal may die-off as well.

PREPARATION

SECTION BACKGROUND

▶ The Triassic Period, the earliest period in the Mesozoic Era, is named for three related units of rock first studied in Germany. The Jurassic Period is named after the Jura Mountains between France and Switzerland, where this age rock was first studied. The most recent period of the Mesozoic Era, the Cretaceous Period, is named for the Latin word for chalk, *creta*. The white chalk cliffs of Dover, England are of this age.

▶ The Pleistocene Epoch is often referred to as the glacial epoch because of the ice ages that occurred during this time in Earth's history.

▶ Humans and their direct ancestors make up a group of animals called hominids. The earliest definite hominids were of the genus *Australopithecus*. Australopithecines had many distinctly human characteristics. They were bipedal and had rounded jaws. Australopithecines lived in the open grasslands of what is now eastern and southern Africa.

▶ Australopithecines were smaller than modern humans. Standing less than 1.5 m tall, they weighed about 20 kg. Their brains were half the size of brains of present-day humans. Fossil evidence indicated these early ancestors of ours used tools made of bone.

PREPLANNING

▶ To prepare for Activity 17-2, obtain adding machine tape, metersticks, and scissors. Also obtain a globe of Earth for the Mini-Lab on page 465.

17-4 Middle and Recent Earth History

New Science Words

Mesozoic Era
Cenozoic Era

Objectives

- ▶ Compare and contrast dominant life-forms in the Mesozoic and Cenozoic Eras.
- ▶ Explain how changes caused by plate tectonics affected the evolution of life during the Mesozoic Era.
- ▶ Identify when humans first appeared on Earth.

The Mesozoic Era

Some of the most distinctive life-forms ever to live on Earth evolved during the Mesozoic Era. One group of organisms you're familiar with—the dinosaurs—appeared during this geologic era.

The **Mesozoic** (mez uh ZOH ihk) **Era,** or era of middle life, began about 225 million years ago. At the beginning of the Mesozoic Era, all continents were joined as a single landmass. Recall from Chapter 13 that this landmass was called Pangaea. Pangaea separated into two large landmasses during the Triassic Period. The northern mass was *Laurasia,* and *Gondwanaland* was in the south. As the Mesozoic Era continued, *Laurasia* and *Gondwanaland* broke up and formed the present-day continents.

Species that survived the mass extinctions of the Paleozoic Era adapted to new environments. Recall that the hard scales of a reptile's skin help to retain body fluids. This trait, along with the hard shell of their eggs, enabled them to readily adapt to the drier climate of the Mesozoic Era. They became the dominant animal life-form in the Jurassic Period. Some reptiles evolved into dinosaurs.

OPTIONS

Meeting Different Ability Levels

For Section 17-4, use the following **Teacher Resource Masters** depending upon individual students' needs.

◆ **Study Guide Master** for all students.

● **Reinforcement Master** for students of average and above average ability levels.

▲ **Enrichment Master** for above average students.

Additional Teacher Resource Package masters are listed in the OPTIONS box throughout the section. The additional masters are appropriate for all students.

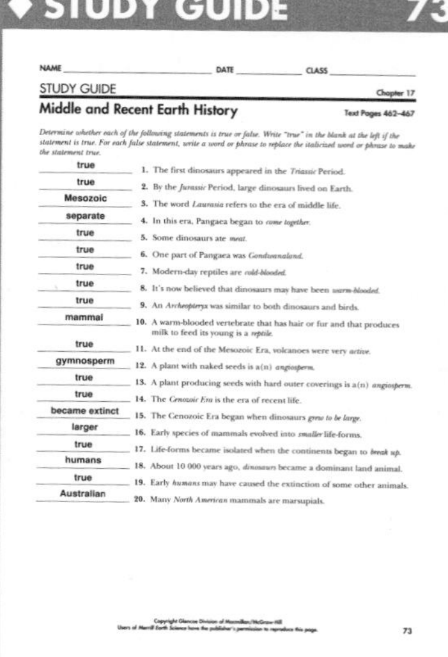

◆ STUDY GUIDE 73

NAME ______ DATE ______ CLASS ______

STUDY GUIDE — Chapter 17

Middle and Recent Earth History — Text Pages 462–467

Determine whether each of the following statements is true or false. Write "true" in the blank at the left if the statement is true. For each false statement, write a word or phrase to replace the italicized word or phrase to make the statement true.

true	1. The first dinosaurs appeared in the *Triassic* Period.
true	2. By the *Jurassic* Period, large dinosaurs lived on Earth.
Mesozoic	3. The word *Laurasia* refers to the era of middle life.
separate	4. In this era, Pangaea began to *come together.*
true	5. Some dinosaurs ate *meat.*
true	6. One part of Pangaea was *Gondwanaland.*
true	7. Modern-day reptiles are *cold-blooded.*
true	8. It's now believed that dinosaurs may have been *warm-blooded.*
true	9. An *Archeopteryx* was similar to both dinosaurs and birds.
mammal	10. A warm-blooded vertebrate that has hair or fur and that produces milk to feed its young is a *reptile.*
true	11. At the end of the Mesozoic Era, volcanoes were very *active.*
gymnosperm	12. A plant with naked seeds is a(n) *angiosperm.*
true	13. A plant producing seeds with hard outer coverings is a(n) *angiosperm.*
true	14. The *Cenozoic Era* is the era of recent life.
became extinct	15. The Cenozoic Era began when dinosaurs *grew to be large.*
larger	16. Early species of mammals evolved into *smaller* life-forms.
true	17. Life-forms became isolated when the continents began to *break up.*
humans	18. About 10 000 years ago, *dinosaurs* became a dominant land animal.
true	19. Early *humans* may have caused the extinction of some other animals.
Australian	20. Many *North American* mammals are marsupials.

73

Figure 17-13. Fossil evidence suggests that some dinosaurs, such as *Maiasaura* and *Protoceratops* (shown above), may have nurtured their young.

Dinosaurs

What were the dinosaurs like? Dinosaurs ranged in height from less than one meter to enormous creatures like *Apatosaurus* and *Tyrannosaurus*. One species of tyrannosaur stood as tall as a two-story building. Some dinosaurs ate meat, whereas others ate only plants.

The first small dinosaurs appeared during the Triassic Period. Larger species of dinosaurs appeared during the Jurassic and Cretaceous Periods. Throughout the Mesozoic Era, new species of dinosaurs evolved as other species became extinct.

Recent studies indicate that dinosaurs may not have been cold-blooded like present-day reptiles. Tracks left in the mud by reptiles are usually close together. This indicates that reptiles generally moved very slowly. Dinosaur tracks have been found that indicate a much faster speed than that of most cold-blooded reptiles. This faster speed would be expected of warm-blooded animals. They need the faster speed to be successful in hunting. *Orodromeus* was three meters long and could reach speeds of 30 km/h.

The fossil record indicates that some dinosaurs nurtured their young and traveled in herds with adults surrounding the young. One such dinosaur is *Maiasaura*. This dinosaur built nests in which it laid its eggs and raised the offspring. Nests have been found in clusters, indicating that more than one family of dinosaurs built in the same area. Some fossils have been found of hatchlings located very close to the adult animal. This has led

What evidence is there that some dinosaurs nurtured their young?

● REINFORCEMENT 73

NAME ______ DATE ______ CLASS ______

REINFORCEMENT — Chapter 17

Middle and Recent Earth History — Text Pages 462–467

Match the descriptions in Column I with the terms in Column II. Write the letter of the correct term in the space provided in the left-hand column.

	Column I	Column II
f	1. Seed plants which first appeared in the Paleozoic Era	a. Gondwanaland
h	2. Era of "middle life"	b. mammals
e	3. Most recent period in the Mesozoic Era	c. Australia
k	4. Oldest period in the Mesozoic Era	d. Laurasia
d	5. Northern part of Pangaea	e. Cretaceous
a	6. Southern part of Pangaea	f. gymnosperms
n	7. Dinosaurs as large as a two-story building	g. angiosperms
q	8. Fast-moving dinosaur	h. Mesozoic
j	9. Dinosaur thought to nurture hatchlings	i. Quaternary
p	10. Winged animal resembling both dinosaurs and birds	j. *Maiasaura*
b	11. Milk-producing animals; first appeared in the Triassic Period	k. Triassic
g	12. Flowering plants	l. Cenozoic
l	13. Most recent era	m. marsupials
i	14. Most recent period in the Cenozoic Era	n. Tyrannosaurs
o	15. Climate change that allowed flowering plants to increase	o. cooling
c	16. Where most marsupials live	p. *Archaeopteryx*
m	17. Animals with pouches	q. *Orodromeus*

Complete the following statements.

18. The bones of cold-blooded animals have **rings similar to growth rings in trees**.
19. The bones of dinosaurs resemble those of **warm**-blooded animals.
20. Dinosaurs may have been much **different from** reptiles today.

 73

▲ ENRICHMENT 73

NAME ______ DATE ______ CLASS ______

ENRICHMENT — Chapter 17

Middle and Recent Earth History — Text Pages 462–467

AUTUMN LEAVES

It's remarkable to find 17 million-year-old fossil leaves. It's more remarkable to find 17 million-year-old leaves themselves. But such fossils have been found. According to the scientist who reported this discovery, Edward Golenberg, about 17 million years ago a storm tore autumn leaves from trees growing near a lake in what is now northern Idaho. The leaves, some green and some red, settled into the cold, oxygen-free sediment at the bottom of the lake. The absence of oxygen keeps bacteria from growing, and bacteria cause plants to decay. The leaves were quickly covered with mud. Over time, the lake dried up. The mud turned to rock, and the leaves were sealed away from destruction for millions of years.

Golenberg found that the rock-encased leaves immediately fell apart when the rocks were broken. But he was able to save some parts by placing them in a solution. This allowed scientists to study the genetic material that made up these ancient plants. The appearance of the leaves indicated that they were an extinct species of magnolia. Examination of the genetic material supported this theory.

This ancient magnolia, like the magnolias of today, is an angiosperm. The seeds of angiosperms are enclosed in a seed case. Insects and birds and sometimes wind carry angiosperm pollen from flower to flower to fertilize the plants. After fertilization, the flowers close and the developing seeds are protected. Gymnosperms, the other kind of seed-producing plant, produce seeds with no seed case. Conifers such as pine and fir trees are typical gymnosperms. The flowers of gymnosperms are hardly noticeable, and gymnosperms depend on wind and gravity for pollination.

Although some scientists believe that angiosperms evolved from gymnosperms, the question of when and how angiosperms like the ancient magnolias first appeared is still a mystery. To date, no magnolialike flower fossils have been found.

1. How does Golenberg's discovery differ from most discoveries that reveal information about ancient plants? **Golenberg discovered actual leaves. Most fossils of plants no longer contain the original organic material.**
2. The flowers of angiosperms are more obvious than those of gymnosperms. Why do you think this is the case? **The flowers of angiosperms have evolved to attract insects and birds, which help spread pollen. Gymnosperms reproduce with the help of the wind and gravity, so bright, colorful flowers serve no purpose.**
3. Do you think trees in autumn looked very different 17 million years ago than they do today? Explain. **Answers will vary. Some may say no—the red magnolia leaves indicate that the leaves probably turned shades of red and gold as they often do now. Others may say there simply isn't enough evidence to decide.**

 73

1 MOTIVATE

FLEX Your Brain

Use the Flex Your Brain activity to have students explore APATOSAURUS. Students may be familiar with the term *Brontosaurus*. This term is no longer used to refer to these large dinosaurs. Apatosaurs were among the largest dinosaurs, with masses up to 36 tonnes. They had long necks and tails supported by massive bodies.

▶ **Video Presentation:** Show the video presentation, *The Great Dinosaur Hunt,* from the Infinite Voyage Home Video Library, available from Inovision, P.O. Box 576, Itasca, IL 60143-0576, phone number 1-800-523-5503. This video presents evidence of the warm-blooded nature of dinosaurs and their possible link to birds.

TYING TO PREVIOUS KNOWLEDGE: Help students recall one theory of the extinction of dinosaurs presented in Chapter 16.

OBJECTIVES AND SCIENCE WORDS: Have students review the objectives and science words to become familiar with this section.

2 TEACH

Key Concepts are highlighted.

CONCEPT DEVELOPMENT

Cooperative Learning: Using the Paired Partners strategy, have students identify characteristics of meat- and plant-eating dinosaurs. Supply students with drawings or models of six different dinosaurs. Have them determine whether the dinosaurs pictured were meat- or plant-eaters. Using a book of dinosaurs, have students identify the drawings or models. Have students describe what characteristics of the various dinosaurs allowed them to determine whether they were meat- or plant-eaters.

CONCEPT DEVELOPMENT

Cooperative Learning: Using the Paired Partners strategy, have students read the article, "Dinosaur Eggs: The Inside Story," by J. R. Horner and D. B. Weishampel, *Natural History*, Dec. 1989. Have students discuss the key concepts of the article and then work together to write a summary of the main ideas of the article.

REVEALING MISCONCEPTIONS

▶ Ask students if humans were alive when dinosaurs lived on Earth. Some students will think they were because of seeing cartoons and movies on television. Explain that humans appeared about 5 million years ago, long after dinosaurs became extinct about 65 million years ago.

TEACHER F.Y.I.

▶ Endotherms have a constant body temperature and are often said to be "warm-blooded."

CROSS CURRICULUM

▶ **Life Science:** It's important to note that plants co-evolve with the animals and other organisms in their environment. Plants aren't "passive bystanders" in the process of natural selection. Plants develop thorns, tough bark, and poisons to thwart predators. For more information on the co-evolution of plants and dinosaurs, direct students to *The Dinosaur Heresies*, by Robert T. Bakker, William Morrow and Company, Inc., New York, 1986, Chapter 9, "When Dinosaurs Invented Flowers."

some scientists to hypothesize that some dinosaurs nurtured their young. In fact, *Maiasaura* hatchlings may have stayed in the nest while they grew in length from about 35 cm to more than one meter.

Other evidence that leads scientists to think that dinosaurs may have been warm-blooded has to do with their bone structure. The bones of cold-blooded animals exhibit rings similar to growth rings in trees. The bones of dinosaurs don't show this ring structure. Instead, they are similar to bones found in birds and mammals. These observations indicate that dinosaurs may have been warm-blooded, fast-moving, nurturing animals somewhat like present-day mammals and birds. They might have been quite different from present-day reptiles.

Figure 17-14. Fossils of *Archaeopteryx* about 150 million years old show both birdlike features, such as feathers, and dinosaur-like features, such as claws and teeth.

Birds

The first birds appeared during the Jurassic Period of the Mesozoic Era. You've learned that the fossil record shows how some traits of the dinosaurs are similar to present-day birds. Scientists think that birds evolved from dinosaurs. The animal *Archaeopteryx* had wings and feathers like a bird, but teeth and claws like a meat-eating dinosaur. It was an ancestor of the birds. Whether it should be classified as a bird or a dinosaur is debatable.

Mammals

During which era and period did mammals evolve?

Mammals first appeared in the Triassic Period. Mammals are warm-blooded vertebrates that have hair or fur covering their bodies. The females produce milk to feed their young. These traits enabled mammals to survive in many changing environments.

OPTIONS

INQUIRY QUESTIONS

▶ **Why do some scientists theorize that birds may have evolved from dinosaurs?** *Archeopteryx had wings and feathers like a bird, but teeth and claws like a meat-eating dinosaur. Present-day birds and extinct dinosaurs share other characteristics as well.*

▶ **Why were mammals able to survive in many different environments?** *Females produce milk to feed the young. They were warm-blooded and had hair or fur to insulate them from extreme cold and warm temperatures.*

▶ **Why did angiosperms survive while other types of plants didn't?** *The hard coating on their seeds protected the seeds from harsh environments. This enabled them to adapt to varied environments.*

Angiosperms

During the Cretaceous Period, seas moved inland and species of plants, animals, and other organisms continued to adapt to new environments. Gymnosperms (JIHM nuh spurmz), which first appeared in the Paleozoic Era, continued to adapt to their changing environment. Gymnosperms are called naked seed plants because they have no fruit covering their seeds. Pines, sequoias, and ginkgos are gymnosperms.

A new classification of plant, called angiosperms (AN jee uh spurmz), evolved from existing plants. Angiosperms, or flowering plants, produce seeds with hard, outer coverings. Common angiosperms were magnolias and willows.

Many angiosperms survived while other organisms did not because their seeds had hard coatings that protected them and allowed them to develop in varied environments. Angiosperms are so adaptive, they remain the dominant land plant today. Present-day angiosperms that evolved during the Mesozoic Era include maple and oak trees.

The end of the Mesozoic Era was a time when landmasses were breaking up and seas were draining from the land. There was also increased volcanic activity. Many life-forms, including the dinosaurs, became extinct. These extinctions were caused by changing environments. What caused the environments to change is still actively investigated by scientists. As discussed in Chapter 16, one event that may have caused a drastic change was a meteorite impact at the very end of the Cretaceous Period.

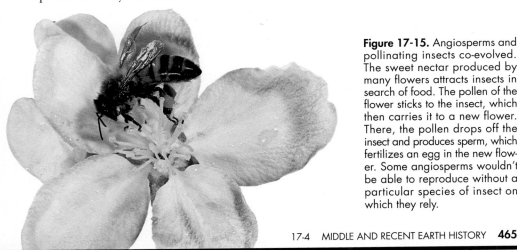

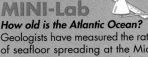

MINI-Lab

How old is the Atlantic Ocean?

Geologists have measured the rate of seafloor spreading at the Mid-Atlantic Ridge at approximately 3.5 to 4.0 centimeters per year. The continents on each side of the Atlantic Ocean are moving away from each other at that rate. On a globe or world map, measure the distance in kilometers between a point near the east coast of North or South America and a corresponding point on the west coast of Europe or Africa. Making the assumption that the rate of motion listed above has been relatively constant through time, calculate how many years it took to create the present Atlantic Ocean if the continents on either side were once joined. Make several other measurements and take the average of your results. Check your predictions with the information provided to you in the geologic time scale in Figure 17-2. How close did you come to the accepted estimate for the beginning of the breakup of Pangaea?

Figure 17-15. Angiosperms and pollinating insects co-evolved. The sweet nectar produced by many flowers attracts insects in search of food. The pollen of the flower sticks to the insect, which then carries it to a new flower. There, the pollen drops off the insect and produces sperm, which fertilizes an egg in the new flower. Some angiosperms wouldn't be able to reproduce without a particular species of insect on which they rely.

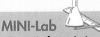

MINI-Lab

Materials: globe or world map, meterstick or metric ruler, string (for measuring the curved surface of the globe)

Teaching Tips

▶Inform students that the rate of sea-floor spread of 3.5 to 4.0 centimeters per year hasn't been constant over the past 200 million years, nor is it presently that value at all points along the mid-Atlantic Ridge. This rate is an average for a number of points along the mid-Atlantic Ridge.

▶Once students have completed their calculations, have them record their estimated time of continental separation for use in constructing the time scale model in Activity 17-2.

Answers to Questions: Although student answers will vary depending on the points on each continent they choose for their measurements, separated distances of 6000 to 7000 kilometers would take from 160 million to 200 million years to achieve. As an example, at 3.5 cm/y rate of spread, two points 7000 km (or 700 million cm) apart would have started separating about 200 million years ago (700 000 000 cm ÷ 3.5 cm/y = 2000 000 000 y). Utilizing the geologic time scale shown in Figure 17-2, 200 million years before present places the beginning of separation in the Triassic Period of the Mesozoic Era.

ENRICHMENT

▶ Have students research the invasion of the northern hemisphere by continental glaciers during the Pleistocene Epoch.

▶ Have students compare and contrast marsupial wolves, rabbits, squirrels, and bears that evolved in Australia to their placental counterparts that evolved in similar environments in Europe and America. Students should note similarities in natural selection despite differences between placental and marsupial evolution caused by the isolation of the life-forms.

PROGRAM RESOURCES

From the **Teacher Resource Package** use:

Activty Worksheets, page 158, Mini-Lab: How old is the Atlantic Ocean?

Cross Curricular Connections, page 21, Word Origins.

Critical Thinking/Problem Solving, page 23, Flightless Birds and Marsupials

CONCEPT DEVELOPMENT

▶ Discuss the path of human evolution shown in Figure 17-16. Relate that there is much controversy among anthropologists as to how many species of *Australopithecus* existed, but many agree that there were at least four. Those species are shown. It's not known which gave rise to our genus, *Homo*. The figure indicates that it was *Australopithecus afarensis*.

▶ Have students note that *Homo habilis,* evolved from *A. afarensis*. *H. habilis* gave rise to *H. erectus* before becoming extinct about 1.5 million years ago. *H. erectus* was the direct ancestor of our species, *H. sapiens*.

▶ Ask students if Neanderthals were contemporaries of modern humans (also called Cro-Magnons). Neanderthals and modern humans existed together from about 100 000 years ago to 34 000 years ago when Neanderthals became extinct. Have students interpret Figure 17-16. Ask them if Neanderthals are their ancestors. According to the diagram, Neanderthals and modern humans had a common ancestor, but the Neanderthals did not give rise to present-day humans.

CHECK FOR UNDERSTANDING

▶ Ask questions 1-3 and the **Apply** Question in the Section Review.

▶ Have students recall when humans first appeared and when they became one of the dominant land animals. Have students summarize how the growing human population may have contributed to the extinction of other life-forms.

RETEACH

Obtain a book on early humans that shows paintings or drawings of humans on a hunting trip after the wooly mammoth and other Pleistocene mammals. Explain how over-hunting can lead to extinction. Relate this to the near extinction of the American Buffalo by over-hunting in the early west.

EXTENSION

For students who have mastered this section, use the **Reinforcement** and **Enrichment** masters or other OPTIONS provided.

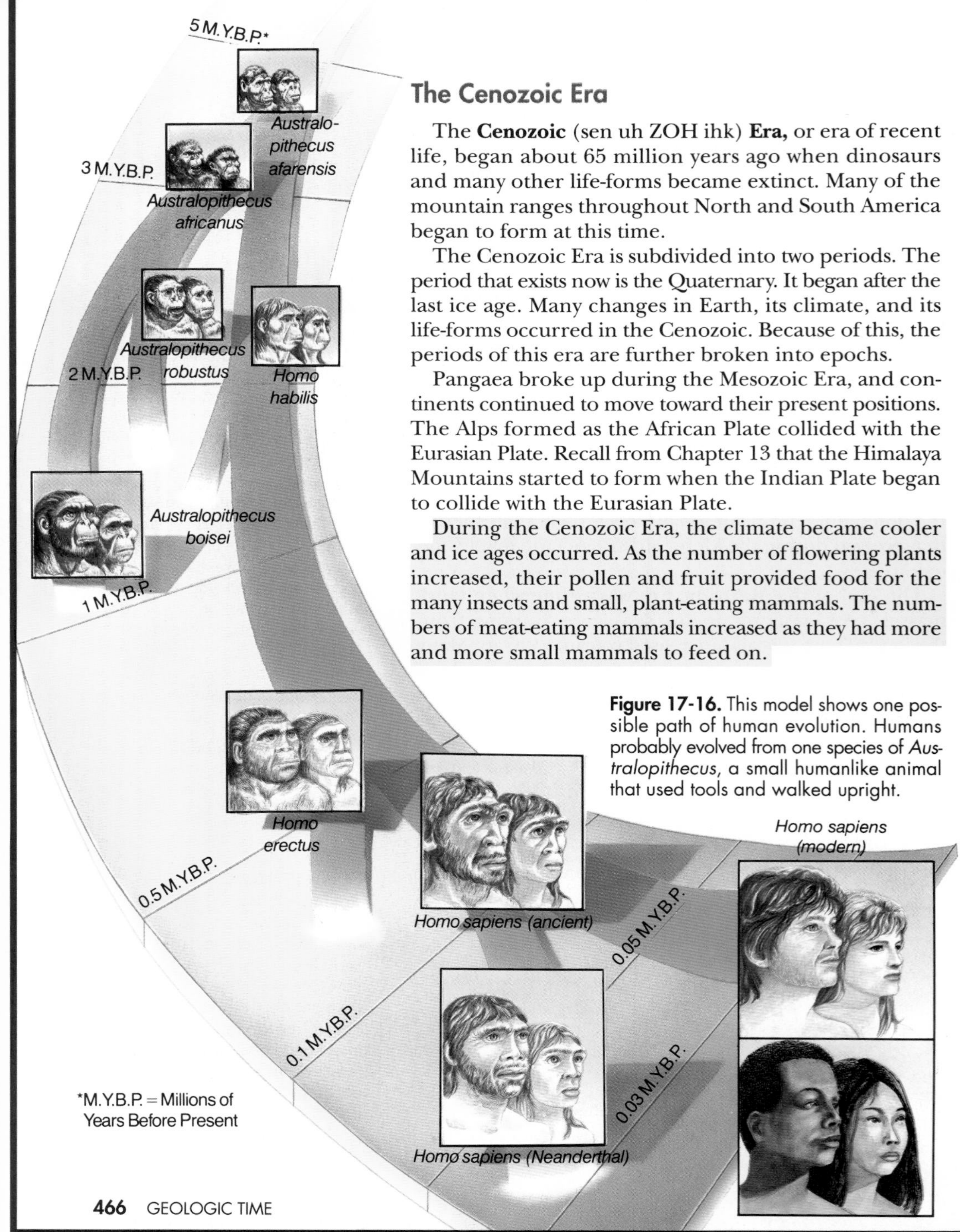

The Cenozoic Era

The **Cenozoic** (sen uh ZOH ihk) **Era,** or era of recent life, began about 65 million years ago when dinosaurs and many other life-forms became extinct. Many of the mountain ranges throughout North and South America began to form at this time.

The Cenozoic Era is subdivided into two periods. The period that exists now is the Quaternary. It began after the last ice age. Many changes in Earth, its climate, and its life-forms occurred in the Cenozoic. Because of this, the periods of this era are further broken into epochs.

Pangaea broke up during the Mesozoic Era, and continents continued to move toward their present positions. The Alps formed as the African Plate collided with the Eurasian Plate. Recall from Chapter 13 that the Himalaya Mountains started to form when the Indian Plate began to collide with the Eurasian Plate.

During the Cenozoic Era, the climate became cooler and ice ages occurred. As the number of flowering plants increased, their pollen and fruit provided food for the many insects and small, plant-eating mammals. The numbers of meat-eating mammals increased as they had more and more small mammals to feed on.

Figure 17-16. This model shows one possible path of human evolution. Humans probably evolved from one species of *Australopithecus*, a small humanlike animal that used tools and walked upright.

OPTIONS

INQUIRY QUESTIONS

▶ **Why did mammals evolve so differently in Australia and South America?** *These areas became isolated from the rest of the world and life forms evolved separately from others.*

▶ **To what fact do some scientists attribute the extinction of some of the larger mammals about 10 000 years ago?** *The appearance of modern humans. Humans competed with the large mammals for food and may have hunted some into extinction.*

PROGRAM RESOURCES

From the **Teacher Resource Package** use:

Activity Worksheets, page 5, Flex Your Brain.

Transparency Masters, pages 75-76, Human Evolution.

Use **Color Transparency** number 38, Human Evolution.

Mammals evolved into larger life-forms. Recall how horses have evolved from small, multi-toed animals into the much larger, hoofed animals of today. Not all mammals remained on land. Ancestors of the present-day whales and dolphins began to make their lives in the sea.

As Australia and South America separated from Antarctica, many life-forms became isolated. They evolved separately from life-forms in other parts of the world. Evidence of this can be seen today with the dominance of marsupials (mar SEW pee ulz) in Australia. Marsupials are mammals that carry their young in a pouch. Kangaroos, wallabies, wombats, and koalas are marsupials that exist only in Australia.

Our species, *Homo sapiens*, probably appeared about 500 000 years ago, but became a dominant land animal only about 10 000 years ago. As the climate remained cool and dry, many larger mammals became extinct. Some scientists think the appearance of humans may have led to the extinction of other mammals. As their numbers grew, humans competed for food that other animals relied on. Also, fossil records indicate early humans were hunters. They may have hunted some animals, such as the woolly mammoth, into extinction.

Did You Know?

Humans have body parts that once served a purpose but now serve no important function. Such parts, called vestigial structures, are no longer useful but have not completely disappeared as we've evolved. Examples include the appendix, wisdom teeth, and a set of muscles in our head to move our ears. Whales and pythons have vestigial hind leg bones. Flightless birds, such as the kiwi, have vestigial wing bones.

SECTION REVIEW

1. In which era, period, and epoch did *Homo sapiens* first appear? According to Figure 17-16, which human ancestor existed 5 million years ago?
2. Did mammals become more or less abundant after the extinction of the dinosaurs? Why do you think this is the case?
3. What characteristic of angiosperms allowed them to adapt to changing environments?
4. **Apply:** Why are the periods of only the Cenozoic Era divided into epochs?

Sequencing

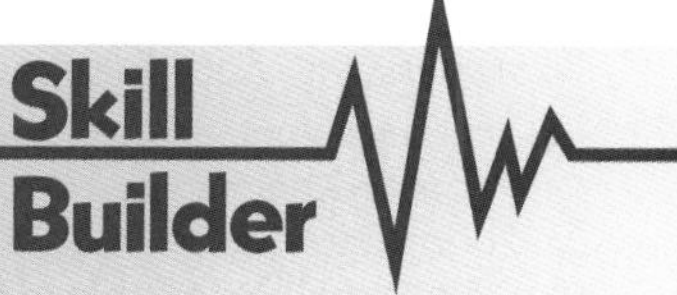

Arrange these organisms in sequence according to when they first appeared on Earth: *mammals, reptiles, dinosaurs, fish, angiosperms, birds, insects, amphibians, first land plants,* and *bacteria*. If you need help, refer to Sequencing in the **Skill Handbook** on page 680.

Skill Builder

Students should use Figure 17-2 on page 448 and the table in Activity 17-2 on page 468 to answer this question. The sequence is bacteria, fish, land plants, amphibians, reptiles, insects, mammals, dinosaurs, birds, angiosperms.

TEACHER F.Y.I.

► Some estimates state that over three fourths of all species on Earth died off at the end of the Mesozoic Era.

► Some anthropologists think that competition with modern humans (Cro-Magnons) for food and space led to the demise of the Neanderthals.

3 CLOSE

► Ask a volunteer to read each lesson objective aloud. Ask another student to summarize how each objective was covered. Ask one or two other students to state whether or not the objective was attained. If any students are unsure if they understand all concepts presented, review the extinction of the dinosaurs and the increasing abundance of mammals at the end of the Mesozoic and beginning of the Cenozoic Eras. Also relate human appearance to animal extinctions.

FLEX Your Brain

Use the Flex Your Brain activity to have students explore THE EVOLUTION OF HOMO SAPIENS.

SECTION REVIEW ANSWERS

1. Cenozoic Era, Quaternary Period, Pleistocene Epoch; *Australopithecus afarensis*

2. Mammals are more abundant during the Cenozoic Era. Mammals became more abundant after the extinction of the dinosaurs. When the dinosaurs became extinct, it reduced competition for food. The pollen and fruit of angiosperms provided food for plant-eating mammals. Increases in plant-eating mammals provided food for meat-eating mammals.

3. These plants had seeds with hard outer coverings. Also, flowering plants often attract insects which are effective pollinators.

4. Apply: This is the recent time in Earth's history and the fossil records are more complete. There are more markers to subdivide geologic time.

ACTIVITY 17-2
30 minutes

OBJECTIVE: Construct a geologic time line.

PROCESS SKILLS applied in this activity:
▶ **Measuring in SI** in Procedure Step 1.
▶ **Using Numbers** in Analyze Question 3.
▶ **Hypothesizing** in Conclude and Apply Question 4.
▶ **Analyzing** in Conclude and Apply Question 5.

COOPERATIVE LEARNING
Have students perform this activity as Paired Partners.

TEACHING THE ACTIVITY

Alternate materials: You may wish to use a roll of industrial paper towels instead of adding machine tape.

▶ Point out that the apparent clustering of events in recent times is a function of available evidence in the fossil and geologic records and not a change in the rate of evolution.

PROGRAM RESOURCES

From the **Teacher Resource Package** use:

Activity Worksheets, pages 153-154, Activity 17-2: Geologic Time Line.

ACTIVITY 17-2
Geologic Time Line

Problem: *How is an absolute time line constructed?*

Materials 

- adding machine tape
- meterstick
- pencil
- scissors

Procedure

1. Using a scale of 1 millimeter equals 1 million years (1 mm = 1 000 000 years), measure and cut a piece of adding machine tape equal to the approximate age of Earth (4.6 billion years).
2. Mark one end of the tape "today" and the other end "4.6 billion years."
3. Using the table shown as a reference, measure and mark the places on the tape that represent the time when each era began.
4. Examine the events and ages listed in the data table. Measuring carefully, include each event on your adding machine tape in the proper place in time. Note that the dates are provided in years B.P. (before present).

Analyze

1. Which events were most difficult to plot?
2. How does the existence of humans on Earth compare with the duration of geologic time?
3. Approximately what percent of geologic time occurred during the Precambrian?

Conclude and Apply

4. Form a hypothesis as to why more is known about recent history than about the Precambrian. How could you test this hypothesis?
5. What can be determined from your time line about the rate at which events have occurred on Earth's surface? Does this rate reflect what has actually happened on Earth? Explain.

Data and Observations

Earth History Events

Event	Years B.P.
1. today	0
2. astronants land on moon	25
3. American Civil War	135
4. Columbus lands in America	500
5. Pompeii destroyed	1 900
6. Eratosthenes calculates Earth's circumference	2 100
7. continental ice retreats from North America	10 000
8. beginning of most recent ice age	1 million
9. early human ancestors	5 million
10. first elephants	40 million
11. first horse	50 million
12. dinosaurs become extinct; beginning of Paleocene	65 million
13. Rocky Mountains begin to rise	80 million
14. beginning of Cretaceous	136 million
15. first birds	150 million
16. beginning of Jurassic	190 million
17. first mammals and dinosaurs	225 million
18. beginning of Permian	280 million
19. first reptiles	325 million
20. coal forests; Appalachians rise	330 million
21. beginning of Mississippian	345 million
22. first amphibians	390 million
23. beginning of Silurian	430 million
24. first land plants and vertebrates	480 million
25. beginning of Ordovician	500 million
26. Animals evolve hard parts	570 million
27. early sponges	600 million
28. oldest microfossils (algae)	3 300 million
29. oldest known rocks	3 800 million

ANSWERS TO QUESTIONS

1. Events occurring in the last few million years were difficult to plot because only several millimeters of tape were available for use.
2. The existence of humans on Earth accounts for only about 0.03 percent of geologic time.
3. approximately 88 percent
4. Acceptable answers would include reference to the availability of more information in younger rocks. Much Precambrian evidence has either been destroyed or has yet to be discovered. This hypothesis could be tested by researching geologic maps showing Precambrian rocks.
5. Students should realize that the abundance of events in recent times can be attributed to the availability of evidence rather than an actual increase in rates of change over earlier periods. Thus, the rate of change probably isn't significantly different in recent times compared to earlier times.

CHAPTER

REVIEW

SUMMARY

17-1: Evolution and Geologic Time

1. Geologic time is divided into eras, periods, and epochs.

2. Divisions within the geologic time scale are based on major evolutionary changes in organisms and on geologic events such as mountain building and plate movements.

3. Plate movements cause changes in Earth's climates that affect organic evolution.

17-2: Science and Society: Present-Day Rapid Extinctions

1. Humans cause extinctions primarily by eliminating natural habitats of organisms.

2. As land is developed by humans, the diversity of life on Earth is reduced.

3. Careful planning, concern for all organisms, and strict laws can help prevent extinctions.

17-3: Early Earth History

1. Cyanobacteria were an early form of life that evolved during the Precambrian Era. Trilobites, brachiopods, fish, and corals were abundant during the Paleozoic Era.

2. By the process of natural selection, bacteria evolved into higher life-forms which evolved into many marine invertebrates during the early Paleozoic. Plants and animals began to move onto land once a protective ozone layer had been established.

3. During the Paleozoic Era, glaciers advanced, and seas withdrew from the continents. Many marine invertebrates became extinct.

17-4: Middle and Recent Earth History

1. Reptiles and gymnosperms were dominant land life-forms in the Mesozoic Era. Mammals and angiosperms began to dominate the land in the Cenozoic.

2. Changes caused by plate tectonics affect the evolution of life.

3. *Homo sapiens* evolved during the Pleistocene.

KEY SCIENCE WORDS

a. **amphibians**
b. **Cenozoic Era**
c. **cyanobacteria**
d. **endangered**
e. **epochs**
f. **eras**
g. **geologic time scale**
h. **habitat**
i. **Mesozoic Era**
j. **natural selection**
k. **organic evolution**
l. **Paleozoic Era**
m. **periods**
n. **Precambrian Era**
o. **reptiles**
p. **species**

UNDERSTANDING VOCABULARY

Match each phrase with the correct term from the list of Key Science Words.

1. change in the hereditary features of a species over a long period of time
2. record of events in Earth history
3. largest divisions of geologic time
4. geologic era with weakest fossil record
5. process by which the best-suited individuals survive in their environment
6. evolved directly from amphibians
7. group of individuals that normally breed only among themselves
8. the geologic era in which we live
9. a species in which only a relatively small number of members exists
10. a place where organisms live and grow

CHAPTER

REVIEW

SUMMARY

Have students read the summary statements to review the major concepts of the chapter.

UNDERSTANDING VOCABULARY

1. k **6.** o
2. g **7.** p
3. f **8.** b
4. n **9.** d
5. j **10.** h

ASSESSMENT

To assess student understanding of material in this chapter, use the resources listed.

COOPERATIVE LEARNING

Consider using cooperative learning in the THINK AND WRITE CRITICALLY, APPLY, and MORE SKILL BUILDERS sections of the Chapter Review.

PROGRAM RESOURCES

From the **Teacher Resource Package** use:

Chapter Review, pages 37-38.

Chapter and Unit Tests, pages 114-117, Chapter Test.

Chapter and Unit Tests, pages 118-119, Unit Test.

CHAPTER
REVIEW

CHECKING CONCEPTS

1. d
2. d
3. a
4. d
5. b
6. b
7. a
8. c
9. b
10. b

UNDERSTANDING CONCEPTS

11. species
12. Quarternary
13. dinosaurs (archeopteryx)
14. *Homo sapiens*
15. endangered

THINK AND WRITE CRITICALLY

16. Natural selection is a theory of how some traits evolve in species and how new species develop. Natural selection is a process that results in evolution. When organisms are selected for naturally, they survive, reproduce, and pass on inheritable traits to their offspring. The species evolves as certain traits become more and more prevalent within the population.

17. Warm shallow seas existed during most of the early Paleozoic Era. Most of the life-forms lived in these seas. As plants and animals evolved, they moved landward during the middle of the era. During this time, vertebrates dominated the land. Changes in climate probably caused many of the extinctions that happened at the close of the era.

18. Both are vertebrates. Ancestors of amphibians were fish, whereas reptiles evolved directly from amphibians. Amphibians need water to reproduce, reptiles do not.

19. changes in climate related to plate movements, meteorite impacts, volcanism, glacial activity, competition with new species, human activities

20. During the Paleozoic Era, most of the organisms were invertebrates. Reptiles and amphibians were common. Life-forms became more complex through time. Mammals became dominating during the late Mesozoic.

CHAPTER
REVIEW

CHECKING CONCEPTS

Choose the word or phrase that completes the sentence.

1. The era in which you live began about ______ million years ago.
   a. 650 c. 2.5
   b. 225 d. 65
2. Process by which better suited organisms survive and reproduce is called ______.
   a. endangerment c. gymnosperm
   b. extinction d. none of these
3. The next smaller division of geologic time after the era is a(n) ______.
   a. period c. epoch
   b. era d. none of these
4. Plate movement can affect ______.
   a. geography c. climate
   b. organisms d. all of these
5. One of the earliest forms of life on Earth was the ______.
   a. gymnosperm c. angiosperm
   b. cyanobacterium d. dinosaur
6. Amphibians evolved from ______.
   a. reptiles c. angiosperms
   b. fish d. gymnosperms
7. Dinosaurs lived during the ______ Era.
   a. Mesozoic c. Precambrian
   b. Paleozoic d. Cenozoic
8. ______ have seeds without protective coverings.
   a. Angiosperms c. Gymnosperms
   b. Flowering plants d. All of these
9. ______ evolved to become the dominant land plant during the Cenozoic Era.
   a. Gymnosperms c. Ginkgos
   b. Angiosperms d. Algae
10. A key factor in preserving many species is ______.
    a. poaching c. construction
    b. law enforcement d. changing habitats

UNDERSTANDING CONCEPTS

Complete each sentence.

11. New ______ evolve from common ancestors.
12. The beginning of the ______ Period was marked by the most recent ice age.
13. The direct ancestors of birds may have been the ______.
14. Our species, ______, may have hunted woolly mammoths into extinction.
15. Some species of elephants are illegally hunted, making them a(n) ______ species.

APPLY

21. Too much harmful ultraviolet radiation from the sun reached Earth's surface prior to the establishment of the ozone layer. UV light causes harmful mutations in the cells of plants.

22. Trilobites were widespread and existed for only a limited segment of geologic time before becoming extinct. Thus, they can be used to accurately date the rocks in which they are contained.

THINK AND WRITE CRITICALLY

16. How is natural selection related to evolution?
17. Briefly describe the major geologic and biological changes that took place during the Paleozoic Era.
18. Compare and contrast the traits of reptiles and amphibians.
19. Describe several causes for extinctions throughout geologic time.
20. Contrast the animal life of the Paleozoic with that of the early Cenozoic.

APPLY

21. Why couldn't plants move onto land prior to the establishment of an ozone layer?
22. Why do trilobites make excellent index fossils?
23. What is the most significant difference between Precambrian and Paleozoic life-forms?
24. How might the extinction of an edible species of plant from a tropical rain forest affect animals that live in the forest?
25. In the early 1800s, a naturalist proposed that the giraffe species has a long neck because the animals stretched their necks to reach tall tree leaves. Explain why this isn't true.

MORE SKILL BUILDERS

If you need help, refer to the Skill Handbook.

1. **Observing and Inferring:** Use the outlines of the present-day continents to make a sketch of the Mesozoic supercontinent Pangaea.
2. **Hypothesizing:** Why did trilobites become extinct at the end of the Paleozoic Era?
3. **Interpreting Data:** Benjamin found what he thought was a piece of coral in a chunk of coal. Was he right? Explain.

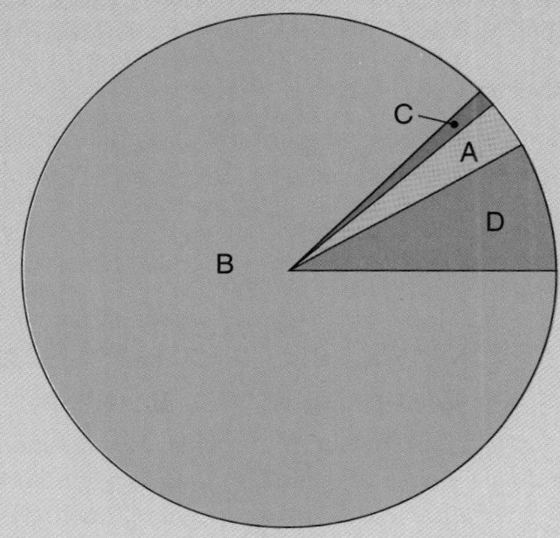

4. **Interpreting Scientific Illustrations:** The pie graph above represents geologic time. Determine which era of geologic time is represented by each portion of the graph.
5. **Interpreting Scientific Illustrations:** The Cenozoic Era has lasted 65 million years. What percentage of Earth's 4.6 billion year history is that? How many degrees on the pie graph represent the Cenozoic Era?

PROJECTS

1. Choose one of Earth's present-day continents and find out how it has changed through geologic time. Include drawings of the different geographic positions it had through time and summaries of the ancient climates, environments, and topography.
2. Research the most recent theories on mass extinctions that occurred at the end of both the Paleozoic and Mesozoic Eras. Compare and contrast the most accepted theories. Form your own hypothesis as to why the extinctions occurred. Support your position with facts.

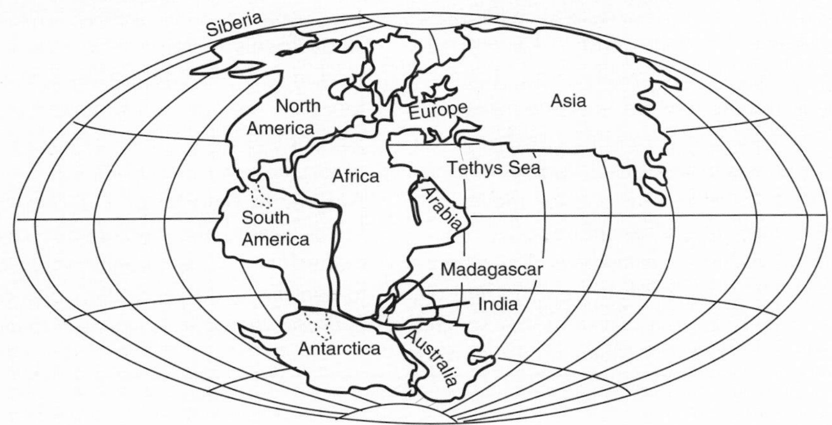

23. Organisms of the Precambrian lacked the hard parts that evolved at the beginning of the Paleozoic.

24. Plants are at the base of most food chains. They make their own food via photosynthesis and are themselves food for primary consumers. The primary consumers, in turn, are food for secondary consumers. If the edible plant becomes extinct, extinctions of primary and secondary consumers may occur because of the disruption of the food chain.

25. This idea states that evolution occurs because an organism acquires a trait for survival and is capable of passing that trait to its offspring. This theory is not accepted today. Our knowledge of genetics has shown that acquired traits are not hereditary. Thus, if a giraffe were capable of stretching its neck during its lifetime, it would not pass on its long neck to its offspring. Similarly, students should realize that if a person has a foot amputated and then he or she has a child, the child is not born without a foot.

MORE SKILL BUILDERS

1. Observing and Inferring: Students' sketches should be similar to the one shown below.

2. Hypothesizing: Accept all reasonable answers. Responses might include plate tectonic processes, withdrawal of the shallow seas, cooler climates, competition with newly evolved organisms.

3. Interpreting Data: No, corals are marine animals. Coal forms from dead plants in freshwater swamps. The "coral" was probably a fossilized twig.

4. Interpreting Scientific Illustrations: Section A represents the Mesozoic Era; Section B represents the Precambrian Era; Section C represents the Cenozoic Era; Section D represents the Paleozoic Era.

5. Interpreting Scientific Illustrations: The Cenozoic Era represents approximately 1.5 percent of Earth's history (65 000 000 ÷ 4 600 000 000 years = 0.015). This is represented by 5 degrees on the graph (360° × 0.015 = 5°).

UNIT 6
GLOBAL CONNECTIONS

Objective

In this unit ending feature, the unit topic, "Change and Earth's History," is extended into other disciplines. Students will see how understanding organic evolution processes and the change in Earth throughout its history has led to advancements in many fields.

Motivate

Cooperative Learning: Assign one Connection to each group of students. Using the Expert Teams strategy, have each group research to find out more about the geographic location of the Connection—its climate, culture, plants and animals, and ecological issues.

Wrap-Up

After students have reviewed all the boxes on this page ask them to form a theory to explain the location of similar fossils on widely separated continents if the theory of plate tectonics had not been developed.

GEOLOGY

Background: The similarity of certain fossils found on the continents on both sides of the Atlantic is hard to explain unless the continents were once connected. Land animals, such as reptiles and insects, and land plants could not have migrated across the Atlantic. Geologic, paleontologic, and paleomagnetic evidence all point to a Devonian collision of Europe with the United States.

Discussion: Discuss that the Appalachians must have formed due to the collision of the two continents. Later, when the two continents were separated, the mountains were on both sides of the ocean.

Answer to Question: The ocean must not have been present at the time the fossils were laid down and the mountains were formed.

Extension: Have students use moist sponges to demonstrate mountain formation at convergent boundaries.

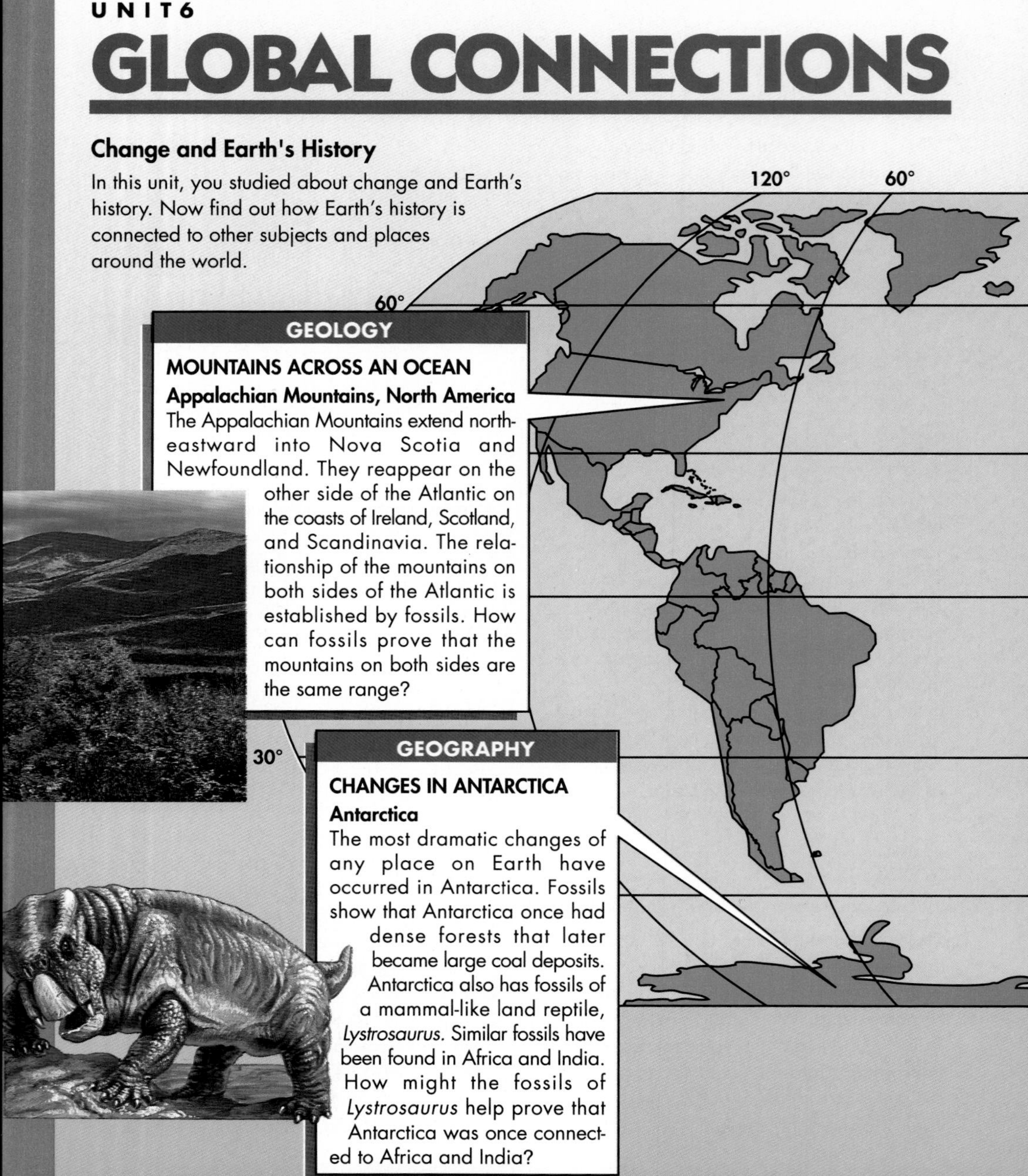

UNIT 6

GLOBAL CONNECTIONS

Change and Earth's History

In this unit, you studied about change and Earth's history. Now find out how Earth's history is connected to other subjects and places around the world.

GEOLOGY

MOUNTAINS ACROSS AN OCEAN

Appalachian Mountains, North America

The Appalachian Mountains extend northeastward into Nova Scotia and Newfoundland. They reappear on the other side of the Atlantic on the coasts of Ireland, Scotland, and Scandinavia. The relationship of the mountains on both sides of the Atlantic is established by fossils. How can fossils prove that the mountains on both sides are the same range?

GEOGRAPHY

CHANGES IN ANTARCTICA

Antarctica

The most dramatic changes of any place on Earth have occurred in Antarctica. Fossils show that Antarctica once had dense forests that later became large coal deposits. Antarctica also has fossils of a mammal-like land reptile, *Lystrosaurus.* Similar fossils have been found in Africa and India. How might the fossils of *Lystrosaurus* help prove that Antarctica was once connected to Africa and India?

472

GEOGRAPHY

Background: The mammal-like reptile *Lystrosaurus* was a land dweller and could not have swum across a wide expanse of water. The fact that its fossil remains are found on three widely separated areas today—Africa, Antarctica, and India—argues for the theory that these places were once connected.

Discussion: Discuss with students that paleontologists study animal fossils not only to find out where animals lived, but also how the species arrived there in the first place. They always study fossils in relation to fossils of the same kind in another place. A fossil of a land animal found in several widely separated places is of special interest because it may indicate that the places have moved apart.

Answer to Question: It shows that when the fossils formed, the landforms were connected.

Extension: Have students study a world map to see the wide separation of locations where *Lystrosaurus* fossils have been found.

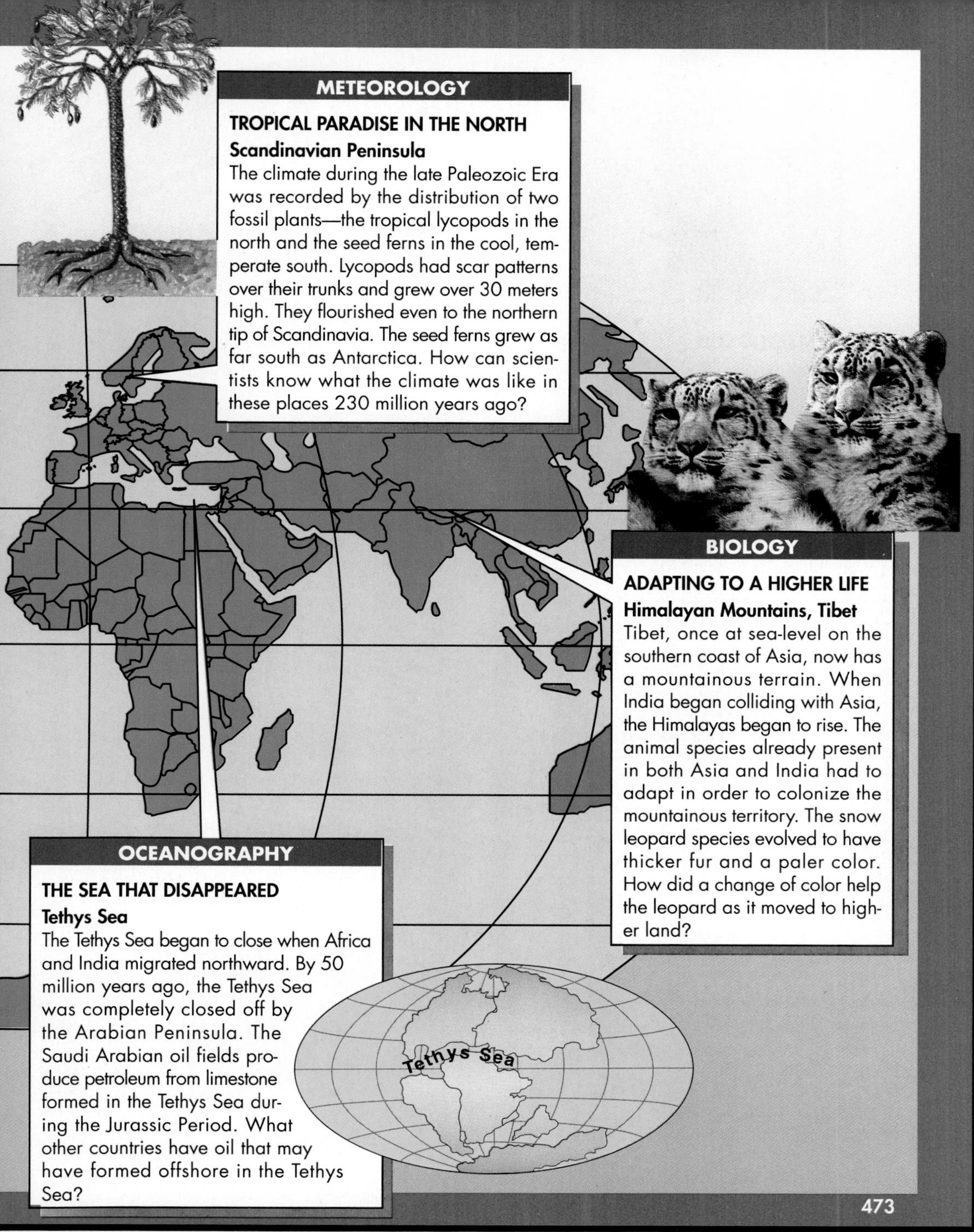

METEOROLOGY

TROPICAL PARADISE IN THE NORTH

Scandinavian Peninsula

The climate during the late Paleozoic Era was recorded by the distribution of two fossil plants—the tropical lycopods in the north and the seed ferns in the cool, temperate south. Lycopods had scar patterns over their trunks and grew over 30 meters high. They flourished even to the northern tip of Scandinavia. The seed ferns grew as far south as Antarctica. How can scientists know what the climate was like in these places 230 million years ago?

BIOLOGY

ADAPTING TO A HIGHER LIFE

Himalayan Mountains, Tibet

Tibet, once at sea-level on the southern coast of Asia, now has a mountainous terrain. When India began colliding with Asia, the Himalayas began to rise. The animal species already present in both Asia and India had to adapt in order to colonize the mountainous territory. The snow leopard species evolved to have thicker fur and a paler color. How did a change of color help the leopard as it moved to higher land?

OCEANOGRAPHY

THE SEA THAT DISAPPEARED

Tethys Sea

The Tethys Sea began to close when Africa and India migrated northward. By 50 million years ago, the Tethys Sea was completely closed off by the Arabian Peninsula. The Saudi Arabian oil fields produce petroleum from limestone formed in the Tethys Sea during the Jurassic Period. What other countries have oil that may have formed offshore in the Tethys Sea?

473

METEOROLOGY

Background: Climatic zones seem to have formed barriers between the lycopods and the seed ferns. Both groups of plants produced immense coal deposits. The seed ferns were probably the ancestors of flowering plants.

Discussion: Discuss with students the importance to scientists of finding the two kinds of plant fossils in late Paleozoic rocks. This information helped meteorologists establish the theory of two climate zones at that time. It also helped geologists to understand more about the position of the continents at that time.

Answer to Question: Scientists can tell what the climate was like by studying the fossils found around the world from that time.

Extension: Have students locate areas of tropical, temperate, and polar climates on a present-day map of the world.

OCEANOGRAPHY

Background: The Tethys Sea extended from the Caribbean region all the way east to what is now Indonesia. It lasted through the Mesozoic Era, allowing the wide migration of Tethyan animals. Several species of corals, sponges, and mollusks not found in other places are found among Tethys fossils.

Discussion: Discuss that deep, wide oceans present an insurmountable barrier for the dispersal of animals living in shelf environments. Most of these animals have larval stages too short to survive long transoceanic voyages. The Tethys Sea, though extensive, was never deep. This fact makes the Tethys animals different from the marine animals that later inhabited the deeper Atlantic Ocean.

Answer to Question: Iran, the former Soviet Union, Iraq, Kuwait, Oman, Abu Dhabi are all oil-producing countries whose oil came from the shelf of the Tethys Sea.

Extension: Have students make a bar graph of amounts of oil produced in countries whose oil came from the shelf of the Tethys Sea.

BIOLOGY

Background: When India began colliding with Asia, it caused Asia to move up and over the Indian plate to form a double thickness of continental rocks in the area. This produced the wide zone of exceptionally high topography in the Himalayas and the Tibetan plateau.

Discussion: Mention to students that the heart and lung systems of the colonizing animal species also changed, allowing them to survive at a higher altitude in which the amount of oxygen in the air is much lower. Studies today show that people who live at high altitudes contain 30 percent more red blood cells than people living at sea level. The additional red blood cells carry more oxygen. High-altitude people also have greater lung capacity, allowing them to take in more air with each breath. The same kind of adaptation has occurred in other animals.

Answer to Question: The paler color made the snow leopard less conspicuous against the gray hillsides or snow.

Extension: Have students list the adaptations in some familiar life-forms.

PALEONTOLOGIST

Background: Paleontologists do research at museums or at universities. Their research may take them to far-away places around the world where fossils are found. They may be called upon when a discovery of fossils is made at an excavation site for a new road.

Related Career	Education
Biostratigrapher	college
Geomorphologist	college
Archaeologist Assistant	high school
Paleogeographer	college

Career Issue: Sometimes work at a construction site is halted because fossils are found. Construction companies are inconvenienced by the loss of time spent digging for fossils. If an important discovery is made at the site, it may halt construction altogether.

What do you think? Have students present opinions of a paleontologist and a construction supervisor concerning fossils found on site.

MUSEUM WORKER

Background: Museum workers may work in one of several departments in a museum. Their work can be exciting because they are surrounded by interesting exhibits that are constantly changing.

Related Career	Education
Museum Librarian	college
Archaeologist	college
Taxonomist	college
Artist	high school or college

Career Issue: A museum worker has enjoyable work and pleasant surroundings but receives little hope of advancement. The worker may decide to work toward a college degree in a field related to the museum.

What do you think? Have students discuss duties that might be performed by museum workers.

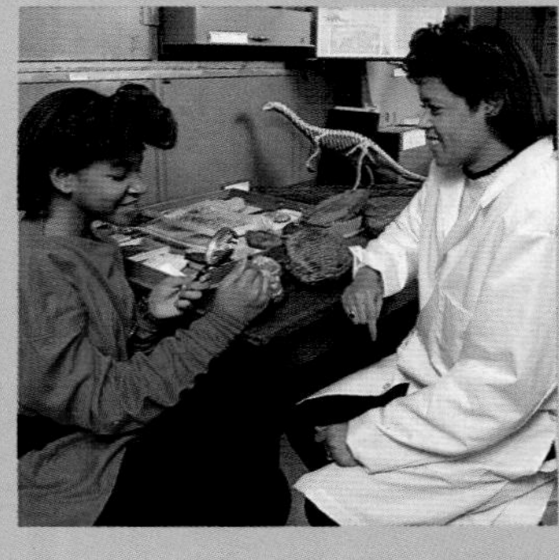

CAREERS

PALEONTOLOGIST

A *paleontologist* studies fossils to find out what kinds of organisms lived during each of the geologic periods. Fossils help paleontologists and geologists determine the age of the rocks in which the fossils are found. Paleontologists can tell from fossils whether the rocks were formed underwater or on land. From this, geologists can form a better picture of how Earth has changed.

Paleontologists usually obtain an advanced degree after college. A student wishing to become a paleontologist should study biology, earth science, and mathematics.

For Additional Information

Contact the Paleontological Society, U.S. Geological Survey, E/501 National Museum Building, Smithsonian Institution, Washington, DC 20506.

MUSEUM WORKER

A *museum worker* may perform any of several functions to keep a museum running smoothly. Since a museum is constantly acquiring new materials, a museum worker may assist the curator in placing these objects in their proper locations. He or she may also assist in preparing an exhibit or caring for the materials once they have been placed on display.

Museum workers usually receive on-the-job training after high school. A student wishing to become a museum worker should study biology and earth science.

For Additional Information

Contact the Museum of Natural History, Smithsonian Institution, Washington, DC 20506.

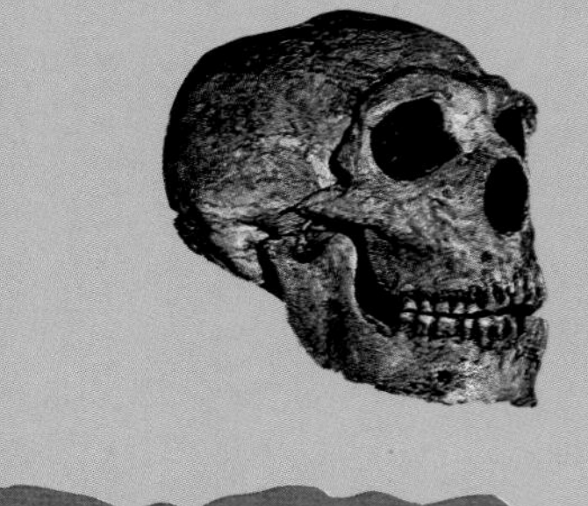

UNIT READINGS

▶Gould, Stephen Jay. *Time's Arrow Time's Cycle.* Cambridge, Massachusetts: Harvard University Press, 1987.

▶Norman, David. *The Illustrated Encyclopedia of Dinosaurs.* New York: Crescent Books, 1985.

▶Weiner, Jonathan. *Planet Earth.* New York, Bantam Books, 1986.

UNIT READINGS

Background

▶ *Time's Arrow Time's Cycle* traces the history of scientists' idea of time and the study of life's history on Earth.

▶ *The Illustrated Encyclopedia of Dinosaurs* provides excellent descriptions of the dinosaurs replete with detailed illustrations.

▶ *Planet Earth* combines the geologic time table with the changes that took place on Earth and with what happened to the dinosaurs.

More Readings

1. "The Dynamic Earth." *Scientific American,* September 1983. This is a special issue on scientists' new vision of our home planet.
2. Levenson, Thomas. *Ice Time.* New York: Harper and Row, Publishers, 1989. This book follows, in rocks, the record of the cycle of the ice sheets.

The Origin
A Biographical Novel of Charles Darwin
by Irving Stone

The following passage reveals Darwin's understanding of how Earth's changing surface was linked to the evolution of living things:

He cruised the bay with Captain FitzRoy and Sulivan. When they reached Punta Alta, Darwin's attention was attracted to low cliffs about a mile in length. At the striking of his geological hammer on the lowest bed, he discovered stratified gravel.

"Captain, look what's showing through! Bones! Fossils! The first I've ever seen *in situ*. Come and help me dig them out."

The conglomerate gave easily. Soon Charles had in his hands the bones of gigantic, ancient mammifers. . . .

Punta Alta was a gold mine of ancient bones. He found the lower jaw of a large animal with a quantity of its teeth; the bones of two or three gnawing animals, bones of the extremities of some great megatherioid quadruped.

"How did these animals get trapped up here in a cliff?" Covington asked.

"They didn't. From the presence of the marine shells and the fact that there are barnacles attached to some of the bones, we can feel certain that these remains were embedded in the bottom of a shallow sea."

"And something pushed that sea bottom up in the air to become cliffs?"

"Yes. Not a volcano, there's no lava here. Probably not an earthquake either, or they might have been sucked down and disappeared. What then? I don't know. Some mysterious boiling force. I wish I had Professor Sedgwick or Charles Lyell here to tell us."

. . . Almost as welcome as the letters from his family was the package containing the second volume of Lyell's *Principles of Geology*, in which Lyell turned his attention to the changes in progress in the animate creations. Lying in his hammock in the stillness of the chart room, he read Lyell's germinal question: ". . . whether there be proofs of the successive extermination of species in the ordinary course of nature, and whether there be any reason for conjecturing that new animals and plants are created from time to time, to supply their place?"

He lay quietly thinking forward to the day when he could show Charles Lyell the fossil bones he had discovered in Punta Alta.

In Your Own Words
▶ In an essay, explain how Darwin showed a reasonable knowledge of changes that occur on Earth.

475

Source: Irving Stone. *The Origin: A Biographical Novel of Charles Darwin.* Garden City, New York: Doubleday and Company, Inc. 1980, pp. 207-209.

Biography: Irving Stone (1903-) is a popular biographer of such famous persons as Vincent Van Gogh, Jack London, Michelangelo, and Abigail Adams. His works are the result of laborious research, and yet his use of imagination helps to make his characters more interesting. To write about Darwin, Stone stayed at Down House, the home of Charles Darwin, to better immerse himself in his subject.

TEACHING STRATEGY

▶ Ask students to discuss the views they supported in their essay about Darwin's knowledge of Earth's changes.

▶ Discuss with students Darwin's friendship with Charles Lyell and the effect of this on Darwin's understanding of geology.

Cooperative Learning: Ask students to work together to identify places in the passage that show Darwin's understanding of Earth's changes. Ask them to find places that show that the author is not a scientist. Ask how these places would have been written differently by a scientist.

Other Works

▶ Other works on Charles Darwin include: Brent, Peter. *Charles Darwin: A Man of Enlarged Curiosity.* New York: Harper, 1981. Eiseley, Loren C. "Charles Darwin." *Oceanography: Readings from Scientific American.* San Francisco: W.H. Freeman and Company, 1971.

Classics

▶ Lyell, K.M. *Life, Letters, and Journals of Sir Charles Lyell.* London: John Murray, 1881. This is a chance to know the thoughts of the great historian of time's cycle.

UNIT

7

NATURAL RESOURCES AND CONSERVATION

In Unit 7, students are introduced to energy sources and their use by humans. Nonrenewable and renewable energy sources are presented, as well as the impact of population on the environment. The causes of pollution are also described.

CONTENTS

ADVANCE PREPARATION

Activities

▶ **Activity 18-2, page 493,** requires 200-watt lamps with reflectors and clamps.

▶ **Activity 19-2, page 515,** requires 2-liter bottles.

▶ **Activity 20-1, page 533,** requires small boxes of plain gelatin, hot plates, and a refrigerator.

▶ **Activity 20-2, page 540,** requires access to home water meters. If water in your area is not metered, obtain the necessary data from an acquaintance whose water is metered.

Audiovisuals

▶ **Section 18-2, page 486:** Arrange to show the video "Green Energy," Films for the Humanities & Sciences.

Field Trips and Speakers

▶ Arrange for an official of a local recycling plant to visit your class.

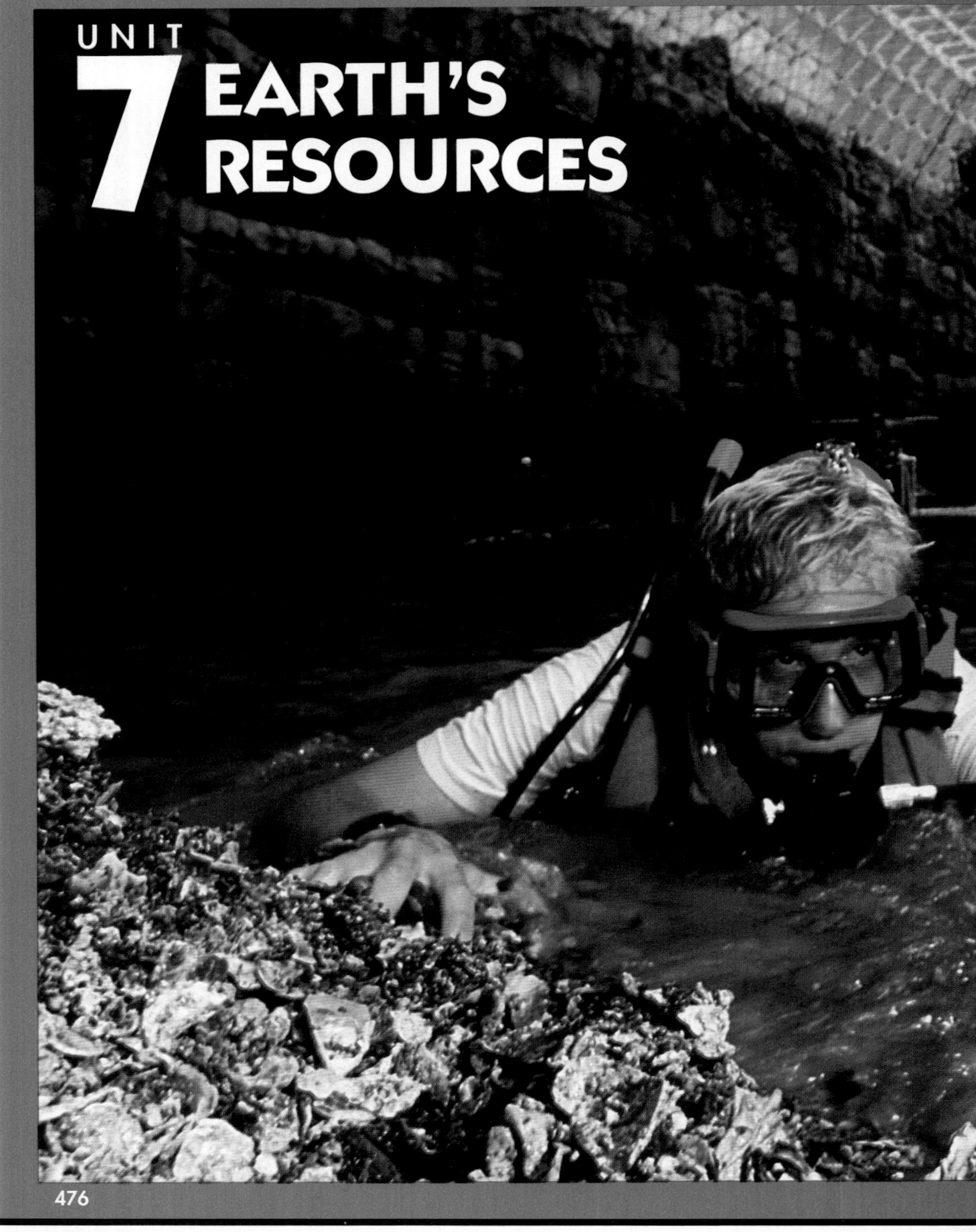

476

OPTIONS

Cross Curriculum

▶ Have students make a list of the wastes produced in domestic arts class and industrial arts class that are recycled.

Cooperative Learning: Inform students that the job of cleaning up pollution all over the world has been given to them. Have groups of three students collaborate on writing papers in which they present possible solutions to the pollution problem.

▶ Ask students to keep a list of times that pollution is discussed in other classes.

Science at Home

▶ Have students observe how people in their hometown use the land. Ask students to write about at least one example of wise land use and one example of where the methods of land use could be improved.

Cooperative Learning: Form groups of three students and have them brainstorm to come up with a list of ways they, or their families, waste energy produced by fossil fuels. As an extension, have students suggest ways that energy conservation could be practiced in their homes.

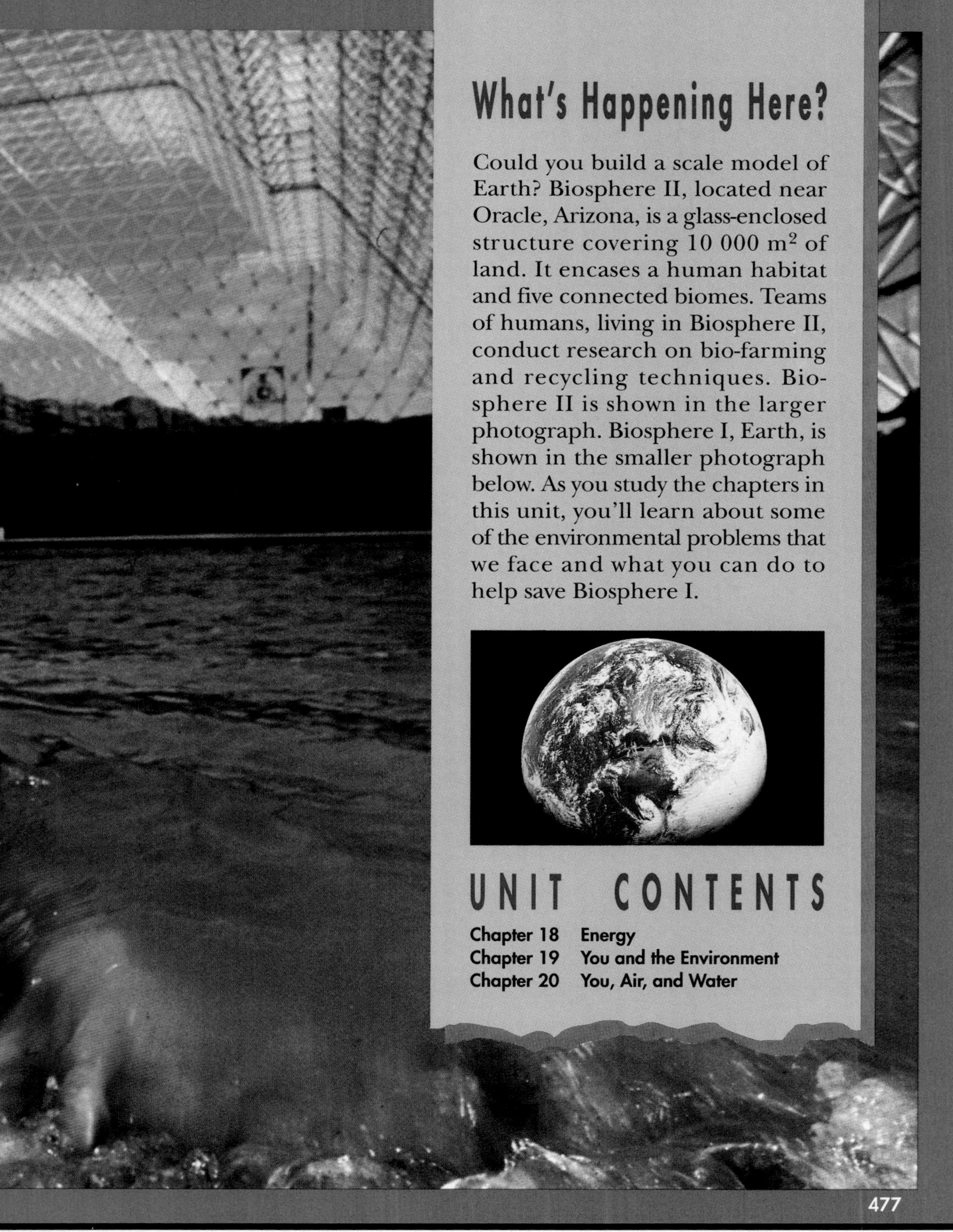

What's Happening Here?

Could you build a scale model of Earth? Biosphere II, located near Oracle, Arizona, is a glass-enclosed structure covering 10 000 m^2 of land. It encases a human habitat and five connected biomes. Teams of humans, living in Biosphere II, conduct research on bio-farming and recycling techniques. Biosphere II is shown in the larger photograph. Biosphere I, Earth, is shown in the smaller photograph below. As you study the chapters in this unit, you'll learn about some of the environmental problems that we face and what you can do to help save Biosphere I.

UNIT CONTENTS

INTRODUCING THE UNIT

What's Happening Here?

▶ Have students look at the photos and read the text. Ask them to tell you what's happening here. Point out to students that in this unit they will be studying the impact of population on energy sources, the environment, and pollution. They will also be studying specific causes of air and water pollution.

▶ **Background:** Biosphere II is separated into an area for humans and an area kept as a wilderness. The area for humans contains living quarters and a farmland. The wilderness contains many different types of plants growing in five different environments. The different environments include a tropical rain forest, a grassland area, a marsh, a mini-ocean, and a desert. The people living in Biosphere II are completely self-sufficient, although they keep in communication with the outside world. The ecological stability was established by carefully selecting the 3800 species of plants, insects, birds, fish, and small mammals that inhabit Biosphere II with the humans.

Previewing the Chapters

▶ Have students use the figures in Chapter 18 to compile a list of energy sources. Have them separate energy sources into two types, nonrenewable and renewable. Encourage students to determine the differences between nonrenewable and renewable energy sources.

▶ Conduct a scavenger hunt through Chapter 20 in search of photographs and new science words that deal with types of air and water pollution.

Tying to Previous Knowledge

▶ Lead students in a discussion of how a greenhouse is similar to, but also different from, Biosphere II.

▶ Ask how many students in the class ever go fishing or know someone who does. Ask them to explain how acid rain might affect the success of a fishing trip if the acid rain has fallen into the lake.

▶ Use the **Inquiry Questions** in the OPTIONS box below to investigate with students the sources of energy available to them.

Multicultural Awareness

▶ Have students research, in groups of three, how the Kuwaiti culture has changed since drilling for oil began in 1936.

▶ Have students research the coal mining industry in China and report on how coal mining affects the everyday life and culture of the people living in that area.

Inquiry Questions

Use the following questions to focus a discussion of the sources of energy available to humans.

1. Which energy source supplies most of our energy needs?
2. Why is the use of this energy not considered good for the environment?
3. What type of energy source is being used when campers build a campfire?

CHAPTER

18 Energy

CHAPTER SECTION	OBJECTIVES	ACTIVITIES
18-1 Nonrenewable Energy Sources (3 days)	1. **Describe** the evolution of fossil fuels—coal, oil, and natural gas. 2. **Explain** why fossil fuels are called nonrenewable energy sources. 3. **Discuss** how you can help conserve fossil fuels.	**MINI-Lab:** *How can you conserve energy?* p. 484 **Activity 18-1:** *Predicting Natural Gas Reserves,* p. 485
18-2 Renewable Energy Sources and Others (2 days)	1. **List** the advantages of using solar power, wind power, and hydroelectric power. 2. **List** the disadvantages of using solar power, wind power, and hydroelectric power.	**Activity 18-2:** *Solar Energy,* p. 493
18-3 Nuclear Energy Science & Society (2 days)	1. **Describe** how nuclear energy is made. 2. **List** the drawbacks and advantages of nuclear energy.	**MINI-Lab:** *Do you have a nuclear "neighbor"?* p. 495
Chapter Review		

ACTIVITY MATERIALS

FIND OUT	ACTIVITIES		MINI-LABS	
Page 479 paper pencil	**18-1 Predicting Natural Gas Reserves, p. 485** pencil paper	**18-2 Solar Energy, p. 493** dry black soil dry brown soil dry white sandy soil clear glass or plastic dishes (3) thermometers (3) 200-watt lamp with reflector and clamp watch or clock with second hand	**How can you conserve energy? p. 484** paper pencil	**Do you have a nuclear "neighbor"? p. 495** none

CHAPTER FEATURES	TEACHER RESOURCE PACKAGE	OTHER RESOURCES
Skill Builder: *Concept Mapping,* p. 484	**Ability Level Worksheets** ◆ ***Study Guide,*** p. 74 ● ***Reinforcement,*** p. 74 ▲ ***Enrichment,*** p. 74 **MINI-Lab Worksheet,** p. 166 **Activity Worksheet,** pp. 160-161 **Critical Thinking/Problem Solving,** p. 24 **Transparency Masters,** pp. 77-78	**Color Transparency 39,** Petroleum Usage
Problem Solving: *Hot Spot,* p. 487 **Technology:** *Solar Powered Plane,* p. 488 **Skill Builder:** *Hypothesizing,* p. 492	**Ability Level Worksheets** ◆ ***Study Guide,*** p. 75 ● ***Reinforcement,*** p. 75 ▲ ***Enrichment,*** p. 75 **Activity Worksheet,** pp. 162-163 **Cross-Curricular Connections,** p. 22 **Technology,** pp. 17-18	**Lab Manual:** *Solar Energy Collector,* p. 141 **Lab Manual:** *Solar Energy Storage,* p. 145 **Lab Manual:** *Solar Energy Application,* p. 147 **Lab Manual:** *Wind Power,* p. 151
You Decide! p. 496	**Ability Level Worksheets** ◆ ***Study Guide,*** p. 76 ● ***Reinforcement,*** p. 76 ▲ ***Enrichment,*** p. 76 **MINI-Lab Worksheet,** p. 167 **Concept Mapping,** pp. 41-42 **Science and Society,** p. 22	
Summary Key Science Words Understanding Vocabulary Checking Concepts Understanding Concepts Think & Write Critically Apply More Skill Builders Projects	**Chapter Review,** pp. 39-40 **Chapter Test,** pp. 125-128	**Chapter Review Software** **Test Bank**

◆ **Basic** ● **Average** ▲ **Advanced**

ADDITIONAL MATERIALS

SOFTWARE	AUDIOVISUAL	BOOKS/MAGAZINES
Geology Search, McGraw-Hill/Webster Division. *Power Grid,* HRM.	*Mineral Challenge,* film, U.S. Bureau of Mines. *The Riches of the Earth,* film, Sterling Educational Films. *Dawn of the Solar Age,* film, Time-Life. *Energy: The Fuels and Man,* film, NGS. *The Petrified River—The Story of Uranium,* film, U.S. Bureau of Mines.	Hassol, Susan and Beth Richman. *Recycling.* Snowmass, CO: Windstar Foundation, 1989. Kaplan Sheila. *Solar Energy.* Milwaukee, WI: Raintree Publishers, Inc., 1982. Kerrill, Edward A. *Environmental Geology.* Columbus, OH: Merrill Publishing Company, 1988. McMullan, John T. *Energy Resources and Supply.* Ann Arbor, MI: Books on Demand.

CHAPTER

18

ENERGY

THEME DEVELOPMENT: Evolution and energy are the themes of this chapter. Fossil fuels, solar energy, energy from water and wind and synfuels, biomass fuels, and sources of nuclear energy are explored.

CHAPTER OVERVIEW

- **Section 18-1:** This section discusses how fossil fuels evolve and how people can help conserve these nonrenewable energy sources.
- **Section 18-2:** The advantages and disadvantages of using energy from the sun, wind, moving water, synfuels, and biomass fuels are presented.
- **Section 18-3: Science and Society:** This section discusses how nuclear energy is produced, and the advantages and disadvantages of using nuclear power. The You Decide feature asks students whether people should continue to develop and build nuclear power plants.

CHAPTER VOCABULARY

energy	solar energy
fossil fuels	solar cell
peat	wind farm
lignite	hydroelectric energy
bituminous coal	synfuel
anthracite	biomass fuel
nonrenewable energy sources	nuclear energy
renewable energy sources	fission

CHAPTER 18 Energy

478

OPTIONS

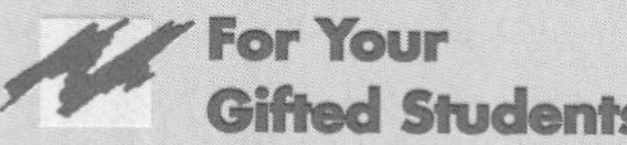

For Your Gifted Students

Have each student write a story describing what daily activities would be like without electricity and/or fossil fuels. Have students discover new forms of energy and write stories about how they can change the way we live today.

Why is energy so important? We use energy for things we do every day, as you'll see when you do the Find Out activity below. There are many different sources of energy. One way is to use solar panels to collect the energy from the sun as shown at the left. Some solar collectors are used to heat water, while solar cells convert energy from the sun into electricity. You probably use hot water and electricity all the time and don't think about where this energy comes from.

FIND OUT!

Do this simple activity to find out how many kinds of energy you will use today.

Make a list of ten things you will do today. Examples might be eat breakfast, travel, be in school, listen to a radio, watch TV, take a bath. Beside each item, write where you think the energy comes from for doing each activity. For example, if your dinner will be cooked on a gas range, the energy comes from gas.

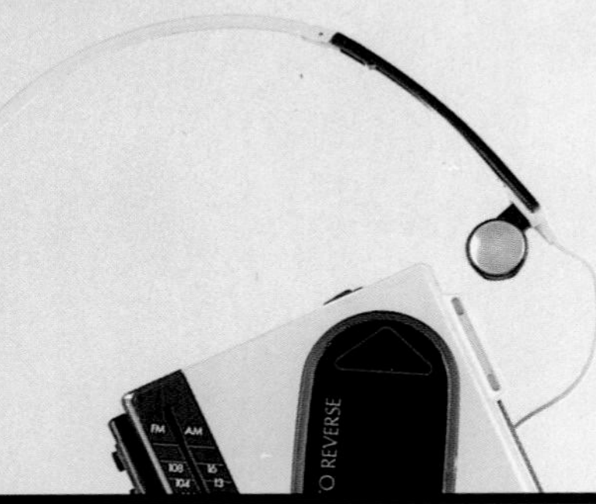

Gearing Up

Previewing the Chapter

Use this outline to help you focus on important ideas in this chapter.

Section 18-1 Nonrenewable Energy Sources
- Fossil Fuels
- Conserving Fossil Fuels

Section 18-2 Renewable Energy Sources and Others
- Renewable Energy
- Solar Energy
- Energy from Wind
- Energy from Water
- Synfuel and Biomass Fuel

Section 18-3 Science and Society Nuclear Energy
- Nuclear Energy
- Nuclear Power Accidents

Previewing Science Skills

- In the **Skill Builders,** you will make a concept map and hypothesize.
- In the **Activities,** you will observe, classify, infer, communicate, predict, and interpret data.
- In the **MINI-Labs,** you will learn about conservation and nuclear reactor safety.

What's next?

Now that you've thought about where the energy comes from for your everyday activities, you'll learn about different energy sources. Then you'll explore alternative sources of energy and look at where energy will come from in the future.

For Your Mainstreamed Students

▶ Have students research the development and use of various energy sources. Have them work as a group to make a time line to hang in the classroom that shows when each energy source was first developed and how it was used.

▶ Have students list the different sources of energy discussed in the chapter. After they have observed their community for a week, have them note which sources are used in the community and how each is used.

INTRODUCING THE CHAPTER

Use the Find Out activity to introduce students to sources of energy. Inform students that they will be learning more about energy sources as they read the chapter.

FIND OUT!

Teaching Tips

▶ After students have compiled their individual lists, ask them to share some of their items with the rest of the class. Write these activities on the chalkboard. Then, have students classify the activities according to energy source used. Sources might include an individual's own energy, energy from natural gas or gasoline, electric power, and so on. See which energy sources are most used by students.

Gearing Up

Have students study the Gearing Up feature to familiarize themselves with the chapter. Discuss the relationships of the topics in the outline.

What's Next?

Before beginning the first section, make sure students understand the connection between the Find Out activity and the topics to follow.

SECTION 18-1

PREPARATION

SECTION BACKGROUND

▶Much of the coal burned today formed from plants that lived during the Mississippian and Pennsylvanian Periods.

▶Coal deposits in the eastern United States generally occur as thin seams among layers of shale, limestone, or sandstone. These seams are typically deep-seated and are mined through deep shafts. In the western U.S., coal generally occurs as a single, thick deposit near the surface. In order to mine it, the overlying rock is stripped away to expose the coal. This type of mining is strip mining.

▶Crude oil is a mixture of hundreds of substances. It forms when marine organisms decompose in an oxygen-free environment.

1 MOTIVATE

▶Have students discuss the fuel efficiency of cars. Ask: **What does MPG mean? Why are consumers concerned about fuel efficiency? Why do automobile manufacturers advertise the MPGs of their cars?** Lead students to think about fossil fuels as finite resources.

Cooperative Learning: Have Paired Partners examine samples of peat, lignite, bituminous coal, and anthracite, but do not tell them what the samples are. Have them contrast the color, texture, and hardness of each sample. Explain that the specimens represent the four different stages in the formation of coal. Have students arrange the samples from least evolved to most evolved.

18-1 Nonrenewable Energy Sources

New Science Words

energy
fossil fuels
peat
lignite
bituminous coal
anthracite
nonrenewable energy sources

Objectives

- ▶ Describe the evolution of fossil fuels—coal, oil, and natural gas.
- ▶ Explain why fossil fuels are called nonrenewable energy sources.
- ▶ Discuss how you can help conserve fossil fuels.

Fossil Fuels

You learned in the Find Out activity how much you depend on energy. Our world depends on energy. **Energy** is the ability to do work. An object has energy if it is able
1 to exert a force or move something. We use energy for heating buildings, running car engines, lighting, farming, making clothes, building roads, cooking—just about everything we do. Where do we get the energy? Right now, we get most of it from fossil fuels.

Fossil fuels include coal, oil, and natural gas. They're called fossil fuels because they actually are fossils, the remains of plants and animals that died and decayed over millions of years. We use fossil fuels to make gasoline for cars, to heat our homes, and for many other uses.

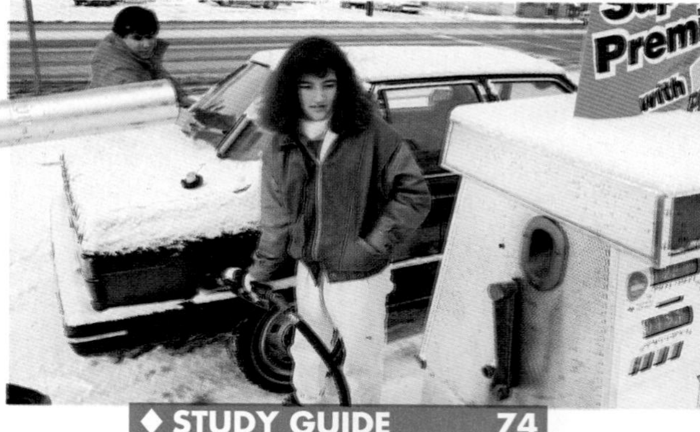

Figure 18-1. Gasoline is one product from fossil fuels we depend on.

OPTIONS

Meeting Different Ability Levels

For Section 18-1, use the following **Teacher Resource Masters** depending upon individual students' needs.

◆ **Study Guide Master** for all students.

● **Reinforcement Master** for students of average and above average ability levels.

▲ **Enrichment Master** for above average students.

Additional Teacher Resource Package masters are listed in the OPTIONS box throughout the section. The additional masters are appropriate for all students.

◆ STUDY GUIDE 74

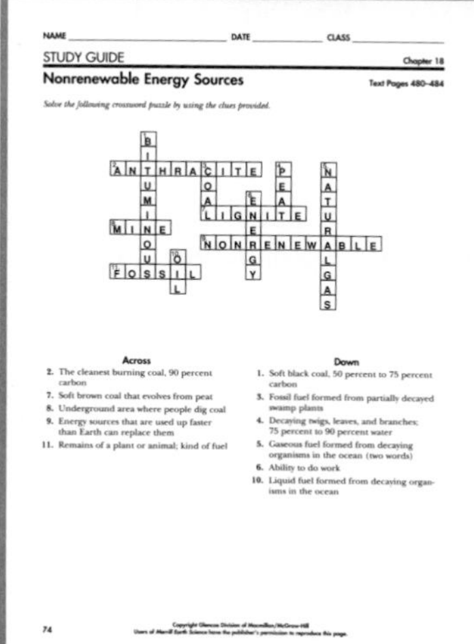

NAME ______ DATE ______ CLASS ______

STUDY GUIDE — Chapter 18

Nonrenewable Energy Sources — Text Pages 480–484

Solve the following crossword puzzle by using the clues provided.

Across

2. The cleanest burning coal, 90 percent carbon
7. Soft brown coal that evolves from peat
8. Underground area where people dig coal
9. Energy sources that are used up faster than Earth can replace them
11. Remains of a plant or animal; kind of fuel

Down

1. Soft black coal, 50 percent to 75 percent carbon
3. Fossil fuel formed from partially decayed swamp plants
4. Decaying twigs, leaves, and branches; 75 percent to 90 percent water
5. Gaseous fuel formed from decaying organisms in the ocean (two words)
6. Ability to do work
10. Liquid fuel formed from decaying organisms in the ocean

74

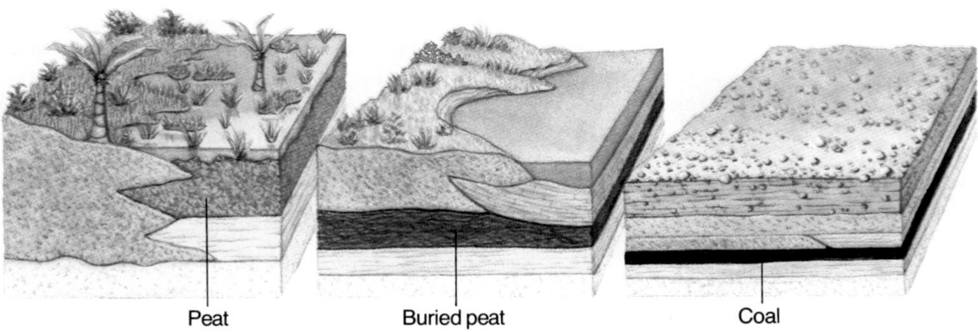

Figure 18-2. If peat becomes buried and compressed, coal may be formed.

Coal

Coal begins forming when swamp plants die and partially decay. Plants are made up of molecules that contain atoms of carbon, hydrogen, and oxygen. Decay occurs when bacteria break apart these molecules, releasing oxygen and hydrogen gases and leaving solid carbon behind. 2
When we burn coal, it is the carbon that releases heat.

The next step occurs when sediments begin piling up on top of the decaying plants. The mass of the sediments compresses the partially decayed plants, squeezing out the moisture. After the decaying plants become buried, coal evolves in the following stages.

The first stage is peat. **Peat** is composed of decaying twigs, leaves, and branches, but is 75 to 90 percent water. Peat is used to heat homes in some parts of the world such as the British Islands, but it is a very poor, smoky fuel that pollutes the air.

As peat becomes buried deeper under more sediment,
it evolves into **lignite.** This soft brown coal has much less 3
moisture and is about 30 percent carbon. Lignite is mined in North Dakota, South Dakota, Montana, and Germany. It's a better fuel for heating homes than peat, but is still very smoky and polluting.

As burial under sediments continues, **bituminous** (bi TOO mihn us) **coal**, or soft coal, forms. It's dense, black, brittle, and has lots of carbon, about 50 to 75 percent. It has lost all but 5 to 15 percent of its water. Bituminous coal is the coal used most often. It provides lots of heat energy when burned, but still pollutes the air. Most of it is mined in the Appalachian Mountains, the Midwest, and the Rocky Mountains of the United States, and in Europe, China, and Australia.

Did You Know?

In one year, burning the coal to light one 100-watt light bulb for 12 hours a day creates more than 936 pounds of carbon dioxide and 7.8 pounds of sulfur dioxide.

What is the most commonly used coal?

TYING TO PREVIOUS KNOWLEDGE: Have students recall from Chapter 16 how fossils form. Explain that coal, oil, and natural gas are formed from plants and animals that lived millions or billions of years ago.

OBJECTIVES AND SCIENCE WORDS: Have students review the objectives and science words to become familiar with this section.

2 TEACH

Key Concepts are highlighted.

CONCEPT DEVELOPMENT

▶ **How does peat evolve into bituminous coal?** *As peat becomes buried under sediments, it loses moisture and becomes lignite. As burial continues, more water is lost and the substance eventually becomes dense, black, brittle bituminous coal.*

▶ **What role do bacteria play in the evolution of coal?** *Bacteria cause the plants to decay by breaking apart molecules of carbon, hydrogen, and oxygen.*

● REINFORCEMENT 74

NAME ______ DATE ______ CLASS ______

REINFORCEMENT Chapter 18

Nonrenewable Energy Sources Text Pages 480–484

Complete the table of fossil fuels.

Fuel	How fuel formed	How fuel obtained	Uses
1. Coal	decayed swamp plants layers of sediments peat lignite bituminous coal anthracite	mines	home heating industries
2. Natural gas	decayed ocean organisms layers of sediments increased pressure and weight chemical reactions	wells	heating cooking
3. Oil	decayed ocean organisms layers of sediments increased pressure and weight chemical reactions	wells	gasoline aircraft fuel furnace fuel lubricants plastics

Answer the following questions on the lines provided.

1. Why is it important to conserve fossil fuels? **Fossil fuels are nonrenewable sources of energy; the more slowly we use them, the longer they will last.**
2. List some ways to conserve fossil fuels. **Answers will vary. They may include: Insulate water heaters; keep windows and doors closed in cold weather; turn off electrical equipment when not in use; run air conditioning as little as possible.**

74

▲ ENRICHMENT 74

NAME ______ DATE ______ CLASS ______

ENRICHMENT Chapter 18

Nonrenewable Energy Sources Text Pages 480–484

WHAT MAKES A GOOD INSULATOR?

Students in Ms. Ohira's science class were studying conservation of energy. They knew that one way to conserve energy was to add insulation in places such as attics and walls and around heaters. To see what kind of materials made good insulators, they performed an experiment.

They collected four empty soft drink cans. They wrapped the first can in newspaper, the second in foil, and the third in polystyrene. They left the fourth can unwrapped. Next, they filled each can with warm water, put a thermometer in each can, and secured the thermometer with clay. They heated the cans under a hot light and measured the temperature every 2 minutes for 20 minutes. Then they turned off the light and measured the temperature every 2 minutes for 20 minutes. Below are their results.

With light on
Can 4 increased in temperature most quickly. Cans 1 and 3 increased in temperature most slowly.
With light off
Can 4 decreased in temperature most quickly. Cans 1 and 3 decreased in temperature most slowly.

Conclude and Apply

1. Of the materials the students used, which were the best insulators against heat gain? **newspaper and polystyrene**
2. Of the materials the students used, which were the best insulators against heat loss? **newspaper and polystyrene**
3. Does insulation prevent heat gain or loss? Explain. **Insulation prevents heat gain, and once heat is gained, it prevents heat loss. The cans wrapped with newspaper and polystyrene heated more slowly and cooled more slowly.**

74

CONCEPT DEVELOPMENT

▶ Stress that peat, lignite, bituminous coal, and anthracite are all used as fuel.

▶ **Which coal is the cleanest burning?** *anthracite* **Which provides the most heat?** *bituminous coal*

CROSS CURRICULUM

▶ **Social Studies:** Have students discuss ways in which economics and politics affect and are affected by crude oil production.

MINI QUIZ

Use the Mini Quiz to check students' recall of chapter content.

1. **_____ is the ability to do work.** *Energy*
2. **As coal forms, bacteria break apart molecules in plants to release oxygen and hydrogen, and leave _____ behind.** *carbon*
3. **Peat evolves into _____ and then into bituminous coal.** *lignite*
4. **_____ is about 90% carbon.** *Anthracite*
5. **Oil and natural gas are removed from underground reservoirs through _____.** *wells*

Figure 18-3. Peat, shown at top, can eventually turn into coal.

4 If heat and intense pressure are applied to bituminous coal, it becomes **anthracite** (AN thruh site). Anthracite is the cleanest burning of all coals and is about 90 percent carbon. It produces less heat than bituminous coal, but industries like it because it burns cleaner and longer. It is mined mostly underground in Pennsylvania and Virginia.

Oil and Natural Gas

We burn vast quantities of oil and gas. In fact, every year we obtain twice the energy from oil and gas than we do from coal. Natural gas is used mostly for heating and cooking. Oil has many more uses.

Most oil is refined into fuels such as gasoline and aircraft fuel. Other oil is made into heating oil for furnaces, lubricants, and plastics. Did you realize that plastic is made from oil?

Both oil and natural gas form over millions of years from the decaying of tiny organisms in the ocean. The process begins when plankton organisms die, fall to the seafloor, and pile up. Later, other sediments are deposited over them, in the same way that coal is buried. They are compacted by the weight, and this pressure on the organic matter helps chemical reactions to occur. This creates the liquid we call oil, as well as gases we call natural gas.

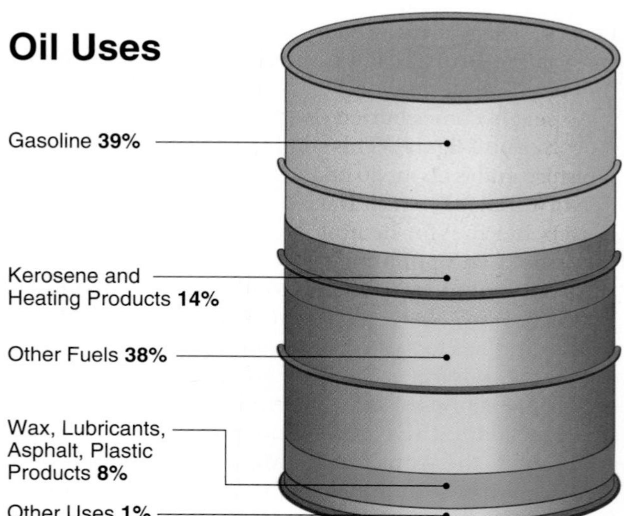

Figure 18-4. This diagram shows what percentages of oil are used for different products. Most oil is used for fuel.

OPTIONS

INQUIRY QUESTIONS

▶ **As coal evolves, what happens to its water and carbon content?** *The water decreases and carbon increases.*

▶ **Compare and contrast the formation of coal with that of oil and natural gas.** *All three fuels originate from living creatures that were buried in sediments and decayed over time. The mass of the sediments compacts the organisms and creates heat and pressure, which cause chemical changes in the organic matter. Coal evolves from swamp plants; oil and natural gas from tiny marine organisms.*

PROGRAM RESOURCES

From the **Teacher Resource Package** use:

Transparency Masters, pages 77-78, Petroleum Usage.

Use **Color Transparency** number 39, Petroleum Usage.

Because oil and natural gas are less dense than water, they migrate upward to get on top of water-saturated rock layers. Sometimes this movement is stopped by impermeable rock, such as shale. This rock traps the oil and gas below it. When this happens, a reservoir of oil or natural gas forms under the impermeable rock.

How do we remove oil and natural gas from these reservoirs? We drill wells down through the rocks until we reach the reservoirs. Wells are lined with pipe to keep them from caving in. Wells are often thousands of meters deep. But they are only centimeters in diameter because oil and natural gas are fluids that travel easily up the pipe to the surface. 5

Science and MATH

Four people living in the same neighborhood each drive 30 km roundtrip to work each day and pay \$4/day to park. How much money could they each save if they car pool, assuming it costs \$.15 per km to operate their cars and they work 5 days/week, 50 weeks/year?

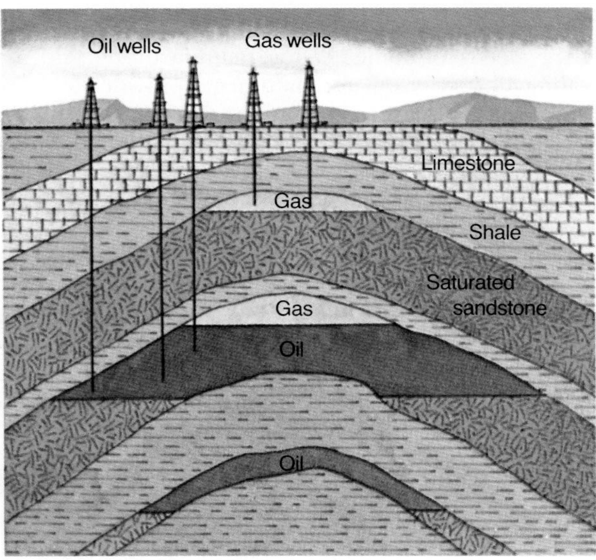

Figure 18-5. Oil and natural gas are often found together. Because gas is less dense than oil, it is found above the oil in the reservoir.

Conserving Fossil Fuels

Do you sometimes forget to turn off the lights when you walk out of a room? Many people waste energy this way. You may not realize that electricity to run our homes and industries will not always be as plentiful and cheap as it is today. Most of the energy sources we are using to generate electricity right now are nonrenewable. **Nonrenewable energy sources** are those that we are using up faster than Earth can replace them. Remember that fossil fuels take millions of years to form.

Is the majority of our current energy sources renewable or nonrenewable?

CONCEPT DEVELOPMENT

▶ **Why do oil and natural gas migrate upward through water-saturated rock?** *They are less dense than water.*

▶ Stress that fossil fuels are considered nonrenewable energy sources because they are being used more quickly than they can be replaced.

Science and MATH

$\frac{\$4.00}{day} \times \frac{5\ days}{wk} \times \frac{50\ wk}{year}$
= \$1000.00/per person parking

$\frac{30\ km}{day} \times \frac{\$0.15}{km} \times \frac{5\ days}{wk} \times \frac{50\ wk}{yr}$
= \$1125.00/person for operation

(\$1000.00 + \$1125.00) × 4 people = \$8500.00 when not car pooling

\$8500.00 – \$2125.00 = \$6375.00

\$6375.00 ÷ 4 = \$1593.75: the amount each person saved by car pooling.

CHECK FOR UNDERSTANDING

Why should people conserve fossil fuel? *Students should be able to explain that ninety percent of our energy needs are provided by fossil fuels. These fuels are being used up very quickly. We will eventually run out.*

RETEACH

Ask students what life might be like once fossil fuel reserves are exhausted. Have them include the effects on transportation, jobs, and the economy.

EXTENSION

For students who have mastered this section, use the **Reinforcement** and **Enrichment** masters or other OPTIONS provided.

INQUIRY QUESTIONS

▶ **Discuss the impact on society if conservation of oil and natural gas is not practiced.** *As these fuels become more scarce, the costs will rise. People will either have to look for alternative fuels or do without some of the conveniences to which they have become accustomed.*

ENRICHMENT

▶ Have interested students research the cause of black lung disease.

▶ Have students report on the products made from crude oil.

▶ Have students make maps showing ancient inland seas and how these correlate to the locations of petroleum and natural gas reservoirs.

MINI-Lab

Teaching Tips

▶ Contact the local utility company for a publication that shows how to read meters.

▶**Answers:** Some synonyms of *conservation* are *care, control, management, preservation, upkeep,* and *maintenance.* When practiced, the quality of life can be maintained and even improved.

3 CLOSE

▶ Have students do Activity 18-1.

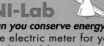

▶ Ask questions 1-3 and the **Apply** Question in the Section Review.

▶ Invite an energy auditor to talk about his or her career.

SECTION REVIEW ANSWERS

1. Plants grow in swamps and eventually die, sink, and decay. Sediments cover the remains and force out water and other impurities leaving the carbon. Chemical reactions occur over time until coal is formed.

2. They are used much more quickly than they are being formed.

3. turn off lights in empty rooms, insulate houses, recycle, car pool, tightly shut doors and windows, reduce the amount of energy used to heat and cool

4. Apply: Natural gas and oil originate from marine organisms. Coal originates from swamp plants. One particular location is not likely to have been covered by both oceans and swamps.

PROGRAM RESOURCES

From the **Teacher Resource Package** use:

Activity Worksheets, page 166, Mini-Lab: How can you conserve energy?

Critical Thinking/Problem Solving, page 24, An Electricity Addiction.

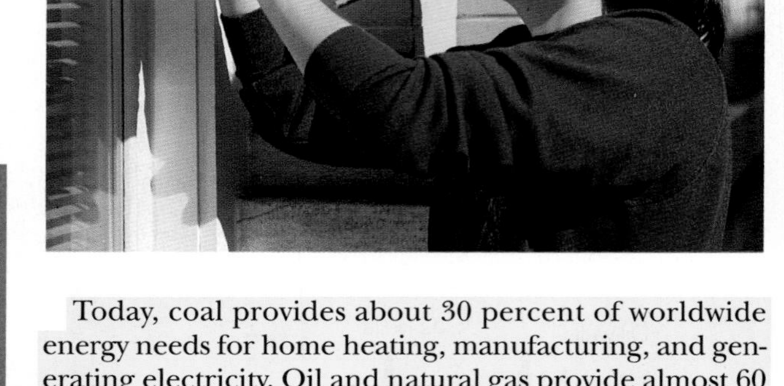

Figure 18-6. Caulking windows is one way to conserve energy.

MINI-Lab 

How can you conserve energy?
Find the electric meter for your home and record the reading on a sheet of paper. Do this for several days, taking your meter readings at approximately the same time each day. Make a list of things you and your family could do to reduce your rate of electricity consumption. Discuss these options with your family, decide which ones you would like to try, and do them for several days. Keep taking the meter readings and see if your efforts seem to be making any difference. If they do, you've not only helped in conserving natural resources, you've also helped your family save some money that can be used for something else instead. What is the meaning of conservation and how might it affect your life?

Today, coal provides about 30 percent of worldwide energy needs for home heating, manufacturing, and generating electricity. Oil and natural gas provide almost 60 percent of our energy needs. At the rate we're burning it, we have enough to last several hundred years, but we will run out someday.

How can you conserve fossil fuels? There are many ways. Turn off lights in rooms as you leave. Do the same with TVs and radios. During cold weather, make sure doors and windows are tightly shut so heated air doesn't leak out of your home. If you have air conditioning, run it as little as possible. Ask adults in your home if more insulation could be added, or if an insulated jacket could be put on the water heater to save energy. All of these steps reduce energy used for heating and cooling.

SECTION REVIEW

1. Describe how coal evolves from plants.
2. Why are fossil fuels nonrenewable energy sources?
3. List five ways you can help conserve fossil fuels.
4. **Apply:** Why are you likely to find natural gas and oil deposits in the same location, but less likely to find coal and oil deposits at the same location?

Skill Builder — **Concept Mapping**

Make a concept map that explains how peat forms. If you need help, refer to Concept Mapping in the **Skill Handbook** on pages 688 and 689.

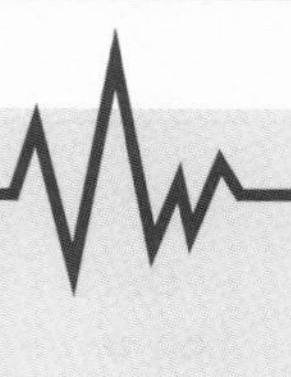

Skill Builder

Possible Solution:

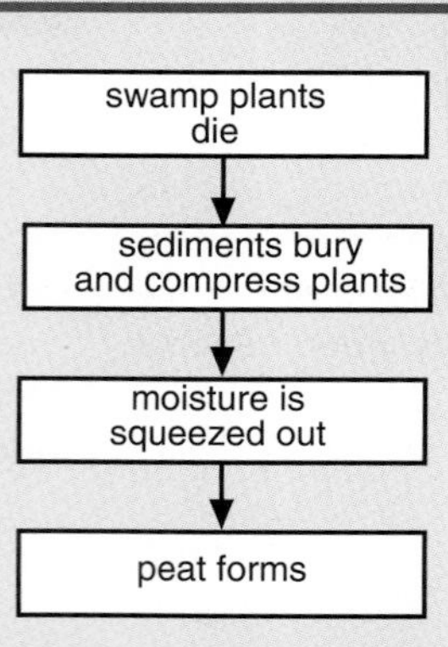
swamp plants die
sediments bury and compress plants
moisture is squeezed out
peat forms

ACTIVITY 18-1
Predicting Natural Gas Reserves

Problem: *At present rates of consumption, what will happen to the United States' known reserves of natural gas?*

Materials
- pencil
- paper

Procedure
1. Many times scientists must be able to predict outcomes. One way of predicting outcomes is to analyze trends. Trends are general movements or directions actions have taken in the past. In this activity, you will learn ways of predicting outcomes.
2. Examine the graph below. It shows the billions of cubic meters of natural gas in U.S. reserves (identified deposits) and in marketed production from 1925 to 1985.
3. Analyze the trends of both the proved reserves and marketed production to predict future outcomes based on present rates by answering the following questions.

Analyze
1. Which best describes the trend in reserves between 1925 and 1965? Between 1965 and 1985?
   a. Reserves increased.
   b. Reserves decreased.
   c. Reserves remained constant.
2. Which best describes the trend in marketed production between 1945 and 1975? Between 1975 and 1985?
   a. Marketed production increased.
   b. Marketed production decreased.
   c. It remained constant.

Conclude and Apply
3. Why do you think the U.S. gas reserves increased from 1925 to 1965, but have decreased since that time?
4. Why did marketed production increase between 1945 and 1975 and then drop?
5. In order to predict the future when examining a graph, a method called extrapolation is used. Extrapolation assumes that the slopes of the curves will not change a great deal and that the latest trend will continue. Use this method to answer the following question. If trends continue in reserves and marketed production, predict what will happen to the U.S. natural gas reserves by 1995.
6. Predict what could happen to the reserves if people really started conserving natural gas and the marketed production dropped to where it was in 1945.

Data and Observations

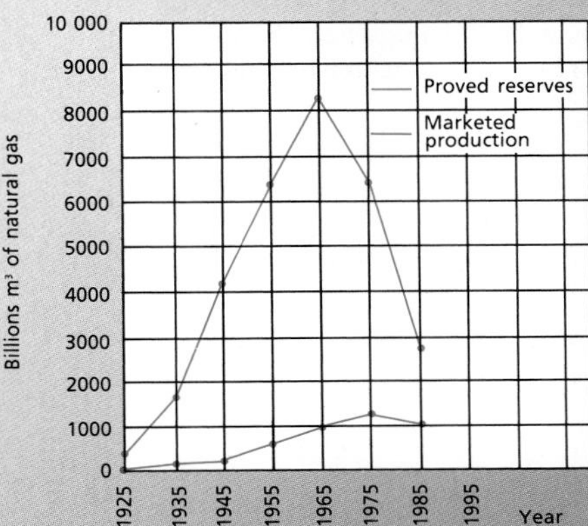

ACTIVITY 18-1
20 minutes

OBJECTIVE: Predict natural gas reserves for the U.S. when given present rates of consumption and declining proven resources.

PROCESS SKILLS applied in this activity:
▶ **Communicating** in Procedure Steps 1 and 2.
▶ **Predicting** in Conclude and Apply Questions 5 and 6.
▶ **Using Numbers** in Analyze Questions 1 and 2, and Conclude and Apply Questions 3-6.
▶ **Interpreting Data** in Analyze Questions 1 and 2.
▶ **Hypothesizing** in Conclude and Apply Questions 3 and 4.

TEACHING THE ACTIVITY
▶ Explain to students that scientists and other experts often predict outcomes by analyzing trends. The graph shows trends in proven natural gas reserves and marketed production over the past 70 years. In order to predict future natural gas levels, students must be able to extrapolate by assuming that the slopes of the curves will not change significantly and that the latest trends will continue.
▶ Point out that the U.S. still has natural gas reserves remaining, even though the trends on the graph indicate that they should be exhausted by at least 1993. Have them infer why the trend lines on the graph must have changed.
▶ On the chalkboard, develop a list of ways in which the rate of natural gas consumption may be lowered.

PROGRAM RESOURCES

From the **Teacher Resource Package** use:

Activity Worksheets, pages 160-161, Activity 18-1: Predicting Natural Gas Reserves.

ANSWERS TO QUESTIONS
1. a; b
2. a; b
3. Between 1925 and 1965, technology led to the discovery of many reservoirs. There was a larger surplus than demand for the gas during those years. Since 1965, there have been few reservoirs found and production has been reduced.
4. There was a great demand for gas from 1945–1975. It was a clean, inexpensive source of energy. After 1975, use decreased due to cost increases. Also, conservation was implemented by the government.
5. Using extrapolation, it appears from this data that proved reserves will be depleted by 1995.
6. The reserves will last longer.

SECTION 18-2

PREPARATION

SECTION BACKGROUND

► One system of heating with solar energy uses black surfaces to absorb sunlight. Other energy-efficient buildings are designed with south-facing vertical windows that absorb solar energy.

► One of the most important uses of flowing water is to extract and process minerals. Aluminum smelters are often located near running water, which is a relatively inexpensive source of energy.

PREPLANNING

► To prepare for Activity 18-2, obtain the materials listed on page 493 for each Science Investigation group.

1 MOTIVATE

FLEX Your Brain

Use the Flex Your Brain activity to have students explore RENEWABLE ENERGY SOURCES.

► **Demonstration:** Use a hand lens, a foil pie pan, and a ball of tissue paper to demonstrate the potential of focused sunlight. Hold the hand lens in the sunlight to focus the rays on the ball of tissue paper. Within a few minutes, the paper should begin to burn. Discuss the reason the paper burns. Have students consider how solar panels focus and collect solar energy for use in heating buildings. **CAUTION:** *Warn students that this demonstration should NOT be repeated.*

PROGRAM RESOURCES

From the **Teacher Resource Package** use:

Activity Worksheet, page 5, Flex Your Brain.

18-2 Renewable Energy Sources and Others

New Science Words

renewable energy sources
solar energy
solar cell
wind farm
hydroelectric energy
synfuel
biomass fuel

Objectives

- ► **List the advantages of using solar power, wind power, and hydroelectric power.**
- ► **List the disadvantages of using solar power, wind power, and hydroelectric power.**

Renewable Energy

Do you think we will we ever run out of fossil fuels? We will, although it will take many decades. Fortunately, we also have **renewable energy sources.** These sources are constant and will not run out in the future as coal will. Renewable energy sources include the sun, wind, water, and geothermal energy that you learned about in Chapter 15.

Figure 18-7. Energy from the sun can be used to make electricity.

OPTIONS

Meeting Different Ability Levels

For Section 18-2, use the following **Teacher Resource Masters** depending upon individual students' needs.

◆ **Study Guide Master** for all students.

● **Reinforcement Master** for students of average and above average ability levels.

▲ **Enrichment Master** for above average students.

Additional Teacher Resource Package masters are listed in the OPTIONS box throughout the section. The additional masters are appropriate for all students.

◆ STUDY GUIDE 75

NAME ____________ DATE ________ CLASS ________

STUDY GUIDE — Chapter 18

Renewable Energy Sources — Text Pages 486–492

Use the words and phrases in the boxes to fill in the blanks.

electricity	geothermal energy	hour
renewable energy sources	solar cells	sun
thermal collectors	water	wind
year	solar energy	

Some energy sources will not run out. These are called **renewable energy sources**. Four of these are the **sun**, **wind**, **water**, and **geothermal energy**.

In one **hour**, enough energy reaches Earth from the sun to supply all the energy we need for a **year**. This is called **solar energy**. Some of this energy heats air or water inside **thermal collectors** and is piped to where heat is needed. **Solar cells** collect energy from the sun and turn it into **electricity**.

advantage	disadvantage	hydroelectric	windmills
running	wind	wind farms	

Another source of energy was used by the Dutch 400 years ago. **Wind** was used to turn **windmills** that ground corn and pumped water. Windmills were also used in the United States and other countries. Today, they are being used again on **wind farms**.

Solar power and wind power are free, and that is an **advantage**. But they can be received only when the sun shines or a strong wind blows, and that is a **disadvantage**. Water power, or **hydroelectric** power, on the other hand, is free and always available. Both tidal energy and energy from **running** water have been used to make electricity.

75

Solar Energy

When you sit in the sun, walk into the wind, or swim against an ocean current, you are feeling the power of solar energy. As you learned in Chapters 9 and 10, the sun's energy not only heats Earth, but it causes Earth's atmosphere and oceans to circulate. Thus, we indirectly use solar energy when we use the wind and moving water to do work.

Many of the nonrenewable energy sources we use today are actually stored solar energy. Plants that formed coal grew using solar energy. Organisms that formed oil and natural gas ate plants, so they also used solar energy. When fossil fuels are burned, stored solar energy is released. These are indirect uses of solar energy.

How is oil indirectly a solar energy?

PROBLEM SOLVING

Hot Spot

It was a hot summer day. Christie decided she wanted to make iced tea. She had heard that "sun tea" was really good. Her friend, Will, had told her that you use a large glass jar with a lid, tea bags, water, and the sun. She decided to make some.

She filled the jar up to the brim with water and put in four small tea bags. Then she screwed the lid tightly on the jar and placed the jar on the patio in the sun. She had forgotten to ask Will how long it took to make it, so she decided to check the jar in a half hour. At the end of the half hour, Christie found that only the top one-fourth of the jar had become tea-colored. Also, she noticed when she touched the jar that the top was warmer than the bottom. She checked it again 30 minutes later to find that the top one-half was tea-colored, but the bottom was still clear. Finally, at the end of one more hour, the whole jar was tea-colored.

Christie added ice cubes to the warm tea and drank a tall glass. As she sipped the long-awaited beverage, she was puzzled by several questions.

Think Critically: Why did only the top part of the water become tea at first? What made the tea so warm? Why was the top part of the jar warm before the bottom part?

● REINFORCEMENT 75

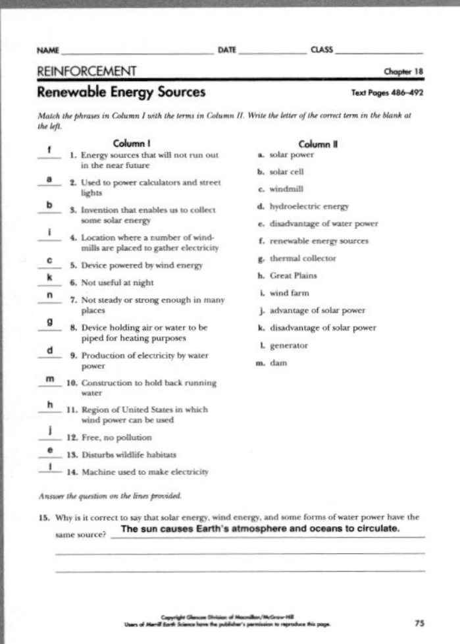

NAME ________ DATE ________ CLASS ________

REINFORCEMENT — Chapter 18

Renewable Energy Sources — Text Pages 486–492

Match the phrases in Column I with the terms in Column II. Write the letter of the correct term in the blank at the left.

Column I	Column II
f 1. Energy sources that will not run out in the near future	a. solar power
a 2. Used to power calculators and street lights	b. solar cell
b 3. Invention that enables us to collect some solar energy	c. windmill
i 4. Location where a number of windmills are placed to gather electricity	d. hydroelectric energy
c 5. Device powered by wind energy	e. disadvantage of water power
k 6. Not useful at night	f. renewable energy sources
n 7. Not steady or strong enough in many places	g. thermal collector
g 8. Device holding air or water to be piped for heating purposes	h. Great Plains
d 9. Production of electricity by water power	i. wind farm
m 10. Construction to hold back running water	j. advantage of solar power
h 11. Region of United States in which wind power can be used	k. disadvantage of solar power
j 12. Free, no pollution	l. generator
e 13. Disturbs wildlife habitats	m. dam
l 14. Machine used to make electricity	

Answer the question on the lines provided.

15. Why is it correct to say that solar energy, wind energy, and some forms of water power have the same source? **The sun causes Earth's atmosphere and oceans to circulate.**

 75

▲ ENRICHMENT 75

NAME ________ DATE ________ CLASS ________

ENRICHMENT — Chapter 18

Renewable Energy Sources — Text Pages 486–492

GROWING FUEL

You know that only a small percentage of the sun's energy can be used by solar cells. For a long time, however, another kind of sun collector has been using solar energy—plants of all kinds. And while they aren't any more efficient than solar cells, there are a lot of them.

Most of the sunlight that falls on plants is reflected back into the atmosphere. Some plants use only 0.01 percent of the solar energy to which they are exposed; others use 3.0 percent or more. The plants convert this small amount of solar energy to stored energy.

The stored energy in wood has served as fuel for thousands of years. Can other plants serve as fuel for today? Yes. Any plant that grows can be converted to energy, but, of course, cost and space might prohibit such use. Forests, for example, take enormous amounts of space and require very long periods to grow. Burning wood directly will never satisfy the modern world's need for fuel.

Recently, plants have been used increasingly to produce a kind of fuel called gasohol. Is gasohol sold in filling stations in your region? Gasohol is usually made from 90 percent gasoline and 10 percent ethyl alcohol. This alcohol is produced from plants.

Most of the ethyl alcohol used in gasohol is made from corn. However, other farm products can also be used to make ethyl alcohol, including most grains. In Brazil, sugar is grown for the purpose of converting it into alcohol that can be mixed with gasoline.

Another kind of alcohol, methanol, may be substituted for gasoline or mixed with it. Methanol is made from organic wastes, such as plant material or animal sewage. Inedible parts of plants can be converted to methanol. The waste is decomposed to make methane gas. The gas can then be burned or converted to methanol.

Possible sources for ethyl alcohol and methanol fuels are many. Cattails, water hyacinths, algae, kelp, and the sap from some types of trees are just some of the sources available. Whether or not they will be used as sources of energy in our future depends on several factors. One, of course, is expense. Another is the development of efficient technologies to use the fuels. A third is politics. Who will pay for new factories to process this fuel? Will growing plants for fuel take too many acres away from needed food supplies? Are there dangers we don't yet know about in this new form of fuel? It's known that such fuel would reduce pollution caused by automobiles.

Some nations without oil reserves are anxious to find alternatives to gasoline. It is possible that Brazil will be growing all its own fuel within another decade or two. Do you think the rest of the world will follow?

1. Where do you think the name gasohol comes from? ***gas* from gasoline and *ohol* from alcohol**
2. Why might people be concerned about using grains to make ethyl alcohol? **Some people might feel that growing grains for fuel would result in a shortage of grains needed for food.**
3. How would you answer a person who said that making ethyl alcohol and methanol is a waste of money because they can never supply all of our needs for gasoline? **They can reduce the amount of oil needed.**

 75

TYING TO PREVIOUS KNOWLEDGE: Have students recall from Chapter 9 that the sun's energy is not distributed equally over Earth. Air that is warmed is pushed aloft by denser cold air. This movement of air creates wind, which can be used as a renewable energy source.

OBJECTIVES AND SCIENCE WORDS: Have students review the objectives and science words to become familiar with this section.

2 TEACH

Key Concepts are highlighted.

CONCEPT DEVELOPMENT

▶ **Where does the energy from wind and moving water originate?** *from the sun*

PROBLEM SOLVING

Think Critically: The water at the top was in contact with the tea bags whereas the water at the bottom of the jar wasn't. As the water heated, the warm water rose because it was less dense than the surrounding water. This warm water came in contact with the tea bags to form tea. Eventually, as the water in the jar warmed, convection currents developed and the tea was carried to the bottom of the jar. The tea was warm because solar radiation struck the jar and conduction transferred heat through the glass to the water.

TECHNOLOGY

▶ For information on solar-powered cars, see "Flying Cockroach Walks to Victory" by Charles Morgan, *Nature*, November 12, 1987, p. 101.

▶ Inform students that research is being done on new types of solar cells. The proposed cells would have no moving parts. The amorphous silicon cells would convert solar energy directly into electricity, are smaller and easier to make, and are cheaper than older solar cell models.

Think Critically: During take-off, the wing tips become horizontal to increase the plane's lift.

CONCEPT DEVELOPMENT

▶ **What are two advantages of using solar energy?** *It is free, inexhaustible, and does not create any pollution.*

▶ Demonstrate how a radiometer or a solar cell works.

Cooperative Learning: Have Science Investigation groups use cardboard and aluminum foil to make solar ovens for cooking a hot dog or a marshmallow. After the ovens have been constructed, take students outside and conduct a test to see which oven cooks the fastest.

TECHNOLOGY

Solar-Powered Plane

Researchers for NASA have designed a solar plane that is able to stay aloft for an entire year. Although the plane will have a wingspan of 98 meters and a 12-meter propeller, it will be made of lightweight wood, and thus will have a low mass.

Energy from the sun will be collected by nearly 4000 square meters of solar cells that will cover the wing tips of the plane and vertical arrays on the wings. During the day, the wing tips will swing to 90-degree angles to receive maximum solar radiation. Excess electricity produced by the cells will be channeled to a fuel cell. The fuel cell will then be used to provide electricity.

Think Critically: Study the photograph. The wing tips are at 90 degrees. Do you think the wing tips stay in this position during take-off? Explain.

What are two advantages of solar energy?

Solar energy is energy from the sun. Enough energy from the sun reaches Earth in one hour to supply all the energy we need for a whole year! The problem is that we can't collect and store all this energy. We can collect part of it, though. One way of doing this is to use solar cells. A **solar cell** collects energy from the sun and transforms it into electricity. Solar energy is free and doesn't create
1 any pollution. Solar cells were invented to generate electricity on satellites, but now they're used to power calculators, TVs, streetlights, and experimental cars.

Solar energy also is used to heat and cool homes and buildings and to heat water. One way this is done is with thermal collectors. Solar energy heats air or water inside the collectors, and then the hot air or water is piped to where the heat is needed.

Solar energy does have some disadvantages. Solar energy can be received only when the sun is shining. That means solar cells work less well on cloudy days, and they don't work at all at night. When seasons cause days to be shorter, solar cells generate less electricity. The closer a

OPTIONS

INQUIRY QUESTIONS

▶ **Why will using the sun and wind as energy sources become more important in the future?** *Fossil fuels are nonrenewable resources and will eventually become exhausted. Resources now too costly will become more economically feasible.*

ENRICHMENT

▶ Have students make models that show how water can be used to produce energy.

▶ Have students research geothermal energy.

▶ Have two groups of students debate the social implications of using food for fuel in a world unable to feed its population.

Figure 18-8. Technology being developed and tested in this experimental solar car will be used to improve solar energy for common use.

solar cell is to the equator, the more direct solar radiation it receives. Solar cells closer to the North Pole or the South Pole receive less solar radiation. ❷

Where would solar energy work best, near the North Pole or near the equator?

Energy From Wind

Have you ever flown a kite on a windy day? Then you know how much energy wind can have. It lifts the kite high in the sky and whips it around.

People have long used the wind for power. As you learned in Chapter 9, one of its first uses was to power sailing ships. The Dutch have used windmills to grind corn and pump water. In the United States during the early 1900s, windmills pumped water on farms. Today, windmills again are capturing energy from wind.

Figure 18-9. Wind has been used as an energy source for many centuries.

CONCEPT DEVELOPMENT

▶ Have a contractor who installs solar energy systems speak to the class or provide additional information about the systems.

▶ Review the information about wind in Chapter 9 before beginning the section on wind as an energy source.

▶ Have students compare and contrast solar heating and wind energy. Students may need to review Section 9-3. Solar heating is not constant throughtout the world. Air that is warmed is pushed aloft by sinking cold air. This movement of air creates wind.

▶ In July 1980, the first solar-powered aircraft, the *Gossamer Penguin*, flew 3.2 kilometers at an altitude of 4.6 meters. This aircraft was powered by 2800 solar cells mounted on a wing span of 22 meters. The solar cells converted sunlight into electricity that powered a motor driving the propeller.

INQUIRY QUESTIONS

▶ **In the future, a large array of solar panels might be placed in space to collect solar energy. The energy would then be transmitted to Earth in the form of microwaves. Explain how this method of collecting solar energy will eliminate some of the problems we presently have in collecting solar energy from Earth's surface.** *Weather, seasons, and latitude will not affect the collection of the energy from space.*

PROGRAM RESOURCES

Use **Laboratory Manual** page 141, Solar Energy Collector; page 145, Solar Energy Storage; page 147, Solar Energy Application; page 151, Wind Power.

CONCEPT DEVELOPMENT

▶ Obtain and show the film *Gusts of Power* (DOE 535), produced by the United States Department of Energy.

▶ Stress that one of the major problems of using the wind to provide power is how to store the energy for use when the wind is not blowing. Interested students could report on storage batteries, the production of hydrogen gas or fuel, the use of a flywheel, or pumping water to a reservoir as potential means of storage.

TEACHER F.Y.I.

▶ At a wind farm at Altamont Pass, California, 7000 turbines produce enough electricity to power almost 1 million homes.

CROSS CURRICULUM

▶ **History:** Have students research the building of hydroelectric power plants by the Tennessee Valley Authority.

TEACHER F.Y.I.

▶ Hydroelectric power plants generate 22 percent of the world's electric power and about 15 percent of the electricity produced in the United States.

CONCEPT DEVELOPMENT

▶ Discuss whether synfuels and biomass fuels are feasible alternatives in your community.

How does a wind farm make electricity?

A **wind farm** is a location where a number of windmills are placed to gather wind and generate electricity. Wind farms usually are on ridges where the wind is strong and
3 steady. The energy from the spinning windmill turns a generator that makes electricity. If the wind changes direction, computers control motors that keep the blades facing into the wind.

Can you think of advantages and disadvantages of using wind energy? Wind is nonpolluting and free. It produces no waste and causes no environmental harm. But only a few regions have winds strong enough to generate elec-
4 tricity. The best locations in the United States are the Great Plains, mountainous areas, and some coastal regions. Also, the wind isn't steady, sometimes stopping and other times blowing too hard. Storing and transporting electricity generated by wind is very expensive.

Figure 18-10. The energy from all these windmills is combined to generate electricity.

Energy from Water

What is hydroelectric energy?

You learned in Chapter 11 how the energy of tides can be used to generate electricity. Obtaining energy from moving water is not new. Mills turned by tidal energy ground grain in England, France, and Spain a thousand years ago. Today, energy from running water is used to turn turbines to make electricity. The production of electricity by water power is called **hydroelectric energy.** We've built dams on many large rivers to generate hydroelectric power.

OPTIONS

INQUIRY QUESTIONS

▶ **What are some advantages of using wind energy?** *Wind is nonpolluting, free, produces no waste, and causes no environmental harm.*

▶ **How is water used to make electricity?** *Water stored in dams is used to generate electricity.*

Figure 18-11. Water flows through the base of this dam where it spins turbines and generators that make electricity.

Hydroelectric dams on rivers work much the same way as the tidal power dam described in Chapter 11. As seen in Figure 18-11, a large concrete dam holds water and forms a lake behind it. As water passes by turbines at the base of the dam, the turbines turn generators that make electricity.

The advantages of hydroelectric energy are that it doesn't make any pollution and the water used is free of cost. However, when dams are built, upstream lakes fill with sediment and downstream erosion increases. Land above the dam is flooded, and wildlife habitats are disturbed.

What are advantages of hydroelectric power?

Synfuel and Biomass Fuel

A **synfuel** is a human-made energy source. Most synfuel products are made by changing fossil fuels into a different form. Coal gasification makes natural gas from coal. This is done by mixing coal with steam and oxygen in a complex process. Some rocks called oil shales contain a waxy oil material. The oil can only be removed in a complex process of crushing and heating.

How can energy be obtained from shale?

If you have ever built a campfire with wood, you have used a biomass fuel. **Biomass fuel** is organic matter used as fuel. Some power plants burn wood to generate electricity. Other power plants add trash and garbage to coal to generate electricity.

Gasohol is a biomass fuel used in cars and trucks. It is 90 percent gasoline and 10 percent alcohol. The alcohol is made from corn or sugarcane.

CHECK FOR UNDERSTANDING

Use the Mini Quiz to check for understanding.

MINI QUIZ

Use the Mini Quiz to check students' recall of chapter content.

1. **Solar cells were invented to generate electricity on _____ .** *satellites*
2. **The _____ a solar cell is to the equator, the more direct solar radiation it receives.** *closer*
3. **The energy from a spinning windmill turns a(n) _____ that makes electricity.** *generator*
4. **The best locations for using energy from the wind are _____ .** *the Great Plains, mountainous regions, and some coastal regions*
5. **A(n) _____ is a human-made energy source.** *synfuel*

RETEACH

Have students make a table by listing Solar, Wind, and Water Power in one column, and listing advantages and disadvantages of each in succeeding columns.

EXTENSION

For students who have mastered this section, use the **Reinforcement** and **Enrichment** masters or other OPTIONS provided.

INQUIRY QUESTIONS

▶ **Classify steam, natural gas, coal, and oxygen as materials either used or produced during coal gasification.** *Coal, steam, and oxygen are used. Natural gas is produced.*

▶ **What do all biomass fuels have in common?** *They are all made of organic matter.*

▶ **Why are biomass fuels renewable energy sources?** *The rate at which they form is much greater than the rate at which they are used.*

3 CLOSE

► Ask questions 1-3 and the **Apply** Question in the Section Review.
► Have students do Activity 18-2.

FLEX Your Brain

Use the Flex Your Brain activity to have students explore BIOMASS FUELS.

SECTION REVIEW ANSWERS

1. Only a few regions have winds strong enough to generate electricity.
2. It is limited by weather, the time of day, season, and latitude. The greatest amount of solar energy is collected on sunny days, during seasons when days are long, and at low latitudes where the solar radiation is most direct.
3. The energy source is free and produces no pollution.
4. Apply: Wind is due to differential heating of air by the sun. Therefore, the source of energy for both is the sun.

Skill Builder

Noise pollution from the hundreds of wind mills on wind farms is one type of pollution associated with using the wind to produce electricity. Some people also view the numerous mills as being a form of visual pollution. Accept all answers that students are able to justify.

Figure 18-12. This trash-burning power plant generates electricity by burning trash and coal.

How have solar cells been improved?

Although these renewable energy sources are limited at the present time, they might become more effective in replacing fossil fuels in the future. Recent advances in solar cell technology have reduced the price of solar cells and increased their efficiency. Other advances in the development of electric cars will help us to be less dependent on oil for transportation. Further improvements in solar and wind technology may enable the sun and wind to be major energy sources in the future.

SECTION REVIEW

1. Why is wind energy limited to certain geographic regions?
2. What are the limitations of solar energy?
3. What are the advantages of hydroelectric power?
4. **Apply:** Why would it be accurate to say that solar energy and wind energy have the same source? What is that source?

Skill Builder — Hypothesizing

You have read that energy from the wind is essentially nonpolluting. Yet, some people claim that there *is* pollution from wind farms. Hypothesize how windmills can cause pollution. If you need help, refer to Hypothesizing in the **Skill Handbook** on page 686.

OPTIONS

PROGRAM RESOURCES

From the **Teacher Resource Package** use:

Activity Worksheets, page 5, Flex your Brain.

Cross-Curricular Connections, page 22, Energy Predictions.

Technology, pages 17-18, Technology on your Roof.

ACTIVITY 18-2
Solar Energy

Problem: *How does the color of a material affect its ability to absorb energy?*

Materials  

- dry black soil
- dry brown soil
- dry white sandy soil
- clear glass or plastic dishes (3)
- thermometers (3)
- 200-watt lamp with reflector and clamp
- watch or clock with second hand
- ring stand
- glass marker
- graph paper
- colored pencils (3)
- metric ruler

Procedure

1. Use the glass marker to label the dishes A, B, and C.
2. Arrange the dishes close together on your desk.
3. Fill dish A with dry black soil to a depth of 2.5 cm.
4. Fill dish B to the same depth with dry brown soil.
5. Fill dish C to the same depth with dry white sandy soil.
6. Place a thermometer in each dish. Be sure to cover the thermometer bulb in each dish completely with the material.
7. Record the temperature of each dish in a table similar to the one shown.
8. Clamp the lamp to the ring stand and position over all three dishes.
9. Turn on the lamp. Be sure the light shines equally on each dish.
10. Read the temperature of each material every 30 seconds for 20 minutes and record in your data table.
11. Use the data to construct a graph. Time should be plotted on the horizontal axis and temperature on the vertical axis. Use a different colored pencil to plot the data and draw the line for each material.

Data and Observations Sample Data

Time minutes	Temperature °C		
	Dish A	Dish B	Dish C
0	22	22	22
0.5	26	23	25

Analyze

1. Which material had the greatest temperature change?
2. Which material had the least change?

Conclude and Apply

3. Why do the curves on the graph flatten?
4. Why do you think flat-plate solar collectors have black plates behind the water pipes?
5. How does the color of a material affect its ability to absorb energy?

ANSWERS TO QUESTIONS

1. black soil
2. white sandy soil
3. The curves flattened out because at a certain point the soil and sand had absorbed the maximum amounts of energy that they were capable of absorbing.
4. The black plates absorb energy quickly and thus the water in the pipes heats more quickly and to a higher temperature than if light-colored plates were used.
5. the darker the color, the greater its ability to absorb energy

ACTIVITY 18-2
45-50 minutes

OBJECTIVE: **Identify** and **describe** at what rate materials absorb solar energy and how the color of a material affects its ability to absorb energy.

PROCESS SKILLS applied in this activity:
▶ **Separating and Controlling Variables** in Procedure Steps 1-11.
▶ **Experimenting** in Procedure Steps 1-11.
▶ **Inferring** in Conclude and Apply Question 4.
▶ **Communicating** in Procedure Steps 1-11.
▶ **Measuring** in Procedure Steps 3-5, 7, and 10.
▶ **Using Numbers** in Procedure Steps 10 and 11.
▶ **Interpreting Data** in Analyze Questions 1 and 2 and Conclude and Apply Questions 3 and 5.

COOPERATIVE LEARNING Have Science Investigation Teams with four students each do this activity.

TEACHING THE ACTIVITY

Troubleshooting: Calibrate all thermometers ahead of time. Be sure that the lamp shines on all three dishes evenly throughout the activity.

▶ Refer students to the concepts of heat and energy transfer discussed in Chapter 9. In this activity, they investigate the rates of solar energy absorption in similar materials of different colors. Have them predict what they think the outcome will be before beginning.

PROGRAM RESOURCES

From the **Teacher Resource Package** use:

Activity Worksheets, page162-163, Activity 18-2: Solar Energy.

SECTION 18-3

PREPARATION

SECTION BACKGROUND

▶ Nuclear reactors have several different systems that control the amount of heat produced by the reactors at any one time. One system consists of control rods made of materials that absorb neutrons. If the reactor gets too hot, the control rods are lowered between the fuel rods, stopping the fission reactions. A reactor's temperature also is controlled by a water cooling system.

▶ One type of fission reactor is a breeder reactor, which actually produces more fissionable fuel than it uses. There are no such reactors in the U.S.

▶ In the future, fusion reactors may be used to produce nuclear energy. Presently, fusion is not practical because temperatures in the millions of degrees Celsius are needed to get the hydrogen nuclei to fuse.

1 MOTIVATE

FLEX Your Brain

Use the Flex Your Brain activity to have students explore NUCLEAR ENERGY.

▶ Ask students to imagine a small room full of mousetraps that are each set to spring when hit. A Ping-Pong ball sits in each trap and will shoot through the air if the mousetrap snaps. Ask students to describe what would happen if a single Ping-Pong ball were thrown into the room. This discussion should be used to present how a chain reaction happens in a nuclear power plant.

PROGRAM RESOURCES

From the **Teacher Resource Package** use:

Activity Worksheets, page 5, Flex Your Brain.

Activity Worksheets, pages 167, Mini-Lab: Do you have a nuclear neighbor?

SCIENCE & SOCIETY 18-3 Nuclear Energy

New Science Words

nuclear energy
fission

Objectives

▶ Describe how nuclear energy is made.
▶ List the drawbacks and the advantages of nuclear energy.

Nuclear Energy

Does your electricity come from a nuclear power plant? It may, because about 20 percent of electricity in the United States comes from nuclear energy.

Nuclear energy is energy produced by fission. **Fission** is the splitting of nuclei of atoms in heavy elements such as uranium. The fuel used in fission power plants is a uranium isotope, uranium-235. You learned about radioactive elements in Chapter 16. Uranium-235 is a radioactive element. It occurs in ore in some sandstones in the Rocky Mountains. After the ore is mined, the uranium is concentrated and then placed in long metal pipes called fuel rods.

A nuclear power plant has a large chamber called a nuclear reactor. In it, the uranium fuel rods sit in a pool of cooling water. Neutrons are fired into the fuel. When the uranium-235 atoms are hit, they break apart, firing out neutrons that hit other atoms. This begins a chain reaction. As each atom fissions, it not only fires neutrons, but also releases heat. This heat is used to boil water to make steam. The steam drives a turbine, which turns a generator, producing electricity.

How is fission used to make electricity?

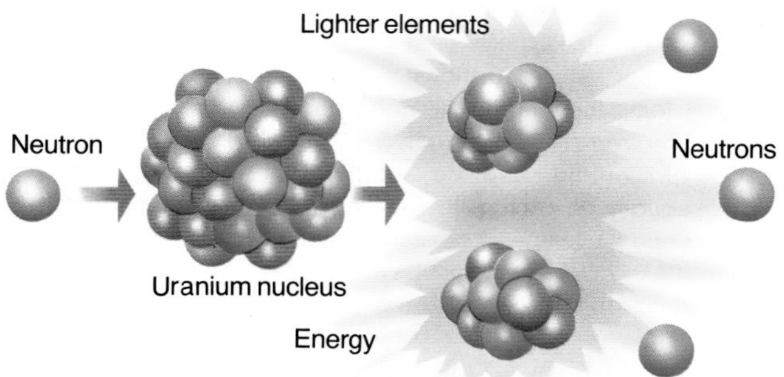

Figure 18-13. Fission occurs when a neutron hits the nucleus of a uranium atom, and the uranium atom splits and releases heat.

OPTIONS

Meeting Different Ability Levels

For Section 18-3, use the following **Teacher Resource Masters** depending upon individual students' needs.

◆ **Study Guide Master** for all students.

● **Reinforcement Master** for students of average and above average ability levels.

▲ **Enrichment Master** for above average students.

Additional Teacher Resource Package masters are listed in the OPTIONS box throughout the section. The additional masters are appropriate for all students.

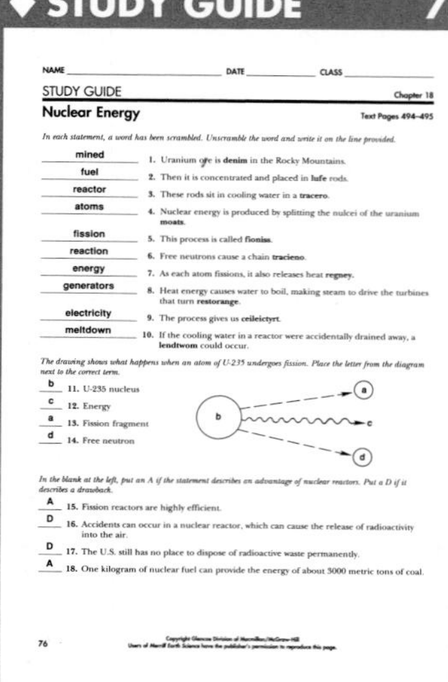

◆ STUDY GUIDE 76

NAME ____ DATE ____ CLASS ____

STUDY GUIDE — Chapter 18

Nuclear Energy — Text Pages 494–495

In each statement, a word has been scrambled. Unscramble the word and write it on the line provided.

mined 1. Uranium ore is **denim** in the Rocky Mountains.
fuel 2. Then it is concentrated and placed in **lufe** rods.
reactor 3. These rods sit in cooling water in a **tracero**.
atoms 4. Nuclear energy is produced by splitting the nulcei of the uranium **moats**.
fission 5. This process is called **fioniss**.
reaction 6. Free neutrons cause a chain **tracieno**.
energy 7. As each atom fissions, it also releases heat **regney**.
generators 8. Heat energy causes water to boil, making steam to drive the turbines that turn **restorange**.
electricity 9. The process gives us **ceileictyrt**.
meltdown 10. If the cooling water in a reactor were accidentally drained away, a **lendtwom** could occur.

The drawing shows what happens when an atom of U-235 undergoes fission. Place the letter from the diagram next to the correct term.

b 11. U-235 nucleus
c 12. Energy
a 13. Fission fragment
d 14. Free neutron

In the blank at the left, put an A if the statement describes an advantage of nuclear reactors. Put a D if it describes a drawback.

A 15. Fission reactors are highly efficient.
D 16. Accidents can occur in a nuclear reactor, which can cause the release of radioactivity into the air.
D 17. The U.S. still has no place to dispose of radioactive waste permanently.
A 18. One kilogram of nuclear fuel can provide the energy of about 3000 metric tons of coal.

76

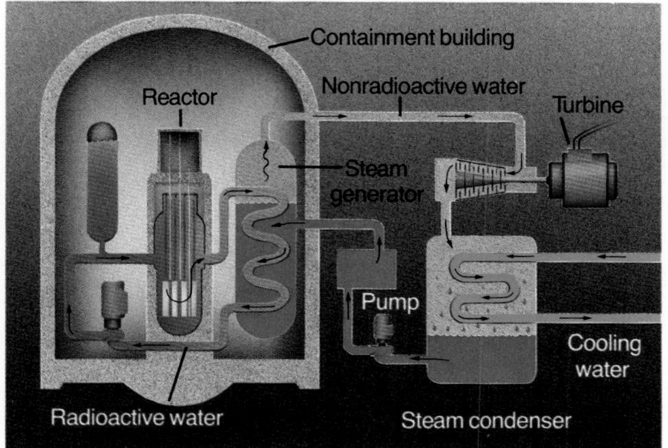

Figure 18-14. In a nuclear power plant, the boiling radioactive water from the reactor is piped into a steam generator. There, it changes nonradioactive water into steam. This steam spins a turbine before it is condensed back into water to repeat the cycle.

Do you know the advantages of fission energy? Fission reactors are very efficient. One kilogram of nuclear fuel can yield the energy of 3000 metric tons of coal! A fission reactor uses 100 tons of fuel each year, compared to millions of tons of fossil fuel needed to produce the same amount of electricity.

Nuclear Power Accidents

What do you think would happen if a nuclear chain reaction in a power plant got out of control? You know that it can't explode like a bomb because the fuel is too weak. But you also know that the used fuel is dangerously radioactive.

We learned what could happen in 1979, when something went wrong in a reactor at Three Mile Island near Harrisburg, Pennsylvania. Part of the uranium-235 fuel melted when most of its cooling water was drained away. The accident was caused by operator confusion and equipment failure. Fortunately, the reactor's walls held all the radioactive materials inside. Only a little radioactive gas was released. Nobody was injured, but thousands of people were very frightened.

A much more serious accident happened at the Chernobyl reactor in the Ukraine in 1986. Operators at the plant ignored warnings that temperatures inside the fuel were getting too high. Steam pressure built up in the pipes and exploded, sending pieces of fuel rods through the roof.

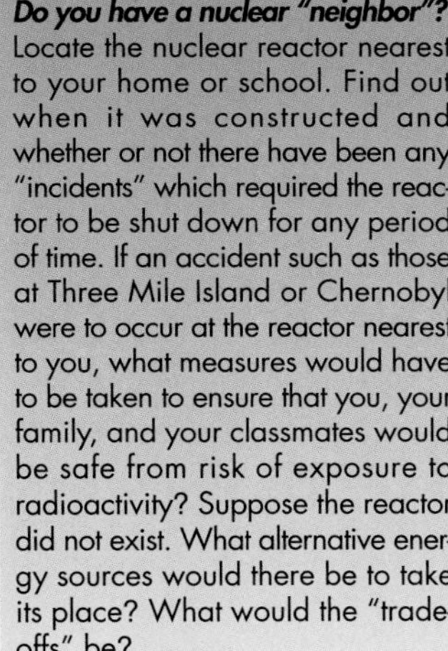

MINI-Lab

Do you have a nuclear "neighbor"?

Locate the nuclear reactor nearest to your home or school. Find out when it was constructed and whether or not there have been any "incidents" which required the reactor to be shut down for any period of time. If an accident such as those at Three Mile Island or Chernobyl were to occur at the reactor nearest to you, what measures would have to be taken to ensure that you, your family, and your classmates would be safe from risk of exposure to radioactivity? Suppose the reactor did not exist. What alternative energy sources would there be to take its place? What would the "trade-offs" be?

● REINFORCEMENT 76

NAME ______ DATE ______ CLASS ______

REINFORCEMENT — Chapter 18

Nuclear Energy — Text Pages 494–495

Answer the following questions on the lines provided.

1. What is the percent of electricity generated by nuclear power plants in the United States? **20%**
2. What isotope is used in fission power plants? **uranium-235**
3. How does a chain reaction occur? **Neutrons are fired into fuel rods of uranium-235. When the uranium-235 atoms are hit, they break apart, firing out neutrons that hit other atoms.**
4. What kind of energy is released by an atom that breaks apart? **heat**
5. A fission reactor uses about 100 tonnes of fuel each year. Would more or less than 100 tonnes of coal be needed to generate the same amount of electricity? Explain. **More, since 3300 tons of coal would produce the same amount of energy as a kilogram of nuclear fuel.**
6. Why do some people want to close all nuclear power plants? **there may be accidents and the problem of nuclear waste disposal**
7. Even if there were never again an accident at a nuclear power plant, what problem still remains? Explain. **The problem of radioactive waste still remains. The waste stays radioactive for thousands of years, and at the present time, there is no permanent way to dispose of it.**
8. Why do some people argue that we should build more nuclear power plants? **America's energy demands are rising. Fossil fuels are running out. Uranium is plentiful.**

The following are steps in producing energy from nuclear power. Number the steps so that they are in the correct order.

2 10. Heat is used to boil water.
4 11. Steam drives a turbine.
6 12. Generator produces electricity.
1 13. Atom splits, releasing neutrons and heat.
5 14. Turbine drives a generator.
3 15. Water turns to steam.

76

▲ ENRICHMENT 76

NAME ______ DATE ______ CLASS ______

ENRICHMENT — Chapter 18

Nuclear Energy — Text Pages 494–495

RECYCLING FUEL

One of the problems with nuclear reactors is how to dispose of the used fuel. Some people believe that the used fuel should be recycled. The reactor uses up only about two-thirds of the uranium in the fuel rods. This means that the used fuel contains the remaining U-235. The used fuel also contains plutonium, strontium, and cesium. These are all radioactive elements that are produced when the U-235 atom splits. Plutonium can undergo fission, just like uranium, and can also be used in fuel rods. Plutonium is also used in making atomic bombs. Both U-235 and plutonium can be recovered from the used fuel, and, in fact, they have been. The U.S. government has used the recovered plutonium to build nuclear weapons.

Used fuel is taken for reprocessing → Recovered uranium and plutonium are reprocessed into fuel → Reactor uses fuel to split atoms → (back to Used fuel is taken for reprocessing)

1. Why is it a good idea to reprocess the reactor fuel? **to recover valuable materials that would otherwise be wasted**
2. Will reprocessing the fuel take care of the problem of disposing of the used fuel? Explain. **It will reduce the problem since some of the material will be recycled. But some material will still have to be disposed of.**
3. Some people see a potential danger in the recycling process and strongly oppose recovering any of the fuel. Why do you think they feel that way? **They are afraid that some group or country will steal the plutonium to make a bomb.**
4. Suppose the following step were added to the flowchart at the top of the page: "The remaining used fuel is buried as waste." Would the flowchart still be a cycle flowchart? Why or why not? **No, because this last step is not part of the direct cycle of going from fuel to used fuel to fuel again.**

76

TYING TO PREVIOUS KNOWLEDGE: Have students recall from Chapter 2 that neutrons are located inside the nuclei of atoms. When neutrons are fired at uranium-235 atoms, the U-235 nuclei split and release more neutrons and energy.

OBJECTIVES AND SCIENCE WORDS: Have students review the objectives and science words to become familiar with this section.

2 TEACH

Key Concepts are highlighted.

CONCEPT DEVELOPMENT

► **Compare the seriousness of the accident at Three Mile Island with that at the Chernobyl plant.** *At Three Mile Island, only a little radioactive gas was released, and there were no injuries. At the Chernobyl plant, wind carried radioactive debris many kilometers, 200 people suffered severe radiation injury, and at least 30 people died.*

REVEALING MISCONCEPTIONS

► Many people believe only nuclear power plants have cooling towers. Coal plants also use these towers.

MINI-Lab

Teaching Tips

►A nuclear power station will provide brochures that will answer some of the questions asked in this activity.

►**Answers:** Factors to be considered are the locations of population centers, available transportation routes away from the reactor area, and the prevailing winds of the area. Generally, if a nearby nuclear reactor doesn't exist, any alternative sources are those utilized before the construction of the facility.

CHECK FOR UNDERSTANDING

Discuss why many people wouldn't choose to live next to a nuclear power plant or a nuclear waste dump.

RETEACH

Have students debate the safety record of nuclear power plants.

EXTENSION

For students who have mastered this section, use the **Reinforcement** and **Enrichment** masters or other OPTIONS provided.

3 CLOSE

FLEX Your Brain

Use the Flex Your Brain activity to have students explore NUCLEAR WASTE STORAGE.

▶ Invite a member of the Environmental Protection Agency or the Nuclear Regulatory Commission to speak about nuclear power safety regulations.

▶ Ask questions 1-3 in the Section Review.

SECTION REVIEW ANSWERS

1. Neutrons are fired into fuel rods that contain uranium-235. When hit, these atoms split, releasing neutrons that hit other atoms. As the atoms split, they release energy.

2. It's efficient—a small amount of fuel can produce a lot of energy.

3. Accidents have leaked radioactive materials into the environment. There is also the problem of radioactive waste storage.

YOU DECIDE!

Some students will say that safety records of nuclear power plants are good, and since the plants are efficient producers of electricity, we should develop and build more of them. Others will say that the problems involved with leaks and waste storage are serious, and that we should emphasize improving and developing other renewable energy sources.

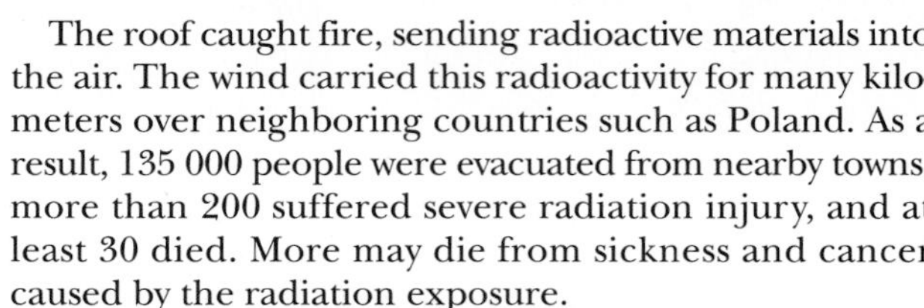

Figure 18-15. Many people fear nuclear energy because of accidents that have released radiation in the past. This photo shows the Chernobyl reactor after it exploded.

The roof caught fire, sending radioactive materials into the air. The wind carried this radioactivity for many kilometers over neighboring countries such as Poland. As a result, 135 000 people were evacuated from nearby towns, more than 200 suffered severe radiation injury, and at least 30 died. More may die from sickness and cancer caused by the radiation exposure.

EcoTip

Save energy! Most ovens today don't have to be preheated, especially when cooking dishes that take a long time, such as casseroles.

Another hazard is the waste products from reactors. The United States has operated nuclear power plants since 1957. Many metric tons of used fuel have piled up. It will remain intensely radioactive for thousands of years before it decays into harmless isotopes. Yet even now, our country still does not have a permanent disposal place ready for this waste.

SECTION REVIEW

1. Describe how nuclear energy is produced.
2. What are the advantages of nuclear energy?
3. What are the drawbacks of nuclear energy?

You Decide!

America's energy demands are rising five percent each year, and we're running out of fossil fuels. Nuclear power may be the only alternative energy source that can produce the large amounts of energy we need very soon. The uranium needed for fuel is plentiful. However, nuclear power plants have the potential for accidents. The problem of disposing of radioactive fuel rods has not been solved. Should we continue to develop and build more nuclear power plants? Or should we place our emphasis on improving renewable energy sources and developing new energy sources?

OPTIONS

ENRICHMENT

▶ Have students research what would happen during a meltdown.

▶ Have students find out how breeder reactors work.

▶ Have students research the claim of room-temperature fusion as a way of producing nuclear energy and discuss its scientific validity.

PROGRAM RESOURCES

From the **Teacher Resource Package** use:

Activity Worksheets, page 5, Flex Your Brain.

Concept Mapping, pages 41-42.

Science and Society, page 22, Low-level Waste.

CHAPTER
REVIEW

SUMMARY

18-1: Nonrenewable Energy Sources

1. Coal forms as plants become buried and decay over millions of years. Oil and natural gas form when marine plants and animals die and accumulate on the ocean floor. Over millions of years, pressure from overlying sediments changes these remains into oil and natural gas.
2. Fossil fuels are nonrenewable energy sources because they take millions of years to form.
3. Turning off lights, radios, and TVs in unoccupied rooms; insulating homes; limiting the use of an air conditioner; recycling; using public transportation; and car pooling are only a few ways to conserve fossil fuels.

18-2: Renewable Energy Sources and Others

1. Solar, wind, and hydroelectric energy are free and don't create the direct pollution that fossil fuels emit.
2. Solar cells are expensive and don't work when the sky is cloudy or dark. Wind energy can be used only where there is constant wind. Hydroelectric dams change the environment.

18-3: Science and Society: Nuclear Energy

1. Nuclear energy is produced by fission, which is the splitting of uranium atoms. Fission produces heat which is used to make steam that drives a turbine, which turns a generator, producing electricity.
2. Releasing radioactive materials into the air, releasing and disposing of wastes, and meltdowns are potential dangers of nuclear energy.

KEY SCIENCE WORDS

a. **anthracite**
b. **biomass fuel**
c. **bituminous coal**
d. **energy**
e. **fission**
f. **fossil fuels**
g. **hydroelectric energy**
h. **lignite**
i. **nonrenewable energy sources**
j. **nuclear energy**
k. **peat**
l. **renewable energy sources**
m. **solar cell**
n. **solar energy**
o. **synfuel**
p. **wind farm**

UNDERSTANDING VOCABULARY

Match each phrase with the correct term from the list of Key Science Words.

1. the ability to do work
2. first stage in coal formation
3. sources of energy that are being used quicker than it takes to replace them
4. collects solar energy and converts it into electricity
5. area with many windmills used to generate electricity
6. energy derived from running water
7. process of splitting of uranium-235 atoms
8. energy sources that won't run out in the near future
9. soft brown coal
10. the cleanest burning coal

OPTIONS

ASSESSMENT

To assess student understanding of material in this chapter, use the resources listed.

COOPERATIVE LEARNING

Consider using cooperative learning in the THINK AND WRITE CRITICALLY, APPLY, and MORE SKILL BUILDERS sections of the Chapter Review.

PROGRAM RESOURCES

From the **Teacher Resource Package** use:
Chapter Review, pages 39-40.
Chapter and Unit Tests, pages 125-128, Chapter Test.

CHAPTER
REVIEW

SUMMARY

Have students read the summary statements to review the major concepts of the chapter.

UNDERSTANDING VOCABULARY

1. d	**6.** g
2. k	**7.** e
3. i	**8.** l
4. m	**9.** h
5. p	**10.** a

CHAPTER
REVIEW

CHECKING CONCEPTS

1. d	**6.** c
2. c	**7.** b
3. d	**8.** d
4. d	**9.** d
5. b	**10.** b

UNDERSTANDING CONCEPTS

11. fossil fuels
12. Lignite
13. Hydroelectric power
14. coal gasification
15. Solar cells

THINK AND WRITE CRITICALLY

16. Both are stages in coal formation. Peat is mostly decaying twigs, leaves, and branches and is 75-90 percent water. Peat is a very poor fuel. Lignite, which is about 30 percent carbon, forms from peat. Lignite is a better fuel than peat.

17. These three fossil fuels occur as different states of matter. Also, oil and gas form from marine organisms, whereas coal forms from swamp plants.

18. Plants use energy from the sun to photosynthesize. Some of the solar energy is stored. If the plants die and become fossil fuels, some of the stored energy is released as heat when the fuel is burned.

19. The possibility of uncontrolled reactions is one problem. Thermal pollution from improperly cooled water can cause damage to nearby bodies of water. Storage and disposal of radioactive wastes are probably the biggest concerns with nuclear energy.

20. Cooling systems help to prevent the reactor from becoming too hot. Concrete walls protect the leakage of radioactive wastes. Trained operators and well maintained equipment are also essential to safe operation of a nuclear power plant.

CHAPTER
REVIEW

CHECKING CONCEPTS

Choose the word or phrase that completes the sentence.

1. ______ is a fossil fuel.
   a. Natural gas **c.** Coal
   b. Oil **d.** All of these
2. Coal forms when ______ die, decay, and become buried for millions of years.
   a. swamp animals **c.** swamp plants
   b. marine plants **d.** marine animals
3. ______ contains the most carbon.
   a. Peat **c.** Bituminous coal
   b. Lignite **d.** Anthracite
4. Oil is used to make ______.
   a. coal **c.** solar energy
   b. nuclear energy **d.** none of these
5. A ______ uses moving water to generate electricity.
   a. wind farm **c.** nuclear reactor
   b. hydroelectric plant **d.** solar cell
6. The most used coal is ______.
   a. peat **c.** bituminous
   b. lignite **d.** anthracite
7. Abundant sunshine is needed for ______.
   a. wind power **c.** hydroelectric power
   b. solar power **d.** all of these
8. The Three Mile Island accident was caused by ______.
   a. too little water
   b. equipment failure
   c. operator confusion
   d. all of these
9. The ability to do work is ______.
   a. solar cell **c.** peat
   b. fission **d.** energy
10. Gas is found in deposits under ______ rock.
    a. permeable **c.** porous
    b. impermeable **d.** unconsolidated

UNDERSTANDING CONCEPTS

Complete each sentence.

11. Today, ______ are burned to provide most of the energy in the United States.
12. ______ is the second stage in coal formation.
13. ______ causes flooding and erosion of nearby land areas.
14. Coal is converted to natural gas in a process called ______.
15. ______ are used to power some satellites, calculators, and street lights.

THINK AND WRITE CRITICALLY

16. Compare and contrast peat and lignite.
17. Describe two ways in which oil and natural gas differ from coal.
18. Explain how energy from the sun becomes trapped in plants and is later released when fossil fuels are burned.
19. Discuss the problems associated with obtaining energy from nuclear fission.
20. What precautions are used in nuclear power plants to prevent accidents?

APPLY

21. Mary found what she thought was a small piece of coral in a chunk of coal. Benjamin thought the fossil was a twig. Who was right? Explain.
22. Why is anthracite a better fuel than bituminous coal?
23. Describe how the windows of a building that uses solar energy should be designed so that the building is most efficient.

24. Which city would be bettter suited for the development of solar energy: a city that has cloud cover 55 percent of the time or a city that has cloud cover 45 percent of the time? Explain.

25. Why are most radioactive wastes so dangerous?

MORE SKILL BUILDERS

If you need help, refer to the Skill Handbook.

1. **Sequencing:** If a well were drilled into a rock containing oil and natural gas, which substance would be encountered first? Explain.
2. **Comparing and Contrasting:** Compare and contrast solar energy with power from the wind.
3. **Interpreting Scientific Illustrations:** Refer to Figure 18-5 on page 483. What lies above gas and oil in this diagram? Why does the gas seem to be trapped directly below this layer?
4. **Making and Using Tables:** Make a table showing the advantages and disadvantages of each energy source discussed in the chapter.
5. **Concept Mapping:** Make a network tree concept map that compares and contrasts the stages of coal formation.

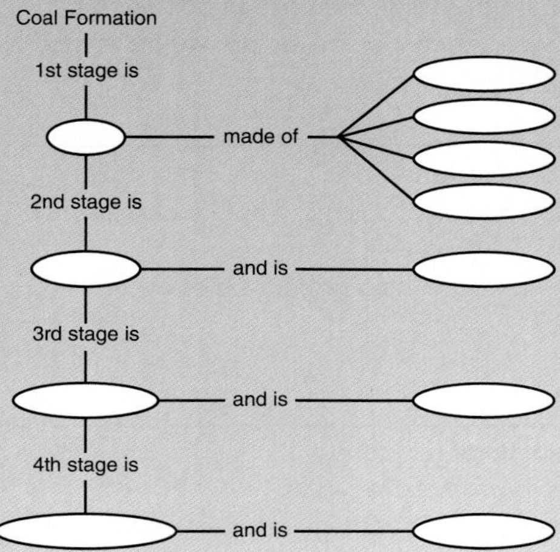

PROJECTS

1. Go to the library to find out about energy-efficient buildings that currently exist in the United States. Then, design and make a three-dimensional model of a futuristic building that is energy efficient.
2. Design and conduct an experiment using a silicon solar cell and a milliammeter to measure the available solar energy.

APPLY

21. Benjamin was correct because coal is made of plants that decay in swamps. Coral is a marine animal.

22. Anthracite is the final stage in coal formation. Most of the impurities have been destroyed by the intense heat and pressure. Thus, anthracite contains about 90 percent carbon and is the cleanest burning coal.

23. Passive solar buildings are designed with vertical windows that face the sun and absorb solar energy, which is converted to heat.

24. The city with cloud cover 45% of the time gets more solar energy and is thus better suited for the development of solar energy plants.

25. The wastes give off radiation, which can be harmful to living organisms. Also, many wastes have long half-lives. Thus, thousands of years must pass before these elements have decayed into stable products.

MORE SKILL BUILDERS

1. Sequencing: Gas, which is less dense than the oil, would be encountered first.

2. Comparing and Contrasting: Both are "free," nonpolluting alternative energy sources to fossil fuels. Although they are "ideal" sources of energy, both are limited by weather and geographic location. Solar energy is also limited by the time of day.

3. Interpreting Scientific Illustrations: Shale overlies the oil and gas. Shale is impermeable and traps the gas below.

4. Making and Using Tables: Tables will vary. Encourage students to paraphrase, rather than copy, the reasons listed in each column.

5. Concept Mapping:

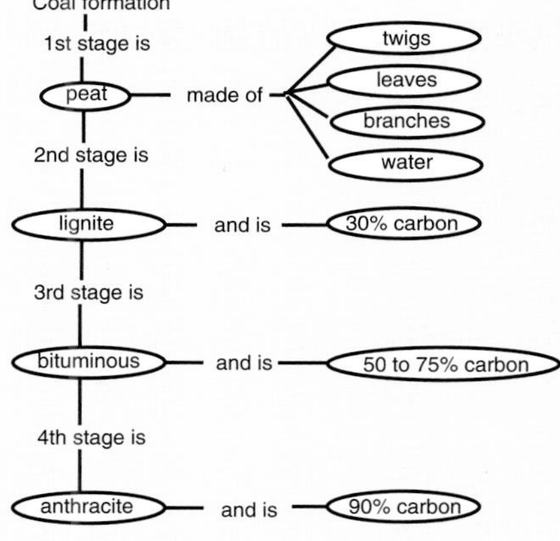

CHAPTER

19 You and the Environment

CHAPTER SECTION	OBJECTIVES	ACTIVITIES
19-1 Population Impact on the Environment (2 days)	1. **Interpret** data from a graph that shows human population growth. 2. **List** reasons for Earth's rapid increase in population. 3. **List** several ways each person in an industrialized nation affects the environment.	**Activity 19-1:** *Human Population Growth Rate,* p. 506
19-2 Using the Land (1 day)	1. **List** ways that we use land. 2. **Discuss** environmental problems created because of land use. 3. **List** things you can do to help protect the environment.	**MINI-Lab:** *Would you use toxic substances to have a weed-free lawn?* p. 510 **MINI-Lab:** *Can one person make a difference?* p. 514 **Activity 19-2:** *A Model Landfill,* p. 515
19-3 Recycling Science & Society (1 day)	1. **List** the advantages of recycling. 2. **Describe** ways to promote recycling. 3. **Express** your feelings about government control of recycling.	
Chapter Review		

ACTIVITY MATERIALS

FIND OUT	ACTIVITIES		MINI-LABS	
Page 501 metric ruler	**19-1 Human Population Growth Rate, p. 506** beaker (250- or 400-mL) paper cups or 50-mL beakers (11) small objects of uniform shape (dried beans, corn kernels, etc.)	**19-2 A Model Landfill, p. 515** 2-liter bottle soil thermometer plastic wrap rubber band graph paper garbage	**Would you use toxic substances to have a weed-free lawn? p. 510** none	**Can one person make a difference? p. 514** will vary according to student choice

CHAPTER FEATURES	TEACHER RESOURCE PACKAGE	OTHER RESOURCES
Skill Builder: *Making and Using Graphs,* p. 505	**Ability Level Worksheets** ◆ ***Study Guide,*** p. 77 ● ***Reinforcement,*** p. 77 ▲ ***Enrichment,*** p. 77 **Activity Worksheet,** pp. 169-170 **Cross-Curricular Connections,** p. 23 **Transparency Masters,** pp. 79-80	**Color Transparency 40,** The Population Explosion **Lab Manual:** *Human Impact on the Environment,* pp. 155-158
Problem Solving: *Will the Landfill Be in Your Back-yard?* p. 511 **Technology:** *Recycling Paper,* p. 513 **Skill Builder:** *Outlining,* p. 514	**Ability Level Worksheets** ◆ ***Study Guide,*** p. 78 ● ***Reinforcement,*** p. 78 ▲ ***Enrichment,*** p. 78 **MINI-Lab Worksheet,** pp. 175-176 **Activity Worksheet,** pp. 171-172 **Critical Thinking/Problem Solving,** p. 25 **Concept Mapping,** pp. 43-44	**Lab Manual:** *Reclamation of Mine Wastes,* pp. 159-160
You Decide! p. 518	**Ability Level Worksheets** ◆ ***Study Guide,*** p. 79 ● ***Reinforcement,*** p. 79 ▲ ***Enrichment,*** p. 79 **Science and Society,** p. 23	**Lab Manual:** *Conservation—Recycling,* pp. 161-162
Summary Key Science Words Understanding Vocabulary Checking Concepts Understanding Concepts Think & Write Critically Apply More Skill Builders Projects	**Chapter Review,** pp. 41-42 **Chapter Test,** pp. 129-132	**Chapter Review Software** **Test Bank**

◆ **Basic** ● **Average** ▲ **Advanced**

ADDITIONAL MATERIALS

SOFTWARE	AUDIOVISUAL	BOOKS/MAGAZINES
Population Control, Focus.	*Understanding the Earth,* film, Coronet/MTI. *The Killing Ground,* video, Coronet/MTI. *The End of One,* video, LCA. *Land Use and Misuse,* video, LCA. *Noise Pollution,* video, LCA. *What'll We Do With the Waste When We're Through?* video, Focus. *The Rock That Glowed: The Importance of Recycling,* video, Focus.	Borrie, W.D. Population, *Environment, and Society.* NY: Oxford University Press, Inc., 1974. Crosson, Pierre R. and Sterling Brubaker. *Resource and Environmental Effects of U.S. Agriculture.* Washington, DC: Resources for the Future Inc., 1982. Hinckley, A.D. *Renewable Resources in Our Future.* Elsmford, NY: Pergamon Press, Inc., 1980.

CHAPTER

19

YOU AND THE ENVIRONMENT

THEME DEVELOPMENT: The theme systems and interactions is focused upon in Sections 19-1 and 19-2 through discussions of how human activities affect the environment. Another theme in this chapter is cycles. In Section 19-3, this theme is emphasized by a presentation on recycling.

CHAPTER OVERVIEW

- **Section 19-1:** This section begins by describing the human population explosion. Then it introduces ways people affect the environment.
- **Section 19-2:** Concepts presented in this section include how people use land, the environmental problems that result from these activities, and ways people can help protect the environment.
- **Section 19-3: Science and Society:** The advantages of recycling are introduced. The You Decide feature asks students to express their opinions concerning whether the government should pass laws requiring people to recycle materials.

CHAPTER VOCABULARY

population
population explosion
landfill
sanitary landfill
hazardous wastes
conservation
composting
recyclable
market
container law

CHAPTER

19 You and the Environment

500

OPTIONS

For Your Gifted Students

Have students call a recycling center in the area and discuss how to begin recycling paper at the school. Survey how much paper is used. Provide boxes in each room for the different kinds of paper (colored, white ledger, computer, etc.) Collect and store the paper for delivery to the recycling center.

The landfill shown is one of many that holds the garbage produced by people. We're running out of space to build new landfills. At the same time, the human population is increasing. Is there enough land and resources to support more people?

FIND OUT!

Do this simple activity to illustrate human population growth.

Draw a square that's 10 cm on each side. This represents one square kilometer of Earth's land surface. In 1977, the average number of people for every square kilometer of land was 28. Draw 28 small circles inside your square to represent this. In 1990, the average rose to 35. Add seven circles to illustrate this increase. It's predicted that in 2075, there will be 98 people per square kilometer. Add circles to represent an average square kilometer of land in 2075. Why is the human population increasing so rapidly? How does the increased population growth affect the environment?

Gearing Up

Previewing the Chapter

Use this outline to help you focus on important ideas in this chapter.

Previewing Science Skills

- ▶ In the **Skill Builders,** you will use a table and outline.
- ▶ In the **MINI-Labs,** you will collect data, apply previous knowledge, and make inferences.
- ▶ In the **Activities,** you will experiment, analyze data, make and use tables and graphs, and draw conclusions.

What's next?

You've seen that the population is rapidly increasing and that land is becoming more and more valuable as a limited resource. In this chapter, you'll discover how the increasing population threatens the environment all over Earth. Most importantly, you'll learn about things you can do to protect the environment.

INTRODUCING THE CHAPTER

Use the Find Out activity to introduce students to human population growth. Inform students that as they read the chapter they will be learning more about human population growth and the effects of human activities on the environment.

FIND OUT!

Preparation: You may want to review the term *map scale* from Chapter 8 before having students perform this activity. The scale of their drawing in this activity is 1:10 000.

Materials: one metric ruler for each student

Teaching Tips

▶ Students should be reminded that the information they are using is the world average. The population density around the world has and will continue to vary a great deal from region to region.

▶ **Answers:** Students may conclude that the population is increasing because the birth rate is increasing and the death rate is decreasing. Students may infer that the environment will be damaged as more and more demands are placed upon it.

Gearing Up

Have students study the Gearing Up feature to familiarize themselves with the chapter. Discuss the relationships of the topics in the outline.

What's Next?

Before beginning the first section, make sure students understand the connection between the Find Out activity and the topics to follow.

For Your Mainstreamed Students

Organize a field trip to a local recycling plant. Have students bring a camera along to take pictures of the process. Have the film developed and make the pictures into a poster showing the process. Have students write under each picture what is taking place in the photo.

SECTION 19-1

PREPARATION

SECTION BACKGROUND

▶ Ninety percent of the world's population increase is expected in developing countries. In western industrial nations, the birthrate is relatively constant, but better diet and disease control extend the life span.

▶ Each year due to population growth, the world's farmers have to feed 93 million more people with 10 886 trillion fewer kilograms of topsoil. There is less topsoil because the land is severely eroded by home construction, road construction, farming practices, etc.

▶ Worldwide, perhaps 450 million people go to bed hungry every night. Millions of people starve every year, and millions more die of diseases brought on by hunger.

PREPLANNING

▶ To prepare for Activity 19-1, obtain the following materials for each Science Investigation group: one beaker (250 or 400 mL), eleven paper cups or beakers (50 mL), and 4096 small objects of uniform shape and size.

1 MOTIVATE

▶ Have students discuss the questions: "How does my being on Earth change Earth? What can I do to make a more positive balance between people and the environment?" These questions will motivate students to learn more about human interactions with the environment.

FLEX Your Brain

Use the Flex Your Brain activity to have students explore HUMAN POPULATION GROWTH.

PROGRAM RESOURCES

From the **Teacher Resource Package** use:

Activity Worksheets, page 5, Flex Your Brain.

19-1 Population Impact on the Environment

New Science Words

population
population explosion

Objectives

- ▶ **Interpret data from a graph that shows human population growth.**
- ▶ **List reasons for Earth's rapid increase in population.**
- ▶ **List several ways each person in an industrialized nation affects the environment.**

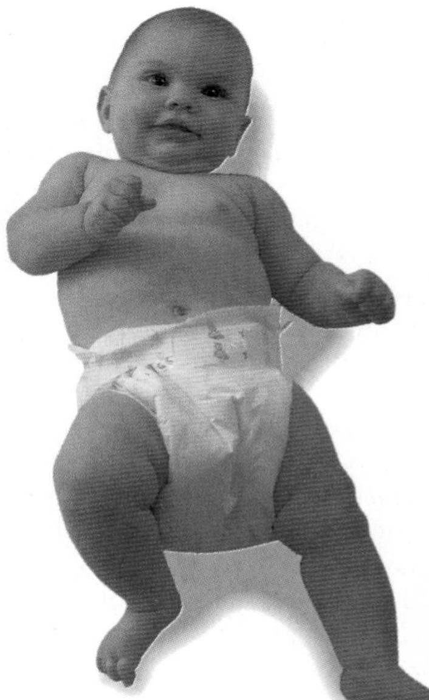

Figure 19-1. The human population is growing at an alarming rate. Will we be able to manage Earth's resources so our species, as well as others, can survive?

The Human Population Explosion

At one time, people thought of Earth as a world with unlimited resources. They thought Earth could provide them with whatever materials they needed. It seemed they would always have enough space to live and to grow food. Earth had an endless supply of metals, fossil fuels, clean water and air, and rich soils. Today, we know this isn't true. Earth's resources are limited. Unless we treat those resources with care, they will disappear. Why have attitudes toward Earth's resources changed? Why have we only recently realized that we need to conserve resources and care for the environment?

When there were fewer people on Earth, it seemed that only a few hundred million people could never use up all of the resources. And, at that time, each individual used fewer resources and produced less waste than people do today. Since that time, the number of people on Earth has increased at an alarming rate. The increase in the world population has changed the way we must view our world and how we care for it.

A **population** is the total number of individuals of a 1
particular species in a particular area. The area can be small or large. For example, we can talk about the human population of one particular community, such as Los Angeles, or about the human population of the entire Earth.

OPTIONS

Meeting Different Ability Levels

For Section 19-1, use the following **Teacher Resource Masters** depending upon individual students' needs.

◆ **Study Guide Master** for all students.

● **Reinforcement Master** for students of average and above average ability levels.

▲ **Enrichment Master** for above average students.

Additional Teacher Resource Package masters are listed in the OPTIONS box throughout the section. The additional masters are appropriate for all students.

◆ STUDY GUIDE 77

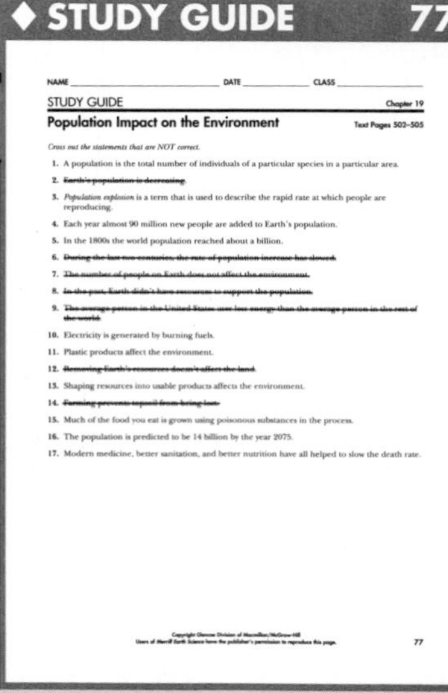

NAME ________ DATE ________ CLASS ________

STUDY GUIDE — Chapter 19

Population Impact on the Environment — Text Pages 502–505

Cross out the statements that are NOT correct.

1. A population is the total number of individuals of a particular species in a particular area.
2. ~~Earth's population is decreasing.~~
3. *Population explosion* is a term that is used to describe the rapid rate at which people are reproducing.
4. Each year almost 90 million new people are added to Earth's population.
5. In the 1800s the world population reached about a billion.
6. ~~During the last two centuries, the rate of population increase has slowed.~~
7. ~~The number of people on Earth does not affect the environment.~~
8. ~~In the past, Earth didn't have resources to support the population.~~
9. ~~The average person in the United States uses less energy than the average person in the rest of the world.~~
10. Electricity is generated by burning fuels.
11. Plastic products affect the environment.
12. ~~Removing Earth's resources doesn't affect the land.~~
13. Shaping resources into usable products affects the environment.
14. ~~Farming prevents topsoil from being lost.~~
15. Much of the food you eat is grown using poisonous substances in the process.
16. The population is predicted to be 14 billion by the year 2075.
17. Modern medicine, better sanitation, and better nutrition have all helped to slow the death rate.

 77

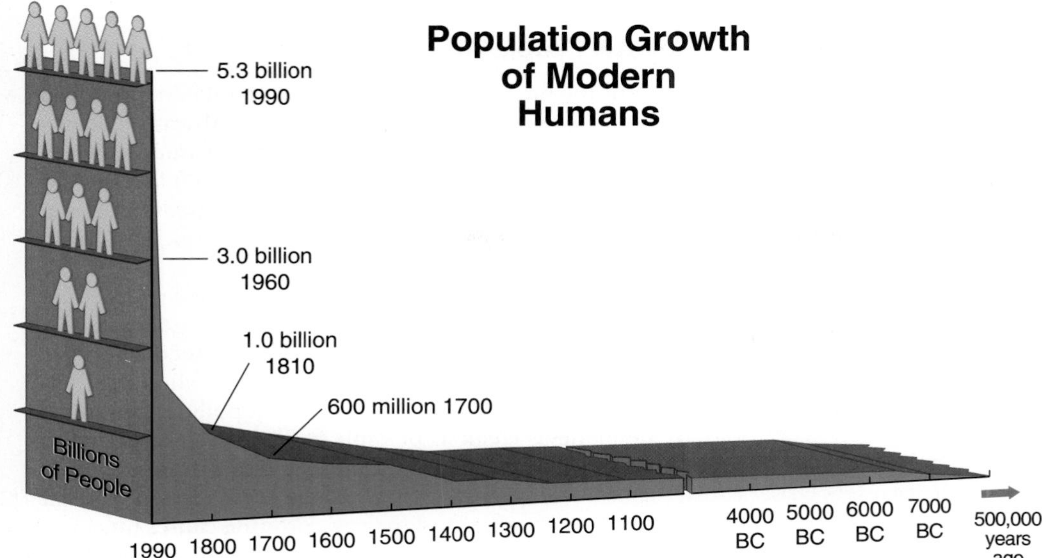

Figure 19-2. The human species, *Homo sapiens,* may have appeared about 500 000 years ago. Our population numbers remained relatively steady until about 200 years ago. Since that time, we have experienced a sharp increase in growth rate.

Have you ever wondered how many people live on Earth? The global population in 1990 was 5.3 billion. Each year, almost 90 million new people are added. Earth is experiencing a **population explosion.** The word *explosion* is used because the rate at which people are ❷
reproducing has rapidly increased in recent history.

Look at Figure 19-2. You can see that it took hundreds of thousands of years for Earth's population to reach 1 billion people. After that, the population increased much faster. Why do you think the population has increased so rapidly in recent years?

What factors have led to an increase in population?

The death rate has been slowed by modern medicines, better sanitation, and better nutrition. This means that more people are living longer and remaining in the population. Also, births have increased because more people are at the age where they can have children. The result is that Earth's population is increasing fast.

Earth's increasing population has seriously changed the environment. Scientists predict even greater changes as more people use Earth's limited resources. By the year 2075, the population is predicted to be 14 billion, nearly three times what it is now. Are there enough natural ❸
resources to support such a large population? How will such a large human population affect our environment?

● REINFORCEMENT 77

NAME ____________ DATE ________ CLASS ________

REINFORCEMENT — Chapter 19

Population Impact on the Environment — Text Pages 502–505

Answer the following questions on the lines provided.

1. What did people long ago think about Earth's resources? Why is that earlier idea incorrect? **People thought Earth had unlimited resources. Today we know that unless we treat resources with care, they will be used up.**
2. Define *population.* **Population is the total number of individuals of a particular species in a particular area.**
3. The term *population explosion* doesn't refer just to increased population, but to the rapid rate at which it is increasing. What does Figure 19-2 in your textbook show about the speed at which our world's population has increased? **The figure shows how rapidly the world population doubles.**
4. How has our improved understanding of nutrition contributed to overpopulation? **The average life span of persons who eat nourishing food has been increased.**
5. What are some of the problems that people on Earth face if the population explosion continues? **Answers will vary but should include: shortage of food supplies, shortage of energy resources, increased pollution, overflowing landfills.**

Complete the following chart using the words in the box.

electricity use — water use — farming — packaging products — making products

Effects on the environment	Caused by
Generated by burning fuels which pollute the atmosphere	**electricity use**
Pollutes the water; cleaning the water adds substances such as chlorine to the environment	**water use**
Erodes topsoil; pesticides and herbicides add poison	**farming**
Uses gasoline to transport resources; processes used to make products add pollutants	**making products**
Using plastic involves refining oil which produces many pollutants; using paper involves cutting down trees and producing pollutants to transform trees into paper	**packaging products**

 77

▲ ENRICHMENT 77

NAME ____________ DATE ________ CLASS ________

ENRICHMENT — Chapter 19

Population Impact on the Environment — Text Pages 502–505

PREDICTING POPULATION GROWTH

In this chapter, you read about population growth. Here are some new facts along with some facts from the chapter.

- The United Nations keeps track of population statistics for the world.
- World population grows every year because the number of births per year is greater than the number of deaths per year.
- In 1990, the world population was 5.3 billion.
- The population of the world is increasing by about 93 million people per year.

Answer the questions below on the lines provided.

1. In what year will the population reach 6 billion? **1997**
2. What will the population be in the year 2000? **about 6 323 000 000**
3. Suppose the world population increases by one percent per year. Do you think, without figuring it out, that a one percent increase would be a big increase? Now figure out how many people a one percent increase of the 1990 population represents. **Students will answer either yes or no. 1% = 53 000 000 people**
4. Suppose the world population increases by two percent per year. How many people does a two percent increase of the 1990 population represent? **2% = 106 000 000 people**
5. How does the predicted increase of 93 million people per year compare with the percentages you just calculated? **It falls between them, though it's closer to 2%.**
6. Some people hope that the world will reach a zero population growth. What do you think this means in relation to the number of births and deaths per year? **The number of births would have to equal the number of deaths.**
7. If zero population growth could be achieved by the year 2000 and continued, what would be the population in 2020? Explain. **The population would be about 6.3 billion because if deaths and births equal each other, there would be no increase in population. It would be the same as it was in 2000, or 6.3 billion.**
8. Why do you think the United Nations keeps information on world population growth? **Answers will vary. Some students may say that the information will help the U.N. plan for areas where people will need more food, or medicine, or housing.**

 77

TYING TO PREVIOUS KNOWLEDGE: In Chapter 18, students learned that fossil fuels are nonrenewable. Ask students how population growth will affect the availability and price of fossil fuels. As human population continues to increase, more and more of these fuels will be burned. Earth's reserves will disappear. The demand will exceed the supply, and prices will likely rise.

OBJECTIVES AND SCIENCE WORDS: Have students review the objectives and science words to become familiar with this section.

2 TEACH

Key Concepts are highlighted.

CONCEPT DEVELOPMENT

▶ Explain how modern health care has actually contributed to the population explosion. With modern medicines, better sanitation, and better nutrition, people are living longer.

▶ Have students interpret Figure 19-2 to discuss population doubling times. Discuss why doubling times have shortened.

STUDENT TEXT QUESTIONS

▶ Page 503, paragraph 4: **Are there enough natural resources to support such a large population?** *probably not* **How will such a large human population affect our environment?** *The environment will probably be severely damaged. Already, there is great damage in some areas.*

TEACHER F.Y.I.

▶ Global population as of April 19, 1990 was 5.3 billion.

CONCEPT DEVELOPMENT

▶ Stress that students' daily activities greatly affect the environment in a variety of ways.

▶ Challenge students to list three daily activities that don't impact the environment.

CROSS CURRICULUM

▶ **Social Studies:** Have students discuss how industrialization and urbanization not only affect, but are affected by, pollution.

MINI QUIZ

Use the Mini Quiz to check students' recall of chapter content.

1. **A(n) _____ is the total number of individuals in a particular species in a particular area.** *population*
2. **The rate at which people are reproducing is so rapid that it's called a(n) _____.** *explosion*
3. **By the year 2075, the population is predicted to be nearly _____ times what it is today.** *three*

PROGRAM RESOURCES

From the **Teacher Resource Package** use:

Cross-Curricular Connections, page 23, Writing a Science Fiction Short Story.

Transparency Masters, pages 79-80, The Population Explosion.

Use **Color Transparency** number 40, The Population Explosion.

Use **Laboratory Manual** pages 155-158, Human Impact on the Environment.

Did You Know?

The United States makes up only 5 percent of the world's human population, yet it consumes 25 percent of the world's natural resources.

How People Affect the Environment

By the time you're 75 years old, you will have produced enough garbage to equal the mass of 16 African elephants (47 000 kilograms). You will have consumed enough water to fill 662 000 bathtubs (163 000 000 liters). And because you live in the United States, you will have used five times as much energy as an average person living elsewhere in the world.

How does the energy consumed by a person in the U.S. compare with that used by other people?

Let's take a look at how your daily activities affect the environment. You use electricity, which is generated by burning fuels. The environment is changed when the fuels are mined, and it's further harmed when the fuels are burned. The water that you use is polluted and must be made as clean as possible before being returned to the environment. Sometimes cleaning the water adds substances such as chlorine to the environment. You eat food which takes land to grow. Farming causes huge volumes of topsoil to be eroded and lost each year. Much of the food you eat is grown using pesticides and herbicides—poisonous substances. How else do you and other people affect the environment?

Many of the products you buy are packaged in plastic and paper. Plastic is refined from oil. The process of refining oil produces many pollutants. The environment is

Table 19-1

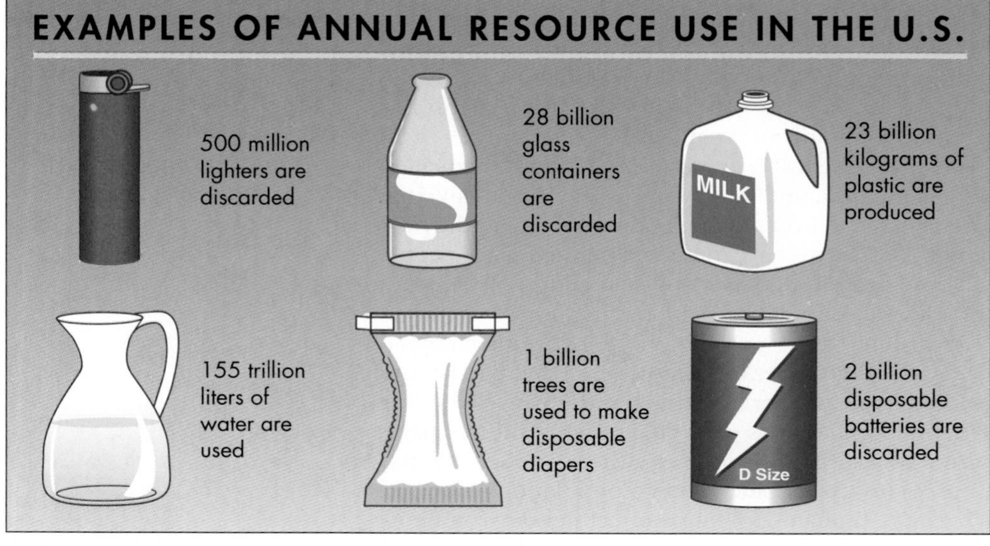

EXAMPLES OF ANNUAL RESOURCE USE IN THE U.S.
500 million lighters are discarded
28 billion glass containers are discarded
MILK
23 billion kilograms of plastic are produced
155 trillion liters of water are used
1 billion trees are used to make disposable diapers
D Size
2 billion disposable batteries are discarded

OPTIONS

ENRICHMENT

Cooperative Learning: Have Study Buddies work together to fill out the following table:

Human Activity	Environmental Effects
Use electricity	fuels are mined and burned, increases greenhouse effect
Use water	pollutants added to environment
Eat food	topsoil is eroded, pesticides and herbicides enter environment
Use plastics	refining oil produces pollutants, waste disposal problem
Use paper	trees removed, increases greenhouse effect, uses nonrenewable resource for transport, pollutants added to environment, waste disposal problem

changed to produce the clean, shiny piece of plastic you buy in the store. Producing paper requires cutting down trees, using gasoline to transport them to a paper mill, and producing pollutants to transform the trees into paper.

We change the land when we remove resources from it, and we further harm the environment when we shape those resources into usable products. The effect on the environment doesn't end there, however. Once we've produced and consumed products, we have to dispose of them. In the next section, you will read about the problems associated with disposal of waste.

As the population continues to grow, more demands will be made on our environment. Becoming all too common are traffic-choked highways, overflowing garbage dumps, shrinking forests, and vanishing wildlife. What can we do? People are the problem, but we also are the solution. As you learn more about how we affect the environment, you'll discover what you can do to make the future world one that everyone can live in.

Figure 19-3. People are beginning to act to protect the environment. For example, egg cartons are made of recycled paper or plastic. Because of consumer demands, grocery stores began selling "environment friendly" materials.

SECTION REVIEW

1. Using Figure 19-2 calculate approximately how many years it took for the *Homo sapiens* population to reach 1 billion. How long did it take to double to 2 billion? to 4 billion?
2. List at least three reasons for Earth's rapid increase in population.
3. **Apply:** In nonindustrialized nations, such as Ethiopia, individuals have less negative impact on the environment than do citizens in industrialized nations. Why do you think this is the case?

Making and Using Graphs

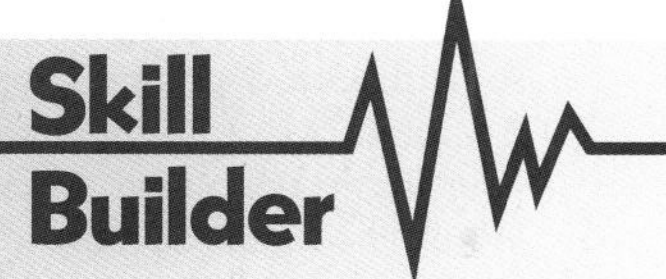

Use Figure 19-2 on page 503 to answer the questions below. If you need help, refer to Making and Using Graphs in the **Skill Handbook** on pages 691 and 692.

1. Early humanlike ancestors existed more than 4 million years ago. Why does the graph indicate that it should extend back only 500 000 years?
2. How would the slope of the graph change if, in the near future, the growth rate were cut in half?

CHECK FOR UNDERSTANDING

▶ Ask questions 1-2 and the **Apply** Question in the Section Review.

RETEACH

Have students keep a diary for one day of all activities they perform that significantly affect the environment. Have them list all ways they use electricity and water, food they eat, and all paper and plastic items they use. In addition to the diary, have them carry a bag with them, into which they throw all personal garbage. At the end of the day, have them weigh their bags and analyze the degree to which they feel they affected the environment.

EXTENSION

For students who have mastered this section, use the **Reinforcement** and **Enrichment** masters or other OPTIONS provided.

3 CLOSE

▶ Have students debate the statement "Progress is more important than the environment."

SECTION REVIEW ANSWERS

1. It took almost 500 000 years for the *Homo sapiens* population to reach 1 billion. It took only 102 years (1810-1912) to double to 2 billion. It reached 4 billion in 62 years (1912-1974).
2. modern medicines, better sanitation, better nutrition, more people are of the age to have children
3. Apply: People living in non-industrialized nations use less water, energy, food, and generate less garbage.

INQUIRY QUESTIONS

▶ **Why do you think people living in the United States use so much more energy than the average person in the world?** *The availability of products is greater in the U.S. More people can afford to have automobiles, heated and air-conditioned homes, and household appliances. They eat food that's grown using energy-consuming farming techniques.*

▶ **Populations near coastlines have doubled over the past 50 years. In what ways has this affected marine environments?** *Pollution has increased, causing organisms to die. Food chains have been disrupted.*

ENRICHMENT

▶ Have students make population charts or graphs that compare the populations of Europe, the Commonwealth of Independent States, Asia, Africa, North America, and Latin America.

▶ Have students determine some of the problems they think will occur as the human population continues to increase. Have them discuss some possible solutions in a report or on a chart, graph, or map.

Skill Builder

1. As indicated in Chapter 17, evidence indicates that *Homo sapiens* evolved about 500 000 years ago. The graph represents the population growth of modern humans.
2. The slope would decrease by half of its current slope. The population would continue to increase, but at a slower rate.

ACTIVITY 19-1
45 minutes

OBJECTIVE: Describe the mathematical nature and potential consequences of human population growth.

PROCESS SKILLS applied in this activity:
▶ **Measuring in SI** and **Estimating** in Procedure Step 3.
▶ **Graphing** in Procedure Step 6.
▶ **Inferring** in Analyze Question 1.
▶ **Comparing** in Analyze Question 3.
▶ **Using Numbers** in Conclude and Apply Question 4.

COOPERATIVE LEARNING Use the Science Investigation strategy to form groups of three or four.

TEACHING THE ACTIVITY

Troubleshooting: Have one extra set-up available in case of an accidental "dumping."

▶ Students may question the reason for the 30-second time intervals. The length of time interval is arbitrary; any constant time interval will do.

▶ It may be impossible to supply students with enough small objects to fill container #11. If so, simply have the students "estimate" what the results would be for container #11, based on their data for containers 1 through 10.

Data and Observations

Time Intervals	Population	% of Empty Volume (400-mL beaker)
0	2	99
1	4	99
2	8	98
3	16	97
4	32	96
5	64	94
6	128	91
7	256	85
8	512	78
9	1024	65
10	2048	48
11	4096	0

PROGRAM RESOURCES

From the **Teacher Resource Package** use:

Activity Worksheets, pages 169-170, Activity 19-1: Human Population Growth Rate.

ACTIVITY 19-1
Human Population Growth Rate

Problem: *What is the mathematical nature of human population growth?*

Materials
- beaker (250 or 400 mL)
- paper cups or 50-mL beakers (11)
- small objects of uniform shape (dried beans, corn kernels, glass or plastic beads, paper clips, wooden markers)

Procedure
1. Place two of the small objects into the large beaker on your desk or table. Place each of the 11 smaller containers in a row beside the larger one. Number each of these containers from 1 to 11.
2. Place two of the objects into the first small container. In each succeeding container, from 2 through 11, place *twice* as many objects as in the one before it (four objects in 2, eight objects in 3, and so on). Record the number of objects in each of the small containers.
3. Estimate the percentage of empty space in the large beaker. Record this estimate in the first line of your data table.
4. Add the contents of container 1 to the large beaker. Record the total "population" (number of objects) and the approximate percentage of empty space in the large beaker.
5. Repeat the procedure for container 2 thirty seconds later. Add the contents of containers 3 through 11 at 30-second intervals. Record your results each time.
6. When the small objects in all of your containers have been added to the large container, make a graph of your results. Place the number of objects (population) on the vertical axis and the time intervals (0 through 11) on the horizontal axis.

Data and Observations
Sample Data

Time interval	Population	Percent of empty volume
0	2	99
1	4	98
2	8	98
10	2048	48
11	4096	0

Analyze
1. Indicate what you think the large beaker and the smaller objects represent.
2. After 11 thirty-second intervals, what is the total number of small objects and percentage of empty space in the large beaker?
3. How does the graph of your data for this activity compare to the graph in Figure 19-2?

Conclude and Apply
4. The radius of Earth is about 6400 kilometers. Approximately 70 percent of its surface is covered by water. Given the present planet population of about 5.5 billion, what is the current population density in people per square kilometer of land surface? (Area of a sphere $= 4\pi r^2$)
5. The present world population is thought to be doubling about every 35 years. Assuming no change in that rate, what will the population density per square kilometer be 35 years from now? 105 years? 1000 years?
6. Identify and describe some "limiting factors" that might determine a maximum population for planet Earth?

ANSWERS TO QUESTIONS

1. The large beaker represents Earth with the small objects representing the human population.
2. 4096; zero percent
3. They are essentially the same.
4. approximately 35.6 people per square kilometer of land surface; Divide 5.5 billion people by a land mass of approximately 154 320 000 square kilometers.
5. In 35 years there would be 71 people for each square kilometer. In 105 years the number would be 286 (44 billion/154 million km^2). In 1000 years there would be about 40 million people per square kilometer.
6. Obviously, from the previous question, space is a limiting factor. Another major factor would be the amount of food available. Other limiting factors might include infectious diseases, climate, war, pollution, and the depletion of natural resources.

Using the Land

19-2

Objectives

- List ways that we use land.
- Discuss environmental problems created because of land use.
- List things you can do to help protect the environment.

New Science Words

landfill
sanitary landfill
hazardous wastes
conservation
composting

Land Usage

You may not think of land as a natural resource. Yet, it is as important to people as oil, gold, clean air, and clean water. Through agriculture, logging, refuse disposal, and urban development, we not only use land, we often abuse it.

Farming

Earth's continents have about 130 million square kilometers of land. We use 15 million square kilometers as farmland. Even so, about 20 percent of the people living in the world live in poverty and hunger. Millions starve to death each year. Unfortunately, advanced farming techniques that produce large volumes of food also create serious environmental problems. To reduce weeds and insects in a field where crops are growing, herbicides and pesticides are often applied. These chemicals

Figure 19-4. Contour plowing is one way farmers reduce erosion. Water follows the natural contour of the land, along the plowed rows, instead of running straight downslope.

OPTIONS

INQUIRY QUESTIONS

- **Why would it be unwise of you to allow your dog to drink water from a stream near a farm?** *Runoff from farms is often contaminated with pesticides and herbicides that can cause animals to develop cancers.*

PROGRAM RESOURCES

From the **Teacher Resource Package** use:

Critical Thinking/Problem Solving, page 25, Chemical Presticides and Biopesticides.

SECTION 19-2

PREPARATION

SECTION BACKGROUND

- Waste deposited in sanitary landfills or open dumps is sometimes called *urban ore* because it contains many materials that could be recycled and used again to provide energy or useful products.
- Most of the biological matter in landfills decays in about 40 years. That could be shortened to five years if air and water are circulated through the landfill.
- Mining wastes are a source of environmental problems particularly in a few western and southwestern states. Runoff from these wastes increases the acidity of streams and pollutes them with toxic metals.

PREPLANNING

- To prepare for Activity 19-2, have each Student Investigation group bring a 2-liter bottle and garbage (including food scraps, yard waste, a plastic item, a metal item, a foam cup, and notebook paper or newsprint). Also obtain the following for each group: soil, thermometer, plastic wrap, and rubber band.

1 MOTIVATE

- Have students read articles or watch a movie about the *Exxon Valdez* oil spill that occurred in Alaska in 1989. Next, ask students to express how they feel about that accident. Then tell them that each year 20 times the amount of oil spilled by the *Exxon Valdez* is dumped into America's environment by "do-it-yourselfers" who change their own motor oil but do not dispose of the used oil properly. This oil pollutes groundwater, fouls water treatment plants, and wastes recyclable oil.
- Show one of the following movies: *Problems of Conservation: Our Natural Resources,* or *Problems of Conservation: Minerals.* Both films are available from Encyclopaedia Britannica Films.

TYING TO PREVIOUS KNOWLEDGE: Have students recall that natural sediments are dissolved by both groundwater and surface water. Chemicals from farms, livestock, landfills, mines, and other industries also become dissolved in these waters.

OBJECTIVES AND SCIENCE WORDS: Have students review the objectives and science words to become familiar with this section.

2 TEACH

Key Concepts are highlighted.

CONCEPT DEVELOPMENT

▶ Have students review the evolution of soil presented in Chapter 5, Section 5-2.

▶ **What are two environmental problems caused by grazing livestock?** *losing land that could be used to grow crops and production of methane gas*

Figure 19-5. Herbicides and pesticides applied to crops run off into streams and poison the environment.

make their way to the waterways where they contaminate the environment. People and other animals can get cancers from consuming food and water polluted by runoff from farmlands.

1 Perhaps the greatest damage caused by farming is excessive topsoil erosion. When croplands are tilled, there's no vegetation covering the soil to prevent it from being carried away by running water. Two or three centimeters of topsoil may be removed in one year. It can take more than 300 years for new topsoil to evolve and replace the eroded topsoil.

Did You Know?

Bacteria living in the intestines of cows and other herbivores break down plant material called cellulose. The cows and other animals can then use the cellulose as an energy source. It's the bacteria, not the animals, that produce methane gas.

Grazing Livestock

Some land is used for grazing livestock. The animals eat the plants on the land and are then often used as food for humans. Two problems associated with grazing livestock include losing land that could be used to grow crops and the production of methane gas.

Figure 19-6. One-third of the land in North America is used to graze livestock. One-half of all croplands is used to grow feed for livestock.

OPTIONS

Meeting Different Ability Levels

For Section 19-2, use the following **Teacher Resource Masters** depending upon individual students' needs.

◆ **Study Guide Master** for all students.

● **Reinforcement Master** for students of average and above average ability levels.

▲ **Enrichment Master** for above average students.

Additional Teacher Resource Package masters are listed in the OPTIONS box throughout the section. The additional masters are appropriate for all students.

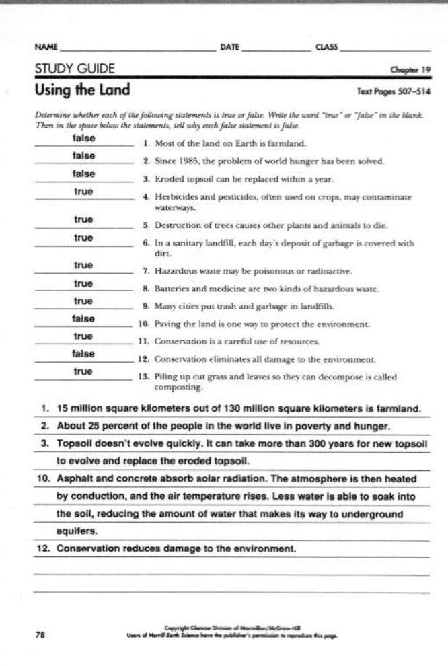

◆ STUDY GUIDE 78

NAME ______ DATE ______ CLASS ______

STUDY GUIDE — Chapter 19

Using the Land — Text Pages 507–514

Determine whether each of the following statements is true or false. Write the word "true" or "false" in the blank. Then in the space below the statements, tell why each false statement is false.

false 1. Most of the land on Earth is farmland.
false 2. Since 1985, the problem of world hunger has been solved.
false 3. Eroded topsoil can be replaced within a year.
true 4. Herbicides and pesticides, often used on crops, may contaminate waterways.
true 5. Destruction of trees causes other plants and animals to die.
true 6. In a sanitary landfill, each day's deposit of garbage is covered with dirt.
true 7. Hazardous waste may be poisonous or radioactive.
true 8. Batteries and medicine are two kinds of hazardous waste.
true 9. Many cities put trash and garbage in landfills.
false 10. Paving the land is one way to protect the environment.
true 11. Conservation is a careful use of resources.
false 12. Conservation eliminates all damage to the environment.
true 13. Piling up cut grass and leaves so they can decompose is called composting.

1. 15 million square kilometers out of 130 million square kilometers is farmland.
2. About 25 percent of the people in the world live in poverty and hunger.
3. Topsoil doesn't evolve quickly. It can take more than 300 years for new topsoil to evolve and replace the eroded topsoil.
10. Asphalt and concrete absorb solar radiation. The atmosphere is then heated by conduction, and the air temperature rises. Less water is able to soak into the soil, reducing the amount of water that makes its way to underground aquifers.
12. Conservation reduces damage to the environment.

78

A square kilometer of vegetable crops can feed many more people than a square kilometer used to raise livestock. Also, cows and other vegetarian animals produce methane. Methane is thought to contribute to the greenhouse effect. 2

Cutting Trees

Some land is used for a source of wood. Trees are cut down and used for lumber, fuel, and paper. Often new trees are planted to take their places. In some cases, especially in the tropical regions, whole forests are cut down without being replaced. Each year an area of rain forest the size of Pennsylvania disappears. It's not just the trees and soil that are destroyed when the trees are cut down. Scientists estimate that 17 500 species die each year because of this loss of habitat.

How large of an area of rain forest is lost each year?

Organisms living outside of the tropics also suffer because of the lost vegetation. Plants remove carbon dioxide from the air and produce oxygen when they photosynthesize. Organisms all over the globe need oxygen to breathe. Reduced vegetation could also result 3
in higher levels of carbon dioxide in the atmosphere. As you know, carbon dioxide is one of the gases that contributes to the greenhouse effect.

How do organisms outside of the rain forest suffer from the loss?

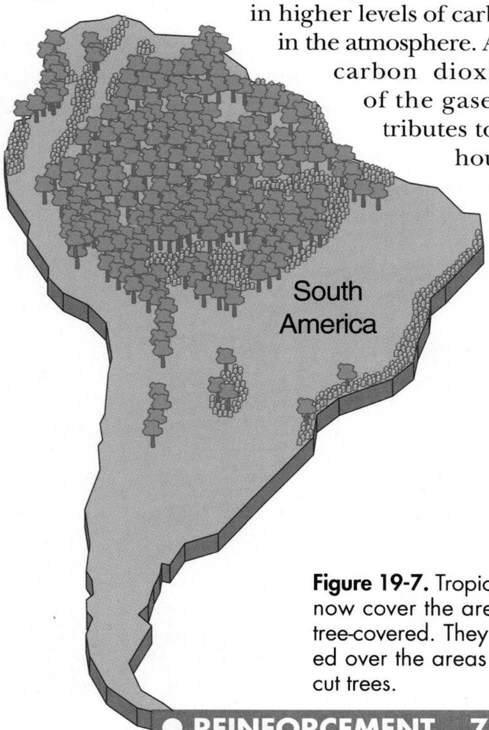

South America

Figure 19-7. Tropical rain forests now cover the areas shown as tree-covered. They once extended over the areas indicated by cut trees.

CONCEPT DEVELOPMENT

▶ **Describe two ways organisms living outside the tropics suffer when rain forests are cut down.** *There is a reduction of oxygen and an addition of carbon dioxide to the atmosphere. Organisms need oxygen to breathe. Carbon dioxide contributes to the greenhouse effect.*

CROSS CURRICULUM

▶ **Geography:** Have students locate the world's rain forests on a globe. In order to do this, they may first need to use a world atlas. Also have them locate Pennsylvania on the globe. Emphasize that each year an area of rain forest the size of Pennsylvania is destroyed.

PROGRAM RESOURCES

From the **Teacher Resource Package** use:

Concept Mapping, pages 43-44.

● REINFORCEMENT 78

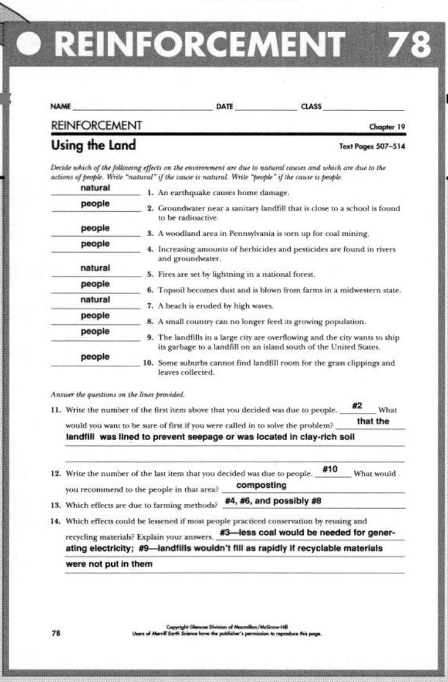

NAME ____ DATE ____ CLASS ____

REINFORCEMENT — Chapter 19

Using the Land — Text Pages 507–514

Decide which of the following effects on the environment are due to natural causes and which are due to the actions of people. Write "natural" if the cause is natural. Write "people" if the cause is people.

natural 1. An earthquake causes home damage.
people 2. Groundwater near a sanitary landfill that is close to a school is found to be radioactive.
people 3. A woodland area in Pennsylvania is torn up for coal mining.
people 4. Increasing amounts of herbicides and pesticides are found in rivers and groundwater.
natural 5. Fires are set by lightning in a national forest.
people 6. Topsoil becomes dust and is blown from farms in a midwestern state.
natural 7. A beach is eroded by high waves.
people 8. A small country can no longer feed its growing population.
people 9. The landfills in a large city are overflowing and the city wants to ship its garbage to a landfill on an island south of the United States.
people 10. Some suburbs cannot find landfill room for the grass clippings and leaves collected.

Answer the questions on the lines provided.

11. Write the number of the first item above that you decided was due to people. **#2** What would you want to be sure of first if you were called in to solve the problem? **that the landfill was lined to prevent seepage or was located in clay-rich soil**
12. Write the number of the last item that you decided was due to people. **#10** What would you recommend to the people in that area? **composting**
13. Which effects are due to farming methods? **#4, #6, and possibly #8**
14. Which effects could be lessened if most people practiced conservation by reusing and recycling materials? Explain your answers. **#3—less coal would be needed for generating electricity; #9—landfills wouldn't fill as rapidly if recyclable materials were not put in them**

78

▲ ENRICHMENT 78

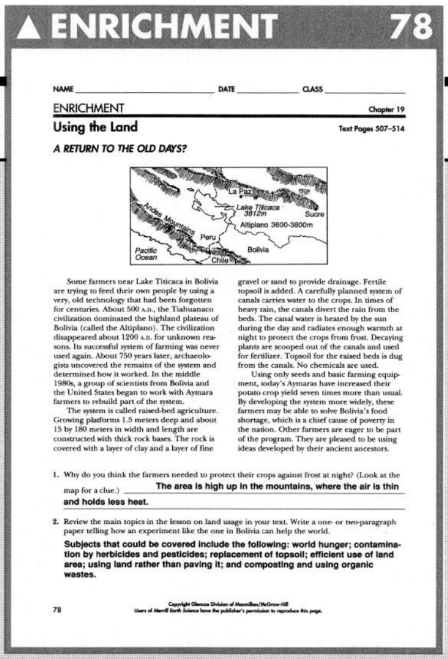

NAME ____ DATE ____ CLASS ____

ENRICHMENT — Chapter 19

Using the Land — Text Pages 507–514

A RETURN TO THE OLD DAYS?

La Paz
Lake Titicaca 3812m
Sucre
Andes Mountains
Altiplano 3600-3800m
Peru
Bolivia
Pacific Ocean
Chile

Some farmers near Lake Titicaca in Bolivia are trying to feed their own people by using a very, old technology that had been forgotten for centuries. About 500 A.D., the Tiahuanaco civilization dominated the highland plateau of Bolivia (called the Altiplano). The civilization disappeared about 1200 A.D. for unknown reasons. Its successful system of farming was never used again. About 750 years later, archaeologists uncovered the remains of the system and determined how it worked. In the middle 1980s, a group of scientists from Bolivia and the United States began to work with Aymara farmers to rebuild part of the system.

The system is called raised-bed agriculture. Growing platforms 1.5 meters deep and about 15 by 180 meters in width and length are constructed with thick rock bases. The rock is covered with a layer of clay and a layer of fine gravel or sand to provide drainage. Fertile topsoil is added. A carefully planned system of canals carries water to the crops. In times of heavy rain, the canals divert the rain from the beds. The canal water is heated by the sun during the day and radiates enough warmth at night to protect the crops from frost. Decaying plants are scooped out of the canals and used for fertilizer. Topsoil for the raised beds is dug from the canals. No chemicals are used.

Using only seeds and basic farming equipment, today's Aymaras have increased their potato crop yield seven times more than usual. By developing the system more widely, these farmers may be able to solve Bolivia's food shortage, which is a chief cause of poverty in the nation. Other farmers are eager to be part of the program. They are pleased to be using ideas developed by their ancient ancestors.

1. Why do you think the farmers needed to protect their crops against frost at night? (Look at the map for a clue.) **The area is high up in the mountains, where the air is thin and holds less heat.**
2. Review the main topics in the lesson on land usage in your text. Write a one- or two-paragraph paper telling how an experiment like the one in Bolivia can help the world.
Subjects that could be covered include the following: world hunger; contamination by herbicides and pesticides; replacement of topsoil; efficient use of land area; using land rather than paving it; and composting and using organic wastes.

78

MINI-Lab

Teaching Tips

The general approach to this activity should be as a problem-solving experience. Because family practices and values are involved, there are no absolutely right or wrong answers to the question. Students in urban areas or from geographic regions where "green" lawns are the exception may not be able to identify with the "problem." In some areas where local water supply is especially sensitive, the application of chemical fertilizers and herbicides may already be legally banned or strictly controlled. It is important that you, as teacher and facilitator, maintain an objective and unbiased position during the discussion. Keep in mind that the parents of your students may have strong opinions one way or the other on this issue. Some families, represented by students in your class, may utilize lawn-care services or apply chemical fertilizers and herbicides themselves. Additionally, be alert to any students whose parent or parents work for a lawn-care service.

CONCEPT DEVELOPMENT

▶ Explain to students that specially designed sites have been constructed to dispose of some forms of hazardous waste. For example, canisters of radioactive waste from nuclear power plants are often placed in abandoned, underground salt mines. The salt prevents groundwater from reaching the stored canisters.

▶ Discuss with students how much of the hazardous waste that ends up in landfills is dumped there legally. Each of us discards materials he or she considers harmless, yet those materials are actually poisonous or carcinogenic.

MINI-Lab

Would you use toxic substances to have a weed-free lawn?

Read the following situation and answer the questions at the end. After you've answered in your own words, compare your responses with those of other students. Suppose you've just purchased a house with a small yard. The yard has many weeds growing among the grass, and the flower beds are overgrown with weeds. You're considering hiring a lawn-care service to come and spray your yard with herbicides and fertilizer. You know that these substances are toxic. Do you decide to have the chemicals applied to your yard? If a neighbor complained that he didn't like the chemicals being sprayed so close to his home, how would you respond?

Landfills

So far, we've discussed ways land is used to produce products we use. Land is also used when we dispose of those products. 4 Eighty percent of all our garbage goes into landfills. A **landfill** is an area where waste is deposited. In a **sanitary landfill,** each day's deposit is covered with dirt. The dirt prevents it from blowing away in the wind, and it reduces the odor produced by the decaying waste. Sanitary landfills are also designed to prevent liquid wastes from draining into the soil and groundwater below. A sanitary landfill is lined with plastic or concrete, or it's located in clay-rich soils that trap the liquid waste.

Some of the wastes we put into landfills are dangerous to organisms. These poisonous, cancer-causing, or radioactive wastes are called **hazardous wastes.** Large quantities of hazardous wastes are put into landfills by industries. But this isn't the only source of these toxic substances. Every year, each person in the United States throws away enough hazardous waste to equal the mass of a small car. Examples of these wastes are insect sprays, fingernail polish removers, batteries, drain cleaners, bleaches, medicines, and paints.

Sanitary landfills greatly reduce the chance that hazardous substances will leak into the surrounding soil and groundwater. However, some of it does find its way into the environment.

OPTIONS

ENRICHMENT

▶ Have students research the status of local landfills. Students should find out how long local landfills can continue to operate. They should discover if any are in danger of closing because of limited space.

PROGRAM RESOURCES

From the **Teacher Resource Package** use:

Activity Worksheets, page 175, Mini-Lab: Would you use toxic substances to have a weed-free lawn?

PROBLEM SOLVING

Will the Landfill be in Your Backyard?

Anthony was on his way home from school when he passed a group of people outside the local government building. They were carrying signs to protest the proposed landfill going up on the edge of their neighborhood. They carried signs that said "NIMBY," or "*Not In My Backyard*."

The protestors were concerned that the landfill would be bad for their neighborhood. They were hoping to prevent it from being built there. Instead, they thought it should be placed elsewhere.

That evening, Anthony saw a news report on the landfill controversy. The report said that the landfill had to be located within city limits. No matter where it was located, it would be in someone's neighborhood. The report went on to say that the current city landfill had to close within the next year because it was almost full. Construction on the new landfill would have to begin soon.

Think Critically: Most people don't want a landfill in their "backyard." Yet, it's their garbage and the garbage of others in the community that must be disposed of. How can people prevent landfills from filling up in the first place? Why would a community refuse to pick up grass clippings if its landfill space were limited?

Another problem is that we're filling up our landfills. We're running out of good areas to build new ones. Many materials placed into landfills don't rot. Instead, they just stay there, taking up space.

The figure on page 510 illustrates the materials commonly put into landfills. Some of these materials decompose rapidly, whereas others do not. It may seem that when we throw something in the garbage can that it's gone and we don't need to be concerned with it anymore. But as you know, our garbage doesn't disappear. It can stay around for hundreds of years. In the case of radioactive waste, it may be around for thousands of years, troubling future generations.

Structures, Mines, and Natural Environments

Another way we change the land is by building structures on it. Concrete and asphalt are quickly replacing grass and woodlands in our communities. The impact on the environment is easy to observe. Asphalt and concrete

CONCEPT DEVELOPMENT

▶ Using the figure on page 510, have students compare the relative volumes of materials in our landfills. Ask them which type of material occupies the most space. How might we significantly reduce the space needed for landfill sites?

TEACHER F.Y.I.

▶ When examined by a researcher, one ten-year-old landfill was found to contain grass clippings that were still green, bread that had not molded, and newspaper headlines that could still be read.

▶ Potentially disease-infected disposable diapers clutter sanitary landfills. About one percent of the landfill space in the United States is filled with soiled disposable diapers. The EPA estimates that 3 million tonnes of feces and urine end up in landfills rather than in sewage treatment plants because people don't wash diapers before they throw them away.

▶ People in the United States annually produce enough garbage to completely fill five million large truck trailers. That would be a fleet stretching end-to-end, twice around the world.

PROBLEM SOLVING

Think Critically: People can help prevent landfills from filling up by recycling and reusing materials. They can also buy products that aren't "overpackaged." Because grass clippings and other organic materials make up a large percentage of the waste going to a landfill, communities may require citizens to compost instead.

INQUIRY QUESTIONS

▶ **What are three problems associated with landfills?** *Wastes leak into the environment; landfills are filling up; people resist the construction of new landfills in their neighborhoods.*

▶ **Why do you suppose many people don't like the idea of landfills being created near their homes?** *Wastes may leak into soil and groundwater. The odor may ruin their property's value.*

Science and MATH

To calculate the water saved by one student, use the following formulas:
16 L – 2 L = 14 L
14 L × 3 = 42 L
42 L × 365 = 15 330 L/year.

To calculate the water that could be saved by the entire U.S. population, use the following:
15 330 L/year × 250 000 000 =
3 832 500 000 000 L/year.

MINI QUIZ

Use the Mini Quiz to check students' recall of chapter content.

1. **People and other animals can get _____ by consuming food and water polluted by farm runoff.** *cancers*
2. **Cows and other herbivores may contribute to the greenhouse effect by producing _____.** *methane*
3. **Reduced vegetation can result in higher levels of _____ in the atmosphere.** *carbon dioxide*
4. **_____ percent of our garbage goes into landfills.** *Eighty*
5. **The temperature in cities tends to be ____ (higher, lower) than in rural areas.** *higher*

TEACHER F.Y.I.

► In the contiguous 48 states, close to half of the land areas in most cities is used for roads, highways, and parking lots. This equals 2% of the total land surface, or an area the size of the state of Georgia.

CONCEPT DEVELOPMENT

► Discuss the term *precycling*. Precycling means to reduce waste before one even buys an item. For example, shoppers precycle by buying food in bulk, thereby reducing the amount of packaging they consume. Precycling also means buying products in "environment-friendly" packages. Students can precycle by purchasing products packaged in materials made from recycled products. For example, they might ask parents or guardians to buy a cereal packaged in recycled cardboard.

5 absorb a lot of solar radiation. The atmosphere is then heated by conduction, and the air temperature rises. You may have observed this if you've ever traveled from a rural area to the city and noticed a rise in temperature.

Another effect of paving over the land is that less water is able to soak into the soil. Instead, it either makes its way to sewer lines or it evaporates. This greatly reduces the amount of water that makes its way to groundwater aquifers. Many communities rely on groundwater for drinking water. At the same time, they're covering more and more of the land with roads, sidewalks, and parking lots that prevent the water from reaching the aquifers.

In previous chapters, you've read about mining and how it adversely affects the environment. As more and more people populate Earth, increased demands for fossil fuels and mineral ores will result in more and more mining operations.

Not all land on Earth is being used to produce usable materials or for storing waste. Some land remains uninhabited by people. National Parks in the United States are protected from much of the pollution and destruction that you've read about in this section. In many countries throughout the world, land is set aside as natural preserves. As the world population continues to increase, the strain on our environment is likely to increase. Let's hope that we will be able to continue preserving some land as natural environments.

Science and MATH

You use16 liters of water if you let the water run while brushing your teeth. Only 2 liters are used if the water is turned off until it's time to rinse. How much water could you save per year by not letting the water run? Base your calculations on brushing your teeth three times a day. How much water could be saved by the entire U.S. population (250 million people)?

Why is paving the land a problem?

Figure 19-8. As we increase our demands for energy, we must find new resources. There are many on-going debates about whether we should mine our national parks and wildlife reserves. One such debate rages over whether to drill for oil here, at the Arctic National Wildlife Reserve in Alaska.

OPTIONS

INQUIRY QUESTIONS

► **Why are cities usually warmer than rural areas?** *The asphalt and concrete in the cities absorb more solar radiation than do the plants in rural areas. Therefore, more heat is conducted to the air in cities.*

► **As the population of the world continues to increase, cities will continue growing, and more and more land will be covered with concrete and asphalt. How will this affect the aquifers under these cities?** *Water levels will keep dropping.*

PROGRAM RESOURCES

From the **Teacher Resource Package** use:

Laboratory Manual pages 159-160, Reclamation of Mine Wastes.

Conserving Resources

People are the cause of our environmental problems, and we also are the solution. What can you do to help? In the United States and other industrialized countries, people have a throwaway life-style. When we are done with something, we throw it away. This means more products have to be produced to replace what we've thrown away; more land is used, and landfills overflow. You can help by conserving resources. **Conservation** is the careful use of resources that reduces damage to the environment. Two ways to conserve resources are by reusing and recycling materials. You'll read more about recycling in the Science and Society section that follows.

What is a "throwaway" lifestyle?

Reusing an item means finding another use for it instead of throwing it away. You can reuse old clothes by giving them to someone else, or by cutting them up into

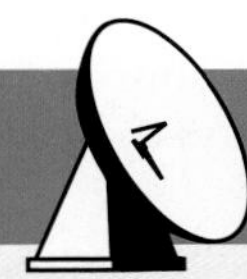

TECHNOLOGY

Recycling Paper

What happens to the newspaper you recycle? After the paper is taken to a plant where it is to be recycled, the paper is put into a device called a pulper. The pulper contains water and other substances that remove any ink from the paper. The paper then becomes part of a soggy mixture called pulp.

Pulp is run through a machine that removes any solid objects such as rubber bands, paper clips, or staples that may have been fastened to the paper. Another device then squeezes the water from the paper mixture. The final stage of processing includes sifting and washing the pulp to remove any unwanted debris.

Water is added to the clean pulp to make a thick, pasty substance. This substance is rolled into thin sheets and dried to form sheets of recycled paper.

Think Critically: If 17 trees are saved when one tonne of paper is recycled, how many trees could be saved in a year if a community recycled 150 000 kilograms of paper each month?

TECHNOLOGY

For more information on recycling paper, see "Save the Trees—and You May Save a Bundle," by C. McAllister, *Business Week*, September 4, 1989, p. 118; or "The Paper Chase," by S.D. Borowitz, *Sierra*, November/December 1989, p. 22.

Think Critically: One tonne (metric ton) is equal to 1000 kg. Therefore:
1 tonne/1000 kg × 17 trees/tonne = 17 trees/1000 kg
150 000 kg/month × 17 trees/1000 kg = 2550 trees/month

CHECK FOR UNDERSTANDING

Ask questions 1-3 and the **Apply** Question in the Section Review.

RETEACH

Cooperative Learning: Have Problem Solving teams list at least five different items that one or more members of the group discarded today. Have them describe at least two ways each of these items could have been reused. An example is that a piece of notebook paper, written on only one side, can still be used for sketching or writing. The paper can also be used to start a fire, or to cover the bottom of a bird cage.

EXTENSION

For students who have mastered this section, use the **Reinforcement** and **Enrichment** masters or other OPTIONS provided.

INQUIRY QUESTIONS

▶ **What is the difference between reusing and recycling?** *Reusing means finding another use for an object. Recycling means materials are changed in form and a new product is made.*

ENRICHMENT

▶ Have students design and build a school compost pile. Be certain that it meets all local health regulations. Use the compost to construct flower beds on school property.

3 CLOSE

FLEX Your Brain

Use the Flex Your Brain activity to have students explore COMPOSTING.

MINI-Lab

Materials: Will depend on student choice. However, tree seedlings appropriate for planting in your locale may often be obtained at little or no cost from an area agricultural extension service or conservation agency. Consult the governmental listings in your phone book for the closest office to your location.

Teaching Tips

▶ Have students agree on the length of time that this activity will be in effect. Try for at least five days or longer.

▶ Compile a list of what each student has done on the chalkboard or overhead projector. Use the list as a basis for discussing what people can do to help conserve Earth's natural resources. Remind students that the preservation of these resources becomes even more critical for each succeeding generation.

Answer to Question: Certainly, if each inhabitant of the planet were to implement environmental conservation practices, Earth would have a far more encouraging future.

SECTION REVIEW ANSWERS

1. farming, grazing, growing trees, landfills, building structures, mining, nature preserves

2. Agriculture: soil erosion, pesticide and herbicide pollution, increased greenhouse effect from methane; Mining: loss of vegetation, polluted runoff into streams, lakes, and aquifers, loss of natural habitats; Trash disposal: leakage into soil and water, landfills take up a lot of space and they are filling up, materials in landfills do not quickly decompose

3. reuse old clothes, reuse plastic and paper bags, compost leaves and grass clippings, dispose of hazardous wastes properly, buy products that are packaged in recycled materials, etc.

4. Apply: Throughout history, this area has been more industrialized than other areas of the country. Industries produce a lot of wastes. Also, the population density is higher there. Thus, the amount of trash is greater, and space available to build landfills is more limited.

MINI-Lab

Can one person make a difference?

This text identifies a number of things people can do to reduce environmental problems. Select at least one and do it. After a length of time that your class has agreed upon, report back on what it was that you did as your part in helping to conserve resources and protect the environment. The population of the United States is about 250 million. What do you suppose would be the result if each person in your country did his or her part in helping save planet Earth also?

rags. The rags can be used in place of paper towels for cleaning jobs around your home.

Reusing plastic and paper bags is another way to reduce waste. Plastic grocery bags are handy for carrying other things. Some grocery stores even pay a few cents when you return and reuse paper grocery bags. Out-of-doors, there are things you can do, too. If you cut grass or rake leaves, compost the leaves and grass clippings instead of putting them into the trash. **Composting** means to pile them up where they can gradually decompose. The decomposed matter can be used in gardens or flower beds to fertilize the soil. Some cities no longer pick up yard waste to take to the landfills. In those places, composting is common. If everyone composted, it would reduce the trash put into landfills by 20 percent.

The human population explosion has already had devastating effects on the environment and the organisms that inhabit Earth. It's unlikely that the population will begin to decline in the near future. To compensate, we must use our resources wisely. Conserving resources by reusing and recycling are two important ways that you can make a difference.

SECTION REVIEW

1. List at least five ways we use land.
2. Discuss environmental problems that are created by agriculture, mining, and trash disposal.
3. List at least five things you can do to help save the environment.
4. **Apply:** Why do you think there is less landfill space left in the northeastern United States than in other areas of the country?

Skill Builder

☑ Outlining

Make an outline of Section 19-2. Use your outline to answer the questions below. If you need help, refer to Outlining in the **Skill Handbook** on page 681.

1. How many uses of land are described in this section?
2. How does farming negatively impact the environment? How does grazing livestock negatively impact it?
3. An open landfill doesn't have many of the characteristics of a sanitary landfill. What do you think an open landfill is like?

Skill Builder

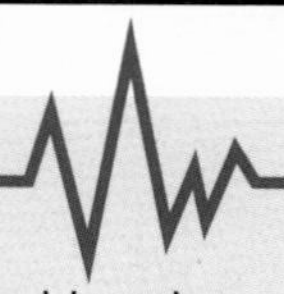

Student outlines will vary, but should reflect the general instructions given in the Skill Handbook.

1. seven (farming, grazing, forestry, landfills, urbanization, mining, preservation)

2. Farming causes excessive topsoil erosion, and it adds poisons to the soil and water. Grazing livestock destroys natural habitats because they have to be transformed into grazing lands. Herbivores also add methane to the atmosphere.

3. An open landfill consists of piles of refuse not covered by dirt. The garbage often blows away in the wind, and it emits a strong odor. Open landfills allow pollutants to leech into groundwater and nearby streams because they aren't sealed.

ACTIVITY 19-2
A Model Landfill

Problem: *What materials rapidly decompose in a landfill?*

Materials  

- 2-liter bottle
- soil
- thermometer
- plastic wrap
- rubber band
- graph paper
- garbage (including food scraps, yard waste, a plastic item, a metal item, a foam cup, and notebook paper or newsprint)

Procedure

1. Cut the top off of the 2-liter bottle.
2. Add soil to the bottle until it is half filled.
3. On graph paper, trace the outline of all the garbage items that you will place into the bottle. Label each outline. Keep the graph paper as a record of the original sizes of the items.
4. Place the items, one at a time, in the bottle. Completely cover each item with soil.
5. Add enough water to the "landfill" until the soil is slightly moist. Place a thermometer in the bottle and seal it up with the plastic wrap and a rubber band.
6. Check the temperature of the "landfill" each day for two weeks. Record the temperatures in your data table.
7. After two weeks, remove all of the items from the soil. Trace the outlines of each on a new sheet of graph paper. Compare the sizes of the items with their original sizes.
8. Wash your hands thoroughly after cleaning up your lab space. Be sure to properly dispose of each item as instructed by your teacher.

Analyze

1. Which items decomposed the most? Which showed the least decomposition?
2. Most decomposition in a landfill is due to the activity of microorganisms. The organisms can live only under certain temperature and moisture conditions. Why was it necessary to add moisture to the soil? How do you think the decomposition rates would have differed if the soil had been completely dry?
3. Compare your results with the results of a bottle that was stored in cold temperatures. What could explain the differences you observe?

Conclude and Apply

4. Why do some items decompose more rapidly than others?
5. What problems are created in landfills by plastics?
6. Yard wastes will eventually decompose, but they take up a lot of space in landfills. What alternatives are there to putting yard wastes in landfills?
7. Why do you think many people buy paper egg cartons instead of foam ones? Why have many stores begun selling only those eggs that come in paper cartons?

ACTIVITY 19-2
30 minutes set up
2 weeks data collection

OBJECTIVE: Observe rate of decomposition of various materials in a model landfill.

PROCESS SKILLS applied in this activity:
▶ **Collecting Data** in Procedure Steps 3 and 6.
▶ **Comparing** in Procedure Step 7 and Question 3.
▶ **Inferring** in Analyze Question 2 and Conclude and Apply Question 4.
▶ **Analyzing Data** in Analyze Questions 1 and 3.

COOPERATIVE LEARNING Have students work in Science Investigation teams of three or four for this activity.

TEACHING THE ACTIVITY

▶ Have members of each group predict what they think will happen to the sizes of the "fill" and to the internal temperatures of the "operating" model landfills.
▶ Set up a "control" landfill model of soil and water only to provide comparative temperature data to that of the "operating" landfills.

PROGRAM RESOURCES

From the **Teacher Resource Package** use:

Activity Worksheets, pages 171-172, Activity 19-2: A Model Landfill.

Activity Worksheets, pages 176, Mini-Lab: Can one person make a difference?

ANSWERS TO QUESTIONS

1. Answers will vary.
2. Microorganism activity is most rapid in warm, moist environments. Decomposition rates tend to be significantly lower under dry conditions.
3. Rates of decomposition tend to be slower at lower temperatures.
4. The items are composed of different materials. Those that are more biodegradable, usually those composed of paper or soft organic materials, tend to decompose faster.
5. Plastics are not biodegradable and therefore do not decompose in a landfill.
6. developing "compost" piles for yard wastes so that they may be "recycled" or allowing them to remain on the ground to decompose in place
7. Foam containers are not biodegradable. Paper containers will decompose within a landfill. Many people are aware of this and will buy only products in containers that are apparently environmentally "safe." As this buying practice becomes more widespread, stores and producers will respond with more environmentally positive packaging.

SECTION 19-3

PREPARATION

SECTION BACKGROUND

▶ Paper loses quality with each reprocessing. Printing and writing paper can only be made from high-grade recycled paper.

▶ Some plastics are melted down and spun into polyester fiber that is used to make sleeping bags, insulation, and fishing line. Also, plastics can be made into rot-resistant materials for picnic tables, waterfront decks, boat hulls, bath tubs, and automobile body panels.

▶ Old tires can be shredded and used for fuel, new rubber, plastic products, and as substitutes for concrete in road pavement.

1 MOTIVATE

Cooperative Learning: Using the Expert Teams strategy, have students set up a trash recycling center at school. Students can maintain areas for collecting glass, metals, and paper. Any money obtained can be used for a class project.

▶ Have students respond to the following fact: Throwing away an aluminum can wastes as much energy as if the can were half full of gasoline. People in the United States throw away about 35 billion aluminum cans each year.

TYING TO PREVIOUS KNOWLEDGE: Most students already know the meaning of the term *recycle.* In this section, students will learn the many ways that the environment is helped when people recycle.

OBJECTIVES AND SCIENCE WORDS: Have students review the objectives and science words to become familiar with this section.

19-3 Recycling

New Science Words

recyclable
market
container law

Objectives

- ▶ List the advantages of recycling.
- ▶ Describe ways to promote recycling.
- ▶ Express your feelings about government control of recycling.

Should We Require Recycling?

1 If you recycle, you may be reducing the trash you will generate in your lifetime by 60 percent. If you don't recycle, you'll generate trash equal to 600 times your mass.

When an object is **recyclable,** it's suitable to be processed and used again. When you recycle, you help the environment in many ways. You save landfill space, energy, and natural resources. You reduce the damage caused by mining, cutting trees, and manufacturing. Let's see how.

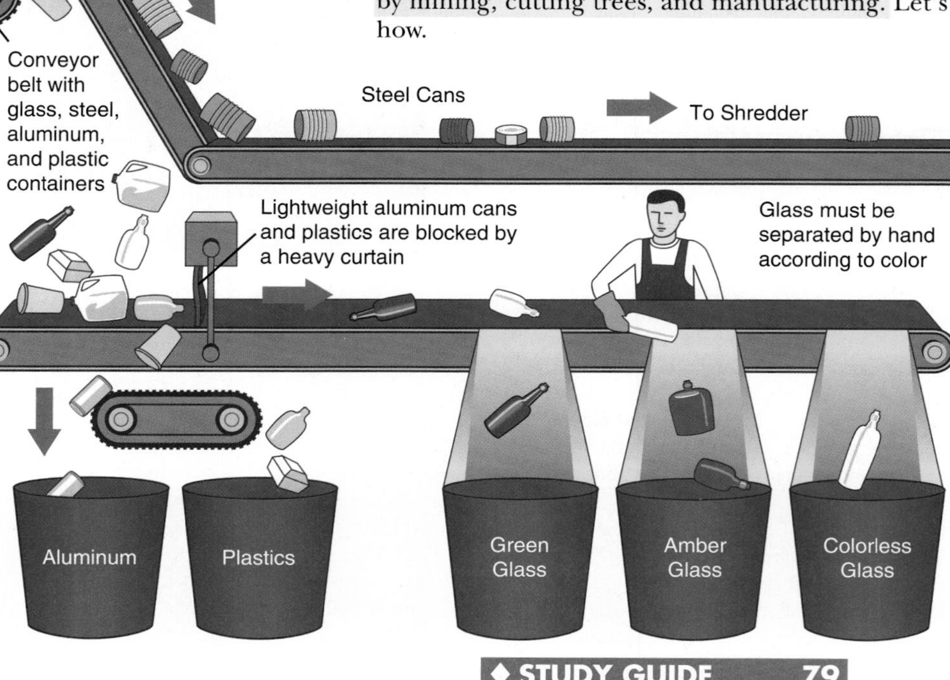

A magnet separates steel cans from the rest of the garbage
Magnet
Conveyor belt with glass, steel, aluminum, and plastic containers
Steel Cans
To Shredder
Lightweight aluminum cans and plastics are blocked by a heavy curtain
Glass must be separated by hand according to color
Aluminum
Plastics
Green Glass
Amber Glass
Colorless Glass

OPTIONS

Meeting Different Ability Levels

For Section 19-3, use the following **Teacher Resource Masters** depending upon individual students' needs.

◆ **Study Guide Master** for all students.

● **Reinforcement Master** for students of average and above average ability levels.

▲ **Enrichment Master** for above average students.

Additional Teacher Resource Package masters are listed in the OPTIONS box throughout the section. The additional masters are appropriate for all students.

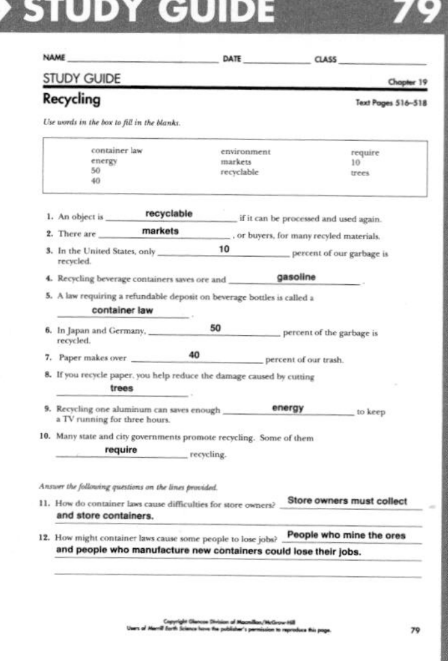

◆ STUDY GUIDE 79

NAME ______ DATE ______ CLASS ______

STUDY GUIDE — Chapter 19

Recycling — Text Pages 516–518

Use words in the box to fill in the blanks.

container law	environment	require
energy	markets	10
50	recyclable	trees
40		

1. An object is **recyclable** if it can be processed and used again.
2. There are **markets**, or buyers, for many recyled materials.
3. In the United States, only **10** percent of our garbage is recycled.
4. Recycling beverage containers saves ore and **gasoline**.
5. A law requiring a refundable deposit on beverage bottles is called a **container law**.
6. In Japan and Germany, **50** percent of the garbage is recycled.
7. Paper makes over **40** percent of our trash.
8. If you recycle paper, you help reduce the damage caused by cutting **trees**.
9. Recycling one aluminum can saves enough **energy** to keep a TV running for three hours.
10. Many state and city governments promote recycling. Some of them **require** recycling.

Answer the following questions on the lines provided.

11. How do container laws cause difficulties for store owners? **Store owners must collect and store containers.**
12. How might container laws cause some people to lose jobs? **People who mine the ores and people who manufacture new containers could lose their jobs.**

 79

Paper makes up more than 40 percent of our trash. If ❷ you recycle paper, you save lots of landfill space. Making brand-new paper from trees uses lots of water and pollutes the air. But recycled paper takes 61 percent less water and produces 70 percent fewer air pollutants.

Paper isn't the only thing that can be recycled. How much energy is saved by recycling one aluminum can? Enough to keep a TV running for about three hours. Twenty aluminum cans can be recycled with the energy needed to produce a single brand-new can from ore.

Why do you suppose more things aren't recycled? One reason is that some people haven't gotten into the habit of recycling. Another is that many areas still do not have recycling centers. But there is a business reason, too. Like anything else, recycling requires money to pay for workers, trucks, buildings, and energy. Recycling businesses have to make a profit, or they can't exist. The only way to make a profit in recycling is to sell the recycled material. This means there must be a market for the material. A **market** is the people and businesses that want to purchase the recycled material. In many cities, old newspapers aren't recycled because there's no market for the recycled paper. Businesses in the community can often buy new paper cheaper than paper that's been recycled.

In the United States, only 10 percent of our garbage ❸ is recycled. In countries with mandatory recycling, like

Did You Know?

It takes more than 500 000 trees to make the newspapers that people in the United States read each Sunday.

Why is a market necessary to the survival of recycling efforts?

● REINFORCEMENT 79

NAME ______ DATE ______ CLASS ______

REINFORCEMENT — Chapter 19

Recycling — Text Pages 516–518

Answer the questions on the lines provided.

1. What is a recyclable object? **A recyclable object is one suitable to be processed and used again.**
2. What are three reasons that paper should be recycled? **Answers should include three of the following: Fewer trees would be cut. Landfills would not fill as fast. Less water is needed to make paper from recycled pulp than from trees. There's less pollution.**
3. Why should aluminum be recycled? **Twenty aluminum cans can be recycled with the energy needed to produce a single brand-new can from ore.**
4. How do container laws help save landfill space? **When consumers return beverage containers, the containers aren't among the garbage taken to landfills.**
5. What do you think are the two best reasons for recycling everything that can be recycled? **Answers may include two of the following: Resources are saved. Energy is saved. Pollution will be less. Landfills will not be filled as soon.**
6. Why are markets important in a recycling program? **If people won't buy recycled products, no business can make a profit from them. Recycling businesses need to make money to pay for trucks, buildings, energy, and workers.**
7. List three ways governments encourage recycling. **Answers should include three of the following: They provide curbside collection or convenient drop-off facilities. They reduce trash-collection fees for a reduced amount of garbage. Some charge fines you if you don't recycle. Some have container laws.**
8. Do you think governments should require recycling? Why or why not? **Some students may say recycling is very important and if consumers will not recycle without laws, then they should be made, by law, to recycle. Others may say there are more important issues for lawmakers and police to concentrate on and so recycling should be voluntary.**

 79

▲ ENRICHMENT 79

NAME ______ DATE ______ CLASS ______

ENRICHMENT — Chapter 19

Recycling — Text Pages 516–518

MOVING DAY

Imagine that your family is moving. You and your sister and brother are responsible for everything in your rooms except the furniture. You are to pack what you want to take, dispose of what you don't want, and leave nothing in the house.

The evening you are to pack, you're the last one to arrive home and find your brother and sister have been very efficient. They tell you they've finished their sorting. The hallway is filled with large plastic bags. Each bag is numbered and labeled. You examine them carefully. The labels read as follows:

- old toys—trash
- summer clothes—move
- old records—trash
- old clothes—trash
- old makeup and medicine—trash
- books—move
- tapes and CD's—move
- school papers—trash
- science experiments from school—trash
- dead plants—trash

Of course you realize your brother and sister need to have conservation explained to them. Suggest they change their containers and explain why.

To help them re-sort their belongings, make a chart showing how to organize the things they want to get rid of. Suggest which items may be separated for reuse and recycling. Show them safe ways to dispose of other trash.

Category	Trash Items
Kind of packing containers to use	**recyclable cardboard cartons or reusable suitcases, trunks, boxes, etc.**
Reusable items	**old toys, old clothes**
Recyclable items	**metal, plastic (including records), school papers**
Hazardous items	**medicines, science experiments (perhaps), makeup**
Compost	**dead plants, science experiments (perhaps)**

 79

2 TEACH

Key Concepts are highlighted.

REVEALING MISCONCEPTIONS

▶ Many students will think that a community has to make money directly from selling recycled materials before recycling is financially worthwhile. However, in many communities, recycling is being done in order to reduce overall costs of waste management and to save landfill space and costs. Recycling is considered to be cost-effective if its operation costs are no more than the costs of waste disposal. A financial loss from a recycling program can be offset by not having to construct new landfill sites.

MINI QUIZ

Use the Mini Quiz to check students' recall of chapter content.

❶ **You can reduce the amount of trash you produce by 60 percent if you ____.** *recycle*

❷ **Paper makes up ____ percent of our trash.** *40*

❸ **In the United States, only ____ percent of our garbage is recycled.** *10*

CHECK FOR UNDERSTANDING

▶ Ask questions 1-2 in the Section Review.

▶ Ask students why people are not recycling more things. Answers will include: *Some people haven't gotten into the habit; many areas do not have recycling centers or the centers only recycle certain items; and there are not markets for some items.*

RETEACH

In order to demonstrate the importance of a market in recycling, have students respond to the following problem. "Suppose one of your friends starts a business by making bracelets out of metal scraps. You decide to help her by starting a recycling center for metal scraps. You offer to pay other friends for metal scraps, which you clean, sort, and sell at a profit to your jeweler friend. Predict what will happen if no one wants to buy her bracelets." *She will quit buying metal scraps, and the recycling business will end.*

3 CLOSE

► Have students research the meaning of the symbols and numbers marked on recyclable materials.

► Invite a local recycling company representative to speak to the class.

SECTION REVIEW ANSWERS

1. saves landfill space, energy, and natural resources; reduces damages from mining, logging, and manufacturing

2. provide curbside collection or convenient drop-off facilities, charge higher garbage fees to people who do not recycle, fine people who do not recycle, require local businesses to use recycled products, have a container law

3. No, many recyclable products are made from first generation raw materials.

EcoTip

Many items on grocery store shelves are packaged in *recyclable* containers. However, these packages are not always made of *recycled* materials. Buying recyclable packages only helps the environment if you make sure they go to a recycling center rather than a landfill.

Japan and Germany, 50 percent of the garbage is recycled. Many state and city governments are now promoting and even requiring recycling.

Some cities encourage people to recycle by providing curbside collection or convenient drop-off facilities. Other cities get even more involved. In Seattle, Washington, people who recycle pay lower trash-collection fees. People who reduce their weekly trash from two bags to one pay a lower fee.

In some places, if you are caught throwing away things that should be recycled, you'll be warned the first time. The next time, your garbage will no longer be picked up. Other governments fine you if you don't recycle.

To provide a market for recycled items, some states require local businesses to use recycled products. For example, the Ohio congress proposed a law to require newspaper publishers in Ohio to use some recycled paper.

Our federal government in Washington, DC, is becoming involved in recycling. A good example is the **container law,** which requires at least a five-cent refundable deposit on most beverage containers nationwide. This means paying five cents extra at the store for a drink, but getting your nickel back if you take the container back to the store. If everyone in the nation would participate in this program, we would save enough energy to light a large city for four years.

SECTION REVIEW

1. List at least four advantages of recycling.
2. List at least four ways that governments encourage recycling.
3. Are all recyclable products made of recycled materials? Explain.

SCIENCE & SOCIETY

You Decide!

The container law saves energy, natural resources, and landfill space. However, it means that store owners must spend time handling the containers and storing them. It forces each of us to recycle, so we can get back our deposits.

Although some new jobs are created by this recycling, some miners and people who make brand-new containers will lose their jobs. Do you think the government should pass laws requiring people to recycle materials? Do you think people will do it without such laws?

OPTIONS

YOU DECIDE!

Some will feel that the government must force recycling because we desperately need to protect the environment, and many people will not bother with the inconveniences of recycling unless forced. Others will feel that people should be allowed to voluntarily recycle. Voluntary recycling is working in many places.

ENRICHMENT

► The following is a quote from Chief Seattle of the Native American Suquamish people. His words were in response to President Franklin Pierce's offer to buy land from the Suquamish people in 1854. Chief Seattle expressed the difference in the way his people viewed the land and the way people of European descent viewed it. "...He treats his mother, the earth, and his brother, the sky, as things to be bought, plundered, sold like sheep or bright beads. His appetite will devour the earth and leave behind only a desert..." Ask students to respond to Chief Seattle's words. Students should relate his thoughts to their own view of how present-day Americans view Earth.

PROGRAM RESOURCES

From the **Teacher Resource Package** use:

Science and Society, page 23, Conservation and the Sierra Club.

Use **Laboratory Manual** pages 161-162, Conservation—Recycling.

CHAPTER
REVIEW

SUMMARY

19-1: Population Impact on the Environment

1. Each year, almost 90 million people are added to Earth's population.
2. The rapid increase in Earth's human population in recent years is due to an increase in the birth rate, advances in medicine, better sanitation, and better nutrition.
3. People in industrial nations strongly impact the environment when they use electricity, burn fossil fuels, contaminate water, and use food that's been grown with pesticides and herbicides.

19-2: Using the Land

1. Land is used for farming, grazing livestock, cutting trees, and mining coal and mineral ores. We also build structures and landfills on the land. Some land is preserved as natural environments.
2. Land becomes polluted by hazardous wastes thrown away by industries and individuals. Fertilizers and pesticides used by farmers pollute groundwater and soil. Mining can leave scars in the landscape and pollute underlying groundwater when the water comes in contact with certain minerals.
3. Recycling and reusing materials are important ways we can conserve natural resources.

19-3: Science and Society: Recycling

1. Recycling saves energy, natural resources, and the much-needed space in landfills.
2. Recycling is encouraged by curbside collection or convenient drop-off facilities. People who recycle may pay lower trash-collection fees. Container laws require a refundable deposit on containers.
3. Some people feel that laws are the only way to get people to recycle and conserve resources. Some people think that recycling should be an individual decision.

KEY SCIENCE WORDS

a. **composting**
b. **conservation**
c. **container law**
d. **hazardous wastes**
e. **landfill**
f. **market**
g. **population**
h. **population explosion**
i. **recyclable**
j. **sanitary landfill**

UNDERSTANDING VOCABULARY

Match each phrase with the correct term from the list of Key Science Words.

1. total number of individuals of a particular species in an area
2. describes the rapid increase in birth rate and decrease in death rate
3. area used to deposit garbage
4. trash that's dangerous to organisms
5. piling up organic material to decompose
6. careful use of resources
7. businesses or people that want to purchase a product or process
8. requires a deposit on containers
9. area lined with plastic, concrete, or clay where garbage is dumped
10. items that can be processed and used again

CHAPTER
REVIEW

SUMMARY

Have students read the summary statements to review the major concepts of the chapter.

UNDERSTANDING VOCABULARY

1. g
2. h
3. e
4. d
5. a
6. b
7. f
8. c
9. j
10. i

ASSESSMENT

To assess student understanding of material in this chapter, use the resources listed.

COOPERATIVE LEARNING
Consider using cooperative learning in the THINK AND WRITE CRITICALLY, APPLY, and MORE SKILL BUILDERS sections of the Chapter Review.

PROGRAM RESOURCES

From the **Teacher Resource Package** use:
Chapter Review, pages 41-42.
Chapter and Unit Tests, pages 129-132, Chapter Test.

CHAPTER

REVIEW

CHECKING CONCEPTS

1. b	**6.** d
2. d	**7.** c
3. c	**8.** c
4. d	**9.** d
5. b	**10.** d

UNDERSTANDING CONCEPTS

11. population explosion
12. landfills
13. composting
14. conservation
15. container law

THINK AND WRITE CRITICALLY

16. 90 000 000 people/365 days × 1 day/24 hours × 1 hour/60 minute = 171 people/minute

17. As the number of persons increases, the rate at which natural resources are used also increases.

18. Much of the energy contained in a plant is used up by livestock. One hectare of land used to grow vegetable crops can feed more humans than a hectare used to graze livestock.

19. Increased cattle populations would increase the amount of methane in the atmosphere.

20. Probably the biggest advantage of recycling paper is that it saves trees. Recycling paper also saves a lot of landfill space, energy, and water. Recycling also reduces air and water pollution.

CHAPTER

REVIEW

CHECKING CONCEPTS

Choose the word or phrase that completes the sentence.

1. Each year, almost ______ people are added to Earth.
a. 90 billion **c.** 90 000
b. 90 million **d.** 900 000 000

2. The population explosion is caused by ______.
a. modern medicine **c.** better nutrition
b. increased birth rate **d.** all of these

3. The United States uses about ______ percent of Earth's resources.
a. 5 **c.** 25
b. 10 **d.** 50

4. Forests are cleared in the U.S. for ______.
a. agriculture **c.** roads
b. mining **d.** all of these

5. Fertilizers and pesticides ______.
a. don't harm Earth **c.** are nontoxic
b. pollute groundwater **d.** fill up landfills

6. Some paper isn't recycled because ______.
a. there's no market **c.** it goes to landfills
b. there's no profit **d.** all of these

7. In a ______, garbage is covered with soil.
a. recycling center **c.** sanitary landfill
b. surface mine **d.** coal mine

8. An empty ______ fruit juice container causes the least harm to the environment.
a. clear plastic **c.** paper
b. glass bottle **d.** foam

9. Planting trees helps ______.
a. reduce erosion
b. slow global warming
c. remove atmospheric carbon dioxide
d. all of these

10. Recycling paper saves ______.
a. energy **c.** water
b. trees **d.** all of these

UNDERSTANDING CONCEPTS

Complete each sentence.

11. A rapid growth in the number of individuals of a certain species is a(n) ______.

12. Most of the trash in the United States is disposed of in ______.

13. Recycling leaves, grass cuttings, and other organic debris is ______.

14. Using less water is one example of the ______ of Earth's resources.

15. Imposing a(n) ______ that would require a deposit on motor oil cans could help reduce pollution.

THINK AND WRITE CRITICALLY

16. On average, how many people are added to Earth's population each minute?

17. What is the relationship between the number of people living on Earth and the rate at which resources are used?

18. Why is raising vegetable crops more efficient than raising livestock?

19. What relationship would you expect between increased cattle populations and methane in the atmosphere?

20. Discuss why recycling paper is good for the environment.

APPLY

21. A ten-minute shower uses 190 liters of water. If a person takes one shower a day and reduces the time to five minutes, how much water would be saved in a year?
22. Oxygen is considered a renewable resource. Explain why.
23. Although land is farmable in many developing countries, hunger is a major problem in many of these countries. Give some reasons why this might be so.
24. Forests in Germany are dying due to acid rain. What effects might this loss have on the environment?
25. Describe how you could encourage your neighbors to recycle their newspapers.

MORE SKILL BUILDERS

If you need help, refer to the Skill Handbook.

1. **Recognizing Cause and Effect:** Suppose a city decided to pave over a large, grassy lot. What effects will this have on the local environment?
2. **Measuring in SI:** If each person in your class produced 47 174 kg of trash in a lifetime, how much trash would be produced by this small population?
3. **Classifying:** Analyze the garbage you throw away in one day. Classify each piece of garbage.
4. **Making and Using Graphs:** In a population of snails, each snail produces two offspring each month. Each offspring also produces two offspring. Using the graph (above right), determine how many snails would be present after five months if the initial population was only two snails.

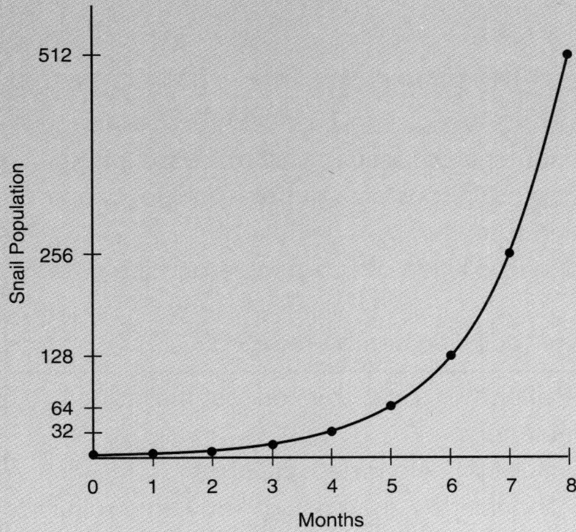

5. **Interpreting Scientific Illustrations:** Why does the curve of the line graph in Question 4 change its slope over time? Suppose half of the snails died after six months and draw a new graph to illustrate the effect.

PROJECTS

1. Use reference books and your knowledge of the environment to determine some of the problems you think will arise as the human population continues to increase. Discuss the problems and some possible solutions in a report.
2. Design an experiment to determine the factors that decrease the time it takes for newspapers or yard wastes to decompose.

APPLY

21. 190 L/2 = 95 L
95 L × 365 days = 34 675 L/year

22. Oxygen is constantly being added to Earth's atmosphere via photosynthesis.

23. Often, farmers can't afford machinery, improved strains of seeds, pesticides, or fertilizers. Insects often destroy crops. Lack of fertilizers causes the soil nutrients to become depleted.

24. Fewer trees are available to produce oxygen. Other vegetation is probably dying, too. The decrease in plants causes an increase in soil erosion. Species of plants and animals that depend on the forest habitat may become extinct if they are unable to adapt to the changes produced by the dying trees.

25. Answers will vary but might include providing collection bins in a convenient place or actually going door to door to collect the papers. If the interest were community wide, people might be given a monetary incentive to recycle.

MORE SKILL BUILDERS

1. Recognizing Cause and Effect: The habitat of many organisms living in the grassy lot would be lost. Less water will soak into the soil. Groundwater may be depleted. Also, the pavement will absorb more heat, causing the air temperature to be greater.

2. Measuring in SI: Answers will depend on the number of students in the class. By multiplying the number of students by 47 174 kg/student, the total amount of trash produced can be calculated.

3. Classifying: Classification schemes will vary but might include sorting by type such as organic or inorganic, or more specifically as organic, glass, aluminum, steel, paper, and plastic. Trash could also be classified as "throw away" or recyclable.

4. Making and Using Graphs: After five months, 64 snails were present.

5. Interpreting Scientific Illustrations: The growth rate is exponential. Each offspring contributes to the population growth, not just the original pair of snails. If half of the population died after six months, the population would drop from 128 snails to 64 snails. The growth would then begin doubling from there.

CHAPTER

20 You, Air, and Water

CHAPTER SECTION	OBJECTIVES	ACTIVITIES
20-1 Air Pollution (1 day)	1. **Identify** the sources of pollutants that cause photochemical smog, sulfurous smog, holes in the ozone layer, and acid rain. 2. **Describe** how air pollution affects people and the environment. 3. **Explain** how air pollution can be reduced.	**MINI-Lab:** *Do we have acid rain?* p. 529
20-2 Acid Rain Science & Society (2 days)	1. **Describe** the effects of acid rain on people, plants, water, and materials. 2. **Describe** activities that help reduce acid rain. 3. **Decide** who should pay the cost of reducing sulfur dioxide emissions.	**Activity 20-1:** *What's in the Air?* p. 533
20-3 Water Pollution (2 days)	1. **List** five water pollutants and their sources. 2. **Describe** ways that international agreements and U.S. laws are designed to reduce water pollution. 3. **Relate** ways you can help reduce water pollution.	**MINI-Lab:** *How hard is your water?* p. 538 **Activity 20-2:** *Water Use,* p. 540
Chapter Review		

ACTIVITY MATERIALS

FIND OUT	ACTIVITIES		MINI-LABS	
Page 523 dust cloth water soap	**20-1 What's in the Air? p. 533** small box of plain gelatin hot plate pan of water plastic lids (4) hand lends binocular microscope marker refrigerator thermal mitt	**20-2 Water Use, p. 540** home water meter	**Do we have acid rain? p. 529** rain/snow plastic container pH ion paper	**How hard is your water? p. 538** distilled water liquid soap samples of water from tap, nearby pond or well, and a local stream baby food jars (3)

CHAPTER FEATURES	TEACHER RESOURCE PACKAGE	OTHER RESOURCES
Skill Builder: *Concept Mapping,* p. 529	**Ability Level Worksheets** ◆ ***Study Guide,*** p. 80 ● ***Reinforcement,*** p. 80 ▲ ***Enrichment,*** p. 80 **MINI-Lab Worksheet,** p. 184 **Concept Mapping,** pp. 45-46 **Transparency Masters,** pp. 81-84	**Color Transparency 41,** Air Pollution Sources **Color Transparency 42,** pH Scale **Lab Manual:** *Smoke Pollution,* pp. 163-166
Technology: *Degradable Plastics,* p. 531 **You Decide!** p. 532	**Ability Level Worksheets** ◆ ***Study Guide,*** p. 81 ● ***Reinforcement,*** p. 81 ▲ ***Enrichment,*** p. 81 **Activity Worksheet,** pp. 178-179 **Science and Society,** p. 24	
Problem Solving: *What's Happening to the Fish?* p. 536 **Skill Builder:** *Interpreting Scientific Illustrations,* p. 539	**Ability Level Worksheets** ◆ ***Study Guide,*** p. 82 ● ***Reinforcement,*** p. 82 ▲ ***Enrichment,*** p. 82 **MINI-Lab Worksheet,** p. 185 **Activity Worksheet,** pp. 180-181 **Critical Thinking/Problem Solving,** p. 26 **Cross-Curricular Connections,** p. 24	**Lab Manual:** *Water Purification,* pp. 167-168
Summary Key Science Words Understanding Vocabulary Checking Concepts Understanding Concepts Think & Write Critically Apply More Skill Builders Projects	**Chapter Review,** pp. 43-44 **Chapter Test,** pp. 133-136 **Unit Test 7,** p. 137-138	**Chapter Review Software** **Test Bank**

◆ **Basic** ● **Average** ▲ **Advanced**

ADDITIONAL MATERIALS

SOFTWARE	AUDIOVISUAL	BOOKS/MAGAZINES
Water Pollution, Soft-Kat, Inc. *Air Pollution,* Educational Materials and Equipment Co. *Earth & Environment Investigations: Pollution Control,* Focus.	*Pollution Solution,* film, NASA. *The Problem with Water is People,* film, CRM Films. *The Big Spill,* video, NOVA (PBS). *Water: A Clear and Present Danger,* video, Coronet/MTI. *Deterioration of Water,* video, LCA. *Pollution of the Upper and Lower Atmosphere,* video, LCA. *Acid Rain,* video, Focus.	Greenland, Davis. *Guidelines for Modern Resource Management.* Westerville, OH: Merrill Publishing Co., 1983. Hardman, T.M. ed. *Water and Food Quality.* NY: Elsevier Science Publishing Company, 1989. Wellburn, Alan. *Air Pollution and Acid Rain: The Biological Impact.* NY: John Wiley and Sons, Inc., 1988.

CHAPTER

20

YOU, AIR, AND WATER

THEME DEVELOPMENT: Systems and interactions are themes of this chapter. Human activities affect and are affected by pollution of Earth's air and water systems. Interactions among humans and these systems are the foci of the chapter.

CHAPTER OVERVIEW

- **Section 20-1:** This section examines the causes of smog and acid rain and describes how air pollution affects human health. Ways of reducing air pollution also are presented.
- **Section 20-2: Science and Society:** How soil type determines the damage caused by acid rain and what can be done about acid rain are discussed. The You Decide feature asks students if people living in the Midwest should assume the entire financial burden to eliminate problems caused by acid rain.
- **Section 20-3:** Some of the causes and effects of water pollution are discussed. A few ways to reduce water pollution are explored.

CHAPTER VOCABULARY

photochemical smog	Clean Air Act
sulfurous smog	scrubber
acid rain	Safe Drinking Water Act
pH scale	Clean Water Act
acids	
bases	

CHAPTER 20

You, Air, and Water

OPTIONS

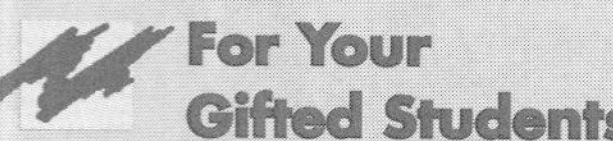

For Your Gifted Students

- Have each student write a story from the point of view of someone who comes to Earth from another planet to find smog, polluted water, and litter. Students could also write from the point of view of someone who lived 100 years ago and sees Earth as it is now.
- Have students brainstorm to compose a list of anti-pollution logos to promote conservation and recycling. They can also construct posters or banners that use the logos.

Most sources of drinking water are polluted. The water has to be treated with chemicals or filters before it's safe to use. Are any streams in your community severely polluted? What about the air in your area? Does it ever have a hazy appearance or unpleasant odor?

FIND OUT!

Do this simple activity to think about how the air and water are polluted.

Find a high shelf or the top of a tall cabinet—some place that hasn't been cleaned for a while. Run a cloth over the top and look at the dirt. This dirt was carried there by the air. This means that you are breathing in dirt like that all the time. Now, wash your hands. The dirt and the soap you used just went down the drain. It's on its way to a stream. Does your drinking water come from a nearby stream? Perhaps it's taken from underground aquifers. Either way, it's water that's been recycled by humans and nature after having been used before. Find out where the water that you use comes from and where it ends up.

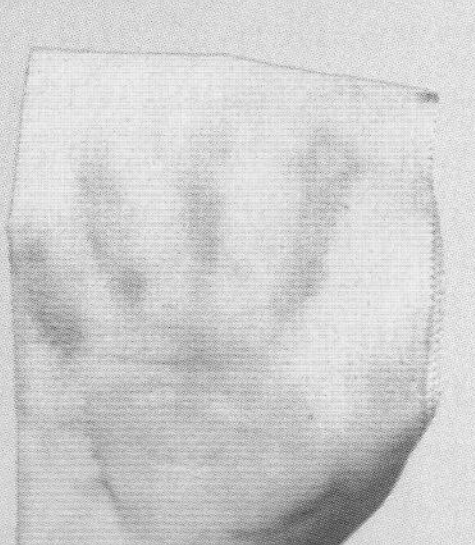

Gearing Up

Previewing the Chapter

Use this outline to help you focus on important ideas in this chapter.

Previewing Science Skills

- ► In the **Skill Builders**, you will make a concept map and make and use tables.
- ► In the **Activities**, you will collect and analyze data, make calculations, make inferences, and draw conclusions.
- ► In the **MINI-Labs**, you will experiment, observe, and infer.

What's next?

You've started thinking about how our air an water become polluted. Now you'll learn how pollutants get into air and water and what you can do to reduce pollution.

INTRODUCING THE CHAPTER

Use the Find Out activity to introduce students to a few air and water pollutants. Inform students that they will be learning more about pollution of Earth's atmosphere and hydrosphere as they read the chapter.

FIND OUT!

Teaching Tips

► You may want to have students review from Chapter 6 how materials are carried by the wind and from Chapter 7 how materials are carried through Earth's water system.

► Have one or two students summarize what was found regarding the local water supply.

Gearing Up

Have students study the Gearing Up feature to familiarize themselves with the chapter. Discuss the relationships of the topics in the outline.

What's Next?

Before beginning the first section, make sure students understand the connection between the Find Out activity and the topics to follow.

For Your Mainstreamed Students

► Invite an Environmental Protection Agency official to the class to talk about local pollution concerns. The official can work with the class to discuss ways they can help fight pollution.

► Ask students to get permission to observe several neighbors for one month. Students should record the number of bags of trash the neighbors put out each week. Have the students think about the correlation between the amount of trash and the number of people in the household.

SECTION 20-1

PREPARATION

SECTION BACKGROUND

▶ Despite the Clean Air Laws, more than 150 million people in the United States live in metropolitan areas where ozone and/or carbon monoxide exceed federal health standards.

▶ In U.S. cities where smog is a serious problem, systems have been installed to warn people when pollution reaches unsafe levels.

▶ Technology exists that enables pollution to be traced to its source when the pollutant is present in as little as one part per trillion parts of air.

PREPLANNING

▶ To prepare for the Mini-Lab on page 529, obtain glass or plastic containers and pH ion paper.

1 MOTIVATE

FLEX Your Brain

Use the Flex Your Brain activity to have students explore SMOG.

▶ Ask students if they think air pollution is much of a problem around the world. Many may think that the problem exists only in large cities in the United States. Inform them that so many children living in the northeast corner of Czechoslovakia have respiratory diseases caused by sulfurous smog that the government issues anti-pollution masks for them to wear to school. The masks help protect their lungs from the sulfur dioxide and dust produced by local coal-burning power plants.

PROGRAM RESOURCES

From the **Teacher Resource Package** use:

Activity Worksheets, page 5, Flex Your Brain.

20-1 Air Pollution

New Science Words

photochemical smog
sulfurous smog
acid rain
pH scale
acids
bases
Clean Air Act

Objectives

- ▶ Identify the sources of pollutants that cause photochemical smog, sulfurous smog, holes in the ozone layer, and acid rain.
- ▶ Describe how air pollution affects people and the environment.
- ▶ Explain how air pollution can be reduced.

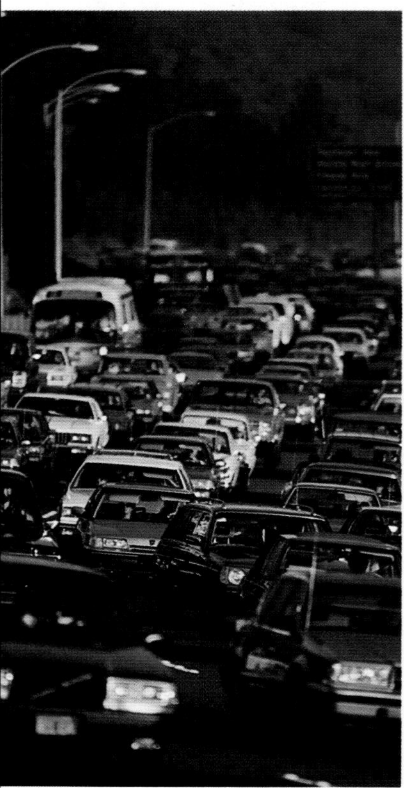

Figure 20-1. Cars are the main source of air pollution in the United States.

What Causes Air Pollution?

Have you ever noticed that the air looks hazy on some days? Do you know what causes this haziness? Air is everywhere, but its quality varies from place to place and day to day. Industries generate dust and chemicals. So, the more industries there are in a region, the more dust and chemicals there are in the air. Other human activities add pollutants to the air, too. For example, cars, buses, trucks, trains, and planes all burn fossil fuels for energy. Their exhaust—the waste products from burning the fossil fuels—adds polluting chemicals to the air. Other sources include smoke from burning trash and dust from plowed fields, construction sites, and mines.

Natural sources add pollutants to the air, too. Examples are volcanic eruptions, forest fires, and grass fires.

Both pollutants produced by human activities and those produced by natural processes cause the haze you sometimes see in the air. Around cities, polluted air is called smog, a word made by combining the words *smoke* and
1 *fog*. Two types of smog are common—photochemical smog and sulfurous smog.

Smog

In areas such as Los Angeles, Denver, and New York, a hazy, brown blanket of smog is created when sunlight reacts with pollutants in the air. This brown smog is called
2 **photochemical smog** because it forms with the aid of light. The pollutants get into the air when fossil fuels are burned. Coal, natural gas, and gasoline are burned by factories, airplanes, and cars. Heat from burning fossil

OPTIONS

Meeting Different Ability Levels

For Section 20-1, use the following **Teacher Resource Masters** depending upon individual students' needs.

◆ **Study Guide Master** for all students.

● **Reinforcement Master** for students of average and above average ability levels.

▲ **Enrichment Master** for above average students.

Additional Teacher Resource Package masters are listed in the OPTIONS box throughout the section. The additional masters are appropriate for all students.

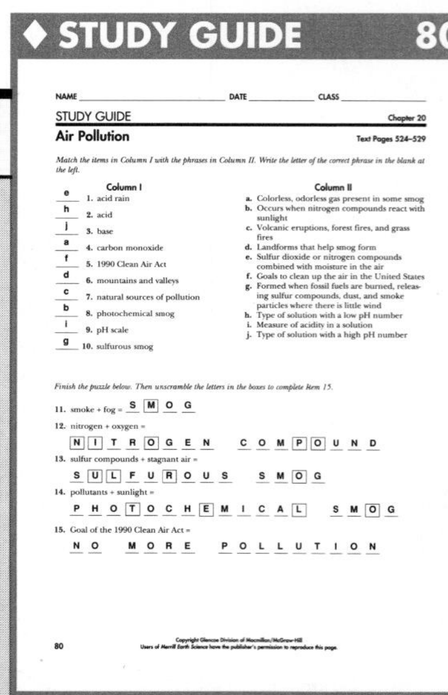

◆ STUDY GUIDE 80

NAME ______ DATE ______ CLASS ______

STUDY GUIDE — Chapter 20

Air Pollution — Text Pages 524–529

Match the items in Column I with the phrases in Column II. Write the letter of the correct phrase in the blank at the left.

Column I	Column II
e 1. acid rain	a. Colorless, odorless gas present in some smog
h 2. acid	b. Occurs when nitrogen compounds react with sunlight
j 3. base	c. Volcanic eruptions, forest fires, and grass fires
a 4. carbon monoxide	d. Landforms that help smog form
f 5. 1990 Clean Air Act	e. Sulfur dioxide or nitrogen compounds combined with moisture in the air
d 6. mountains and valleys	f. Goals to clean up the air in the United States
c 7. natural sources of pollution	g. Formed when fossil fuels are burned, releasing sulfur compounds, dust, and smoke particles where there is little wind
b 8. photochemical smog	h. Type of solution with a low pH number
i 9. pH scale	i. Measure of acidity in a solution
g 10. sulfurous smog	j. Type of solution with a high pH number

Finish the puzzle below. Then unscramble the letters in the boxes to complete Item 15.

11. smoke + fog = S M O G
12. nitrogen + oxygen = N I T R O G E N C O M P O U N D
13. sulfur compounds + stagnant air = S U L F U R O U S S M O G
14. pollutants + sunlight = P H O T O C H E M I C A L S M O G
15. Goal of the 1990 Clean Air Act = N O M O R E P O L L U T I O N

80

fuels causes nitrogen and oxygen to chemically combine to form nitrogen compounds. These compounds react with sunlight and produce other substances.

One of the substances created when sunlight reacts with waste gases is ozone. Recall that ozone in the stratosphere protects us from the sun's ultraviolet radiation. But ozone that forms in smog near Earth's surface causes health problems.

A second type of smog is called **sulfurous smog.** It's created when fossil fuels are burned in electrical power
3 plants and home furnaces. The burning releases sulfur compounds, dust, and smoke particles into the air. Sulfurous smog forms when these substances collect in an area where there's little or no wind. The stagnant air fills with a blanket of gray smog. It may hang over a city for several days and is hazardous to breathe.

Nature plays an important role in creating smog. Sunlight helps form photochemical smog. Sulfurous smog forms when weather systems are calm and the air is not being moved around. Also, sometimes a layer of warm air lies on top of cooler air. Normally, the warmer air is near Earth's surface. But in cases where the warm air is above, it becomes a barrier that prevents the cool air below from rising. The result is that cool, dense air full of pollutants is trapped near the ground. Eventually, the weather changes and cleaner air is blown in, dispersing the polluted air.

Science and MATH

Cars emit about 20 pounds of carbon dioxide for each gallon of gas they use. How much more carbon dioxide will a car that gets 20 miles per gallon emit than one that gets 30 miles per gallon if they both drive 18 000 miles per year? Convert your answer from pounds to kilograms.

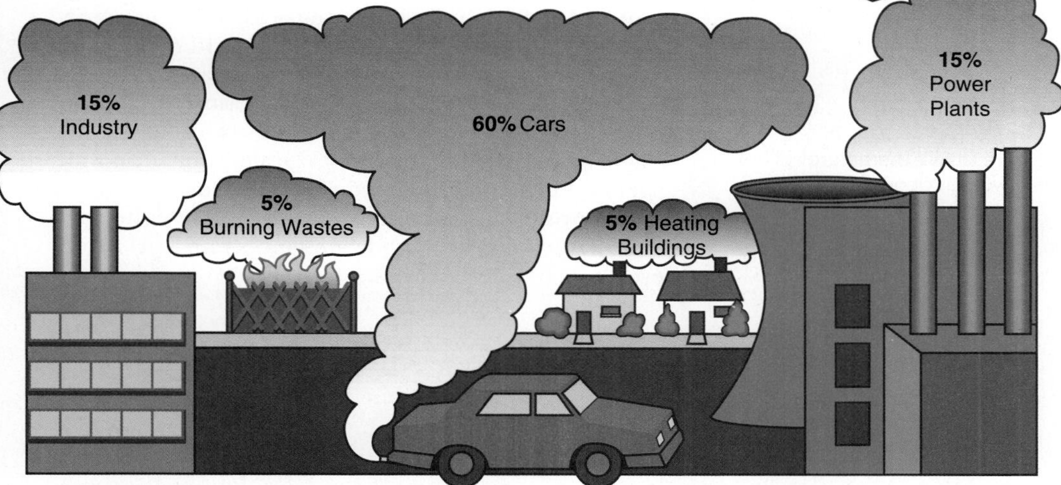

Figure 20-2. Proportions of Smog Caused by the Major Sources of Air Pollution

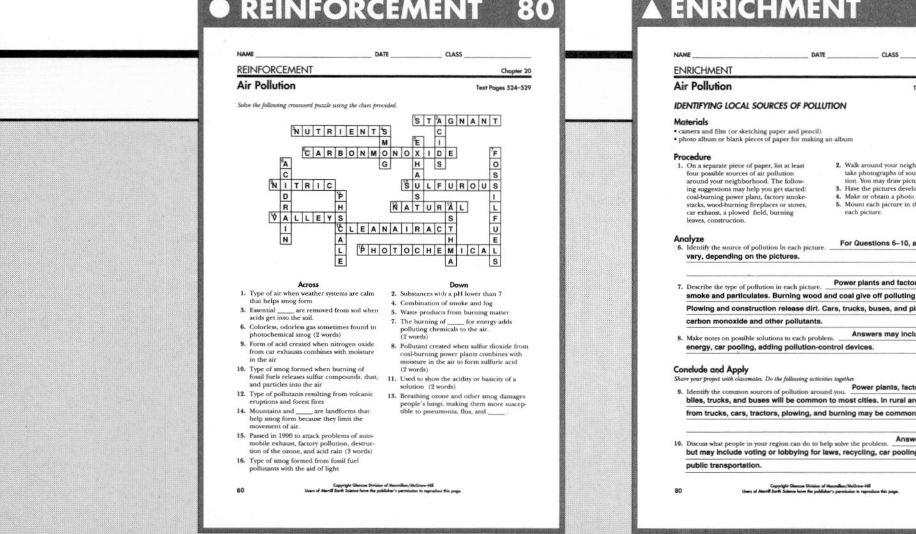

● REINFORCEMENT 80

NAME ______ DATE ______ CLASS ______

REINFORCEMENT Chapter 20

Air Pollution Text Pages 524–529

Solve the following crossword puzzle using the clues provided.

STAGNANT, NUTRIENTS, SMOG, ACIDS, EXHAUSTS, CARBONMONOXIDE, FOSSILFUELS, ACIDRAIN, NITRIC, SULFUROUS, PHSCALE, NATURAL, ASTHMA, VALLEYS, CLEANAIRACT, PHOTOCHEMICAL

Across

1. Type of air when weather systems are calm that helps smog form
3. Essential _____ are removed from soil when acids get into the soil.
6. Colorless, odorless gas sometimes found in photochemical smog (2 words)
9. Form of acid created when nitrogen oxide from car exhausts combines with moisture in the air
10. Type of smog formed when burning of fossil fuels releases sulfur compounds, dust, and particles into the air
12. Type of pollutants resulting from volcanic eruptions and forest fires
14. Mountains and _____ are landforms that help smog form because they limit the movement of air.
15. Passed in 1990 to attack problems of automobile exhaust, factory pollution, destruction of the ozone, and acid rain (3 words)
16. Type of smog formed from fossil fuel pollutants with the aid of light

Down

2. Substances with a pH lower than 7
4. Combination of smoke and fog
5. Waste products from burning matter
7. The burning of _____ for energy adds polluting chemicals to the air. (2 words)
8. Pollutant created when sulfur dioxide from coal-burning power plants combines with moisture in the air to form sulfuric acid (2 words)
11. Used to show the acidity or basicity of a solution (2 words)
13. Breathing ozone and other smog damages people's lungs, making them more susceptible to pneumonia, flus, and _____.

80

▲ ENRICHMENT 80

NAME ______ DATE ______ CLASS ______

ENRICHMENT Chapter 20

Air Pollution Text Pages 524–529

IDENTIFYING LOCAL SOURCES OF POLLUTION

Materials

- camera and film (or sketching paper and pencil)
- photo album or blank pieces of paper for making an album

Procedure

1. On a separate piece of paper, list at least four possible sources of air pollution around your neighborhood. The following suggestions may help you get started: coal-burning power plant, factory smokestacks, wood-burning fireplaces or stoves, car exhaust, a plowed field, burning leaves, construction.
2. Walk around your neighborhood and take photographs of sources of air pollution. You may draw pictures if you prefer.
3. Have the pictures developed.
4. Make or obtain a photo album.
5. Mount each picture in the album. Label each picture.

Analyze

6. Identify the source of pollution in each picture. **For Questions 6–10, answers will vary, depending on the pictures.**
7. Describe the type of pollution in each picture. **Power plants and factories emit smoke and particulates. Burning wood and coal give off polluting chemicals. Plowing and construction release dirt. Cars, trucks, buses, and planes produce carbon monoxide and other pollutants.**
8. Make notes on possible solutions to each problem. **Answers may include using less energy, car pooling, adding pollution-control devices.**

Conclude and Apply

Share your project with classmates. Do the following activities together.

9. Identify the common sources of pollution around you. **Power plants, factories, automobiles, trucks, and buses will be common to most cities. In rural areas, pollution from trucks, cars, tractors, plowing, and burning may be common.**
10. Discuss what people in your region can do to help solve the problem. **Answers will vary but may include voting or lobbying for laws, recycling, car pooling, and using public transportation.**

80

TYING TO PREVIOUS KNOWLEDGE: Have students recall from Chapter 9 that chlorofluorocarbons pollute the stratosphere by destroying the ozone layer. In Chapter 10, students learned how carbon dioxide and several other gases contribute to the greenhouse effect. Assure students that they will be adding to their existing knowledge of air pollution.

OBJECTIVES AND SCIENCE WORDS: Have students review the objectives and science words to become familiar with this section.

2 TEACH

Key Concepts are highlighted.

CONCEPT DEVELOPMENT

▶ Have volunteers differentiate among the natural and human-made sources of pollution.

▶ After students have read pages 524 and 525, ask these questions. **What kind of weather is usually associated with sulfurous smog?** *The air is calm. Sometimes a layer of warm air overlies cooler air, trapping pollutants in the cooler air.* **Explain the role of sunlight in producing photochemical smog.** *Sunlight reacts with gases produced when fossil fuels are burned. The pollutants that are formed are known as smog.*

TEACHER F.Y.I.

▶ Each year crop losses amount to about $5 billion due to ozone at Earth's surface.

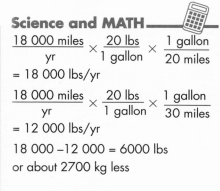

Science and MATH

$$\frac{18\ 000 \text{ miles}}{\text{yr}} \times \frac{20 \text{ lbs}}{1 \text{ gallon}} \times \frac{1 \text{ gallon}}{20 \text{ miles}}$$
= 18 000 lbs/yr

$$\frac{18\ 000 \text{ miles}}{\text{yr}} \times \frac{20 \text{ lbs}}{1 \text{ gallon}} \times \frac{1 \text{ gallon}}{30 \text{ miles}}$$
= 12 000 lbs/yr

18 000 –12 000 = 6000 lbs
or about 2700 kg less

CONCEPT DEVELOPMENT

▶ Before continuing with the section, be sure students can answer the following questions. **How do landforms affect smog development?** *Mountains restrict the movement of air.* **How do cars contribute to the acid rain problem?** *Nitrogen oxide from car exhausts combines with moisture in air to form nitric acid.* **If the pH of a substance is 4, is this substance an acid or a base?** *an acid*

TEACHER F.Y.I.

▶ The carbon dioxide content in Earth's atmosphere has increased 27% since the 1850s.

▶ It takes one large tree about 12 hours to convert the carbon dioxide exhaled by one person in one day into breathable oxygen.

Figure 20-3. Fraser firs on Mt. Mitchell, North Carolina, are dying from the effects of acid rain.

Landforms also affect smog development. For example, mountains may help cause smog by restricting the movement of air. Los Angeles has this problem because of nearby mountains. So does the city of Denver, in the Rocky Mountains. Some cities are in valleys, where dense, dirty air tends to stay.

Smog isn't the only air pollution problem we have. Recall from Chapters 9 and 10 that chlorofluorocarbons from air conditioners, refrigerators, and spray cans are destroying the ozone layer in the stratosphere. Carbon dioxide from burning coal, oil, natural gas, and forests is worsening the greenhouse effect.

Acid Rain

Another major pollution problem is acid rain. It has two sources. Acid rain is created when sulfur dioxide from
4 coal-burning power plants combines with moisture in the air to form sulfuric acid. Acid rain also is created when nitrogen oxide from car exhausts combines with moisture in the air to form nitric acid. The moisture becomes so acidic that when it falls to the ground, we call it **acid rain.**

What forms of precipitation can be acidic?

Actually, acid rain can fall as rain, snow, sleet, mist, or fog. As you might suspect, acid rain is very harmful to the environment.

What do you think would happen if you watered a plant with lemon juice instead of water? As you might guess, it would die. Lemon juice is a strong acid. Acid rain sometimes is as strong as lemon juice. Thus, acid rain can be strong enough to kill plants. To understand this, let's learn how the strength of an acid is measured.

We describe how acidic a solution is by using the **pH scale.** Figure 20-4 illustrates the pH scale. Substances with
5 a pH lower than seven are considered **acids.** The lower the pH number, the stronger the acid. The higher the number, the weaker the acid. Substances with a pH above seven are considered **bases.**

Figure 20-4. The natural pH of rainwater is about 5.0 in the eastern states. In the west, natural pH levels range between 5.3 and 6.5. Acid rain can have a pH of less than 3.0.

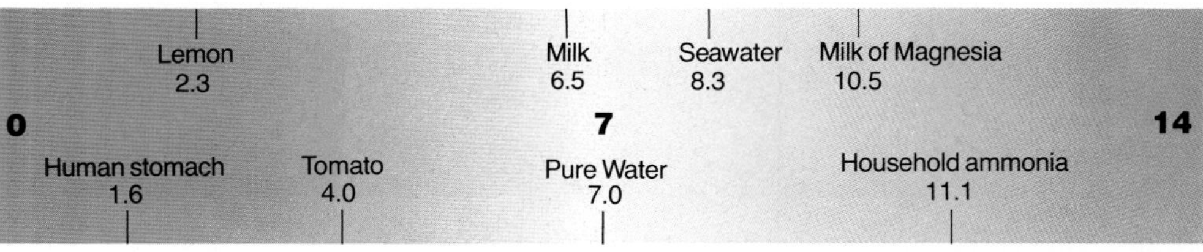

OPTIONS

PROGRAM RESOURCES

From the **Teacher Resource Package** use:

Transparency Masters, pages 81-82, Air Pollution Sources.

Transparency Masters, pages 83-84, pH Scale.

Use **Color Transparency** number 41, Air Pollution Sources.

Use **Color Transparency** number 42, pH Scale.

When acids get into soil, they remove essential nutrients. Acids also lower a plant's resistance to diseases, insects, and bad weather. This explains why many of Earth's forests are dying. Acid rain also increases the acidity of streams, rivers, and lakes, killing organisms that live in the water. It even damages the surfaces of buildings and cars.

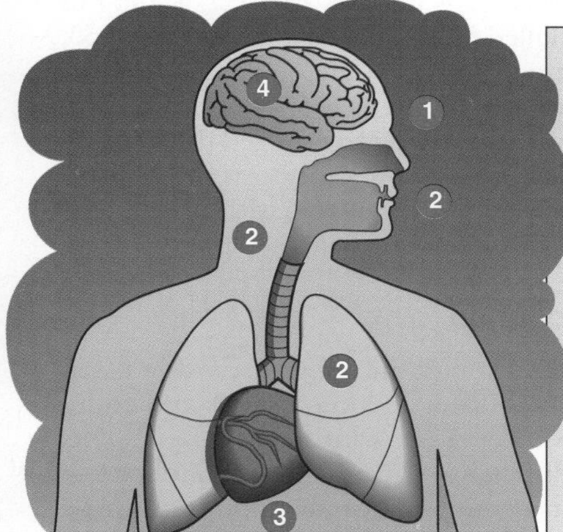

Effects of Air Pollution on the Body

1 Eyes
Compounds found in smog cause the eyes to water and sting. If conditions are bad enough, vision may be blurred.

2 Nose, throat, and lungs
Ozone irritates the nose and throat, causing burning. It reduces the ability of the lungs to fight infections.

3 Heart
Inhaled carbon monoxide is absorbed by red blood cells, rendering them incapable of transporting oxygen throughout the body. Chest pains result because of low oxygen levels.

4 Brain
Motor functions and coordination are impaired because oxygen levels in the brain are reduced when carbon monoxide is inhaled.

How Air Pollution Affects Our Health

Suppose you're an athlete in a large city and you're training for the big, upcoming competition. You have to get up at 4:30 A.M. to exercise. Later in the day, the smog levels will be so high that it won't be safe for you to do strenuous exercise. In southern California, Denver, and other areas, athletes adjust their training schedules to avoid exposure to ozone and other smog. Schools schedule football games for Saturday afternoons when the smog levels are low. Parents are warned to keep their children indoors when smog levels exceed certain levels. Breathing dirty air, especially taking deep breaths of it when you're actively exercising, causes health problems.

How hazardous is dirty air? Every year, between 40 000 and 100 000 people in the United States die from diseases related to air pollution. Breathing ozone and other smog damages people's lungs, making them more susceptible to diseases like pneumonia, flus, and asthma. Less severe symptoms of breathing ozone include a stinging chest, burning eyes, dry throat, and headache.

What are the physical symptoms of breathing ozone?

MINI QUIZ

Use the Mini Quiz to check students' recall of chapter content.

1. **What is smog?** *polluted air around cities*
2. **When nitrogen compounds react with sunlight, _____ smog forms.** *photochemical*
3. **When sulfur compounds, dust, and smoke particles collect in the air, _____ smog forms.** *sulfurous*
4. **_____ forms when sulfur dioxide or nitrogen oxide combines with moisture in the air.** *Acid rain*
5. **A substance with a pH lower than seven is a(n) _____ .** *acid*

CONCEPT DEVELOPMENT

► Have students write one or two paragraphs to describe the effects of acid rain on soil, plants, streams, and buildings. *Acid rain removes essential nutrients from soil. It lowers a plant's resistance to diseases, insects, and bad weather. Acid rain can kill organisms living in streams. Finally, it damages the surfaces of buildings and other structures.*

► Ask students if they or their relatives have suffered from health problems as a result of air pollution. Ask students to list health disorders related to polluted air. *pneumonia, flus, asthma, stinging chests, burning eyes, dry throats, headaches*

CROSS CURRICULUM

► **Health:** Have students research to find sources of indoor air pollution. Have them study the health effects of asbestos, formaldehyde, radon, cigarette smoke, and other substances found in houses.

PROGRAM RESOURCES

From the **Teacher Resource Package** use:

Concept Mapping, pages 45-46.

Use **Laboratory Manual,** pages 163-166, Smoke Pollution.

CHECK FOR UNDERSTANDING

Ask students who is responsible for protecting Earth's resources for future generations.

RETEACH

Cooperative Learning: Have Study Buddies review Section 9-2 on the ozone layer; Section 10-4 on the greenhouse effect; Section 18-1 on conserving fossil fuels; Section 19-2 on conserving resources, and Section 19-3 on recycling. Have the Buddies make lists of at least 15 things they can do to help reduce air pollution. Have a class contest to see which pair of Study Buddies can list the most items.

EXTENSION

For students who have mastered this section, use the **Reinforcement** and **Enrichment** masters or other OPTIONS provided.

3 CLOSE

▶ Have students identify sources of local air pollution. Then have them refer to maps showing the locations of the sources and local wind patterns. Have students predict where pollutants from the sources would be most concentrated.

▶ Invite a physician to talk with your class about health problems associated with air pollution.

▶ Ask questions 1-3 and the **Apply** Question in the Section Review.

Name two substances that compose photochemical smog.

Substances other than ozone make up photochemical smog. One is carbon monoxide, a colorless, odorless gas. Even in small concentrations carbon monoxide makes people ill. When the concentration rises, people can die. You've probably heard of people who died from carbon monoxide poisoning when they left their car running in a garage or when their car's exhaust leaked into the car.

Sulfurous smog also kills people. In 1952, a smog in London, England, killed more than 4000 people. In 1953, a New York City smog caused about 200 deaths.

What do you suppose happens when you inhale the humid air from acid rain? Acid is deposited deep inside your lungs. This causes irritation, reduces your ability to fight respiratory infections, interferes with oxygen circulation, and puts stress on your heart.

Reducing Air Pollution

Why does pollution in one state affect other states?

Pollutants moving through the atmosphere don't stop when they reach the borders between states and countries. They float wherever the winds carry them. This makes them very difficult to control. Even if one state or country reduces its production of air pollutants, those from another state or country can blow in. However, cooperation among states and nations can help. So can controls by governments. Let's examine what's being done.

In 1987, officials from more than 30 countries wrote a treaty to reduce the use of chlorofluorocarbons (CFCs). These nations agreed to cut the production of CFCs in half by the year 2000.

Table 20-1

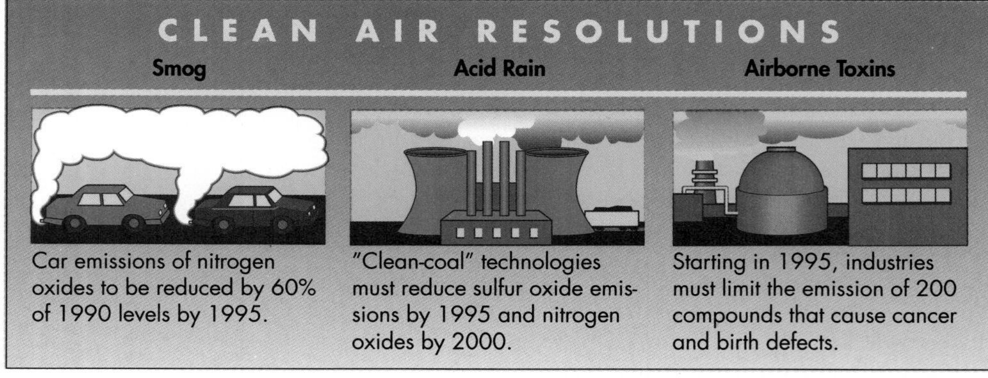

CLEAN AIR RESOLUTIONS
Smog
Acid Rain
Airborne Toxins
Car emissions of nitrogen oxides to be reduced by 60% of 1990 levels by 1995.
"Clean-coal" technologies must reduce sulfur oxide emissions by 1995 and nitrogen oxides by 2000.
Starting in 1995, industries must limit the emission of 200 compounds that cause cancer and birth defects.

OPTIONS

INQUIRY QUESTIONS

▶ **Why must all countries work together to control air pollution?** *Air pollutants float wherever the winds carry them. They are not stopped by political boundaries.*

PROGRAM RESOURCES

From the **Teacher Resource Package** use:

Activity Worksheets, page 184, Mini-Lab: Do we have acid rain?

The Congress of the United States passed several laws to protect the air. The 1990 **Clean Air Act** attacks the problems of automobile exhaust, factory pollution, destruction of ozone, and acid rain. In the figure on page 528, you can see some of the goals of the Clean Air Act.

Governments are passing laws to make everyone achieve the goals. The role of the federal Environmental Protection Agency is to check on progress toward the goals. The role of taxpayers and consumers is to pay the $50 billion or more each year to make the changes in industry and products necessary to clean up the air.

Governments are starting to do their part to protect our environment, but it's up to all of us to do what we can. The Clean Air Act can work only if you and everyone else cooperates. In Chapters 18 and 19 you discovered several ways you can save energy and reduce trash, such as using less electricity, recycling, and sharing rides. When you do these things, you also are reducing air pollution. We all must do our share to clean up the air.

MINI-Lab

Do we have acid rain?

The next time it rains or snows, use a glass or plastic container to collect a sample of several milliliters or centimeters of the rain or snow. Use pH ion paper to determine the acidity level of your sample. If you have collected snow, melt it before measuring its pH. Record the indicated pH of your sample and compare it to the results of other classmates who have followed the same procedure. What is the average pH of the samples obtained from this precipitation? How does the level of acidity in the samples compare to those shown on the pH scale in Figure 20-4 on page 526?

SECTION REVIEW

1. List the air pollutants, and their sources, that cause photochemical smog, sulfurous smog, holes in the ozone layer, and acid rain.
2. In what ways does air pollution affect the health of people?
3. How can you help reduce air pollution?
4. **Apply:** An earlier Clean Air Act, passed in 1970, required that coal-burning power plants use very tall smokestacks so that air pollutants would be injected high in the sky, where high-altitude winds would disperse them. Power plants in the midwestern states complied with the new law, but people in eastern Canada began complaining about acid rain. Explain the connection.

Skill Builder

Concept Mapping

Make a concept map that explains how sulfurous smog forms and how weather affects how long it persists. If you need help, refer to Concept Mapping in the **Skill Handbook** on pages 688 and 689.

Skill Builder

One possible solution is shown:

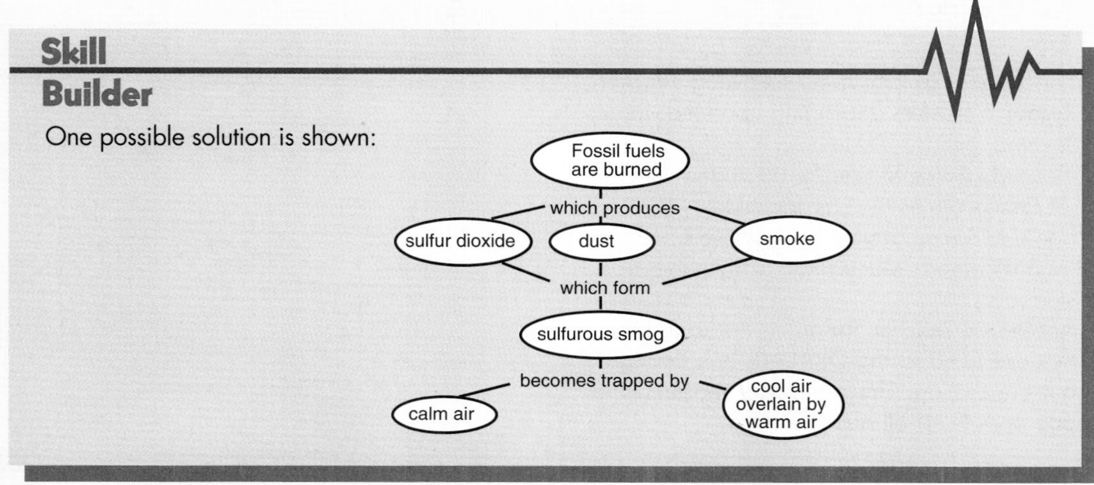

MINI-Lab

Materials: pH paper, small container

Teaching Tips

►Try to have students collect their samples at about the same time or, at least, from the same source of precipitation. Have students use the same chart to determine the pH levels of the samples.

Answers

►Students' samples should have reasonably similar pHs. The acidity of the precipitation will depend on the geographic location and the prevailing wind direction of the area.

SECTION REVIEW ANSWERS

1. Photochemical smog is produced when fossil fuels are burned and the wastes react with sunlight. Sulfurous smog results from sulfur oxide, dust, and smoke combining with moisture in the air. Holes in the ozone layer are caused by chlorofluorocarbons. Acid rain forms when sulfur dioxide and nitrogen oxide combine with moisture in the air. Most pollutants are the result of human activities.

2. Air pollution increases susceptibility to pneumonia, flus, and asthma; causes stinging chests, burning eyes, dry throats, headaches, stress on hearts, and sometimes deaths.

3. Answers may include: share in cost of cleaning air, use less energy, recycle, car pool, plant trees, stop using products with CFCs.

4. Apply: Sulfur in the smoke goes up the stacks and mixes with water vapor in the air to form sulfuric acid. Clouds drift northeast and drop acid rain onto Canada.

SECTION 20-2

PREPARATION

SECTION BACKGROUND

▶ Pyrite, or "fool's gold," is a common component of coal beds. When coal containing this mineral is burned, sulfur dioxide is produced.

▶ From 1950 to 1989, emissions of sulfur dioxide and nitrogen oxides doubled.

▶ Water with a pH of 5 or less is considered unlikely to be able to support most forms of life.

PREPLANNING

▶ To prepare for Activity 20-1, obtain the following materials for each Science Investigation group: a small box of plain gelatin, a hot plate, a pan, four plastic lids, a hand lens, a binocular microscope, a marker, and thermal mitts.

1 MOTIVATE

FLEX Your Brain

Use the Flex Your Brain activity to have students explore ACID RAIN.

Cooperative Learning: Have Paired Partners simulate acid rain by adding a few drops of lemon juice to a sample of tap water. Have them use pH ion paper and a pH color chart to determine the pH of the water. Then instruct them to slowly add just enough of a base, like baking soda or ammonia, to the water to neutralize the acid.

PROGRAM RESOURCES

From the **Teacher Resource Package** use:

Science and Society, page 24, Get the Lead Out.

Activity Worksheets, page 5, Flex Your Brain.

SCIENCE & SOCIETY 20-2 Acid Rain

New Science Words

scrubber

Objectives

- ▶ Describe the effects of acid rain on people, plants, water, and materials.
- ▶ Describe activities that help reduce acid rain.
- ▶ Decide who should pay the cost of reducing sulfur dioxide emissions.

Figure 20-5. pH levels of rainfall in the eastern states and Canada are dangerously low.

pH levels of rainfall

4.1–4.2 | 4.3–4.4 | 4.5–4.6 | 4.7–4.8 | 4.9–5.0 | 5.1–5.7

How Soil Type Determines Acid Rain Damage

You may live in an area where there is very little acid rain. The amount of acid rain in an area depends on the number of factories and cars in the area. They are the sources of the sulfur and nitrogen gases that become acid rain. Whether acid rain falls where you live also depends on patterns of precipitation and wind direction where you are. Even if industry and cars are producing a lot of pollution near you, much of it may be carried away by the wind before it falls back down as acid rain.

It's not just the volume of acid rain that falls that determines how much damage is
done in an area. There's another important 1
factor: the soil. Different types of soil react differently to acid rain. Some soils already are acidic, and acid rain makes them even more acidic. But other soils are basic. If you mix an acidic solution with a basic solution, they neutralize each other. Therefore, if acid rain falls on basic soil, the acid rain becomes partly neutralized and causes less damage.

Soils in the midwestern states are basic. So, when acid rain falls in the Midwest, it's neutralized in the soil. But some areas, such as the northeastern states and eastern Canada, don't have basic soils. In these places, acid rain makes the ground and groundwater even more acid. Plants and fish have evolved to live in the naturally acidic soil and water. The additional acidity from acid rain injures them.

OPTIONS

Meeting Different Ability Levels

For Section 20-2, use the following **Teacher Resource Masters** depending upon individual students' needs.

◆ **Study Guide Master** for all students.

● **Reinforcement Master** for students of average and above average ability levels.

▲ **Enrichment Master** for above average students.

Additional Teacher Resource Package masters are listed in the OPTIONS box throughout the section. The additional masters are appropriate for all students.

◆ STUDY GUIDE 81

NAME ______ DATE ______ CLASS ______

STUDY GUIDE — Chapter 20

Acid Rain — Text Pages 530–532

Use the words in the boxes to fill in the blanks.

acidic	factories	soil
basic	nitrogen gases	wind
cars	Midwest	sulfur

The amount of acid rain in an area depends on the number of **factories** and **cars** in the area. This is because they are the sources of **sulfur** and **nitrogen gases** that become acid rain.

Does acid rain fall where the pollution starts? It depends on the **wind**, which sometimes carries the pollution away.

When acid rain does fall, the damage it does depends partly on the kind of **soil** in the area. Some soils are already **acidic**, and plants that grow in them can't survive when more acid is added. Other soils are **basic**, and the damage is less when acid rain falls on these. As a rule, soils in the **Midwest** are basic and soils in the northeastern states are acidic.

sulfur	coal-burning	jobs
car exhaust	public transportation	car pooling
cost	scrubber	coal

Acid rain is created when moisture in the air combines with nitrogen oxide to form nitric acid. Do you know what the main source of nitrogen oxide is? It comes from **car exhaust**. Two ways people can help to reduce nitric acid are by **car pooling** and using **public transportation**.

Another source of acid rain comes from **coal-burning** power plants that release **sulfur** into the air. Power plants can help this situation in two ways. They can wash the **coal**, and they can run the smoke through a **scrubber**.

Why don't people insist that the power plants make their exhaust cleaner? Because the **cost** of electricity would increase and because many people could lose their **jobs**.

81

What Can Be Done about Acid Rain?

The main source of the nitric acid in acid rain is car 2
exhaust. Better emission control devices on cars will help
reduce acid rain. So will car pooling and public trans- 3
portation, because they reduce the number of trips, and
thus the amount of fuel used.

Coal-burning power plants can help correct the problem. Some coal has lots of sulfur in it. When the coal is
burned, the sulfur combines with moisture in the air to 4
form sulfuric acid. Power plants can wash coal to remove some sulfur before the coal is burned. This way, burning produces less sulfur in the smoke. And they can run the smoke through a scrubber. A **scrubber** sprays the exhaust with basic compounds that increase the pH to a safe level.

How does burning coal create acid rain?

Washing sulfur from the coal and using a scrubber lower sulfur emissions from coal-burning plants up to 90 percent. Unfortunately, taking these steps also raises the cost of generating electricity.

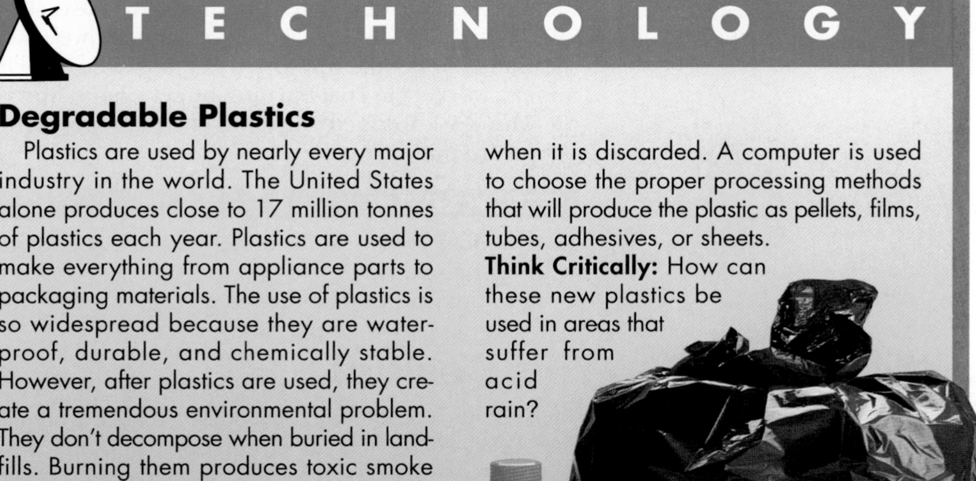

TECHNOLOGY

Degradable Plastics

Plastics are used by nearly every major industry in the world. The United States alone produces close to 17 million tonnes of plastics each year. Plastics are used to make everything from appliance parts to packaging materials. The use of plastics is so widespread because they are waterproof, durable, and chemically stable. However, after plastics are used, they create a tremendous environmental problem. They don't decompose when buried in landfills. Burning them produces toxic smoke that pollutes the air.

Concerns for these problems have caused a company in Switzerland to invent a new type of plastic that repels water during use, but decomposes into harmless residues when it is discarded. A computer is used to choose the proper processing methods that will produce the plastic as pellets, films, tubes, adhesives, or sheets.

Think Critically: How can these new plastics be used in areas that suffer from acid rain?

● REINFORCEMENT 81

NAME ____________ DATE ________ CLASS ________

REINFORCEMENT — Chapter 20

Acid Rain — Text Pages 530–532

Write an explanation for each statement on the lines provided.

1. A city produces a lot of air pollution, but never has acid rain.
Much of the pollution may be carried away by the wind before it falls as rain.
2. Some soils are damaged very little by acid rain.
Acid rain on a basic soil is partially neutralized.
3. Acid rain is not a serious problem in the Midwest.
Soils in the Midwest are basic.
4. Areas in the northeastern states and eastern Canada have problems with acid rain.
Soils in these areas are acidic.
5. Some plants and fish that live in acidic soils and waters die from acid rain.
They have evolved to live in naturally acidic soil and water, but the additional acidity from acid rain injures them.
6. Many power plants do not have scrubbers.
Scrubbers cost a great deal of money and add to the cost of electricity.
7. It will take years for fuel sources other than coal to be used.
Changing the kind of fuel used costs money because furnaces and boilers must be replaced.
8. The 1990 Clean Air Act gives companies until the year 2000 to reduce auto exhaust and sulfur dioxide emissions instead of asking them to do it immediately.
Such changes will cost billions of dollars.
9. Many people in the Midwest may lose their jobs as a result of the 1990 Clean Air Act.
Coal miners, workers in coal-burning power plants, and people who work for factories that burn coal may be without jobs if bituminous coal is banned.
10. People do not agree about who will pay to clean up the air.
Some people think the Midwest should pay for scrubbers and new power plants. Others think the whole United States should help pay for this.

81

▲ ENRICHMENT 81

NAME ____________ DATE ________ CLASS ________

ENRICHMENT — Chapter 20

Acid Rain — Text Pages 530–532

FINGERPRINTING POLLUTANTS

Public concern over acid rain has been growing. As a result, several laws have been passed in an effort to control it. In 1987, the National Acid Precipitation Assessment Program released a report that was based on the study of effects of some pollutants on major types of forests. Three of the pollutants are sulfuric acid, nitric acid, and ozone.

The data show that the effect of air pollutants is very complex. For example, acid rain alone appears to have little or no effect on seedling trees or on most farm crops. But ozone, often found with acid rain, seems to damage pine trees in mountain forests. Also, acid precipitation has been known to acidify lake water. The acid interferes with the ability of fish to obtain oxygen. The acid also interrupts the lake food chains by causing plants fed on by other organisms to die. Recent research shows that the local geological conditions and types of soil beneath and around lakes influence the amount of lake damage caused by acid rain. Lakes underlain by limestone show little or no damage. That is because limestone contains calcium carbonate, which is a base. The calcium carbonate neutralizes the acid. Most of the lakes that can be harmed by acid rain are those that are underlain by bedrock made of granite or quartz. They are located in the northeastern part of the United States.

Researchers now can "fingerprint" pollutants. They can tell, using special equipment, what part of the world or country a pollutant comes from. Researchers studying lakes Ontario and Erie were able to determine that the lead found in western Lake Ontario came from Canada. The lead found in southern Lake Erie came from the United States. Using "fingerprinting," or chemical analysis, investigators determined that most of the sulfur dioxide falling in the northeastern United States originated in the Midwest.

Shortly after the 1987 National Acid Precipitation Assessment Program report was published, the American Forestry Association recommended that Congress provide measures to control air pollutants that damage and kill trees. They made their recommendations. They were afraid that a delay in legislation would lead to more serious forest damage. In 1990, Congress did pass another Clean Air Act.

1. Why is it important to know where pollutants come from? **Once you know the source, you can begin to make changes to eliminate or reduce the pollution.**
2. If you were searching for the source of an airborne pollutants such as sulfur dioxide, what weather pattern would you look at to begin your search? Why? **The wind pattern, since the winds carry the pollutants from one place to another.**
3. What do you think is the value of legislation designed to reduce air pollution? **Answers will vary, but may include: Laws against air pollution have value because they require regulation that reduces damage to forests and lakes.**
4. What might be a drawback of such legislation? **Answers will vary, but may include: The costs of making changes to reduce air pollution may be so high that companies might have to go out of business or drastically raise their prices.**

81

TYING TO PREVIOUS KNOWLEDGE: Have students recall from Chapter 5 that soils evolve from weathered rock and organic matter. Because rocks and organic matter vary from one location to another, soils have very distinct pH values.

OBJECTIVES AND SCIENCE WORDS: Have students review the objectives and science words to become familiar with this section.

2 TEACH

Key Concepts are highlighted.

CONCEPT DEVELOPMENT

▶ Have students bring in soil samples and use a soil testing kit to determine the pH of each sample.

TEACHER F.Y.I.

▶ Nearly 14 000 lakes in Canada are "biologically dead" because of acid rain. Many lakes in the New England states and New York are also "dead."

TECHNOLOGY

▶ For information on recycling plastics, see "Recycling Polystyrene," by V. Elaine Gilmore, et al., *Popular Science,* February, 1990, pp. 41-42.

▶ Have students discuss whether or not "degradable" plastics are really "good" for the environment. Some students will realize that in order to decompose, the plastics must be subjected to conditions in which the presence of organisms, light, and heat are ideal. Because trash is buried daily in landfills, most plastics, even those promoted as "degradable," will remain in tact for hundreds of years.

Think Critically: The plastics can be applied to cars instead of wax and sprayed onto statues to protect them from the corrosive effects of acid rain.

CHECK FOR UNDERSTANDING

Use the Mini Quiz to check for understanding.

MINI QUIZ

Use the Mini Quiz to check students' recall of chapter content.

1. **Two factors that determine the amount of damage done by acid rain are _____ .** *the amount of acid rain that falls; soil type*
2. **The main source of nitric acid in acid rain is _____ .** *car exhaust*
3. **Car emissions can be reduced by emission control devices, car pooling, and _____ .** *using public transportation*
4. **Sulfur from burning coal combines with _____ to produce sulfuric acid.** *moisture in the air*

RETEACH

Have students debate whether people living in the United States should switch to fuel sources other than coal. Have students review the material in Chapter 18 before debating this issue.

EXTENSION

For students who have mastered this section, use the **Reinforcement** and **Enrichment** masters or other OPTIONS provided.

3 CLOSE

▶ Have students perform Activity 20-1.
▶ Ask questions 1-2 in the Section Review.
▶ Take students to visit a local coal-burning power plant.

SECTION REVIEW ANSWERS

1. Basic soils neutralize acid. If soil is acidic, acid rain will do a lot of damage.
2. Better emission-control devices on cars, car pooling, and mass transit will reduce nitric acid. Washing coal and scrubbing the exhaust gases from coal-burning plants will reduce sulfuric acid. Other fuel sources could be used in place of coal.

Figure 20-6. Pressure from environmental groups and the government is forcing coal-burning power plants to make expensive changes to reduce emissions. How much are we willing to pay for cleaner air?

Another thing we could do is switch to other fuel sources. However, recall from Chapter 18 that these have disadvantages, too. And even if everyone agreed to make fuel changes, it would take many years for some areas to change. This is because many people, especially in the midwestern states, depend on coal for home heating and generating electricity. Changing the kind of fuel used costs money, because furnaces and boilers must be replaced.

As you read in the last section, the 1990 Clean Air Act requires great reductions in auto exhaust and sulfur dioxide emissions by the year 2003. This will cost all of us billions of dollars. It especially affects the Midwest, where thousands of people will lose their jobs. These include miners, workers in coal-burning power plants, and people who work for factories. The economy where these people live will suffer.

SECTION REVIEW

1. How does soil type determine the amount of damage done by acid rain?
2. How can acid rain be reduced?

You Decide!

Much of the acid rain problem comes from coal-burning power plants in the Midwest. Some people think that these midwestern states should pay to clean up the problem. But others propose that everyone in the nation should pay for the cleanup. This would reduce the financial burden on the midwestern states. They also propose a job-protection program to help coal miners and others who might lose their jobs. Is this fair to everyone? Why or why not?

YOU DECIDE!

Some students will feel that the states with sulfur dioxide emission problems should be the ones to pay. Other students will argue that everyone should help pay for the cleanup because for many years the people living in the Midwest have been providing the rest of the country with energy and items it has manufactured using this energy. The job protection program would retrain people. This would help the nation's economy.

ACTIVITY 20-1
What's in the Air?

Problem: *What types of dust or particles are in the air in your area?*

Materials 

- small box of plain gelatin
- hot plate
- pan of water
- plastic lids (4)
- hand lens
- binocular microscope
- marker
- refrigerator
- thermal mitt

Procedure

1. Follow the mixing directions on the box of gelatin. Pour a thin layer of gelatin into each lid. **CAUTION:** *Wear a thermal mitt while working with a hot plate and while pouring the gelatin from the pan into the lids.*
2. Place the lids in a refrigerator until the gelatin is set.
3. Place the lids in four different locations in your community. Make sure that you choose places where the gelatin will not be disturbed.
4. After one week, collect the lids. Label each lid with its location.
5. Examine each lid with a hand lens.
6. Record your observations in a data table similar to the one shown in Data and Observations. Record whether the material on each lid is dust, large particles, or other materials.
7. Sketch some of the material found on each of your lids.
8. Sort the particulate matter (large pieces of dust, plant pieces, seeds, parts of insects, and so on) from each sample site.
9. Arrange these materials on microscope slides for each location.
10. Label the slides with the location from which each sample came.
11. Examine each slide with the microscope.
12. Try to identify what type of particulate matter you have collected.

Data and Observations

Location	Type of material	Description of material
1		
2		
3		
4		

Analyze

1. What sort of materials collected on each lid?
2. Rank the lids in order from the most solid particles to the least solid particles.
3. Which of the materials that were collected might be a result of human activities?
4. Explain why some areas had more and larger particles in the air.

Conclude and Apply

5. How does your body filter solid particles from the air you breathe?
6. Do any of the seeds that you might have collected suggest how some plants migrate from one area to another? Explain.
7. Try to identify what plants are responsible for the plant material on your slides. Try to identify the insect material. Were there any particles you could not identify?
8. Do you think any of the material you collected might be harmful to humans? Explain your answer.

ACTIVITY 20-1
25 minutes

OBJECTIVE: Determine the types of particulate matter in the air.

PROCESS SKILLS applied in this activity:
▶ **Observing** in Procedure Steps 5 and 11.
▶ **Classifying** in Procedure Steps 6, 8, and 12.
▶ **Inferring** in Analyze Questions 3 and 4 and Conclude and Apply Questions 5 and 8.
▶ **Interpreting Data** in Analyze Questions 1, 2, and 4 and Conclude and Apply Questions 6 and 7.
▶ **Experimenting** in Procedure Steps 1-12.

COOPERATIVE LEARNING Have Science Investigation teams of 3 or 4 students each perform this activity.

TEACHING THE ACTIVITY

▶ Most of the materials collected will be particulate matter, dust, and soot. Have students study maps that show the locations of nearby industries and weather maps that show local wind patterns. See if they can establish a correlation.
▶ Review the procedures for preparing and using microscope slides.
▶ Have groups reach a consensus about harmful effects of the samples collected and ways this pollution could be curbed.

PROGRAM RESOURCES

From the **Teacher Resource Package** use:

Activity Worksheets, pages 178-179, Activity 20-1: What's in the Air?

ANSWERS TO QUESTIONS

1. Most of the materials will be very small particles of dust and soot.
2. A hand lens should be used to assist the sorting.
3. Soot may come from industries, automobiles, public transportation, and sources of open burning. Dust may be in construction areas or where land has been stripped of vegetation.
4. Sources of the particles will vary. Also, wind patterns would keep some areas free of particulate matter.
5. fine hairs in the nose and mucous surfaces in the throat
6. Seeds migrate by wind, or are carried by animals or insects in some fashion. Some seeds have exterior "stickers," that become attached to animals.
7. Most students will find some they cannot identify.
8. Large particulate matter may be harmful if present in large quantities. Students may cite persons with respiratory illnesses as being at higher risk.

SECTION 20-3

PREPARATION

SECTION BACKGROUND

- The Clean Water Act of 1972 forbids cities to discharge sewage until 85% of the bacteria and pollutants have been removed. Some cities still do not comply with this law.
- Nitrogen and phosphorus are difficult to remove from sewage and wastewater. Large amounts of these elements are released into surface waters from household detergents, soaps, and other cleaning agents.
- Some of the toxins in Lake Erie originate from as far away as Central America. The toxins are carried there by wind.
- Substantial amounts of pesticides have percolated into well water in 34 states. Harmful levels of these pollutants are found in at least one of every nine wells tested. Unfortunately, more than 117 million people in the United States rely on underground wells for drinking water.

PREPLANNING

- Obtain samples of well or pond water, stream water, and distilled water, baby food jars, and liquid soap for the Mini-Lab on page 538.

1 MOTIVATE

FLEX Your Brain

Use the Flex Your Brain activity to have students explore SEWAGE TREATMENT.

- Invite a hydrogeologist to discuss the "health" of local streams and the groundwater supply.

PROGRAM RESOURCES

From the **Teacher Resource Package** use:

Activity Worksheets, page 5, Flex Your Brain.

20-3 Water Pollution

New Science Words

Safe Drinking Water Act
Clean Water Act

Objectives

- List five water pollutants and their sources.
- Describe ways that international agreements and U.S. laws are designed to reduce water pollution.
- Relate ways you can help reduce water pollution.

Causes and Effects of Water Pollution

Suppose you were hiking along a stream or lake and became very thirsty. Do you think it would be safe to drink the water? In most cases, it wouldn't. Many streams and lakes in the United States are quite polluted.

You learned in Chapter 12 how pollutants get into the oceans. Groundwater, streams, and lakes are polluted by similar sources. These pollutants cause health problems such as cancer, dysentery, birth defects, and liver damage in humans and other animals.

Our water is being contaminated from many sources. How do you think these pollutants get into the water? **1** Bacteria and viruses get into the water because some cities illegally dump raw sewage directly into the water. Underground septic tanks can leak, too. Radioactive materials can get into the water from leaks at nuclear power plants and radioactive waste dumps.

Figure 20-7. Your drinking water comes from nearby streams, lakes, or underground aquifers. In most cases, pollutants have to be removed before the water is safe to drink.

OPTIONS

Meeting Different Ability Levels

For Section 20-3, use the following **Teacher Resource Masters** depending upon individual students' needs.

- ◆ **Study Guide Master** for all students.
- ● **Reinforcement Master** for students of average and above average ability levels.
- ▲ **Enrichment Master** for above average students.

Additional Teacher Resource Package masters are listed in the OPTIONS box throughout the section. The additional masters are appropriate for all students.

◆ STUDY GUIDE 82

NAME ______ DATE ______ CLASS ______

STUDY GUIDE — Chapter 20

Water Pollution — Text Pages 534–539

A word has been scrambled in each of the following statements. Unscramble the word and write it on the line provided.

bacteria 1. Tests of rivers, streams, and lakes show that some have been polluted by **beairact** from raw sewage.
illegal 2. Dumping raw sewage is an **aglille** act.
radioactive 3. Barrels of waste from nuclear power plants may leak materials that are **taciodivera.**
aquifers 4. Water running through mines carries pollutants to underground **quaierfs.**
wash 5. Water is polluted every time you **shaw**.
reduce 6. Sometimes countries work together to **drecue** pollution.
quality 7. Canada and the United States made two water **lautiqy** agreements.
hazardous 8. **zhousdara** wastes poured directly onto the ground may move through the soil.
disposal 9. If you have a question about how to get rid of hazardous wastes, call your garbage **plaidoss** service for information.
energy 10. A way for individuals to reduce water pollution is to conserve **neegry**.

Complete the chart by listing each of the following sentences under the correct heading.

- The United States passed it in 1986.
- The United States passed it in 1987.
- It ensures that drinking water is safe.
- It gives money to states to build sewage plants.
- It gives money to states to build wastewater treatment facilities.
- It requires states to develop water quality standards for all streams.
- Some cities still do not meet its standards.

Safe Drinking Water Act	Clean Water Act
1. The United States passed it in 1986.	1. The United States passed it in 1987.
2. It ensures that drinking water is safe.	2. It gives money to states to build sewage plants.
3. Some cities still do not meet its standards.	3. It gives money to states to build wastewater treatment facilities.
	4. It requires states to develop water quality standards for all streams.

82

Pesticides and herbicides from farms and lawns are picked up by rainwater and carried into streams. Oil and gasoline spilled on city streets and highways are carried through storm sewers, or they run over the ground and into the nearest stream. Some people dump motor oil into sewers after they've changed the oil in their cars. Water running through mines also carries pollutants to streams and underground aquifers. Industrial chemicals get into the water because some factories illegally dump toxic materials directly into the water. Waste from landfills and hazardous waste dumps leaks into the surrounding soil and groundwater.

It may seem as if the greatest causes of water pollution are illegal dumping, carelessness, and accidents. However, this isn't the case. Most pollution is caused by legal, everyday activities. Water is polluted when we flush our toilets, wash our hands, brush our teeth, and water our lawns. It's also polluted when oil and gas run off of pavement into streams. We all contribute to polluting Earth's waters.

The average shower uses 19 liters per minute. If you take a 5-minute shower each day, how much water do you use in one year by showering?

Figure 20-8. Before our wastewater can be safely returned to the environment, it must be cleaned. The plant known as water hyacinth removes many pollutants from water. Water hyacinths can be used at wastewater treatment facilities to clean up water before it flows back into streams and aquifers.

Reducing Water Pollution

Several countries have worked together to reduce water
pollution. Let's look at one example. Lake Erie is on the
border between the United States and Canada. In the 2
1960s, Lake Erie was so polluted by phosphorus from
sewage, soaps, and fertilizers that it was turning into a
green, soupy mess. Large areas of the lake bottom had
no oxygen and, therefore, no life. Some people said the
whole lake was dead.

● REINFORCEMENT 82

NAME ______ DATE ______ CLASS ______

REINFORCEMENT — Chapter 20

Water Pollution — Text Pages 534–539

Complete the sentences below.

1. Most pollution is caused by **everyday, legal activities**.
2. Bacteria and viruses in the water can come from **raw sewage**.
3. Leaks from a nuclear power plant cause the water to be polluted by **radioactive materials**
4. Pesticides and herbicides in the water come from **farms and lawns**.
5. Factories pollute water by **illegally dumping toxic materials into the water**

Answer the following questions on the lines provided.

6. Both the Clean Water Act and the Safe Drinking Water Act were passed by Congress. How are the two acts different? **The Safe Drinking Water Act requires that cities provide safe drinking water for citizens. The Clean Water Act gives money to states for building sewage and wastewater treatment facilities. They may use the money to control runoff from streets, mines, and farms. The states are also required to develop water quality standards for all streams.**
7. If you wanted to dispose of hazardous materials, such as household chemicals or used oil from the car, where would you get information about their proper disposal? **Read labels on containers. Call sewage office, water office, or garbage disposal service for information.**
8. How does home water use add to pollution? **Any water that is used must be purified before it reaches the home, and it must be treated as wastewater after use in the home. Using fossil fuels for energy for these treatments adds to pollution.**

82

▲ ENRICHMENT 82

NAME ______ DATE ______ CLASS ______

ENRICHMENT — Chapter 20

Water Pollution — Text Pages 534–539

TRACKING TRACE ELEMENTS

Site	Trace element concentrations (mg/m^3)			
	Manganese	Copper	Lead	Zinc
1	9	12	38	11
2	11	14	42	13
3	10	13	39	10
4	11	14	41	13
5	13	13	44	13
6	13	13	44	14
7	13	13	44	15
8	9	11	41	14
9	11	11	44	13
10	12	13	46	15
11	11	11	43	11
12	10	10	41	10
13	12	11	35	10
14	7	8	31	8
15	6	7	31	6
16	11	11	42	11
17	16	14	43	16
18	13	11	38	12

Lakes and streams contain trace elements, or certain ions in solution, that are used by organisms for life processes. Recommended trace amounts of four elements are manganese, 50 mg/m^3; copper, 1000 mg/m^3; lead, 50 mg/m^3; and zinc 5000 mg/m^3. Larger amounts are toxic. The map shows a region where these four elements are mined and processed. To minimize pollution in some areas, all waste water is contained in settling ponds. Particles that carry much of the chemical waste are allowed to settle in these ponds before the water is pumped back into streams. The numbers on the map represent sites where water samples were collected. The table shows trace element concentrations at those sites.

1. What causes concentrations of trace elements to rise from Site 9 to Site 10? **A tributary from a mine region flows into Shenk's Creek between Sites 9 and 10.**
2. What causes concentrations to decrease from Site 10 to Site 11? **Rocky Creek flows into Shenk's Creek and dilutes the concentrations.**
3. Why would concentrations be low at Site 8, compared to the sites that feed into it? **Jones River may dilute the concentrations.**
4. Do settling ponds seem to be working? Explain. **Yes. The mine near Site 17 has no settling pond; its concentrations are higher than those at Site 18, which has one.**

82

TYING TO PREVIOUS KNOWLEDGE: Have students recall that in Section 12-4 they learned about one kind of water pollution—ocean pollution.

OBJECTIVES AND SCIENCE WORDS: Have students review the objectives and science words to become familiar with this section.

2 TEACH

Key Concepts are highlighted.

CONCEPT DEVELOPMENT

▶ Have students discuss various sources of water pollution. If there are any water pollution problems in your area, students may want to report on their causes and the steps being taken to correct the problems.

▶ After students have studied page 535, ask the following questions. **What causes most water pollution?** *everyday activities like flushing toilets, washing hands, brushing teeth, watering lawns, and water running off pavement* **How can runoff from a coal mine pollute groundwater with sulfuric acid?** *The sulfur in the coal mixes with the water, producing sulfuric acid. This acidic water travels through pores in the soil and into the groundwater.*

TEACHER F.Y.I.

▶ The Great Lakes contain 95% of the fresh water in the United States.

Science and MATH

$$\frac{19\ \text{L}}{\text{min}} \times \frac{5\ \text{min}}{\text{day}} \times \frac{365\ \text{days}}{\text{year}}$$

$= 41\ 975$ L/yr

PROBLEM SOLVING

Think Critically: The boys hoped to discover a phosphate source that was entering the farm pond. The pollution could be decreased by using different detergents and fertilizers and by altering the drainage pattern around the pond.

REVEALING MISCONCEPTIONS

▶ Many students probably think that if a particular pollutant is no longer added to a lake, it will disappear from the lake over time. However, this is not true with some pollutants. A group of chemicals called polychlorinated biphenyls (PCBs) were banned in the United States in 1979. However, they remain in high concentrations at the bottom of many lakes, where they have become trapped in the mud and have been passed through food chains.

CROSS CURRICULUM

▶ **Government:** Have students find out how a bill becomes a law in Congress.

PROBLEM SOLVING

What's Happening to the Fish?

Joe and Scott had been fishing the same pond for seven years. However, they had noticed that they seemed to be catching fewer fish during the past two years than they had when they first started fishing there. They were also aware that the algae cover seemed to be getting thicker each year.

Joe and Scott were learning about air and water pollution in their science class.

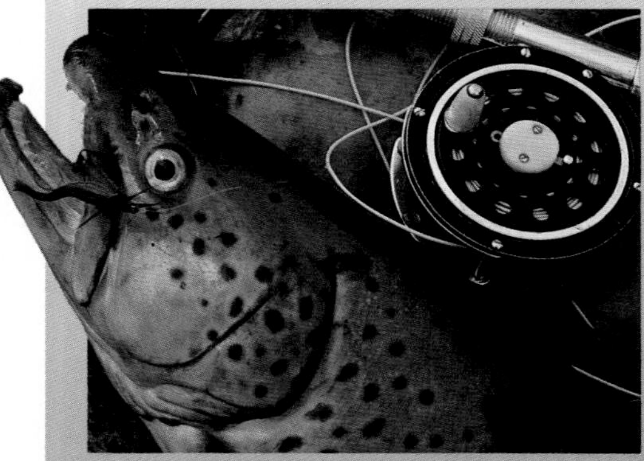

They learned that high levels of phosphates and nitrates in water can cause an increase in algae populations. As these algae populations die, they sink to the bottom of the body of water. Then, the decomposer populations increase. Oxygen in the water is used up by the large numbers of decomposers. Fish and other aquatic populations do not have enough oxygen to survive.

Joe and Scott decided to make some careful observations near their fishing spot. They found that a nearby farm had a septic tank system for waste disposal. They questioned the owners about the types of soaps and detergents that were used for doing laundry. They also asked if fertilizers were being used on the crops.

Think Critically: Why were Joe and Scott interested in this information? If they determine that the pond is being polluted, what could be done to decrease the pollution?

3 In the 1970s, the United States and Canada made two water quality agreements. The two countries spent $15 billion to stop the sewage problem. Today, the green slime is gone, and the fish are back. However, more than 300 human-made chemicals still are in Lake Erie, and some of them are very hazardous. The United States and Canada now are studying ways to get them out of the lake.

How has the U.S. government helped to reduce water pollution?

The U.S. Congress also has reduced water pollution by passing several laws. Two important laws are the 1986 Safe Drinking Water Act and the 1987 Clean Water Act.

The 1986 **Safe Drinking Water Act** is a law to ensure that drinking water in our country is safe. Most cities have been able to comply with this law. In fact, 87 percent of the 58 000 public water systems met the government

OPTIONS

PROGRAM RESOURCES

From the **Teacher Resource Package** use:

Cross-Curricular Connections, page 24, Making Posters.

Critical Thinking/Problem Solving, page 26, Pests or Pollution?

Use **Laboratory Manual,** pages 167-168, Water Purification.

standards in 1986. However, some cities still don't meet these standards. In 1990, about 30 million U.S. citizens still drank from potentially unsafe water supplies.

4 The 1987 **Clean Water Act** gives money to the states for building sewage and wastewater treatment facilities. It also is for controlling runoff from streets, mines, and farms. Runoff caused up to half of the water pollution in the United States before 1987. This act also requires states to develop quality standards for all their streams.

5 The U.S. Environmental Protection Agency (EPA) makes sure that cities comply with both the Safe Drinking Water Act and the Clean Water Act. Most cities and states are working hard to clean up their water. Many streams that once were heavily polluted by sewage and industrial wastes are now safe for swimming and fishing. However, there is still much more to be done.

For example, the EPA discovered that one-half of the 5000 disposal sites for hazardous wastes are leaking into the groundwater. Also, mineral residues from 10 000 abandoned mines are killing aquatic life in streams in the Rocky Mountains. At least ten percent of the nation's lakes are contaminated with enough toxic chemicals and metals to make them dangerous to aquatic life. Worst of all, much of the groundwater in the United States is polluted. Groundwater provides drinking water for more than 50 percent of the nation's population.

Did You Know?

About 380 liters of water are used to produce one pat of butter.

What is one function of the EPA?

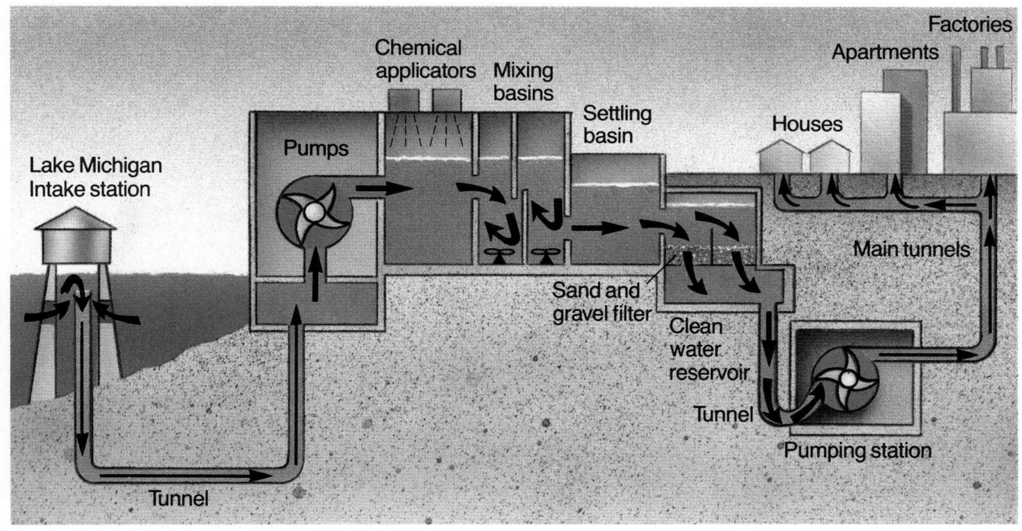

Figure 20-9. This water purification plant in Chicago provides drinking water for millions of people. Water taken from Lake Michigan is pumped into a tank where alum, chlorine, lime, and other compounds are added to kill microorganisms. It's thoroughly mixed and the large particles of matter settle out. Some smaller particles are filtered by sand and gravel. Clean water is then pumped to consumers.

CHECK FOR UNDERSTANDING

Use the Mini Quiz to check for understanding.

MINI QUIZ

Use the Mini Quiz to check students' recall of chapter content.

1. **Bacteria and viruses get into water because some cities illegally dump raw ____ directly into water.** *sewage*
2. **Lake Erie was so polluted by ____ in the 1960s that the water turned green.** *phosphorus*
3. **In the 1970s, the United States and ____ made two water quality agreements to stop polluting Lake Erie.** *Canada*
4. **The 1987 ____ Act gives money to the states for building sewage and wastewater treatment facilities.** *Clean Water*
5. **The ____ makes sure that cities comply with the Safe Drinking Water Act and the Clean Water Act.** *Environmental Protection Agency*

RETEACH

Cooperative Learning: Have Paired Partners make posters depicting sources and solutions to various kinds of water pollution. Hang the posters throughout the school building.

EXTENSION

For students who have mastered this section, use the **Reinforcement** and **Enrichment** masters or other OPTIONS provided.

ENRICHMENT

▶ Have students find out the source of the local water supply. Have them investigate who determines whether or not the supply is pure; how often the supply is tested; and how the wastewater is treated.

▶ Have students research the problems involved when polychlorinated biphenyls (PCBs) get into water.

CONCEPT DEVELOPMENT

▶ **Why should you never dump paint or oil directly onto the ground?** *They can leach into the soil and reach the groundwater.*

MINI-Lab

Materials: small containers with caps, liquid soap, water samples, distilled water, glass marking pen

Teaching Tips

▶ The temperature of each sample, the amount of each sample, the amount of liquid soap added, and the amount and force of the shaking all must be constant.

▶ Remind students to label the contents of each container.

▶ The distilled water will produce the most soapsuds and, therefore, will be the "softest" water sample.

Answers

The hardest water will be the sample producing the least amount of suds when the sample and liquid soap are combined and shaken. Scale in teakettles, clothes, dishwashing machines, hot water tanks, hot water heating systems, and industrial boilers is due to hard water.

PROGRAM RESOURCES

From the **Teacher Resource Package** use:

Activity Worksheets, page 185, MINI-Lab: How hard is your water?

MINI-Lab

How hard is your water?

When minerals such as calcium carbonate, magnesium carbonate, or sulfates are dissolved in water, the water is said to be "hard." This is a type of natural "pollution" that occurs in some areas. Test the hardness of the water in your area by placing samples of water from the tap, a nearby pond or well, and a local stream into a small container such as a baby food jar. Place an equal amount of distilled water into another container. Add one drop of liquid soap to each, cap each container tightly and shake each rapidly. Observe how many soapsuds are produced. Repeat the procedure several times with each container. The container with the most suds contains the softest water. What was the source of the hardest water in your experiment? What problems might be caused by having a hard-water supply in your home or community?

How Can You Help?

As you discovered in Chapter 19, we are the cause of our environmental problems. We also are the solution. What can you do to help? You can help by following some simple steps. For example, if you dispose of household chemicals such as paints and motor oil, don't pour them down the drain or onto the ground. Also, don't put them out with your other trash. Why not?

If you pour hazardous wastes directly onto the ground, they move through the soil and reach the groundwater below. When you pour them down the drain, they flow through the sewer, through the wastewater treatment plant, and into wherever the wastewater is drained, usually into a stream. This is how rivers become polluted. If you put wastes out with the trash, they end up in landfills, where they may leak out.

What should you do with these wastes? First, read the label on the container for instructions on disposal. Don't throw the container into the trash if the label specifies a different method of disposal. Recycle if you can. Many cities have recycling facilities for metal, glass, and plastic containers. Store chemical wastes so that they can't leak. If you live in a city, call the sewage office, water office, or garbage disposal service and ask them how to safely dispose of the others.

Another way you can reduce water pollution is to conserve energy. With less use of fuels there will be less acid rain falling into forests and streams. And with less nuclear power, there will be a reduced risk of radioactive materials leaking into the environment.

Another way you can help is to conserve water that comes from your tap. How much water do you use every

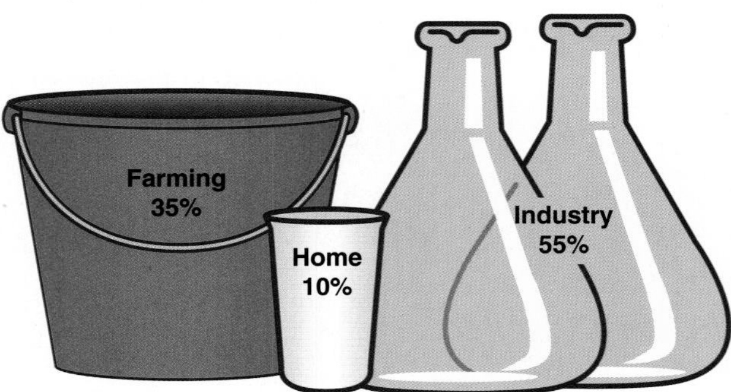

Figure 20-10. The industries that produce the products you use each day consume more than half of the freshwater used in the United States.

OPTIONS

INQUIRY QUESTIONS

▶ **Identify and explain the trade-offs involved when a person changes his or her lifestyle in order to conserve Earth's resources.** *Recycling takes time that could be spent doing other things. Conserving energy and water may require that a person give up some conveniences. For example, walking instead of driving to the store will save energy, but will take more time and effort.*

▶ **What is meant by the statement "one person's sewage is another person's drinking water?"** *The sewage produced by one community is treated and returned to streams or aquifers. It flows downstream to the next community where it is used as drinking water.*

day? Think of all the ways you depend on water. How many times do you flush a toilet each day? How much water do you use every day for taking a bath or cleaning your clothes? How much water do you use when you wash dishes, wash a car, or use a hose or lawn sprinkler? Typical U.S. citizens like you use between 265 and 568 liters every day.

All of this water must be purified before it reaches your home. Then it must be treated as wastewater after you use it. It takes a lot of energy to treat this water and pump it to your home. Remember, when you use energy, you add to the pollution problem. Therefore, when you reduce the amount of water you use, you prevent pollution. Simple things you can do to use less water include taking a shower instead of a bath and turning off the water while brushing your teeth. Can you think of other things you can do?

Water pollution is everybody's problem, and we must do our part to help reduce it. Consider changes you can make in your life that will make a difference.

EcoTip

After obtaining an adult's permission, fill a two-liter soft-drink bottle with water and seal it. Place it in your toilet tank. You can save more than ten percent of the water used to flush the toilet.

SECTION REVIEW

1. List five water pollutants and their sources.
2. Describe how the United States and Canada reduced pollution in Lake Erie.
3. What is the purpose of the 1987 Clean Water Act?
4. What are three things you can do to help reduce water pollution?
5. **Apply:** Southern Florida is home to nearly 5 million people, many dairy farms, and sugarcane fields. It's also the location of Everglades National Park—a shallow river system with highly polluted waters that are drying up. Why do you think they're drying up? What kinds of pollutants do you think are in the Everglades?

Interpreting Scientific Illustrations

Skill Builder

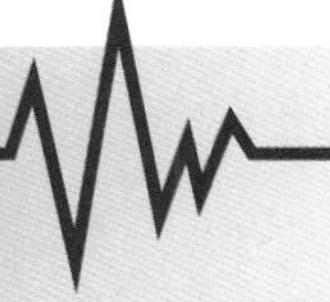

Use Figure 20-9 to answer the following questions: *Why are mixing basins needed? What's the purpose of the sand and gravel filter? Gravity forces the water through the system until it reaches the reservoir. Why is a pump needed after this point?* If you need help, refer to Interpreting Scientific Illustrations in the **Skill Handbook** on page 693.

Skill Builder

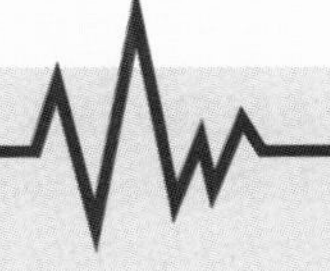

The mixing basin ensures that the added chemicals are dispersed throughout the water. The sand and gravel filter out microscopic impurities as the water drains through the pores. The reservoir is lower than the buildings that receive the water. Therefore, a pump is needed to work against the force of gravity and push the water upward.

STUDENT TEXT QUESTION

▶ Page 539, paragraph 1: **Can you think of other things you can do?** *Possible answers include making sure the water is turned off when not in use and only using dishwasher and washing machines for full loads.*

3 CLOSE

▶ Have students perform Activity 20-2.
▶ Ask questions 1-4 and the **Apply** Question in the Section Review.
▶ Have students produce a newspaper that deals with environmental problems. Distribute it throughout the school or community.

SECTION REVIEW ANSWERS

1. bacteria and viruses: human and other animal fecal materials; radioactive materials: radioactive wastes and some geologic deposits; pesticides and herbicides: agriculture; fossil fuels: spills, carelessness, and underground gasoline tanks, mines, and oil wells; industrial chemicals: manufacturing
2. They jointly spent $15 billion to stop sewage from polluting the lake.
3. The act allows monies to be given to build sewage and wastewater treatment facilities and reduce storm-water runoff from streets, mines, and farms. It also requires states to develop water quality standards for streams within their boundaries.
4. properly dispose of hazardous wastes or recycle them, conserve energy, and conserve water
5. Apply: They're drying up because more water is being removed than can be replaced by rainfall and runoff. Pollutants include bacteria and viruses from the cattle feces; pesticides and herbicides from the sugarcane fields; and fossil fuels and industrial wastes from the cities.

ACTIVITY 20-2
20 minutes

OBJECTIVE: Determine home water usage.

PROCESS SKILLS applied in this activity:
▶ **Observing** in Procedure Steps 1 and 3.
▶ **Using Numbers** in Procedure Steps 2 and 4 and Analyze Questions 2 and 3.
▶ **Interpreting Data** in Analyze Question 1 and Conclude and Apply Question 4.
▶ **Inferring** in Conclude and Apply Question 5.
▶ **Communicating** in Conclude and Apply Question 6.

TEACHING THE ACTIVITY

Alternate Materials: If your community uses only water from wells, you may supply hypothetical meter readings for the eight days so students can complete the activity.

▶ Be sure students understand the differences among the water meters and can identify which type is used in their homes.

▶ Make sure students understand the units in which water use is measured.

▶ After students have collected their data, make a list on the chalkboard or overhead projector showing the range of water use from highest to lowest for the class. This should be done without identifying which family is which. This will allow students to see how the rate of water use in their home compares to the usage by other families.

▶ For an interesting comparison, make arrangements with an earth science teacher from another part of the country, preferably an area that has a quite different climate or altitude, to do this activity during the same period of time with his or her class. Compare results and discuss the reasons for any significant differences.

PROGRAM RESOURCES

From the **Teacher Resource Package** use:

Activity Worksheets, pages 180-181, Activity 20-2: Water Use.

ACTIVITY 20-2
Water Use

Problem: *How much water does your family use?*

Materials
- home water meter

Background
There are several different types of water meters. Meter *a* has six dials. As water moves through the meter, the pointers on the dials rotate. To read a meter similar to *a,* find the dial with the lowest denomination indicated. The bottom dial is labeled 10. Record the last number that the pointer on that dial has passed. Continue this process for each dial. Meter *a* shows 18 853 gallons. Meter *b* is read like a digital watch. It indicates 1959.9 cubic feet. Meter *c* is similar to meter *b,* but indicates water use in cubic meters.

Procedure
1. Record your home water meter reading at the same time of the day for eight days.
2. Subtract the previous day's reading to determine the amount of water used each day.
3. Record how much water is used in your home each day. Also, record the activities in your home that used water each day.
4. Plot your data on a graph like the one shown. Label the vertical axis with the units used by your meter.

Analyze
1. During which day is the most water used? Why?
2. Calculate the total amount of water used by your family during the week.
3. Calculate the average amount of water each person used during the week by dividing the total amount of water used by the number of persons. Calculate a monthly average.

Conclude and Apply
4. Why is your answer to Question 3 only an estimate of the amount of water used?
5. How might the time of year affect the rate at which your family uses water?
6. What are some things your family could do to conserve water?

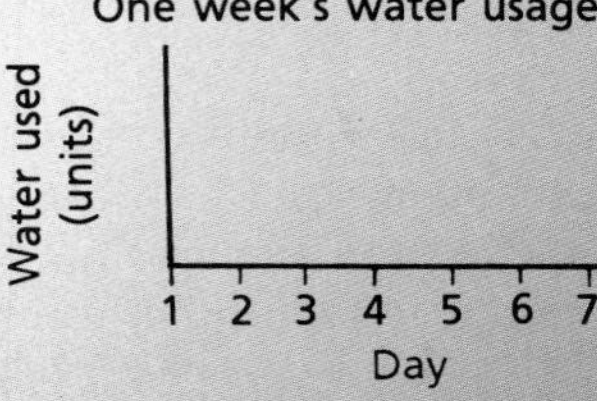

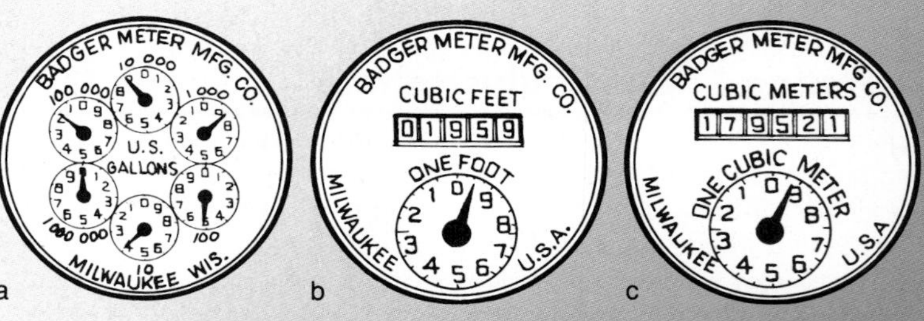

ANSWERS TO QUESTIONS

1. Answers will vary, but watering lawns or doing laundry may increase home water use.
2. Adding daily totals will give a weekly total.
3. Answers will vary. Discuss how the size of a family affects the average. Also, discuss reasons for weekly variations in the average.
4. This amount is an estimate because the week in which data were collected may not be typical.
5. It might be affected because lawn watering and car washing are seasonal activities.
6. Answers may include fixing leaky faucets, taking shorter showers, and not letting water run while brushing teeth.

CHAPTER REVIEW

SUMMARY

20-1: Air Pollution

1. Photochemical smog forms when fossil fuels are burned. Sulfurous smog is created when fuels are burned in electrical power plants and home furnaces. CFCs cause holes in the ozone layer. Acid rain is the result of burning coal and gasoline, which produce gases that react to form acids in the air.
2. Air pollution causes health problems in people and other organisms.
3. Recycling and conservation of Earth's resources reduce pollution.

20-2: Science and Society: Acid Rain

1. Acid rain can lower a plant's resistance to disease, insects, and bad weather. It can also kill organisms that live in fresh water by increasing the acidity of the water.
2. Better emission control devices on cars, car pooling, and the use of public transportation can help reduce acid rain. Washing coal that contains a lot of sulfur and using scrubbers can also reduce acid rain.
3. The cost of reducing sulfur dioxide emissions could be shared by everyone or could be limited to the areas that produce the emissions.

20-3: Water Pollution

1. Bacteria and viruses from animal wastes, radioactive waste, pesticides and herbicides used in agriculture, fossil fuels from mines and wells, and industrial chemicals from manufacturing processes all pollute freshwater bodies.
2. The passing of laws and the enforcement of these laws by the EPA and other agencies has helped to reduce water pollution.
3. Safely disposing of hazardous wastes is one way to reduce water pollution. Recycling and conservation are also important.

KEY SCIENCE WORDS

a. **acid rain**
b. **acids**
c. **bases**
d. **Clean Air Act**
e. **Clean Water Act**
f. **photochemical smog**
g. **pH scale**
h. **Safe Drinking Water Act**
i. **scrubber**
j. **sulfurous smog**

UNDERSTANDING VOCABULARY

Match each phase with the correct term from the list of Key Science Words.

1. smog that forms with the aid of light
2. smog that forms when pollutants mix with a layer of stagnant air
3. acidic rain, snow, sleet, or hail
4. law passed to protect air in the U.S.
5. a scale used to measure the acidity or basicity of a solution
6. device that lowers sulfur emissions from coal-burning power plants
7. law assuring water is safe to drink
8. law that controls stormwater runoff
9. substances with low pH numbers
10. substances with high pH numbers

OPTIONS

ASSESSMENT

To assess student understanding of material in this chapter, use the resources listed.

COOPERATIVE LEARNING

Consider using cooperative learning in the THINK AND WRITE CRITICALLY, APPLY, and MORE SKILL BUILDERS sections of the Chapter Review.

PROGRAM RESOURCES

From the **Teacher Resource Package** use:
Chapter Review, pages 43-44.
Chapter and Unit Tests, pages 133-136, Chapter Test.
Chapter and Unit Tests, pages 137-138, Unit Test.

CHAPTER REVIEW

SUMMARY

Have students read the summary statements to review the major concepts of the chapter.

UNDERSTANDING VOCABULARY

1. f	**6.** i
2. j	**7.** h
3. a	**8.** e
4. d	**9.** b
5. g	**10.** c

CHAPTER
REVIEW

CHECKING CONCEPTS

1. d
2. b
3. d
4. b
5. d
6. b
7. a
8. c
9. c
10. a

UNDERSTANDING CONCEPTS

11. Photochemical smog
12. sulfurous smog
13. acid rain
14. scrubber
15. Safe Drinking Water Act

THINK AND WRITE CRITICALLY

16. Both are forms of air pollution produced by the burning of fossil fuels. Photochemical smog forms when fossil fuels are burned by cars, planes, and factories. The waste gases react with sunlight to produce the smog. Sulfurous smog forms when fossil fuels are burned in electrical power plants and home furnaces.

17. Acid rain can form when sulfur dioxide from coal-burning power plants combines with moisture in the air to form sulfuric acid. Acid rain can also form when nitrogen oxide from car exhausts combines with moisture in the air to form nitric acid.

18. The number of factories and motor vehicles in an area increases the damage done by acid rain. Damage also is dependent upon certain weather factors. Finally, soil type can increase or decrease the effects of acid rain on the vegetation and groundwater of an area.

19. Radioactive wastes, pesticides, herbicides, and fossil fuels in freshwater sources are thought to cause cancer in humans.

20. Both were passed to help reduce water pollutants. The Safe Drinking Water Act ensures that all drinking water is safe. The Clean Water Act allots monies to states for building water treatment facilities. The Clean Water Act also requires that water quality standards be developed for all streams.

CHAPTER
REVIEW

CHECKING CONCEPTS

Choose the word or phrase that completes the sentence.

1. Dust gets into the air from ______.
a. cars and buses **c.** trucks and trains
b. factories and farms **d.** all of these

2. _____ forms when chemicals mix with sunlight.
a. pH **c.** Sulfurous smog
b. Photochemical smog **d.** Acid rain

3. Smog development is controlled by ______.
a. weather patterns **c.** mountains
b. sunlight **d.** all of these

4. Acid rain can form when ______ combines with moisture in the air.
a. ozone **c.** carbon dioxide
b. sulfur dioxide **d.** none of these

5. Air pollution can be reduced by ______ .
a. using less CFCs **c.** recycling
b. sharing rides **d.** all of these

6. One goal of the ______ Act is to reduce the level of car emissions.
a. Clean Water **c.** Safe Drinking Water
b. Clean Air **d.** all of these

7. Acid rain has a pH ______.
a. less than 5.5 **c.** greater than 7.0
b. between 5.5 and 7.0 **d.** greater than 9.5

8. The damage done by acid rain depends on ______.
a. the pH scale **c.** soil type
b. nitrogen emissions **d.** groundwater sources

9. Most water pollution is caused by ______.
a. illegal dumping
b. industrial chemicals
c. everyday water use in the home
d. wastewater treatment facilities

10. The ______ Act gives money to local governments to treat wastewater.
a. Clean Water **c.** Safe Drinking Water
b. Clean Air **d.** all of these

UNDERSTANDING CONCEPTS

Complete each sentence.

11. ______ forms when the gases produced by burning fossil fuels react with sunlight.
12. Weather plays an important role in the time it takes for ______ to disperse from an area.
13. Precipitation that forms when certain gases mix with the air is called ______.
14. A(n) ______ can prevent harmful substances from burning coal from getting into the air.
15. The ______ requires that water for human consumption be safe.

THINK AND WRITE CRITICALLY

16. Compare and contrast photochemical smog and sulfurous smog.
17. Explain two ways in which acid rain can form.
18. Discuss the factors that affect the severity of the damage done by acid rain.
19. Which water pollutants are thought to cause cancer in humans?
20. Compare and contrast the Safe Drinking Water Act with the Clean Water Act.

APPLY

21. How might cities with smog problems lessen the dangers to people who live and work in the cities?
22. How are industries both helpful and harmful to humans?
23. How do trees help to reduce air pollution?
24. Thermal pollution occurs when heated water is dumped into a nearby water body. What effects does this type of pollution have on organisms in the water bodies?
25. What steps might a community in a desert area take to cope with the water supply problems?

MORE SKILL BUILDERS

If you need help, refer to the Skill Handbook.

1. **Hypothesizing:** Earth is nearly 75 percent water. Yet, much of this water is not available for many uses. Explain.
2. **Recognizing Cause and Effect:** What effect will an increase in the human population have on the need for fresh water?
3. **Classifying:** If a smog is brownish in color, is it sulfurous or photochemical smog?
4. **Concept Mapping:** Copy and complete the concept map of the water cycle. Indicate how humans interrupt the cycle. Use the phrases: *Evaporation occurs, Purified, Drinking water, Atmospheric water,* and *Wastewater.*

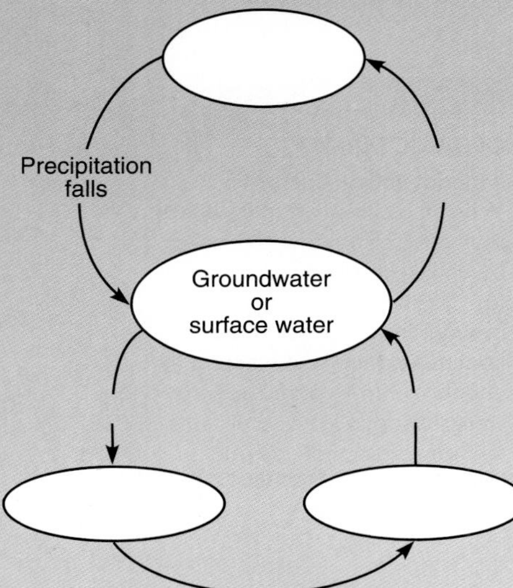

5. **Outlining:** Make an outline that summarizes what you personally can do to reduce air pollution.

PROJECTS

1. Design an experiment to test the effects of acid rain on various kinds of vegetation.
2. Design an experiment to determine which kind of sediment—gravel, sand, or clay—is most effective in filtering pollutants from water.

APPLY

21. Cities could broadcast health alerts that would take effect when the amount of pollutants in the air surpasses a certain level. At these times, factories that contribute to the pollution could be closed and people with respiratory problems would be advised to stay indoors.
22. Most industries provide products that improve the quality of life. However, many by-products of industrial processes pollute Earth's air, water, and soil.
23. Trees reduce the amount of carbon dioxide in the air because all green plants use this gas to photosynthesize.
24. The heat could kill organisms and cause excessive evaporation of water. Evaporation can cause substances in the water to become concentrated, which could cause organisms to become sick and perhaps die.
25. Desert dwellers must pump groundwater or pipe in surface waters. The water must then be stored in covered containers to reduce evaporation. Conservation also would be important in such communities.

MORE SKILL BUILDERS

1. Hypothesizing: Much of the water at Earth's surface is salt water, which must be processed before being used in most instances.
2. Recognizing Cause and Effect: An increase in the human population would increase the demand for fresh water.
3. Classifying: photochemical smog
4. Concept Mapping: One possible solution is shown below.

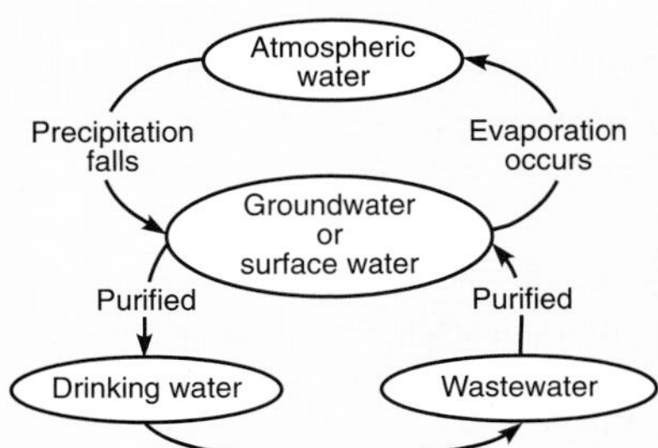

5. Outlining: Outlines will vary. Points may include walking or cycling to nearby places, recycling resources, planting trees, reducing wastes, and conservation of all resources.

UNIT 7
GLOBAL CONNECTIONS

Objective
In this unit ending feature, the unit topic, "Earth's Resources," is extended into other disciplines. Students will see how the study of natural resources is related to other disciplines as well as aspects of everyday life.

Motivate
Cooperative Learning: Assign one Connection to each group of students. Using the Expert Teams strategy have each group research to find out more about the geographic locations of the Connection—its climate, cultures, plants, animals, and ecological issues.

Wrap-Up
After students have reviewed all the boxes on these pages, ask them to form a hypothesis about why industrialized nations are the biggest air polluters, even though they are making the greatest effort to clean up the air.

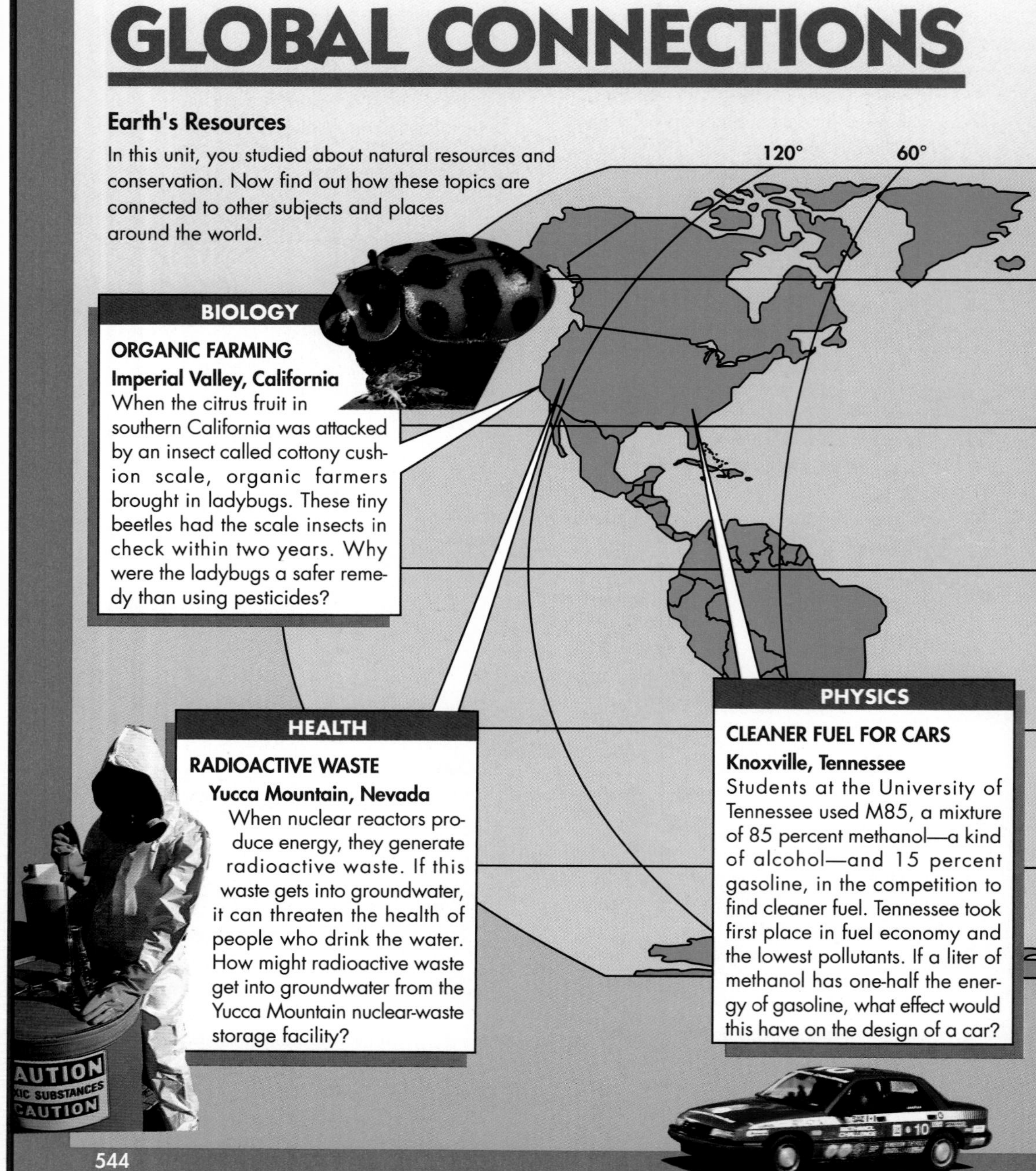

UNIT 7
GLOBAL CONNECTIONS
Earth's Resources
In this unit, you studied about natural resources and conservation. Now find out how these topics are connected to other subjects and places around the world.
120°
60°
BIOLOGY
ORGANIC FARMING
Imperial Valley, California
When the citrus fruit in southern California was attacked by an insect called cottony cushion scale, organic farmers brought in ladybugs. These tiny beetles had the scale insects in check within two years. Why were the ladybugs a safer remedy than using pesticides?
HEALTH
RADIOACTIVE WASTE
Yucca Mountain, Nevada
When nuclear reactors produce energy, they generate radioactive waste. If this waste gets into groundwater, it can threaten the health of people who drink the water. How might radioactive waste get into groundwater from the Yucca Mountain nuclear-waste storage facility?
PHYSICS
CLEANER FUEL FOR CARS
Knoxville, Tennessee
Students at the University of Tennessee used M85, a mixture of 85 percent methanol—a kind of alcohol—and 15 percent gasoline, in the competition to find cleaner fuel. Tennessee took first place in fuel economy and the lowest pollutants. If a liter of methanol has one-half the energy of gasoline, what effect would this have on the design of a car?
CAUTION
TOXIC SUBSTANCES
CAUTION
544

BIOLOGY
Background: Once organic farmers have made the transition from using artificial fertilizers and pesticides, it usually takes four or five years before their profits begin to rise. Their production per unit area will be lower by about 10 percent, but, because they no longer have the huge expense of fertilizers, they become more profitable.
Discussion: Discuss why it is healthier to eat organic foods. Mention that if more people buy organic foods, more farmers will grow foods without poisons.
Answer to Question: The ladybugs caused no recognizable harm to the environment or to the food produced. Pesticides pollute the environment and may also cause harm to the people who eat the food.
Extension: Have students use an encyclopedia to make a pie graph of goods produced in California by agriculture.

HEALTH
Background: During nuclear reactions, uranium-238 absorbs a neutron and is changed to plutonium-239. Plutonium has a half-life of 24 000 years, so half of the plutonium waste would still be present after 24 000 years. Radiation damages living tissue and may cause death or lasting injury.
Discussion: Discuss that some radioactive materials have a half-life of only 30 years. Compare this to a long half-life of thousands or millions of years. However, all radiation can cause harm to living tissue. Mention that it is very difficult to find a way to store nuclear wastes safely. The Department of Energy wants to build an underground waste depository. This worries many people.
Answer to Question: It might leak, or rainwater might carry the radioactive wastes to the groundwater.
Extension: Have students make a bar graph that shows the amount of nuclear power produced by countries around the world.

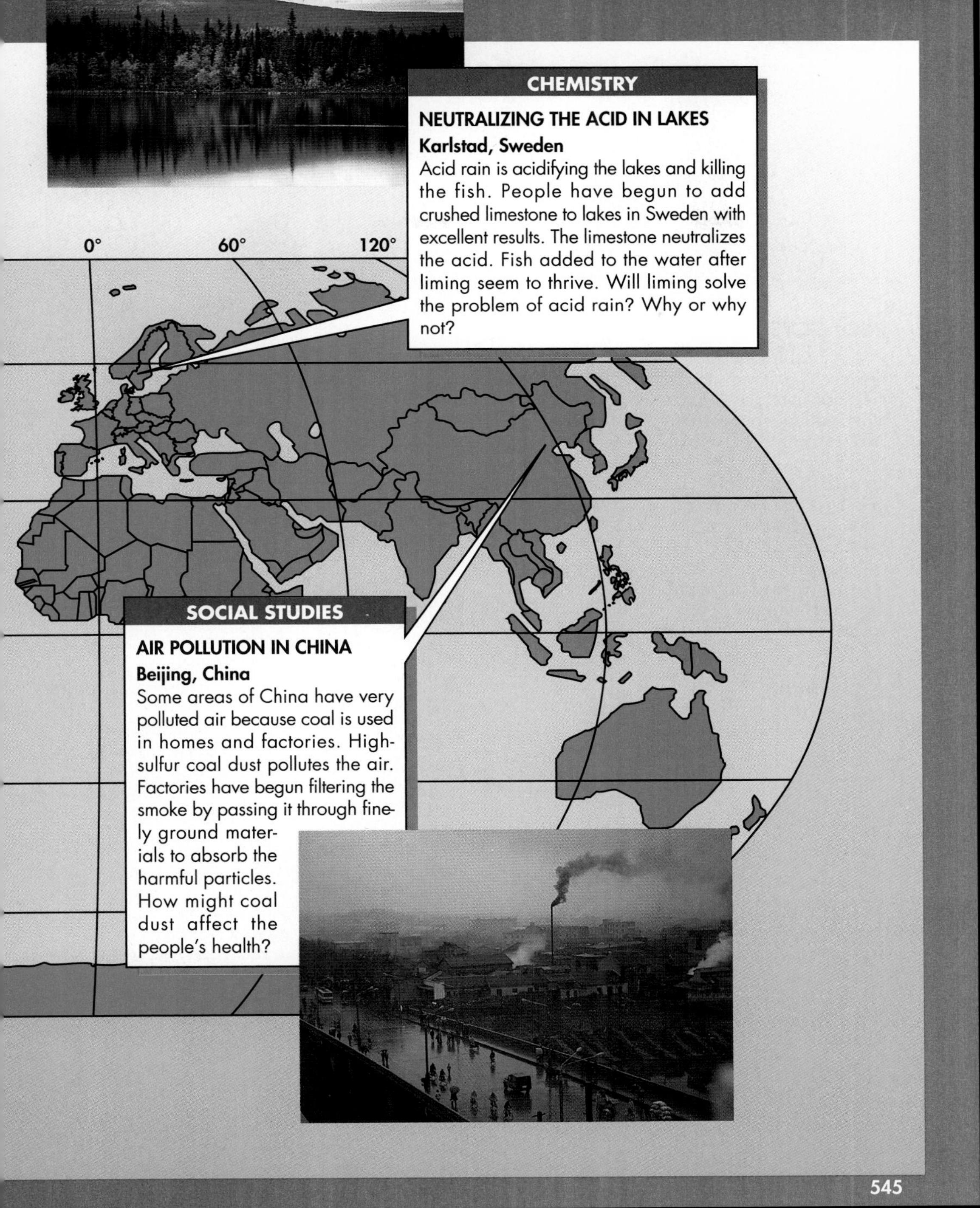

CHEMISTRY

NEUTRALIZING THE ACID IN LAKES
Karlstad, Sweden
Acid rain is acidifying the lakes and killing the fish. People have begun to add crushed limestone to lakes in Sweden with excellent results. The limestone neutralizes the acid. Fish added to the water after liming seem to thrive. Will liming solve the problem of acid rain? Why or why not?

SOCIAL STUDIES

AIR POLLUTION IN CHINA
Beijing, China
Some areas of China have very polluted air because coal is used in homes and factories. High-sulfur coal dust pollutes the air. Factories have begun filtering the smoke by passing it through finely ground materials to absorb the harmful particles. How might coal dust affect the people's health?

SOCIAL STUDIES

Background: The World Health Organization's (WHO) guideline for particles in the air is 60 to 90 micrograms. WHO has found that the industrialized nations have been able to reduce emissions of pollutants and improve air quality in the cities. This progress has been offset by the rapid urbanization and industrialization of developing nations.
Discussion: Discuss with students that in Kuwait the concentration of particles was measured at 603 micrograms and in Beijing the concentration was at 399. Mention that Kuwait's level of particles is due to wind-blown sand, which is not as dangerous as particles caused by combustion. Dust particles are too large to be absorbed by the lungs.
Answer to Question: The people would inhale the particles into their lungs. This would cause lung diseases such as cancer and emphysema.
Extension: Have students place flat dishes coated with petroleum jelly around the school to check for air-born particles.

PHYSICS

Background: Methanol has decided advantages over gasoline from an environmental perspective: (1) Its combustion is more complete, cutting down on hydrocarbon emissions between 20 and 50 percent in present cars and 90 percent in engines built to use methanol. (2) It cuts down on nitrogen oxide emitted at high temperatures because methanol burns at lower temperatures. (3) Carbon monoxide emissions are also lower because methanol burns in oxygen.
Discussion: After discussing the advantages of methanol, mention the disadvantages—(1) It is an eye irritant. However, the fumes are easily dispersed and cause no problem. (2) It gives off formaldehyde, a carcinogen. It would be a problem in unventilated garages but could be eliminated with modified engines.
Answer to Question: You would probably need a larger gas tank or have to fill up more often to travel the same distance. The car would have to be lighter to compensate for the extra mass.
Extension: Have students use an encyclopedia to research what methanol is made from and what some of its other uses are.

CHEMISTRY

Background: In the United States, fishery experts are dumping granulated limestone into some affected lakes. The technique is a stopgap measure—not a permanent solution to acid rain. Acid rain will continue until power plants, factories, and automobiles reduce the amounts of sulfur dioxide and nitrogen oxides they release into the air.
Discussion: Discuss that when sulfuric or nitric acid reacts with limestone, a chemical reaction occurs. The acid is neutralized and causes little or no harm to the fish.
Answer to Question: Liming will not solve the problem of acid rain. It only helps reduce the acid content of the lakes for a time.
Extension: Have students list ways that emissions of sulfur dioxide and nitrogen oxides could be reduced.

ECOLOGIST

Background: Ecologists may work for a government agency, such as the Environmental Protection Agency. They may also teach at universities. This career provides a great service because it helps make the world a safer place to live.

Related Career	Education
Envrionmental Engineer	college
Wastewater Treatment Operator	two-year college
Hydrologist	college
Landscaper	high school

Career Issue: Ecologists are often required to call attention to what is damaging the environment. Without the watchful eyes of ecologists, the water and air would be even more polluted than they are now.

What do you think? Have students discuss how ecologists with the EPA help to control water and air pollution.

POLLUTION-CONTROL TECHNICIAN

Background: Pollution-control technicians may work in laboratories or for local, state, or federal government agencies. They may also work for private "watch-dog" groups.

Related Career	Education
Emissions Control Inspector	high school
Laboratory Technician	two-year college
Science Writer	college
Automobile Designer	two-year college

Career Issue: Pollution-control technicians are sometimes at the center of controversy. Those who pollute the environment may not wish anyone to monitor their activities or to report on the extent of the damage caused.

What do you think? Lead students in a discussion of how pollution-control technicians might monitor water and air pollutants.

CAREERS

ECOLOGIST

An *ecologist* studies the relationships between living things and their habitats. One of the most important roles of ecologists is to help manage and control the environment. They study the effect of air and water pollution on living things. They also try to foresee the effect on wildlife of activities such as building dams or cutting down forests. Ecologists make people aware of the need to conserve natural resources.

An ecologist's job requires a college degree in ecology or related fields. A student interested in becoming an ecologist should take courses in biology and mathematics.

For Additional Information

Contact the American Institute of Biological Sciences, Office of Career Services, 730 11th Street NW, Washington, DC 20001-4584.

POLLUTION-CONTROL TECHNICIAN

Pollution-control technicians help improve the environment by monitoring the pollutants being released into the air or water. They may test the drinking water or the air quality to make certain it meets health standards. They may even check on noise pollution caused by cars and airplanes.

A pollution-control technician needs an associate degree from a community college. A student interested in a career as a pollution-control technician should study biology, chemistry, and mathematics.

For Additional Information

Contact the National Environmental Health Association, 720 S. Colorado Boulevard, Denver, CO 80222.

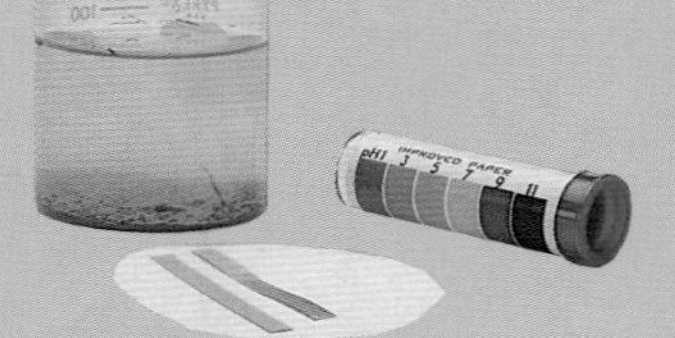

UNIT READINGS

►Berger, John J. *Restoring the Earth.* New York: Alfred A. Knopf, 1985.

►Seymour, John and Herbert Girardet. *Blueprint for a Green Planet: Your Practical Guide to Restoring the World's Environment.* New York: Prentice-Hall, 1987.

►Wild, Russel, ed. *The Earth Care Annual 1990.* Emmaus, Pennsylvania: National Wildlife Federation, Rodale Press, 1990.

546

UNIT READINGS

Background

► *Restoring the Earth* introduces the reader to people working to restore those natural resources crucial to the future of the planet.

► *Blueprint for a Green Planet* prescribes concretely how individuals and communities can halt and reverse environmental damage.

► *The Earth Care Annual 1990* is a collection of current newspaper and magazine articles on the environment, arranged according to topic.

More Readings

1. The Earth Works Group. *50 Simple Things You Can Do to Save the Earth.* Berkeley, California: Earthworks Press, 1989. This book offers fifty suggestions of how to improve the environment.
2. Dubos, Rene. *The Wooing of Earth: New Perspective of Man's Use of Nature.* New York: Charles Scribner's Sons, 1980. This book looks at our relation to nature in broad historical and biological perspectives.

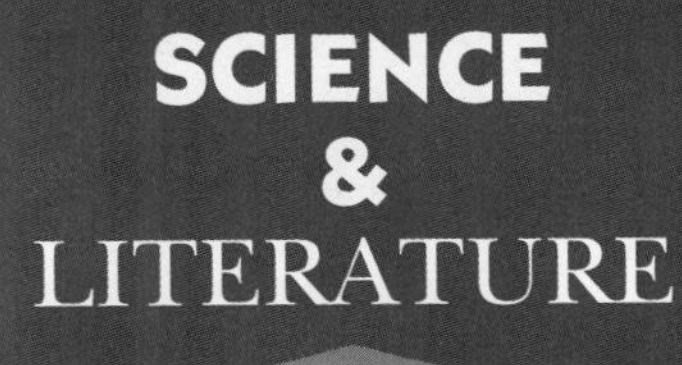

Rachel Carson's *Silent Spring*

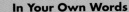

Rachel Carson was a scientist, a writer, and a lover of nature. She, like so many others, looked forward each year to the coming of spring with its songs of birds. She began to notice in the early 1960s that in some parts of America, spring was strangely silent because many of the birds were dead.

Her book *Silent Spring* tells about people's reckless attempt to control the environment by using large quantities of pesticides, particularly DDT. This effort was responsible for poisoning the birds in the air and the fish in the rivers. In *Silent Spring*, she writes:

Over increasingly large areas of the United States, spring now comes unheralded by the return of the birds, and the early mornings are strangely silent where once they were filled with the beauty of bird song. This sudden silencing of the song of birds, this obliteration of the color and beauty and interest they lend to our world have come about swiftly, insidiously, and unnoticed by those whose communities are as yet unaffected. From the town of Hinsdale, Illinois, a housewife wrote in despair to one of the world's leading ornithologists, Robert Cushman Murphy, Curator Emeritus of Birds at the American Museum of Natural History.

"Here in our village the elm trees have been sprayed for several years. When we moved here six years ago, there was a wealth of bird life . . . After several years of DDT spray, the town is almost devoid of robins and starlings; chickadees have not been on my shelf for two years, and this year the cardinals are gone, too; the nesting population seems to consist of one dove pair and perhaps one catbird family."

Who has decided—who has the right to decide—for the countless legions of people who were not consulted that the supreme value is a world without insects, even though it is also a sterile world ungraced by the curving wing of a bird in flight?

In Your Own Words

▶ The use of DDT has been banned, but other pesticides still harm wildlife. Write a newspaper article to express your views about the use of pesticides.

547

SCIENCE & LITERATURE

Source: Rachel Carson's *Silent Spring*. Boston: Houghton, Mifflin Company, 1962, pp. 103-127.

Biography: Rachel Carson (1907-1964) was a marine biologist who worked for the U.S. Fish and Wildlife Service during most of her life. She alerted the world to the dangers of pesticides and helped restrict their use.

TEACHING STRATEGY

▶ Ask students to support the opinions they expressed about the dangers of pesticides with other quotes from *Silent Spring*.

Cooperative Learning: Have groups of students work together to prepare a poster or collage to point out the problems exposed by Rachel Carson. Have them display their work.

▶ Possible essay topics include "What I Can Do to Improve the Environment," "What Will the World be Like if Pollution Continues?"

Other Works

▶ Other books on the environment include: Myers, N. *The Gaia Atlas of Planet Management*. London: Pan Books, 1985. Weisskopf, Michael. "In the Sea, Slow Death by Plastic." *Smithsonian*. March 1988, pp. 58-67.

Classics

▶ Carson, Rachel. *Silent Spring*. Boston: Houghton, Mifflin, 1962. This classic calls attention to the damage being done to the environment by increased use of pesticides.

▶ Fisher, J., N. Simon, and J. Vincent. *Wildlife in Danger*. New York: The Viking Press, 1969. This book shows where the responsibility lies for endangering the planet's wildlife.

UNIT

8

ASTRONOMY

In Unit 8, students are introduced to the size and structure of the universe. The unit is organized as an exploration outward from Earth, with chapters on exploring space, the Earth-moon system, the solar system, and, finally, stars and galaxies.

CONTENTS

ADVANCE PREPARATION

Activities

▶ **Activity 21-1, page 557,** requires plane, convex, and concave mirrors.

▶ **Activity 21-2, page 566,** requires a portable screen, a remote-controlled car, an instant camera or video camera, and a stopwatch.

▶ **Activity 22-2, page 594,** requires light sources and polystyrene balls.

▶ **Activity 23-2, page 617,** requires adding machine tape.

▶ **Activity 24-2, page 641,** requires a small tripod and refracting telescope.

Audiovisuals

▶ **Section 24-2, page 634:** Arrange to show the video "Stardust," The Astronomers, Episode 5, PBS Video.

UNIT 8 THE SOLAR SYSTEM

548

OPTIONS

Cross Curriculum

▶ Have students keep a list of times that constellation names are mentioned in stories they read in other classes.

▶ Lead students in a discussion of how familiar constellations and stars have been used to help people avoid getting lost.

▶ Have students write papers on how the history of the crewed space program is related to the politics and interactions between nations at the time the space program began.

Science at Home

▶ Have students attempt to find the Big Dipper, the Little Dipper, and Polaris in the night sky. Ask them to draw the major stars that they see and to connect the drawings into familiar patterns.

Cooperative Learning: Have groups of three students read the mythology of different constellations. Each of the group members is to teach the other group members what he or she has learned about the mythology of his or her specific constellation.

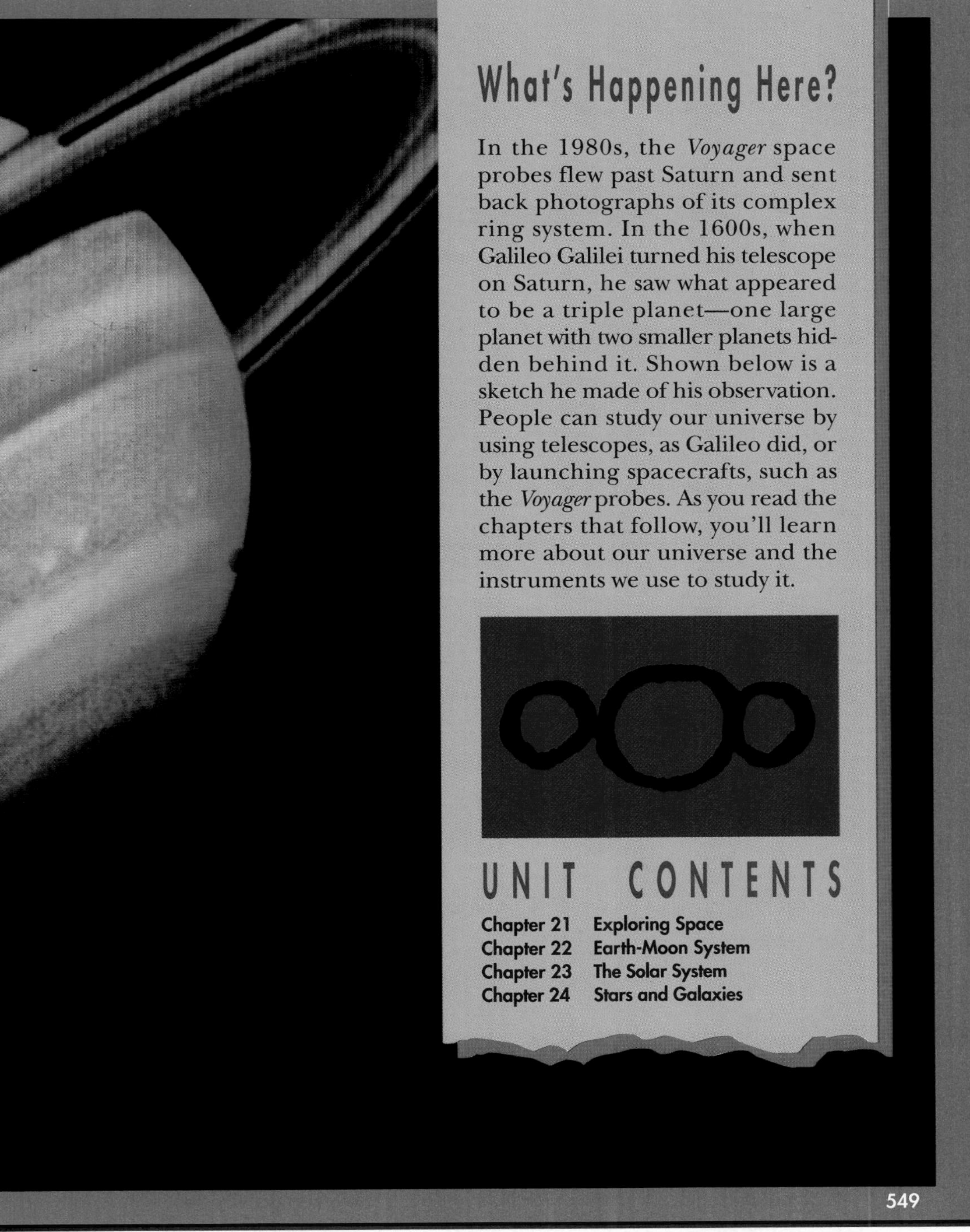

What's Happening Here?

In the 1980s, the *Voyager* space probes flew past Saturn and sent back photographs of its complex ring system. In the 1600s, when Galileo Galilei turned his telescope on Saturn, he saw what appeared to be a triple planet—one large planet with two smaller planets hidden behind it. Shown below is a sketch he made of his observation. People can study our universe by using telescopes, as Galileo did, or by launching spacecrafts, such as the *Voyager* probes. As you read the chapters that follow, you'll learn more about our universe and the instruments we use to study it.

UNIT CONTENTS

549

INTRODUCING THE UNIT

What's Happening Here?

▶ Have students look at the photos and read the text. Ask them to tell you what's happening here. Point out to students that in this unit they will be studying Earth's position in space and its relationship to other objects in the universe.

▶ **Background:** In 1609, Galileo first described Saturn as a triple planet system. His observations of Saturn showed a large planet with two small bulges on either side. In 1655, Christian Huygens described Saturn as a ringed planet. He was able to determine that at least one ring of material completely surrounded the planet. In 1675, G.D. Cassini observed what appeared to be a split in the ring. This split is called the Cassini division and was evidence for at least a double ring system. By the mid-1800s, a third and, in 1970, a fourth ring were discovered from Earth. When the *Voyager* space probes flew by Saturn, its rings were resolved into thousands. It was noted that the Cassini division, as well as other divisions, also contain particles of the ring system. However, these areas are less dense than the rings proper.

Previewing the Chapters

▶ Give students a list of topics to be studied in this unit. Have students refer to the Gearing Up section of each chapter to determine where each topic will be covered.

▶ Have students search for a figure that shows the relative sizes of all the planets in our solar system. Students should discover it on page 601.

Tying to Previous Knowledge

▶ Ask students to speculate on how the impact of a large meteorite with Earth might have caused the extinction of lifeforms in Earth's past. Inform students that many fires might be started by such a collision. Also, large amounts of dust may be thrown into the atmosphere, blocking light from the sun.

▶ Use the **Inquiry Questions** in the OPTIONS box below to investigate with students how Earth is affected by objects from space.

Multicultural Awareness

Have students research how cultures in developing nations have been changed by global communication and weather satellite transmissions. Some governments forbid their citizens to have dish antennas that would be able to receive world news programs. Have students discuss why this might be the case.

Inquiry Questions

Use the following questions to focus a discussion of the effects of space objects on Earth.

1. Have students refer to Figure 23-16, page 620, and then ask, "What may have caused Barringer Crater in Arizona?"
2. What might have collided with Earth, just after it formed, that could have caused the moon to form?
3. What might happen if Earth were to pass through the tail of a comet?
4. What causes "shooting stars" visible in the night sky?

CHAPTER

21 Exploring Space

CHAPTER SECTION	OBJECTIVES	ACTIVITIES
21-1 Radiant Energy from Space (2 days)	1. **Define** the electromagnetic spectrum. 2. **Compare** and **contrast** refracting and reflecting telescopes. 3. **Compare** and **contrast** optical and radio telescopes.	**Activity 21-1:** *Telescopes,* p. 557
21-2 Light Pollution Science & Society (1 day)	1. **Explain** how light pollution affects the ability to see dim objects in the sky. 2. **Discuss** the controversy over light pollution as it relates to security and safety lighting.	**MINI-Lab:** *How much light pollution is there?* p. 558
21-3 Artificial Satellites and Space Probes (2 days)	1. **Compare** and **contrast** natural and artificial satellites. 2. **Differentiate** between an artificial satellite and a space probe. 3. **Outline** the history of the race to the moon.	**Activity 21-2:** *Simulated Probe to Mars,* pp. 566-567
21-4 The Space Shuttle and the Future (1 day)	1. **Describe** the benefits of the space shuttle. 2. **Evaluate** the usefulness of orbital space stations.	**MINI-Lab:** *How can gravity be simulated in a space station?* p. 569
Chapter Review		

ACTIVITY MATERIALS

FIND OUT	ACTIVITIES		MINI-LABS	
Page 551 white paper flashlights (3) different colored filters (3)	**21-1 Telescopes, p. 557** candle cardboard, white 50 cm × 60 cm flashlight magnifying glass glass of water aluminum or silver spoon plane mirror convex mirror concave mirror empty paper towel roll masking tape	**21-2 Simulated Probe to Mars, pp. 566-567** portable screen remote controlled car large rocks (30 cm) camera (instant), film stopwatch	**How much light pollution is there? p. 558** cardboard tube from an empty roll of paper towels	**How can gravity be simulated in a space station? p. 569** turntable LP record scissors construction paper masking tape marbles

CHAPTER FEATURES	TEACHER RESOURCE PACKAGE	OTHER RESOURCES
Problem Solving: *A Homemade Antenna,* p. 555 **Skill Builder:** *Sequencing,* p. 556	**Ability Level Worksheets** ◆ ***Study Guide,*** p. 83 ● ***Reinforcement,*** p. 83 ▲ ***Enrichment,*** p. 83 **Activity Worksheet,** pp. 187-188 **Technology,** pp. 19-20 **Transparency Masters,** pp. 85-86	**Color Transparency 43,** Telescopes **Lab Manual:** *Refraction of Light,* pp. 169-170 **Lab Manual:** *Spectral Analysis,* pp. 171-174
You Decide! p. 559	**Ability Level Worksheets** ◆ ***Study Guide,*** p. 84 ● ***Reinforcement,*** p. 84 ▲ ***Enrichment,*** p. 84 **MINI-Lab Worksheet,** p. 195	
Technology: *Spin-offs,* p. 564 **Skill Builder:** *Concept Mapping,* p. 565	**Ability Level Worksheets** ◆ ***Study Guide,*** p. 85 ● ***Reinforcement,*** p. 85 ▲ ***Enrichment,*** p. 85 **Activity Worksheet,** pp. 189-191 **Cross-Curricular Connections,** p. 25	
Skill Builder: *Outlining,* p. 570	**Ability Level Worksheets** ◆ ***Study Guide,*** p. 86 ● ***Reinforcement,*** p. 86 ▲ ***Enrichment,*** p. 86 **MINI-Lab Worksheet,** p. 196 **Concept Mapping,** pp. 47-48 **Critical Thinking/Problem Solving,** p. 27 **Science and Society,** p. 25	
Summary Key Science Words Understanding Vocabulary Checking Concepts Understanding Concepts Think & Write Critically Apply More Skill Builders Projects	**Chapter Review,** pp. 45-46 **Chapter Test,** pp. 146-147	**Chapter Review Software** **Test Bank**

◆ **Basic** ● **Average** ▲ **Advanced**

ADDITIONAL MATERIALS

SOFTWARE	AUDIOVISUAL	BOOKS/MAGAZINES
Sky Lab, MECC. *Space Database,* Sunburst.	*Mission of Apollo/Soyuz,* film, NASA. *Measuring in Astronomy,* film, BFA. *To Boldly Go... (Voyager),* video, NOVA (PBS). *Infinite Horizons: Space Beyond Apollo,* video, Coronet/MTI. *Voyage of the SS Columbia: Just Short of a Miracle,* video, Coronet/MTI. *The Dream is Alive,* laserdisc, Lumivision. *Footsteps of Giants,* laserdisc, Image Entertainment. *Space Shuttle: Space Disc Vol. 3,* laserdisc, Optical Data Corp.	Burdett, Gerald L. and Gerald A. Soffen. *The Human Quest in Space.* San Diego, CA: American Astronautical Society, 1987. Ebbinghausen, E.B. *Astronomy.* 5th rev. ed. Westerville, OH: Merrill Publishing Co., 1985. Pasachaff, Jay M. *Contemporary Astronomy.* 3rd ed. Troy, MO: Saunders College Publishing, 1985.

CHAPTER

21

EXPLORING SPACE

THEME DEVELOPMENT: Energy is one of the themes presented in this chapter. The properties of radiant energy have enabled scientists to describe the scale and structure of our solar system and beyond.

CHAPTER OVERVIEW

- **Section 21-1:** This section discusses forms of radiant energy and the electromagnetic spectrum. Optical and radio telescopes used to study energy from space are briefly discussed.
- **Section 21-2: Science and Society:** The effects of light pollution on observing the night sky are presented. The You Decide feature asks students to consider whether people with security lighting should be required to use less-polluting types, or whether the lights should be turned off after a certain time.
- **Section 21-3:** This section relates the initial events that put humans into space. Artificial satellites and space probes are described. A synopsis of the space programs that led to putting people on the moon also is presented.
- **Section 21-4:** Section 21-4 discusses the benefits of the space shuttle, and the usefulness of space stations.

CHAPTER VOCABULARY

electromagnetic spectrum
refracting telescope
reflecting telescope
observatories
radio telescope
light pollution
satellite
orbit
space probe
Project Mercury
Project Gemini
Project Apollo
space shuttle
space station

CHAPTER

21 Exploring Space

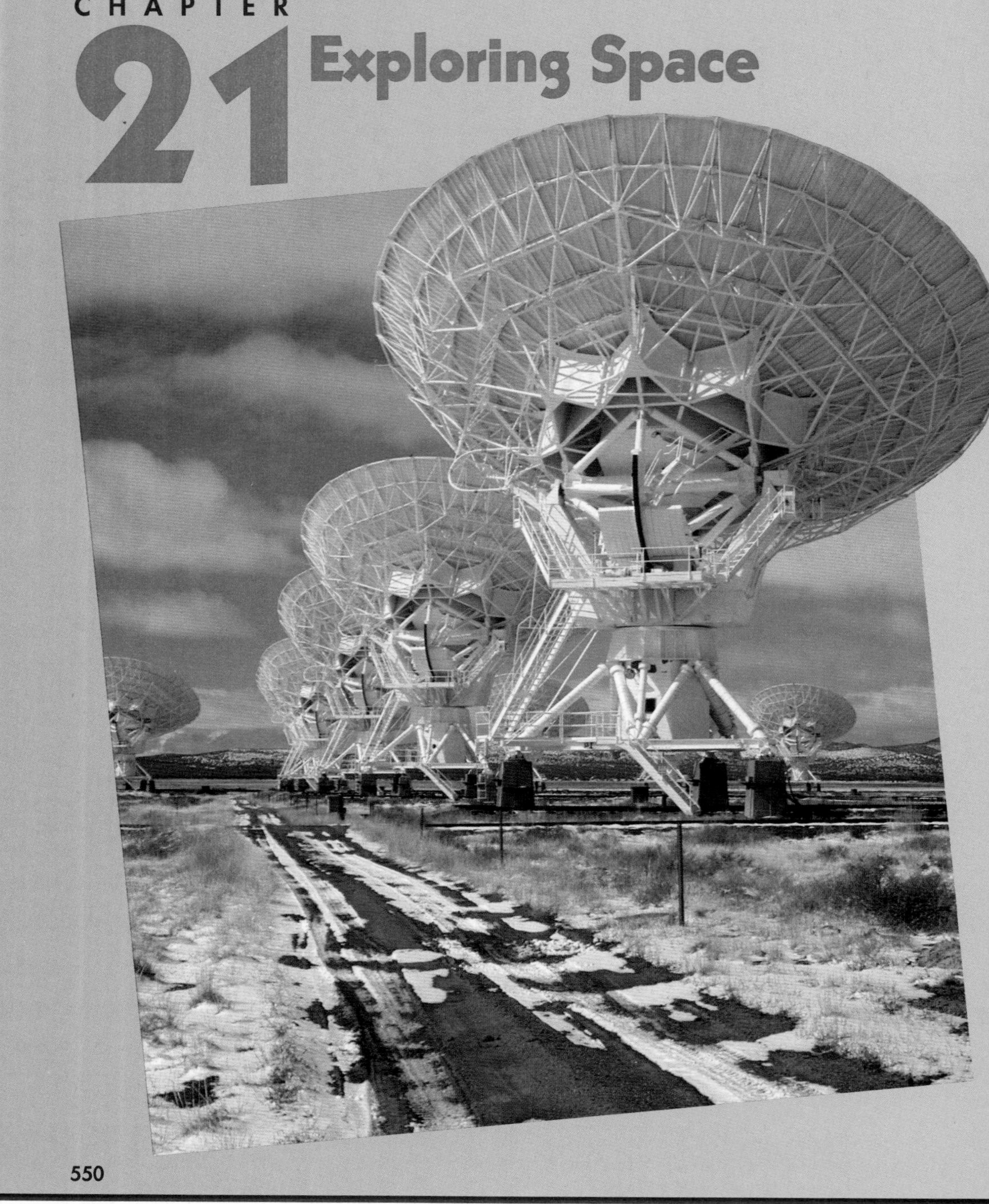

550

OPTIONS

For Your Gifted Students

Have students research "space junk." Inform students that space junk includes unused and nonfunctioning materials and machines in orbit around Earth. Space junk ranges from sand-grain sized paint chips to large communication satellites. Have them discuss this growing problem and how it can be reduced or eliminated. Students can write to NASA to ask for information on the issue and also to find out what they are doing about space junk. Students should discuss the growing concern that space junk may pose a threat to the safety of future crewed space flights. Have students find out how long it takes items to fall out of orbit and re-enter Earth's atmosphere.

The radio telescopes shown detect energy from space that we can't see. But even visible energy holds information that isn't at first apparent. Some of the radiation we receive from stars is in the form of white light. White light is a mixture of the colors of the rainbow—red, orange, yellow, green, blue, indigo, and violet. By studying the visible light and invisible energy coming from objects in space, we have learned a great deal about the universe.

FIND OUT!

Do this simple activity to see how colors combine to form white light.

Cover the end of a flashlight with a green gelatin (or plexiglass) filter. Cover another flashlight with a blue filter and a third with a red filter. In a darkened room, shine the red light on a sheet of white paper. Then, keeping the red light on, shine the blue light at the same spot on the paper. What do you observe? Add the green light. What do you observe when all three lights are shining at the same spot?

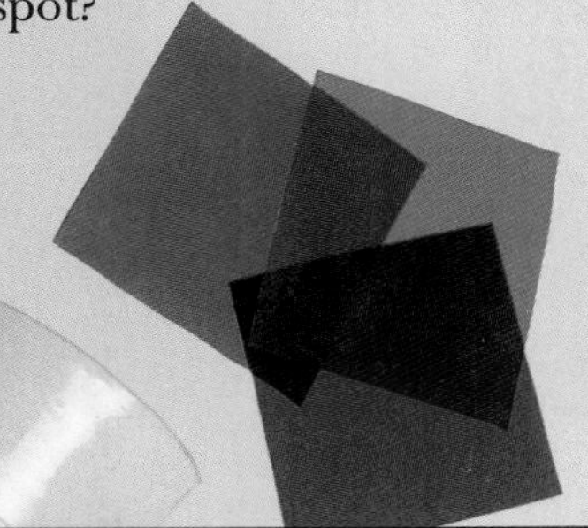

Gearing Up

Previewing the Chapter

Use this outline to help you focus on important ideas in this chapter.

Previewing Science Skills

- In the **Skill Builders,** you will sequence events, make concept maps, and outline.
- In the **Activities,** you will observe, analyze data, make inferences, and draw conclusions.
- In the **MINI-Labs,** you will experiment, construct models, and draw conclusions.

What's next?

You've seen how colored light combines to form new colors and white light. But visible light is just one form of energy we receive from the sun and other stars in space. In Section 21-1, you'll read about the forms of energy radiated by objects in space and the tools we use to study that energy.

INTRODUCING THE CHAPTER

Use the Find Out activity to introduce students to the composition of white light. Inform students they will be learning about radiant energy and how it can be used to find out about objects in space.

FIND OUT!

Preparation: Several days before you begin the chapter, have students bring in flashlights. Also obtain green, blue, and red gelatin or plexiglass filters.

Materials: white paper, three flashlights, and three different colored filters for each group

Cooperative Learning: Form Science Investigation groups of four students per group.

Teaching Tips

- Make sure that the flashlights used by a group are identical.
- Have students attach the filters to the flashlights with transparent tape. Make the room as dark as possible. Cover the windows if necessary.
- Check flashlight batteries ahead of time. Have extra batteries available.

Gearing Up

Have students study the Gearing Up feature to familiarize themselves with the chapter. Discuss the relationships of the topics in the outline.

What's Next?

Before beginning the first section, make sure students understand the connection between the Find Out activity and the topics to follow.

For Your Mainstreamed Students

Assist students as they make models of space machines such as space probes, space capsules, or the space shuttle. Have them discuss some of the proposed future spacecraft and space stations. Students can draw or make models of their own ideas about future space machines.

SECTION 21-1

PREPARATION

SECTION BACKGROUND

▶ The primary mirror of the *Hubble Space Telescope* was incorrectly ground and now produces spherical aberration. Light from the inner and outer portions of the primary mirror is not focused in the same focal plane. Thus, the image is never quite sharp and is surrounded by a diffuse halo.

▶ Presently, the largest optical telescope on Earth is the 10-m Keck reflecting telescope on Mauna Kea in Hawaii. Its primary mirror has been constructed from 36 hexagonal glass segments, each 1.8 m in diameter.

▶ The Very Large Array (VLA) of telescopes near Socorro, New Mexico is composed of 27 radio telescopes. All 27 telescopes can be used at once to operate as one large telescope.

1 MOTIVATE

FLEX Your Brain

Use the Flex Your Brain activity to have students explore THE ELECTROMAGNETIC SPECTRUM.

Cooperative Learning: Have Paired Partners use a prism to separate white light, such as sunlight, into its components. Explain that as white light passes through a prism, different colors are refracted or bent different amounts to form a spectrum. Violet light bends the most and red light bends the least.

PROGRAM RESOURCES

From the **Teacher Resource Package** use:

Activity Worksheets, page 5, Flex Your Brain.

21-1 Radiant Energy from Space

New Science Words

electromagnetic spectrum
refracting telescope
reflecting telescope
observatories
radio telescope

Objectives

- ▶ Define the electromagnetic spectrum.
- ▶ Compare and contrast refracting and reflecting telescopes.
- ▶ Compare and contrast optical and radio telescopes.

Did You Know?

If it were possible for you to travel at the speed of light, you could travel around the world seven times in one second.

The Electromagnetic Spectrum

On this crisp autumn evening, you take a break from your homework to gaze out the window at the many stars filling the night sky. You think about your future and how humans might someday attempt to travel to one of those distant stars. Looking up at the night sky, it's easy to imagine future spaceships venturing through space and large space stations circling above Earth where people work and live. But when you look into the night sky, what you're really seeing is the distant past, not the future.

When you look at a star, you see the light that left it many years ago. The light that you see travels very fast, but the distances across space are so great that it takes years for the light to reach Earth—sometimes tens of thousands of years.

The light and other energy leaving a star are forms of radiant energy. Recall that radiant energy, or radiation,

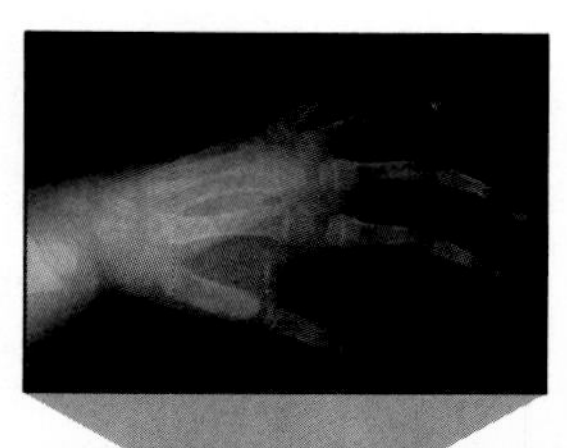

OPTIONS

Meeting Different Ability Levels

For Section 21-1, use the following **Teacher Resource Masters** depending upon individual students' needs.

◆ **Study Guide Master** for all students.

● **Reinforcement Master** for students of average and above average ability levels.

▲ **Enrichment Master** for above average students.

Additional Teacher Resource Package masters are listed in the OPTIONS box throughout the section. The additional masters are appropriate for all students.

◆ STUDY GUIDE 83

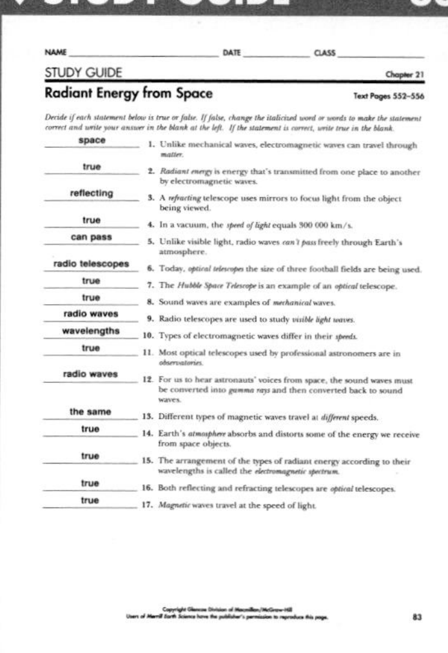

NAME ______________ DATE ________ CLASS ________

STUDY GUIDE — Chapter 21

Radiant Energy from Space — Text Pages 552–556

Decide if each statement below is true or false. If false, change the italicized word or words to make the statement correct and write your answer in the blank at the left. If the statement is correct, write true in the blank.

space	1. Unlike mechanical waves, electromagnetic waves can travel through *matter*.
true	2. *Radiant energy* is energy that's transmitted from one place to another by electromagnetic waves.
reflecting	3. A *refracting* telescope uses mirrors to focus light from the object being viewed.
true	4. In a vacuum, the *speed of light* equals 300 000 km/s.
can pass	5. Unlike visible light, radio waves *can't pass* freely through Earth's atmosphere.
radio telescopes	6. Today, *optical telescopes* the size of three football fields are being used.
true	7. The *Hubble Space Telescope* is an example of an *optical* telescope.
true	8. Sound waves are examples of *mechanical* waves.
radio waves	9. Radio telescopes are used to study *visible light waves*.
wavelengths	10. Types of electromagnetic waves differ in their *speeds*.
true	11. Most optical telescopes used by professional astronomers are in *observatories*.
radio waves	12. For us to hear astronauts' voices from space, the sound waves must be converted into *gamma rays* and then converted back to sound waves.
the same	13. Different types of magnetic waves travel at *different* speeds.
true	14. Earth's *atmosphere* absorbs and distorts some of the energy we receive from space objects.
true	15. The arrangement of the types of radiant energy according to their wavelengths is called the *electromagnetic spectrum*.
true	16. Both reflecting and refracting telescopes are *optical* telescopes.
true	17. *Magnetic* waves travel at the speed of light.

83

is energy that's transmitted from one place to another by electromagnetic waves. Electromagnetic waves carry energy through empty space as well as through matter.

Recall what you learned about earthquake waves. Earthquake waves are mechanical waves and, unlike electromagnetic waves, they need matter to be transmitted. Sound waves, another type of mechanical wave, can't travel through empty space. How do we hear the voices of the astronauts while they're in space? When they speak into a microphone, the sound is converted into electromagnetic waves called radio waves. The radio waves travel through space and through our atmosphere. They are then converted back into sound waves by electronic equipment and audio speakers.

Radio waves and visible light from the sun are just two types of electromagnetic waves. The other types include gamma rays, X rays, ultraviolet waves, infrared waves, and microwaves. Figure 21-1 shows these forms of radiant energy arranged according to their wavelengths. This arrangement of radiant energy is called the **electromagnetic spectrum.** 1

Although the types of electromagnetic waves differ in their wavelengths, they all travel at the speed of 300 000 km/s in a vacuum. You're probably more familiar with this speed as the "speed of light." Visible light and other forms of radiant energy travel at this incredible speed, but the universe is so large that it takes billions of years for the light from some objects to reach Earth.

Once radiant energy from the stars and other objects reaches Earth, we can use it to learn about the objects. What tools and methods do scientists use to discover what lies beyond our planet?

Why aren't sound waves included in the electromagnetic spectrum?

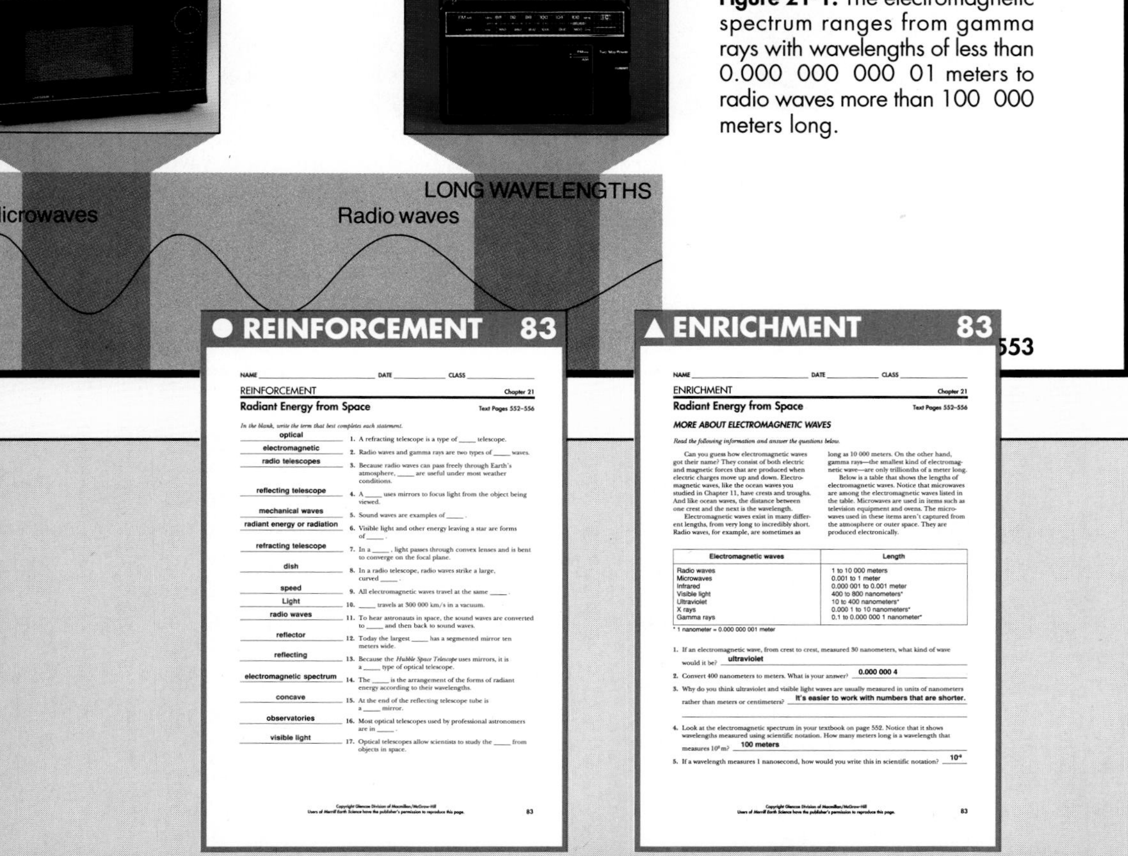

Figure 21-1. The electromagnetic spectrum ranges from gamma rays with wavelengths of less than 0.000 000 000 01 meters to radio waves more than 100 000 meters long.

● REINFORCEMENT 83

NAME ______ DATE ______ CLASS ______

REINFORCEMENT — Chapter 21

Radiant Energy from Space — Text Pages 552–556

In the blank, write the term that best completes each statement.

optical	1. A refracting telescope is a type of ____ telescope.
electromagnetic	2. Radio waves and gamma rays are two types of ____ waves.
radio telescopes	3. Because radio waves can pass freely through Earth's atmosphere, ____ are useful under most weather conditions.
reflecting telescope	4. A ____ uses mirrors to focus light from the object being viewed.
mechanical waves	5. Sound waves are examples of ____ .
radiant energy or radiation	6. Visible light and other energy leaving a star are forms of ____ .
refracting telescope	7. In a ____ , light passes through convex lenses and is bent to converge on the focal plane.
dish	8. In a radio telescope, radio waves strike a large, curved ____ .
speed	9. All electromagnetic waves travel at the same ____ .
Light	10. ____ travels at 300 000 km/s in a vacuum.
radio waves	11. To hear astronauts in space, the sound waves are converted to ____ and then back to sound waves.
reflector	12. Today the largest ____ has a segmented mirror ten meters wide.
reflecting	13. Because the *Hubble Space Telescope* uses mirrors, it is a ____ type of optical telescope.
electromagnetic spectrum	14. The ____ is the arrangement of the forms of radiant energy according to their wavelengths.
concave	15. At the end of the reflecting telescope tube is a ____ mirror.
observatories	16. Most optical telescopes used by professional astronomers are in ____ .
visible light	17. Optical telescopes allow scientists to study the ____ from objects in space.

 83

▲ ENRICHMENT 83

NAME ______ DATE ______ CLASS ______

ENRICHMENT — Chapter 21

Radiant Energy from Space — Text Pages 552–556

MORE ABOUT ELECTROMAGNETIC WAVES

Read the following information and answer the questions below.

Can you guess how electromagnetic waves got their name? They consist of both electric and magnetic forces that are produced when electric charges move up and down. Electromagnetic waves, like the ocean waves you studied in Chapter 11, have crests and troughs. And like ocean waves, the distance between one crest and the next is the wavelength.

Electromagnetic waves exist in many different lengths, from very long to incredibly short. Radio waves, for example, are sometimes as long as 10 000 meters. On the other hand, gamma rays—the smallest kind of electromagnetic wave—are only trillionths of a meter long.

Below is a table that shows the lengths of electromagnetic waves. Notice that microwaves are among the electromagnetic waves listed in the table. Microwaves are used in items such as television equipment and ovens. The microwaves used in these items aren't captured from the atmosphere or outer space. They are produced electronically.

Electromagnetic waves	Length
Radio waves	1 to 10 000 meters
Microwaves	0.001 to 1 meter
Infrared	0.000 001 to 0.001 meter
Visible light	400 to 800 nanometers*
Ultraviolet	10 to 400 nanometers*
X rays	0.000 1 to 10 nanometers*
Gamma rays	0.1 to 0.000 000 1 nanometer*

* 1 nanometer = 0.000 000 001 meter

1. If an electromagnetic wave, from crest to crest, measured 30 nanometers, what kind of wave would it be? **ultraviolet**
2. Convert 400 nanometers to meters. What is your answer? **0.000 000 4**
3. Why do you think ultraviolet and visible light waves are usually measured in units of nanometers rather than meters or centimeters? **It's easier to work with numbers that are shorter.**
4. Look at the electromagnetic spectrum in your textbook on page 552. Notice that it shows wavelengths measured using scientific notation. How many meters long is a wavelength that measures 10^2 m? **100 meters**
5. If a wavelength measures 1 nanosecond, how would you write this in scientific notation? **10^{-9}**

 83

TYING TO PREVIOUS KNOWLEDGE: Most students have used binoculars to observe distant objects. Inform students that binoculars can be used to view large areas of the sky. Binoculars are actually two refracting telescopes side by side.

OBJECTIVES AND SCIENCE WORDS: Have students review the objectives and science words to become familiar with this section.

2 TEACH

Key Concepts are highlighted.

CONCEPT DEVELOPMENT

Cooperative Learning: Using the Paired Partner strategy, have students construct a simple refracting telescope. Supply each group of three students with two convex lenses of different sizes. Explain that one student should hold the larger lens in front of an object, while the second student lines up the smaller lens with the larger one. Have students move the lenses back and forth until the third student can see an image of the object through the lenses. If the lenses are held correctly, students will observe an enlarged image of the object being viewed.

▶ Have volunteers compare and contrast refracting and reflecting telescopes.

▶ Have students, as a group, compile a list of advantages and disadvantages of the *Hubble Space Telescope.*

CROSS CURRICULUM

▶ **Physics:** Have students find out how concave and convex lenses affect the path of light that passes through them.

MINI QUIZ

Use the Mini Quiz to check students' recall of chapter content.

1. **The arrangement of radiant energy according to its wavelengths is the _____.** *electromagnetic spectrum*
2. **_____ telescopes bend light to produce an image.** *Refracting*
3. **A(n) _____ telescope uses mirrors to focus light from the object being viewed.** *reflecting*
4. **Professional astronomers house their telescopes in dome-shaped buildings called _____.** *observatories*
5. **Which type of telescope is used to study radio waves traveling through space?** *radio telescope*

REVEALING MISCONCEPTIONS

▶ Ask students what power of a telescope is important to consider when purchasing a telescope. Most students will believe that magnifying power is the most important. Inform them that resolving power, the ability of a telescope to separate two points of light without blurring, is more important than the magnification. If the resolving power is poor, the telescope will magnify a poorly resolved image.

TEACHER F.Y.I.

▶ The *Hubble Space Telescope* is so powerful that if you were in Washington, D.C., you could use the telescope to read a newspaper headline in Missouri.

▶ The largest radio telescope in the world is located near Arecibo, Puerto Rico. The curved dish, made of more than 38 400 aluminum panels, is 305 meters in diameter.

▶ The photo on page 651 in Chapter 24 is of the Arecibo radio telescope.

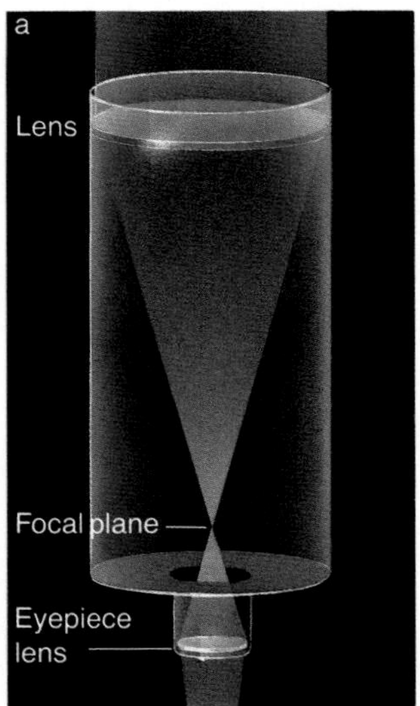

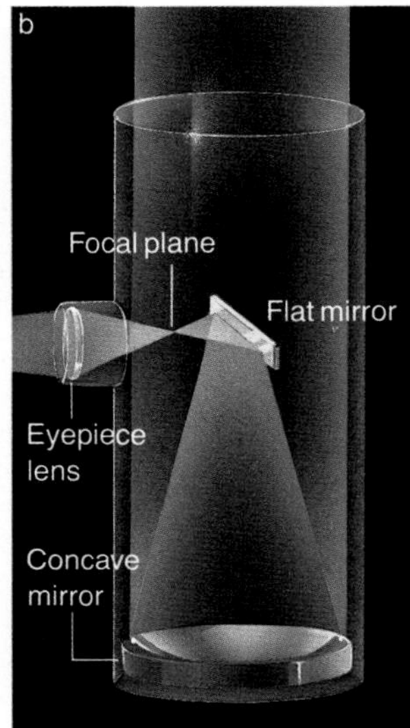

Figure 21-2. In a refracting telescope (a), a convex lense focuses light to form an image. In a reflecting telescope (b), a concave mirror focuses light to form an image. The image is then magnified by the eyepiece.

Optical Telescopes

Optical telescopes produce magnified images of objects. The two types of optical telescopes are refracting telescopes and reflecting telescopes. In a **refracting**
2 **telescope,** the light from an object passes through convex lenses and is bent to converge on one plane called the focal plane. It is then bent again as it passes through another lens, the eyepiece, and a magnified image of the object forms in your eye.

A **reflecting telescope** uses mirrors to focus light from
3 the object being viewed. At the end of the telescope tube is a concave mirror. When visible light strikes this mirror, it is reflected to the focal plane. A smaller mirror is often used to reflect the light into the eyepiece lens so the image can be viewed.

Most optical telescopes used by professional
4 astronomers are housed in buildings called **observatories.** Observatories often have a dome-shaped roof that opens up so light can reach the telescopes. However, not all telescopes are in observatories. You've probably read about the *Hubble Space Telescope* launched in 1990 by the space shuttle *Discovery.*

Hubble was placed in space so scientists could avoid looking through our atmosphere. Earth's atmosphere absorbs and distorts some of the energy we receive from space. Because *Hubble* wouldn't have to view space through our atmosphere, it should have produced very clear images. Some images haven't been as clear as hoped. When the largest mirror of this reflecting telescope was being shaped, a mistake was made. Because of its distorted shape, about half of the programs scheduled for *Hubble* don't work as well as planned.

Radio Telescopes

Optical telescopes allow scientists to study the visible light coming from objects in space. But as you know, stars and other objects radiate more than visible light. They radiate energy throughout the electromagnetic spectrum.
5 A **radio telescope** is used to study radio waves traveling through space. Unlike visible light, radio waves pass freely through Earth's atmosphere. Because of this, radio telescopes are useful under most weather conditions and at all times of day and night.

OPTIONS

INQUIRY QUESTIONS

▶ **What is the function of the concave mirror in a reflecting telescope?** *The mirror focuses light onto the focal plane, where the image is formed.*

▶ **How do reflecting and refracting telescopes differ in the way they form images?** *A reflecting telescope uses a concave mirror to reflect light to the focal plane, while a refracting telescope uses a convex lens to bend light to the focal plane.*

▶ **What advantage does a radio telescope have over optical telescopes?** *Because radio waves are not affected by cloud cover, radio telescopes can be used in almost all kinds of weather and at all times of the day and night. Radio telescopes can receive energy from objects that cannot be observed with optical telescopes.*

▶ **How are the curved dish of a radio telescope and the concave mirror of a reflecting telescope similar?** *Both concentrate electromagnetic waves by reflecting them to a single plane. Both reflect onto the focal plane.*

Radio waves reaching Earth's surface strike the large, curved dish of a radio telescope. This dish reflects the waves to a focal plane where a receiver is located. Computers record the waves picked up by the receiver. The recorded information allows us to map the universe, detect objects in space, and to search for intelligent life that might be broadcasting radio waves.

Since the early 1600s when the Italian scientist Galileo Galilei first turned a telescope toward the stars, people have been searching for better ways to study what lies beyond our atmosphere. Bigger and better mirrors and lenses have been constructed for use in optical telescopes. Today, the largest reflector has a segmented mirror ten meters wide, and the largest radio telescope is 300 meters wide. These telescopes are quite an improvement over Galileo's small, handheld model. Still, Galileo was able to see what others had not even dreamed of. He saw shadows in the craters of our moon and discovered four moons orbiting Jupiter. In the remainder of this chapter, you'll learn about the instruments we've sent into space to send back information that could never be collected through the eyepiece or radio receiver of a telescope.

EcoTip

Military satellites broadcast radio waves that are picked up by radio telescopes searching the galaxy for newly forming stars. These radio waves are a type of "pollution" to sensitive radio telescopes

PROBLEM SOLVING

A Homemade Antenna

Calid and Hiroshi had been looking forward to their camping trip for several weeks. They had just set up camp when some large clouds began to roll in and the wind began to stir.

Calid pulled out their radio to listen to the weather forecast. He thought a storm might be approaching and they would need to seek better shelter. The radio reception was poor and they could barely hear the weather report.

Hiroshi dug through their camping supplies and found some aluminum foil wrap, an umbrella, and some string. He suggested that they could use these items to improve the radio reception.

Think Critically: How could Calid and Hiroshi improve the radio reception with the items from their supplies? How are the parts of their radio and antenna like those of a radio telescope?

CHECK FOR UNDERSTANDING

Ask the following questions of the class as a group. Have available labeled cross-sections showing the path of radiant energy through refracting, reflecting, and radio telescopes. Have students study the diagrams, then ask: **What is the function of the objective of each telescope?** *The objective is the lens, mirror, or dish antenna that collects visible light or radio waves and focuses them onto the focal plane.* **Why was the *Hubble Space Telescope* placed into orbit?** *Astronomers can use the* Hubble Space Telescope *to observe objects deep in space without having to look through Earth's atmosphere.*

PROBLEM SOLVING

Teaching Tip: You may wish to have students experiment with an umbrella, foil, and radio to see if reception can be improved. Be sure students tune the radio to a weak station, just barely audible to begin with. Then, have them move the umbrella with foil back and forth until they find the position that gives the best results.

Think Critically: Calid and Hiroshi can improve the reception of their radio by increasing the ability of its antenna to collect radio waves. They can cover the inside of the umbrella with the aluminum foil, making it reflective. The handle of the umbrella can then be bound to the metal antenna of the radio with the string. The umbrella reflects incoming radio waves onto the radio's small antenna, increasing the number of waves received by the radio. The umbrella is like the giant dishes of radio telescopes. The radio is similar to a receiver of a radio telescope.

ENRICHMENT

- Have students research the discoveries made by Galileo with his refracting telescope.
- Have interested students find out about Search for Extraterrestrial Intelligence, or SETI, programs.
- Have students work in teams to determine what astronomers can learn from a radio-wave map of the Milky Way.

PROGRAM RESOURCES

From the **Teacher Resource Package** use:

Transparency Masters, pages 85-86, Telescopes.

Technology, pages 19-20, Radio Telescopes.

Use **Color Transparency** number 43, Telescopes.

RETEACH

Show students a picture of the *Hubble Space Telescope* and some photographs of objects taken by the telescope. Refer to *Astronomy* and *Sky and Telescope* magazines beginning with the September 1990 issues. Have students see if they are able to detect any distortions in the photos taken by the telescope.

EXTENSION

For students who have mastered this section, use the **Reinforcement** and **Enrichment** masters or other OPTIONS provided.

3 CLOSE

▶ Ask questions 1-4 and the **Apply** Question in the Section Review.

Cooperative Learning: Have Paired Partners compile a list of the types of radiant energy they have been exposed to or have used. Visible light from light bulbs, dentists' X rays, microwaves from microwave ovens, radio waves from radio station transmitters, and ultraviolet rays and infrared radiation from the sun are a few examples students may list.

SECTION REVIEW ANSWERS

1. the arrangement of all forms of radiant energy according to their wavelengths
2. a reflecting telescope
3. A radio telescope uses a curved dish antenna to collect and focus radio waves, whereas an optical telescope uses lenses or mirrors to collect and focus visible light.
4. Such telescopes would be located above the distorting effects of Earth's atmosphere.
5. Apply: about eight years—four years for the message to reach them and four years for their reply to travel back to us

Skill Builder

radio waves, microwaves, infrared waves, visible light, ultraviolet waves, X rays, gamma rays

Figure 21-3. The *Hubble Space Telescope* was deployed from the cargo bay of the space shuttle *Discovery* on April 25, 1990. It's now orbiting Earth, sending back images and data about distant space objects.

SECTION REVIEW

1. What is the electromagnetic spectrum?
2. Which type of telescope reflects light from a mirror to form an image?
3. How are radio telescopes and optical telescopes different from one another?
4. Why should telescopes such as the *Hubble Space Telescope* produce more detailed images than Earth-based telescopes?
5. **Apply:** It takes light from the closest star to Earth (other than the sun) about four years to reach us. If there was intelligent life on a planet circling that star, how long would it take for us to send them a radio transmission and for us to receive their reply?

Sequencing

Sequence these electromagnetic waves from longest wavelength to shortest wavelength: *gamma rays, visible light, X rays, radio waves, infrared waves, ultraviolet waves,* and *microwaves.* If you need help, refer to Sequencing in the **Skill Handbook** on page 680.

OPTIONS

PROGRAM RESOURCES

Use **Laboratory Manual**, pages 169-170, Refraction Of Light.

Use **Laboratory Manual,** pages 171-174, Spectral Analysis.

ACTIVITY 21-1
Telescopes

Problem: *How do the paths of light differ in reflecting and refracting telescopes?*

Materials  

- candle
- cardboard, white, 50 cm × 60 cm
- flashlight
- magnifying glass
- glass of water
- aluminum or silver spoon
- plane mirror
- convex mirror
- concave mirror
- empty paper towel roll
- masking tape

Procedure

1. Observe your reflection in a plane, convex, and concave mirror. Note differences in your image in the three mirrors.
2. Hold an object in front of each of the mirrors. Compare the images as to relative size and position.
3. Darken the room and hold the convex mirror at a 45° angle, slanting downward from your body. Direct the flashlight beam toward the mirror from right angles to your body. Note the size and position of the reflected light.
4. Repeat Step 3 using a plane mirror. Draw a diagram to show what happens to the beam of light.
5. Place the spoon in a glass of water. Diagram the shape of the spoon at the water line.
6. Attach the empty paper towel roll to the flashlight with masking tape so that the narrow beam of light will pass through the roll. Direct the light into a large glass of water, first directly from above, then from a 45° angle to the water surface. Compare the direction of the light rays when viewed from the side of the glass.
7. Light a candle and set it up some distance from the vertically held cardboard screen. **CAUTION:** *Keep hair and clothing away from the flame.* Using the magnifying glass as a convex lens, hold it between the candle and the screen until you have the best possible image.
8. Move the glass closer to the candle. Note what happens to the size of the image. Move the cardboard until the image is in focus.

Analyze

1. What is the purpose of the concave mirror in a reflecting telescope?
2. How did you determine the position of the focal plane of the magnifying glass in Step 7? What does this tell you about the position of all the light rays?
3. In one type of reflecting telescope, a plane mirror is in the tube near the eyepiece. What is the purpose of this mirror?
4. The eyepiece of a telescope is convex. What is its purpose?
5. What is the effect of the concave mirror on your reflection? Of the convex mirror? Of the plane mirror?
6. What effect did the convex mirror have on the beam of light in Step 3?

Conclude and Apply

7. Discuss your observations of the relationship of the distance between the object and lens and the clearest and largest image you could obtain in Steps 7 and 8.
8. How does the path of light differ in refracting and reflecting telescopes?

ACTIVITY 21-1
50-60 minutes

OBJECTIVE: Compare and contrast the paths taken by light in reflecting and refracting telescopes.

PROCESS SKILLS applied in this activity:
▶ **Observing** in Procedure Steps 1-8.
▶ **Inferring** in Analyze Questions 1-4.
▶ **Communicating** in Procedure Steps 1-8.
▶ **Interpreting Data** in Analyze Questions 5 and 6.
▶ **Experimenting** in Procedure Steps 1-8.
▶ **Defining Operationally** in Conclude and Apply Questions 7 and 8.
▶ **Separating and Controlling Variables** in Procedure Steps 1-8.

TEACHING THE ACTIVITY

▶ Review the difference between reflection and refraction, if necessary.
▶ Light pollution in most urban areas is usually at its peak during the early evening.
▶ When long exposures are used on telescope cameras, the light of the night sky builds up a "background fog" that masks the fainter objects in the sky.

PROGRAM RESOURCES

From the **Teacher Resource Package** use:

Activity Worksheets, pages 187-188, Activity 21-1: Telescopes.

ANSWERS TO QUESTIONS

1. collects incoming light and produces a small real image at the focal point
2. The focus of the lens is determined to be where the light from the candle is concentrated almost to a single point of light. An inverted, smaller image will occur on the cardboard at a distance between the focus and twice the focus. The rays must have been bent by the lens to be concentrated to one point.
3. to reflect the image 90° to the eyepiece
4. The eyepiece is moved toward the image until the inverted image is just inside the focus of the eyepiece. The eye then sees an enlarged virtual image.
5. A concave mirror enlarges an image. The image in the convex mirror is smaller and farther away than the object. The image in a plane mirror is the same size and at the same distance as the object.
6. Light rays diverge or spread out.
7. The real image occurs between the focal length and twice the focal length. Light passing through the lens converges to form the image. The real image is always inverted and smaller than the object. The focal length of the convex lens depends on the shape of the lens and the index of refraction of the lens material.
8. In refracting telescopes, light is bent into focus as it passes through a series of lenses. Reflecting telescopes use a series of mirrors to reflect light rays to a focus.

SCIENCE & SOCIETY SECTION 21-2

1 MOTIVATE

TYING TO PREVIOUS KNOWLEDGE: Have students list common sources of light pollution that they've probably taken for granted such as string lights at car dealerships, advertising and security lighting at shopping centers, and street lights.

OBJECTIVES AND SCIENCE WORDS: Have students review the objectives and science words to become familiar with this section.

2 TEACH

Key Concepts are highlighted.

MINI-Lab

Materials: cardboard tube from an empty roll of paper towels

Teaching Tips

► In most cases, an observer in a rural or high altitude location will be able to detect three or four times the number of objects that can be seen by an observer in an urban or suburban setting.

Answers: Students will generally find that observations made before sunrise, when light pollution is at a minimum, will reveal more observable objects in the night sky than those made in the early evening. The difference is usually due to a difference in the levels of human activities at these two times.

PROGRAM RESOURCES

From the **Teacher Resource Package** use:

Activity Worksheets, page 195 Mini-Lab: How much light pollution is there?

SCIENCE & SOCIETY 21-2 Light Pollution

New Science Words

light pollution

Objectives

- ► Explain how light pollution affects the ability to see dim objects in the sky.
- ► Discuss the controversy over light pollution as it relates to security and safety lighting.

Should Light Pollution Be Controlled?

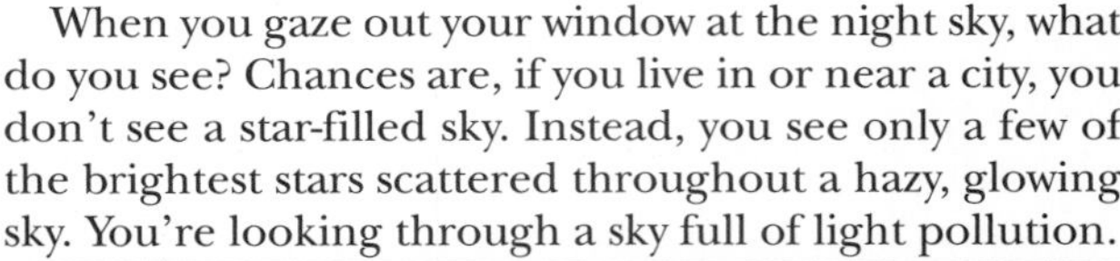

When you gaze out your window at the night sky, what do you see? Chances are, if you live in or near a city, you don't see a star-filled sky. Instead, you see only a few of the brightest stars scattered throughout a hazy, glowing sky. You're looking through a sky full of light pollution.

City lights cause a glow in the sky called **light pollution.** Light pollution makes the sky glow bright enough that dim stars can't be seen. What effect does light pollution have on your ability to stargaze? How do you think this affects astronomers working near large cities? Many people feel that their right to a dark night sky has been taken away.

Observing objects through Earth's atmosphere can be difficult even without light pollution. As you learned in Chapter 9, the atmosphere absorbs some of the radiant energy entering it. Visible light from objects in space can't pass through clouds or smog. Light pollution makes observing even more difficult. If an object is faint, it's difficult to distinguish between visible light from the object in space and visible light from the city.

Most people agree that lights are needed on city streets and parking lots for safety and security. What can be done to reduce light pollution without reducing public safety and security?

In several cities in the United States, work has begun to reduce light pollution. Tucson, Arizona, located only 80 km from Kitt Peak Observatory, has replaced its street lights with low-pressure sodium lamps. These lights shine at wavelengths that can be filtered out by astronomers. They produce better lighting for the streets and even cost

MINI-Lab

How much light pollution is there? Use a cardboard tube from an empty roll of paper towels. Select a night when clear skies are predicted. Go outside approximately two hours after sunset, look through the cardboard tube, and count the number of stars you are able to see without moving the observing tube. Follow the same procedure for two other areas of the sky and determine the average number of observable stars at each location. Approximately two hours before sunrise, later on the same night, repeat the procedure. What differences appear to exist between the two different sets of observations? Explain what might account for these differences.

OPTIONS

Meeting Different Ability Levels

For Section 21-2, use the following **Teacher Resource Masters** depending upon individual students' needs.

◆ **Study Guide Master** for all students.

● **Reinforcement Master** for students of average and above average ability levels.

▲ **Enrichment Master** for above average students.

Additional Teacher Resource Package masters are listed in the OPTIONS box throughout the section. The additional masters are appropriate for all students.

◆ STUDY GUIDE 84

NAME ______ DATE ______ CLASS ______

STUDY GUIDE — Chapter 21

Light Pollution — Text Pages 558–559

Each number in the code below represents a letter. Use the code to decode the message. After you've decoded the message, answer the question.

Code:

1	2	3	4	5	6	7	8	9	10	11	12	13	14	15	16	17	18	19	20	21	22	23	24	25	26
A	C	E	G	I	K	M	O	Q	S	U	W	Y	B	D	F	H	J	L	N	P	R	T	V	X	Z

23 17 3 / 10 23 1 22 10 / 8 16 / 23 17 3
T H E / S T A R S / O F / T H E

20 5 4 17 23 / 10 6 13 / 2 1 20 ' 23 / 14 3
N I G H T / S K Y / C A N ' T / B E

10 3 3 20 / 16 22 8 7 / 17 3 22 3
S E E N / F R O M / H E R E

23 17 3 / 14 22 5 4 17 23 / 2 5 23 13
T H E / B R I G H T / C I T Y

19 5 4 17 23 10 / 1 22 3 / 18 11 10 23 / 23 8 8
L I G H T S / A R E / J U S T / T O O

20 3 1 22
N E A R

23 17 3 13 / 2 1 11 10 3 / 1 / 4 19 8 12
T H E Y / C A U S E / A / G L O W

2 1 19 19 3 15 / 19 5 4 17 23
C A L L E D / L I G H T

21 8 19 19 11 23 5 8 20 / 16 8 22 / 12 17 5 2 17
P O L L U T I O N / F O R / W H I C H

12 3 / 17 1 24 3 / 20 8 / 3 1 10 13
W E / H A V E / N O / E A S Y

10 8 19 11 23 5 8 20
S O L U T I O N

Name two things that can be done to reduce light pollution. **Answers will vary but could include: Use low-pressure sodium lights, put hoods on lights such as flood lights, and turn off unnecessary outdoor lighting.**

84

Figure 21-4. The photographs show Tucson, Arizona, as seen from Kitt Peak National Observatory. The top photo was taken in 1959, the bottom photo in 1980.

less to operate. Another solution is to put hoods on billboard, parking lot, and flood lights so they illuminate the object or the ground rather than the sky.

The problem of light pollution is not just a problem for the big cities. In some cases, even in rural towns security lighting at one home can cause light pollution. For example, suppose you decide to have a few friends over to sit outside and watch for meteors, or so-called "shooting stars." You set up your chairs and sit down for an evening of searching the skies. Soon you realize that the sky is too bright. Your neighbor's security lights are casting a glow into the sky. When you ask your neighbor to turn off the lights, he refuses. He is concerned about some recent robberies and wants to keep his yard completely lit up. He has a right to protect his property; you have a right to observe the skies unspoiled by glare. What's the solution to this problem?

SECTION REVIEW

1. Why does light pollution interfere with nighttime observations?
2. Why would it be difficult to pass laws that ban light pollution?

You Decide!

Security lighting causes light pollution that interferes with nighttime observations. What can be done to ensure the safety of people and also eliminate light pollution? Do you think people who are not interested in night-sky observing should be required to replace their lights with less-polluting types? Should they have to turn off all outside lights after a certain time?

● REINFORCEMENT 84

NAME ______ DATE ______ CLASS ______

REINFORCEMENT — Chapter 21

Light Pollution — Text Pages 558–559

Choose the correct sentences to make two events-chain concept maps—one for light pollution and one for a solution to light pollution.

- Lights are installed on city streets.
- Dim stars can't be seen.
- The lights cause a glow in the sky.
- The city installs new low-pressure sodium lamps.
- At a nearby observatory, the light pollution interferes with observations.
- Astronomers can see better, and the city saves money.

Light pollution

People need to be safe on city streets at night.
↓
Lights are installed on city streets.
↓
The lights cause a glow in the sky.
↓
Dim stars can't be seen.

One solution to light pollution

The street lights used by a city cause light pollution.
↓
At a nearby observatory, the light pollution interferes with observations.
↓
The city installs new low-pressure sodium lamps.
↓
Astronomers can see better, and the city saves money.

84

▲ ENRICHMENT 84

NAME ______ DATE ______ CLASS ______

ENRICHMENT — Chapter 21

Light Pollution — Text Pages 558–559

HOW MUCH DOES LIGHT POLLUTION AFFECT YOUR ABILITY TO SEE POINTS OF LIGHT?

Materials
- large cardboard carton
- small lamp without shade
- large lamp with shade
- large piece of heavy cloth
- large needle
- small nail
- hammer

Procedure
1. Use the hammer, needle, and nail to poke a number of holes of different sizes in the bottom of the box. **CAUTION:** *Be very careful when poking the holes so that you do not puncture yourself with the needle or nail or hit yourself with the hammer.*
2. Put the box on its side and place a small unshaded lamp in the box. **CAUTION:** *To avoid the chance of a fire, make sure the light bulb of the lamp does not touch any surface.*
3. In a darkened room, turn on the lamp.
4. Stand about three meters from the box. Count the number of holes through which you can see light shining.
5. Record the number.
6. Repeat Steps 3–5 three times, using the large lamp in front of the box. First have the large lamp with the shade covered in front of the box. Then use the lamp with the shade uncovered. Finally, take the shade off the lamp.

Data and Observations

	Number of holes seen
Darkened room	**Data will vary.**
Room with lamp shade covered	
Room with shaded lamp	
Room with unshaded lamp	

Analyze
1. Under what conditions did you see the most holes? **in the darkened room without the lamp**
2. When did you see the least number of holes? **when the unshaded lamp was used**

Conclude and Apply
3. How did the light affect your ability to see? **The light made it more difficult to see because it interfered with the light shining through the holes.**
4. Compare your results to the effect of light pollution on the visibility of the stars. **The effect is similar. The light from the lamp interfered with the ability to see holes just as light pollution interferes with the ability to see the stars.**

84

CHECK FOR UNDERSTANDING

Ask Questions 1 and 2 in the Section Review.

RETEACH

Demonstration: Set up two identical light bulbs on a table in the front of the room. Shield one by taping a cardboard tent over its top. Have students observe that in a darkened room, placing a shield over the top of a light reduces the amount of light directed upward.

EXTENSION

For students who have mastered this section, use the **Reinforcement** and **Enrichment** masters or other OPTIONS provided.

Cooperative Learning: Using the Paired Partners strategy, have students write a proposal for a city ordinance that would control security lighting so amateur astronomers could enjoy unrestricted observation.

3 CLOSE

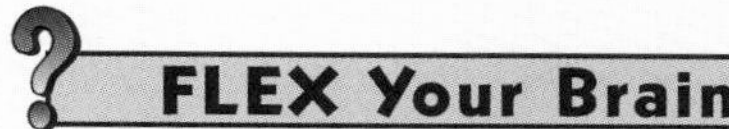

Use the Flex Your Brain activity to have students explore LOCAL LIGHT POLLUTION LAWS.

SECTION REVIEW ANSWERS

1. The glow caused by the numerous artificial lights masks the light from some stars.

2. Many people would resist legislation that forced them to turn off their security lights because these people feel it's their right to have safety lighting around their homes and yards. Businesses want to leave lights on to advertise.

YOU DECIDE!

Form three discussion panels. Assign each panel one of the questions presented in the You Decide feature. Have each group debate possible answers to its question and present the conclusions to the class.

SECTION 21-3

PREPARATION

SECTION BACKGROUND

▶ The first United States weather satellite, *Vanguard 2,* was launched in February 1959. Its mission was to take photographs of Earth's cloud patterns.

▶ Since *Sputnik I* was launched in 1957, over 15 000 artificial satellites have been sent into space. Of these, only six percent are still functioning. The remaining nonfunctioning satellites are classified as space junk. Other space junk includes satellite fragments, booster rockets, tools such as wrenches and screwdrivers, and items as small as paint chips.

▶ In July 1975, one of the Apollo spacecraft built (but not used) during Project Apollo moon flights was placed into orbit where it linked up with a Soyuz spacecraft. The joint mission showed that docking two vastly different spacecraft was possible. To achieve a successful dock, a special docking module was carried into space by the Apollo crew.

▶ *Apollo 13* did not land on the moon. While on its way to the moon, an oxygen tank in the service module exploded. This crippled the command module and the astronauts had to use the lunar module to power the spacecraft back to Earth.

▶ Space probes that helped locate landing sites on the moon were the *Ranger, Surveyor,* and *Lunar Orbiter. Ranger* took pictures of the moon's surface prior to its crash landing on the moon's surface. *Surveyor* landed on the moon, took pictures, and tested the lunar soil for landing possibilities. *Lunar Orbiter* took detailed photographs of the moon while orbiting the satellite.

21-3 Artificial Satellites and Space Probes

New Science Words

satellite
orbit
space probe
Project Mercury
Project Gemini
Project Apollo

Objectives

- ▶ **Compare and contrast natural and artificial satellites.**
- ▶ **Differentiate between an artificial satellite and a space probe.**
- ▶ **Trace the history of the race to the moon.**

The First Steps into Space

If you had your choice of watching your favorite team on television or from the stadium, which would you prefer? You would probably want to be as close as possible so you wouldn't miss any of the action. Some scientists feel the same way. Even though telescopes have taught them a great deal about the moon and planets, they want to learn more by actually going to those places, or by sending spacecraft where they can't go.

Space exploration began in 1957 when the former Soviet Union used a rocket to send *Sputnik I* into space. It was
1 the first artificial satellite. A **satellite** is any object that revolves around another object. When an object enters space, it will travel in a straight line unless a force such

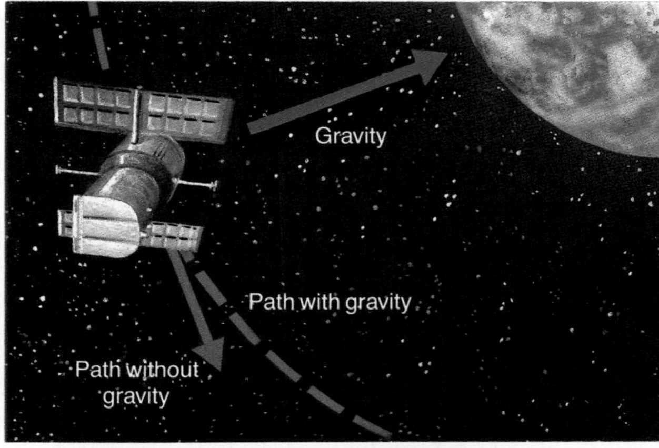

Figure 21-5. The combination of the satellite's forward movement and the gravitational attraction of Earth causes the satellite to travel in a curved path, or orbit.

OPTIONS

Meeting Different Ability Levels

For Section 21-3, use the following **Teacher Resource Masters** depending upon individual students' needs.

◆ **Study Guide Master** for all students.

● **Reinforcement Master** for students of average and above average ability levels.

▲ **Enrichment Master** for above average students.

Additional Teacher Resource Package masters are listed in the OPTIONS box throughout the section. The additional masters are appropriate for all students.

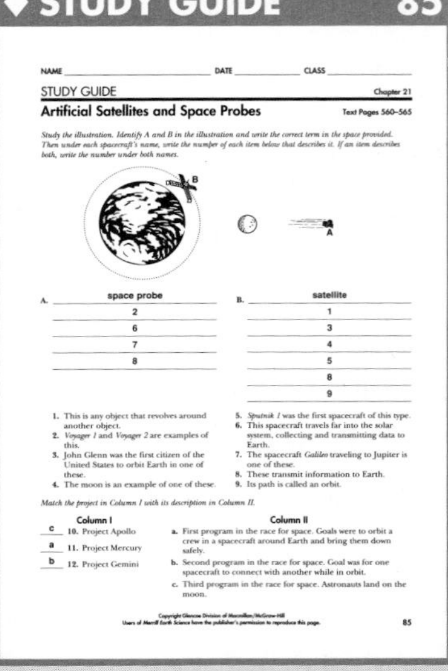

◆ STUDY GUIDE 85

NAME ________ DATE ________ CLASS ________

STUDY GUIDE — Chapter 21

Artificial Satellites and Space Probes — Text Pages 560-565

Study the illustration. Identify A and B in the illustration and write the correct term in the space provided. Then under each spacecraft's name, write the number of each item below that describes it. If an item describes both, write the number under both names.

A. space probe	B. satellite
2	1
6	3
7	4
8	5
	8
	9

1. This is any object that revolves around another object.
2. *Voyager 1* and *Voyager 2* are examples of this.
3. John Glenn was the first citizen of the United States to orbit Earth in one of these.
4. The moon is an example of one of these.
5. *Sputnik I* was the first spacecraft of this type.
6. This spacecraft travels far into the solar system, collecting and transmitting data to Earth.
7. The spacecraft *Galileo* traveling to Jupiter is one of these.
8. These transmit information to Earth.
9. Its path is called an orbit.

Match the project in Column I with its description in Column II.

Column I

c 10. Project Apollo
a 11. Project Mercury
b 12. Project Gemini

Column II

a. First program in the race for space. Goals were to orbit a crew in a spacecraft around Earth and bring them down safely.
b. Second program in the race for space. Goal was for one spacecraft to connect with another while in orbit.
c. Third program in the race for space. Astronauts land on the moon.

 85

as gravity deflects it. When Earth's gravity pulls on a satellite, it falls toward Earth. The result of the satellite traveling forward while at the same time falling toward Earth is that the satellite travels in a curved path around Earth. Such a path is called an **orbit.** 2

The moon is a natural satellite of Earth. It completes one orbit every month. *Sputnik I* orbited Earth for three months before gravity pulled it back into the atmosphere, where it burned up. *Sputnik I* was an experiment to show that artificial satellites could be made. Today, thousands of artificial satellites are in orbit around Earth.

Compare and contrast natural and artificial satellites.

Present-day communication satellites transmit radio and television programs to locations around the world. Other satellites gather scientific data that can't be obtained from Earth, and weather satellites constantly monitor Earth's global weather patterns.

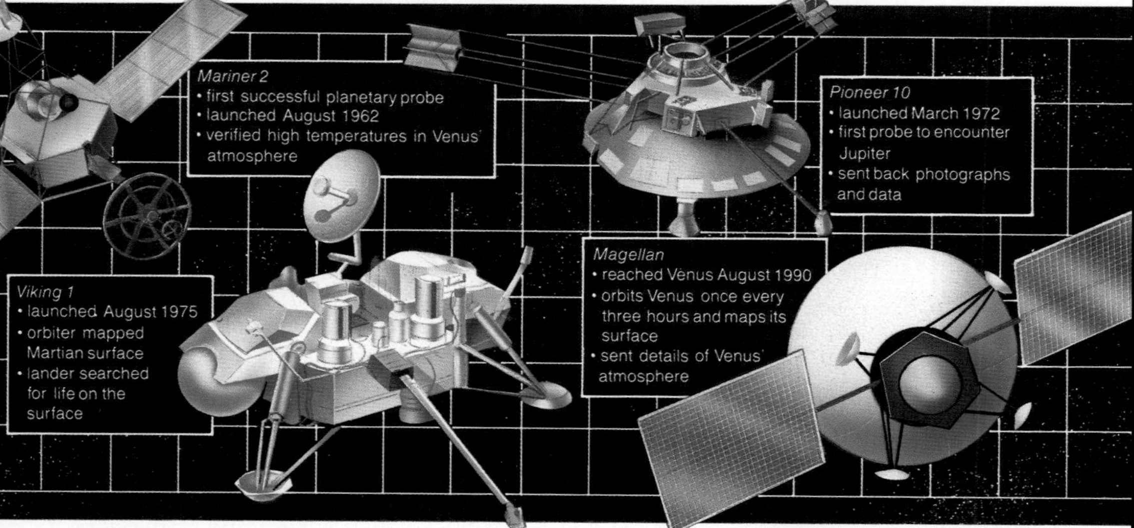

Mariner 2
• first successful planetary probe
• launched August 1962
• verified high temperatures in Venus' atmosphere
Pioneer 10
• launched March 1972
• first probe to encounter Jupiter
• sent back photographs and data
Magellan
• reached Venus August 1990
• orbits Venus once every three hours and maps its surface
• sent details of Venus' atmosphere
Viking 1
• launched August 1975
• orbiter mapped Martian surface
• lander searched for life on the surface

Figure 21-6. Examples of U.S. Space Probes

Space Probes

Not all objects carried into space by rockets become satellites. Rockets can also be used to send instruments far into space. A **space probe** is an instrument that gathers information and sends it back to Earth. Unlike satellites that orbit Earth, space probes travel far into the solar system. Some have even traveled out of the solar system. Space probes carry cameras and other data-gathering 3

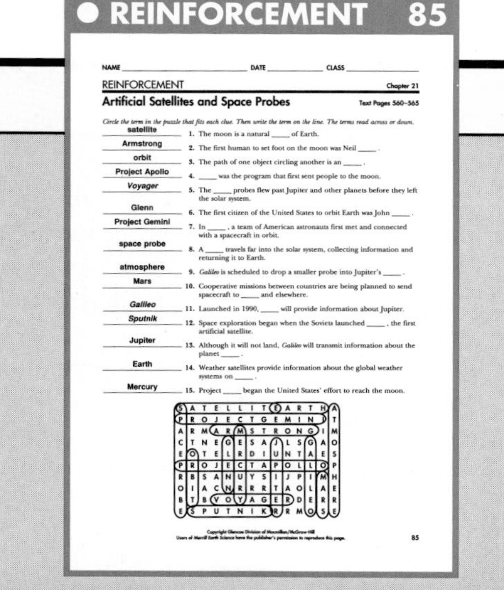

● REINFORCEMENT 85

NAME ____________ DATE ________ CLASS ________

REINFORCEMENT Chapter 21

Artificial Satellites and Space Probes Text Pages 560–565

Circle the term in the puzzle that fits each clue. Then write the term on the line. The terms read across or down.

satellite 1. The moon is a natural _____ of Earth.

Armstrong 2. The first human to set foot on the moon was Neil _____ .

orbit 3. The path of one object circling another is an _____ .

Project Apollo 4. _____ was the program that first sent people to the moon.

Voyager 5. The _____ probes flew past Jupiter and other planets before they left the solar system.

Glenn 6. The first citizen of the United States to orbit Earth was John _____ .

Project Gemini 7. In _____ , a team of American astronauts first met and connected with a spacecraft in orbit.

space probe 8. A _____ travels far into the solar system, collecting information and returning it to Earth.

atmosphere 9. *Galileo* is scheduled to drop a smaller probe into Jupiter's _____ .

Mars 10. Cooperative missions between countries are being planned to send spacecraft to _____ and elsewhere.

Galileo 11. Launched in 1990, _____ will provide information about Jupiter.

Sputnik 12. Space exploration began when the Soviets launched _____ , the first artificial satellite.

Jupiter 13. Although it will not land, *Galileo* will transmit information about the planet _____ .

Earth 14. Weather satellites provide information about the global weather systems on _____ .

Mercury 15. Project _____ began the United States' effort to reach the moon.

S A T E L L I T E A R T H A
P R O J E C T G E M I N I T
A R M A R M S T R O N G I M
C T N E G E S A J L S G A O
E O T E L R D I U N T A E S
P R O J E C T A P O L L O P
R B S A N U Y S I J P I M H
O I A C N R R R T A O L A E
B T B V O Y A G E R D E R R
E S P U T N I K R R M O S E

 85

▲ ENRICHMENT 85

NAME ____________ DATE ________ CLASS ________

ENRICHMENT Chapter 21

Artificial Satellites and Space Probes Text Pages 560–563

MAGELLAN

Read the following information and answer the questions below.

After it was launched by the space shuttle, *Magellan* began its long journey into space. *Magellan* headed for Venus, the planet closest to Earth. By August 10, 1990, *Magellan* began to orbit Venus. Once in orbit, the spacecraft began mapping the topography of the planet. By October, it had mapped only about 1.5 percent of the planet.

Magellan sends to Earth radar images of Venus. Its radar can detect features that are only 120 meters across. This is ten times smaller than anything ever detected on Venus before. The spacecraft has revealed many features of the planet's surface, including volcanic mountains and craters as large as major American cities.

After completing the mapping of Venus, which took about 250 days, *Magellan* started mapping the planet again. Scientists use the two sets of maps to compare sights on Venus. They look for changes that may have occurred between the times the two sets of maps were completed.

Scientists expect the images sent back to Earth by *Magellan* to help solve many mysteries about Venus. They hope to learn if Venus, like Earth, is divided into tectonic plates. They hope to learn how some features of its landscape have formed. They have learned already how one mountain peak was formed—by three upward thrusts of Venus's surface.

1. What might scientists conclude if a new space probe mapped Venus in 1999 and showed new lava not seen on the earlier maps? **The scientists might conclude that volcanoes are active on Venus. They might conclude that one or more volcanoes erupted between the time the different sets of maps were imaged.**

2. Radar images sent back to Earth by October 1990 have shown that Venus's surface has faultlike cracks. Based on the information available by October 1990, could we generalize that the entire planet has these cracks? **Because such a small percentage of the planet had been mapped by October 1990, a generalization about the entire planet's surface based on that information might prove incorrect.**

 85

1 MOTIVATE

FLEX Your Brain

Use the Flex Your Brain activity to have students explore ROCKET PROPULSION.

Cooperative Learning: Have Paired Partners collaborate on a brief written report about information that could be obtained by artificial satellites in orbit around Earth. Then have the class discuss how this information is used by humans on Earth's surface. To help students get started, list various types of artificial satellites: weather, communications, military, and astronomical.

TYING TO PREVIOUS KNOWLEDGE: Blow up a balloon and release it. Have students note that the balloon travels in the direction opposite where the air is escaping from its neck. Explain that rockets are propelled forward as gases escape from the nozzle at the back of the rocket.

OBJECTIVES AND SCIENCE WORDS: Have students review the objectives and science words to become familiar with this section.

2 TEACH

Key Concepts are highlighted.

CONCEPT DEVELOPMENT

FLEX Your Brain

Use the Flex Your Brain activity to have students explore the DATA COLLECTED BY SPACE PROBES. Have them contrast this with data collected by artificial satellites.

PROGRAM RESOURCES

From the **Teacher Resource Package** use:

Activity Worksheets, page 5, Flex Your Brain.

CONCEPT DEVELOPMENT

▶Show the video "Sail On, Voyager!" from the Infinite Voyage Home Video Library, which is available from Inovision, P.O. Box 576, Itasca, IL 60143-0576, or by calling 1-800-523-5503. This video describes the *Voyager* program as well as problems the spacecraft endured as it toured the outer planets.

Cooperative Learning: Using the Paired Partner strategy, have students use the school library to research the Mercury Seven astronauts. Students should collaborate on a written report about the missions each astronaut performed in the Mercury and other space programs, and what they are doing now.

Science and READING

After students find out about gravity-assisted space travel, have them compare and contrast the travel as it was used for the *Voyager* spacecraft and as it is presently being used for the *Galileo* space probe.

REVEALING MISCONCEPTIONS

▶Many people think artificial satellites and space probes gather identical data. Explain that artificial satellites orbit Earth or the object under observation. Probes are spacecraft sent far into space by rockets. They don't orbit other objects. Both satellites and probes send information back to Earth.

CROSS CURRICULUM

▶**Social Studies:** Have students research and report on the space programs of Japan and Europe. Students' reports should focus on the artificial satellites and probes launched by these space agencies.

Earth
• *Voyagers 1* and *2* are launched in 1977
Jupiter
• July 1979
• found ring around Jupiter
• discovered three new moons and erupting volcanoes on Io
Saturn
• August 1981
• revealed the complexity of Saturn's rings

Figure 21-7. Major Discoveries of *Voyager 2*

equipment as well as radio transmitters and receivers that allow them to communicate with scientists on Earth. Figure 21-6 is a timeline showing the space probes launched by NASA.

4 You've probably heard of the space probes *Voyager 1* and *Voyager 2*. These two probes were launched in 1977 and have now left our solar system. On their journeys, they flew past Jupiter, Saturn, Uranus, and Neptune. In Chapter 23, you will see many of the spectacular photographs obtained from the *Voyager* probes and read about what we've learned from them. Scientists expect these probes to continue to transmit data to Earth from beyond the solar system for at least 20 more years.

5 The *Voyager* probes didn't land on any of the planets they visited. Some probes, such as *Viking*, do land. *Galileo*, launched in 1989, will reach Jupiter in 1995 if all goes as planned. Once there, *Galileo* will drop a smaller probe into Jupiter's atmosphere. The small probe will take a parachute ride through Jupiter's violent atmosphere. Before being crushed by the atmospheric pressure, it will transmit information about Jupiter's composition, temperature, and pressure to the mother ship orbiting above. *Galileo* will then relay this information back to scientists eagerly awaiting it on Earth.

Science and READING

The *Galileo* craft is scheduled to rendezvous with Jupiter after it first flies by Venus, circles the sun, and then comes past Earth. Research newspaper articles to find out why *Galileo* is taking such an indirect path to Jupiter. Research NASA's method of gravity-assisted space travel.

OPTIONS

INQUIRY QUESTIONS

▶**How do space probes differ from artificial satellites?** *A space probe is launched into space, beyond Earth's orbit, where it gathers and transmits information back to Earth. Artificial satellites are placed into orbit around the object being studied and transmit information back to Earth's surface.*

▶**How did the *Voyager* probes differ from the *Viking* probes?** *The* Voyager *probes did not land on any planet they studied; the* Viking *probes landed on Mars.*

▶**Why was the success of *Sputnik I* so important to the explorations of space?** *The success of* Sputnik I *indicated to many people that placing a human into space was possible.*

▶**How did Project Mercury prepare the U.S. for future moon explorations?** *The Mercury program was devised to test the ability of humans to perform in space. It also provided experience in spaceflight.*

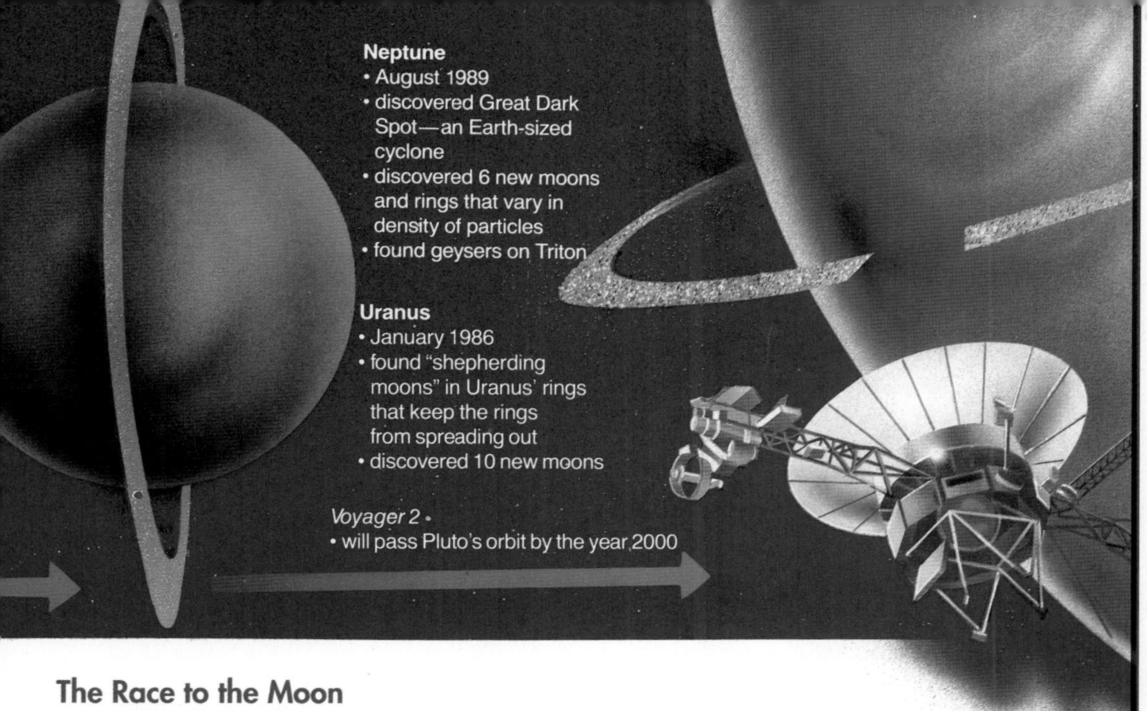

Neptune
• August 1989
• discovered Great Dark Spot—an Earth-sized cyclone
• discovered 6 new moons and rings that vary in density of particles
• found geysers on Triton
Uranus
• January 1986
• found "shepherding moons" in Uranus' rings that keep the rings from spreading out
• discovered 10 new moons
Voyager 2
• will pass Pluto's orbit by the year 2000

The Race to the Moon

It was quite a shock to people throughout the world when they turned on their radio and television sets and heard the radio transmissions from *Sputnik I* as it orbited over their heads. All that *Sputnik I* transmitted was a sort of "beeping" sound, but people quickly realized that putting a human into space wasn't far off.

In 1961, the Soviet cosmonaut Yuri A. Gagarin became the first human in space. He orbited Earth and then returned safely. Soon, President John F. Kennedy called for the United States to place people on the moon by the end of that decade. The "race for space" had begun.

Who was the first human in space?

The U.S. program to reach the moon began with **Project Mercury.** The goals of Project Mercury were to orbit a crewed spacecraft around Earth and to bring it safely back. The program provided data and experience in the basics of spaceflight. On May 5, 1961, Alan B. Shepard became the first U.S. citizen in space. In 1962, Mercury astronaut John Glenn became the first U.S. citizen to orbit Earth.

Project Gemini was the next step in reaching the moon. Teams of two astronauts in the same Gemini spacecraft orbited Earth. One Gemini team met and connected with

ENRICHMENT

▶Have students research geostationary satellites to find out what these satellites are used for and how the term describes the type of orbit of such a satellite.

▶Most communications satellites are placed in a geostationary or synchronous, orbit. This type of orbit permits the satellite to be constantly over a particular location of Earth's surface. The satellite circles Earth at exactly the same speed as Earth rotates below. Thus, it appears to be stationary to an Earth-based observer because it is always in the same location relative to Earth's surface.

▶Satellites not in a geostationary orbit pass over a particular location only once per orbit for only a brief time. This limits their usefulness for communication purposes. An Earth-based station would be in range of a non-synchronous satellite for only a brief time period. Communication satellites in geostationary orbits are within range of a station at all times.

CONCEPT DEVELOPMENT

▶Have students write to the regional NASA spaceflight center to request information about astronaut training and/or Space Camp. Then have students write reports, give oral presentations, or design bulletin boards that describe astronaut training or Space Camp.

CROSS CURRICULUM

▶**Social Studies:** Have students speculate on why so many developments occurred in the space program during the 1960s. Students should realize that the United States and the former Soviet Union were participating in a "race for space."

CHECK FOR UNDERSTANDING

Use the Mini Quiz to check for understanding.

MINI QUIZ

Use the Mini Quiz to check students' recall of chapter content.

1. **An object that revolves around another object is a(n) _____ .** *satellite*
2. **Define *orbit*.** *the curved path that an object follows as it travels in space*
3. **A(n) _____ is an instrument sent into space, beyond Earth's orbit, to gather information and send it back to Earth.** *space probe*
4. **The _____ space probes flew past Jupiter, Saturn, Uranus, and Neptune.** *Voyager*
5. **In 1995, if all goes as planned, _____ will drop a smaller probe into Jupiter's atmosphere.** *Galileo*

RETEACH

Cooperative Learning: Have Paired Partners make outlines of the material presented in Section 21-3. Have partners quiz other partners to review the material.

EXTENSION

For students who have mastered this section, use the **Reinforcement** and **Enrichment** masters or other OPTIONS provided.

CONCEPT DEVELOPMENT

▶ Pose the following questions. **What was the goal of Project Mercury?** *The goal of Project Mercury was to orbit a crewed spacecraft and to bring it safely back to Earth.* **What was the goal of Project Gemini?** *to have two astronauts in one craft meet and connect with two astronauts in another craft while in orbit* **What was the goal of Project Apollo?** *to place humans on the moon and to bring them back safely to Earth*

▶ **Demonstration:** Obtain models of the Mercury, Gemini, and Apollo spacecraft. Open the hatches of each model and show students how the astronauts would sit inside. Make sure students note that only one astronaut could fit in the Mercury spacecraft, two in the Gemini spacecraft, and that three sat side-by-side in the Apollo spacecraft.

TECHNOLOGY

▶ For more information, see *Spinoff,* a NASA publication that can be obtained by writing to Directory, Technology Utilization Division, P.O. Box 8756; Baltimore-Washington International Airport, MD 21240.

▶ Have interested students briefly report on the proposed research planned for future space stations.

Think Critically: Quartz watches are only one of the many spin-offs of the space program. Other responses that students might mention include calculators, computers, and battery-powered hand tools.

another spacecraft in orbit—a skill that would be needed on a voyage to the moon.

Along with the Mercury and Gemini programs, a series of probes was sent to the moon. Their mission was to take pictures of its surface that would be used to determine the best landing sites on the moon.

When did humans first reach the moon?

The final stage of the U.S. program to reach the moon was **Project Apollo.** On July 20, 1969, *Apollo 11* landed on the lunar surface. Neil Armstrong was the first human to set foot on the moon. His first words as he stepped onto its surface were: "That's one small step for a man, one giant leap for mankind." Edwin Aldrin, the second of the three *Apollo 11* astronauts, joined Armstrong on the moon and they explored its surface for two hours. Michael Collins remained in the Command Module

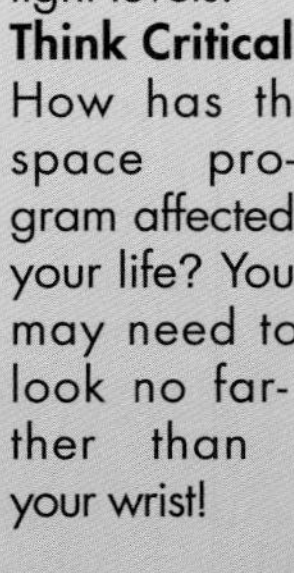

TECHNOLOGY

Spin-offs

The technology developed by NASA to achieve its goals in space has been remarkable. Much of it is now being used by people throughout the world. The technologies developed by NASA that are later used by the general public are called spin-offs.

NASA had to develop lightweight, compact breathing systems for the astronauts to carry as they ventured out of their spacecraft and onto the moon. Today, firefighters use these breathing systems as well as fire-resistant uniforms originally designed as flight suits for NASA pilots. The lightweight material in the suits won't burn or crack.

Another material, designed for boots worn by astronauts on the moon, is now found in some athletic shoes. Other materials have been incorporated into ski goggles, blankets, and bicycle seats.

Persons who are visually impaired have benefited from spin-offs too. They are able to use a device that vibrates ink on a printed page. This enables them to read materials that aren't in braille. Another device determines the denomination of currency and generates an audible signal.

Other spin-offs include pens that write without the help of gravity and sunglasses that adjust to various light levels.

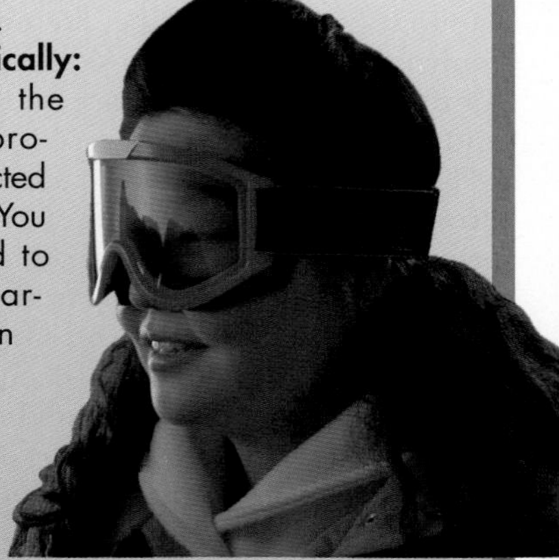

Think Critically: How has the space program affected your life? You may need to look no farther than your wrist!

OPTIONS

INQUIRY QUESTIONS

▶ **How did the information gained in Project Gemini lead to success in the Apollo mission?** *Project Gemini provided the opportunity for astronauts to work in space. It also showed that one spacecraft could successfully meet and rendezvous with another spacecraft while in orbit.*

▶ **Why do you think Michael Collins remained in the Command Module while Neil Armstrong and Edwin Aldrin landed on the moon?** *Collins operated the Command Module during the rendezvous and connection with the lunar lander. It was considered safer to have a person in the Command Module in case of problems during the connection of the spacecraft.*

▶ **What would be some of the advantages of sharing space missions with other countries?** *The cost of the space missions could be shared. Also, if the data gathered were shared by all nations, repetitive missions would be reduced. This would provide funds for other space missions and research.*

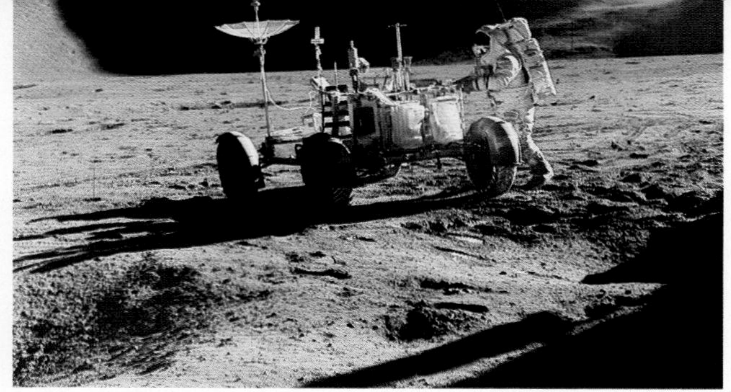

Figure 21-8. The Lunar Rover Vehicle was first used during the Apollo 15 mission. Riding in the "moon buggy," Apollo 15, 16, and 17 astronauts explored large areas of the lunar surface.

orbiting the moon, where Armstrong and Aldrin returned before beginning the journey home. A total of six lunar landings brought back more than 2000 samples of moon rock for study before the program ended in 1972.

During the past three decades, most missions in space have been carried out by individual countries, often competing to be the first or the best. Today, there is much more cooperation among countries of the world to work together and share what each has learned. Projects are now being planned for cooperative missions to Mars and elsewhere. As you read the next section, you'll see how the U.S. program has progressed since the days of Project Apollo, and where it may be going in the future.

SECTION REVIEW

1. Currently, no human-made objects are orbiting Neptune, yet Neptune has eight major satellites. Explain.
2. Galileo is considered a space probe as it travels to Jupiter. Once there, however, it will become an artificial satellite. Explain.
3. List the NASA projects that led to landing humans on the moon.
4. **Apply:** Is Earth a satellite of any other body in space? Explain your answer.

Concept Mapping — Skill Builder

Make a network-tree concept map that compares the first event in the U.S. space program to the first event in the former Soviet space program. If you need help, refer to Concept Mapping in the **Skill Handbook** on pages 688 and 689.

TEACHER F.Y.I.

▶ While the Apollo Command Module remained in orbit around the moon, a smaller Lunar Module (LM) took two astronauts down to the moon's surface. A portion of the LM was designed to be a launching pad and it stayed on the moon when the astronauts blasted off to rejoin the Command Module.

3 CLOSE

FLEX Your Brain

Use the Flex Your Brain activity to have students explore PROJECT APOLLO.

▶ Ask questions 1-3 and the **Apply** Question in the Section Review.

SECTION REVIEW ANSWERS

1. These eight satellites are natural satellites of the planet.

2. Once the probe arrives at Jupiter, it will go into orbit around that planet and become an artificial satellite.

3. Crewed NASA projects included Project Mercury, Project Gemini, and Project Apollo. Several uncrewed missions included *Ranger, Surveyor,* and *Lunar Orbiter.*

4. Apply: Yes, Earth is a natural satellite of the sun.

PROGRAM RESOURCES

From the **Teacher Resource Package** use:

Cross-Curricular Connections, page 25, Where do Names Come From?

Activity Worksheets, page 5, Flex Your Brain.

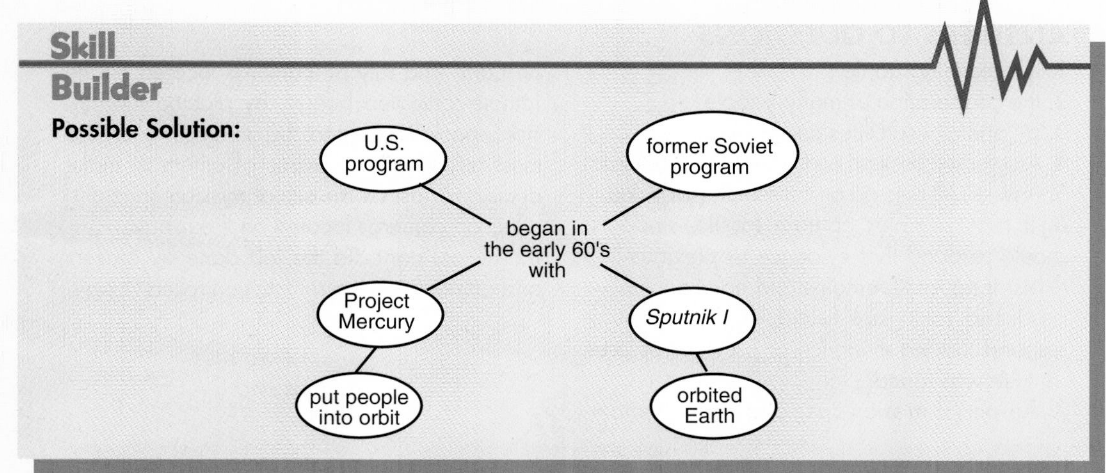

ACTIVITY 21-2

two class periods

OBJECTIVE: Plan, organize, and **perform** a simulated landing of a robot surface probe on Mars.

PROCESS SKILLS applied in this activity:
▶ **Formulating Models** in Procedure Step 1.
▶ **Observing** in Procedure Step 7.
▶ **Interpreting Data** in Procedure Steps 3, 4, 8, and 9.
▶ **Measuring** in Procedure Step 7.
▶ **Separating and Controlling Variables** in Procedure Steps 1, 5, and 7 and in Analyze Questions 1 and 2.
▶ **Inferring** in Conclude and Apply Questions 4-6.
▶ **Communicating** in Procedure Steps 1-9.

COOPERATIVE LEARNING Use the Science Investigation strategy to have students perform this activity. Assign roles as described in the Procedure.

TEACHING THE ACTIVITY

▶ Select an area of the school grounds to be used as the Martian surface. Dig "craters" in the area and move in several large rocks.
▶ Set up a screen behind which the mission specialist is to work.
▶ During the phase of the mission planning, have students brainstorm to devise the most workable method of completing the mission. Have one or two students list all ideas on the chalkboard.

ACTIVITY 21-2
Probe to Mars

Problem: *How is a mission involving a robot surface probe to Mars organized and carried out?*

Materials

- portable screen
- remote controlled car
- bag to hold rock and mineral samples
- large rocks (30 cm)
- camera (instant), film
- stopwatch

Background

- During this activity, you and your classmates will conduct a role playing space camp mission to successfully land an exploration probe on the surface of Mars, retrieve samples, and return those samples to Earth for analysis.
- To achieve this goal, you must do what NASA does before, during, and after a mission.
- You and your classmates will perform individual and group tasks that will lead to a successful mission.

Procedure

1. **Mission Planning:** The entire class will plan the mission. Include methods to be used for observing, mapping, choosing a landing site, operating the robot surface probe (a battery operated remote control car), collecting samples, analyzing the success of the mission, and designing a mission emblem.
2. **Orbital Photographic Study of the Martian Surface:** Two students will photograph all parts of the martian surface to be studied.

3. **Mapping the Martian Surface:** Three students will use photographs from the orbital study and draw a map of the martian surface. Be sure to identify large boulders, craters, flat areas, locations of samples to be retrieved, and any other key surface features.
4. **Landing Site Selection:** Three students will study the maps of the surface and decide on a landing site and route for the robot surface probe.
5. **Design of RSR (Remote Sample Retrieval) System:** Three students will design a method of retrieving a container of rock samples from Mars' surface. Rock samples will be encased in a baglike container, so the retrieval system must be able to pick up the bag of samples. The retrieval system might also include a cart, attached to the rear of the robot surface probe, to hold the samples.
6. **Mission Control (part 1):** A team of five students will conduct the countdown, blast off, flight, and landing of the robot surface probe.
7. **Mission Control (part 2):** A mission specialist and assistant will operate remote controls that will enable the robot surface probe to move around on the martian surface. A second mission specialist will operate the RSR System and collect samples for study. A successful mission is one in which the lander explores all parts of the martian surface within range, without colliding with boulders or falling into craters. A successful mission also involves retrieving rock samples from the planet's surface and returning them to Earth for study. NOTE: AS THE MISSION SPECIALIST OPERATES CONTROLS FROM BEHIND A SCREEN, THE ASSISTANT WILL GIVE DIRECTIONS ON WHICH WAY TO MOVE THE SURFACE PROBE. THE ASSISTANT DOES THE JOB THAT SENSORS OR CAMERAS WOULD.

ANSWERS TO QUESTIONS

1. the planning portion
2. the cooperation of many people
3. by artificial satellites and probes
4. Answer will depend on the samples provided.
5. Answer will depend on the samples provided.
6. If rock samples contain fossils, students should respond that evidence of previous life exists. If no fossil remains and no organically-produced rocks are found, students should respond that no evidence of previous or present life was found.
7. An actual mission specialist would remain on Earth and rely on cameras located on the remote-controlled buggy. By placing the mission specialist behind the screen, he or she must rely on observations of others to make decisions, just as an actual mission specialist relies on cameras located on the robots.
8. The assistant did the job done by sensors and cameras on the remote-controlled buggy.

8. **Sample Analysis:** A team of eight students will conduct an analysis of the rocks brought back from Mars' surface. This team of students is to use methods of identifying minerals and rocks learned in Chapters 3 and 4.
▶ Separate all samples into two main groups. Group one will be those that are recognized as mineral samples. Group two will be those that are recognized as rocks.
▶ Four students are to complete Activity 3-2 on page 73 of Chapter 3 for the identification of the mineral samples in group one. Include a copy of this activity as part of the final mission report.
▶ Four students are to study the rock samples in group two.
   - Determine the type of rocks present.
   - Determine the mineral content of each rock sample.
   - Look for any evidence of life on the surface of Mars by searching for fossils in the rocks brought back from the planet.

9. **Mission Debriefing:** A team of three students will:
▶ Observe the probe mission.
▶ Record the time required to conduct the surface probe mission.
▶ Judge when the mission is complete.
▶ Record the number of times the probe is delayed or hindered by various features.
▶ Review the reports of the sample analysis teams for general conclusions regarding the content of rocks on Mars' surface.

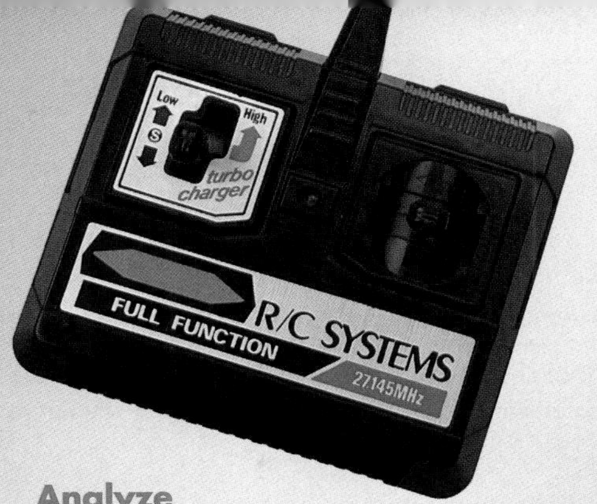

Analyze

1. What part of the mission did all other parts depend on?
2. What feature of the total project brought about a successful mission?
3. In an actual mission, how would photographs of possible landing sites be obtained?
4. What was the most common mineral found on the "martian" surface?
5. What types of rocks were found?

Conclude and Apply

6. What conclusion can be drawn from the mission about the past or present existence of life on Mars?
7. Why was the mission specialist placed behind a screen?
8. What task did the assistant perform when working with the mission specialist?
9. From your observations, list some likely sources of problems for an actual mission of this type.

Data and Observations

Sample Data

Time of Mission		Accuracy of Mission	
Mission start	1:03:00 EST	Were all sites visited?	yes
Mission stop	1:31:17 EST	List the number of times the mission was delayed by surface features.	7
Mission length	28 min	Was the mission completed?	yes

▶ Have five students conduct the countdown, blast off, and flight of the space probe. You may wish to have students build a model rocket and launch it to simulate this portion of the activity. If so, be sure an adult supervises any launches students conduct using model-rocket engines.
▶ Have one student move the remote-controlled buggy to the area to be studied. (This simulates the landing on the Martian surface.)
▶ Obtain a copy of "Launching A Dream, A Teacher's Guide to a Simulated Space Shuttle Mission" from NASA, Lewis Research Center, Cleveland, OH 44135. Use the book to provide ideas on how to set up and organize this activity.
Troubleshooting: Several days before doing this activity obtain the remote-controlled buggy, camera, and stopwatch, so they can be checked to see that they operate properly. Be sure to have plenty of fresh batteries for the remote-controlled buggy. Obtain a camera with instant-developing film to photograph the Martian surface.

PROGRAM RESOURCES

From the **Teacher Resource Package** use:

Activity Worksheets, pages 189-191, Activity 21-2: Probe to Mars.

9. Problem areas may include obtaining detailed photographs of Mars' surface, omitting key steps in the mission planning, breakdown of the remote-controlled buggy, destruction of the buggy by colliding with rocks or falling into a crater, or breakdown in communication from the robot to the mission specialist, among others.

SECTION 21-4

PREPARATION

SECTION BACKGROUND

▶ The space shuttle *Challenger* exploded 75 seconds after its launch on January 28, 1986. The explosion occurred when one of two solid fuel booster rockets developed a leak. The hot gases burned through the main fuel tank causing it to explode. All people on board were killed.

▶ Cosmonauts lost calcium from their bones and were weak after spending a year aboard *Mir*. Prolonged stays in space may have other harmful effects on humans and other organisms.

PREPLANNING

▶ To prepare for the Mini-Lab, obtain a record album and three marbles for each Science Investigation group.

1 MOTIVATE

▶ If possible, obtain a working model of a space shuttle. Use the model to demonstrate how the cargo bay is used to carry satellites to and from Earth and how the mobile arm is used to place satellites into orbit and to bring them back into the cargo bay for repairs.

PROGRAM RESOURCES

From the **Teacher Resource Package** use:

Critical Thinking/Problem Solving, page 27, Students and the Space Program.

Concept Mapping, pages 47-48.

Science and Society, page 25, Space Pollution.

Activity Worksheets, pages 196, Mini-Lab: How can gravity be simulated in a space station?

21-4 The Space Shuttle and the Future

New Science Words

space shuttle
space station

Objectives

- ▶ Describe the benefits of the space shuttle.
- ▶ Evaluate the usefulness of orbital space stations.

The Space Shuttle: A Reusable Spacecraft

Imagine spending millions of dollars to build a machine, sending it off into space, and watching its 3000 tonnes of metal and other materials burn up after only a few minutes of work. That's exactly what NASA did for many years. The early rockets lifted into orbit a small capsule holding the astronauts. Sections of the rocket separated from the rest of the rocket body and burned as they re-entered the atmosphere.

NASA administrators, like many people, realized that it can be less expensive and less wasteful to reuse resources. Just as you may reuse a paper bag to pack your lunch, NASA has begun to reuse the spacecrafts that carry astronauts and cargo into space. The reusable spacecraft that transports astronauts, satellites, and other materials to and from space is the **space shuttle.** 1

At launch, the space shuttle orbiter stands on end and is connected to an external liquid-fuel tank and two solid-fuel booster engines. When the shuttle reaches an altitude of about 40 km, the emptied solid-fuel booster rockets drop off and parachute back to Earth. They are recovered and used again. The larger external liquid-fuel tank eventually separates and falls back to Earth. It isn't recovered.

OPTIONS

Meeting Different Ability Levels

For Section 21-4, use the following **Teacher Resource Masters** depending upon individual students' needs.

◆ **Study Guide Master** for all students.

● **Reinforcement Master** for students of average and above average ability levels.

▲ **Enrichment Master** for above average students.

Additional Teacher Resource Package masters are listed in the OPTIONS box throughout the section. The additional masters are appropriate for all students.

◆ STUDY GUIDE 86

NAME ____________ DATE ________ CLASS ____________

STUDY GUIDE Chapter 21

The Space Shuttle and the Future Text Pages 568–569

*Read the following statements. If a statement is true of a space shuttle, write **SH** in the blank. If a statement is true of a space station, write **ST**. If the statement is true of both, write **B** in the blank.*

B 1. The United States has developed this type of spacecraft.
SH 2. This is a reusable space transport.
SH 3. Its solid-fuel booster engines are recovered after they are parachuted to Earth.
B 4. This has orbited Earth.
ST 5. Cosmonauts spent a record 365 days on one of these.
ST 6. NASA plans on assembling a future one of these in orbit.
ST 7. This provides living quarters and places for work and exercise for people living in space.
B 8. Astronauts have conducted experiments in these.
SH 9. This glides back to Earth and lands like an airplane.
ST 10. NASA plans call for crews to remain on board this several months at a time.
SH 11. This would be used in the future to send equipment and goods back and forth to people working in space.
SH 12. Its mechanical arm can be used to launch, retrieve, and repair satellites.
ST 13. The Soviets called theirs *Mir.*
ST 14. We called ours *Skylab.*
SH 15. The *Hubble Space Telescope* was launched by this in 1990.
ST 16. A purpose of this is to serve as a repair site for satellites and other vehicles.
SH 17. Its liquid-fuel tank is not recovered when it returns to Earth.
SH 18. Astronauts can only spend a short time in space in one of these.
ST 19. In one of these, American crews have spent up to 84 days collecting data about the effects of living in space.
B 20. NASA has plans for the future use of this.
B 21. Astronauts on this perform many duties.
ST 22. Several nations will cooperate in working on a future project for this.
ST 23. While in this, researchers will make products that will be returned to Earth.

86

Once the space shuttle orbiter reaches space, it begins to orbit Earth. There, astronauts perform many different tasks. The cargo bay can carry a self-contained laboratory where astronauts conduct scientific experiments and determine the effects of space flight on the human body. On missions in which the cargo bay isn't used as a laboratory, the shuttle can launch, repair, and retrieve satellites.

To retrieve a satellite, a large mechanical arm in the cargo bay is extended. An astronaut inside the shuttle orbiter moves the arm by remote control. The arm grabs the satellite and pulls it back into the cargo bay doors. It can then be returned to Earth.

Similarly, the mechanical arm can be used to lift a satellite or probe out of the cargo bay and place it into space. In some cases, a defective satellite can be pulled in by the mechanical arm, repaired while in the cargo bay, and then placed into space once more.

After the completion of each mission, the space shuttle orbiter glides back to Earth and lands like an airplane. A very large landing field is needed because the gliding speed of the orbiter is 335 km/hr.

Space Stations

Astronauts can spend only a short time in space in the space shuttle orbiter. Its living space is very small, and the crew needs more space to live, exercise, and work. A **space station** has living quarters, work and exercise space, 2 and all the equipment and support systems needed for humans to live and work in space.

The United States had such a station in the past. The space station *Skylab* was launched in 1973. Crews of astronauts spent up to 84 days in it performing experiments and collecting data on the effects on humans living in space. In 1979, the abandoned *Skylab* fell out of orbit and burned up as it entered Earth's atmosphere.

Crews from the former Soviet Union have spent the most time in space aboard their space station, *Mir.* 3 Two cosmonauts spent a record 365 days on board.

Presently, NASA is planning a space station that would be larger than *Skylab* or *Mir.* Construction of this space station is scheduled to begin in the late 1990s or early twenty-first century. Previous space stations have been assembled on Earth and then rocketed to space. If NASA

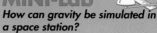

MINI-Lab

How can gravity be simulated in a space station?

Locate an LP record album you can use for this activity. Measure the circumference of the record. Now cut a piece of construction paper so it's the same length as the record's circumference and 8 cm wide. Fold the paper in half so that it is now 4 cm wide. Score the paper along the fold and then open it back up.

Wrap the paper around the record so the score line contacts the record all the way around. Fold the paper under one side of the record and tape it securely. Leave the other 4 cm of paper standing, so you have a wall around the outside of the record disc.

Place the record on a turntable and place three marbles at its center. Switch the turntable to its slowest setting, and turn it on.

Why do the marbles move to the wall of paper? How does this simulate gravity? How could a space station simulate gravity using the same method? Make a sketch of a space station that would be able to spin to simulate gravity.

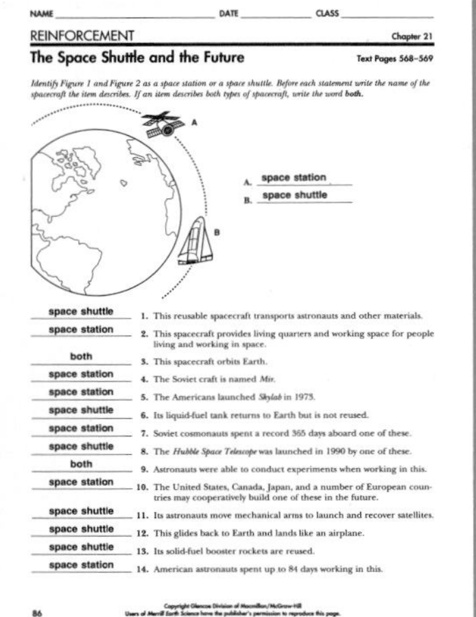

● REINFORCEMENT 86

NAME ________ DATE ________ CLASS ________

REINFORCEMENT — Chapter 21

The Space Shuttle and the Future — Text Pages 568–569

Identify Figure 1 and Figure 2 as a space station or a space shuttle. Before each statement write the name of the spacecraft the item describes. If an item describes both types of spacecraft, write the word **both.**

A. space station

B. space shuttle

space shuttle 1. This reusable spacecraft transports astronauts and other materials.

space station 2. This spacecraft provides living quarters and working space for people living and working in space.

both 3. This spacecraft orbits Earth.

space station 4. The Soviet craft is named *Mir.*

space station 5. The Americans launched *Skylab* in 1973.

space shuttle 6. Its liquid-fuel tank returns to Earth but is not reused.

space station 7. Soviet cosmonauts spent a record 365 days aboard one of these.

space shuttle 8. The *Hubble Space Telescope* was launched in 1990 by one of these.

both 9. Astronauts were able to conduct experiments when working in this.

space station 10. The United States, Canada, Japan, and a number of European countries may cooperatively build one of these in the future.

space shuttle 11. Its astronauts move mechanical arms to launch and recover satellites.

space shuttle 12. This glides back to Earth and lands like an airplane.

space shuttle 13. Its solid-fuel booster rockets are reused.

space station 14. American astronauts spent up to 84 days working in this.

86

▲ ENRICHMENT 86

NAME ________ DATE ________ CLASS ________

ENRICHMENT — Chapter 21

The Space Shuttle and the Future — Text Pages 568–569

PLANNING SPACE COLONIES

Some scientists are planning colonies in space. In this activity you will analyze their ideas and consider the answer to a related problem. Read each idea carefully and then answer the questions.

1. One group has decided that a satellite colony should include 10 000 people. In the population, 30 percent will produce materials and perform services for the colony's needs. In the population, 44 percent will produce materials for export to Earth.
   a. How many of people are to produce materials and perform services for the colony? 3000
   b. How many people are to produce materials for export to Earth? 4400

   Problem: Why do you suppose 26 percent of the colony's population is unaccounted for in the production of materials and the performance of services? Answers will vary but students may point out that some may be scientists or astronauts who have different responsibilities.

2. One design for a space colony is a large doughnut-shaped structure. The "doughnut" would be spun to give people inside a sense of gravity like that on Earth.
   a. If 60 percent of the inside volume of the structure can be inhabited and the total volume of the structure is 29 000 000 cubic meters, what is the actual volume that can be inhabited? 17 400 000 m^3
   b. What would be the average volume of living space for each of the 10 000 people? 1740 m^3

   Problem: Think of necessary human activities. Describe one way designers might use space in the colony very efficiently for one or more human activities. Answers may include such ideas as using large cafeterias for recreation.

3. It's suggested that each person in the colony will need 1.7 tonnes of material from Earth each year. Also, it's thought that to help people avoid boredom, half of the people in the colony will return to Earth each year.
   a. How much material would be needed by 10 000 people in one year? 17 000 tonnes
   b. How many of the 10 000 people would be rotated with people from Earth each year? 5000

   Problem: If you were permitted only 50 kilograms for your personal belongings (excluding food, furniture, and your spacesuit), what would you take with you to spend a year as a space colonist? Answers will vary but may include entertainment items such as radios or books.

86

TYING TO PREVIOUS KNOWLEDGE: Have students recall the details of the most recent space shuttle mission by sharing magazine articles and photographs that describe the accomplishments of space shuttle missions. Have students hypothesize why space shuttle missions occur more frequently than other missions.

OBJECTIVES AND SCIENCE WORDS: Have students review the objectives and science words to become familiar with this section.

2 TEACH

Key Concepts are highlighted.

MINI-Lab

Materials: turntable, LP record, scissors, construction paper, masking tape, marbles

Teaching Tips

► Inform students that only the *slowest* speed of the turntable should be used.

Answers: The marbles are directed away from the center of the turntable (or from the axis of rotation) by centrifugal force. This force is defined as the apparent force on a body in curvilinear motion directed away from the axis of rotation. It simulates gravity by forcing objects (in this case the marbles) outward, away from the center of the rotating body. The surface of the construction paper that stops the marbles becomes the floor or artificial ground. In that spinning body, the direction "up" would be toward the center or axis of rotation. "Down" would be away from the axis of rotation or outward in all directions. Any space station would simulate this "artificial" gravity by spinning slowly around a central axis of rotation.

CHECK FOR UNDERSTANDING

Use the Mini Quiz to check for understanding.

MINI QUIZ

Use the Mini Quiz to check students' recall of chapter content.

1. **The ____ is a reusable spacecraft that transports astronauts, satellites, and other materials to and from space.** *space shuttle*
2. **What is a space station?** *a spacecraft that has everything needed to live and work in space*
3. **What was *Skylab*?** *a U.S. space station that orbited Earth for 4 years.*

RETEACH

Have students research the final flight of *Challenger*. Have students describe the effects the explosion has had on the U.S. space program.

EXTENSION

For students who have mastered this section, use the **Reinforcement** and **Enrichment** masters or other OPTIONS provided.

Science and WRITING

Make sure students realize that the 100 people don't have to be known to them personally, but rather should include occupations such as farmers, mechanics, writers, and so on.

3 CLOSE

▶ Ask questions 1-2 and the **Apply** Question in the Section Review.

SECTION REVIEW ANSWERS

1. It is a reusable spacecraft.
2. It has a large cargo bay that enables it to carry satellites to and from Earth; it can be used to repair defective satellites; and it can land like an airplane.
3. Apply: A future space station could be located at a greater distance from Earth, reducing drag caused by the atmosphere. Also, rockets could be used to occasionally adjust the orbit of the space station to compensate for any decay of its orbit.

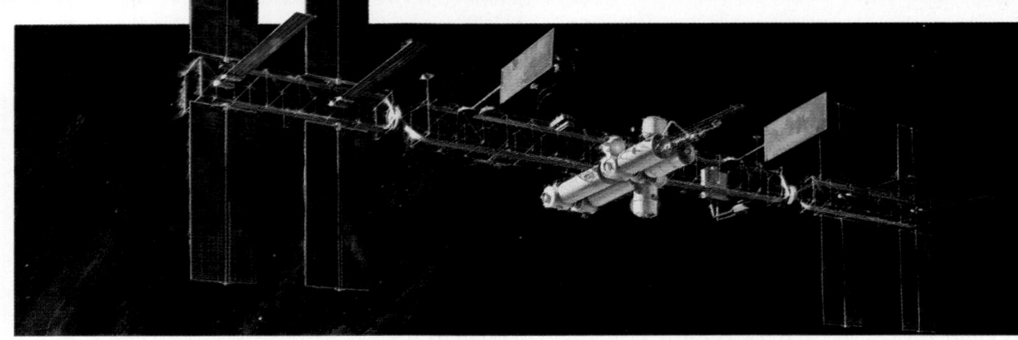

Figure 21-9. This is one proposal for the next space station. NASA will consider many models before deciding on a final plan for the new space station.

carries out its plan, the future space station will be assembled in orbit. The space shuttle will carry up the pieces and astronauts will connect them.

NASA plans for crews to stay on board the station for several months at a time. While there, researchers will make products that are returned for use on Earth. These products might include perfect crystals grown in the weightlessness of space that are useful in medical research. Robots may work in the vacuum and low temperatures of space to produce better and cheaper computer chips.

Another purpose for the space station is for it to serve as a refueling and repair station for satellites and other vehicles. In the future, plans call for it to be used as a construction site for ships to the moon and Mars.

Like many projects today, the future space station is planned as a cooperative effort of several countries. Japan, Canada, and the 13 countries of the European Space Agency may all contribute.

Science and WRITING

Suppose it's the year 2010 and you're in charge of assembling a crew for a new space station. Select the 100 people you want to fill the station. Remember, you will need people to do a variety of jobs, such as farming, maintenance, scientific experimentation, and so on. You will have to live with them and rely on them for the next year. Discuss, in writing, whom you would select and why.

SECTION REVIEW

1. What is the main advantage of the space shuttle?
2. Why is the space shuttle more versatile than earlier spacecraft?
3. **Apply:** *Skylab's* forward motion was slowed by friction caused by Earth's outer atmosphere. How could NASA prevent this from happening with a new space station?

Skill Builder — ☑ Outlining

Outline the possible uses of the mechanical arm of the space shuttle's cargo bay. If you need help, refer to Outlining in the **Skill Handbook** on page 681.

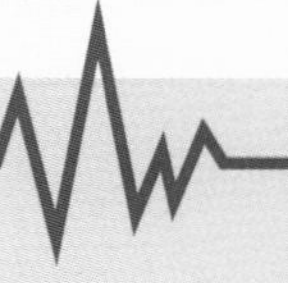

Skill Builder

Outlines will vary, but students should include at least the activities described in Section 21-4. Some students may know of other uses for the arm.

CHAPTER

REVIEW

SUMMARY

21-1: Radiant Energy from Space

1. The arrangement of radiant energy waves according to their wavelengths is the electromagnetic spectrum.
2. Optical telescopes produce magnified images of objects. A refracting telescope bends light to form an image. A reflecting telescope uses mirrors to focus light to produce an image.
3. Optical telescopes magnify visible light so that objects can be viewed. Radio telescopes collect and record radio waves given off by some space objects.

21-2: Science and Society: Light Pollution

1. City lights cause a glow in the night sky that obscures dim stars.
2. Lights are needed in towns and cities for safety and security reasons. However, light pollution can cause problems for amateur stargazers as well as professional astronomers.

22-3: Artificial Satellites and Space Probes

1. A satellite is an object that revolves around another object. The moons of the planets are natural satellites. Artificial satellites are those made by people.
2. An artificial satellite collects data as it orbits Earth. A space probe travels far out into the solar system, gathers data, and sends it back to Earth.
3. Early American space programs included the Mercury, Gemini, and Apollo projects.

21-4: The Space Shuttle and the Future

1. The space shuttle is a reusable spacecraft that carries astronauts, satellites, and other payloads to and from space.
2. Space stations provide the opportunity to do research not possible on Earth. Future space stations could also serve as refueling and repair stations for space vehicles.

KEY SCIENCE WORDS

a. **electromagnetic spectrum**
b. **light pollution**
c. **observatories**
d. **orbit**
e. **Project Apollo**
f. **Project Gemini**
g. **Project Mercury**
h. **radio telescope**
i. **reflecting telescope**
j. **refracting telescope**
k. **satellite**
l. **space probe**
m. **space shuttle**
n. **space station**

UNDERSTANDING VOCABULARY

Match each phrase with the correct term from the list of Key Science Words.

1. the arrangement of radiant energy waves according to their wavelengths
2. uses lenses to bend light toward a focal plane
3. uses mirrors to collect light and form an image
4. glow in the night sky caused by city lights
5. an object that revolves around another object
6. the path traveled by a satellite
7. the first crewed U.S. space program
8. space program that reached the moon
9. carries people and tools to and from space
10. a place in space to live and work

CHAPTER

REVIEW

SUMMARY

Have students read the summary statements to review the major concepts of the chapter.

UNDERSTANDING VOCABULARY

1. a	**6.** d
2. j	**7.** g
3. i	**8.** e
4. b	**9.** m
5. k	**10.** n

OPTIONS

ASSESSMENT

To assess student understanding of material in this chapter, use the resources listed.

COOPERATIVE LEARNING

Consider using cooperative learning in the THINK AND WRITE CRITICALLY, APPLY, and MORE SKILL BUILDERS sections of the Chapter Review.

PROGRAM RESOURCES

From the **Teacher Resource Package** use:
Chapter Review, pages 45-46.
Chapter Tests, pages 146-147, Chapter Test.

CHAPTER
REVIEW

CHECKING CONCEPTS

1. d	**6.** a
2. d	**7.** c
3. a	**8.** c
4. c	**9.** b
5. b	**10.** d

UNDERSTANDING CONCEPTS

11. the moon
12. Optical telescopes
13. Light pollution
14. artificial satellite
15. space station

THINK AND WRITE CRITICALLY

16. Electromagnetic waves can carry energy through matter and empty space, whereas mechanical waves need matter through which to travel.
17. Reflecting and refracting telescopes both gather light from the object being viewed and magnify the light to produce an image. A refracting telescope uses lenses to accomplish this while a reflecting telescope uses mirrors.
18. Natural sources are clouds, precipitation, and the moon; artificial sources include city lights, security lights, street lights, and air pollution, among others.
19. An object in motion tends to move in a straight line. But gravity acts on the object and pulls it toward Earth. The resultant force keeps the object traveling in a curved path.
20. Students' responses will vary. Reasons for flying might include the intrigue of getting to travel, live, and work in space. Reasons for declining the opportunity might include the potential dangers involved during lift-off, the stay in space, and landing.

APPLY

21. Earth-based observations are obscured by the atmosphere. The atmosphere absorbs and distorts incoming radiation. Because the moon has no atmosphere, visible light and other forms of energy can reach its surface without being distorted.
22. Most students should realize that the surface temperature of the sun and the immense heat that is radiated from it would make a space-probe encounter useless as the probe would burn up before getting close enough to gather data.
23. Answers will vary. Crewless probes need fewer resources and can provide more data about our outer solar system and deep space. Space flights with people aboard provide information about living in space and also valuable technological data.
24. No, sound requires matter through which to travel. Space is a virtual vacuum.
25. A portion of Pluto's orbit lies closer to the sun than Neptune. The *Voyager 2* probe crossed Pluto's orbit as it traveled to Neptune. Also, a probe destined for a region of space beyond our solar system could cross Pluto's orbit without actually visiting the planet.

CHAPTER
REVIEW

CHECKING CONCEPTS

Choose the word or phrase that completes the sentence.

1. ______ are electromagnetic waves.
   a. Gamma rays **c.** Microwaves
   b. Visible light waves **d.** All of these
2. ______ telescopes use mirrors to collect light.
   a. Radio **c.** Refracting
   b. Electromagnetic **d.** Reflecting
3. A(n) ______ telescope can be used during the day or at night and during bad weather.
   a. radio **c.** refracting
   b. electromagnetic **d.** reflecting
4. ______ reduce light pollution.
   a. Radio telescopes **c.** Sodium lamps
   b. Observatories **d.** All of these
5. *Sputnik I* was the first ______.
   a. telescope **c.** observatory
   b. artificial satellite **d.** U.S. space probe
6. Goals of ______ were to put a spacecraft in orbit and bring it safely back.
   a. Project Mercury **c.** Project Gemini
   b. Project Apollo **d.** *Viking I*
7. The ______ of the space shuttle are reused.
   a. liquid-fuel tanks **c.** booster engines
   b. Gemini rockets **d.** none of these
8. The ______ of the space shuttle can place a satellite into space and retrieve it.
   a. liquid-fuel tank **c.** mechanical arm
   b. booster rocket **d.** carbo bay
9. *Skylab* was a(n) ______ that fell from its orbit.
   a. space probe **c.** space shuttle
   b. space station **d.** optical telescope
10. Microwaves are ______.
    a. invisible
    b. longer than visible waves
    c. shorter than gamma waves
    d. both a and b

UNDERSTANDING CONCEPTS

Complete each sentence.

11. A natural satellite of Earth is ______.
12. ______ use mirrors and lenses rather than radio receivers to gather electromagnetic waves.
13. ______ is caused by the use of many artificial lights.
14. The *Hubble Space Telescope* is a(n) ______ of Earth.
15. A(n) ______ provides astronauts with more living and working space than the space shuttle orbiter.

THINK AND WRITE CRITICALLY

16. How do electromagnetic waves differ from mechanical waves? Give an example to support your answer.
17. Compare and contrast two types of optical telescopes.
18. List one natural and two artificial sources that prevent clear observations of the night sky.
19. Explain what two motions keep a satellite in orbit around Earth.
20. If given the chance, would you choose to fly on a shuttle mission? Give reasons for your answer.

APPLY

21. How would a moon-based telescope have advantages over the Earth-based telescopes being used today?
22. Would a space probe to the sun's surface be useful? Explain.

23. Suppose NASA had to choose between continuing either the spaceflight programs with people aboard or the crewless space probes. Which do you think is the more valuable program? Explain your choice.
24. Suppose two astronauts were outside of the space shuttle orbiter while orbiting Earth. The audio speaker in the helmet of one of the astronauts quits working. The other astronaut is only one meter away, so she shouts a message to him. Can he hear her? Explain.
25. No space probes have visited the planet Pluto, the outermost planet of our solar system. Nevertheless, probes have crossed Pluto's orbit. Explain how this is possible.

MORE SKILL BUILDERS

If you need help, refer to the Skill Handbook.

1. **Sequencing:** Arrange these events in order from earliest to the most recent. Galileo discovered four moons orbiting Jupiter, *Sputnik I* orbited Earth, humans landed on the moon, *Galileo* began its journey to Jupiter, Yuri Gagarin orbited Earth, Project Apollo began, *Discovery* launched the *Hubble Space Telescope.*
2. **Measuring in SI:** Explain whether or not each of the following pieces of equipment could be used aboard the space shuttle as it orbits Earth: a balance, a graduated cylinder, a meterstick, and a thermometer.
3. **Concept Mapping:** Make an events chain map that explains what happens to different parts of the space shuttle including the orbiter, liquid fuel tank, and solid fuel booster engines, from takeoff to landing.
4. **Classifying:** Classify each of the following as a satellite or a space probe: Mercury spacecraft, *Sputnik I*, the *Hubble Telescope,* the space shuttle orbiter, and *Voyager 2*.
5. **Making and Using Tables:** Copy the table below. Use information in the chapter as well as news articles and other resources to complete your table.

Several U.S. Space Probes			
Probe	**Launch Date**	**Destinations**	**Planets or objects visited**
Mariner 4			
Vikings 1 & 2			
Pioneers 10 & 11			
Voyagers 1 & 2			
Magellan			
Galileo			

PROJECTS

1. Design and build a three-dimensional model of a space station. Be sure to include a way for people and equipment to be transported into and out of the station.
2. Construct working models of the two kinds of optical telescopes. Demonstrate their uses to your class.

MORE SKILL BUILDERS

1. Sequencing: Galileo discovered four moons orbiting Jupiter; *Sputnik I* orbited Earth; Yuri Gagarin orbited Earth; Project Apollo began; humans landed on the moon; *Galileo* began its journey to Jupiter; *Discovery* launched the *Hubble Space Telescope.*

2. Measuring in SI: The balance and the graduated cylinder couldn't be used because the objects and fluids to be measured wouldn't stay on the pans or in the cylinder. Distances and temperature, however, are not affected by the weightless environment of space.

3. Concept Mapping: Students' maps will vary. Most should include the following steps:
Orbiter takes off from launch pad. At height of 40 km, booster rockets drop off and parachute to Earth. Liquid-fuel tank eventually drops off. When mission is over, shuttle orbiter returns to Earth.

4. Classifying: All were satellites except Voyager 2. It did not orbit any object and is therefore a space probe.

5. Making and Using Tables: *Mariner 4* was launched in 1964. Its destination was Mars, which was the only planet that it visited. *Vikings 1* and *2* were launched in 1975, destined for the Martian surface. Both probes visited only Mars. *Pioneers 10* and *11* were launched in 1973 and 1974, respectively. *Pioneer 10* was destined to leave the solar system. *Pioneer 11's* destination was an orbit of Saturn. *Pioneer 10* visited only Jupiter. *Pioneer 11* visited both Jupiter and Saturn. *Voyagers 1* and *2* were launched in 1977. Both were destined to leave our solar system. *Voyagers 1* and *2* visited Jupiter and Saturn. *Voyager 2* went on to visit Uranus and Neptune. *Magellan* was launched in 1989, destined to orbit Venus. It visited only Venus. *Galileo* was launched in 1989. It's destiny is to achieve an orbit of Jupiter. *Galileo* will circle Venus, Earth, Mars, and Earth again before reaching Jupiter.

CHAPTER

22 Earth-Moon System

CHAPTER SECTION	OBJECTIVES	ACTIVITIES
22-1 Planet Earth (2 days)	1. **Describe** Earth's shape and list physical data about Earth. 2. **Compare** and **contrast** rotation and revolution of Earth. 3. **Demonstrate** how Earth's revolution and tilt cause seasons to change on Earth.	**MINI-Lab:** *How round is Earth?* p. 582 **Activity 22-1:** *The Egg and the Equinox,* p. 583
22-2 Earth's Moon (1 day)	1. **Demonstrate** how the moon's phases depend on the relative positions of the sun, the moon, and Earth. 2. **Describe** why eclipses occur, and **compare** solar and lunar eclipses. 3. **Hypothesize** what surface features of the moon tell us about its history.	**MINI-Lab:** *How does the moon affect tides?* p. 586
22-3 Building a Moon Colony Science & Society (2 days)	1. **Describe** how a moon colony might be constructed. 2. **List** advantages and disadvantages of constructing a moon colony.	**Activity 22-2:** *Moon Phases and Eclipses,* p. 594
Chapter Review		

ACTIVITY MATERIALS

FIND OUT	ACTIVITIES		MINI-LABS	
Page 575 lamp without shade globe of Earth	**22-1 The Egg and the Equinox, p. 583** raw egg	**22-2 Moon Phases and Eclipses, p. 594** light source (unshaded) polystyrene ball on pencil globe Figure 22-6	**How round is Earth? p. 582** string globe of Earth basketball or volleyball Table 22-1 ruler	**How does the moon affect tides? p. 586** tidal range graph from Chapter 11 Review

CHAPTER FEATURES	TEACHER RESOURCE PACKAGE	OTHER RESOURCES
Technology: *Clocks: The Old and the New,* p. 580 **Skill Builder:** *Recognizing Cause and Effect,* p. 582	**Ability Level Worksheets** ◆ ***Study Guide,*** p. 87 ● ***Reinforcement,*** p. 87 ▲ ***Enrichment,*** p. 87 **MINI-Lab Worksheet,** p. 204 **Activity Worksheet,** pp. 198-199 **Critical Thinking/Problem Solving,** p. 28 **Transparency Masters,** pp. 87-88	**Color Transparency 44,** Earth-Sun Relationships **Lab Manual:** *Earth's Spin,* pp. 175-176 **Lab Manual:** *Earth's Magnetism,* pp. 177-178
Problem Solving: *Marooned on the Moon,* p. 590 **Skill Builder:** *Measuring in SI,* p. 591	**Ability Level Worksheets** ◆ ***Study Guide,*** p. 88 ● ***Reinforcement,*** p. 88 ▲ ***Enrichment,*** p. 88 **MINI-Lab Worksheet,** p. 205 **Concept Mapping,** pp. 49-50 **Cross-Curricular Connections,** p. 26 **Transparency Masters,** pp. 89-90	**Color Transparency 45,** Moon Phases **Lab Manual:** *Moon Phases,* pp. 179-180
You Decide! p. 593	**Ability Level Worksheets** ◆ ***Study Guide,*** p. 89 ● ***Reinforcement,*** p. 89 ▲ ***Enrichment,*** p. 89 **Activity Worksheet,** pp. 200-201 **Science and Society,** p. 26	
Summary Key Science Words Understanding Vocabulary Checking Concepts Understanding Concepts Think & Write Critically Apply More Skill Builders Projects	**Chapter Review,** pp. 47-48 **Chapter Test,** pp. 150-153	**Chapter Review Software** **Test Bank**

◆ **Basic** ● **Average** ▲ **Advanced**

ADDITIONAL MATERIALS

SOFTWARE	AUDIOVISUAL	BOOKS/MAGAZINES
Moon Rise/Set, Micro Learningware. *Time and Seasons,* Rand McNally. *The Earth and Moon Simulator,* Focus. *Our Home Planet,* Focus.	*How We Know the Earth Moves,* film, BFA. *The Earth in Motion,* film, EBEC. *The Lunar Orbiter,* film, NASA. *Controversy Over the Moon,* film, EBEC. *Moonwalk,* video, LCA. *For All Mankind,* laserdisc, The Voyager Company.	Press, Frank and Raymond Siever. *Earth.* 4th ed. NY: W.H. Freeman and Company, 1986. Sneider, Cary I. *Earth, Moon and Stars.* Berkley, CA: Lawrence Hall of Science, 1986. Whipple, L.C. Earth, *Moon and Planets.* Cambridge, MA: Harvard University Press.

CHAPTER

22

EARTH-MOON SYSTEM

THEME DEVELOPMENT: Cycles and systems and interactions are emphasized in this chapter. Earth's rotation and revolution cause daily and seasonal cycles. Phases of the moon occur monthly and rely on the interaction among the sun, the moon, and Earth. Eclipses not only occur several times a year but the same cycle recurs every 18 years. The interactions of the Earth-moon system and the phenomena that result should be emphasized as you teach all sections of the chapter.

CHAPTER OVERVIEW

- **Section 22-1:** Section 22-1 presents some of the physical data of Earth. The planet's rotation and revolution also are described. The causes for seasons are explained in terms of Earth's position in space with respect to the sun and the tilt of Earth's axis.
- **Section 22-2:** The reasons why the moon goes through phases are presented. The types and causes of eclipses are described. The origin of Earth's only natural satellite also is explored.
- **Section 22-3: Science and Society:** Methods that might be employed to build a moon colony are explored. The You Decide feature asks students to consider whether benefits of a moon colony are worth the risks involved.

CHAPTER VOCABULARY

sphere
axis
rotation
revolution
ellipse
equinox
solstice
moon phases
new moon
waxing
first quarter
full moon
waning
third quarter
solar eclipse
lunar eclipse
maria
moon colony

CHAPTER

22 Earth-Moon System

574

OPTIONS

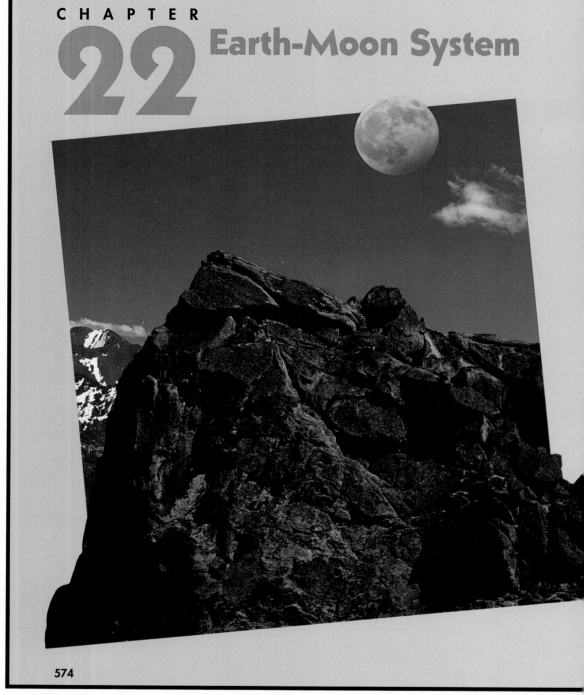

For Your Gifted Students

Have students work in pairs to make time-lapse videos of the phases of the moon. Every night, the partners should videotape the moon for a few seconds. They should do this for one month. A regular 35 mm camera can be used if a video camera is not available.

You have experienced the changing of the seasons many times, but do you know what causes seasons? When it's winter in Earth's northern hemisphere, it's summer in the southern hemisphere and vice versa. Why is this the case?

FIND OUT!

Do this simple activity to see what causes the seasons to change.

Use a lamp without a shade to represent the sun. Turn the lamp on. Hold a globe of Earth about 2 m from the lamp. Tilt the globe slightly, so the northern half of it points toward the "sun." What season do you think this represents for Earth's northern hemisphere? What season would be occurring in the southern hemisphere? Now, keeping it tilted, walk the globe around the "sun." Don't turn or twist the globe as you walk. When you're halfway around the "sun," notice that the northern hemisphere is no longer pointing toward the "sun." What season is it in the northern hemisphere now?

Gearing Up

Previewing the Chapter

Use this outline to help you focus on important ideas in this chapter.

Section 22-1 Planet Earth
- ▶ Planet Earth Data
- ▶ Seasons
- ▶ Equinoxes and Solstices

Section 22-2 Earth's Moon
- ▶ Motions of the Moon
- ▶ Phases of the Moon
- ▶ Eclipses
- ▶ Structure of the Moon
- ▶ Origin of the Moon

Section 22-3 Science and Society
Building a Moon Colony
- ▶ Should Humans Colonize the Moon?

Previewing Science Skills

- ▶ In the **Skill Builders,** you will recognize cause and effect relationships and measure in SI.
- ▶ In the **Activities,** you will make models, analyze and interpret data, and make inferences.
- ▶ In the **MINI-Labs,** you will measure in SI, analyze data, interpret graphs, and draw conclusions.

What's next?

In the Find Out activity you learned that seasons on Earth change because Earth is tilted and sunlight hits it differently as Earth moves around the sun. As you read this chapter, you'll also learn what causes day and night, and how Earth and the moon interact.

For Your Mainstreamed Students

Have students research myths about the full moon. After gathering the information, they can write and perform skits that illustrate some of the myths.

INTRODUCING THE CHAPTER

Use the Find Out activity to introduce students to the causes of seasons. Inform students that they will be learning more about the interactions of Earth, the moon, and the sun as they read the chapter.

FIND OUT!

Preparation: Several days before you begin this chapter, have students bring in small lamps from home. Also obtain several globes of Earth.

Materials: one lamp without shade and one globe for each group of students

Cooperative Learning: Form Science Investigation groups of three students per group. As two students perform the activity, the third should observe and record what he or she observes. Students could alternate roles so that each has a chance to observe the activity.

Teaching Tips

▶ Caution students not to touch the lamp bulb as it may get very hot.

▶ Be sure students understand that the orientation or "tilt" of the globe must remain constant. If necessary, place tape on the wall and explain that the globe must be tilted toward the tape as students move the globe around the "sun."

Answers to Questions: When the northern hemisphere points toward the sun, the northern hemisphere experiences summer. When the northern hemisphere points away from the sun, it experiences winter.

Gearing Up

Have students study the Gearing Up feature to familiarize themselves with the chapter. Discuss the relationships of the topics in the outline.

What's Next?

Before beginning the first section, make sure students understand the connection between the Find Out activity and the topics to follow.

SECTION 22-1

PREPARATION

SECTION BACKGROUND

▶ Convection currents of molten iron deep in Earth's core produce huge electrical currents. These electrical currents, in turn, cause Earth's magnetic field.

▶ Magnetic compass directions can be corrected to true geographic directions by either adding or subtracting the declination value listed on a map. If the declination is east, the value is subtracted from the compass reading. If the declination is west, the value is added.

▶ The Tropics of Cancer and Capricorn mark the latitudes where the noonday sun is directly overhead at summer solstice for each hemisphere. At 66.5° latitudes, the sun's rays strike Earth at a glancing angle. These latitudes are designated the Arctic Circle in the north and the Antarctic Circle in the south. When the sun is directly over the Tropic of Cancer, no light strikes Earth farther south than the Antarctic Circle. No light strikes Earth farther north than the Arctic Circle when the sun is directly above the Tropic of Capricorn.

▶ Seasons aren't marked by great climatic changes at the equator. The sun is overhead 12 hours per day, and the amount of solar energy received doesn't vary much from one day to the next.

PREPLANNING

▶ To prepare for Activity 22-1, obtain a raw egg for each group of students. You may wish to have several extra eggs in case some are broken. Also obtain a ball of string to be used in the Mini-Lab and basketballs or other large, playground balls to be used in various demonstrations throughout the section.

22-1 Planet Earth

New Science Words

sphere
axis
rotation
revolution
ellipse
equinox
solstice

Objectives

▶ Describe Earth's shape and list physical data about Earth.
▶ Compare and contrast rotation and revolution of Earth.
▶ Demonstrate how Earth's revolution and tilt cause seasons to change on Earth.

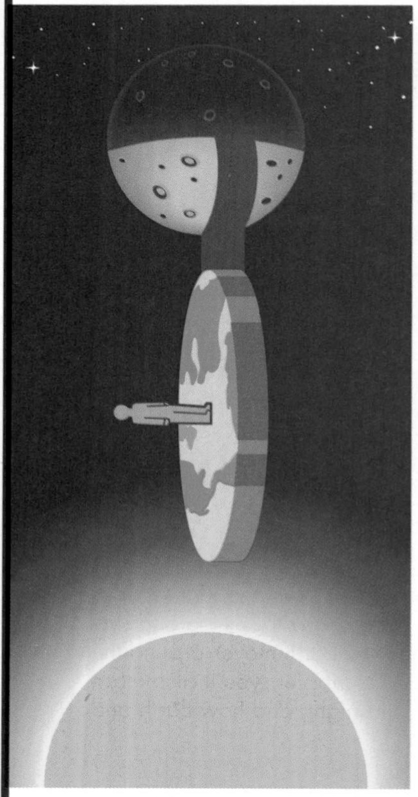

Figure 22-1. Aristotle's Proof That Earth Is Not Flat

Planet Earth Data

You rise early in the morning while it's still dark outside. You sit by the window and watch the sun come up. Finally, day breaks and the sun begins its journey across the sky. But is it the sun that's moving, or is it you?

Today, we know that the sun appears to move across the sky because Earth is spinning. You may take it for granted that Earth is traveling around the sun. But it wasn't long ago that people believed Earth was the center of the universe. They believed Earth stood still and the sun traveled around it.

As recently as the days of Christopher Columbus, there were people who also believed Earth was flat. They noticed the surface appeared to stretch out flat in all directions. They thought that if you sailed far out to sea, you would eventually fall off the edge of the world. How do you know this isn't true? How have scientists determined what Earth is shaped like?

Space probes and artificial satellites have sent back images that show Earth is sphere-shaped. A **sphere** is a round, three-dimensional object whose surface at all points is the same distance from its center. Tennis balls and basketballs are examples of spheres. But people had evidence of Earth's true shape long before cameras were sent into space.

In the 3rd century, B.C., Greek astronomer Aristotle reasoned that if Earth were flat, it would sometimes cast a shadow of a straight line on the moon. Because such a shadow is never observed, he concluded that Earth was spherical rather than flat.

OPTIONS

Meeting Different Ability Levels

For Section 22-1, use the following **Teacher Resource Masters** depending upon individual students' needs.

◆ **Study Guide Master** for all students.

● **Reinforcement Master** for students of average and above average ability levels.

▲ **Enrichment Master** for above average students.

Additional Teacher Resource Package masters are listed in the OPTIONS box throughout the section. The additional masters are appropriate for all students.

◆ STUDY GUIDE 87

NAME ______ DATE ______ CLASS ______

STUDY GUIDE — Chapter 22

Planet Earth — Text Pages 576–582

Use the words in the box to fill in the blanks in the statements.

revolution	ellipse	seasons
sphere-shaped	sphere	center
24 hours	365 days	rotation
axis		

1. A round, three dimensional object is a **sphere**.
2. All points on a sphere's surface are the same distance from the **center** of the sphere.
3. Images from space probes and artificial satellites show that Earth is **sphere-shaped**.
4. The North and South Poles are located at the ends of Earth's **axis**, the imaginary line around which Earth spins.
5. The spinning of Earth on its axis that causes day and night is called **rotation**.
6. One complete rotation of Earth takes about **24 hours**.
7. Earth's yearly orbit around the sun is its **revolution**.
8. One complete revolution of Earth takes about **365 days**.
9. The path of Earth's orbit is in the shape of an elongated closed curve called an **ellipse**.
10. Earth's tilted axis causes **seasons**.

Answer the following questions on the lines provided.

11. What is inclined at an angle of 11.5° to Earth's rotational axis? **magnetic axis**
12. What is the sun directly over at the equinoxes? **the equator**
13. Which season begins in the northern hemisphere when the sun reaches its greatest distance south of the equator? **winter**
14. On what date does the southern hemisphere begin spring? **September 22, 23**
15. At the March equinox, what season begins in the northern hemisphere? **spring**
16. At the summer solstice in the northern hemisphere, at what point is the sun? **at its northernmost point—over the Tropic of Cancer**

87

Table 22-1

PHYSICAL PROPERTIES OF EARTH	
Diameter (pole to pole)	12 714 km
Diameter (equator)	12 756 km
Circumference (poles)	39 776 km
Circumference (equator)	39 843 km
Mass	5.98×10^{27} g
Density	5.52 g/cm^3
Average distance to the sun	149 600 000 km
Period of rotation (1 day)	23 hr, 56 min
Period of revolution (1 year)	365 day, 6 hr, 9 min

Axis

Rotation

Other evidence for Earth's shape was observed by early sailors. They watched ships approach from across the ocean and saw that the top of the ship would come into view first. As they continued to watch the ship, more and more of it would come into view. As the ship moved over the curved surface of Earth, they could see all of it.

Today, we know that Earth is sphere-shaped, but it's not a perfect sphere. It bulges slightly at the equator and is somewhat flattened at the poles. The poles are located at the north and south ends of Earth's axis. Earth's
1 **axis** is the imaginary line around which Earth spins. The spinning of Earth on its axis, called **rotation,** causes day
2 and night to occur.

What is Earth's axis?

As Earth rotates, the sun comes into view at daybreak. Earth continues to spin, making it appear that the sun moves across the sky until it sets at night. During night, the area of Earth that you're on has spun away from the sun. Because of this, the sun is no longer visible. Earth continues to steadily rotate, and the sun eventually comes into view the next morning. One complete rotation takes about 24 hours, or one day. How many rotations does Earth complete during one revolution around the sun? As you can see, it completes about 365 rotations during one year. Table 22-1 lists some other physical properties of Earth.

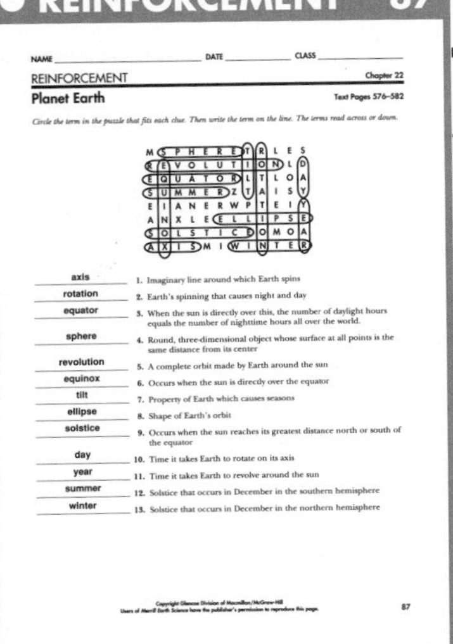

● REINFORCEMENT 87

NAME ______ DATE ______ CLASS ______

REINFORCEMENT — Chapter 22

Planet Earth — Text Pages 576–582

Circle the term in the puzzle that fits each clue. Then write the term on the line. The terms read across or down.

M S P H E R E T R L E S
R E V O L U T I O N L D
E Q U A T O R L T L O A
S U M M E R Z T A I S Y
E I A N E R W P T E I Y
A N X L E E L L I P S E
S O L S T I C E O M O A
A X I S M I W I N T E R

axis 1. Imaginary line around which Earth spins
rotation 2. Earth's spinning that causes night and day
equator 3. When the sun is directly over this, the number of daylight hours equals the number of nighttime hours all over the world.
sphere 4. Round, three-dimensional object whose surface at all points is the same distance from its center
revolution 5. A complete orbit made by Earth around the sun
equinox 6. Occurs when the sun is directly over the equator
tilt 7. Property of Earth which causes seasons
ellipse 8. Shape of Earth's orbit
solstice 9. Occurs when the sun reaches its greatest distance north or south of the equator
day 10. Time it takes Earth to rotate on its axis
year 11. Time it takes Earth to revolve around the sun
summer 12. Solstice that occurs in December in the southern hemisphere
winter 13. Solstice that occurs in December in the northern hemisphere

 87

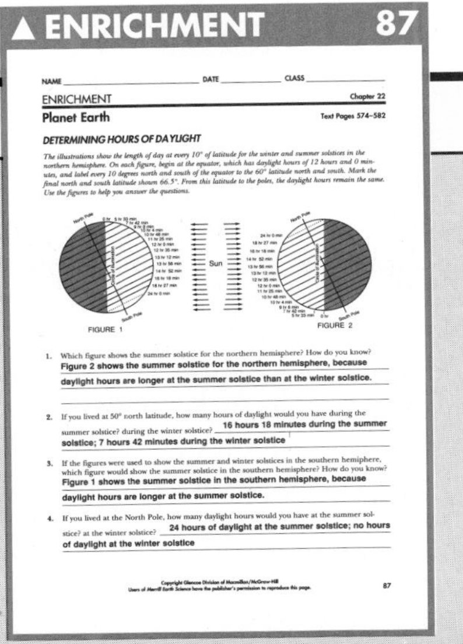

▲ ENRICHMENT 87

NAME ______ DATE ______ CLASS ______

ENRICHMENT — Chapter 22

Planet Earth — Text Pages 574–582

DETERMINING HOURS OF DAYLIGHT

The illustrations show the length of day at every 10° of latitude for the winter and summer solstices in the northern hemisphere. On each figure, begin at the equator, which has daylight hours of 12 hours and 0 minutes, and label every 10 degrees north and south of the equator to the 60° latitude north and south. Mark the final north and south latitude shown 66.5°. From this latitude to the poles, the daylight hours remain the same. Use the figures to help you answer the questions.

1. Which figure shows the summer solstice for the northern hemisphere? How do you know? **Figure 2 shows the summer solstice for the northern hemisphere, because daylight hours are longer at the summer solstice than at the winter solstice.**
2. If you lived at 50° north latitude, how many hours of daylight would you have during the summer solstice? during the winter solstice? **16 hours 18 minutes during the summer solstice; 7 hours 42 minutes during the winter solstice**
3. If the figures were used to show the summer and winter solstices in the southern hemiphere, which figure would show the summer solstice in the southern hemisphere? How do you know? **Figure 1 shows the summer solstice in the southern hemisphere, because daylight hours are longer at the summer solstice.**
4. If you lived at the North Pole, how many daylight hours would you have at the summer solstice? at the winter solstice? **24 hours of daylight at the summer solstice; no hours of daylight at the winter solstice**

 87

1 MOTIVATE

FLEX Your Brain

Use the Flex Your Brain activity to have students explore THE CAUSE OF NIGHT AND DAY ON EARTH.

TYING TO PREVIOUS KNOWLEDGE: Have students recall from Chapter 2 physical properties of matter. Remind them that physical properties can be measured without changing a substance into a new substance. Have students list some physical properties of Earth.

OBJECTIVES AND SCIENCE WORDS: Have students review the objectives and science words to become familiar with this section.

2 TEACH

Key Concepts are highlighted.

CONCEPT DEVELOPMENT

▶ Have a volunteer contrast circles and spheres. Have other students give at least five examples of each. Compile the list on the chalkboard.

▶ Review the definitions of *diameter, circumference, mass,* and *density,* if necessary.

Cooperative Learning: Using the Paired Partners strategy, have students demonstrate evidence of Earth's shape. First, have one student in each group hold a basketball at eye level, about 0.33 m from his or her face. Have the second student slowly move a small object up and over the basketball from the opposite side. The first student should see the top of the object first, then the bottom. Have partners reverse roles. Relate this to how the top of a ship approaching from across the ocean is the first part seen. Then have the partners use a flashlight to cast shadows of a book and a ball against a wall. Have students relate this to the fact that Earth casts a curved shadow on the moon during a lunar eclipse.

CONCEPT DEVELOPMENT

Cooperative Learning: Have Paired Partners use basketballs to represent Earth to demonstrate the difference between Earth's rotation and revolution.

▶ **Demonstration:** Make a sketch of Earth on an overhead transparency. Label the geographic poles. Place the transparency over a bar magnet on an overhead projector. Rotate the figure so that the magnet makes an 11.5° angle with the rotational axis of Earth. Sprinkle iron shavings over the transparency and tap it lightly. Have a volunteer explain the relationship between this demonstration and Earth's magnetic field. Be sure to tape a border around the transparency so iron filings do not get into the projector.

TEACHER F.Y.I.

▶ Earth's diameter is 42 km greater at the equator than at the poles, causing an object's weight to be 0.3 percent less at the equator than at the poles.

▶ The speed of Earth's rotation is gradually slowing down. Most scientists think this slowing is due to the friction caused by ocean tides and the gravitational "drag" of the moon.

PROGRAM RESOURCES

Use **Laboratory Manual** pages 175-176, Earth's spin.

Use **Laboratory Manual** pages 177-178, Earth's Magnetism.

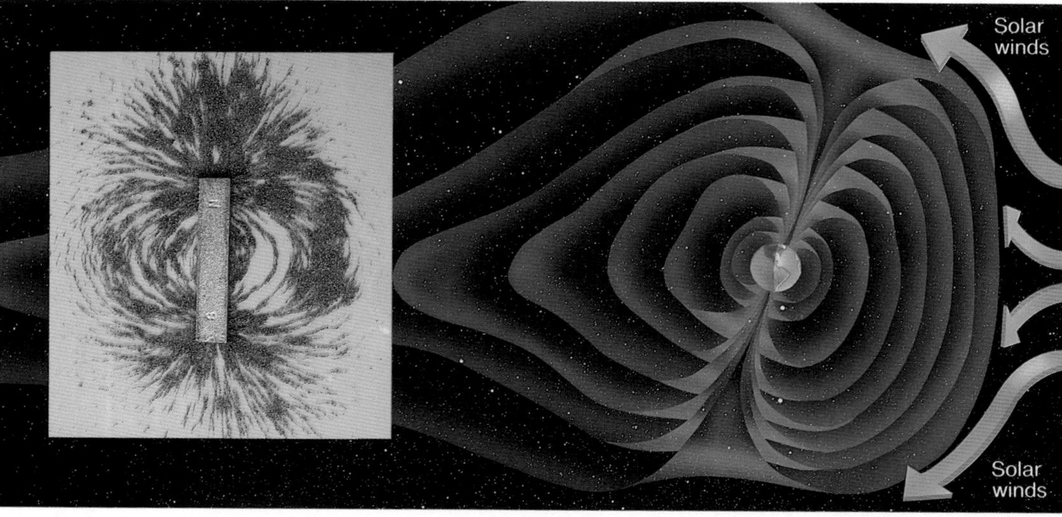

Figure 22-2. Particles streaming through space from the sun distort Earth's magnetic field. As a result, it doesn't have the same shape as a magnetic field surrounding a bar magnet.

3 Another physical property that you've observed the effects of is Earth's magnetic field. Recall from Chapter 13 that convection currents deep inside Earth's mantle power the movement of tectonic plates. Scientists hypothesize that movement of material inside Earth also generates a magnetic field.

The magnetic field of Earth is much like that of a bar magnet. Earth has a north and a south magnetic pole, just as a bar magnet has opposite magnetic poles at its ends. Figure 22-2 illustrates the effects of sprinkling iron shavings over a bar magnet. The shavings align with the magnetic field of the magnet. Earth's magnetic field is similar, almost as if Earth had a giant bar magnet in its core.

When you observe a compass needle pointing toward the north, you're seeing evidence of Earth's magnetic field. Earth's magnetic axis, the line joining its north and south magnetic poles, doesn't align with its rotational axis. The magnetic axis is inclined at an angle of 11.5° to the rotational axis. If you followed a compass needle pointing north, you'd end up at the magnetic north pole rather than the geographic (rotational) north pole.

You're now aware of some of Earth's physical properties. But how do these properties affect you? What everyday events can you explain in terms of Earth's physical properties and movement in space?

OPTIONS

INQUIRY QUESTIONS

▶ **Where on Earth's surface is the magnetic field the strongest?** *Because all magnetic force lines merge at Earth's poles, the magnetic field is strongest at these two locations.*

▶ **Why does the sun appear to rise in the east and set in the west?** *Earth rotates from west to east, causing the sun to appear to rise in the east, move across the sky, and set in the west.*

▶ **How does revolution differ from rotation?** *Revolution is the orbital movement of one object around another. Rotation is the spinning of an object on its axis.*

▶ **Why does Earth's distance from the sun change during the year?** *Earth's orbit around the sun is an ellipse. The sun is not at the center of the ellipse, so Earth is closer to the sun at some times during the year than at others.*

Seasons

Autumn is coming and each day it gets colder outside. The sun rises later each day and is lower in the sky. A month ago, it was light enough to ride your bike at 8:00 PM. Now it's dark at 6:30 PM. What is causing this change?

You learned earlier that Earth's rotation causes day and night to occur. Another important motion of Earth is its **revolution,** or yearly orbit around the sun. Just as the moon is a satellite of Earth, Earth is a satellite of the sun. If Earth's orbit were a circle, and the sun were at the center of the circle, Earth would maintain a constant distance from the sun. However, this isn't the case. Earth's orbit is an **ellipse,** an elongated closed curve. The sun is offset from the center of the ellipse. Because of this, the distance between Earth and the sun changes during Earth's yearlong orbit. Earth gets closest to the sun—about 147 million km away—on January 3. The farthest point in Earth's orbit is about 152 million km away from the sun and is reached on July 4. Is this elliptical orbit causing the changing temperatures on Earth? If it were, you would expect the warmest days in January. You know this isn't the case in the northern hemisphere. Something else is causing the change. 4

Why does Earth's distance from the sun change?

Figure 22-3. The northern hemisphere experiences summer when Earth is farthest from the sun. It experiences winter when Earth is closest to the sun. Earth's tilt on its axis causes the northern and southern hemispheres to be alternately tilted toward the sun. This diagram is drawn from a view below Earth's orbital plane.

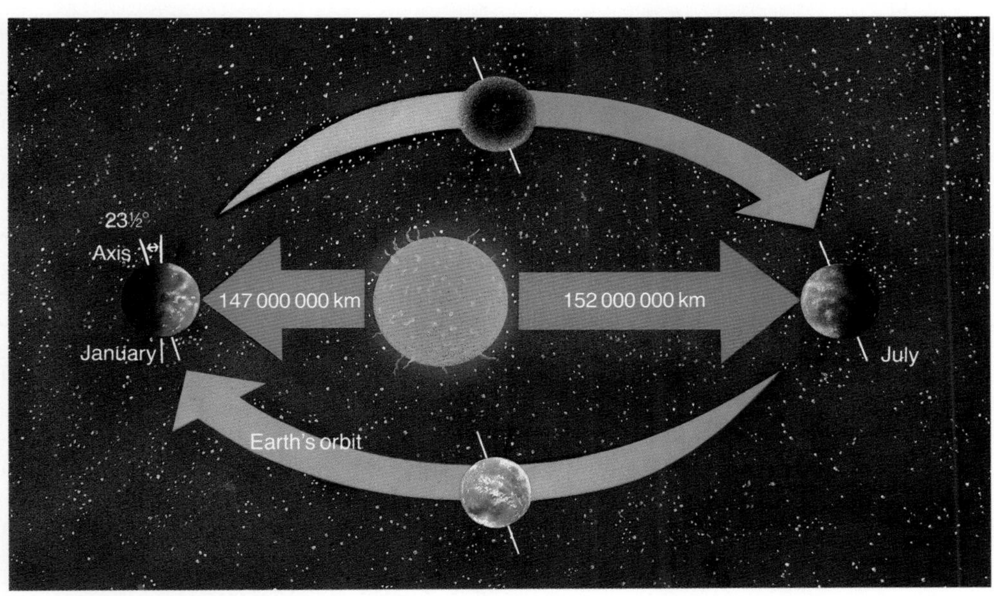

CROSS CURRICULUM

▶ **Mathematics:** Have students compute Earth's circumference using the equation, $C = \pi \times d$, where π equals 3.14 or 22/7 and d, the diameter of Earth, equals 12 756 km. Answers will be 40 054 km or *40 090* km, depending on which value of π was used.

REVEALING MISCONCEPTIONS

▶ Some students think that the planets move around the sun in circular orbits. In fact, many early astronomers believed that orbits were circular. Have students use string, thumbtacks, and pencils to construct a model of Earth's orbit, which averages about 150 million km along its major axis.

STUDENT TEXT QUESTIONS

▶ Page 578, paragraph 4: **But how do these properties affect you? What everyday events can you explain in terms of Earth's physical properties and movement in space?** *Answers will vary. Responses might include that day and night are caused by Earth's rotation and seasons are caused in part by the tilt of Earth's axis.*

MINI QUIZ

Use the Mini Quiz to check students' recall of chapter content.

1. **Earth's _____ is the imaginary line around which Earth spins.** *axis*
2. **Describe Earth's rotation.** *It's the spinning of Earth on its axis.*
3. **_____ currents deep inside Earth are thought to generate its magnetic field.** *Convection*
4. **The yearly orbit of Earth around the sun is Earth's _____ .** *revolution*

FLEX Your Brain

Use the Flex Your Brain activity to have students explore CAUSES OF EARTH'S SEASONS.

ENRICHMENT

▶ Have students find out about and then sketch the geocentric and heliocentric models of our solar system. The geocentric model, which places Earth at the center of the solar system was once widely accepted. The heliocentric model places the sun at the solar system's center. Have students list the evidence used to support both models. Have them explain why the heliocentric model is accepted as the correct model.

PROGRAM RESOURCES

From the **Teacher Resource Package** use:

Critical Thinking/Problem Solving, page 28, Sick of Winter.

Transparency Masters, pages 87-88, Earth-Sun Relationships.

Use **Color Transparency** number 44, Earth-Sun Relationships.

TECHNOLOGY

Think Critically: The length of a day will increase. The length of a year will not be affected. Earth's period of revolution is not dependent on its period of rotation. However, students should realize that there will be fewer days in a year, but the length of a year will not change.

TEACHER F.Y.I.

▶ Earth's orientation in space gradually changes with time. Presently, Earth's axis points toward Polaris, the North Star. In about 12 000 years, Earth's axis will point toward the star Vega in the constellation Lyra. This change is the result of Earth's "wobbling" on its axis.

CONCEPT DEVELOPMENT

Cooperative Learning: Form Science Investigation groups with four students per group. Have students consider what would happen inside the Arctic and Antarctic Circles during summer solstice for each hemisphere. Then supply each group of students with a globe of Earth and a flashlight. Instruct them to shine the flashlight directly on the Tropics of Cancer and Capricorn to illustrate why the areas within the Arctic and Antarctic circles are called the lands of the midnight sun during summer solstice.

TECHNOLOGY

Clocks: The Old and the New

Atomic clocks measure time by recording the frequency of electromagnetic waves given off by atoms. Unlike conventional clocks, atomic clocks aren't affected by changes in temperature or the wearing of their parts. As a result, they gain or lose less than one second in 200 000 years.

Using atomic clocks, scientists have found that each successive day on Earth is getting longer. Evidence indicates that Earth's rotation is slowing down.

Apparently, Earth's rotation has been slowing down for millions of years. By studying the growth lines on 375-million-year-old corals, scientists have determined that there were 440 days in a year at the time these corals were growing. Corals deposit monthly growth lines on their shells in much the same way trees develop yearly growth rings.

Atomic clocks and ancient corals have proven that Earth's rotation is slowing down. Scientist think that it's being "dragged" on by the gravitational attraction of the moon. **Think Critically:** As this drag continues, what will happen to the length of a day on Earth? To the length of a year?

Even though Earth is closest to the sun in January, the overall amount of energy Earth receives from the sun changes very little throughout the year. However, the amount of energy any one place on Earth receives can vary quite a bit.

Recall the Find Out activity at the beginning of the chapter. You worked with a model of Earth revolving around the sun. Do you remember how you tilted the Earth slightly? Earth's axis is tilted 23.5° from a line perpendicular to its orbit. It's this tilt that causes the seasons.

Daylight hours are longer for the hemisphere tilted toward the sun. Think of how early it gets dark in the winter compared to in the summer. The hemisphere tilted toward the sun receives more hours of sunlight than the hemisphere tilted away from the sun.

Another effect of Earth's tilt is that the sun's radiation strikes the hemisphere tilted toward it at a higher angle than it does the other hemisphere. Because of this, the

Did You Know?

The slowing of Earth's rotation has been documented by Babylonian records of solar eclipses. The recorded dates of the eclipses only could have occurred if the Earth was rotating slightly faster in the past.

OPTIONS

INQUIRY QUESTIONS

▶ **During which season in the United States is Earth closest to the sun?** *Earth is closest to the sun when it is winter in the United States.*

▶ **Would Earth's seasons change if Earth's axis were not tilted? Explain.** *If Earth's axis weren't tilted, the amount of daylight would equal the amount of nighttime everywhere on Earth. The angle at which sunlight shone on any location would be the same. Thus, Earth would not experience seasons.*

▶ **Why is the area near Earth's equator hotter than the areas near the poles?** *Earth's equatorial region receives the most direct sunlight. Polar areas receive less sunlight per unit area than other regions; therefore, the poles are always colder than the other regions of Earth.*

▶ **If Earth's tilt on its axis measured 33°, how might seasonal changes and temperature ranges differ?** *Seasonal changes, and therefore temperatures in any given area would probably be more extreme.*

▶ **How many hours of daylight occur all over the world at spring and fall equinoxes?** *12 hours*

hemisphere tilted toward the sun receives more radiant energy per unit area than the hemisphere tilted away. In other words, if you measured the amount of radiation received in a one-square-kilometer area in the northern hemisphere and, at the same time, measured it for one-square-kilometer in the southern hemisphere, you would find a difference. The hemisphere tilted toward the sun would be receiving more energy.

A summer season results when the sun is in the sky longer and its radiant energy strikes Earth at a higher angle. Just the opposite occurs during winter. Figure 22-3 shows how Earth's tilted axis results in the change of seasons.

What causes the seasons to change?

Equinoxes and Solstices

Because of the tilt of Earth's axis, the sun's position relative to Earth's equator constantly changes. Most of the time the sun is north or south of the equator. Two times during the year, however, the sun is directly over the equator.

When the sun reaches an **equinox,** it is directly above Earth's equator, and the number of daylight hours equals the number of nighttime hours all over the world. At that

Figure 22-4. At summer solstice, the sun's rays directly strike the Tropic of Cancer, 23.5° north latitude. The sun is directly over the Tropic of Capricorn, 23.5° south latitude, at winter solstice. At both fall and spring equinoxes, the sun is directly over the equator.

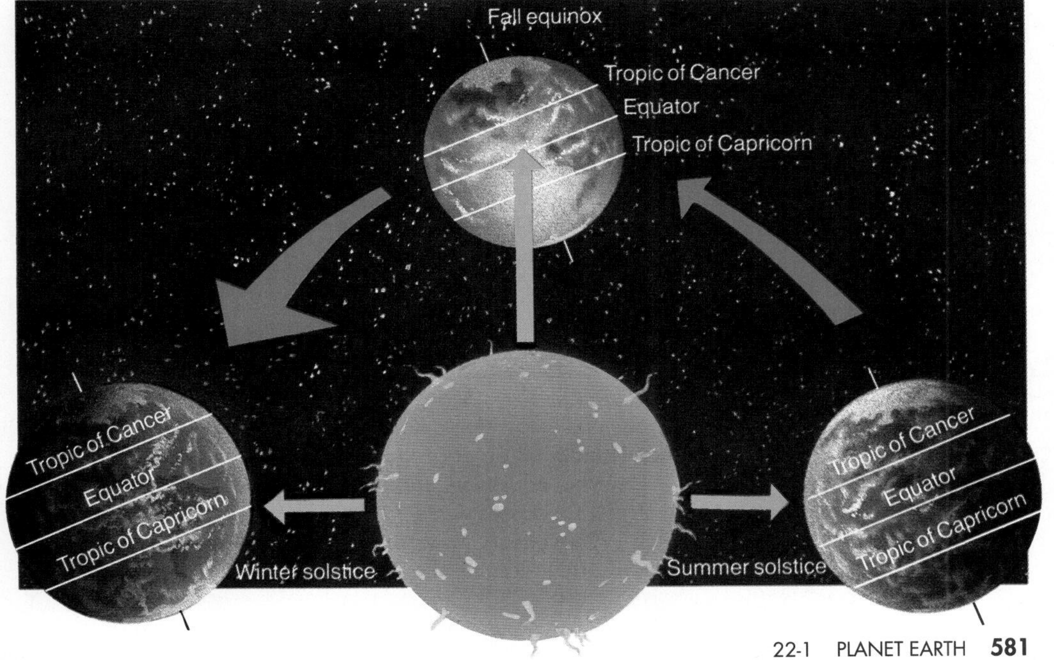

CHECK FOR UNDERSTANDING

▶ Ask students the questions that follow. **Where is the sun during an equinox?** *directly over the equator* **What is a solstice?** *the time when the sun reaches its greatest distance north and south of the equator* **At what time during the year are there the most hours of daylight?** *during summer solstice* **During which season does the shortest day of the year occur?** *winter*

RETEACH

Demonstration: Darken the room and place a globe of Earth next to a light source. Tilt the globe 23.5°. Hold the globe so that its axis points toward and then away from the light. Slowly spin the globe to demonstrate how the amount of light striking each hemisphere of the globe changes. Help students conclude that days are shorter in the Northern Hemisphere when Earth's axis is tilted away from the sun and longer when Earth's axis is tilted toward the sun.

EXTENSION

For students who have mastered this section, use the **Reinforcement** and **Enrichment** masters or other OPTIONS provided.

3 CLOSE

▶Ask students to speculate why people long ago thought Earth was flat. Students should be able to state that Earth is so big relative to our viewpoint that it seems to stretch out in all directions. Show photographs of Earth from space to reaffirm its spherical shape.

▶Ask questions 1-3 and the **Apply** Question in the Section Review.

ENRICHMENT

▶ Have students describe how a compass needle would react if held directly over Earth's equator and then directly over Earth's North or South Pole. *A compass needle will point north when held over the equator and spin when held directly over Earth's poles.*

MINI-Lab

Materials: string, ruler, globe of Earth, basketball or volleyball, Table 22-1

Teaching Tips

▶ Best results are obtained by using string with limited "stretchability."

▶ Stress that precise measurements must be made as approximations will not produce accurate results.

▶ **Answers:** Earth has a "roundness" ratio of 1.003. Usually, student measurements will confirm that the globe and the ball are actually less "round" than Earth; that is, they will have "roundness" ratios greater than 1.003.

▶ Earth's year is slightly more than six hours longer than 365 days. Because of this, an extra day is added to the calendar every four years. When this day is added during leap year, the days on which the solstices and equinoxes fall shift.

SECTION REVIEW ANSWERS

1. Earth bulges slightly at the equator, making its diameter at the equator slightly larger than that at the poles.

2. rotation

3. summer

4. Apply: Seasons, would not occur. The climate of a particular location would depend only on the angle at which the sun's rays struck the location. Hot areas would remain hot all year, and cold areas would remain cold.

Skill Builder

1. the tilt of Earth's axis

2. The sun being in the sky for a shorter amount of time and its radiant energy striking Earth at a low angle cause winter.

3. It has little effect. The seasons are primarily due to the tilt of Earth on its axis, not its distance from the sun. It may cause the average summer temperatures of the southern hemisphere to be slightly warmer than they would otherwise be. But the effect is essentially insignificant.

MINI-Lab

How round is Earth?

Use a long piece of string to measure the circumference of a globe of Earth at the equator. Make a second measurement of the circumference along the prime meridian and International Date Line (180° meridian). Determine the roundness ratio of the globe by dividing its larger circumference by its smaller circumference. Continue all divisions to four decimal places. Repeat this procedure with a basketball or volleyball. Use any two circumferences that are at a right (90°) angle to each other. Use these data and the data of Earth's circumference provided in Table 22-1 to compare Earth's "roundness" to the ball and the globe. Which is more "round"? How "round" is Earth? Explain how your data support your answer.

time, neither the northern nor the southern hemisphere is tilted toward the sun. Figure 22-4 shows how this happens. In the northern hemisphere, the sun reaches the spring equinox on March 20 or 21 and fall equinox on September 22 or 23. In the southern hemisphere, the equinoxes are reversed. These are the first days of spring and fall.

Solstice is where the sun reaches its greatest distance north or south of the equator. In the northern hemisphere, the sun reaches the summer solstice on June 21 or 22, and winter solstice occurs on December 21 or 22. Just the opposite is true for the southern hemisphere. When the sun is at the summer solstice, there are more daylight hours than during any other day of the year. When it's at the winter solstice, on the shortest day of the year, we have the most nighttime hours.

As you've seen, the rotation of Earth causes day and night. Earth's tilted axis is responsible for the seasons you experience, and our revolution around the sun marks the passing of a year. Earth is just one of many planetary bodies revolving around the sun. In the next section, you will read how Earth's nearest neighbor, the moon, is also in constant motion and how you observe this motion each day.

SECTION REVIEW

1. Why can't you give just one number to describe Earth's diameter?
2. Which Earth motion causes night and day?
3. What season occurs in Earth's northern hemisphere when Earth's north pole is tilted toward the sun?
4. **Apply:** How would a year on Earth be different if Earth's axis weren't tilted?

Skill Builder — Recognizing Cause and Effect

Answer these questions about the Earth-moon relationship. If you need help, refer to Recognizing Cause and Effect in the **Skill Handbook** on page 683.

1. What causes seasons on Earth?
2. What causes winter?
3. What effect on seasons does the sun being closest to Earth in January have?

OPTIONS

PROGRAM RESOURCES

From the **Teacher Resource Package** use:

Activity Worksheets, pages 204, Mini-Lab: How round is Earth?

Activity Worksheets, pages 198-199, Activity 22-1: The Egg and the Equinox.

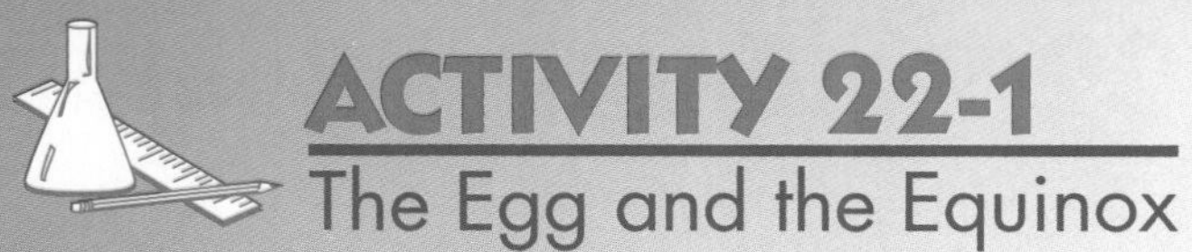

ACTIVITY 22-1
The Egg and the Equinox

Problem: *Is there any reason an egg would balance on end when the sun reaches equinox but not at other times?*

Materials
- raw egg

Procedure
1. Perform this activity on a day on which the sun is NOT at equinox.
2. The following article is similar to ones that appear in newspapers across the United States each year during the spring equinox. Read it before proceeding to Step 3.

   Believe it or not, spring arrived today. And because it's the first day of spring, you can balance a raw egg on its end. It sounds strange, but it's true. For centuries, people have been welcoming spring's arrival by balancing eggs on their large ends. In fact, several hundred people gathered in Bates Park this morning to watch as school children put 12 dozen eggs through their balancing acts. How does it work? Legends state that at the moment of spring equinox, the sun and Earth are in harmony, and everything is in balance—eggs included. Celebrate spring's arrival. Go balance an egg!
3. Hypothesize whether or not you would be able to stand an egg on end when the sun is at equinox. Hypothesize whether you will be able to today, when the sun is not at equinox.
4. Attempt to stand an egg on its large end. You may have to try many times, but it's probable that you will be able to do it.

Analyze
1. What is the position of the sun, relative to Earth's latitude, when it reaches equinox?
2. Is the sun directly overhead at the latitude at which you live?
3. On what days of the year does the sun reach equinox? How do those days differ from all others?
4. Is it possible to stand an egg on end on days other than when the sun is at equinox?

Conclude and Apply
5. Do you think that the gravitational attraction between the sun and Earth is significantly different during times of equinox and other days of the year?
6. Many people read articles such as the one on this page and then succeed in standing an egg on end on the day of equinox. Why would they believe that it's possible only on that day?
7. How does this activity prove that you shouldn't believe everything that you read?

ACTIVITY 22-1
15-20 minutes

OBJECTIVE: Experiment to test a hypothesis on some effects of the Earth-sun relationship during an equinox.

PROCESS SKILLS applied in this activity:
- **Hypothesizing** in Procedure Step 3.
- **Inferring** in Analyze Question 4 and Conclude and Apply Question 5.
- **Experimenting** in Procedure Step 4.
- **Interpreting Data** in Conclude and Apply Questions 6 and 7.
- **Communicating** in Procedure Step 2 and Analyze Questions 1-3.

TEACHING THE ACTIVITY
- Discuss the fact that the article doesn't state that eggs can be balanced only during equinox and at no other time. However, most people infer that such is the case. Only by experimenting can it be proven that it's possible at other times.
- Discuss students' responses to Conclude and Apply Question 6. Emphasize the importance of experimenting, observing, and inferring in establishing "facts."

Troubleshooting: Prior to distributing the eggs to students, place all eggs large-end-down in egg cartons. This will allow the yolk and other fluids within the egg to settle to the "bottom," or large end of the egg. Students should be able to balance their eggs without much difficulty if they've been resting with their large ends down prior to beginning this activity.

ANSWERS TO QUESTIONS
1. The sun is positioned in such a way that its rays fall directly on the equator. To an observer on the equator, the sun would appear directly overhead at noon.
2. No, unless you live in Hawaii. The sun is *never* directly overhead in the continental United States.
3. Depending on which year of the four-year cycle it is, equinox will fall on or about March 21 and September 21. During a leap year, it will be a day or so earlier. In the year preceding leap year, it will be a day or so later.
4. It can be done, although it is extremely difficult. Some students will lack the patience and/or delicate touch to do it.
5. There is no significant difference. Some students may equate equal number of hours of daylight and darkness with some sort of gravity balance. There is no relationship between the two.
6. Probably because they only attempt to balance an egg on the day of the equinox. During the rest of the year, they aren't concerned with their ability to balance an egg. People reading the article would have to conduct a scientific investigation to conclude that it's possible on any day. The investigation would simply be to attempt to balance the egg on days that are not during an equinox.
7. It's important to note that the article is factual and doesn't state any inaccuracies. However, it does *imply* that there is a phenomenon unique to the equinoxes responsible for one's ability to balance an egg. Students should realize that by conducting this activity, they have proven that the *inferences* made by people reading the article are false though the *stated facts* are true.

SECTION 22-2

PREPARATION

SECTION BACKGROUND

▶ The same side of the moon always faces Earth because the moon rotates on its axis every 27.3 days, which is the same amount of time it takes it to revolve around Earth.

▶ Lunar librations do allow humans to see a little more than half of the moon from Earth. Because the moon's orbit is an ellipse, its orbital speed varies. Because of this variation, humans can see a little more of its western hemisphere and then a little more of its eastern hemisphere throughout a month.

▶ The moon's gravitational force is not strong enough to hold gases at its surface. Gases have probably been released by volcanic activity on the moon's surface in the past, but they have escaped into space.

▶ One of the current hypotheses on the formation of the moon states that a Mars-sized asteroid collided with Earth shortly after Earth formed. The collision caused enormous amounts of surface matter from the asteroid and Earth to be thrown into orbit. This matter later formed Earth's moon.

1 MOTIVATE

FLEX Your Brain

Use the Flex Your Brain activity to have students explore WHY THE MOON GOES THROUGH PHASES.

22-2 Earth's Moon

New Science Words

moon phases
new moon
waxing
first quarter
full moon
waning
third quarter
solar eclipse
lunar eclipse
maria

Objectives

- ▶ **Demonstrate how the moon's phases depend on the relative positions of the sun, the moon, and Earth.**
- ▶ **Describe why eclipses occur, and compare solar and lunar eclipses.**
- ▶ **Hypothesize what surface features of the moon tell us about its history.**

Motions of the Moon

You have probably noticed how the moon's apparent shape changes from day to day. Sometimes, just after sunset, you can see a full, round moon low in the sky. Other times only half of the moon is visible and it's high in the sky at sunset. Sometimes the moon is visible during the day. Why does the moon look the way it does? What causes it to change its appearance and position in the sky?

Just as Earth rotates on its axis and revolves around the sun, the moon rotates on its axis and revolves around Earth. The moon's revolution causes changes in its appearance. If the moon rotates on its axis, why don't we see it spin around in space? The moon rotates on its axis once every 27.3 days. It takes the same amount of time to revolve once around Earth. Because these two motions take the same amount of time, the same side of the moon always faces Earth. The other side is never turned toward us.

You can demonstrate this by having a friend hold a ball in front of you. Instruct your friend to move the ball around you while keeping the same side of it facing you. Everyone else in the room will see all sides of the ball. You will see only one side. The ball rotated once as it revolved around you once.

Figure 22-5. In about a one-month period, the moon orbits Earth. It also completes one rotation on its axis during the same period. As a result, the same side of the moon is always facing Earth.

OPTIONS

Meeting Different Ability Levels

For Section 22-2, use the following **Teacher Resource Masters** depending upon individual students' needs.

◆ **Study Guide Master** for all students.

● **Reinforcement Master** for students of average and above average ability levels.

▲ **Enrichment Master** for above average students.

Additional Teacher Resource Package masters are listed in the OPTIONS box throughout the section. The additional masters are appropriate for all students.

◆ STUDY GUIDE 88

NAME ______ DATE ______ CLASS ______

STUDY GUIDE — Chapter 22

Earth's Moon — Text Pages 584–591

In the blank at the left, write the term from the box that matches the description.

lunar eclipse	first quarter	full moon	waning gibbous
new moon	solar eclipse	maria	third quarter
waxing	waxing gibbous	waning	waning crescent
moon phases			

moon phases 1. Changing appearances of the moon as seen from Earth
third quarter 2. Phase of the moon when you see only half of the lighted side after a full moon
waning 3. Period when the amount of the lighted side that can be seen becomes increasingly smaller
waning gibbous 4. Phase that starts just after the full moon
waxing 5. Period after a new moon when more and more of the lighted side of the moon becomes visible
new moon 6. Phase when the lighted half of the moon is facing the sun and the dark side faces Earth
first quarter 7. Waxing phase of the moon when you can see half of the lighted side, or one-quarter, of the moon's surface
full moon 8. Phase of the moon when the half of the moon's surface facing Earth is lighted
waxing gibbous 9. Waxing period when more than one-quarter but less than half of the lighted side of the moon's surface can be seen
solar eclipse 10. Occurs when the moon moves directly between the sun and Earth and casts a shadow on part of Earth
lunar eclipse 11. Occurs when Earth's shadow falls on the moon
maria 12. Dark-colored, flat regions of lava on the moon's surface
waning cresent 13. Occurs just before a new moon

Write an F next to the statements that are false.

F 14. The moon rotates on its axis once every 365 days.
___ 15. The moon completes one revolution around Earth every 27.3 days.
F 16. The large depressions on the moon that are caused by meteorites are called crescents.
___ 17. One half of the moon is always lighted because it faces the sun.
F 18. At full moon, we see 100 percent of the moon.

88

The moon shines by reflecting sunlight from its surface. Just as half of Earth experiences day as the other half experiences night, half of the moon is lighted while the other half is dark. As the moon revolves around Earth, you see different portions of its lighted side, causing the moon's appearance to change. **Moon phases** are the changing appearances of the moon as seen from Earth. The phase you see depends on the relative positions of the moon, Earth, and the sun.

Phases of the Moon

New moon occurs when the moon is between Earth and the sun. During **new moon**, the lighted half of the moon is facing the sun and the dark side faces Earth. The moon is in the sky, but it can't be seen.

Shortly after new moon, more and more of its lighted side becomes visible—the phases are **waxing.** About 24 hours after new moon, you can see a thin slice of the lighted side. This phase is called the waxing crescent. About a week after new moon, you can see half of the lighted side, or one-quarter of the moon's surface. This phase is **first quarter.**

The phases are continuing to wax—more and more of the lighted side can be seen. When more than one-quarter is visible, but less than half, it is called waxing gibbous. **Full moon** occurs when the half of the moon's surface facing Earth is lit up.

Define waxing and waning.

Figure 22-6. The Phases of the Moon: (a) New moon, (b) Waxing crescent, (c) First quarter, (d) Waxing gibbous, (e) Full moon, (f) Waning gibbous, (g) Third quarter, (h) Waning crescent

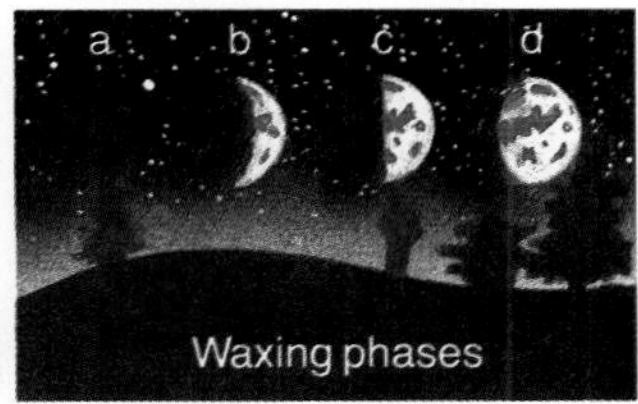

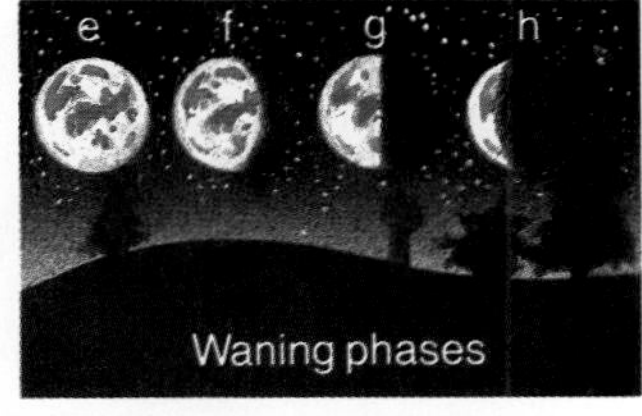

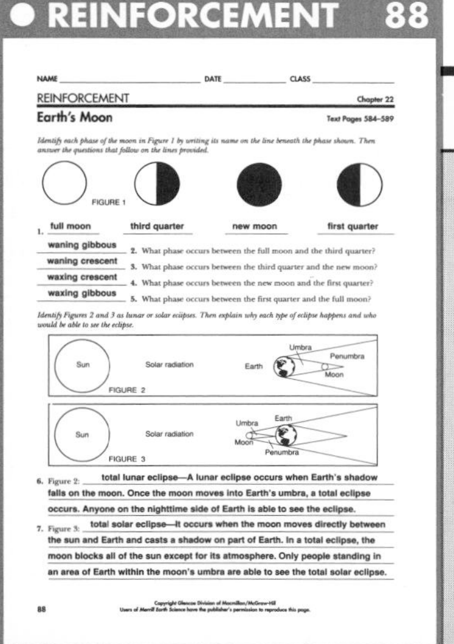

● REINFORCEMENT 88

NAME ______ DATE ______ CLASS ______

REINFORCEMENT — Chapter 22

Earth's Moon — Text Pages 584–589

Identify each phase of the moon in Figure 1 by writing its name on the line beneath the phase shown. Then answer the questions that follow on the lines provided.

FIGURE 1

1. full moon — third quarter — new moon — first quarter

waning gibbous 2. What phase occurs between the full moon and the third quarter?

waning crescent 3. What phase occurs between the third quarter and the new moon?

waxing crescent 4. What phase occurs between the new moon and the first quarter?

waxing gibbous 5. What phase occurs between the first quarter and the full moon?

Identify Figures 2 and 3 as lunar or solar eclipses. Then explain why each type of eclipse happens and who would be able to see the eclipse.

Sun — Solar radiation — Earth — Umbra — Penumbra — Moon — FIGURE 2

Sun — Solar radiation — Umbra — Earth — Moon — Penumbra — FIGURE 3

6. Figure 2: total lunar eclipse—A lunar eclipse occurs when Earth's shadow falls on the moon. Once the moon moves into Earth's umbra, a total eclipse occurs. Anyone on the nighttime side of Earth is able to see the eclipse.

7. Figure 3: total solar eclipse—It occurs when the moon moves directly between the sun and Earth and casts a shadow on part of Earth. In a total eclipse, the moon blocks all of the sun except for its atmosphere. Only people standing in an area of Earth within the moon's umbra are able to see the total solar eclipse.

88

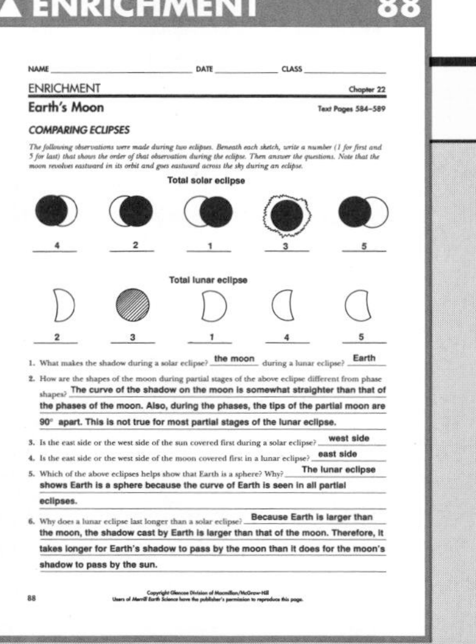

▲ ENRICHMENT 88

NAME ______ DATE ______ CLASS ______

ENRICHMENT — Chapter 22

Earth's Moon — Text Pages 584–589

COMPARING ECLIPSES

The following observations were made during two eclipses. Beneath each sketch, write a number (1 for first and 5 for last) that shows the order of that observation during the eclipse. Then answer the questions. Note that the moon revolves eastward in its orbit and goes eastward across the sky during an eclipse.

Total solar eclipse

4 — 2 — 1 — 3 — 5

Total lunar eclipse

2 — 3 — 1 — 4 — 5

1. What makes the shadow during a solar eclipse? the moon during a lunar eclipse? Earth
2. How are the shapes of the moon during partial stages of the above eclipse different from phase shapes? The curve of the shadow on the moon is somewhat straighter than that of the phases of the moon. Also, during the phases, the tips of the partial moon are 90° apart. This is not true for most partial stages of the lunar eclipse.
3. Is the east side or the west side of the sun covered first during a solar eclipse? west side
4. Is the east side or the west side of the moon covered first in a lunar eclipse? east side
5. Which of the above eclipses helps show that Earth is a sphere? Why? The lunar eclipse shows Earth is a sphere because the curve of Earth is seen in all partial eclipses.
6. Why does a lunar eclipse last longer than a solar eclipse? Because Earth is larger than the moon, the shadow cast by Earth is larger than that of the moon. Therefore, it takes longer for Earth's shadow to pass by the moon than it does for the moon's shadow to pass by the sun.

88

CONCEPT DEVELOPMENT

▶**Demonstration:** Fill a large, flat pan with very fine-grained, dry sand to a depth of 10 cm. Have volunteers drop various objects, such as marbles, rocks of different sizes, and steel ball bearings, from different heights above the pan. Carefully remove the objects and help students relate this demonstration to the formation of craters on the moon.

TYING TO PREVIOUS KNOWLEDGE: Have students recall from Chapter 11 the cause of tides. Students should remember that the gravitational pull of the moon on Earth causes water to bulge on the side of Earth facing the moon and on the side opposite the moon. Also have students recall that large tidal ranges occur when Earth, the sun, and the moon are lined up.

OBJECTIVES AND SCIENCE WORDS: Have students review the objectives and science words to become familiar with this section.

2 TEACH

Key Concepts are highlighted.

CONCEPT DEVELOPMENT

▶**Demonstration:** Obtain a globe of the moon or use a volleyball to represent the moon. Darken the room and place three overhead projectors across the front of the room with their lights aimed toward the back of the room at an angle above students' heads. Then have students cluster near the center of the room. Inform students that the projectors represent the sun, they are on Earth, and the globe or ball represents the moon. Keep the same side of the moon facing the students as you make it revolve around them. Students should be able to see the moon go through phases beginning with new moon. Point out that the side of the moon that we aren't able to see is lighted during new moon.

REVEALING MISCONCEPTIONS

▶ Some students may think that the far side of the moon is not seen because it is dark. Explain that the back of the moon receives as much light as the side that faces Earth.

CONCEPT DEVELOPMENT

▶ After students read page 586, ask the following question. **How does a waxing moon differ from a waning moon?** *As more and more of the lighted side of the moon becomes visible, the moon is waxing. When less of the lighted side is visible, the moon is waning.*

MINI-Lab

Materials: tidal range graph from Chapter 11 Review

Answers: A new or full moon probably occurred on January 7 to 9 and 20 to 23, because tidal range was greatest at these times. First and third quarter moons probably occurred on January 1, January 14 or 15, and January 28 to 30 when tidal range was lowest. When the sun, Earth, and moon are aligned along an imaginary straight line during new and full moon phases, tidal range is greatest. When the sun, Earth, and moon are at right angles to one another, tidal range is its lowest.

TEACHER F.Y.I.

▶ A sidereal month is 27.3 days long, the actual period of the moon's revolution around Earth. A synodic month, the time from one phase until the same phase occurs again, is 29.5 days long. The discrepancy is due to Earth's revolution. It takes the moon about two days to "catch up" with Earth's advancement around the sun.

MINI-Lab

How does the moon affect tides? Refer back to the graph showing tidal ranges which you constructed in the More Skill Builders section of the Chapter 11 Review. If you didn't make that graph, you should do so now. Recalling what you know about the position of the moon during neap and spring tides, answer the following questions. On what days in your graph do you suspect that the moon was at new or full phase? On what days do you think it was in first or third quarter phase? How are the position of the moon, the moon's phase, and the tidal range related?

After passing full moon, the amount of the lighted side that can be seen becomes smaller. The phases are said to be **waning.** Waning gibbous begins just after full moon. When you can see only half of the lighted side, the **third quarter** phase occurs. The amount of the moon that can be seen continues to become smaller. Waning crescent occurs just before another new moon. Once again you can see a small slice of the lighted side.

The complete cycle of the moon's phases takes about 29.5 days. During the span of a month, you can watch the moon pass through all of its phases. You may also notice that the moon rises about 50 minutes later each day. In the time that it takes Earth to rotate once, the moon has moved forward in its revolution. So it takes an extra 50 minutes for a location on Earth to "catch up" with the new position of the moon.

Eclipses

Imagine yourself as one of your ancient ancestors, living 50 000 years ago. You're out foraging for nuts and other fruit in the bright afternoon sun. Gradually, the sun disappears from the sky, as if being swallowed by a giant sky creature. You can see stars coming out, crickets begin to chirp to signal the nightfall, and birds return to the trees to settle down for the night. But the darkness lasts only a short time, and as quickly as the sun disappeared, it returns to full brightness. You realize something unusual has happened, but you don't know what caused it. It will be almost 48 000 years before anyone can explain the event that you just experienced.

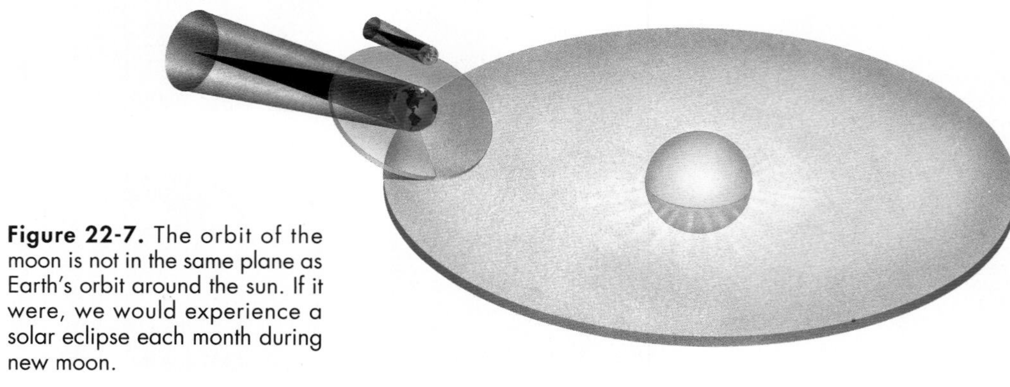

Figure 22-7. The orbit of the moon is not in the same plane as Earth's orbit around the sun. If it were, we would experience a solar eclipse each month during new moon.

OPTIONS

INQUIRY QUESTIONS

▶**Is the far side of the moon ever completely lit? Explain.** *Yes, the far side of the moon is completely lit during new moon phase.*

▶**What causes moon phases?** *As the moon revolves around Earth, the relative positions of Earth, the moon, and the sun change. This causes the side of the moon visible from Earth to receive different amounts of solar radiation, changing the moon's appearance.*

PROGRAM RESOURCES

From the **Teacher Resource Package** use:

Activity Worksheets, page 205, Mini-Lab: How does the moon affect tides?

Use **Laboratory Manual** pages 179-180, Moon Phases.

The event just described was a total solar eclipse. Today, we know what causes such eclipses; but for our early ancestors, they must have been terrifying events. Many animals act as if night has come; cows return to their barns, and chickens go to sleep. But what causes the day to suddenly change into night and suddenly back into day?

Revolution of the moon causes more than just a change in its phases, it also causes eclipses. Eclipses occur when Earth or the moon temporarily blocks the sunlight reaching the other. Sometimes during new moon, a shadow cast by the moon falls on Earth and causes a solar eclipse. During full moon, a shadow of Earth can be cast on the moon, resulting in a lunar eclipse.

Eclipses can occur only when the sun, the moon, and Earth are perfectly lined up. Because the moon's orbit is not in the same plane as Earth's orbit around the sun, eclipses happen only a few times per year. If the moon's orbit were not inclined at an angle compared to Earth's, an eclipse would occur with every new and full moon.

Why don't solar eclipses occur with each new moon?

Solar Eclipses

A **solar eclipse** occurs when the moon moves directly between the sun and Earth and casts a shadow on part of Earth. The darkest portion of the moon's shadow is called the umbra. A person standing in an area of Earth within the umbra sees a total solar eclipse. The only portion of the sun that's visible is part of its atmosphere, which appears as a pearly white glow around the edge of the eclipsing moon. 1

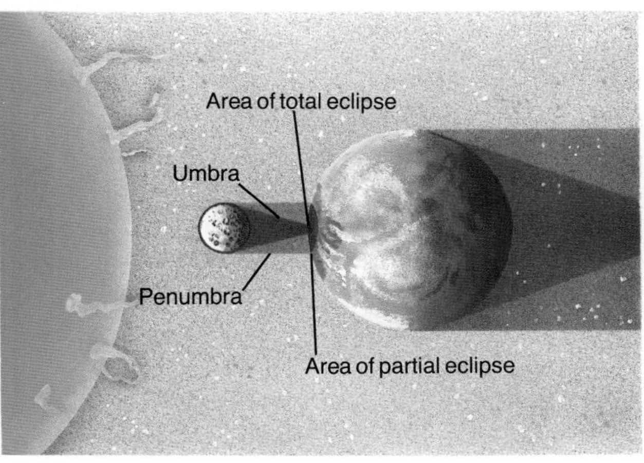

Figure 22-8. Only a small area of Earth experiences a total solar eclipse during the eclipse event. Only the outer portion of the sun's atmosphere is visible during a total solar eclipse.

CROSS CURRICULUM

▶ **Language Arts:** Have students research the origin and meaning of the phrase *once in a blue moon.*

CONCEPT DEVELOPMENT

▶ Have students quickly sketch and label the positions of the sun, moon, and Earth during a solar eclipse. After they read page 588, have them do the same for a lunar eclipse.

▶ **What is an eclipse?** *a phenomenon during which the moon or Earth temporarily blocks the sunlight reaching the other* **What is a solar eclipse?** *an event during which the moon moves directly between the sun and Earth and casts a shadow on part of Earth*

INQUIRY QUESTIONS

▶ **How can you prove that the moon revolves around Earth?** *By observing the moon nightly, you can observe that the position of the moon on successive nights moves slightly toward the east relative to stars in the night sky.*

▶ **How can an object as small as the moon completely block out the sun?** *The moon is much closer to Earth than the sun and thus appears to be the same size as the sun.*

PROGRAM RESOURCES

From the **Teacher Resource Package** use:

Cross-Curricular Connections, page 26, The Moon and Abraham Lincoln in Court.

Transparency Masters, pages 89-90, Moon Phases.

Use **Color Transparency** number 45, Moon Phases.

CONCEPT DEVELOPMENT

▶Present students with the following questions as you discuss the material on page 588: **What is an umbra?** *the darkest part of the moon's shadow cast on Earth during an eclipse* **What's a penumbra?** *a lighter shadow that surrounds the umbra during an eclipse* **What do people standing in the umbra see?** *a total solar eclipse* **What do people standing in the penumbra see?** *a partial solar eclipse*

TEACHER F.Y.I.

▶In 1966, the Soviet *Luna 9* probe became the first spacecraft to land on the moon. Four months later, the American *Surveyor 1* spacecraft landed on Earth's only natural satellite.

EcoTip

Unlike the moon, Earth has large bodies of water full of wildlife. But the wildlife is threatened by our garbage. One type of deadly garbage is the rings of plastic six-pack holders—the rings used on soft drink cans and motor oil. Seals and sea lions get them caught around their necks. As the animals grow, the rings slowly choke them to death. Clip the rings with scissors before you throw them in the garbage.

Surrounding the umbra is a lighter shadow on Earth's surface called the penumbra. Persons standing in the penumbra see a partial solar eclipse. Photographs can be taken of the curved edge of the moon moving over a portion of the sun. **CAUTION:** *Never look directly at a solar eclipse. The light will permanently damage your eyes.*

Lunar Eclipses

2 When Earth's shadow falls on the moon, a **lunar eclipse** occurs. A lunar eclipse begins with the moon moving into Earth's penumbra. As the moon continues to move, it enters Earth's umbra and you see a curved shadow on the moon's surface. It was from this shadow that Aristotle concluded that Earth was a sphere. When the moon moves completely into Earth's umbra, the moon becomes very dark because light from the sun is blocked by Earth. A total lunar eclipse has occurred.

A partial lunar eclipse occurs when only a portion of the moon moves into Earth's umbra. The remainder of the moon is in Earth's penumbra and it therefore receives some direct sunlight.

A total solar eclipse occurs from zero to two times every year, yet most people live their entire lives never witnessing one. You may not be lucky enough to see a total solar eclipse, but it's almost certain you will have a chance to see a total lunar eclipse in your lifetime. Although total solar eclipses are more common than total lunar eclipses, only those people in the very small region where the moon's umbra strikes Earth can witness a total solar eclipse. In contrast, anyone on the nighttime side of Earth can see a total lunar eclipse.

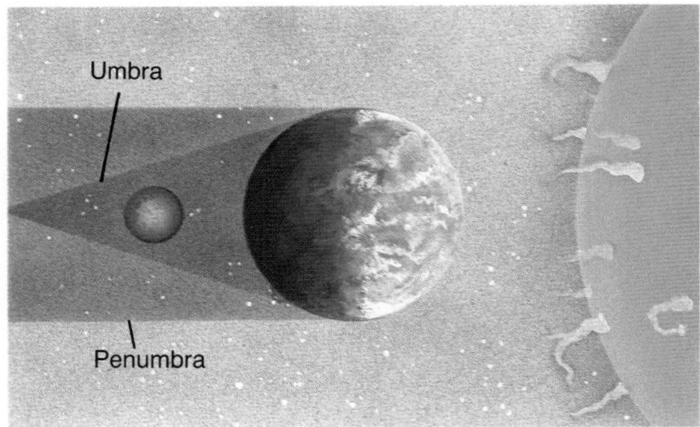

Figure 22-9. During a total lunar eclipse, Earth's shadow blocks light coming from the sun.

OPTIONS

INQUIRY QUESTIONS

▶**Why should you never look directly at a solar eclipse?** *Although the sun may appear dimmer than usual, it is still bright enough to permanently damage your eyes with harmful radiation.*

▶**During a lunar eclipse, Earth blocks off sunlight to the moon, yet the moon appears deep red. Explain.** *Sunlight is bent, or refracted, by Earth's atmosphere and falls on the moon. Of all the colors that compose sunlight, red light is bent the least; therefore, more of it travels on to the moon.*

▶**Why can anyone on the night side of Earth witness a total lunar eclipse?** *Because Earth's shadow is large, the entire moon can be eclipsed by the umbra. This then is visible anywhere the moon is in the sky.*

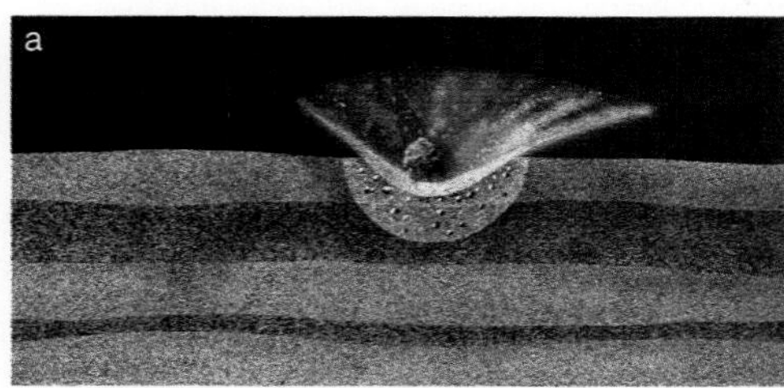

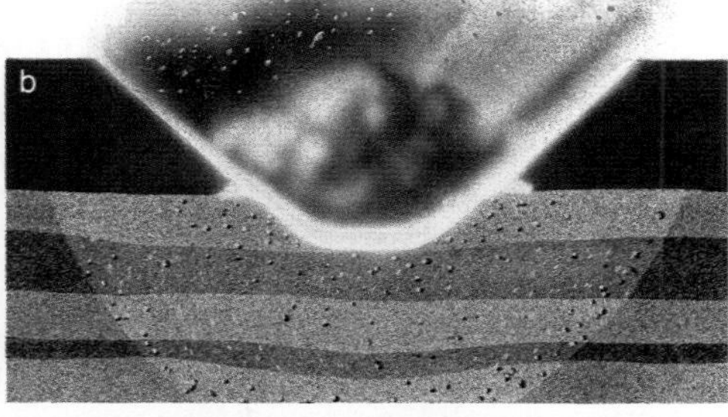

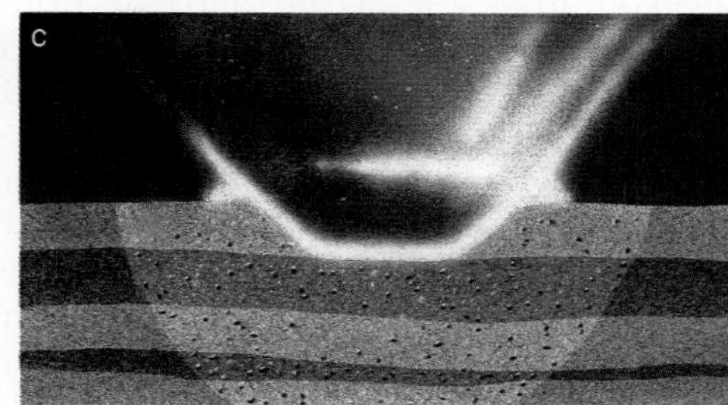

Figure 22-10. A meteorite impact (a) sends shock waves through the moon's surface (b). Some of the moon's surface is ejected upward along with fragments from the exploding meteorite (c). Eventually, the crater stops growing as gravity overcomes the forces of expansion (d).

Structure of the Moon

When you look at the moon, you can see many of its larger surface features, especially if you use a telescope. The dark-colored, flat regions called **maria** are very easy 3
to find. Maria were formed when lava from the moon's interior flooded over and filled large basins on the moon's surface. The basins formed early in the moon's history.

Many depressions on the moon were formed by meteorites, space objects that strike the surfaces of planets and their satellites. These depressions caused by meteorite impacts are called craters. During impact, cracks 4
may have formed in the moon's crust, allowing lava to reach the surface and fill in the large craters. The igneous rocks of the maria are 3 to 4 billion years old. They are the youngest rocks found on the moon thus far.

Seismographs left on the moon by Apollo astronauts have enabled scientists to study moonquakes. Recall from Chapter 14 that the study of earthquakes allows scientists to map Earth's interior. Likewise, studying moonquakes has led to a model of the moon's interior. One model of the moon shows that its crust is about 60 km thick on the side facing Earth and about 100 km thick on the far side. Below the crust, a solid mantle extends to a depth of about 800 km. A partly molten zone of the mantle extends farther down. Below this is an iron-rich solid core.

Did You Know?

The word *maria* comes from the Latin word for "sea." In the 17th century, astronomers thought the moon had oceans of water and named these areas maria. Today, we know the moon has little atmosphere and no water.

CONCEPT DEVELOPMENT

Cooperative Learning: Form Problem Solving groups with four students per group. Provide each group with a map of the moon's surface. Have students find and describe key surface features and explain how each feature might be formed.

▶**How did the moon's craters form?** *during impacts with space objects such as meteorites*

CROSS CURRICULUM

▶**History:** Provide small groups of students with a map of the moon's surface. Have them locate some of the more prominent craters. Have students find out a little about the lives of the persons after whom the craters were named.

CHECK FOR UNDERSTANDING

Use the Mini Quiz to check for understanding.

MINI QUIZ

Use the Mini Quiz to check students' recall of chapter content.

1. **Which type of eclipse occurs when the moon moves directly between Earth and the sun?** *solar eclipse*
2. **Which type of eclipse occurs when Earth's shadow falls on the moon?** *lunar eclipse*
3. **What are maria and how did they form?** *dark-colored flat areas on the moon that formed when lava filled large basins on the surface*
4. **Meteorite impacts have caused many depressions called _____ on the moon's surface.** *craters*

RETEACH

Using a globe of Earth, a tennis ball, and a large beach ball, simulate solar and lunar eclipses with the help of volunteers.

EXTENSION

For students who have mastered this section, use the **Reinforcement** and **Enrichment** masters or other OPTIONS provided.

ENRICHMENT

▶Have each student keep a two-week log of moon observations, including the moon phase, the time it was observed, and the moon's altitude above the horizon. The width of a fist when held at arm's length is approximately equal to 10° of altitude.

▶Have students find out what kinds of equipment were left behind on the moon and how these instruments have given scientists a better understanding of the moon's structure and history. Students should discover that instruments left by *Apollo* astronauts have recorded vibrations caused by meteorite impacts as well as seismic waves produced by moonquakes deep within the moon's interior. The instruments are extremely sensitive, recording 3000 moonquakes a year. Each moonquake releases energy equivalent to that released by an exploding firecracker. Reflectors, also left by astronauts, allow us to measure variations in the distance between Earth and the moon. Variations of a few centimeters can be measured by bouncing a laser beam off of the reflectors.

Origin of the Moon

List four theories of the moon's origin.

A recent theory about the moon's origin states that in Earth's early history, a Mars-sized object collided with Earth, throwing gas and debris into orbit. Within about 1000 years the gas and debris condensed into one large mass, forming the moon. Figure 22-11 illustrates several theories of the moon's origin.

Regardless of the moon's true origin, it has played an important role in our history. It was the source of curiosity for many early astronomers. Studying the phases of the moon and eclipses led people to conclude that Earth and the moon were in motion around the sun. Earth's shadow on the moon proved that Earth wasn't flat. When Galileo first turned his telescope to the moon, he found a surface scarred by craters and maria. Before that time, many people believed that all planetary bodies were "perfect," without surface features.

By studying the moon, we have learned about ourselves and the planet we live on. As you will read in the next section, the moon is not only important as an object from our past, but it is important to our future as well.

PROBLEM SOLVING

Marooned on the Moon

You and your crew have crash-landed on the moon, far from your intended landing site at the moon colony. It will take you one day to reach the moon colony on foot. The side of the moon that you're on will be facing away from the sun during your entire trip back to the colony. You manage to salvage the following items from your wrecked ship: food, rope, solar-powered heating unit, battery operated heating unit, three 70-kilogram oxygen tanks, map of the moon's constellation, magnetic compass, oxygen-burning signal flares, matches, 8 liters of water, solar-powered radio receiver and transmitter, 3 flashlights and extra batteries, signal mirror, and binoculars.

Keep in mind that the moon's gravity is much less than that of Earth's, and it lacks a magnetic field.

Think Critically: Which of these items do you and the other two members of your crew decide to take? Why is each item useful or not useful?

OPTIONS

INQUIRY QUESTIONS

▶ **In what ways might Earth be different if it had no moon?** *Nights would be much darker, there would be no eclipses, and there would be no tides.*

PROGRAM RESOURCES

From the **Teacher Resource Package** use:

Concept Mapping, pages 49-50.

PROBLEM SOLVING

Think Critically: The food, rope, battery-operated heating unit, oxygen tanks, water, constellation map, flashlights, and possibly binoculars would be useful. The other items wouldn't be useful due to the lack of sunlight and atmosphere on the moon. Also, the moon has no magnetic field, so the compass couldn't be used. Food and water will be needed to complete the difficult journey. A battery-operated heating unit is also necessary because of the extremely low temperatures on the nightside. Oxygen tanks are the most important items to bring. A map of the moon's constellations may help if the crew becomes lost. They can obtain general information about their location. This is their only means of navigation since a magnetic compass is useless. A flashlight is absolutely necessary on the nighttime side. Binoculars will be useless unless they transverse into the daytime side on their way to the colony. Rope may be needed to cross rough terrain or to rescue a crew member who has fallen into a crater. The solar-powered heating unit and radio are not operable without sunlight. A signal mirror is useless for the same reason. Signal flares and matches cannot be used in the oxygen-free environment.

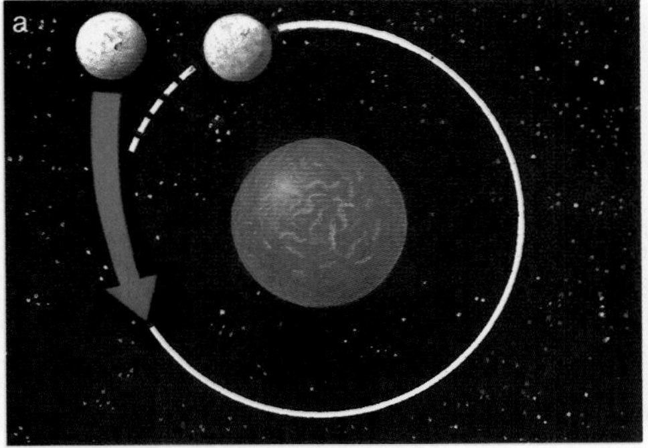

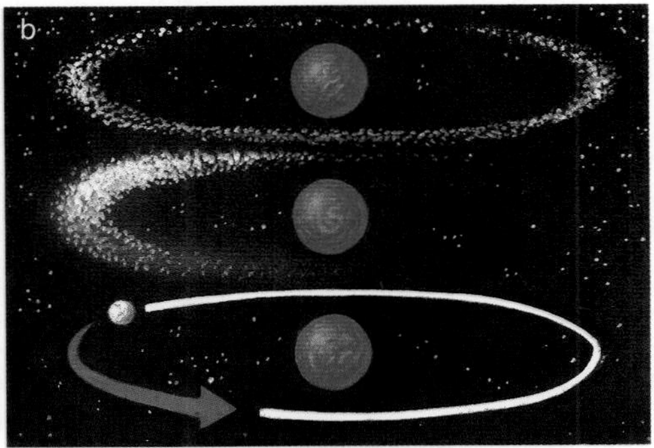

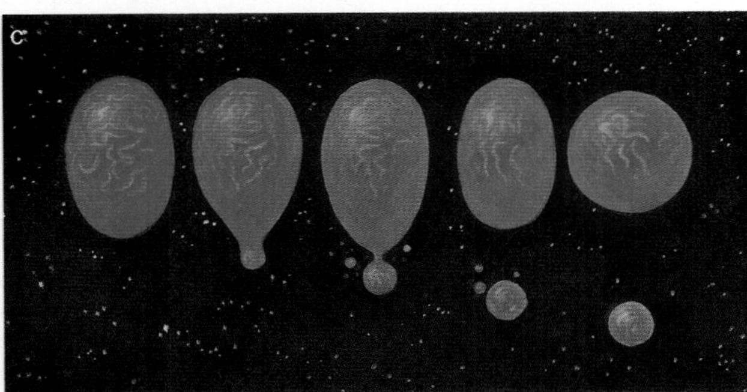

Figure 22-11. Three models of the moon's formation: (a) The moon is captured by Earth's gravity. The moon would have formed elsewhere and then "wandered" into Earth's vicinity. (b) The moon is condensed from loose material surrounding Earth during the early formation of the solar system. (c) A blob of molten material may have been ejected while Earth was still in its early, molten state.

SECTION REVIEW

1. What are the relative positions of the sun, moon, and Earth during a full moon?
2. Which type(s) of eclipse(s) can occur during full moon?
3. What caused the formation of maria on the moon?
4. **Apply:** Suppose the moon's diameter were one-half what it is now. Describe how a solar eclipse would differ from the solar eclipses that actually occur. Make a sketch of what would be observed.

Measuring in SI — Skill Builder

The moon's mass is 1/81 of Earth's mass. The moon's density is 3.3 g/cm^3. Calculate the moon's volume using the formula: *volume = mass/density.* If you need help, refer to Measuring in SI in the **Skill Handbook** on pages 684 and 685.

3 CLOSE

▶ Ask questions 1-3 and the **Apply** Question in the Section Review.

FLEX Your Brain

Use the Flex Your Brain activity to have students explore SURFACE FEATURES OF THE MOON and what they tell us about its history.

SECTION REVIEW ANSWERS

1. Earth is between the sun and the moon.
2. a lunar eclipse
3. Large floods of dark-colored lava covered low areas on the moon's surface, forming the maria.
4. Apply: There would never be a total solar eclipse. The moon would appear much smaller than the sun. During a solar eclipse, a portion of the sun would form a thick halo completely surrounding the darkened moon. Sketches should illustrate the disc of the sun with only its central portion eclipsed by the small moon.

Skill Builder

Recall that the mass of Earth is 5.98×10^{27} g.

$$\text{moon's mass} = 5.98 \times 10^{27}\text{ g} \div 81 = 7.4 \times 10^{25}\text{ g}$$

$$\text{volume of moon} = \frac{7.4 \times 10^{25}\text{ g}}{3.3\text{ g/cm}^3} = 2.2 \times 10^{25}\text{ cm}^3$$

SECTION 22-3

PREPARATION

SECTION BACKGROUND

▶ Biosphere II, a closed ecological system containing a human habitat and five connected biomes, is an Earth-based first step in devising a successful, self-sufficient moon colony.

1 MOTIVATE

TYING TO PREVIOUS KNOWLEDGE: Most students have learned that the various biomes on Earth depend on one another. Have students speculate on how scientists might create mini-biomes to support life within a moon colony. Direct students to the introduction to Unit 7 on pages 476 and 477. Discuss how information obtained from experiments conducted in Biosphere II could assist in the planning of a moon colony.

OBJECTIVES AND SCIENCE WORDS: Have students review the objectives and science words to become familiar with this section.

2 TEACH

Key Concepts are highlighted.

CONCEPT DEVELOPMENT

▶ Have students research moon colonies in the library. Sources to suggest include *Voyage through the Universe, Spacefarers,* Time-Life Books Inc., Richmond, VA, 1989, pp. 48-68, and "Biosphere 2," *Odyssey,* by Mary Algozin, Nov. 1990, pp. 4-9.

22-3 Building a Moon Colony

New Science Words

moon colony

Objectives

- ▶ Describe how a moon colony might be constructed.
- ▶ List advantages and disadvantages of constructing a moon colony.

Should Humans Colonize the Moon?

NASA is now considering plans for a colony on the moon early in the twenty-first century. A **moon colony** would be a permanent structure on the moon in which scientists could live and work for extended periods of time. Would benefits of a moon colony outweigh the cost and dangers involved in building one? What would a moon colony be like? Where would the materials needed to survive on the moon come from?

One idea for a moon colony includes living quarters made of a high-strength, multiple-layer fabric. The fabric would be supported by a framework inside, forming a dome about 15 m in diameter. At first, astronauts would take the supplies they needed with them. Eventually, the moon colony would become self-sufficient.

Oxygen can be extracted from moon rocks and soil. This oxygen could be used for breathing and to combine with hydrogen to produce water for the colony. Food could be grown in lunar soil that has been enclosed under protecting domes.

There are several advantages to building a moon colony. Scientists would learn more about the moon itself by studying it up close. The more we learn about the moon, the more we might learn about the evolution of our solar system.

OPTIONS

Meeting Different Ability Levels

For Section 22-3, use the following **Teacher Resource Masters** depending upon individual students' needs.

◆ **Study Guide Master** for all students.

● **Reinforcement Master** for students of average and above average ability levels.

▲ **Enrichment Master** for above average students.

Additional Teacher Resource Package masters are listed in the OPTIONS box throughout the section. The additional masters are appropriate for all students.

◆ STUDY GUIDE 89

NAME ________ DATE ________ CLASS ________

STUDY GUIDE — Chapter 22

Building a Moon Colony — Text Pages 592–593

Circle the word in parentheses that makes each sentence correct.

1. NASA is exploring plans to establish a colony on the moon in the (twentieth, twenty-first) century.
2. A moon colony would be a (permanent, temporary) structure on the moon where scientists could live and work.
3. One suggestion for a moon colony is using a high-strength, multiple-layer (metal, fabric) to construct living quarters.
4. (Oxygen, Hydrogen) for breathing could be extracted from moon rocks and soil.
5. Oxygen combined with hydrogen could be used to produce (soil, water).
6. Scientists could use the moon colony to do a close-up study of (the moon, Earth).
7. The study of the moon would help scientists learn more about the evolution of (the sun, the solar system).
8. A moon colony would provide opportunities to study long-term exposure to a space (environment, program).

Put an X by the sentences that are true about a moon colony.

X 9. The moon would be an excellent location from which to study the universe because it has almost no atmosphere.
X 10. Oxygen could be extracted from the soil and used for breathing.
____ 11. Building a moon colony would be a low-cost program.
X 12. Life in a moon colony could expose the inhabitants to the dangers of radiation.
____ 13. People in a moon colony would be breathing an oxygen-rich atmosphere.
____ 14. From the beginning, a moon colony would be self-sufficient.
X 15. People in the moon colony would experience nights that were two weeks long.
____ 16. It would take three years for people to arrive at the moon colony once they left Earth.
X 17. The moon colonists would build domes for living quarters.
____ 18. The buildings for a moon colony would be moved from place to place on the moon.
X 19. One goal of the moon colony would be to supply propellant fuel for spacecraft.
____ 20. Food supplies for a moon colony would have to be provided by Earth.
X 21. The moon colony's sky would be half as bright as the darkest Earth sky.
X 22. A moon colony could supply space exploration needs.

89

Before astronauts travel into interplanetary space, many scientists want the opportunity to study how they will react to long missions. Mars missions may require three years to complete. A moon colony would provide the opportunity to study long-term exposure to a space environment.

The moon would make an excellent location from which to study the universe. The moon has almost no atmosphere. The sky is half as bright as the darkest Earth sky. Nighttime on the moon is two weeks long. These characteristics make the moon a great place to study objects in deep space.

Moon rocks may contain large deposits of usable resources. Although products from the moon may not be used on Earth, they could supply many of the needs of space exploration. Oxygen could be extracted from moon rocks to be used in spacecraft propellants. One of the goals of a moon colony would be to supply spacecraft with fuel and other materials.

Building a moon colony would have its problems. The cost of a colony on the moon could reach into the billions of dollars. Some people would rather see this money spent on Earth-based research. A second problem would be the danger to astronauts who live and work on the moon. They would spend long periods of time exposed to the dangers of possible radiation and no breathable atmosphere.

Science and MATH

It's the summer of 2025, and you're planning your family's vacation to the new resort on the moon. How long will it take you to get there if you cruise at 4000 km/h?

SECTION REVIEW

1. What is a moon colony?
2. What are the advantages and disadvantages of a moon colony?

You Decide!

Some scientists believe the economic cost and the risks of human space travel are too great. They believe that recent improvements in the use of robots show that humans are not needed in space. They want to see funds used to explore the solar system with noncrewed spacecraft.

Are the benefits humans would receive from such a colony worth the risks involved? Are there other missions in space that should be funded in place of a moon colony?

● REINFORCEMENT 89

NAME ____________ DATE ________ CLASS ________

REINFORCEMENT — Chapter 22

Building a Moon Colony — Text Pages 592–593

Identify each of the following statements as an advantage or disadvantage of building a moon colony. Write A next to advantages and D next to disadvantages.

A 1. Oxygen that could be used for breathing, making water, and making propellants can be obtained from moon rocks and soil.
D 2. The cost of building a moon colony would be very high.
A 3. People could learn more about the moon by studying it up close.
A 4. Because the moon has almost no atmosphere, objects in space could be seen more clearly than they can from the Earth.
D 5. Astronauts and others living on the moon would have no breathable atmosphere.
A 6. Moon rocks may contain large deposits of usable resources.
A 7. Moon products could supply many of the needs of space exploration.
D 8. People in the colony could be exposed to the dangers of radiation.
A 9. Moon soil could be used to grow food under protective domes.
D 10. At first all the supplies needed by a moon colony would have to be shipped from Earth.

Use the following terms in the box to complete the statements.

atmosphere	twenty-first	hydrogen	interplanetary
permanent	radiation	goals	

11. NASA scientists are considering the possibility of building a moon colony in the **twenty-first** century.
12. Scientists would live and work in the **permanent** structure built on the moon for the colony.
13. Scientists could extract oxygen from moon rocks and combine it with **hydrogen** to make the water the colony would need.
14. Many scientists want to study how astronauts would react to long-term space missions before astronauts travel into **interplanetary** space.
15. Because night is two weeks long and the moon has almost no **atmosphere**, the moon would be a good place to study objects in space.
16. Supplying spacecraft fuel is among the **goals** of a moon colony.
17. Exposure to **radiation** is one of the dangers people living in a moon colony might face.

89

▲ ENRICHMENT 89

NAME ____________ DATE ________ CLASS ________

ENRICHMENT — Chapter 22

Building a Moon Colony — Text Pages 592–593

INTERPRETING FACTS

Use the information in the table and a calculator to help you answer the questions.

Facts about the moon	
Diameter at the equator: 3476 km	Period of rotation: about 27.3 days
Circumference at the equator: 10 920 km	Period of revolution around Earth: about 27.3 days
Density: 3.3 g/cm³	Length of day and night: about 15 Earth days each
Gravity: 1/6 of Earth's	Temperature: high: 127°C daytime; low: −170°C nighttime
Distance from Earth: closest: 356 400 km; farthest: 406 700 km; average: 384 400 km	Atmosphere: almost none

1. Earth's circumference at the equator is 39 843 km. How many times larger is it than the moon's circumference? **3.65 times larger**
2. How many times will the moon revolve around Earth in 92 days? **3.37 times**
3. How many times will the moon rotate on its axis in 92 days? **3.37 times**
4. If a rock has a mass 0.15 kg on the moon, what will its mass be on Earth? **An object's mass doesn't change from one gravitational field to another. The rock's mass would still be 0.15 kg.**
5. If a colonist weighs 800.15 newtons on Earth, what would the colonist weigh on the moon? **133.36 newtons**
6. Use the average distance to the moon to answer this question. If astronauts travel to the moon and back to Earth again in 144 hours, how many kilometers per hour do they travel? **5338.9 km/h**
7. If colonists travel at 6000 km/h, how long will it take them to get to the moon from Earth when the moon is at its farthest point from Earth? its nearest point to Earth? Round your answers to the nearest hour. **68 hours; 59 hours**
8. How much time would the colonists in Question 7 save if they traveled to the moon when it was at its nearest point rather than at its farthest point from Earth? **9 hours**
9. With the extremes of temperatures on the moon, what would a colony need to protect its people from the temperatures? **A colony would need effective heating and air conditioning systems. Back-up sources of power would be needed to ensure these systems worked if there were a power outage.**

89

Science and MATH

400 000 km ÷ 4000 km/hr = 100 hrs

CHECK FOR UNDERSTANDING

Ask questions 1-2 in the Section Review.

RETEACH

Lead a discussion on how food, oxygen, and water, which are needed to survive in a moon colony, could be obtained.

EXTENSION

For students who have mastered this section, use the **Reinforcement** and **Enrichment** masters or other OPTIONS provided.

3 CLOSE

Cooperative Learning: Form Numbered Heads Together groups. Have students list and discuss advantages and disadvantages of constructing a moon colony.

SECTION REVIEW ANSWERS

1. a permanent structure on the moon in which scientists could live and work for extended periods of time

2. Advantages include the possibility of doing various kinds of research not possible on Earth, setting up astronomical observatories, and having access to the moon's resources. Disadvantages include the enormous expense of building the colony and the possible dangers to humans at the colony.

YOU DECIDE!

When attempting to answer the questions posed, students should consider costs, the main purpose or function of colony to be built, and possible uses of a moon colony.

PROGRAM RESOURCES

From the **Teacher Resource Package** use:

Science and Society, page 26, Space Colony on Earth.

ACTIVITY 22-2
30-40 minutes

OBJECTIVE: Demonstrate the relative positions of Earth and the moon during lunar phases and **distinguish** between a lunar and solar eclipse.

PROCESS SKILLS applied in this activity:
▶ **Observing** in Procedure Steps 1, 4, 5, and 6.
▶ **Inferring** in Analyze Questions 2 and 3 and Conclude and Apply Questions 4-6.
▶ **Recognizing and Using Spatial Relationships** in Procedure Steps 1-6.
▶ **Interpreting Data** in Analyze Question 1.
▶ **Formulating Models** in Procedure Steps 2-6.
▶ **Experimenting** in Procedure Steps 1-6.

COOPERATIVE LEARNING Have Science Investigation teams perform this activity.

TEACHING THE ACTIVITY

▶ It is important for the room to be dark enough for the light source to cast an observable shadow on the model Earth or moon when in the appropriate phase for an eclipse to occur.
▶ Before students attempt to answer Analyze Question 2, point out that the distance between the moon and Earth is not constant. The moon's orbit is an ellipse; therefore, its distance from Earth varies throughout its revolution.

PROGRAM RESOURCES

From the **Teacher Resource Package** use:

Activity Worksheets, pages 200-201, Activity 22-2: Moon Phases and Eclipses.

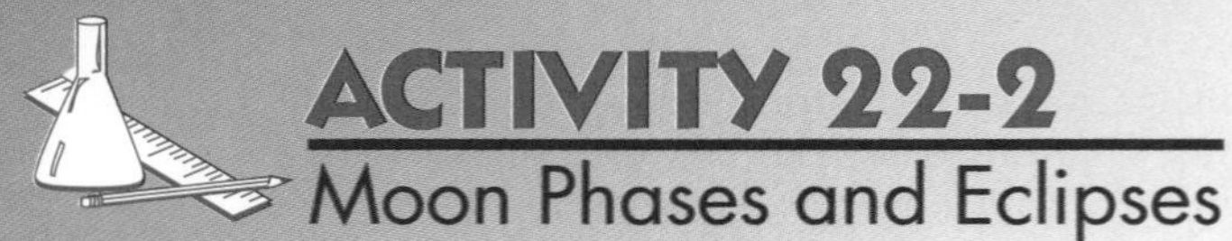

ACTIVITY 22-2
Moon Phases and Eclipses

Problem: *How do the motions and size of the moon cause moon phases and eclipses?*

Materials 

- light source (unshaded)
- polystyrene ball on pencil
- globe
- Figure 22-6

Procedure

1. Study the positions of the sun, the moon, and Earth in Figure 22-6.
2. Use a polystyrene ball on a pencil as a model moon. Move the model moon around the globe to duplicate the exact position that would have to occur for a lunar eclipse to take place.
3. Move the model moon to the position that would cause a solar eclipse.
4. Place the model moon at each of the following phases: first quarter, full moon, third quarter, and new moon. Identify which, if any, eclipse could occur during each phase. Record you data.
5. Place the model moon at the location where a lunar eclipse could occur. Move it slightly toward and away from Earth. Note the amount of change in the size of the shadow causing the eclipse. Record this information.
6. Repeat Step 5 with the model moon in a position where a solar eclipse could occur.

Analyze

1. During which phase(s) of the moon is it possible for an eclipse to occur?
2. Describe the effect that a small change in the distance between Earth and the moon has on the size of the shadow causing the eclipse.
3. As seen from Earth, how does the apparent size of the moon compare to the apparent size of the sun? How can an eclipse be used to confirm this?

Data and Observations

Moon Phase	Observations
first quarter	
full	
third quarter	
new	

Conclude and Apply

4. Why don't a lunar and solar eclipse occur every month?
5. Suppose you wanted to more accurately model the movement of the moon around Earth. How would your model moon move around the globe? Would it always be in the same plane as the light source and the globe?

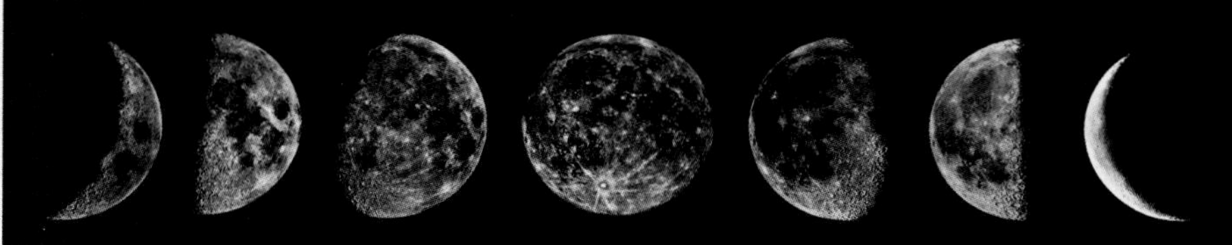

ANSWERS TO QUESTIONS

1. Eclipses of the moon may occur only at full moon phase. Solar eclipses occur only during new moon phase.
2. The distance between Earth and the moon has little effect on lunar eclipses. During solar eclipses, the closer the two bodies, the larger the moon's shadow on Earth's surface and the longer the duration of the eclipse.
3. The moon and sun *appear* similar in size. This relationship is most observable during a solar eclipse as the moon just seems to exactly fit the solar disk being eclipsed.
4. Eclipses are possible only when the moon is crossing Earth's orbital plane around the sun. Except for a few minutes each month, the moon is always located either above or below Earth's orbital plane.
5. In order to accurately demonstrate lunar motions around Earth, the moon must spend most of its time either above or below Earth's orbital plane. Additionally, it will move slightly away from and closer to Earth during its elliptical orbit.

CHAPTER

REVIEW

SUMMARY

22-1: Planet Earth

1. Earth is a sphere that is slightly flattened at its poles. Earth's mass is nearly 6.0×10^{27} grams and its density is 5.52 g/cm^3. Earth's magnetic field is due to convection currents in its mantle.
2. Earth rotates, or spins, on its axis once each day and revolves about the sun in a little more than 365 days.
3. Seasons on Earth are due to the amount of solar energy received by a hemisphere at a given time. The tilt of Earth on its axis causes the amount of solar energy to vary, thus causing changes in seasons.

22-2: Earth's Moon

1. Earth's moon goes through phases that depend on the relative positions of the sun, the moon, and Earth.
2. Eclipses occur when Earth or the moon temporarily blocks out the sunlight reaching the other. A solar eclipse occurs when the moon moves directly between the sun and Earth. A lunar eclipse occurs when Earth's shadow falls on the moon.
3. The moon's maria are the result of ancient volcanism. Craters on the moon's surface formed from impacts with meteorites.

22-3: Science and Society: Building a Moon Colony

1. One proposed moon colony would be made of layers of fabric supported by an inner, dome-shaped framework. Air and water could be obtained from gases in the moon's rocks. Food could be grown in lunar soil within the colony.
2. Advantages of a moon colony include learning more about Earth's natural satellite, learning how people would adapt to living in space, and learning more about the universe. Disadvantages include high costs, and risks of radiation and no breathable atmosphere.

KEY SCIENCE WORDS

a. **axis**
b. **ellipse**
c. **equinox**
d. **first quarter**
e **full moon**
f. **lunar eclipse**
g. **maria**
h. **moon colony**
i. **moon phases**
j. **new moon**
k. **revolution**
l. **rotation**
m. **solar eclipse**
n. **solstice**
o. **sphere**
p. **third quarter**
q. **waning**
r. **waxing**

UNDERSTANDING VOCABULARY

Match each phrase with the correct term from the list of Key Science Words.

1. Earth's shape
2. causes day and night to occur on Earth
3. Earth's path around the sun
4. shape of Earth's orbit
5. the sun's position when it's directly above the equator
6. the moon can't be seen during this phase
7. moon phase in which all of the lighted side is seen
8. eclipse that occurs when the moon is between Earth and the sun
9. flat regions on the moon
10. a place to live and work on the moon

OPTIONS

ASSESSMENT

To assess student understanding of material in this chapter, use the resources listed.

COOPERATIVE LEARNING

Consider using cooperative learning in the THINK AND WRITE CRITICALLY, APPLY, and MORE SKILL BUILDERS sections of the Chapter Review.

PROGRAM RESOURCES

From the **Teacher Resource Package** use:

Chapter Review, pages 47-48.

Chapter and Unit Tests, pages 150-153, Chapter Test.

CHAPTER

REVIEW

SUMMARY

Have students read the summary statements to review the major concepts of the chapter.

UNDERSTANDING VOCABULARY

1. o
2. l
3. k
4. b
5. c
6. j
7. e
8. m
9. g
10. h

CHAPTER

REVIEW

CHECKING CONCEPTS

1. c	**6.** b
2. a	**7.** a
3. c	**8.** b
4. d	**9.** d
5. d	**10.** b

UNDERSTANDING CONCEPTS

11. axis
12. ellipse
13. southern
14. maria
15. moon colony

THINK AND WRITE CRITICALLY

16. Rotation is the spinning of an object about its axis. Revolution is the movement of one object around another. Both the moon and Earth rotate and revolve.

17. The moon's period of rotation equals its period of revolution. Thus, the same side of the moon is always facing Earth. Only astronauts who have orbited the moon have directly observed craters on the far side of the moon.

18. During an equinox, the number of daylight hours equals the number of nighttime hours and the sun is directly above Earth's equator. Solstice occurs when the sun reaches its greatest distance north or south of the equator. At summer solstice, the number of daylight hours is greatest; the shortest day of the year is winter solstice.

19. These are shadows formed by the moon during eclipses. The umbra is the darker shadow cast on Earth's moon. The penumbra is the lighter shadow cast on Earth's surface.

20. There is no atmosphere to obscure telescope observations. The night sky from the moon has no light pollution. Nights on the moon are longer than those on Earth.

CHAPTER

REVIEW

CHECKING CONCEPTS

Choose the word or phrase that completes the sentence.

1. The sun rises and sets because ______.
a. Earth revolves
b. it moves in space
c. Earth rotates
d. none of these

2. Earth's circumference at the ______ is greater than it is at the ______.
a. equator, poles **c.** poles, equator
b. axis, mantle **d.** mantle, axis

3. When the sun reaches equinox, the ______ is facing the sun.
a. southern hemisphere
b. northern hemisphere
c. equator
d. none of these

4. The moon rotates once every ______.
a. 24 hours **c.** 27.3 hours
b. 365 days **d.** 27.3 days

5. Moon phases depend on the position of ______.
a. Earth **c.** the sun
b. the moon itself **d.** all of these

6. As the moon appears to get larger, it is said to ______.
a. wane **b.** wax
c. rotate **d.** be crescent-shaped

7. During a ______ eclipse, the moon is directly between the sun and Earth.
a. solar **c.** full
b. new **d.** lunar

8. The ______ is the darkest part of the moon's shadow during a solar eclipse.
a. waxing gibbous **c.** waning gibbous
b. umbra **d.** penumbra

9. ______ are depressions on the moon.
a. Maria **c.** Phases
b. Moonquakes **d.** Craters

10. Oxygen for a moon colony could be obtained from the ______.
a. lunar atmosphere
b. lunar rocks and soil
c. lunar water
d. none of these

UNDERSTANDING CONCEPTS

Complete each sentence.

11. Even if you could view Earth from space, you wouldn't be able to see its ______ because it's an imaginary line about which Earth rotates.

12. The shape of the path Earth makes around the sun is a(n) ______.

13. In the ______ hemisphere, fall equinox is reached on March 20 or 21.

14. The moon's ______ formed from ancient lava flows.

15. A(n) ______ would make a great "observatory" from which to study space.

APPLY

21. An observer in space would see no lunar phases because he or she would be outside the moon's orbit. The moon would appear to loop around Earth.

22. Earth bulges at the equator. Its gravitational attraction there is less than that at the poles. Thus, a person weighs less at the equator.

23. During full and new moons, Earth, the sun, and the moon, align, thus the gravitational attraction is greatest. High tides are the highest and low tides are the lowest during these two phases.

THINK AND WRITE CRITICALLY

16. Compare and contrast rotation and revolution. Give an example of each.
17. Why have observers on Earth never seen craters on one side of the moon?
18. How do equinoxes and solstices differ?
19. What causes umbras and penumbras?
20. What advantages would astronomers on the moon have over astronomers on Earth for studying the universe?

APPLY

21. How would the moon appear to an observer in space during its revolution? Would phases be observable? Explain.
22. Would you weigh more at Earth's equator or at the North Pole? Explain.
23. Recall that tides occur due to the gravitational attraction among the sun, moon, and Earth. During which phases of the moon are tides the highest? Explain.
24. If you were lost on the moon's surface, why would it be more beneficial to have a star chart rather then a compass?
25. Which of the moon's motions are real? Which are apparent? Explain why each occurs.

MORE SKILL BUILDERS

If you need help, refer to the Skill Handbook.

1. **Hypothesizing:** Hypothesize why locations near Earth's equator travel faster during one rotation than places near the poles.
2. **Using Variables, Constants, and Controls:** Describe a simple activity that would show that direct rays from the sun provide more energy than slanted rays.
3. **Inferring:** The moon doesn't produce its own light. Why can we see it in the night sky?
4. **Comparing and Contrasting:** Compare and contrast a waning moon with a waxing moon.
5. **Concept Mapping:** Copy and complete the cycle map below. Show the sequences of the moon's phases.

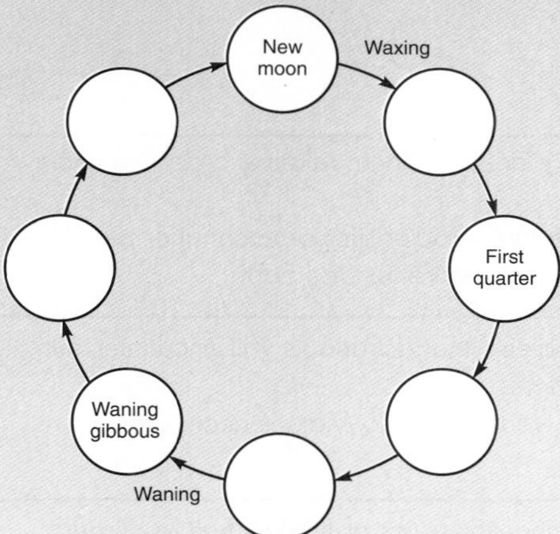

PROJECTS

1. Construct a model that demonstrates how all the phases of the moon are seen from Earth *and* from space.
2. Research the work done by a Greek mathematician named Eratosthenes. How does his circumference of Earth compare with the value used today?

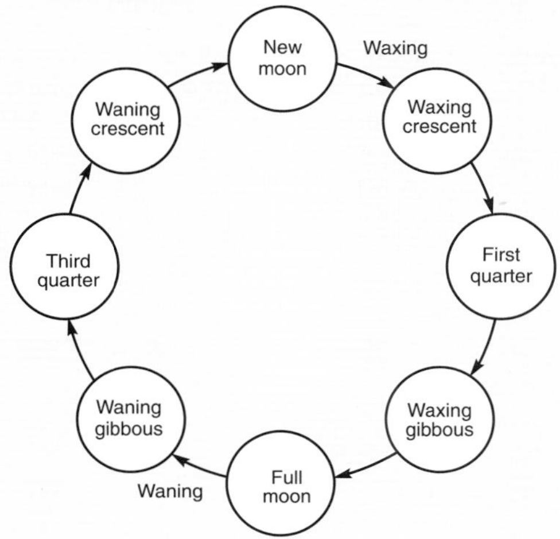

24. The moon does not have a magnetic field. Star charts could be used to navigate, but a compass could not.
25. The changing position of the moon from night to night is a real motion because the moon is orbiting Earth. The moon appears to move westward across the sky due to Earth's rapid rotation. Though the moon is progressing westward in its revolution around Earth, its trip across the sky in a single night is due to Earth's rotation. Seeing the same side of the moon seems to indicate a lack of rotation. This is an apparent motion because the moon's period of rotation equals its period of revolution.

MORE SKILL BUILDERS

1. Hypothesizing: The circumference of Earth is greater at low latitudes than at high latitudes. Thus locations near the equator have a greater distance to travel to complete one rotation than do locations near the poles. Both tropic and polar locations must complete their journeys during the same time period (24 hours); therefore, the locations at low latitudes must travel faster.
2. Using Variables, Constants, and Controls: Shining a flashlight onto a piece of paper from directly above and then at an angle would show that the rays traveling at an angle are spread over a larger area and thus provide less energy per unit area than direct rays. The angle would be the variable; the energy emitted and the height of the flashlight would be the constants.
3. Inferring: The moon shines because it reflects sunlight from its surface.
4. Comparing and Contrasting: Both are due to the moon's going through phases. A waxing moon is one that gets larger each night. A waning moon becomes smaller each night.
5. Concept Mapping: The solution is shown at left.

CHAPTER

23 The Solar System

CHAPTER SECTION	OBJECTIVES	ACTIVITIES
23-1 The Solar System (2 days)	1. **Compare** and **contrast** the sun-centered and Earth-centered models of the solar system. 2. **Describe** the theory for the formation of the solar system.	**Activity 23-1:** *Planetary Orbits,* p. 605
23-2 The Inner Planets (2 days)	1. **List** the inner planets in their relative order from the sun. 2. **Identify** important characteristics of each inner planet. 3. **Compare** and **contrast** Venus and Earth.	**MINI-Lab:** *How would construction be different on Mars?* p. 609
23-3 Mission to Mars Science & Society (1 day)	1. **Recognize** problems that astronauts will encounter during a trip to Mars. 2. **Decide** if a crewed mission to Mars is necessary.	
23-4 The Outer Planets (3 days)	1. **List** the major characteristics of Jupiter, Saturn, Uranus, and Neptune. 2. **Recognize** how Pluto differs from the other outer planets.	**MINI-Lab:** *How can you draw planets to scale?* p. 614 **Activity 23-2:** *Solar System Distance Model,* p. 617
23-5 Other Objects in the Solar System (2 days)	1. **Explain** where a comet comes from and describe how a comet develops as it approaches the sun. 2. **Differentiate** among comets, meteoroids, and asteroids.	
Chapter Review		

ACTIVITY MATERIALS

FIND OUT	ACTIVITIES		MINI-LABS	
Page 599 color comics from newspaper magnifying glass	**23-1 Planetary Orbits, p. 605** thumbtacks or pins string cardboard (21.5 cm × 28 cm) metric ruler pencil paper	**23-2 Solar System Distance Model, p. 617** adding machine tape meterstick scissors pencil	**How would construction be different on Mars? p. 609** paper pencil	**How can you draw planets to scale? p. 614** metric ruler drawing compass pencil paper

CHAPTER FEATURES	TEACHER RESOURCE PACKAGE	OTHER RESOURCES
Skill Builder: *Concept Mapping,* p. 604	**Ability Level Worksheets** ◆ ***Study Guide,*** p. 90 ● ***Reinforcement,*** p. 90 ▲ ***Enrichment,*** p. 90 **Activity Worksheet,** pp. 207-208 **Concept Mapping,** pp. 51-52 **Cross-Curricular Connections,** p. 27 **Transparency Masters,** pp. 91-94	**Color Transparency 46,** Relative Sizes of Planets **Color Transparency 47,** Planets in Solar System **Lab Manual:** *Newton's First Law of Motion,* p. 181
Problem Solving: *The Hotter It Gets???* p. 607 **Skill Builder:** *Interpreting Data,* p. 609	**Ability Level Worksheets** ◆ ***Study Guide,*** p. 91 ● ***Reinforcement,*** p. 91 ▲ ***Enrichment,*** p. 91 **MINI-Lab Worksheet,** p. 213	**Lab Manual:** *Venus—The Greenhouse Effect,* p. 183
You Decide! p. 611	**Ability Level Worksheets** ◆ ***Study Guide,*** p. 92 ● ***Reinforcement,*** p. 92 ▲ ***Enrichment,*** p. 92 **Science and Society,** p. 27	
Skill Builder: *Recognizing Cause and Effect,* p. 616	**Ability Level Worksheets** ◆ ***Study Guide,*** p. 93 ● ***Reinforcement,*** p. 93 ▲ ***Enrichment,*** p. 93 **MINI-Lab Worksheet,** p. 214 **Activity Worksheet,** pp. 209-210 **Critical Thinking/Problem Solving,** p. 29	**Lab Manual:** *Jupiter and Its Moons,* p. 187
Technology: *Garbage in Space,* p. 621 **Skill Builder:** *Interpreting Scientific Illustrations,* p. 622	**Ability Level Worksheets** ◆ ***Study Guide,*** p. 94 ● ***Reinforcement,*** p. 94 ▲ ***Enrichment,*** p. 94	
Summary Key Science Words Understanding Vocabulary Checking Concepts Understanding Concepts Think & Write Critically Apply More Skill Builders Projects	**Chapter Review,** pp. 49-50 **Chapter Test,** pp. 154-157	**Chapter Review Software** **Test Bank**

◆ **Basic** ● **Average** ▲ **Advanced**

ADDITIONAL MATERIALS

SOFTWARE	AUDIOVISUAL	BOOKS/MAGAZINES
Astronomy—Planets, Educational Courseware. *Sundisk,* Sunshine Computer Software Co. *The Solar System,* Queue. *Easy Search: Solar System Rescue,* Focus. *Planetarium on Computer: The Solar System,* Focus.	*Mars—Is There Life?,* film, NASA. *Mercury,* film, NASA. *Our Planets—No Place Like Earth,* film, Time-Life. *The Wanderers: Paths of Planets,* film, BFA. *Neptune's Cold Fury,* video, NOVA (PBS). *The Planets,* laserdisc, NGS. *Planetscopes: Space Disc Vol. 2,* laserdisc, Optical Data Corp. *Voyager Gallery: Space Disc Vol. 1,* laserdisc, Optical Data Corp. *Voyager Odyssey,* laserdisc, Lumivision.	Brandt, Keith. *Planets and the Solar System.* Mahwah, NJ: Troll Associates, 1985. Branley, Franklyn M. *Planets in Our Solar System.* NY: Harper and Row Junior Books Group, 1987. Sagan, Carl. *Broca's Brain.* NY: Ballantine Books, Inc., 1986.

CHAPTER

23

THE SOLAR SYSTEM

THEME DEVELOPMENT: The theme of this chapter is the scale and structure of the solar system. All objects in this system are compared and contrasted according to size and composition.

CHAPTER OVERVIEW

▶ **Section 23-1:** This section describes how the present-day sun-centered model of the solar system evolved. One hypothesis of the formation of the solar system is also presented.

▶ **Section 23-2:** This section lists and describes characteristics of each of the inner planets.

▶ **Section 23-3: Science and Society:** Section 23-3 asks students to consider whether robots or humans should explore Mars.

▶ **Section 23-4:** This section lists and describes each of the outer planets. Information gathered from the *Voyager* space probes is presented.

▶ **Section 23-5:** Section 23-5 describes comets, meteoroids, and asteroids.

CHAPTER VOCABULARY

solar system
inner planets
outer planets
Mercury
Venus
Earth
astronomical unit
Mars
data gloves
Jupiter
Great Red Spot
Saturn
Uranus
Neptune
Pluto
comet
Oort Cloud
meteor
meteorite
asteroid

CHAPTER

23 The Solar System

598

OPTIONS

For Your Gifted Students

Have students do some research to find out about famous astronomers and their contributions to astronomy. Students can work in groups of 5 or 6 to write plays in which these astronomers are brought together in time to debate their ideas. Students can dress in period costumes and perform the plays for the class.

Some of the planets in the solar system have systems of rings around them. The image at the left is a photo collage of several planets in the solar system. The rings of Saturn are seen in the center. From Earth, planetary rings look like solid bands that circle the planet. Actually, planetary rings are made up of millions of individual particles of dust, rock, and ice that are orbiting around some planets in bands.

FIND OUT!

Do this simple activity to find out about planetary rings.

Bring in some color comics from your local newspaper. First, examine the color while holding the comics at arm's length from your eyes. The colors of areas within the lines seem solid and made up of just one color, don't they? Now examine the comics up close with a magnifying glass. Try to observe tan or orange colors in the comics. What does the magnifying glass reveal? Are all of the colors really solid? What does this comparison help to explain about planetary rings?

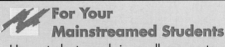

Gearing Up

Previewing the Chapter

Use this outline to help you focus on important ideas in this chapter.

Section 23-1 The Solar System
- Early Ideas about the Solar System
- Formation of the Solar System
- Motions of the Planets

Section 23-2 The Inner Planets
- Inner Planets

Section 23-3 Science and Society Mission to Mars
- Who Should Explore Mars—Humans or Robots?

Section 23-4 The Outer Planets
- Outer Planets

Section 23-5 Other Objects in the Solar System
- Other Objects in the Solar System
- Comets
- Meteoroids, Meteors, and Meteorites
- Asteroids

Previewing Science Skills

- In the **Skill Builders,** you will make a concept map and interpret a scientific illustration.
- In the **Activities,** you will measure, predict, interpret, and use numbers.
- In the **MINI-Labs,** you will make a model and plan for a trip to Mars.

What's next?

Many objects in the solar system are different than they appear from Earth. As you read this chapter, you'll learn about many new discoveries about the planets and their moons. You will also learn about other objects that are part of our solar system.

INTRODUCING THE CHAPTER

Use the Find Out activity to introduce students to the fact that planetary rings are composed of millions of individual particles. Inform students that they will be learning about the scale and structure not only of planetary rings, but of all objects in the solar system.

FIND OUT!

Preparation: Have students bring in color comics from the local newspapers. Also obtain magnifying glasses.
Materials: color comics from a newspaper and a magnifying glass for each student
Teaching Tips
- Call on volunteers to answer the questions asked.
- Show students distant and close-up photographs taken of Saturn's rings.

Gearing Up

Have students study the Gearing Up feature to familiarize themselves with the chapter. Discuss the relationships of the topics in the outline.

What's Next?

Before beginning the first section, make sure students understand the connection between the Find Out activity and the topics to follow.

For Your Mainstreamed Students

Have students work in small groups to make mobiles of the solar system to display in class. On the backside of each planet students should include all the pertinent facts, such as temperature extremes, whether or not the planet has an atmosphere, length of orbit around the sun, the numbers of moons, and so on.

SECTION 23-1

PREPARATION

SECTION BACKGROUND

▶ Most objects in the solar system rotate and revolve toward the east. Any motion different from this eastward motion is retrograde motion. Retrograde motion of Mars' orbit was one piece of evidence used by Copernicus to support his sun-centered model of the solar system.

▶ In 1543, Copernicus published his sun-centered solar system but had incorrectly concluded that planets orbited the sun in circular paths. Between 1609 and 1619, Johannes Kepler devised three laws of planetary motion, which mathematically proved that planets' orbits were elliptical.

▶ Recent theories on the formation of our solar system suggest that a nearby star may have exploded, sending shock waves through the cloud that was to become the solar system. The shock waves caused the particles in the cloud to condense. Then, gravity acted on the particles to pull them toward the center of the cloud.

▶ Astronomers have found evidence of disks of matter surrounding other stars, which may be other solar systems in their initial stages of formation. β Pictoris is one such star.

PREPLANNING

▶ To prepare for Activity 23-1, obtain thumbtacks or pins, string, cardboard, and metric rulers.

PROGRAM RESOURCES

From the **Teacher Resource Package** use:

Transparency Masters, pages 91-92, Relative Sizes of the Planets; pages 93-94, Planets in the Solar System.

Use **Color Transparency** number 46, Relative Sizes of the Planets.

Use **Color Transparency** number 47, Planets in the Solar System.

23-1 The Solar System

New Science Words

solar system
inner planets
outer planets

Objectives

- ▶ Compare and contrast the sun-centered and the Earth-centered models of the solar system.
- ▶ Describe the theory for the formation of the solar system.

Early Ideas about the Solar System

Imagine yourself lying in the grass on a warm, clear summer night gazing at the stars and the moon. The stars and the moon seem so still and beautiful. You may even have looked at other planets in the solar system thinking they were stars. Although the planets are very different from stars, they blend in with the stars and are usually hard to pick out.

As you learned in Chapter 22, the sun and the stars appear to move through the sky because Earth is moving. This wasn't always a known fact. Many early Greek scientists thought the planets, the sun, and the moon

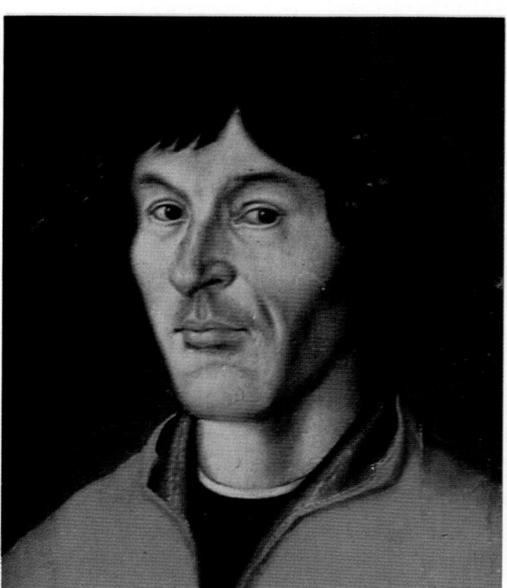

Figure 23-1. Nicholas Copernicus (at left) and Galileo Galilei

OPTIONS

Meeting Different Ability Levels

For Section 23-1, use the following **Teacher Resource Masters** depending upon individual students' needs.

◆ **Study Guide Master** for all students.

● **Reinforcement Master** for students of average and above average ability levels.

▲ **Enrichment Master** for above average students.

Additional Teacher Resource Package masters are listed in the OPTIONS box throughout the section. The additional masters are appropriate for all students.

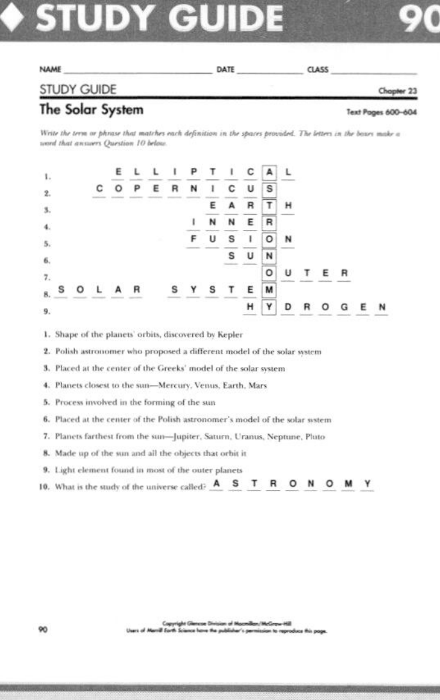

◆ STUDY GUIDE 90

NAME ______ DATE ______ CLASS ______

STUDY GUIDE Chapter 23

The Solar System Text Pages 600-604

Write the term or phrase that matches each definition in the spaces provided. The letters in the boxes make a word that answers Question 10 below.

1. E L L I P T I C [A] L
2. C O P E R N I C U [S]
3. E A R [T] H
4. I N N E [R]
5. F U S I [O] N
6. S U [N]
7. [O] U T E R
8. S O L A R S Y S T E [M]
9. H [Y] D R O G E N

1. Shape of the planets' orbits, discovered by Kepler
2. Polish astronomer who proposed a different model of the solar system
3. Placed at the center of the Greeks' model of the solar system
4. Planets closest to the sun—Mercury, Venus, Earth, Mars
5. Process involved in the forming of the sun
6. Placed at the center of the Polish astronomer's model of the solar system
7. Planets farthest from the sun—Jupiter, Saturn, Uranus, Neptune, Pluto
8. Made up of the sun and all the objects that orbit it
9. Light element found in most of the outer planets
10. What is the study of the universe called? A S T R O N O M Y

90

were each embedded in a separate sphere that rotated around Earth. The stars were embedded in another sphere that also rotated around Earth. Early observers described moving objects in the night sky using the term planet, which means "to wander." This model is called the Earth-centered model of the solar system. To the astronomers who believed in this model of the solar system, there were seven planets. They were Mercury, Venus, the moon, the sun, Mars, Jupiter, and Saturn.

This idea of an Earth-centered solar system was held for centuries until the Polish
1 astronomer Nicholas Copernicus published a different view in 1543. Copernicus proposed that Earth was also a planet and that it, along with the other planets, revolved around the sun. He also stated that the movement of the planets and the stars was due to the rotation of Earth. This is the sun-centered model of the solar system.

Using his telescope, Galileo found evidence that supported the ideas of Copernicus. He did this by discovering that Venus went through phases like the moon's. These phases could only be explained if Venus and Earth were orbiting the sun. From this, he concluded that Venus revolves around the sun, and the sun is the center of the solar system.

We now know that Earth is one of nine planets and many smaller objects that orbit the sun, making up the
2 **solar system.** The nine planets and the sun, at right, are shown here at the correct scale. The dark areas on the sun are sunspots that you will learn about in Chapter 24. You can see how small Earth is compared to some of the other planets and the sun, which is much larger than any of the planets.

The solar system includes a vast territory extending billions of kilometers in all directions from the sun. If all the matter in the solar system, excluding the sun, were combined, it would make up less than one percent of the sun's total mass. The sun contains 99.86 percent of the mass of the whole solar system. Because of its gravitational pull, the sun is the central object around which other objects of the solar system revolve.

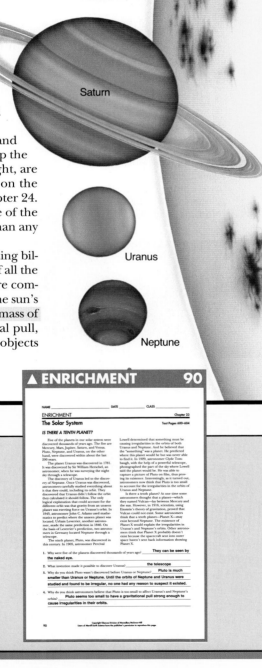

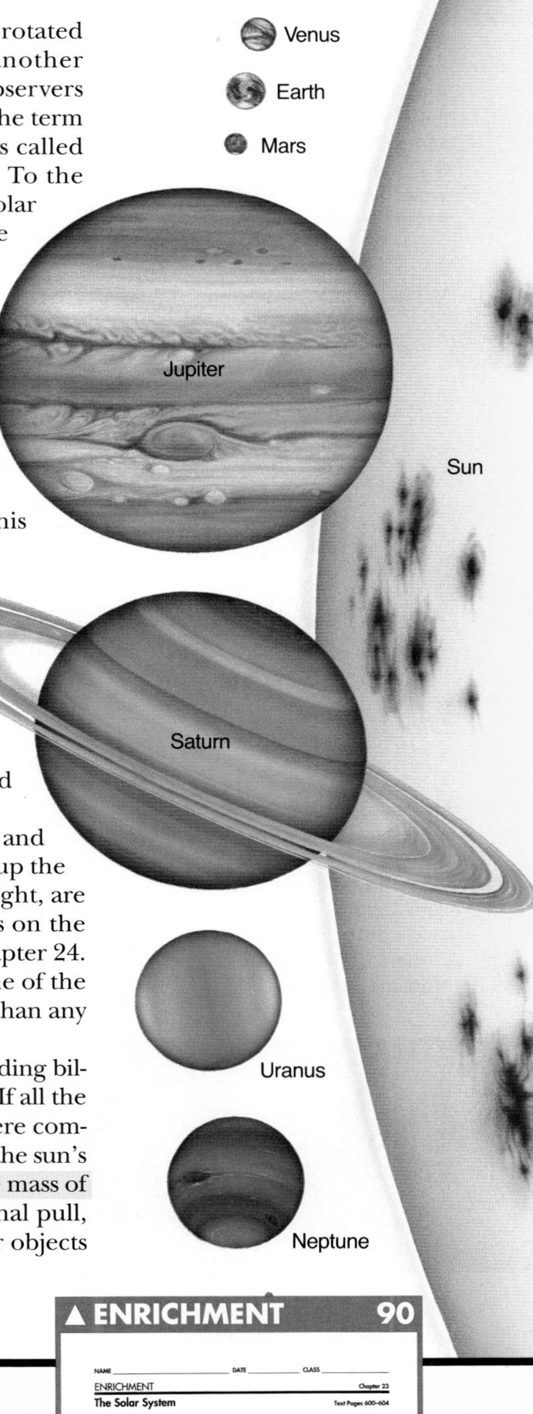

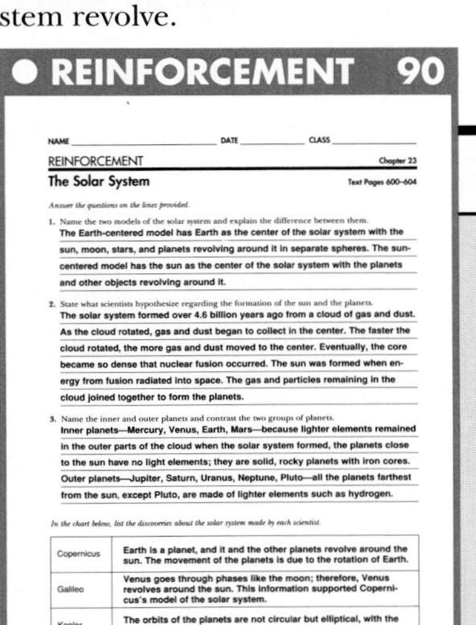

● REINFORCEMENT 90

NAME ________ DATE ________ CLASS ________

REINFORCEMENT — Chapter 23

The Solar System — Text Pages 600–604

Answer the questions on the lines provided.

1. Name the two models of the solar system and explain the difference between them.
The Earth-centered model has Earth as the center of the solar system with the sun, moon, stars, and planets revolving around it in separate spheres. The sun-centered model has the sun as the center of the solar system with the planets and other objects revolving around it.

2. State what scientists hypothesize regarding the formation of the sun and the planets.
The solar system formed over 4.6 billion years ago from a cloud of gas and dust. As the cloud rotated, gas and dust began to collect in the center. The faster the cloud rotated, the more gas and dust moved to the center. Eventually, the core became so dense that nuclear fusion occurred. The sun was formed when energy from fusion radiated into space. The gas and particles remaining in the cloud joined together to form the planets.

3. Name the inner and outer planets and contrast the two groups of planets.
Inner planets—Mercury, Venus, Earth, Mars—because lighter elements remained in the outer parts of the cloud when the solar system formed, the planets close to the sun have no light elements; they are solid, rocky planets with iron cores. Outer planets—Jupiter, Saturn, Uranus, Neptune, Pluto—all the planets farthest from the sun, except Pluto, are made of lighter elements such as hydrogen.

In the chart below, list the discoveries about the solar system made by each scientist.

Copernicus	Earth is a planet, and it and the other planets revolve around the sun. The movement of the planets is due to the rotation of Earth.
Galileo	Venus goes through phases like the moon; therefore, Venus revolves around the sun. This information supported Copernicus's model of the solar system.
Kepler	The orbits of the planets are not circular but elliptical, with the sun offset from the center.

90

▲ ENRICHMENT 90

NAME ________ DATE ________ CLASS ________

ENRICHMENT — Chapter 23

The Solar System — Text Pages 600–604

IS THERE A TENTH PLANET?

Five of the planets in our solar system were discovered thousands of years ago. The five are Mercury, Mars, Jupiter, Saturn, and Venus. Pluto, Neptune, and Uranus, on the other hand, were discovered within about the last 200 years.

The planet Uranus was discovered in 1781. It was discovered by Sir William Herschel, an astronomer, when he was surveying the night sky through a telescope.

The discovery of Uranus led to the discovery of Neptune. Once Uranus was discovered, astronomers carefully studied everything about it that they could, including its orbit. They discovered that Uranus didn't follow the orbit they calculated it should follow. The only logical explanation that could account for the different orbit was that gravity from an unseen planet was exerting force on Uranus's orbit. In 1843, astronomer John C. Adams used mathematics to predict where the unseen planet was located. Urbain Leverrier, another astronomer, made the same prediction in 1846. On the basis of Leverrier's prediction, two astronomers in Germany located Neptune through a telescope.

The ninth planet, Pluto, was discovered in this century. In 1905, astronomer Percival Lowell determined that something must be causing irregularities in the orbits of both Uranus and Neptune. And he believed that the "something" was a planet. He predicted where this planet would be but was never able to find it. In 1929, astronomer Clyde Tombaugh, with the help of a powerful telescope, photographed the part of the sky where Lowell said the planet would be. He was able to capture a picture of Pluto on film, thus proving its existence. Interestingly, as it turned out, astronomers now think that Pluto is too small to account for the irregularities in the orbits of Uranus and Neptune.

Is there a tenth planet? At one time some astronomers thought that a planet—which they named Vulcan—lay between Mercury and the sun. However, in 1916, scientists, using Einstein's theory of gravitation, proved that Vulcan could not exist. Some astronomers think that a tenth planet—Planet X—may exist beyond Neptune. The existence of Planet X would explain the irregularities in Uranus's and Neptune's orbits. Other astronomers think that Planet X probably doesn't exist because the spacecraft sent into outer space haven't sent back information showing Planet X.

1. Why were five of the planets discovered thousands of years ago? **They can be seen by the naked eye.**
2. What invention made it possible to discover Uranus? **the telescope**
3. Why do you think Pluto wasn't discovered before Uranus or Neptune? **Pluto is much smaller than Uranus or Neptune. Until the orbits of Neptune and Uranus were studied and found to be irregular, no one had any reason to suspect it existed.**
4. Why do you think astronomers believe that Pluto is too small to affect Uranus's and Neptune's orbits? **Pluto seems too small to have a gravitational pull strong enough to cause irregularities in their orbits.**

90

1 MOTIVATE

FLEX Your Brain

Use the Flex Your Brain activity to have students explore THE SUN-CENTERED AND EARTH-CENTERED MODELS OF THE SOLAR SYSTEM.

Cooperative Learning: Have Paired Partners make flash cards of the planets in the solar system. They can draw the planet on one side of the card and write anything they know about it on the other side. Students should keep their flash cards handy so they can correct or update their information as they read this chapter.

TYING TO PREVIOUS KNOWLEDGE: Have students recall from Chapter 22 that Earth rotates on its axis. Remind them that the "rising" and "setting" of the sun, moon, and stars are caused by this movement of Earth. Ask students to speculate why these same observations caused people long ago to think Earth was in the center of the solar system.

OBJECTIVES AND SCIENCE WORDS: Have students review the objectives and science words to become familiar with this section.

2 TEACH

Key Concepts are highlighted.

CONCEPT DEVELOPMENT

▶ Have volunteers compare and contrast the sun-centered solar system with the Earth-centered model by making sketches on the chalkboard.

▶ **What evidence was found that led to the sun-centered model of the solar system?** *Copernicus discovered that the movement of stars and planets as observed from Earth was due to Earth's rotation. Galileo discovered that Venus went through phases. Both discoveries led to the sun-centered model.*

CONCEPT DEVELOPMENT

▶ Ask students why an ice skater will pull his or her arms toward the body as he or she spins. Compare this increase in rotational speed to that of the cloud that formed the solar system, which spun more quickly as more material was pulled toward its center.

▶ **Demonstration:** Take students out into a long hallway. Inform them that you are going to use some of them to construct a model that shows the distances among the planets. Place one student as the sun at one end of the hallway. Choose a distance, based on the length of the hall, to represent one astronomical unit. Planetary distances from the sun are given in Appendix I. Position students to show how distances vary among the planets. Students should notice that the inner planets are clustered near the sun, while the distances among outer planets are much greater. You may wish to position other students here and there to represent comets, as well as several students between Mars and Jupiter to represent the asteroids.

PROGRAM RESOURCES

From the **Teacher Resource Package** use:

Concept Mapping, pages 51-52.

Cross-Curricular Connections, page 27, Solar System Scale Model.

Did You Know?

Mars has the largest volcano in the solar system. Olympus Mons is more than ten times larger than the Hawaiian volcano island of Mauna Loa. Mauna Loa is over 9 kilometers tall from its underwater base to its peak.

Formation of the Solar System

Scientists hypothesize that the sun and the solar system formed more than 4.6 billion years ago from a cloud of gas and dust. Gravitational forces acting on the cloud probably caused it to begin to contract. Initially, the cloud was rotating very slowly. But, as the density of the cloud became greater, increased gravity pulled more gas and dust into the cloud center. This caused the cloud to rotate faster, which in turn caused it to flatten into a disk.

What is fusion?

Eventually, the core of the cloud became so dense that nuclear fusion began. Fusion occurs when hydrogen atoms combine, forming helium. The new helium atom has less mass than that of the original hydrogen atoms. The lost mass is converted to energy. Once energy formed by fusion radiated into space, the cloud center formed into the sun.

Why are the inner planets solid and rocky?

Not all gas and dust was drawn into the core of the cloud. Remaining gas and dust particles combined, attracting more particles as they became larger. Because of the greater heat in the inner solar system, most of the elements with low atomic mass could not condense into solids. This accounts for the fact that planets close to the sun lack light elements and have formed into rocky
3 planets with iron cores.

The **inner planets,** Mercury, Venus, Earth, and Mars, are the solid, rocky planets closest to the sun. The **outer planets,** Jupiter, Saturn, Uranus, Neptune, and Pluto, are
4 those farthest from the sun and are made mostly of lighter elements such as hydrogen. You'll learn in Section 23-4, however, that Pluto is more like an inner planet.

Figure 23-2. This diagram shows the relative distances between the planets. Notice how relatively close the inner planets Mercury, Venus, Earth, and Mars (at left) are compared to the outer planets Jupiter, Saturn, Uranus, Neptune, and Pluto.

Motions of the Planets

When Nicholas Copernicus developed his sun-centered model of the solar system, he thought that the

OPTIONS

INQUIRY QUESTIONS

▶ **When the cloud that formed the solar system condensed, fusion began. Explain.** *Immense amounts of heat were generated inside the cloud, causing the hydrogen atoms to move very rapidly. The rapidly moving atoms collided and combined, or fused.*

▶ **What was Johannes Kepler's contribution to the sun-centered solar system model?** *He used mathematics to determine the shapes of the orbits and to calculate that the sun was not at the center of the elliptical paths.*

▶ **How do the planets' revolutions support the idea that the cloud that formed the solar system spun faster as it contracted?** *The inner planets revolve faster than the outer planets.*

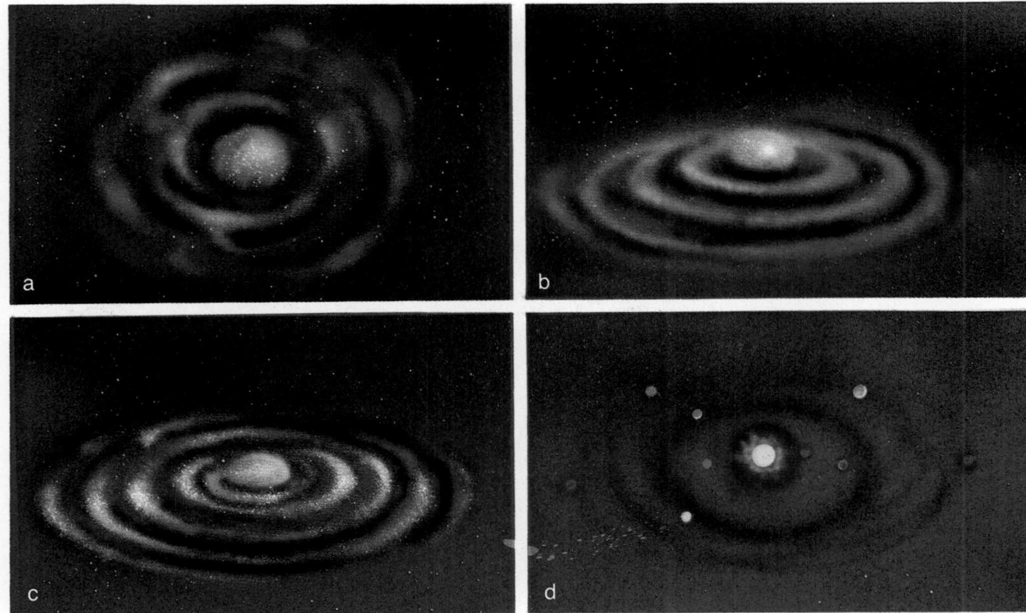

Figure 23-3. The solar system may have formed from a rotating cloud of gas and dust.

planets orbited the sun in circles. In the early 1600s, the German mathematician Johannes Kepler began studying the orbits of the planets. He discovered that the shapes of the orbits are not circular, but are elliptical. He also calculated that the sun is not at the center of the ellipse, but is offset from the center.

Kepler also discovered that the planets travel at different speeds in their orbits around the sun. The planets closer to the sun travel faster than planets farther away from the sun. Mercury orbits the sun at about 48 kilometers per second, whereas Neptune orbits the sun at about 5 kilometers per second. As a result, the outer planets take much longer to orbit the sun than the inner planets do.

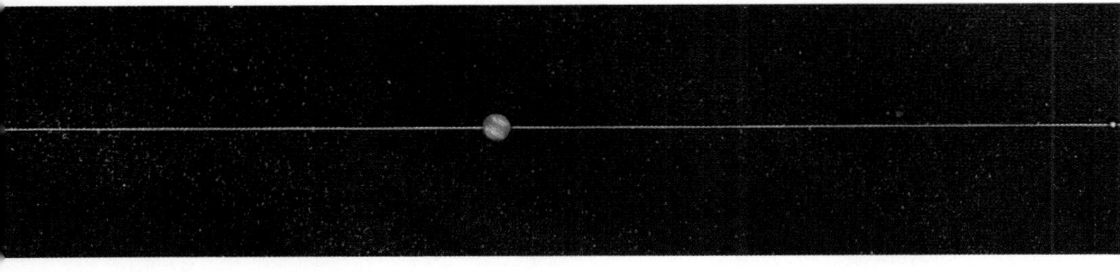

ENRICHMENT

▶ Have students find out about Kepler's three laws of planetary motion and the work done by Kepler that enabled him to devise the laws. They should also briefly explain what each law states about planetary motion.

PROGRAM RESOURCES

Use **Laboratory Manual** page 181, Newton's First Law of Motion.

CROSS CURRICULUM

▶ **Mathematics:** Have students calculate how many years it would take to travel from Earth's orbit to Mars' orbit, if they were traveling at 88 km/hr, the speed of a car. The average distance between the orbits is about 78 million km. The trip would take about 100 years.

REVEALING MISCONCEPTIONS

▶ Some students may still think that the sun and all other objects in the sky revolve around Earth. Explain that Earth's rotation on its axis causes the sun to "rise" and "set."

CHECK FOR UNDERSTANDING

Use the Mini Quiz to check for understanding.

MINI QUIZ

Use the Mini Quiz to check students' recall of chapter content.

1. **The _____ model of the solar system was proposed by Copernicus in 1543.** *sun-centered*
2. **The sun, nine planets, and many smaller objects make up the _____.** *solar system*
3. **The _____ planets are small and rocky and have iron cores.** *inner*
4. **The _____ planets are composed mostly of lighter elements.** *outer*

RETEACH

Have students compare and contrast labeled photographs or illustrations of the planets. Have students divide the planets into two groups based on size alone. Discuss where Pluto fits in this classification.

EXTENSION

For students who have mastered this section, use the **Reinforcement** and **Enrichment** masters or other OPTIONS provided.

TEACHER F.Y.I.

▶ Tycho Brahe maintained an observatory on an island near mainland Denmark. At this observatory, Brahe made some observations that proved very helpful to Kepler in his calculations of planetary orbits.

3 CLOSE

▶ Ask questions 1-3 and the **Apply** Question in the Section Review.

Cooperative Learning: Have Paired Partners work on the Skill Builder activity on this page.

FLEX Your Brain

Use the Flex Your Brain activity to have students explore one theory on THE FORMATION OF THE SOLAR SYSTEM.

SECTION REVIEW ANSWERS

1. In the sun-centered model, all objects orbit the sun, whereas in the Earth-centered model, the sun, planets, and other objects in the solar system orbit Earth.

2. More than 4.6 billion years ago, a large cloud of gas and dust began to condense. The center of the cloud formed the sun. The planets and other objects in the solar system formed from outer portions of the cloud.

3. Light elements did not condense near the sun because of the heat. They condensed and formed the gaseous planets in the outer solar system.

4. Apply: It would be longer because Uranus' orbit is much larger than Earth's. Eighty-four Earth years equal one Uranus year.

PROGRAM RESOURCES

From the **Teacher Resource Package** use:

Activity Worksheets, page 5, Flex Your Brain.

Figure 23-4. This device is an early model of the solar system.

Copernicus and his ideas, considered radical at the time, led to the birth of modern astronomy. Early scientists didn't have technology such as space probes to learn about the planets. Nevertheless, they discovered a great deal about our solar system and developed theories about the solar system that we use today.

SECTION REVIEW

1. What is the difference between the sun-centered and the Earth-centered models of the solar system?
2. How do scientists think the sun and the solar system formed?
3. Why are most of the outer planets made of lighter elements?
4. **Apply:** Would a year on the planet Uranus be longer or shorter than an Earth year?

Skill Builder — Concept Mapping

Make a concept map that compares and contrasts the Earth-centered universe with the sun-centered model. If you need help, refer to Concept Mapping in the **Skill Handbook** on pages 688 and 689.

Skill Builder

Possible Solution:

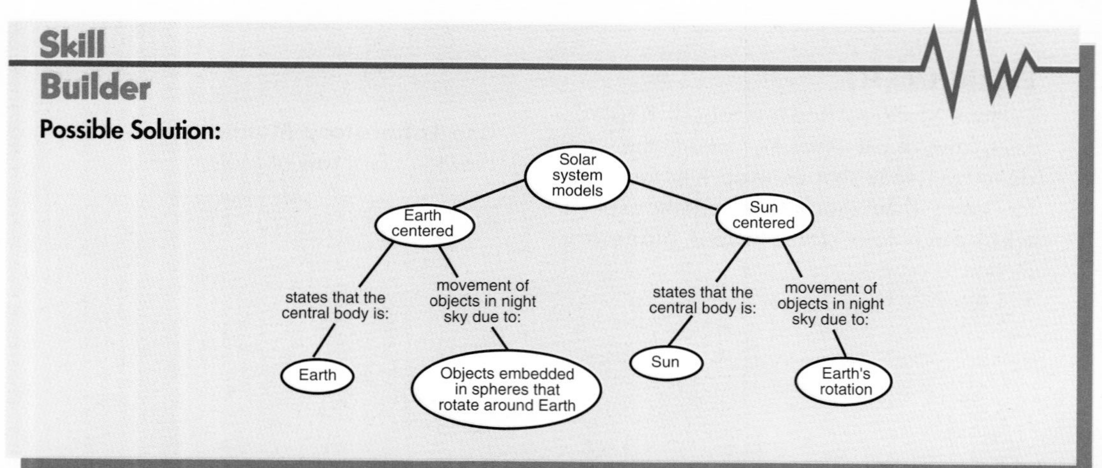

ACTIVITY 23-1
Planetary Orbits

Problem: *What is the most accurate model of the shape of a planet's orbit around the sun?*

Materials 

- thumbtacks or pins
- string
- cardboard (21.5 cm × 28 cm)
- metric ruler
- pencil
- paper

Procedure

Part A

1. Place a blank sheet of paper on top of the cardboard and place two thumbtacks or pins about 3 cm apart.
2. Tie the string into a circle with a circumference of 15 to 20 cm. Loop the string around the thumbtacks. With someone holding the tacks or pins, place your pencil inside the loop and pull it taut.

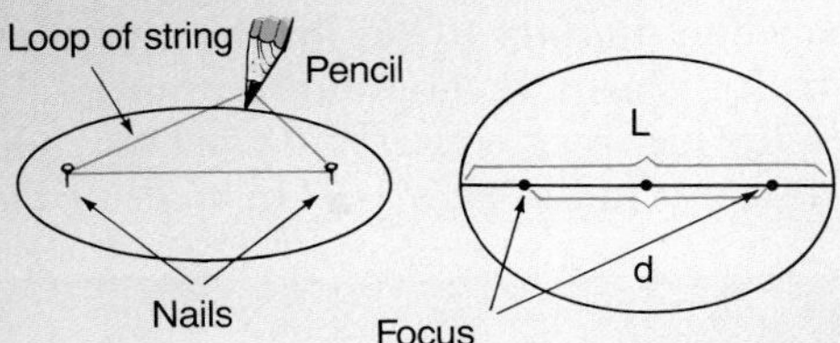

3. Move the pen or pencil around the tacks, keeping the string taut, until you have completed a smooth, closed curve or an ellipse.
4. Repeat Steps 1 through 3 several times. First vary the distance between the tacks and then vary the circumference of the string. However, change only one of these each time. Note the effect on the size and shape of the ellipse with each of these changes.
5. Orbits are usually described in terms of eccentricity (e). The eccentricity of any ellipse is determined by dividing the distance (d) between the foci (here, the tacks) by the length of the major axis (L). See the diagram above.
6. Calculate and record the eccentricity of the ellipses that you constructed.

Part B

7. Refer to Appendix I to determine the eccentricities of planetary orbits.
8. Construct an ellipse with the same eccentricity as Earth's orbit.
9. Repeat Step 8 with the orbit of either Pluto or Mercury.

Data and Observations Sample Data

Constructed Ellipse	d (cm)	L (cm)	e (d/L)
#1	3	15.6	0.19
#2	5	13.5	0.37
#3	5	8.7	0.57
Earth's orbit	.48	28	.017
Mercury's orbit			.206
Pluto's orbit			.248

Analyze

1. What effect does a change in the length of the string or the distance between the tacks have on the shape of the ellipse?
2. What must be done to the string or placement of tacks to decrease the eccentricity of a constructed ellipse?

Conclude and Apply

3. Describe the shape of Earth's orbit. Where is the sun located within the orbit?
4. Name the planets that have the most eccentric orbits.

ACTIVITY 23-1
40 minutes

OBJECTIVE: Describe a model that best represents the shape of planetary orbits.

PROCESS SKILLS applied in this activity:
▶ **Measuring** in Procedure Steps 1 and 2.
▶ **Inferring** in Analyze Question 2 and Conclude and Apply Questions 3 and 4.
▶ **Using Numbers** in Procedure Steps 5, 6, 8, and 9.
▶ **Interpreting Data** in Analyze Question 1.
▶ **Separating and Controlling Variables** in Procedure Step 4.

TEACHING THE ACTIVITY

▶ Although thumbtacks are easier for students to control, hat pins are excellent for this activity, since they allow students to observe all parts of the taut string. Time can be saved by having a number of pieces of string already tied in loops of varied sizes.

▶ Provide students with several values for d and L for imaginary ellipses and allow them to solve for e.

Troubleshooting: If students have any problem with the equation $e = d/L$, show them how $3 = 6/2$ or $3 = 12/4$ relates to it. Some students may become frustrated in attempting to construct an ellipse with Earth's orbital eccentricity of 0.017, thinking it impossible. If so, discuss with them the answers to Analyze Questions 1 and 2, and then apply their answers to this task.

PROGRAM RESOURCES

From the **Teacher Resource Package** use:

Activity Worksheets, pages 207-208, Activity 23-1:Planetary Orbits.

ANSWERS TO QUESTIONS

1. Increasing the length of the string or decreasing the distance between the tacks makes the ellipse more circular. Decreasing the string's length or increasing the distance between foci makes the shape more elliptical.
2. Lengthen the string or move the tacks closer to each other.
3. It appears to be circular with the sun near one of the foci.
4. Pluto (0.247), Mercury (0.206), and Mars (0.093)

SECTION 23-2

PREPARATION

SECTION BACKGROUND

▶ Carbon dioxide dissolves in water, therefore much of the carbon dioxide in Earth's atmosphere has been removed by rain. If it weren't for the presence of liquid water on Earth, the amount of carbon dioxide in the air would be similar to that in Venus' atmosphere, causing a tremendous increase in the greenhouse effect on Earth.

▶ All planets except Earth can be classified as inferior or superior. Inferior planets, Mercury and Venus, have orbits that are inside Earth's orbit. Superior planets have orbits that lie outside Earth's orbit. These include Mars, Jupiter, Saturn, Uranus, Neptune, and Pluto.

1 MOTIVATE

FLEX Your Brain

Use the Flex Your Brain activity to have students explore THE INNER PLANETS.

▶ Have students make up sentences that allow them to remember the planets in their order from the sun. For example, *my very exceptional mother just served us nutritious pizza*.

TYING TO PREVIOUS KNOWLEDGE: Have students recall from Chapter 21 that much of what we know about the solar system has been sent back to Earth by space probes.

OBJECTIVES AND SCIENCE WORDS: Have students review the objectives and science words to become familiar with this section.

PROGRAM RESOURCES

From the **Teacher Resource Package** use:

Activity Worksheets, page 5 Flex Your Brain.

23-2 The Inner Planets

New Science Words

Mercury
Venus
Earth
astronomical unit
Mars

Objectives

- ▶ List the inner planets in their relative order from the sun.
- ▶ Identify important characteristics of each inner planet.
- ▶ Compare and contrast Venus and Earth.

Inner Planets

We know much more about the solar system since the days of Copernicus and Galileo. Advancements in telescopes have allowed us to observe the planets from Earth. And space probes have explored much of our solar system, obtaining much of the knowledge we have about the planets. Let's take a tour of the solar system through the "eyes" of the space probes.

Mercury

Which planet is closest to the sun?

1 The closest planet to the sun is **Mercury.** It's also the second smallest planet. Our first close look at Mercury came in 1974, when *Mariner 10* flew by the planet and sent pictures back to Earth, as shown in Figure 23-5. The surface of Mercury has many craters and looks much like our moon. It also has cliffs as high as 3 km on its surface.

Figure 23-5. Mercury looks very much like Earth's moon.

OPTIONS

Meeting Different Ability Levels

For Section 23-2, use the following **Teacher Resource Masters** depending upon individual students' needs.

◆ **Study Guide Master** for all students.

● **Reinforcement Master** for students of average and above average ability levels.

▲ **Enrichment Master** for above average students.

Additional Teacher Resource Package masters are listed in the OPTIONS box throughout the section. The additional masters are appropriate for all students.

◆ STUDY GUIDE 91

NAME ____ DATE ____ CLASS ____

STUDY GUIDE — Chapter 23

The Inner Planets — Text Pages 606-609

In the blank at the left, write the letter of the term or phrase that correctly completes each statement.

b 1. Mars is the ____ planet outward from the sun.
a. third b. fourth

b 2. Because of similar size and mass, ____ is called Earth's twin.
a. Mars b. Venus

a 3. ____ has great extremes in temperature –450°C during the day and –170°C at night.
a. Mercury b. Mars

b 4. Venus is the ____ planet outward from the sun.
a. fourth b. second

a 5. The ____ space probes made many discoveries about Mars.
a. *Viking* b. *Mariner*

b 6. The atmosphere of ____ is mostly carbon dioxide.
a. Mercury b. Venus

b 7. The largest volcano in the solar system is ____ on Mars.
a. *Valles Marineras* b. *Olympus Mons*

a 8. One astronomical unit (AU) is equal to the average distance between the sun and ____.
a. Earth b. Mercury

a 9. One astronomical unit (AU) equals ____.
a. 150 million km b. 15 million km

b 10. Water exists as a solid, liquid, and gas on ____.
a. Mercury b. Earth

a 11. Polar ice caps are a visible feature of ____.
a. Mars b. Venus

b 12. Mars appears red because of ____ in its rocks.
a. sulfuric acid b. iron oxide

b 13. ____ is the third planet outward from the sun.
a. Venus b. Earth

a 14. ____ is the larger of Mars's two moons.
a. Phobos b. Deimos

a 15. The ____ space probe mapped the surface of Venus.
a. *Magellan* b. *Mariner*

91

PROBLEM SOLVING

The Hotter It Gets???

Carol and Salvatore were pretending to be a part of an astronaut team whose next mission was to land on the surface of one of the inner planets. In researching information about the surface conditions that they might expect to find on the inner planets, Carol and Sal were surprised to note that Mercury, which is the closest planet to the sun, does not have the highest average surface temperature. Venus, shown at right, which is almost twice as far from the sun, averages higher surface temperatures.

Think Critically: How can you explain this fact?

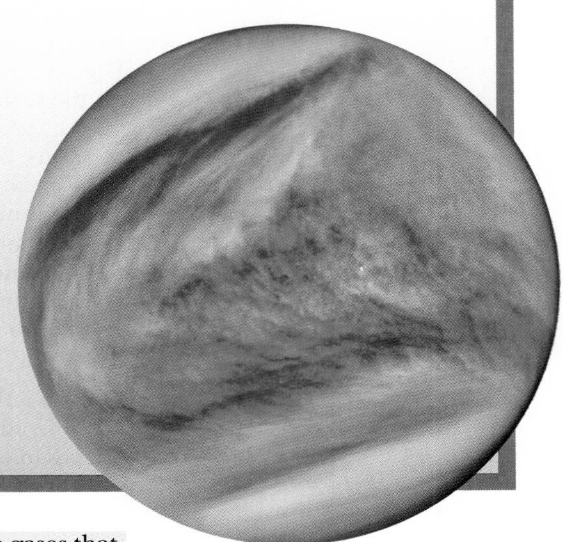

Because of a low force of gravity, most of the gases that could form an atmosphere have escaped the planet into space. Mercury has a very thin atmosphere composed mostly of sodium, helium, potassium, and hydrogen. Because it has almost no atmosphere and is very close to the sun, Mercury has great extremes in temperature. Because Mercury is a relatively dark object, it does not reflect much of the sunlight falling on it. Mercury's surface can reach temperatures of 450°C during the day—hot enough to melt lead. The very thin atmosphere allows heat to escape the surface rapidly and temperatures drop to −170°C at night.

Why does Mercury have great extremes in temperature?

Venus

The second planet outward from the sun is **Venus.** Venus is sometimes called Earth's twin because its size and mass are very similar to Earth's. One major difference is that the entire surface of Venus is blanketed by an atmosphere of dense clouds. The atmosphere of Venus, which has 90 times the pressure of Earth's, is mostly carbon dioxide. The clouds in the atmosphere contain droplets of sulfuric acid which give the clouds a slightly yellow color. 

● REINFORCEMENT 91

NAME ____________ DATE ________ CLASS ________

REINFORCEMENT — Chapter 23

The Inner Planets — Text Pages 606–609

Write the names of the inner planets as headings in the chart in the order of their position from the sun. Then fill in the chart using information from your textbook.

	1 Mercury	2 Venus	3 Earth	4 Mars
Size and composition	small, solid, rocky	small, solid, rocky	small, solid, rocky	small, solid, rocky with iron oxide
Atmosphere	thin; oxygen, sodium, helium, other gases—gases escape into space	dense clouds of mostly carbon dioxide, droplets of sulfuric acid	nitrogen, oxygen, other gases	
Temperatures	great extremes 450°C in day −170°C at night	greenhouse effect, 470°C	allow water to exist as solid, liquid, and gas	
Surface features	craters, high cliffs, moonlike surface	craters, cracks, volcanoes with lava flows	oceans, land masses, polar ice caps	red rocks, rifts, craters, channels, volcanoes, polar ice caps
Moons (number/names)			1	2 Phobos, Deimos
Space probes/ year(s)	*Mariner 10* 1974	*Venera* 1970 *Magellan* 1990		*Viking 1 and 2* 1976

91

▲ ENRICHMENT 91

NAME ____________ DATE ________ CLASS ________

ENRICHMENT — Chapter 23

The Inner Planets — Text Pages 606–609

VIEWS OF VENUS

The figure below shows the positions of Venus in its orbit in relation to an Earth position. Study the views of the sun and Venus in our sky and the phases of Venus below. Match the position of Venus in its orbit with the view in our sky. Write the matching letter in the blank below each telescope image of Venus.

View from north of Earth and Venus orbits
A B C D E
Venus orbit
Earth orbit

Venus — Western horizon — Telescope image of Venus: C
Venus — Western horizon — B
Venus — Western horizon — D
Venus — Eastern horizon — A
Venus — Eastern horizon — E

1. Why does Venus's shape appear to change for different phases in its orbit? **When Venus is on the opposite side of the sun, the sunlit side of Venus faces Earth. When Venus is on the nearside of Earth, the sunlit side of Venus faces the sun. As Venus orbits, either more or less light is visible on Earth, depending on Venus's position.**

2. Describe the view of Venus from Earth when Venus forms a right angle with the sun and Earth. **Venus is in a quarter phase—the sunlight makes a straight rather than curved line on Venus.**

91

PROBLEM SOLVING

Think Critically: The thick atmosphere of Venus absorbs solar energy and prevents it from rapidly radiating back into space. Mercury, which has little atmospheric gas, loses energy rapidly from its surface. Even though Venus is farther from the sun than Mercury, its atmosphere holds and circulates solar energy to a much greater extent. This creates a higher average surface temperature on Venus.

2 TEACH

Key Concepts are highlighted.

CONCEPT DEVELOPMENT

Cooperative Learning: Have Paired Partners use Appendix I to compare and contrast the sizes of the inner planets. Then have them draw each planet to scale on a sheet of paper.

PROGRAM RESOURCES

Use **Laboratory Manual,** page 183, Venus—The Greenhouse Effect.

CONCEPT DEVELOPMENT

Cooperative Learning: Have four Problem Solving Teams devise advertisement packages intended to entice people to travel to one of the inner planets. Encourage students to create posters, slogans, and songs to promote their planet. Call on students from each group to share their advertisements with the class.

CROSS CURRICULUM

▶ **Mathematics:** Have students compute the volumes of the inner planets using the equation: $V = 0.17\pi d^3$, where V is volume and d is diameter.

CHECK FOR UNDERSTANDING

Use the Mini Quiz to check for understanding.

MINI QUIZ

Use the Mini Quiz to check students' recall of chapter content.

1. **Which planet is closest to the sun?** *Mercury*
2. **Which planet is considered to be Earth's twin?** *Venus*
3. **What did detailed maps of Venus' surface reveal?** *Venus' surface has huge craters, faultlike cracks, and volcanoes.*
4. **What is an AU?** *the average distance from Earth to the sun*
5. **_____ is the red planet.** *Mars*

RETEACH

Show the filmstrip program, *Exploration of the Universe, Inner Planets,* available from the National Geographic Society, Washington, DC.

EXTENSION

For students who have mastered this section, use the **Reinforcement** and **Enrichment** masters or other OPTIONS provided.

Why does Venus have a greenhouse effect?

Clouds on Venus are so dense that only two percent of the sunlight that strikes the top of the clouds reaches the planet's surface. This solar energy is trapped by the carbon dioxide gas and causes a greenhouse effect similar to Earth's greenhouse effect you read about in Chapter 10. Due to this intense greenhouse effect, the temperature on the surface of Venus is 470°C.

The former Soviet Union has led in the exploration of Venus. Beginning in 1970 with the first *Venera* probe, the Russians have photographed and mapped the surface of Venus using radar. But in 1990, the United States' *Magellan* probe began using its radar to make the most
3 detailed maps yet of the surface of Venus. *Magellan* revealed huge craters, faultlike cracks, and volcanoes with visible lava flows.

Earth

Earth is the third planet from the sun. The average distance from Earth to the sun is 150 million km, or one
4 **astronomical unit** (AU). Astronomical units are used to measure distances to objects in the solar system. Surface temperatures on Earth allow water to exist as a solid, liquid, and gas.

Mars

Mars is the fourth planet from the sun. It's referred to
5 as the red planet because iron oxide in the weathered rocks on its surface gives it a reddish color. Mars actually appears red from Earth. Other features of Mars visible

Figure 23-6. Like Earth, Mars has ice caps at both poles.

OPTIONS

INQUIRY QUESTIONS

▶ **What do radar images of Venus gathered by the *Magellan* space probe indicate about the planet's history?** *The craters on Venus indicate that it has been hit by large space objects. The planet was geologically active at some time in its past, as shown by the volcanoes and faultlike cracks.*

▶ **Why isn't Earth's surface marked by large numbers of craters like the surfaces of Mars and Mercury?** *Water on Earth's surface, along with other agents, is constantly eroding the surface. Moving wind, water, and ice may have "erased" the ancient craters.*

▶ **If oxygen ever did exist in the Martian atmosphere, where might it be now?** *The oxygen might have combined with iron in the rocks of Mars' surface to form the red iron oxide surface visible from Earth.*

from Earth are its polar ice caps which get larger during the Martian winter and shrink during the summer.

Most of the information we now have about Mars came from the *Viking* probes. *Viking 1* and *2* landed on Mars in 1976. The *Viking* probes sent back pictures of a reddish-colored, barren, rocky, and windswept surface. Mars also has many craters.

The *Viking* probes also discovered long channels on the planet that look like they were carved by flowing water at some time in Mars' past. Also discovered was the largest volcano in the solar system, Olympus Mons. Large rift zones have formed in the Martian crust. One such rift, Valles Marineras, is more than 4000 km long, up to 240 km wide in places, and more than 6 km deep.

Viking probes also discovered that Mars has ice caps at the north and south poles that change with the seasons. The southern polar ice cap changes little with the seasons and is made mostly of frozen carbon dioxide. The northern polar ice cap is much smaller in the summer and is made of water ice. Frozen carbon dioxide accumulates in the winter, enlarging the ice cap.

Mars has two small moons, both of which are highly cratered. Phobos is only 25 km in diameter and Deimos is 13 km in diameter.

As you toured the inner planets using the "eye" of the space probes, you saw how each planet is unique. Mercury, Venus, Earth, and Mars are quite different from the outer planets that you'll tour in the next section.

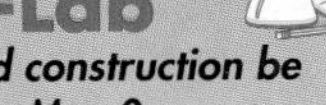

MINI-Lab

How would construction be different on Mars?

Suppose you are a crane operator who is sent to Mars to help build a Mars colony. You know that your crane can lift 44 500 newtons on Earth, but the gravity of Mars is only 0.4 of Earth's gravity. How much mass could your crane lift on Mars? How could this be an advantage over construction on Earth?

Why does Mars' northern ice cap get bigger in the winter?

SECTION REVIEW

1. List the inner planets in order from the sun.
2. How are Mercury and Earth's moon similar?
3. Why is Venus called Earth's twin?
4. List one important characteristic for each inner planet.
5. **Apply:** Why is the surface temperature of Venus higher than Mercury's, even though Mercury is closer to the sun?

Interpreting Data — Skill Builder

Using the information given, explain how Mars is like Earth. If you need help, refer to Interpreting Data in the **Skill Handbook** on page 687.

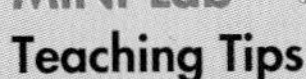

MINI-Lab

Teaching Tips

▶ Remind students that force equals the mass times the gravitational constant: F = mg.

▶ Earth's gravitational constant, g, is 9.8 m/s^2. Thus, Mars' gravitational constant is 0.4 times 9.8 m/s^2 or 3.92 m/s^2.

Answers:

$F_e = mg_e$

$m = 44\,500 \text{ N}/9.8 \text{ m/s}^2$

$= 4540$ kg on Earth

$F_m = mg_m$

$m = 44\,500 \text{ N}/3.92 \text{ m/s}^2$

$= 11\,352$ kg on Mars

The crane could lift more material on Mars and thus speed up construction.

3 CLOSE

▶ Ask questions 1-4 and the **Apply** Question in the Section Review.

SECTION REVIEW ANSWERS

1. Mercury, Venus, Earth, Mars

2. The surfaces of both are very heavily cratered. The amount of light reflected from both objects is low because of the dark-colored surfaces.

3. Venus and Earth are similar in size, mass, and shape.

4. Answers might include that Mercury is heavily cratered; Venus has a dense cloud cover; water exists on Earth in three states; and Mars appears red due to the iron oxide on its surface.

5. Apply: Venus' dense atmosphere traps heat, causing a tremendous greenhouse effect. Because of this, Venus' surface temperature is greater than Mercury's even though Mercury is closer to the sun.

Skill Builder

Answers should include that both are inner planets. The processes of volcanism and weathering helped to form each planet. Both have polar ice caps.

ENRICHMENT

▶ Have students research the discoveries made by the *Magellan* space probe as it orbited Venus.

▶ Have students contact NASA for publications that review the *Mariner 10* space probe to Mercury, the *Pioneer Venus* space probe to Venus, and the *Viking* space probe missions to Mars. Have them prepare brief written summaries of each probe's accomplishments.

PROGRAM RESOURCES

From the **Teacher Resource Package** use:

Activity Worksheets, page 213, Mini-Lab: How would construction be different on Mars?

SECTION 23-3

PREPARATION

SECTION BACKGROUND

▶Data gloves and Eye Phones allow the user not to interface with a situation, but rather to be included within the made-up environment.

1 MOTIVATE

FLEX Your Brain

Use the Flex Your Brain activity to have students explore A TRIP TO MARS.

▶Have students design a spacecraft that would take humans to Mars.

TYING TO PREVIOUS KNOWLEDGE: Have students recall from Chapter 21 the achievements and problems experienced by former Soviet cosmonauts aboard their space station.

OBJECTIVES AND SCIENCE WORDS: Have students review the objectives and science words to become familiar with this section.

2 TEACH

Key Concepts are highlighted.

CONCEPT DEVELOPMENT

▶Have each student draw a model of a robot that could move around and work on Mars. Ask them to explain how their robots would be controlled.

PROGRAM RESOURCES

From the **Teacher Resource Package** use:

Activity Worksheets, page 5, Flex Your Brain.

Science and Society, page 27, To Mars or Not?

SCIENCE & SOCIETY 23-3 Mission to Mars

New Science Words

data gloves

Objectives

- ▶ Recognize problems that astronauts will encounter during a trip to Mars.
- ▶ Decide if a crewed mission to Mars is necessary.

Who Should Explore Mars—Humans or Robots?

You learned about exploring space in Chapter 21. Scientists are currently developing plans to further explore Mars. Because Mars is 55 million kilometers at the closest, it will take about three years to get to Mars and back. Because of the long duration of the flight, astronauts would face much more danger than they currently do in space shuttle missions.

Because of the near zero gravity in outer space, bones lose calcium and weaken. Bones might fracture more easily once astronauts land on Mars or return to Earth. Also, muscles get weak because they don't have to hold the body up as they do under Earth's gravity.

In addition to these problems, body fluids move upward because no gravity is pulling them down. The movement of fluids could signal the kidneys to excrete more fluids, causing dehydration. Also, astronauts will be exposed to more radiation from the sun than during space shuttle flights.

Some scientists are suggesting that advanced robots being developed can be used to explore Mars instead of humans. They say that robots could operate equipment, build space stations, make repairs, or carry out scientific experiments in space or on Mars.

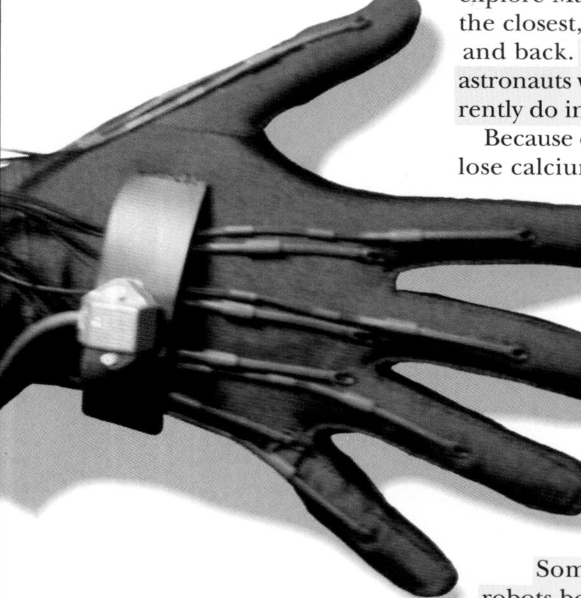

Figure 23-7. Fiber-optic sensors in data gloves transfer the movement of the operator to a robot.

This new technology uses video and artificial touch sense. The artificial senses of the robot are connected to the real senses of a human. The robot has video cameras

OPTIONS

Meeting Different Ability Levels

For Section 23-3, use the following **Teacher Resource Masters** depending upon individual students' needs.

◆ **Study Guide Master** for all students.

● **Reinforcement Master** for students of average and above average ability levels.

▲ **Enrichment Master** for above average students.

Additional Teacher Resource Package masters are listed in the OPTIONS box throughout the section. The additional masters are appropriate for all students.

◆ STUDY GUIDE 92

NAME ______ DATE ______ CLASS ______

STUDY GUIDE Chapter 23

Mission To Mars Text Pages 610-611

Determine whether each of the following statements is true or false. Write the word "true" or "false" in the blank. If the statement is false, rewrite it so that it's true.

false 1. Only humans can carry out scientific experiments on Mars. **Robots might also carry out scientific experiments on Mars.**

true 2. The near zero gravity in space can cause human bones to lose calcium, weaken, and break more easily.

false 3. Human muscles are not affected by the lack of gravity in space. **Human muscles are weakened by the lack of gravity in space.**

false 4. It would take about three months to get to Mars and back. **It would take about three years to get to Mars and back.**

true 5. A robot's hands are controlled by sensors connected to data gloves worn by a human operator.

true 6. A robot "sees" with tiny video cameras.

false 7. Radio signals travel from Earth to Mars in a few seconds. **Radio signals travel from Earth to Mars in 20 minutes.**

false 8. Scientists have already developed robots with sufficient artificial intelligence to work on Mars. **Scientists haven't yet developed robots with sufficient artificial intelligence to work on Mars.**

true 9. Because of the long flight to Mars, humans would face more danger than they do on current missions.

true 10. Body fluids move upward because there's no gravity to pull them down.

92

Figure 23-8. "Eye Phones" contain small video screens that are worn as goggles.

for eyes and special touch sensors in its limbs. The human operator looks at tiny video screens worn as goggles and sees exactly what the robot sees. **Data gloves** worn by the operator have sensors connected to the robot's hands. Any movement performed by the operator is duplicated by the robot's hands.

One problem facing the robot technology is the long distance from Earth to Mars. Radio signals from the operator to a robot on Mars would take about 20 minutes—too long to be practical. Researchers would like to develop the robot technology for use on the moon or on a space station at first, then work on developing artificial intelligence for robots on Mars. A robot with artificial intelligence would be programmed to do a task and would have some ability to "think" on its own.

How might scientists deal with the problems of delayed radio signals to robots on Mars?

SECTION REVIEW

1. What are two problems astronauts will experience during extended space travel?
2. How could we benefit from a crewed mission to Mars?

You Decide!

Even with the drawback of crewed flight to Mars, scientists think that humans should go because of the challenge of human exploration. Also, humans might find more clues about the formation of the solar system and life on other planets. Should astronauts or robots explore Mars?

● REINFORCEMENT 92

NAME ______ DATE ______ CLASS ______

REINFORCEMENT — Chapter 23

Mission to Mars — Text Pages 610–611

Answer the questions on the lines provided.

1. How far away is Mars from Earth? **55 million kilometers** How long would it take to travel from Earth to Mars and back? **three years**
2. How could the near zero gravity in space affect astronauts' bones? **Their bones would lose calcium and weaken. Then the bones would fracture more easily when the astronauts returned to Earth.**
   Their muscles? **Their muscles would become weak because in space they didn't have to work to hold the body up against gravity as they do on Earth.**
   Their body fluids? **Their body fluids would move upward. This might cause the kidneys to excrete more fluids, which would lead to dehydration.**
3. Why would astronauts be exposed to more radiation from the sun? **Out in space they wouldn't be shielded from some of the radiation by the gases in Earth's atmosphere. Also, because the trip would take longer than a shuttle flight, they would be exposed to radiation for a longer period of time.**
4. How are robots controlled by human operators? **The human operators control the robots using video cameras and sensors. The operators "see" through the video cameras that are the robots' eyes. Using data gloves which are connected to sensors in the robots' hands, the operators can control the robots' movements .**
5. What could robots do on Mars? **Scientists suggest that robots could carry out scientific experiments, operate equipment, build space stations, and make repairs—virtually anything that humans can do.**
6. Why is current robot technology not practical for use on Mars? **The radio signals that an operator uses to control a robot take too long—20 minutes—to travel from Earth to Mars.**
7. What are the advantages and disadvantages of sending a human-crewed mission to Mars? **Disadvantages—major dangers to the humans' health and safety, which could be avoided by sending robots instead of humans; Advantages—the greater amount of information that humans could probably find out on the mission and the challenge that humans find in the exploration of new frontiers**

92

▲ ENRICHMENT 92

NAME ______ DATE ______ CLASS ______

ENRICHMENT — Chapter 23

Mission to Mars — Text Pages 610–611

A MARS COLONY?

Sometime in the future, maybe within the next century, humans may establish a colony on Mars. What do you think a colony on Mars would be like? Read the following information about Mars and then answer the questions.

Mars, one of Earth's nearest neighbors, has been the focus of speculation for years. Even now, with all the information that the *Viking* probes provided about Mars, the question of whether there is life on Mars is still unanswered. It's possible that although there's no life now on Mars, there was life there in the past. Where there was life once, scientists theorize, there's the possibility of life again. Mars once had a thicker atmosphere, its temperatures were warmer, and it had water on its surface. Scientists think these things existed on Mars at about the same time that life began on Earth. Thus, some forms of life may have also evolved on Mars. They may have later disappeared when conditions changed and would no longer support life. At the very least, the *Viking* probes showed that Mars, while not a livable place for humans, does have the basic components available to sustain life.

Mars's atmosphere is 95 percent carbon dioxide with some nitrogen and water vapor. The planet is very cold, with an average temperature of −50°C, which varies depending on season and location. Mars is cold not only because it is farther from the sun, but because the thin atmosphere does not help retain heat. In an atmosphere as cold as that of Mars, ice evaporates into a gas without turning into a liquid. Mars is very dry. It's drier than Earth's driest desert. But it does have some water frozen in its polar ice caps. (As you read in the chapter, the northern polar ice cap contains much more water than the southern polar ice cap.) It possibly has permafrost, or layers of frozen soil below the surface. Large areas of Mars are covered with reddish, fine-grained soil. Its canyons, dry river beds, and lava flows may bring to mind the landscape of the southwestern United States. The region near the equator has giant volcanoes. Tremendous dust storms occur in the southern hemisphere.

Because Mars has a smaller mass than Earth, its gravity is three eighths as strong as Earth's. A day on Mars lasts about as long as a day on Earth. But a year on Mars lasts twice as long as a year on Earth. Mars is slightly tilted on its rotational axis. This means, as it does on Earth, that its poles get varying amounts of sunlight and that Mars has seasons. Each season, though, lasts twice as long as a season on Earth.

1. Approximately how many hours does it take for Mars to complete one rotation? **24 hours**
2. If an object weighs 40 newtons on Earth, how much would it weigh on Mars? **15 newtons**
3. The polar caps on Mars, especially the northern polar cap, grow larger or get smaller, depending on the time of year in Mars. Why do you think that is? **Because Mars is tilted on its axis, the poles are tilted toward or away from the sun, depending on the season. When a pole is tilted toward the sun, the sun causes some of the ice cap to evaporate. The opposite process occurs when the pole is tilted away from the sun.**

92

Cooperative Learning: Form Numbered Heads Together groups of four students per group. Have students compile lists of tasks a robot with artificial intelligence might perform on a Mars mission.

CHECK FOR UNDERSTANDING

Have students hypothesize how robots on Mars could be controlled from Earth.

RETEACH

Refer to "Telepresence," by Grant Fjermedal, *Final Frontier,* July/August 1990. Show students pictures of the data gloves and visual sensors used to operate robots. Ask students to speculate on other ways this equipment could be used.

EXTENSION

For students who have mastered this section, use the **Reinforcement** and **Enrichment** masters or other OPTIONS provided.

3 CLOSE

▶Ask questions 1-2 in the Section Review.

▶Have students list and discuss advantages and disadvantages of using robots rather than humans on a mission to Mars.

SECTION REVIEW ANSWERS

1. Answers may include that bones lose calcium, muscles become weak, and body fluids shift upward causing dehydration.

2. Humans can make judgments about what is being observed. They can change the mission if there is a need. Humans might also be able to find clues about the formation of the solar system or life on other planets.

YOU DECIDE!

Make sure students support their choices with facts.

SECTION 23-4

PREPARATION

SECTION BACKGROUND

▶ Not counting the sun, Jupiter contains 99 percent of the solar system's mass.

▶ Jupiter, Saturn, and Neptune all radiate more energy than they receive from the sun because of internal heat sources.

▶ Uranus doesn't appear to have an internal heat source. Some scientists believe a collision with another object may have turned Uranus on its side and destroyed its heat source.

▶ Pluto is very different from the other outer planets. Hypotheses suggest that it may not have formed in the orbit it now occupies and that it may have been a moon of Uranus or Neptune.

PREPLANNING

▶ To prepare for Activity 23-2, obtain adding machine tape, a meterstick, and scissors for each group of students.

1 MOTIVATE

FLEX Your Brain

Use the Flex Your Brain activity to have students explore CHARACTERISTICS OF THE OUTER PLANETS.

▶ If you didn't show the video program *Sail On, Voyager!* from the Infinite Voyage Home Video Library while teaching Chapter 21, show it now. It is available from Inovision, P.O. Box 576, Itasca, IL 60143-0576 or by calling 1-800-523-5503. This video presents an overview of the *Voyager* program.

PROGRAM RESOURCES

From the **Teacher Resource Package** use:

Activity Worksheets, page 5, Flex Your Brain.

23-4 The Outer Planets

New Science Words

Jupiter
Great Red Spot
Saturn
Uranus
Neptune
Pluto

Objectives

▶ **List the major characteristics of Jupiter, Saturn, Uranus, and Neptune.**

▶ **Recognize how Pluto differs from the other outer planets.**

Outer Planets

You have learned that the inner planets are small, solid, rocklike bodies in space. By contrast, the outer planets, except for Pluto, are very large, gaseous objects.

You first heard of the *Voyager* probes in Chapter 21. Although they were not the first probes to the outer planets, they have discovered a wealth of new information about Jupiter, Saturn, Uranus, and Neptune. Let's follow the *Voyager* probes on their journeys to the outer planets of the solar system.

Jupiter

1 In 1979, *Voyager 1* flew by **Jupiter,** the largest planet and the fifth planet from the sun. *Voyager 2* flew by Jupiter later that same year. The major discoveries of the probes include new information about the motions of Jupiter's atmosphere and the discovery of three new moons. *Voyager* probes also discovered that Jupiter has a faint ring around it and that one of its moons has volcanoes on it.

Jupiter is composed mostly of gaseous and liquid hydrogen, helium, and some ammonia, methane, and water vapor. Scientists believe the atmosphere of hydrogen and helium gradually changes to a planetwide ocean of liquid hydrogen and helium toward the middle of the planet. Below this liquid layer, there is a solid core of ice and rock.

You've probably seen pictures from the *Voyager* probes of Jupiter's colorful clouds. Its atmosphere has bands of white, red, tan, and brown clouds. Continuous storms of swirling, high pressure

Figure 23-9. Jupiter's cloud bands are its most visible feature.

OPTIONS

Meeting Different Ability Levels

For Section 23-4, use the following **Teacher Resource Masters** depending upon individual students' needs.

◆ **Study Guide Master** for all students.

● **Reinforcement Master** for students of average and above average ability levels.

▲ **Enrichment Master** for above average students.

Additional Teacher Resource Package masters are listed in the OPTIONS box throughout the section. The additional masters are appropriate for all students.

◆ STUDY GUIDE 93

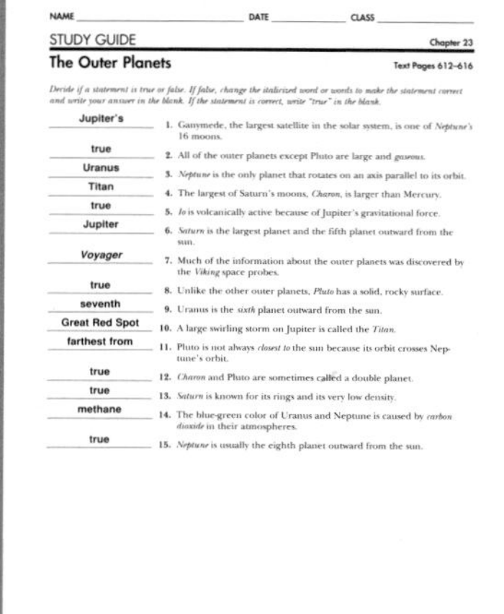

NAME ______ DATE ______ CLASS ______

STUDY GUIDE — Chapter 23

The Outer Planets — Text Pages 612-616

Decide if a statement is true or false. If false, change the italicized word or words to make the statement correct and write your answer in the blank. If the statement is correct, write "true" in the blank.

Jupiter's — 1. Ganymede, the largest satellite in the solar system, is one of *Neptune's* 16 moons.

true — 2. All of the outer planets except Pluto are large and *gaseous.*

Uranus — 3. *Neptune* is the only planet that rotates on an axis parallel to its orbit.

Titan — 4. The largest of Saturn's moons, *Charon,* is larger than Mercury.

true — 5. *Io* is volcanically active because of Jupiter's gravitational force.

Jupiter — 6. *Saturn* is the largest planet and the fifth planet outward from the sun.

Voyager — 7. Much of the information about the outer planets was discovered by the *Viking* space probes.

true — 8. Unlike the other outer planets, *Pluto* has a solid, rocky surface.

seventh — 9. Uranus is the *sixth* planet outward from the sun.

Great Red Spot — 10. A large swirling storm on Jupiter is called the *Titan.*

farthest from — 11. Pluto is not always *closest to* the sun because its orbit crosses Neptune's orbit.

true — 12. *Charon* and Pluto are sometimes called a double planet.

true — 13. *Saturn* is known for its rings and its very low density.

methane — 14. The blue-green color of Uranus and Neptune is caused by *carbon dioxide* in their atmospheres.

true — 15. *Neptune* is usually the eighth planet outward from the sun.

93

Table 23-1

LARGE MOONS OF JUPITER			
Io	Europa	Ganymede	Callisto
The most volcanically active object in the solar system. Sulfur lava gives it its distinctive red and orange color.	Rocky interior is covered by a 100 km thick ice crust, which has a network of cracks, indicating tectonic activity.	Has an ice crust about 100 km thick, covered with grooves. Crust surrounds a 900 km thick slushy mantle of water and ice. Has a rocky core.	Has a heavily cratered ice-rock crust several hundred km thick. Crust surrounds a water or ice mantle around a rocky core.

gas have been observed on Jupiter. The **Great Red Spot** is the most spectacular of these storms. Lightning has also been observed within Jupiter's clouds.

In orbit around Jupiter are 16 moons. Io is the closest of these moons to Jupiter. Jupiter's tremendous gravitational force pulls on Io, causing it to be the most volcanically active object in the solar system. The next moon out is Europa. it is composed mostly of rock with a thick coating of ice. Another significant moon of Jupiter is Ganymede, which is the largest satellite in the solar system. It's larger than the planet Mercury. Callisto is the fourth moon out, composed of ice and rock.

Why do scientists think Io is so volcanically active?

Saturn

The next planet for the *Voyager* probes was Saturn in 1980 and 1981. **Saturn** is the sixth planet from the sun, also known as the ringed planet. Saturn is the second largest planet in the solar system, but has the lowest density. Its density is so low that it would float on water.

Similar to Jupiter, Saturn is a large, gaseous planet with a thick outer atmosphere composed mostly of hydrogen and helium. Saturn's atmosphere also contains ammonia, methane, and water vapor. As you go deeper into Saturn, the gases gradually change to liquid hydrogen and helium. Below the atmosphere and liquid ocean, Saturn has a core of rock and ice.

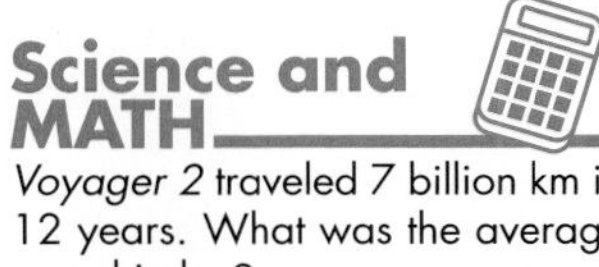

Science and MATH

Voyager 2 traveled 7 billion km in 12 years. What was the average speed in km?

TYING TO PREVIOUS KNOWLEDGE: Have students recall from Chapter 21 that space probes are instruments that gather information and send it back to Earth.

OBJECTIVES AND SCIENCE WORDS: Have students review the objectives and science words to become familiar with this section.

2 TEACH

Key Concepts are highlighted.

Cooperative Learning: Form Numbered Heads Together groups of four students each. Have students play "Planet Jeopardy" by reading statements from this section and Section 23-2 and calling on a student to form an appropriate question. Award points for every correct question by a group.

Science and MATH

$$\frac{7\ 000\ 000\ 000 \text{ km}}{12 \text{ yr}} =$$

583, 333, 333 km/yr
1, 598, 173 km/day
66, 591 km/hr

TEACHER F.Y.I.

▶ About every 30 years, when Saturn's Northern Hemisphere is tilted toward the sun, a Great White Spot develops in the planet's atmosphere. The latest occurrence was on September 24, 1990. The storm encircled the globe by October 23, 1990. Astronomers believe the "spot" is caused when moist air is carried to an altitude where ammonia crystallizes to form the brilliant clouds.

PROGRAM RESOURCES

Use **Laboratory Manual,** page 187, Jupiter and its Moons.

● REINFORCEMENT 93

NAME ______ DATE ______ CLASS ______

REINFORCEMENT — Chapter 23

The Outer Planets — Text Pages 612–616

List the outer planets across the top of the chart in the order of their usual position from the sun. Then fill in the chart using information from your textbook.

	5 Jupiter	6 Saturn	7 Uranus	8 Neptune	9 Pluto
Size and composition	large, gaseous	large, gaseous	large, gaseous	large, gaseous	small, solid
Atmosphere	hydrogen, helium, ammonia, methane, water vapor	hydrogen, helium, ammonia, methane, water vapor	hydrogen, helium, methane	similar to Uranus's	no dense atmosphere
Below the atmosphere	ocean of liquid hydrogen and helium, core of ice and rock	liquid hydrogen and helium, core of ice and rock	liquid water, methane, ammonia, rocky core	liquid water, methane, ammonia, rocky core	solid rocky surface
Notable features	white, tan, red, brown clouds, storms (Great Red Spot), faint rings	hundreds of rings, lowest density of all planets	thin dark rings, blue-green color, sideways rotation	blue-green color, storms in atmosphere, rings with gaps	sometimes the eighth planet, not like other outer planets
Moons (number/names)	16 Io, Europa, Ganymede, Castillo	18 Titan	15	8 Triton	1 Charon
Space probes/year(s)	*Voyager 1* 1979 *Voyager 2* 1979	*Voyager 2* 1980, 1981	*Voyager 2* 1986	*Voyager 2*	

 93

▲ ENRICHMENT 93

NAME ______ DATE ______ CLASS ______

ENRICHMENT — Chapter 23

The Outer Planets — Text Pages 612–616

PLANETARY SIZES

Materials
- your textbook
- knife
- metric ruler
- cookie sheet
- two packages of ready mixed cookie dough
- shortening or cooking spray

Procedure
1. Refer to Appendix I in your textbook.
2. In the space provided, write the scale model diameter for each planet. Use a scale of 1 mm equals 1000 km.
3. Using the scale model sizes above, use the knife to cut round, flat cookies of each of the appropriate diameters. Measure the diameters using a metric ruler. Round off each to the nearest millimeter.
4. Coat the cookie sheet with shortening or cookie spray.
5. Place your cookie "planets" on the sheet, starting with Mercury and proceeding through Pluto.
6. Study the comparative sizes of your "planets" and answers the questions below.
7. Once you have completed the questions, you can bake and eat your "planets."

Mercury 4.9 mm
Venus 12.1 mm
Earth 12.8 mm
Mars 6.8 mm
Jupiter 142.8 mm
Saturn 120.7 mm
Uranus 51.8 mm
Neptune 49.5 mm
Pluto 3.0 mm

Analyze
1. Which planet is the largest? Jupiter Which is the smallest? Pluto
2. How many Earth models would fit across the model of Jupiter? 11

Conclude and Apply
3. Based on the planets' diameters, which planets would you expect to be most like Earth in basic characteristics? Venus, Mars, and perhaps Mercury
4. The diameter of Jupiter is about one-tenth that of the sun. How many Earth models could you fit across a model of the sun? 110
5. Four planets are called the major planets. Which do you think they are? the four largest: Jupiter, Saturn, Uranus, and Neptune

 93

CONCEPT DEVELOPMENT

Cooperative Learning: Supply students with the following diameters of the larger moons in the solar system: Earth's moon (3476 km), Io (3630 km), Europa (3138 km), Ganymede (5262 km), Callisto (4800 km), Titan (5150 km), and Triton (2760 km). Have Paired Partners compare and contrast the sizes of these moons with the sizes of the inner planets. Using a scale of 1 mm = 100 km, have students draw to scale the inner planets and moons listed above. Students should notice that some of the moons are larger than Mercury.

MINI-Lab

Materials: metric ruler, drawing compass, pencil, and paper

Teaching Tips

Cooperative Learning: Have Paired Partners do this activity.

►The scale size for each planet is the product of the scale size of the model Earth times the other planet's multiple of Earth size. For example, if the scale Earth were 2 cm in diameter, Jupiter would be 2 cm × 11.23, or 22.46 cm, in scale diameter.

Answers: Students' answers will vary depending on the scale size chosen for Earth's diameter. Have them compute the answers to the first two questions by multiplying Earth's scale diameter by 11 765, which is the number of Earth diameters in 1 AU. At 1 AU = 2 m, the sun would be 14 millimeters in diameter. The model Earth would be considerably smaller—0.12 millimeters or 0.012 cm.

PROGRAM RESOURCES

From the **Teacher Resource Package** use:

Activity Worksheets, page 214, Mini-Lab: How can you draw planets to scale?

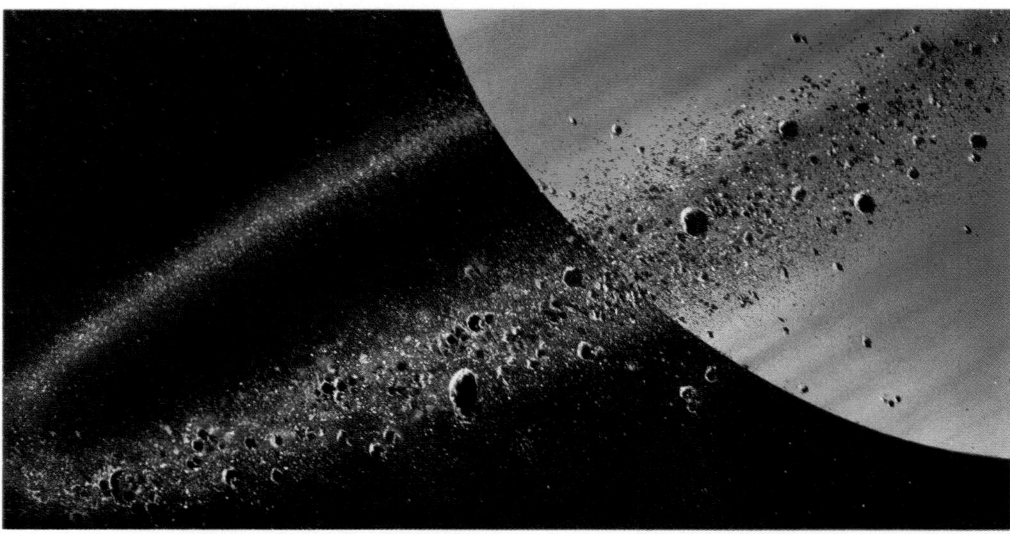

Figure 23-10. Saturn's rings are made of pieces of rock and ice.

MINI-Lab

How can you draw planets to scale?

To determine how the sizes of the planets in the solar system compare to each other, use the information on planet diameters in Appendix I. Select a scale diameter of Earth and draw a circle with this diameter on paper. Using Earth's diameter as 1.0, draw each of the other planets to scale also. At this scale, how far would your model Earth have to be located from the sun? What would 1 AU be for this model? Using a scale of 1 AU = 2 m, how large would the sun and Earth models have to be to remain in scale?

The *Voyager* probes gathered new information about Saturn's ring system and its moons. Scientists once believed that Saturn had only three rings around it. 2 The *Voyager* probes showed that Saturn has several broad rings, each of which is composed of hundreds of thin ringlets. Each ring is composed of countless particles ranging from the size of a speck of dust to tens of meters across. This makes Saturn's ring system the most complex of all outer gaseous planets.

At least 18 moons orbit Saturn. That's more than any other planet in our solar system. The largest of these, 3 Titan, is also larger than Mercury. It has an atmosphere of nitrogen, argon, and methane.

Uranus

After Saturn, *Voyager 2* flew by Uranus in 1986. **Uranus** is the seventh planet from the sun. It is a large, gaseous planet with 15 satellites and a system of thin, dark rings.

Voyager discovered numerous new thin rings and ten new moons that were not seen earlier. *Voyager* also detected that the magnetic field is tilted 60° from its rotational poles. This is odd because most magnetic fields are nearly aligned with a planet's poles. Scientists think Uranus may be undergoing a magnetic reversal.

OPTIONS

INQUIRY QUESTIONS

► **Why do most of the outer planets have relatively low densities compared to the inner planets?** *The outer planets, except for Pluto, are composed of lighter elements and compounds, such as hydrogen, helium, ammonia, and methane.*

► **How is Saturn's moon Titan similar to an inner planet?** *It is relatively large and has an atmosphere of nitrogen, argon, and methane.*

► **Saturn's ring system can be seen from Earth. All the gaseous outer planets have rings, but we can't see them from Earth. Why?** *The rings around Jupiter, Uranus, and Neptune are very thin and dark in color.*

► **What causes the blue-green colors of Uranus and Neptune?** *the presence of methane in their atmosphere*

The atmosphere of Uranus is composed of hydrogen, helium, and some methane. The methane gives the planet its blue-green color. Methane absorbs the red and yellow light, and the clouds reflect the green and blue. Under its atmosphere, scientists believe Uranus has a mantle of liquid water, methane, and ammonia surrounding a rocky core.

One of the most unique features of Uranus is that its axis of rotation is tilted on its side compared to the other planets. The axes of rotation of the other planets are nearly perpendicular to the planes of their orbits. Uranus, however, has a rotational axis nearly parallel to the plane of its orbit.

Figure 23-11. Pictured here are the blue planets Uranus (above) and Neptune (below).

Neptune

From Uranus, *Voyager 2* traveled on to **Neptune,** a large, gaseous planet very similar to Uranus. Most of the time, Neptune is the eighth planet from the sun. However, Pluto's orbit crosses inside Neptune's during a part of its voyage around the sun. Currently, Pluto is closer to the sun than Neptune, and it will remain closer to the sun until 1999. 4

Neptune's atmosphere is very similar to that of Uranus. The methane content gives Neptune its distinctive blue-green color just as it does for Uranus. Neptune has dark-colored, stormlike features in its atmosphere that are similar to the Great Red Spot on Jupiter.

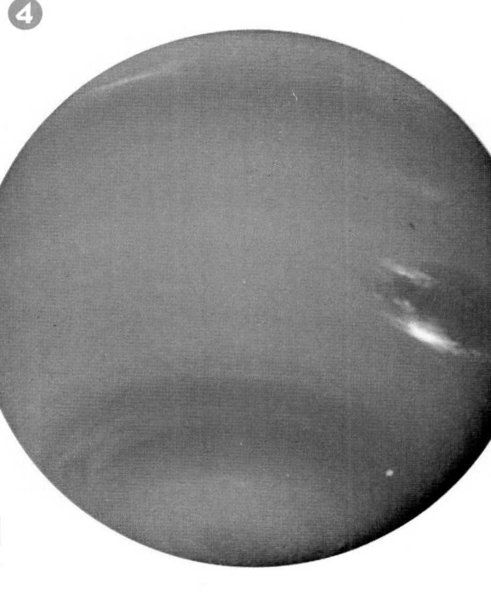

Under its atmosphere, Neptune is thought to have liquid water, methane, and ammonia. Neptune probably has a rocky core.

With *Voyager 2* discovering six new moons, the total for Neptune is now eight. Of these, Triton is most interesting. Triton has a diameter of 2700 km and has a thin atmosphere composed mostly of nitrogen. *Voyager* also discovered that Neptune also has rings that are thin in some places and thick in other places. At a certain distance, the thin places are not visible, and the rings seem broken.

CHECK FOR UNDERSTANDING

Use the Mini Quiz to check for understanding.

MINI QUIZ

Use the Mini Quiz to check students' recall of chapter content.

1. **The largest planet in the solar system is _____ .** *Jupiter*
2. **_____ has the most complex ring system of all the planets.** *Saturn*
3. **Which moon of Saturn has an atmosphere and is larger than Mercury?** *Titan*
4. **Which planet is currently closer to the sun—Pluto or Neptune?** *Pluto*

RETEACH

Cooperative Learning: Using the Paired Partners strategy, have students prepare flash cards of the outer planets by sketching each planet on a separate card. On the reverse side of the card, instruct students to write down the characteristics of each planet. Partners can then test each other using the flash cards.

EXTENSION

For students who have mastered this section, use the **Reinforcement** and **Enrichment** masters or other OPTIONS provided.

ENRICHMENT

▶ Have each student compile a list of the physical properties of all known moons orbiting the outer planets. Suggest students use data available from the *Voyager* missions.

PROGRAM RESOURCES

From the **Teacher Resource Package** use:

Critical Thinking/Problem Solving, page 29, Voyager Probes.

REVEALING MISCONCEPTIONS

▶ Some students may think planets give off light like the sun. Inform students that planets "shine" due to reflected sunlight.

3 CLOSE

▶ Ask questions 1-4 and the **Apply** Question in the Section Review.

▶ **How does Pluto differ from the other outer planets?** *It doesn't have a dense atmosphere and has a solid, rocky surface.* **How are Jupiter, Saturn, Uranus, and Neptune similar?** *They all have low densities and are large and gaseous. Each has a dense atmosphere.*

SECTION REVIEW ANSWERS

1. The outer planets are very large, gaseous objects, except for Pluto. The inner planets are small, solid, rocklike bodies in space.

2. It is a very large, swirling storm.

3. Yes, Ganymede and Titan are larger than Mercury and Pluto.

4. It is not surrounded by a dense atmosphere, and it has a solid, rocky surface.

5. Apply: Pluto's orbit is more elliptical than the orbits of other planets. This causes Pluto to come closer to the sun than Neptune for about 20 years of its orbit.

Skill Builder

1. bands of red, tan, and brown clouds

2. High pressure causes the gases in the storm to flow inward toward its center.

3. Jupiter is the largest planet and thus has the greatest gravitational force of the nine planets. The force is in fact large enough to hold a moon that is larger than Mercury in orbit around the planet.

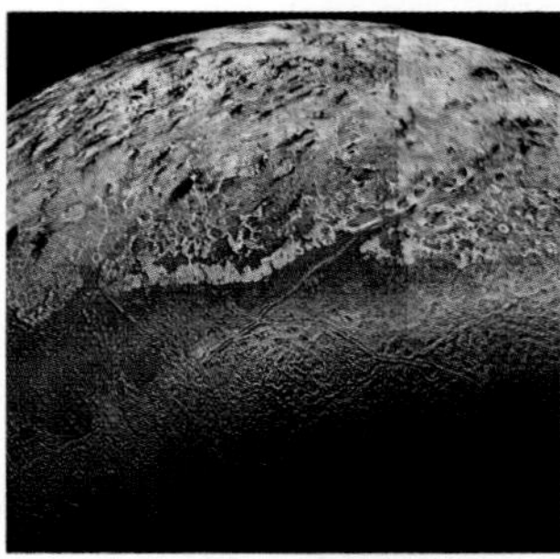

Figure 23-12. Neptune's Moon Triton

Voyager ended its tour of the solar system with Neptune. Scientists were not able to direct *Voyager* to Pluto because Neptune's gravity deflected it toward Triton, away from the direction of Pluto. Both *Voyager* probes are now out of the solar system. They will continue into space searching for the extent of the sun's effect on charged particles.

Pluto

Because **Pluto** is farther from the sun during most of its orbit around the sun, it is considered the ninth planet from the sun. Pluto is not like the other outer planets. It's not surrounded by a dense atmosphere, and it's the only outer planet with a solid, rocky surface. Some scientists believe that Pluto may have been a moon that escaped from an orbit around Neptune.

Why are Charon and Pluto considered a double planet?

Pluto's only moon, Charon, has a diameter equal to half of Pluto's. Charon orbits very close to Pluto. Because of their close size and orbit, Charon and Pluto are often considered a double planet.

With the *Voyager* probes leading the way, we have entered a new age of knowledge about the solar system. Other new probes such as the *Galileo* will continue to extend our understanding of the solar system.

SECTION REVIEW

1. What's the difference between the outer planets and the inner planets?
2. What causes the Great Red Spot on Jupiter?
3. Are there moons in the solar system that are larger than planets? What are they?
4. How is Pluto different from the other outer planets?
5. **Apply:** Why is Neptune sometimes the farthest planet from the sun?

Skill Builder — Recognizing Cause and Effect

Answer the following questions about Jupiter. If you need help, refer to Recognizing Cause and Effect in the **Skill Handbook** on page 683.

1. What causes Jupiter's surface color?
2. How is the Great Red Spot affected by Jupiter's atmosphere?
3. How does Jupiter's size affect its gravitational force?

OPTIONS

ENRICHMENT

▶ Have students make and display three-dimensional models of the outer planets and their moons.

▶ Have interested students summarize the data gathered by *Voyager* and present this information to the class.

ACTIVITY 23-2
Solar System Distance Model

Problem: *How can you construct a scale model showing the distance between the sun and planets in the solar system?*

Materials 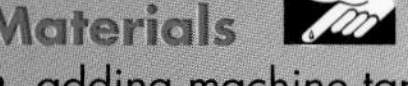

- adding machine tape
- meterstick
- scissors
- pencil

Procedure

1. Use Appendix I to obtain the mean distance from the sun in AUs for each planet. Record these data in the table.
2. Using 10 centimeters as the distance between Earth and the sun (10 cm = 1 AU), determine the length of adding machine tape you will need to do this investigation.
3. Calculate the scale distance that each planet would be from the sun on the adding machine tape. Record this information.
4. Cut the tape to the proper length.
5. Mark one end of the tape to represent the position of the sun.
6. Put a label at the proper location on the tape where each planet would be if the planets were in a straight line outward from the sun.
7. Complete the table by calculating the scale distance of each planet from the sun if 1 AU equals 2 meters on a model.

Analyze

1. Explain how the scale distance is determined.
2. How much adding machine tape would be required to construct a model with a scale distance 1 AU = 2 m?

Conclude and Apply

3. In addition to scale distances, what other information do you need before you can construct an exact scale model of the solar system?
4. Proxima Centauri, the next closest star to our sun, is 4.3 light-years from the sun. Using the scale of 10 cm = 1 AU, how long a piece of adding machine tape would you need to include this star on your scale model?

Data and Observations

Sample Data

Planet	Distance to sun (km)	Distance to sun (AU)	Scale distance (1 AU = 10 cm)	Scale distance (1 AU = 2 m)
Mercury	58×10^6	0.38	3.9 cm	77.4 cm
Venus	108×10^6	0.72	7.2 cm	1.45 m
Earth	150×10^6	1.00	10.0 cm	2.0 m
Mars	228×10^6	1.52	15.2 cm	3.05 m
Jupiter	780×10^6	5.20	52.0 cm	10.4 m
Saturn	143×10^7	9.54	95.4 cm	19.08 m
Uranus	288×10^7	19.18	191.8 cm	38.4 m
Neptune	451×10^7	30.06	300.6 cm	60.1 m
Pluto	592×10^7	39.44	394.4 cm	78.9 m

ACTIVITY 23-2
40 minutes

OBJECTIVE: Construct a scale model of the distances between the sun and planets.

PROCESS SKILLS applied in this activity:
▶ **Measuring** in Procedure Steps 2 and 6.
▶ **Predicting** in Conclude and Apply Question 4.
▶ **Using Numbers** in Procedure Steps 1-3 and 7, Analyze Question 2, and Conclude and Apply Question 4.
▶ **Interpreting Data** in Analyze Question 1 and Conclude and Apply Question 3.
▶ **Formulating Models** in Conclude and Apply Question 3.

COOPERATIVE LEARNING Have Paired Partners do this activity.

TEACHING THE ACTIVITY

▶ You may need to help students with the math in order for them to understand how to set up the scale distances and construct the scale model. Allow students to calculate the amount of tape needed to construct the scale model and begin, even if incorrect. If students have any errors in their calculations, it will become apparent to them before they progress very far in the procedure.

PROGRAM RESOURCES

From the **Teacher Resource Package** use:

Activity Worksheets, pages 209-210, Activity 23-2: Solar System Distance Model.

ANSWERS TO QUESTIONS

1. The scale distance is determined by multiplying the AU-distance of each planet by the scale (in AUs) selected.
2. 78.9 meters, or any answer approaching 80 meters
3. In order to construct a scale model of the solar system, students must also know the planet diameters. This information would have to be converted to the same scale as the distance to the sun in AUs.
4. At a scale of 10 cm = 1 AU, one light year to scale would be about 6.3 km. This would place Proxima Centauri approximately 27 kilometers away from the sun, if Earth were 10 cm, or 1 AU, away.

SECTION 23-5

PREPARATION

SECTION BACKGROUND

▶ Comets appear to orbit the sun in a belt called the Oort Comet Cloud some 50 000 km from the sun. Some comets take more than one million years to complete one orbit.

▶ When Halley's comet came close to Earth in 1986, five space probes were launched to study it: the Soviet *Vega 1* and *Vega 2* probes; the Japanese *Suisei* and *Sakigake* probes; and the European Space Agency's *Giotto* probe. *Giotto* traveled closest to the comet's nucleus. Data sent back by the probes indicate the nucleus is black, measures about 15 km in length and 8 km in width, and rotates once every 2 days. It was also noted that the coma contains boulder-size rocks as well as fine dust particles.

▶ On the average, 66 meteorites crash to Earth every 24 hours. Although most are very small and land in the oceans, astronomers are constantly searching the skies for asteroids or comets that could cause damage. In recent years, several large asteroids have been observed passing very close to Earth. Some have even been seen streaking across Earth's upper atmosphere and traveling back into space.

▶ There are three general types of meteorites. Iron meteorites are made mostly of iron and are rich in nickel. Stony meteorites resemble rocks on Earth. Stony-iron meteorites are composed of iron, nickel, and other elements.

23-5 Other Objects in the Solar System

New Science Words

comet
Oort Cloud
meteor
meteorite
asteroid

Objectives

- ▶ **Explain where a comet comes from and describe how a comet develops as it approaches the sun.**
- ▶ **Differentiate between comets, meteoroids, and asteroids.**

Other Objects in the Solar System

Although the planets and their satellites are the most noticeable members of the sun's family, there are many other objects that orbit the sun. Comets, meteors, and asteroids are other objects in the solar system.

You've probably heard of Halley's comet. It was last seen from Earth in 1986. English astronomer Edmund Halley realized that comet sightings that had taken place about every 76 years were really sightings of the same comet. This comet that takes about 76 years to orbit the sun was named after him. Halley's comet is just one example of the many other objects in the solar system beside the planets. Figure 23-13 describes comets.

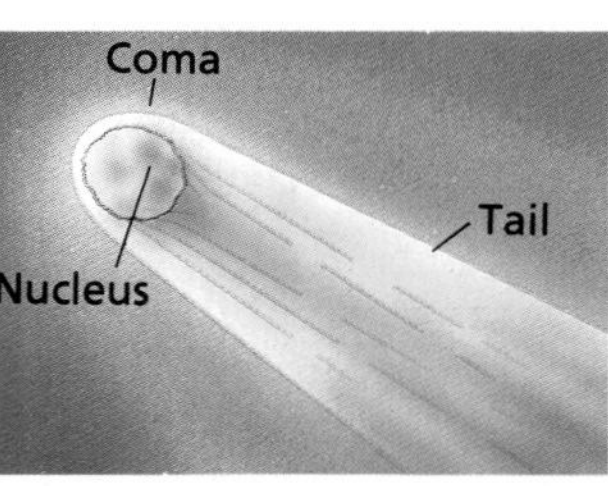

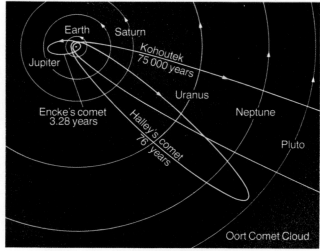

Figure 23-13. A comet consists of a nucleus, a coma, and a tail, as shown above. The orbits of three famous comets are shown at right.

OPTIONS

Meeting Different Ability Levels

For Section 23-5, use the following **Teacher Resource Masters** depending upon individual students' needs.

◆ **Study Guide Master** for all students.

● **Reinforcement Master** for students of average and above average ability levels.

▲ **Enrichment Master** for above average students.

Additional Teacher Resource Package masters are listed in the OPTIONS box throughout the section. The additional masters are appropriate for all students.

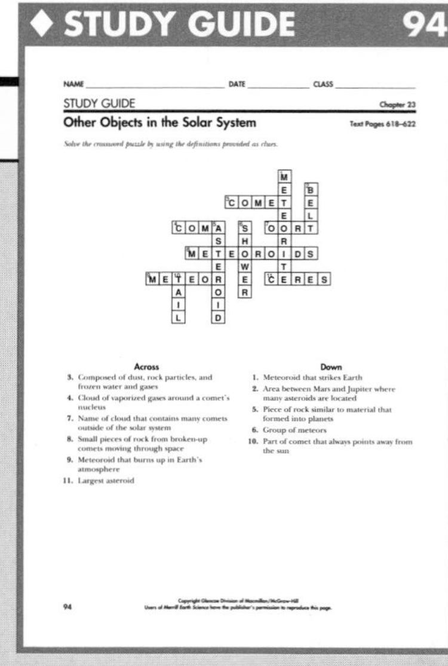

◆ STUDY GUIDE 94

NAME ______ DATE ______ CLASS ______

STUDY GUIDE Chapter 23

Other Objects in the Solar System Text Pages 618–622

Solve the crossword puzzle by using the definitions provided as clues.

Across

3. Composed of dust, rock particles, and frozen water and gases
4. Cloud of vaporized gases around a comet's nucleus
7. Name of cloud that contains many comets outside of the solar system
8. Small pieces of rock from broken-up comets moving through space
9. Meteoroid that burns up in Earth's atmosphere
11. Largest asteroid

Down

1. Meteoroid that strikes Earth
2. Area between Mars and Jupiter where many asteroids are located
5. Piece of rock similar to material that formed into planets
6. Group of meteors
10. Part of comet that always points away from the sun

94

Copyright Glencoe Division of Macmillan/McGraw-Hill
Users of Merrill Earth Science have the publisher's permission to reproduce this page.

Comets

A **comet** is composed of dust and rock particles mixed ❶ in with frozen water, methane, and ammonia. The Dutch astronomer Jan Oort proposed the idea that a large collection of comets lies in a cloud that completely surrounds the solar system. This cloud is located beyond the orbit of Pluto and is called the **Oort Cloud.** ❷ Scientists believe the gravity of nearby stars or another planet interacts with the Oort Cloud, changing the orbits of some comets. The sun's gravity then pulls the comet toward it. The comet then either escapes from the solar system or gets captured into a much smaller orbit.

The structure of a comet is like a large, dirty snowball, or a mass of frozen ice and rock. But as the comet approaches the sun, it develops a very distinctive structure. Ices of water, methane, and ammonia begin to vaporize because of the heat from the sun. The vaporized gases form a bright cloud called a coma around the nucleus, or solid part, of the comet. The solar wind, a stream of charged particles from the sun, pushes on the gases in the coma. These particles form a bright tail that always points away from the sun.

After many trips around the sun, most of the frozen ice in a comet has vaporized. All that is left are small particles which spread out in the orbit of the original comet.

Figure 23-14. This is a computer-enhanced image of Halley's comet.

Why do comets move toward the center of the solar system?

Did You Know?

There are about 25 comets visible to the naked eye every century.

● REINFORCEMENT 94

NAME ______ DATE ______ CLASS ______

REINFORCEMENT — Chapter 23

Other Objects in the Solar System — Text Pages 618–622

Answer Questions 1–3 on the lines provided.

1. What is the Oort Cloud, and where is it located? **The Oort Cloud is a large collection of comets; it completely surrounds the solar system beyond the orbit of Pluto.**
2. What is an asteroid, and where are most asteroids located? **An asteroid is a piece of rock similar to the material that later formed into the planets; most asteroids are located in between the orbits of Mars and Jupiter.**
3. How do scientists explain the location of the asteroid belt? **One theory is that the gravity of Jupiter kept the asteroids in the belt from forming into another planet.**

Identify Figure 1 and its parts and then answer the questions that follow.

4. Figure 1: **comet**
   A. **coma** B. **nucleus**
   C. **tail**
5. How does a comet begin? **It's pulled from the Oort Cloud by the gravity of a nearby star or planet. Then it's pulled by the sun's gravity to the center of the solar system. At first it's like a large, dirty snowball. Heat from the sun begins to vaporize its ice into gases.**
6. How does the comet end? **After the comet has made many trips around the sun, its frozen ice has all been vaporized. The remaining particles are spread out in the orbit of the comet. The small pieces of rock are called meteoroids.**

Identify the parts of Figure 2 and then answer the questions that follow.

7. A. **meteoroids** B. **meteors**
   C. **meteorites**
8. Which begin as meteroids? **A, B, and C**
9. Which are pieces of rock moving through space? **A, B, and C**

94

▲ ENRICHMENT 94

NAME ______ DATE ______ CLASS ______

ENRICHMENT — Chapter 23

Other Objects in the Solar System — Text Pages 618–622

NEW INFORMATION FROM AN OLD COMET

Read the following information and answer the questions that follow.

Comet Halley was observed as early as 240 B.C. Since the first record of its appearance, the comet has been a great mystery. In 1986, the European Space Agency (representing a number of countries in Europe), the Soviet Union, and Japan sent space probes to get a closer look at Comet Halley. These probes provided us with startling new information about the comet.

The most exciting new information was the detail of the comet's elongated, peanut-shaped nucleus. Scientists think the comet has a nucleus composed of some combination of rock and ice. It measures 15 km × 8 km × 8 km and contains several shallow craters. Each crater is about 1 km in diameter. Comet Halley's mass is 10^{17} g, with an average density of about 0.3 g/cm^3. The nucleus is covered with a layer of dust which retains heat. When Comet Halley is closest to the sun, temperatures can rise to about 77°C. Each large dust grain is thought to consist of many tiny particles with spaces in between. Some of these pores are filled with ice, and others are empty.

On the side of the comet facing the sun, ice changes to water vapor. Jets of water vapor with dust particles spray from the comet. Near the sun, several tons of gas and dust are emitted each second in the jets.

1. Why do we have new information about Comet Halley? **because spacecraft have recently studied it**
2. What countries sent space probes? **several European countries, the Soviet Union, and Japan**
3. What is the shape of the nucleus? **elongated, peanut-shaped**
4. Calculate the volume of the nucleus. **15 km × 8 km × 8 km = 960 km^3**
5. What and where are jets? **sprays of dust with water vapor; on the comet's sunlit side**
6. Name an object with the same diameter or a distance equal to the diameter of a crater on Halley's nucleus. **Student answers will vary; possible answers are about three football fields end to end or ten city blocks.**
7. Describe what you think you would see if you could stand on the sunward side of Comet Halley. **You would see dark dust around your feet and a sky that was bright with dust and water vapor jets scattering the sun's light. The dust of the comet would fill the sky and also scatter sunlight.**

94

1 MOTIVATE

FLEX Your Brain

Use the Flex Your Brain activity to have students explore COMETS.

▶ Obtain and display photos of Halley's comet's most recent visit.

TYING TO PREVIOUS KNOWLEDGE: Have students recall from Chapter 22 that the moon's surface is heavily cratered. Relate that most craters on the moon were probably formed by impacts with meteorites.

OBJECTIVES AND SCIENCE WORDS: Have students review the objectives and science words to become familiar with this section.

2 TEACH

Key Concepts are highlighted.

CONCEPT DEVELOPMENT

▶ After students have read pages 618 and 619, ask these questions. **What is a comet?** *an object made of dust; rocks; and frozen water, methane, and ammonia* **What is the Oort Cloud and where is it located?** *The Oort Cloud is a large collection of comets that orbit beyond Pluto.*

▶ Have two volunteers demonstrate how the speed at which a comet orbits the sun increases as it approaches the sun.

PROGRAM RESOURCES

From the **Teacher Resource Package** use:

Activity Worksheets, page 5, Flex Your Brain.

CONCEPT DEVELOPMENT

Cooperative Learning: Have Expert Teams compare and contrast comets, meteoroids, meteors, and meteorites.

REVEALING MISCONCEPTIONS

▶ Many people incorrectly refer to meteors as "shooting stars." Explain that meteors are relatively small, rock-like bodies that move through space. Stars, however, are enormous balls of gas that tend to remain in their "places" in space.

MINI QUIZ

Use the Mini Quiz to check students' recall of chapter content.

1. **What is a comet?** *a space object composed of dust and rock particles mixed with frozen water, methane, and ammonia*
2. **A large collection of comets beyond Pluto's orbit is the ____ .** *Oort Cloud*
3. **A meteoroid that burns up in Earth's atmosphere is a(n) ____** *meteor*

Figure 23-15. This meteor was seen in the daytime sky over the Grand Tetons.

Meteoroids, Meteors, and Meteorites

Where do meteroids come from?

You learned earlier that comets tend to break up after they have passed close to the sun many times. The small pieces of the comet nucleus spread out into a loose group within the original orbit of the broken comet. These small pieces of rock moving through space are then called meteoroids.

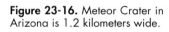

If the path of a meteoroid crossed the position of Earth, it would enter our atmosphere at between 12 and 72 km/s. Most meteoroids are so small that they are completely vaporized in Earth's atmosphere. 3 A meteoroid that burns up in Earth's atmosphere is called a **meteor.** People often see these and call them "shooting stars."

Figure 23-16. Meteor Crater in Arizona is 1.2 kilometers wide.

OPTIONS

INQUIRY QUESTIONS

▶ **What causes comets to break up after they pass close to the sun many times?** *The sun causes most of the frozen ice to vaporize. The remaining parts of the comet spread out into the comet's original orbit.*

▶ **When does a meteoroid become a meteor?** *When a meteoroid enters Earth's atmosphere and burns up, it becomes a meteor.*

▶ **What causes a meteor shower?** *A meteor shower occurs when Earth passes within the orbit of a comet that has broken apart.*

▶ **What do meteorites tell us about the solar system?** *Meteorites come from comets or asteroids, thus they provide data about the material that formed the solar system.*

Each time Earth passes through the loose group of particles within the path of a broken-up comet, many small particles of rock and dust enter the atmosphere. Because more meteors than usual are seen, this is called a meteor shower. Some meteor showers will have more than 50 meteors per hour.

If the meteoroid is large enough, it may not completely burn up in Earth's atmosphere. When it strikes Earth, it is called a **meteorite.** Meteor Crater in Arizona was formed when a large meteorite struck Earth. Because meteorites originally come from comets or asteroids, scientists believe they are made of material that formed at the beginning of the solar system. 4

What happens to the smallest meteroids as they fall to Earth?

TECHNOLOGY

Garbage in Space

Since the 1950s, people have been exploring space. And since then, more than 3.5 million kilograms of garbage—from wrenches to satellites—has been dumped in space! Much of the space trash is only a few centimeters in size, but in the zero gravity environment of space, such particles could move at speeds that exceed 24 000 kilometers per hour and cause much damage to spacecraft!

NASA scientists are currently working on designs that would protect spacecraft and space station *Freedom,* in particular, from space debris. One proposed system is a collision warning system that would alert astronauts and ground controllers to potentially dangerous debris. The system would use infrared sensors mounted like headlights onto a spacecraft or space station to detect objects. Space-based radars would then determine the path of the object and allow the astronauts time to either avoid or prepare for the collision.

Think Critically: One estimate has 3.5 million particles of garbage in space. What is the average mass of each particle?

CROSS CURRICULUM

▶ **Economics:** Have students research the nickel mines of Sudbury Basin in Ontario, Canada. It is thought that about 2 billion years ago, an asteroid 6 km in diameter collided with Earth at this location. The collision caused the formation of rich deposits of nickel, cobalt, and platinum.

CHECK FOR UNDERSTANDING

Ask: **What happens when a meteoroid strikes Earth?** *Students should be able to explain that, if the meteoroid is large enough, an impact crater will form.*

RETEACH

Place 10 cm of fine-grained sand or dry cement in a flat pan so that the substance completely covers the bottom of the pan. Have volunteers drop various-sized "meteorites" into the pan. Have students carefully remove the objects and observe the craters made.

EXTENSION

For students who have mastered this section, use the **Reinforcement** and **Enrichment** masters or other OPTIONS provided.

TECHNOLOGY

▶ For more information, see "Tackling the Menace of Space Junk" by Mark D. Uehling, *Popular Science*, July, 1990, pp. 82+.

▶ Have students discuss ways to reduce future space trash. Reusing many parts and instruments has currently been implemented by NASA.

Think Critically: 3.5 million kilograms ÷ 3.5 million particles = 1.0 kg/particle

INQUIRY QUESTIONS

▶ **Why are most asteroids between Mars and Jupiter?** *One theory is that Jupiter's enormous gravitational force kept a planet from forming in that area.*

▶ **Where else in the solar system besides the asteroid belt can asteroids be found?** *Some of the larger asteroids may have been thrown out of the belt and may have been captured as moons.*

TEACHER F.Y.I.

▶ The asteroid belt is not as dense as many people think. The *Pioneer* and *Voyager* space probes flew through the asteroid belt without detecting a single asteroid.

▶ The four largest asteroids are Ceres, Pallas, Vesta, and Hygeia.

3 CLOSE

▶ Ask questions 1-3 and the **Apply** Question in the Section Review.

FLEX Your Brain

Use the Flex Your Brain activity to have students explore ASTEROIDS.

Cooperative Learning: Provide students with metric rulers. Have Paired Partners contrast the sizes of the larger asteroids, Earth, and the moon, using a scale of 1 mm = 100 km. Have students use these data: Earth (12 756 km), the moon (3476 km), Ceres (940 km), Pallas (540 km), Vesta (510 km), and Hygeia (410 km).

SECTION REVIEW ANSWERS

1. As a comet approaches the sun, heat causes some of the comet to vaporize. Solar wind pushes on these gases to form a tail on the comet.

2. A meteoroid is a rocky object traveling through space; a meteor is a meteoroid that has entered Earth's atmosphere; a meteorite is a meteor that has reached Earth's surface.

3. a crater

4. Apply: Comets are collections of frozen gas and rocky particles that generally travel in elliptical orbits around the sun. Meteoroids are usually small fragments of rock that move independently through space. Asteroids generally orbit the sun between Mars and Jupiter. Their sizes can range from small particles to objects as large as 1000 km in diameter.

Skill Builder

The coma is the yellowish ball near the left edge of the photo. The tail comprises the rest of the comet. The sun is to the left.

Asteroids

Where do asteroids come from?

An **asteroid** is a piece of rock similar to the material that later formed into the planets. Most asteroids are located in an area between the orbits of Mars and Jupiter called the asteroid belt.

Why are they located there? One theory states that the gravity of Jupiter kept a planet from forming in the area where the asteroid belt is now located. In addition to this, some of the larger asteroids may have been thrown out of the belt and are probably scattered throughout the present-day solar system. Many have since been captured as moons around other planets.

The size of the asteroids in the asteroid belt range from tiny particles to almost 1000 km in diameter. The largest asteroid, and the first one ever discovered, is Ceres. Its diameter is 940 km.

Comets, meteoroids, and asteroids are probably composed of material that formed early in the history of the solar system. Scientists study the structure and composition of these space objects in order to better understand what the solar system may have been like long ago. Understanding what the early solar system was like could help scientists to better understand the formation of Earth and its relationship to other objects in the solar system.

Did You Know?

Venus rotates in the opposite direction from Earth. It also takes longer to rotate one complete turn than it does to complete one revolution around the sun. This means that a day on Venus is longer than its year.

SECTION REVIEW

1. Why does a comet's tail form as it approaches the sun?
2. How do a meteoroid, a meteor, and a meteorite differ?
3. What type of feature might be formed on Earth if a large meteorite reached its surface?
4. **Apply:** Describe differences among comets, meteoroids, and asteroids.

Skill Builder — Interpreting Scientific Illustrations

Identify the coma and tail of the comet shown in Figure 23-14 on page 619. In which direction is the sun relative to the comet? If you need help, refer to Interpreting Scientific Illustrations in the **Skill Handbook** on page 693.

OPTIONS

ENRICHMENT

▶ Have students research Sir Edmund Halley's study of the comet that is named for him.

▶ Obtain a table of regular meteor showers. Determine when the next meteor shower is to occur. Have students observe meteors and keep records on how many they see. Discuss the meteor shower the day after it occurs.

PROGRAM RESOURCES

From the **Teacher Resource Package** use:

Activity Worksheets, page 5, Flex Your Brain.

CHAPTER

REVIEW

SUMMARY

23-1: The Solar System

1. The Earth-centered model proposed that Earth was inside a sphere and that the planets and the stars rotated around Earth. The sun-centered model states that the sun is the center of the solar system.

2. Our solar system formed about 4.6 billion years ago from a cloud of gas and dust. The cloud rotated and pulled much matter into its center. Eventually, the central part formed the sun and the remaining matter formed the planets.

23-2: The Inner Planets

1. The inner planets, in increasing distance from the sun, are Mercury, Venus, Earth, and Mars.

2. The moonlike Mercury has a very thin atmosphere. Venus has a dense atmosphere of carbon dioxide and sulfuric acid. On Earth, water exists in three states. Mars appears red due to weathering of its rocks.

3. Venus and Earth are similar in size and mass. Both have greenhouse effects.

23-3: Science and Society: Mission to Mars

1. Problems that astronauts to Mars would face include muscle and bone weakness and exposure to dangerous levels of radiation.

2. A crewed mission to Mars would be dangerous to the astronauts involved. Robots may be a better alternative than sending humans to Mars.

23-4: The Outer Planets

1. A faint ring and 16 moons orbit the gaseous Jupiter. Jupiter's Great Red Spot is a storm. Saturn is made of mostly gas and has rings. Uranus is a large, gaseous planet with many moons and several rings. Neptune is similar to Uranus in composition and has stormlike features similar to Jupiter.

2. Pluto doesn't have a dense atmosphere, and its surface is rocky.

23-5: Other Objects in the Solar System

1. As a comet approaches the sun, vaporized gases form a bright coma around the comet's nucleus. A tail that points away from the sun is formed by solar wind.

2. Meteoroids are small pieces of rock moving through space. An asteroid is a piece of rock that is a part of the asteroid belt.

KEY SCIENCE WORDS

a. **asteroid**
b. **astronomical unit**
c. **comet**
d. **data gloves**
e. **Earth**
f. **Great Red Spot**
g. **inner planets**
h. **Jupiter**
i. **Mars**
j. **Mercury**
k. **meteor**
l. **meteorite**
m. **Neptune**
n. **Oort Cloud**
o. **outer planets**
p. **Pluto**
q. **Saturn**
r. **solar system**
s. **Uranus**
t. **Venus**

UNDERSTANDING VOCABULARY

Match each phrase with the correct term from the list of Key Science Words.

1. solid, rocky planets closest to the sun
2. planet most like Earth in size and mass
3. planet with carbon dioxide ice caps
4. Ganymede and Io are two of its moons
5. planet that could float on water
6. large gaseous planets
7. currently the farthest planet from the sun
8. large group of comets beyond Pluto's orbit
9. a rock that enters Earth's atmosphere
10. a meteoroid that strikes Earth

OPTIONS

ASSESSMENT

To assess student understanding of material in this chapter, use the resources listed.

COOPERATIVE LEARNING

Consider using cooperative learning in the THINK AND WRITE CRITICALLY, APPLY, and MORE SKILL BUILDERS sections of the Chapter Review.

PROGRAM RESOURCES

From the **Teacher Resource Package** use:

Chapter Review, pages 49-50.

Chapter and Unit Tests, pages 154-157, Chapter Test.

CHAPTER

REVIEW

SUMMARY

Have students read the summary statements to review the major concepts of the chapter.

UNDERSTANDING VOCABULARY

1. g
2. t
3. i
4. h
5. q
6. o
7. m
8. n
9. k
10. l

CHAPTER
REVIEW

CHECKING CONCEPTS

1. b
2. c
3. b
4. d
5. d
6. c
7. d
8. b
9. a
10. b

UNDERSTANDING CONCEPTS

11. Earth
12. inner
13. Venus, Earth
14. data gloves or humans
15. Pluto

THINK AND WRITE CRITICALLY

16. Copernicus thought the planets moved around the sun in circular orbits and that the sun was in the center of the circles. Kepler discovered that the orbits were ellipses and the sun was offset from the center of the orbits.
17. The inner planets are rocky, more dense, and are composed of heavier elements. With the exception of Pluto, the outer planets are larger than the inner planets, are less dense, have more satellites, and move more slowly.
18. In space, a comet resembles a large, dirty snowball. As it nears the sun, a comet forms a coma around its nucleus. Solar wind pushes on the particles of a comet to form a tail that points away from the sun.
19. Unlike the other planets, Uranus' axis of rotation is nearly parallel to the plane of its orbit.
20. Both are small, rocky planets in the solar system. Mercury is closest to the sun; Pluto is usually the farthest. Mercury has no satellites; Pluto has one.

CHAPTER
REVIEW

CHECKING CONCEPTS

Choose the word or phrase that completes the sentence.

1. ____ proposed a sun-centered solar system.
   - **a.** Ptolemy
   - **b.** Copernicus
   - **c.** Galileo
   - **d.** Oort
2. ______ formed the sun.
   - **a.** Rotation
   - **b.** Revolution
   - **c.** Nuclear fusion
   - **d.** The greenhouse effect
3. Planets orbit the sun in ______.
   - **a.** circles
   - **b.** ellipses
   - **c.** rotation
   - **d.** none of these
4. ______ has very extreme temperatures because it has little atmosphere.
   - **a.** Earth
   - **b.** Jupiter
   - **c.** Mars
   - **d.** Mercury
5. Water is a solid, liquid, or gas on ______.
   - **a.** Pluto
   - **b.** Uranus
   - **c.** Saturn
   - **d.** Earth
6. The largest volcano in the solar system is on ______.
   - **a.** Earth
   - **b.** Jupiter
   - **c.** Mars
   - **d.** Uranus
7. A problem with living in space is ______.
   - **a.** bones lose calcium
   - **b.** dehydration
   - **c.** muscles weaken
   - **d.** all of these
8. ______ has a very complex ring system made of hundreds of ringlets.
   - **a.** Pluto
   - **b.** Saturn
   - **c.** Uranus
   - **d.** Mars
9. The magnetic pole of ______ is tilted 60°.
   - **a.** Uranus
   - **b.** Earth
   - **c.** Jupiter
   - **d.** Pluto
10. The tail of a comet always points ______.
   - **a.** toward the sun
   - **b.** away from the sun
   - **c.** toward Earth
   - **d.** away from the Oort Cloud

UNDERSTANDING CONCEPTS

Complete each sentence.

11. The object around which all planets and stars were once believed to have orbited is ______.
12. Although it is the ninth planet from the sun, Pluto is like a(n) ______ planet.
13. A greenhouse effect occurs on _____ and _____.
14. Robots imitate the motions made by ______.
15. In 2001, ______ will be the farthest planet from the sun.

THINK AND WRITE CRITICALLY

16. Contrast Copernicus' model of the solar system with Kepler's model.
17. Describe the general characteristics of the inner and outer planets.
18. Describe how the structure of a comet changes as it nears the sun.
19. How is Uranus different from the other eight planets?
20. Compare and contrast Mercury and Pluto.

APPLY

21. Why is the surface temperature on Venus so much higher than that on Earth?
22. Describe the relationship between the mass of a planet and the number of satellites it has.
23. Why are probe landings on Jupiter or Saturn unlikely events?
24. What evidence suggests that water is or once was present on Mars?
25. An observer on Earth can watch Venus go through phases much like Earth's moon does. Explain why this is so.

MORE SKILL BUILDERS

If you need help, refer to the Skill Handbook.

1. **Concept Mapping:** Make a concept map that explains how a comet changes as it travels through space.

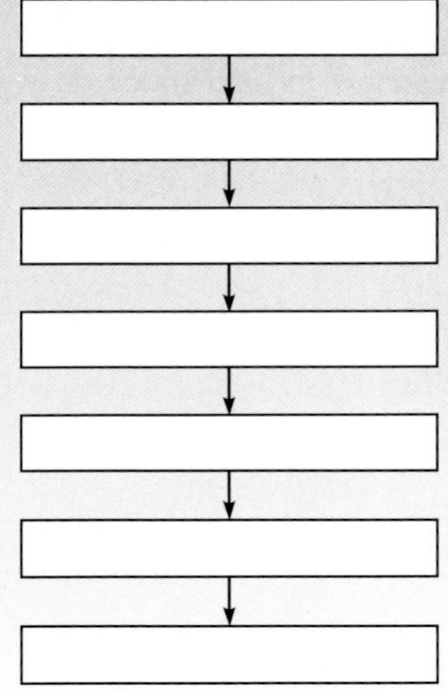

2. **Hypothesizing:** Mercury is the closest planet to the sun, yet it does not reflect much of the sun's light. What can you say about Mercury's color?
3. **Measuring in SI:** The Great Red Spot of Jupiter is about 40 000 km long and about 12 000 km wide. What is its area in km^2?
4. **Sequencing:** Arrange the following planets in order from the planet with the most natural satellites to the one with the least number: Earth, Jupiter, Saturn, Neptune, Uranus, and Mars.
5. **Making and Using Tables:** Make a table that summarizes the main characteristics of each planet in the solar system.

PROJECTS

1. Build a three-dimensional scale model of the solar system.
2. Mercury, Venus, Mars, Jupiter, and Saturn can be observed by the unaided eye. Research where in the sky these planets can be observed for the next five years. Construct a display with your findings.

APPLY

21. The greenhouse effect on Venus is much greater than that on Earth because the clouds on Venus are very dense and the amount of carbon dioxide in the air is greater. The CO_2 retains the heat.

22. In general, the more massive planets have more satellites.

23. The extreme heat, the gaseous state of the planets' surfaces, and the dense atmospheres would probably destroy any space probe before it could reach either of the planets' surfaces.

24. Rocks have been weathered to produce iron oxide. Channels appear to have been carved by flowing water. The northern ice cap is composed partly of ice.

25. Any planet orbiting the sun inside the orbit of another planet appears to go through phases. The orbit of Venus is inside the orbit of Earth.

MORE SKILL BUILDERS

1. Concept Mapping: See below.

2. Hypothesizing: Mercury is relatively

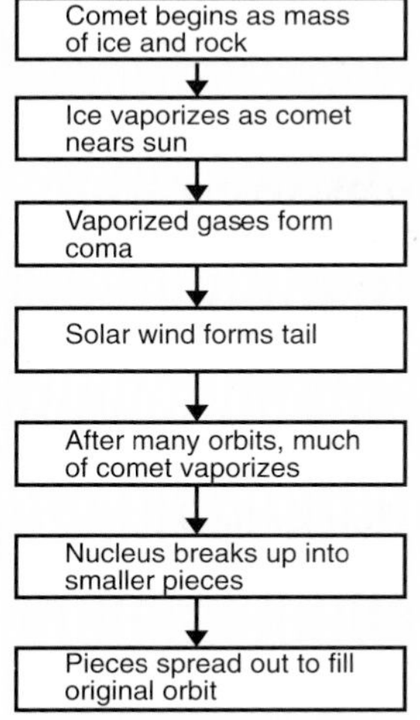

dark in color, and like dark-colored objects, it doesn't reflect much of the light that reaches its surface.

3. Measuring in SI:

area = length × width
= 40 000 km × 12 000 km
= 480 000 000 km^2

4. Sequencing: Saturn, Jupiter, Uranus, Neptune, Mars, Earth

5. Making and Using Tables: Answers will vary, but students should include the number of satellites, the type of atmosphere, and other unique characteristics in their tables.

CHAPTER

24 Stars and Galaxies

CHAPTER SECTION	OBJECTIVES	ACTIVITIES
24-1 Stars (2 days)	1. **Explain** why the positions of the constellations change throughout the year. 2. **Compare** and **contrast** absolute magnitude and apparent magnitude. 3. **Describe** how parallax is used to determine distances.	**Activity 24-1:** *Measuring Parallax,* p. 633
24-2 Evolution of Stars (3 days)	1. **Diagram** how stars are classified. 2. **Relate** the temperature of a star to its color. 3. **Outline** the evolution of a main sequence star.	**Activity 24-2:** *Sunspots,* p. 641
24-3 The Sun (1 day)	1. **Describe** how energy is produced in the sun. 2. **Recognize** that sunspots, prominences, and solar flares are related. 3. **Explain** why our sun is considered an average star and how it differs from stars in binary systems.	**MINI-Lab:** *What are the relative sizes of stars?* p. 644
24-4 Galaxies and the Expanding Universe (2 days)	1. **Describe** a galaxy and list the three main types of galaxies. 2. **Identify** several characteristics of the Milky Way Galaxy. 3. **Explain** how the big bang theory explains observed Doppler shifts.	**MINI-Lab:** *How far into space do we "see"?* p. 650
24-5 The Search for Extraterrestrial Life Science & Society (1 day)	1. **Name** locations in our solar system where life may have existed in the past or could exist now. 2. **Describe** methods used to search for extraterrestrial life within and beyond our solar system. 3. **Decide** if methods used by scientists might cause contamination of other worlds.	
Chapter Review		

ACTIVITY MATERIALS

FIND OUT	ACTIVITIES		MINI-LABS	
Page 627 balloon clothespin felt tip marker string metric ruler	**24-1 Measuring Parallax, p. 633** meterstick metric ruler masking tape	**24-2 Sunspots, p. 641** several books clipboard small tripod refracting telescope cardboard scissors	**What are the relative sizes of stars? p. 644** string (125 cm in length) chalk meterstick	**How far into space do we "see"? p. 650** large sheet of paper metric ruler or meterstick

CHAPTER FEATURES	TEACHER RESOURCE PACKAGE	OTHER RESOURCES
Problem Solving: *Star Light, Star Bright,* p. 630 **Skill Builder:** *Recognizing Cause and Effect,* p. 632	**Ability Level Worksheets** ◆ ***Study Guide,*** p. 95 ● ***Reinforcement,*** p. 95 ▲ ***Enrichment,*** p. 95 **Activity Worksheet,** pp. 216-217 **Critical Thinking/Problem Solving,** p. 30	**Lab Manual:** *Astronomical Distances,* pp. 189-190 **Lab Manual:** *Star Trails,* pp. 193-194 **Lab Manual:** *Star Positions,* pp. 195-196
Technology: *Studying Supernovas,* p. 639 **Skill Builder:** *Sequencing,* p. 640	**Ability Level Worksheets** ◆ ***Study Guide,*** p. 96 ● ***Reinforcement,*** p. 96 ▲ ***Enrichment,*** p. 96 **Activity Worksheet,** pp. 218-219 **Concept Mapping,** pp. 53-54 **Transparency Masters,** pp. 95-98	**Color Transparency 48,** Relative Sizes of Stars **Color Transparency 49,** H-R Diagram **Lab Manual:** *Star Colors,* pp. 191-192
Skill Builder: *Interpreting Scientific Illustrations,* p. 645	**Ability Level Worksheets** ◆ ***Study Guide,*** p. 97 ● ***Reinforcement,*** p. 97 ▲ ***Enrichment,*** p. 97 **MINI-Lab Worksheet,** p. 222 **Transparency Masters,** pp. 99-100	**Color Transparency 50,** Evolution of a Main Sequence Star
Skill Builder: *Recognizing Cause and Effect,* p. 651	**Ability Level Worksheets** ◆ ***Study Guide,*** p. 98 ● ***Reinforcement,*** p. 98 ▲ ***Enrichment,*** p. 98 **MINI-Lab Worksheet,** p. 223	
You Decide! p. 654	**Ability Level Worksheets** ◆ ***Study Guide,*** p. 99 ● ***Reinforcement,*** p. 99 ▲ ***Enrichment,*** p. 99 **Cross-Curricular Connections,** p. 28 **Science and Society,** p. 28	
Summary Key Science Words Understanding Vocabulary Checking Concepts Understanding Concepts Think & Write Critically Apply More Skill Builders Projects	**Chapter Review,** pp. 51-52 **Chapter Test,** pp. 158-161 **Unit Test 8,** pp. 162-163	**Chapter Review Software** **Test Bank**

◆ **Basic** ● **Average** ▲ **Advanced**

ADDITIONAL MATERIALS

SOFTWARE	AUDIOVISUAL	BOOKS/MAGAZINES
Astronomy II—Constellations, Educational Courseware. *Astronomy Demonstrations,* John Wiley and Sons, Inc. *Stars and Galaxies,* Queue. *Journey to the Stars,* Queue.	*Charting the Universe with Optical and Radio Telescopes,* film, EBEC. *Galaxies and the Universe,* film, Coronet/MTI. *The Night Sky,* film, EBEC. *Space Science: Galaxies and the Universe,* film, EBEC. *Universe,* film, Coronet/MTI.	Kaufmann, William J. III. *Universe.* 3rd ed. NY: W.H. Freeman & Co., 1991. Osterbrook, Donald E. *Stars and Galaxies: Citizens of the Universe.* NY: W.H. Freeman & Co., 1990.

CHAPTER

24

STARS AND GALAXIES

THEME DEVELOPMENT: Scale, structure, and evolution are the major themes of this chapter. The size and structure of stars and galaxies are presented. The evolution of stars and the universe should be emphasized as you teach all sections in the chapter.

CHAPTER OVERVIEW

- **Section 24-1:** This section compares the absolute and apparent brightness of stars. Other properties of stars are also presented.
- **Section 24-2:** The evolution of main-sequence stars from one stage to another is presented in this section. Energy production in stars is also discussed.
- **Section 24-3:** The structure and surface features of the sun are discussed in this section.
- **Section 24-4:** This section illustrates the different types of galaxies. The big bang theory of the evolution of the universe is also presented.
- **Section 24-5: Science and Society:** The You Decide feature asks students to consider whether humans should risk contaminating other worlds while in search of extraterrestrial life.

CHAPTER VOCABULARY

constellations
absolute magnitude
apparent magnitude
parallax
light-year
main sequence
nebula
giant
white dwarf
supergiant
neutron star
black hole
photosphere
chromosphere
corona
sunspots
binary system
galaxy
big bang theory
extraterrestrial life

CHAPTER 24

Stars and Galaxies

OPTIONS

For Your Gifted Students

This activity will show the apparent motion of the stars. Away from city lights, have students place an SLR camera on a tripod. Sighting through the lens, aim the camera so that the North Star (Polaris) is directly in the center of the viewfinder. Use a film that's fast, such as 1000 ASA. Open the shutter for 20 to 30 minutes and have the aperture as wide open as possible. As Earth rotates, the light from the stars will expose the film and appear as circular streaks around the North Star. Students can experiment by opening the shutter for longer periods of time.

The collection of stars, gas, and dust shown at left is a galaxy similar to the one that contains our solar system. There are countless galaxies in the universe, most of which are moving away from each other. Our universe is expanding.

FIND OUT!

Do this simple activity to model the expansion of the universe.

Partially inflate a balloon. Fold the neck and clip it shut with a clothespin so air doesn't escape. Draw six evenly spaced dots on the balloon with a felt-tip marker. Label the dots A through F. Use a string and ruler to measure the distance, in millimeters, from dot A to each of the other dots. Remove the clothespin and inflate the balloon some more. Measure the distance of each dot from A again. Inflate the balloon once more and take the new measurements. Which distances changed the most? The least? If each dot represents a galaxy, describe the motion of the galaxies relative to one another. Is the universe expanding?

Gearing Up

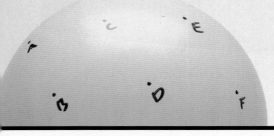

Previewing the Chapter

Previewing Science Skills

- ▶ In the **Skill Builders,** you will recognize cause and effect, sequence events, interpret scientific illustrations, and observe and infer.
- ▶ In the **Activities,** you will collect and analyze data and draw conclusions.
- ▶ In the **MINI-Labs,** you will interpret scientific illustrations and make inferences.

What's next?

You've discovered that the galaxies are moving away from each other. But what are galaxies, and why are they moving? In this chapter, you'll learn that galaxies are large groups of stars, and you'll discover how we know they are moving apart.

INTRODUCING THE CHAPTER

Use the Find Out activity to introduce students to the concept of an expanding universe. Inform students that they will be learning more about the universe and the stars and galaxies it contains as they read the chapter.

FIND OUT!

Preparation: Several days before you begin this chapter, have students bring in large, round balloons and clothespins.

Materials: one balloon, one clothespin, one felt-tip marker, string, and a metric ruler for each group

Cooperative Learning: Form Science Investigation groups of four students per group. Assign student roles that include a reader, a materials handler, a recorder, and a reporter. One student should blow up the balloon and clip it shut. Another should draw the dots on the balloon. The other two students should measure the distance between the dots.

Teaching Tips

▶ Caution students not to blow the balloons up so much that they break.

▶ Call on the reporters of each group to answer the text questions.

Gearing Up

Have students study the Gearing Up feature to familiarize themselves with the chapter. Discuss the relationship of the topics in the outline.

What's Next?

Before beginning the first section, make sure students understand the connection between the Find Out activity and the topics to follow.

For Your Mainstreamed Students

Students can practice identifying the constellations by performing the following activity. Have students cut black construction paper into several 4-cm squares. On each square, students should put pin holes to form a design of the stars of major constellations. Students then place a constellation square at one end of a cardboard tube. Pointing the tube toward a light source, students should be able to view the constellation through the tube. Have students switch constellation squares and make a game of identifying various constellations.

SECTION 24-1

PREPARATION

SECTION BACKGROUND

▶ The brightest star in the winter sky, Sirius, is actually two stars. One of the two stars of this binary system, Sirius B, is one of the first white dwarf stars ever discovered.

▶ The absolute magnitude of a star is affected by its size and temperature. The apparent magnitude of a star is affected by its size, temperature, and distance. If the absolute and apparent magnitudes of a star are known, its distance can be determined.

▶ Clouds of gas and dust in space can obscure starlight, reducing a star's apparent brightness.

▶ Another unit used for stating distances to stars and galaxies is the parsec. One parsec equals 3.26 light-years.

1 MOTIVATE

▶ Supply students with star charts that contain only dots as stars. Ask students to make up their own constellations using the stars. Ask students to explain why they chose the drawings they did. Relate this to how the original constellations were named.

TYING TO PREVIOUS KNOWLEDGE: Help students recall what they know about constellations. Ask how many students have seen the Big Dipper. Draw the stars of the Big Dipper on the chalkboard and show why it's called a dipper.

▶ Some students may know that they can use the North Star (Polaris) to determine direction if they're lost at night.

OBJECTIVES AND SCIENCE WORDS: Have students review the objectives and science words to become familiar with this section.

24-1 Stars

New Science Words

constellations
absolute magnitude
apparent magnitude
parallax
light-year

Objectives

▶ Explain why the positions of the constellations change throughout the year.
▶ Compare and contrast absolute magnitude and apparent magnitude.
▶ Describe how parallax is used to determine distances.

Constellations

Have you ever watched clouds drift by on a summer day? It's fun to look at the clouds and imagine they have shapes familiar to you. One may look like a face. You might see a cloud that resembles a rabbit or a bear. People long ago did much the same thing with patterns of stars in the sky. They named certain groups of stars, called **constellations,** after animals, characters in mythology, or familiar objects.

From Earth, a constellation looks like a group of stars that are relatively close to one another. In most cases, the stars in a constellation have no relationship to each other in space. Figure 24-1 illustrates how this is possible.

The position of a star in the sky can be given as a specific location within a constellation. For example, you can say that the star Betelgeuse (BEET ul joos) is in the

Figure 24-1. The star at the end of the "handle" of the Big Dipper is 210 light-years away. The star second from the end is only 88 light-years away, yet they appear next to each other in the sky.

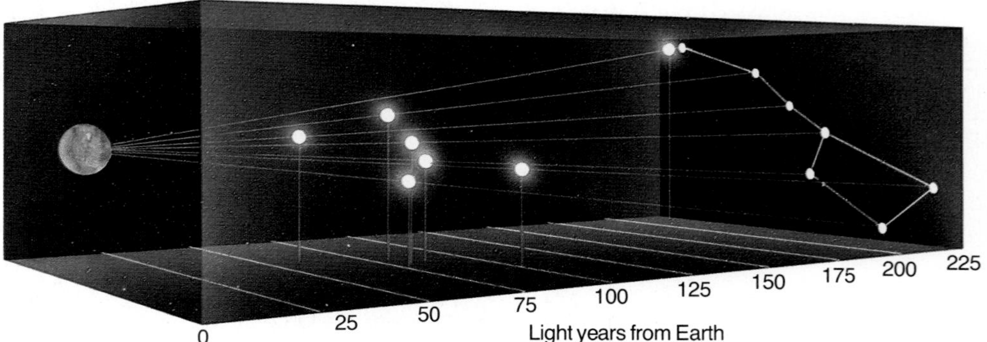

OPTIONS

Meeting Different Ability Levels

For Section 24-1, use the following **Teacher Resource Masters** depending upon individual students' needs.

◆ **Study Guide Master** for all students.

● **Reinforcement Master** for students of average and above average ability levels.

▲ **Enrichment Master** for above average students.

Additional Teacher Resource Package masters are listed in the OPTIONS box throughout the section. The additional masters are appropriate for all students.

◆ STUDY GUIDE 95

NAME ______ DATE ______ CLASS ______

STUDY GUIDE — Chapter 24

Stars — Text Pages 628–632

Decide if each statement below is true or false. If false, change the italicized word or words to make the statement correct and write your answer in the blank at the left. If the statement is correct, write "true" in the blank.

true 1. A group of stars that form a pattern is called a *constellation.*
apparent magnitude 2. The amount of light that Earth receives from a star is called the star's *absolute magnitude.*
light-years 3. The distances of stars from Earth are measured in *parallaxes.*
true 4. Very hot stars are a *blue-white* color.
absolute magnitude 5. The *apparent magnitude* of a star is the amount of light it actually gives off.
true 6. Another name for the North Star is *Polaris.*
greater than 7. The absolute magnitude of Rigel is *less than* that of Sirius.
true 8. The apparent shift in an object when viewed from two different positions is called *parallax.*
true 9. The pattern of dark lines recorded by a spectrograph can be used to identify the *elements* that are in a star's atmosphere.
true 10. The stars appear to change positions in the sky throughout the year because the *Earth revolves around the sun.*
distance 11. A light-year is the *speed* that light travels in one year.
true 12. The apparent magnitude of stars is *greater* when they are closer to Earth.
true 13. Constellations that circle Polaris and are visible year-round are called *circumpolar* constellations.
Polaris 14. The star *Betelgeuse* is almost directly over Earth's north pole.
true 15. All of the constellations appear to be moving because *Earth* is moving.

95

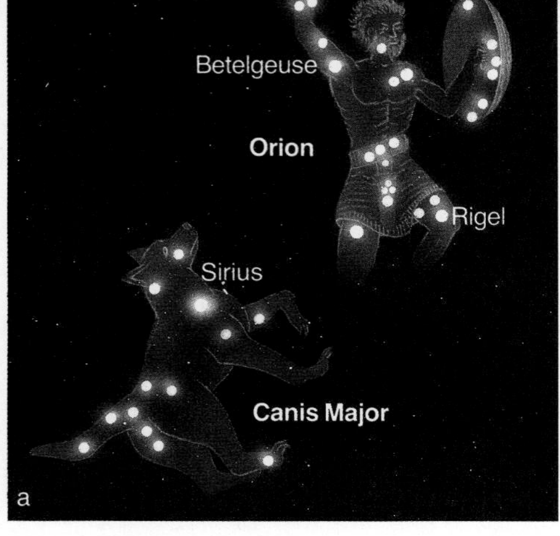

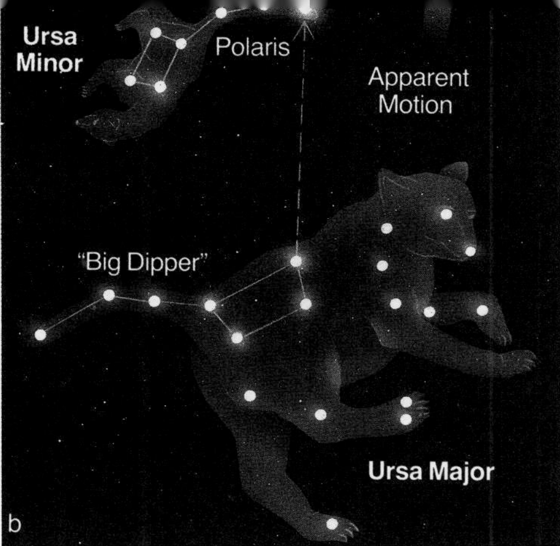

right shoulder of the mighty hunter Orion. Orion's faithful companion is his dog, Canis Major. The brightest star in the winter sky, Sirius (SIHR ee us), is in the constellation Canis Major.

Early Greek astronomers named many constellations, and today astronomers have divided the sky into 88 constellations. You may already know some of them. Have you ever tried to find the Big Dipper? It's part of the constellation Ursa Major. Notice how the front two stars of the Big Dipper point directly at the star Polaris. Polaris, also known as the North Star, is located at the end of the Little Dipper—part of Ursa Minor. Polaris is almost directly over Earth's north pole.

As Earth rotates, you can watch Ursa Major, Ursa Minor, and other constellations in the northern sky circle around Polaris. Because these constellations circle Polaris they are called circumpolar constellations.

All of the constellations appear to move because Earth is moving. The stars appear to complete one full circle in the sky in just under 24 hours as Earth rotates on its axis. The stars also appear to change positions in the sky throughout the year as Earth revolves around the sun.

Circumpolar constellations are visible all year long, but other constellations are not. As Earth orbits the sun, different constellations come into view while others disappear. Orion, which is visible in the winter, can't be seen in the summer because the daytime side of Earth is facing it. The various constellations visible each season are shown in Appendix J on pages 674 and 675.

Figure 24-2. Orion and Canis Major (a) are visible in the winter sky, but rest below the horizon during other seasons. Circumpolar constellations such as Ursa Major (b) are visible year-round.

Figure 24-3. This photograph shows the path of the circumpolar stars over a period of several hours. Because Polaris is almost directly over the North Pole, it doesn't appear to move much as Earth rotates.

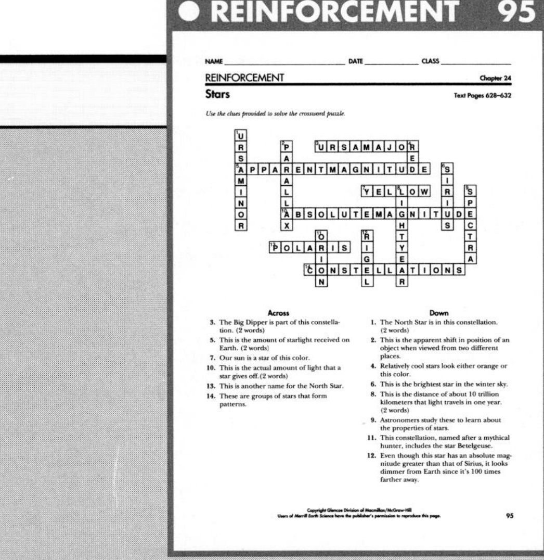

● REINFORCEMENT 95

NAME ______ DATE ______ CLASS ______

REINFORCEMENT — Chapter 24

Stars — Text Pages 628–632

Use the clues provided to solve the crossword puzzle.

Across

3. The Big Dipper is part of this constellation. (2 words)
5. This is the amount of starlight received on Earth. (2 words)
7. Our sun is a star of this color.
10. This is the actual amount of light that a star gives off. (2 words)
13. This is another name for the North Star.
14. These are groups of stars that form patterns.

Down

1. The North Star is in this constellation. (2 words)
2. This is the apparent shift in position of an object when viewed from two different places.
4. Relatively cool stars look either orange or this color.
6. This is the brightest star in the winter sky.
8. This is the distance of about 10 trillion kilometers that light travels in one year. (2 words)
9. Astronomers study these to learn about the properties of stars.
11. This constellation, named after a mythical hunter, includes the star Betelgeuse.
12. Even though this star has an absolute magnitude greater than that of Sirius, it looks dimmer from Earth since it's 100 times farther away.

95

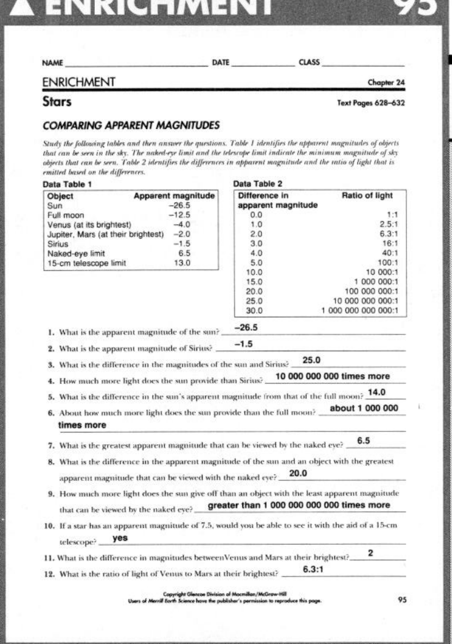

▲ ENRICHMENT 95

NAME ______ DATE ______ CLASS ______

ENRICHMENT — Chapter 24

Stars — Text Pages 628–632

COMPARING APPARENT MAGNITUDES

Study the following tables and then answer the questions. Table 1 identifies the apparent magnitudes of objects that can be seen in the sky. The naked-eye limit and the telescope limit indicate the minimum magnitude of sky objects that can be seen. Table 2 identifies the differences in apparent magnitude and the ratio of light that is emitted based on the differences.

Data Table 1

Object	Apparent magnitude
Sun	−26.5
Full moon	−12.5
Venus (at its brightest)	−4.0
Jupiter, Mars (at their brightest)	−2.0
Sirius	−1.5
Naked-eye limit	6.5
15-cm telescope limit	13.0

Data Table 2

Difference in apparent magnitude	Ratio of light
0.0	1:1
1.0	2.5:1
2.0	6.3:1
3.0	16:1
4.0	40:1
5.0	100:1
10.0	10 000:1
15.0	1 000 000:1
20.0	100 000 000:1
25.0	10 000 000 000:1
30.0	1 000 000 000 000:1

1. What is the apparent magnitude of the sun? **−26.5**
2. What is the apparent magnitude of Sirius? **−1.5**
3. What is the difference in the magnitudes of the sun and Sirius? **25.0**
4. How much more light does the sun provide than Sirius? **10 000 000 000 times more**
5. What is the difference in the sun's apparent magnitude from that of the full moon? **14.0**
6. About how much more light does the sun provide than the full moon? **about 1 000 000 times more**
7. What is the greatest apparent magnitude that can be viewed by the naked eye? **6.5**
8. What is the difference in the apparent magnitude of the sun and an object with the greatest apparent magnitude that can be viewed with the naked eye? **20.0**
9. How much more light does the sun give off than an object with the least apparent magnitude that can be viewed by the naked eye? **greater than 1 000 000 000 000 times more**
10. If a star has an apparent magnitude of 7.5, would you be able to see it with the aid of a 15-cm telescope? **yes**
11. What is the difference in magnitudes between Venus and Mars at their brightest? **2**
12. What is the ratio of light of Venus to Mars at their brightest? **6.3:1**

95

2 TEACH

Key Concepts are highlighted.

CONCEPT DEVELOPMENT

FLEX Your Brain

Use the Flex Your Brain activity to have students explore the CHANGING SHAPES OF THE CONSTELLATIONS. Students may think that the star patterns viewed from Earth are permanent. They should discover that the stars are changing their relative positions in space. As a result, the constellations are changing shape. For example, in several thousand years, Polaris will no longer be at the North Pole. Eventually, the stars of the Big Dipper will have moved so that it's no longer dipper shaped.

▶ **Demonstration:** Position student "constellations" around the edge of the classroom. Place one student at the center of the classroom to act as the sun. Have another student act as Earth and begin slowly rotating. Ask "Earth" for the names of "constellations" visible when "the sun" is not visible. Now have "Earth" revolve around "the sun." When "Earth" is at a different position, ask for the names of "constellations" that are visible when his or her back is to "the sun." Students should realize that constellations change during the year because Earth revolves around the sun.

▶ **Demonstration:** Use a planetarium to show the position and shape of prominent constellations visible in each season.

REVEALING MISCONCEPTIONS

▶ Ask students why stars are part of a particular constellation. Many students may think that stars within one constellation are close to one another in space. Explain that two stars that appear side by side may be separated by hundreds of light-years. Likewise, two stars that are only a few light-years apart may appear to be quite far apart in the night sky.

MINI QUIZ

Use the Mini Quiz to check students' recall of chapter content.

1. **The amount of light received on Earth from a star, called ______, is affected by distance.** *apparent magnitude*
2. **_____ is the apparent shift in the position of an object caused by viewing it from two locations.** *Parallax*
3. **A(n) _____ is the distance light travels in one year.** *light-year*

CONCEPT DEVELOPMENT

Cooperative Learning: Form Numbered Heads Together groups with four students per group and ask the following question. **What can be said about a star whose spectrum contains dark lines corresponding to the wavelengths absorbed by calcium, hydrogen, helium, and argon?** *The atmosphere of the star contains calcium, hydrogen, helium, and argon.*

PROBLEM SOLVING

Think Critically: When the distance between the light and the light meter was doubled from 20 cm to 40 cm, light intensity decreased by 1/4. When the distance was tripled, intensity decreased by 1/9; at four times, 1/16. The relationship can be expressed as 1 divided by the square of how many times distance is increased. At 100 cm, the light intensity will be decreased by 1/25.

Did You Know?

The brightest known stars shine as bright as one million of our suns. It would take 10 000 of the dimmest stars to equal the brightness of our sun.

Absolute and Apparent Magnitudes

When you look at constellations, you'll notice that some stars are brighter than others. Sirius looks much brighter than Rigel (RI juhl). But is Sirius actually a brighter star, or is it just closer to Earth, which makes it appear brighter? As it turns out, Sirius is 100 times closer to Earth than Rigel. If Sirius and Rigel were the same distance from Earth, Rigel would appear much brighter in the night sky than would Sirius.

When you refer to the brightness of a star, you can refer to either its absolute magnitude or its apparent magnitude. The **absolute magnitude** of a star is a measure of the amount of light it actually gives off. The amount of
1 light received on Earth is called the **apparent magnitude.** A star that's actually rather dim can appear quite bright in the sky if it's close to Earth. A star that's actually bright can appear dim if it's far away.

PROBLEM SOLVING

Star Light, Star Bright

Mary conducted an activity to determine the relationship between distance and the brightness of stars. She used a meterstick, a light meter, and a light bulb. The bulb was mounted at the zero end of the meterstick. Mary placed the light meter at the 20-cm mark on the meterstick and recorded the distance and the light meter reading in the data table. Readings are in luxes, which are units for measuring light intensity. Mary doubled and tripled the distance and took more readings.

Distance (cm)	Meter Reading (luxes)
20	4150
40	1050
60	460
80	262.5

Think Critically: What is the relationship between light intensity and distance? What would it be at 100 cm?

OPTIONS

INQUIRY QUESTIONS

▶**Two stars in the sky have the same apparent magnitude but one is much closer to you than the other. What can you determine about the absolute magnitudes of the two stars?** *The star that is farther away must have a greater absolute magnitude in order to appear as bright as the closer star.*

▶**Why would one star have a greater absolute magnitude than another?** *The star with the greater absolute magnitude gives off more energy than the other star. This might be because it is larger and/or hotter.*

▶**What property of a star could you determine if you knew the star's absolute and apparent magnitudes?** *The star's distance could be calculated.*

▶**If a star 100 light-years out in space suddenly exploded, how long would it be before humans on Earth would know of the explosion?** *It would take 100 years for the light from the explosion to reach Earth; a light-year is the distance light travels in one year.*

Determining the Distances to Stars

How do we know when a star is close to our solar system? One way is to measure its parallax. **Parallax** is the apparent shift in the position of an object when viewed from two different positions. You can easily observe parallax. Hold your hand at arm's length and look at one finger first with your left eye and then with your right eye. Your finger appears to change position with respect to the background. Now try the same experiment with your finger closer to your face. What do you observe? The nearer an object is to the observer, the greater its parallax. 2

Why are parallax measurements useful only for nearby stars?

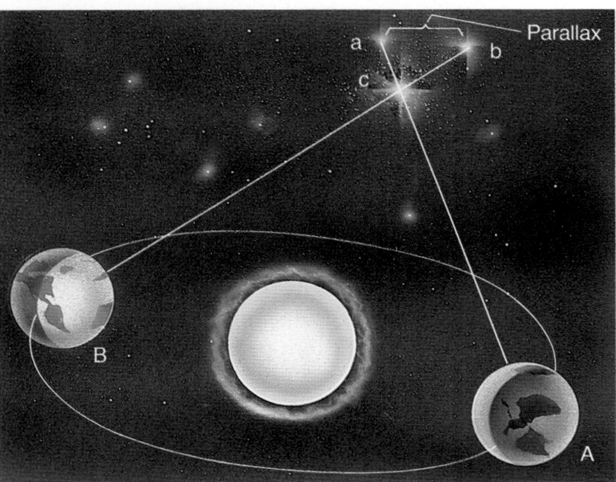

Figure 24-4. When Earth is in position A, the star appears to be in position a. The star appears to be in position b when Earth is in position B. This apparent shift in the star's position is its parallax. The actual position of the star is c.

We can measure the parallax of relatively close stars to determine their distances from Earth. When astronomers first realized how far away stars actually are, it became apparent that a new unit of measure would be needed to record their distances. Measuring star distances in kilometers would be like measuring the distance between cities in millimeters.

Distances in space are measured in light-years. A **light-year** is the distance that light travels in one year. Light travels at 300 000 km/s, or about 9.5 trillion kilometers in one year. The nearest star to Earth, other than the sun, is Proxima Centuri. Proxima Centuri is 4.2 light-years away, or about 40 trillion kilometers. It takes 4.2 years for its light to reach your eyes. 3

TEACHER F.Y.I.

▶ There are 360 degrees (°) in a circle. In each degree, there are 60 minutes (′) and in each minute there are 60 seconds (″). This means that one second equals 1/3600 of a degree. The largest measured parallax angle for any star is 0.77 seconds.

CROSS CURRICULUM

▶ **Mathematics:** Use the following equation to calculate the distance in light-years to two stars. Star 1 has a parallax angle (p) of 0.77″ and Star 2 has a parallax angle (p) of 0.04″.

$$d \text{ (light-years)} = 3.26/p$$

Star 1: d = 4.23 light-years
Star 2: d = 81.50 light-years

CHECK FOR UNDERSTANDING

Ask questions 1-3 and the **Apply** Question in the Section Review.

RETEACH

Activity: Use a soccer, football, or baseball playing field to conduct this activity demonstrating parallax. Have one student stand at one end of the field, approximately 50 meters away from another student using a compass. The compass should have a sighting mirror. Have the student determine the exact compass heading to the student at the far end of the field. Now have the student holding the compass move approximately 20 meters to his or her left or right. Have the student determine the new compass heading to the stationary student at the end of the field. Repeat this activity but vary the distances between students.

EXTENSION

For students who have mastered this section, use the **Reinforcement** and **Enrichment** masters or other OPTIONS provided.

ENRICHMENT

▶ After they have studied the star charts in Appendix J, have students look for ways to associate constellation drawings to familiar items. For example, the main part of Sagittarius is often called the teapot. Also have them look for ways that one constellation can help them find others. For example, the curve of the Big Dipper's handle points at the star Arcturus in Boötes. Have students draw star maps to show the relationships they have discovered.

PROGRAM RESOURCES

Use **Laboratory Manual,** pages 189-190, Astronomical Distances.
Use **Laboratory Manual,** pages 193-194, Star Trails.

3 CLOSE

FLEX Your Brain

Use the Flex Your Brain activity to have students explore OUR SOLAR SYSTEM'S NEAREST NEIGHBOR. The nearest stellar system to the sun is a group of three stars. To the naked eye they appear as one star called Alpha Centauri. Alpha Centauri is actually two stars revolving around each other. Near them is a third star, Proxima Centauri, believed to be closest to our solar system.

SECTION REVIEW ANSWERS

1. As Earth revolves around the sun, the nighttime side of Earth faces different directions in space. As a result, different constellations become visible on the nighttime side. The daytime side is too bright to allow constellations to be seen.

2. Because both stars give off the same amount of light, they have the same absolute magnitude. If one star looks brighter than the other, it's probably closer to Earth. However, interstellar gases could obscure a close star, making one that's far away appear brighter.

3. The parallax for faraway stars is too small to be measured accurately.

4. Apply: Because the nearest stars are mostly invisible when viewed from Earth, they must not be very bright. Their absolute magnitudes aren't very bright.

Skill Builder

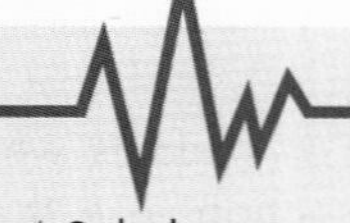

Proxima Centauri is 4.2 light-years away. Ages will vary, but should equal the students' ages minus 4.2 years. Proxima Centauri is close but it doesn't give off much light. Both the absolute and apparent magnitudes of Betelgeuse are brighter than Proxima Centauri's.

Figure 24-5. A triangle-shaped glass called a prism can be used to produce a spectrum. The various wavelengths making up white light bend at different angles when they pass through the prism. They separate from each other, and the colors of the spectrum become visible.

Determining a Star's Temperature and Composition

The color of a star indicates its temperature. For example, very hot stars are a blue-white color. A relatively cool star looks orange or red. Stars the temperature of our sun have a yellow color.

Astronomers learn about other properties of stars by studying their spectra. They use spectrographs to break visible light from a star into its component colors. If you look closely at the spectrum of a star, such as the one shown on page 650, you will see dark lines in it. The lines are caused by elements in the star's atmosphere. As light radiated from a star passes through the star's atmosphere, some of it is absorbed by elements in the atmosphere. The wavelengths of visible light that are absorbed appear as dark lines in the spectrum. Each element absorbs certain wavelengths, producing a certain pattern of dark lines. The patterns of lines can be used to identify which elements are in a star.

SECTION REVIEW

1. Explain how Earth's revolution affects constellations that are visible throughout the year.
2. If two stars give off the same amount of light, what might cause one of them to look much brighter than the other?
3. Measuring distances in space using parallax is only useful for relatively near stars. Explain why it can't be used for objects that are very far away.
4. **Apply:** Only about 700 stars have large enough parallaxes that their distances can be determined using parallax. Most of them are invisible to the naked eye. What does this indicate about their absolute magnitudes?

Skill Builder — Recognizing Cause and Effect

Suppose you viewed Proxima Centuri through a telescope. How old were you when the light that you see left Proxima Centuri? Why might Proxima Centuri look dimmer than the star Betelgeuse, a very large star 489 light-years away? If you need help, refer to Recognizing Cause and Effect in the **Skill Handbook** on page 683.

OPTIONS

INQUIRY QUESTIONS

▶ **If you observe two stars in space and one of them is blue in color while the other is orange in color, which of the two stars is hotter?** *The blue star would be very much hotter than the orange star.*

▶ **What can be learned about a star by studying the pattern of dark lines in its spectrum?** *The pattern of dark lines indicates the element content of the star's atmosphere.*

PROGRAM RESOURCES

From the **Teacher Resource Package** use:

Critical Thinking/Problem Solving, page 30, Archaeoastronomy.

Activity Worksheets, page 5, Flex Your Brain.

Use **Laboratory Manual,** pages 195-196, Star Positions.

ACTIVITY 24-1
Measuring Parallax

Problem: *How does distance affect parallax?*

Material 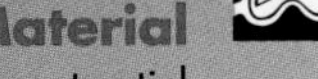

- meterstick
- metric ruler
- masking tape

Procedure

1. Place a piece of masking tape next to the 20-, 40-, and 60-cm marks of the meterstick so that a pencil will stop at the tape and be aligned with the 20-, 40-, or 60-cm mark.
2. Use tape to attach the metric ruler to a bulletin board in the room. Make sure the metric ruler is in a horizontal position so that it reads left to right.
3. Carefully place the 1-cm end of the meterstick on the bridge of your nose. **CAUTION:** *Be sure to wear goggles to protect your eyes. Don't walk with the meterstick in this position.* Place the other end of the meterstick against the 1-cm mark on the ruler.
4. Move a pencil along the meterstick to where the first piece of tape is located.
5. Close your left eye. Align the pencil with the end of the meterstick and the 1-cm mark on the ruler. Close your right eye and open your left eye. Observe the number of centimeters from the metric ruler that the pencil shifted. Record the number in the data table.
6. Write a hypothesis stating how moving the pencil farther from the eye will affect the distance the pencil shifts.
7. Repeat Steps 5 and 6 with the pencil at the 40- and 60-cm marks.

Data and Observations Sample Data

Distance of pencil from eye (cm)	Apparent movement (cm)
20	18.4
40	8.5
60	4.9

Analyze

1. What happened to the pencil when the right eye was closed and the left eye was opened?
2. At what distance from the eye did the pencil shift the greatest distance?
3. What happened to the shift of the pencil as the distance of the pencil from the eye increased?

Conclude and Apply

4. How does your hypothesis compare with the results of the activity?
5. How does the distance of an object from an observer affect parallax?
6. How might astronomers use parallax?

ACTIVITY 24-1
25 minutes

OBJECTIVE: Determine and **describe** the effect of distance on the parallax of an object.

PROCESS SKILLS applied in this activity:
▶ **Formulating Models** in Procedure Steps 1-4.
▶ **Observing** in Procedure Step 5.
▶ **Hypothesizing** in Procedure Step 6.
▶ **Interpreting Data** in Conclude and Apply Question 5.
▶ **Inferring** in Conclude and Apply Question 6.

COOPERATIVE LEARNING
Using the Paired Partners strategy, assign one member of each group the role of recorder. The other partner should carry out the experiment. Students can then switch roles.

TEACHING THE ACTIVITY

▶ The recorder may need to hold the end of the meterstick against the ruler for stability during the measurement readings.

▶ Remind students that they are to predict what they will observe at the 40- and 60-cm marks *after* they take the 20-cm reading but *before* they continue with the measurements.

▶ **Expected Results:** Answers for the apparent movement of the pencil will vary somewhat because they depend on the distance between the right and left eye of each student. Typical answers, however, approach 20 cm of apparent movement from the 20-cm mark, 8.5 cm apparent movement from the 40-cm mark, and 4.9 cm apparent movement from the 60-cm mark.

ANSWERS TO QUESTIONS

1. The pencil appeared to shift to the right. In actuality, nothing happened to the pencil; the movement was only apparent.
2. at the 20-cm mark
3. The amount of apparent shift decreased.
4. Answers will vary. Some will have hypothesized that the apparent shift will decrease as distance between the object (pencil) and observer (eye) increases. These students should indicate that experimental data supported their hypotheses.
5. As the distance of an object from an observer increases, the parallax of the object decreases at a constant and predictable rate.
6. Astronomers use parallax angles (or shifts in the apparent position of astronomical objects) to determine distances to the objects. Parallax angles can also be used to determine sizes and actual motions of the objects (by analyzing their apparent motions). Once the distance and size of an object are determined, other characteristics of the object, such as energy emission, can be inferred.

PROGRAM RESOURCES

From the **Teacher Resource Package** use:
Activity Worksheets, pages 216-217, Activity 24-1: Measuring Parallax.

SECTION 24-2

PREPARATION

SECTION BACKGROUND

▶ Not all stars shine with a steady light. Stars that change in brightness are called variable stars. Stars may vary because the outer layers of the star may expand and contract, causing a change in the temperature and the absolute magnitude of the star. Betelgeuse in Orion can change its surface area by more than 40 percent, causing it to vary in brightness.

▶ One class of variable star, called a Cepheid variable, is very important to the study of the universe. These stars vary regularly and their period of variation is an indication of their absolute magnitudes. Because of this, they can be used to determine distances to faraway clusters and galaxies. Polaris is a Cepheid variable.

▶ In a star that has a mass similar to our sun, outer layers become unstable and begin escaping into space when the core runs out of hydrogen fuel. The escaping gases form a shell around the star, producing a planetary nebula. The Ring Nebula in the constellation Lyra is an example of this stage of stellar evolution.

1 MOTIVATE

FLEX Your Brain

Use the Flex Your Brain activity to have students explore WHAT POWERS A STAR. Have students investigate the process of fusion in stars.

PROGRAM RESOURCES

From the **Teacher Resource Package** use:

Activity Worksheets, page 5, Flex Your Brain.

24-2 Evolution of Stars

New Science Words

main sequence
nebula
giant
white dwarf
supergiant
neutron star
black hole

Objectives

- ▶ Diagram how stars are classified.
- ▶ Relate the temperature of a star to its color.
- ▶ Outline the evolution of a main sequence star.

The H-R Diagram

In the early 1900s, Ejnar Hertzsprung and Henry Russell noticed that for most stars, the higher their temperatures, the brighter their absolute magnitudes. They developed a graph to show this relationship.

Hertzsprung and Russell placed the temperatures of the stars across the bottom of the graph and the absolute magnitudes of the stars up one side. A graph that shows the relationship of a star's temperature to its absolute magnitude is called a Hertzsprung-Russell (H-R) diagram. Figure 24-7 shows a typical H-R diagram.

As you can see, stars seem to fit into specific areas of the chart. Most stars fit into a diagonal band that runs from the upper left to the lower right of the chart. This band, called the **main sequence,** contains hot, blue, bright

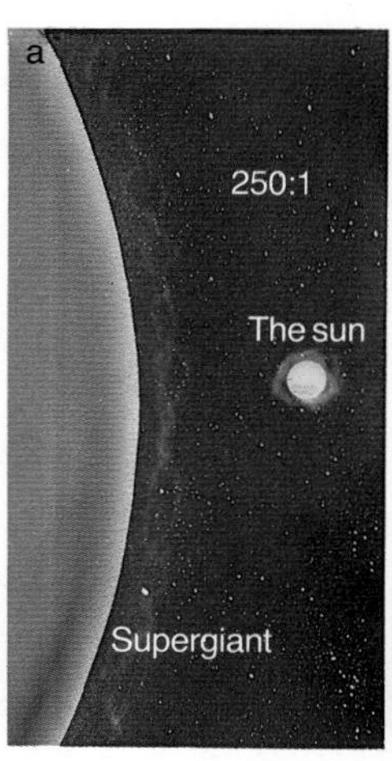

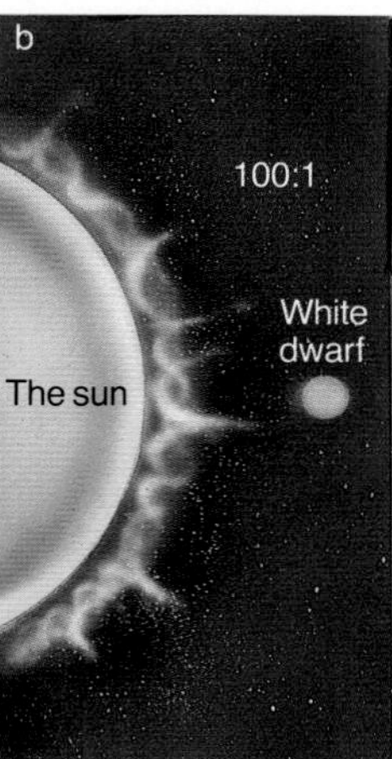

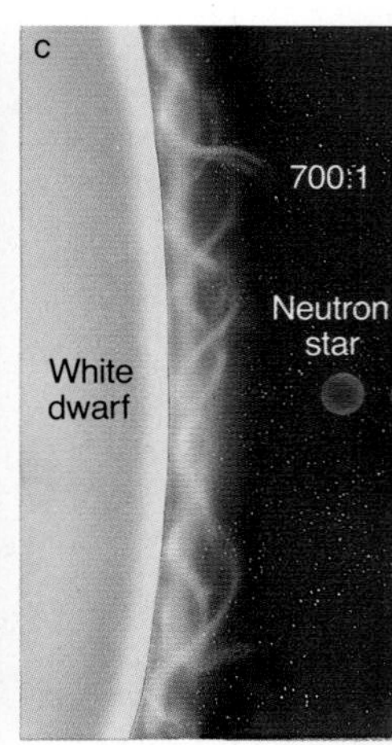

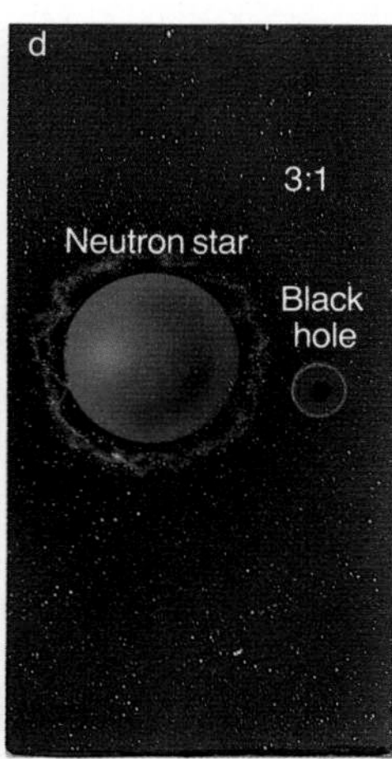

Figure 24-6. The Relative Sizes of Stars: (a) A supergiant can be 250 times as large as our sun. (b) The sizes of white dwarfs vary considerably, but a typical white dwarf is planet-sized, or about 100 times smaller than our sun. (c) A typical white dwarf is 700 times larger than a typical neutron star. (d) A black hole is about one-third the size of a neutron star.

OPTIONS

Meeting Different Ability Levels

For Section 24-2, use the following **Teacher Resource Masters** depending upon individual students' needs.

◆ **Study Guide Master** for all students.

● **Reinforcement Master** for students of average and above average ability levels.

▲ **Enrichment Master** for above average students.

Additional Teacher Resource Package masters are listed in the OPTIONS box throughout the section. The additional masters are appropriate for all students.

◆ STUDY GUIDE 96

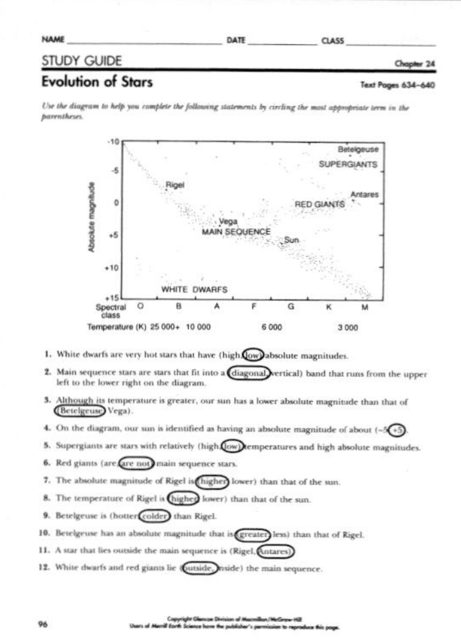

NAME ____________ DATE ________ CLASS ________

STUDY GUIDE — Chapter 24

Evolution of Stars — Text Pages 634–640

Use the diagram to help you complete the following statements by circling the most appropriate term in the parentheses.

1. White dwarfs are very hot stars that have (high, low) absolute magnitudes.
2. Main sequence stars are stars that fit into a (diagonal, vertical) band that runs from the upper left to the lower right on the diagram.
3. Although its temperature is greater, our sun has a lower absolute magnitude than that of (Betelgeuse, Vega).
4. On the diagram, our sun is identified as having an absolute magnitude of about (−5, +5).
5. Supergiants are stars with relatively (high, low) temperatures and high absolute magnitudes.
6. Red giants (are, are not) main sequence stars.
7. The absolute magnitude of Rigel is (higher, lower) than that of the sun.
8. The temperature of Rigel is (higher, lower) than that of the sun.
9. Betelgeuse is (hotter, colder) than Rigel.
10. Betelgeuse has an absolute magnitude that is (greater, less) than that of Rigel.
11. A star that lies outside the main sequence is (Rigel, Antares).
12. White dwarfs and red giants lie (outside, inside) the main sequence.

96

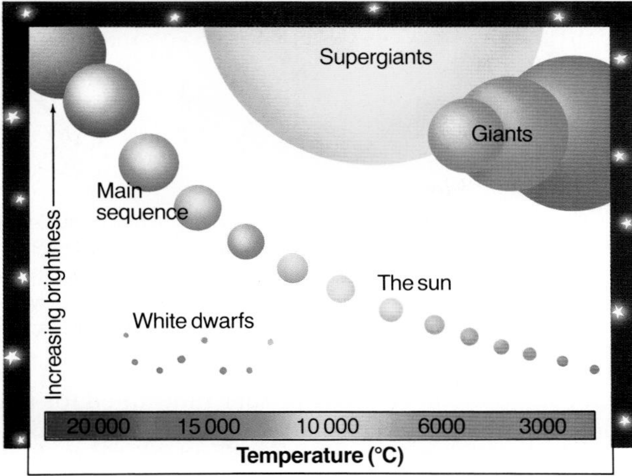

Figure 24-7. Hot, blue stars in the upper left of the main sequence are as large as giants but they are much hotter. Moderate, yellow stars are near the middle of the main sequence. Very dim, small red stars are in the lower right of the main sequence. Giants and supergiants are bright but cool and don't fall within the main sequence. White dwarfs are hot but not very bright.

stars in the upper left and cool, red, dim stars in the lower right. Yellow, medium temperature, medium brightness stars fall in between. The sun is a yellow main sequence star.

About 90 percent of all stars are main sequence stars. Among main sequence stars, the hottest stars generate the most light and the coolest generate the least. But what about the remaining ten percent? Some of these stars are hot but not very bright. These small stars are located on the lower left of the H-R diagram and are called white dwarfs. Other stars are extremely bright but not very hot. These large stars on the upper right of the H-R diagram are called giants, or red giants because they are usually red in color. The largest giants are called supergiants.

Fusion

When the H-R diagram was developed, scientists didn't know what caused stars to shine. Hertzsprung and Russell developed their diagram without knowing what produced the light and heat of stars.

For centuries, people had been puzzled by the question of what stars were and what made them shine. It wasn't until the early part of this century that scientists were forced to explain how a star could shine for billions of years. Until that time, many had estimated the age of Earth as only a few thousand years old. The

Did You Know?

In 1600, Giordano Bruno was burned at the stake for suggesting that the stars were like our sun. He thought perhaps they even had planets orbiting them as the sun of our solar system does. Bruno's beliefs are accepted today as common knowledge, but during his time they were unacceptable.

● REINFORCEMENT 96

NAME ______ DATE ______ CLASS ______

REINFORCEMENT — Chapter 24

Evolution of Stars — Text Pages 634–640

Circle the term in the puzzle that fits each clue. Then write the term on the line. In the puzzle, the terms read across or down.

E I B L A C K H O L E N S
H N E U T R O N S T A R T
R M A I N S E Q U E N C E
D C E I E N P R P O P O G
I O S E B L U E E D T H I
A L A T U M A S R S C A A
G O Y E L L O W G N B E N
R R C O A N V E I R T E T
A W H I T E D W A R F D I
M N T S U P E R N O V A O
E N F U S I O N T E R G Y

1. A **nebula** is a large cloud of dust and gas that becomes a star.
2. A graph that shows the relationship between a star's absolute magnitude and temperature is an **H-R diagram**.
3. A star that is a **giant** uses helium for fuel and has expanding outer layers.
4. The **fusion** of atoms powers the sun and other stars.
5. The temperature and brightness of stars are indicated by **color**.
6. About 90 percent of the stars including our sun are **main sequence** stars.
7. A **supernova** is produced when the outer core of a star explodes after the core collapses.
8. The hottest, brightest stars in the main sequence are a **blue** color.
9. Medium hot and bright stars like our sun are **yellow** in color.
10. When a star has no fuel left and its outer layers escape into space, it is a **white dwarf**.
11. As heavier and heavier elements are formed by fusion, a star expands into a **supergiant**.
12. When a collapsed core becomes so dense only neutrons can exist there, a **neutron star** is formed.
13. A **black hole** is so dense that nothing, including light, can escape its gravity field.
14. Write the remaining letters in the puzzle to reveal a famous scientist's theory.
Einstein proposed that mass can be converted into energy.

96

▲ ENRICHMENT 96

NAME ______ DATE ______ CLASS ______

ENRICHMENT — Chapter 24

Evolution of Stars — Text Pages 634–640

CLASSIFYING STARS

Use the H-R diagram on page 635 of your textbook to classify each of the stars listed in the table as white dwarf, main sequence, giant, or supergiant stars. Also identify the color of the star based on its spectral class.

Spectral classifications	
Class	Color
O	blue
B	bluish-white
A	white
F	yellowish-white
G	yellow
K	orange
M	red

Star	Surface temperature, K	Absolute magnitude	Type of star	Spectral color
Hadar	21 000	−5	main sequence	blue
Sirius A	10 400	+1.4	main sequence	bluish-white
Sirius B	10 700	+11.6	white dwarf	bluish-white
Arcturus	4 500	−0.3	giant	orange
Antares	2 900	−4.5	supergiant	red
Altair	8 000	+2.2	main sequence	white
Ross	2 800	+13.3	main sequence	red
Beta Pegasi	2 000	−1.4	giant	red
Capella	5 900	−0.7	giant	orange
Van Maanen's	5 800	+10.4	white dwarf	yellow
Bernard's	2 600	+13.2	main sequence	red
Pollux	4 100	+1.0	giant	orange
Procyon	6 500	+2.8	giant	yellowish-white
Betelgeuse	2 700	−5.6	supergiant	red
Mintaka	21 000	−5.1	main sequence	bluish-white

96

Cooperative Learning: Using the Paired Partners strategy, have students prepare and display a bulletin board version of a Hertzsprung-Russell diagram. Use Figure 24-7 as a guide.

TYING TO PREVIOUS KNOWLEDGE: Help students recall the states of matter from Chapter 2. Remind them that stars are composed of matter in the plasma state. Have them describe what happens to matter in the plasma state.

OBJECTIVES AND SCIENCE WORDS: Have students review the objectives and science words to become familiar with this section.

2 TEACH

Key Concepts are highlighted.

CONCEPT DEVELOPMENT

Cooperative Learning: Form Expert Teams with three students in each team. Have members of the Expert Teams answer the following questions. **What properties of stars are plotted on the H-R diagram?** *Absolute magnitude is plotted against temperature.* **What process generates energy in the core of a star? Explain.** *Fusion generates energy in the core of a star. Four hydrogen atoms fuse to become one helium atom. Mass that is lost in the reaction is changed to energy.* **What process occurs to mark the birth of a star?** *Once the gas and dust in a nebula have contracted so much that temperatures inside the cloud center reach 10 000 000°C, fusion begins and energy is radiated outward. Once the energy makes its way to the surface of the dense cloud and radiates into space, a star is formed.*

CONCEPT DEVELOPMENT

▶ **Demonstration:** Using tongs, hold the end of a wire (an unfolded paper clip will work) over the flame of a Bunsen burner. Gradually heat the wire until it begins to glow. Ask students to record the color of the glowing wire. Continue to hold the wire over the flame to allow it to become hotter. Ask students to record any changes they see in the wire while it's being heated. Ask one student to summarize what happened to the wire. As the wire was heated, it started to glow and gradually changed from a reddish-orange color to a yellow-white as it became hotter. Relate this to the different colors of stars on the main sequence. **CAUTION:** *Wear goggles and handle the hot wire carefully.*

TEACHER F.Y.I.

▶ Matter in the core of a star is in the plasma state. In a plasma, atoms have been stripped of their electrons. The atomic nuclei are so energetic that they approach each other at high rates of speed and fuse into heavier atoms.

CROSS CURRICULUM

▶ **Physical Science:** Have students research the controversy over the possibility of achieving "cold fusion" in the near future. Cold fusion is the theoretical fusion of hydrogen nuclei at room temperature. In 1990, two scientists (British chemist Martin Fleischmann and University of Utah colleague, B. Stanley Pons) claimed to have observed heat from fusion when they inserted palladium rods into jars of heavy water in electrolysis devices. To date, no one has been able to confirm that such electrolytic cells produce heat or other radiation that could be attributed to fusion reactions.

▶ **Science and Math:**
4 (H) = 4 (1.008 amu) = 4.032
Mass lost:
4.032 − 4.004 = 0.028 amu lost
Lost mass is converted into energy.

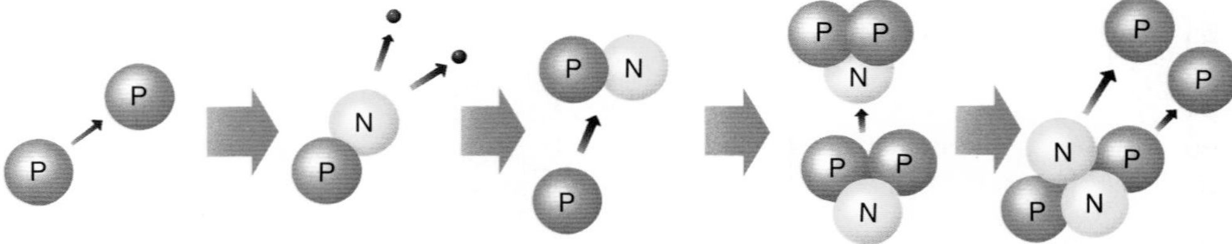

Two hydrogen nuclei (protons) are forced together in the core of a star. | One of the protons decays to a neutron, releasing subatomic particles. | Another proton fuses with the proton and neutron to form an isotope of helium. | Another helium isotope fuses with the previously formed isotope. | A helium nucleus is formed as two protons break away. Energy is released in the process.

sun could have been made of coal and shined for that long. But what material could possibly burn for billions of years?

In 1920, A. S. Eddington suggested that hydrogen atoms in the sun fused, or combined, to form helium atoms. Recall that the nucleus of a hydrogen atom is a single proton. A helium atom contains two protons and two neutrons in its nucleus. The diagram above illustrates how four hydrogen nuclei could combine to create one helium nucleus. The mass of one helium nucleus is less than the mass of four hydrogen nuclei, so some mass is lost in the reaction.

Years earlier, in 1905, Albert Einstein had proposed a theory stating that mass can be converted into energy. The mass "lost" when hydrogen atoms fuse to form a helium atom is converted to energy. Eddington concluded that hydrogen fusion powered the sun and other stars.

Fusion occurs in the cores of stars. Only there, are temperatures and pressures high enough to cause atoms to fuse. Normally, they would repel each other, but in the core of a star, atoms are forced close enough together that their nuclei attract.

Science and MATH

The mass of a hydrogen nucleus is 1.008 atomic mass units (amu). A helium nucleus' mass is 4.004 amu. Calculate the mass lost when four hydrogen nuclei fuse to form one helium nucleus. What happens to this mass?

The Evolution of Stars

The H-R diagram and Eddington's theory explained a lot about stars. But, they also led to more questions. Many wondered why some stars didn't fit in the main sequence group and what happened when a star exhausted its supply of hydrogen fuel. Today, we have a theory of how stars evolve, what makes them different from one another, and what happens when they die.

OPTIONS

INQUIRY QUESTIONS

▶ **Why is the mass of the helium atom formed by fusion less than the combined masses of the four hydrogen atoms that fused to form it?** *Some of the mass of the hydrogen atoms is converted to energy.*

▶ **When the hydrogen fuel inside a star is used up, why does the star become unbalanced?** *The outward pressure caused by fusion is reduced and can no longer balance the force of gravity. When this happens, the core begins to contract.*

▶ **If the temperature inside a star's contracting core heats up, why does the outer layer of the star turn reddish in color?** *The increased heat inside the star causes the outer layers of the star to expand. As the outer layers expand outward, the gases contained in them cool down, thus becoming red in color.*

1 A star begins as a large cloud of gas and dust called a **nebula.** The particles of gas and dust exert a gravitational force on each other, and the nebula begins to contract. As the particles in the cloud move closer together, the temperatures in the nebula increase. When temperatures inside the nebula reach 10 000 000°C, fusion begins. The energy released radiates outward through the condensing ball of gas. As the energy radiates into space, a star is born.

What determines when fusion begins within a nebula?

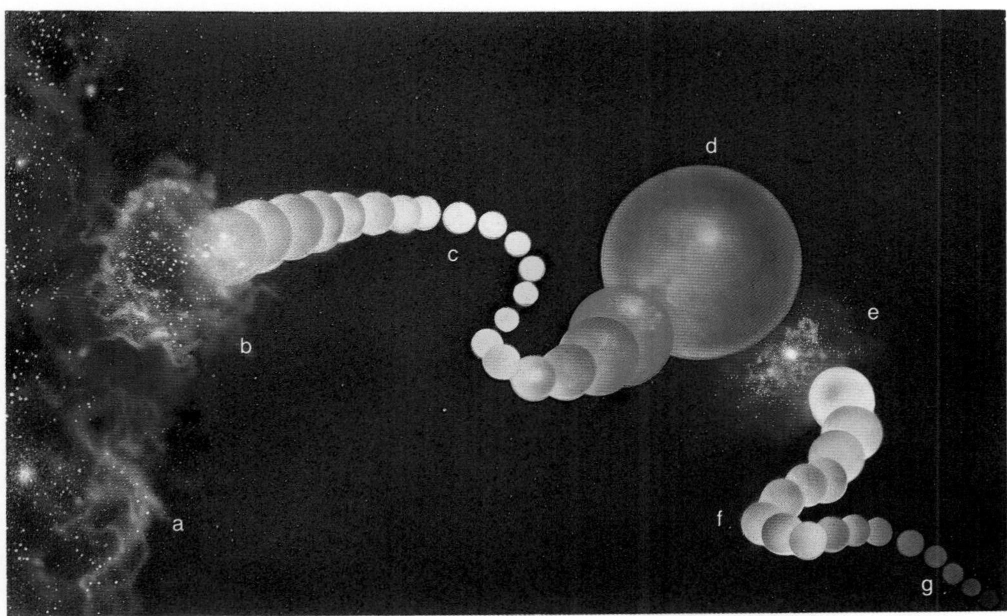

Figure 24-8. The Life of a Main Sequence Star the size of our sun: A nebula (a) condenses and stars begin to form within it as temperatures rise (b). A main sequence star forms (c). When its hydrogen fuel is exhausted, it expands and becomes a giant (d). The core collapses while the outer portions of the giant are blown away (e), forming a white dwarf (f). Eventually, the white dwarf uses up it fuel and becomes a cold, dead star (g). Note that stars are not shown to scale.

The heat from the fusion causes pressure that balances the attraction due to gravity, and the star becomes a main sequence star. It continues to use up its hydrogen fuel.

When the hydrogen in the core of the star is exhausted, there is no longer a balance between pressure and gravity. The core contracts, and the temperatures inside the star increase. This causes the outer layers of the star 2 to expand. The star has evolved into a **giant.**

Unless a giant has a small mass, helium nuclei fuse to form carbon in its core. By this time, the star has expanded to an enormous size, and its outer layers are much cooler than they were when it was a main sequence star. In about 5 billion years, our sun will become a giant.

CONCEPT DEVELOPMENT

▶ Refer students to Figure 24-7 and ask the following questions of the class as a group. **What is true about the absolute magnitude and temperature of supergiant stars?** *Supergiant stars have very high absolute magnitudes but very low temperatures.* **Based on this fact and their name, what can be said about supergiant stars?** *Supergiant stars are very large compared to other stars.* **Why do the stars located in the upper left portion of the H-R diagram have such a high absolute magnitude?** *These stars are fairly large and have very high temperatures.*

Cooperative Learning: Form Problem Solving Teams of four students per team. Have students construct a concept map showing the evolution of a star from beginning to end. Have students include branches in the map for stars of low, medium, and high mass.

▶ Ask the following questions of the class as a group. **What type of object forms if the core of a star more than 30 times more massive than the sun collapses?** *black hole* **Why is this object called a black hole?** *Nothing, not even light, can escape its tremendous gravity.* **If black holes can't be seen, how have astronomers found what they think are black holes?** *As matter is drawn into a black hole, it is thought that large amounts of X rays are given off. Astronomers have found several strong X-ray sources that appear to have very high mass but that can't be seen.*

ENRICHMENT

▶ Have students use astronomy books and magazine articles to research the Horsehead and Orion Nebulas located in the constellation of Orion. Have them determine why the Horsehead Nebula is a dark nebula and the Orion Nebula is a bright nebula. Also have them explain the relationship of the brightness of the nebulas and star formation processes occurring within them.

PROGRAM RESOURCES

From the **Teacher Resource Package** use:

Transparency Masters, pages 95-96, Relative Sizes of Stars.

Transparency Masters, pages 97-98, H-R Diagram.

Use **Color Transparency** number 48, Relative Sizes of Stars.

Use **Color Transparency** number 49, H-R Diagram.

REVEALING MISCONCEPTIONS

▶ Ask students to describe how big stars are. Many students will consider them to be rather small. Others will think they are about the size of our sun. Refer students to Figure 24-6 to show the relative sizes of stars.

TEACHER F.Y.I.

▶ A white dwarf will eventually use up its fuel supply and evolve into a burned out black dwarf. This is not necessarily true for a white dwarf that is part of a binary system. If the white dwarf is close enough to its companion star, it may pull hydrogen from it. The hydrogen is compressed and fusion occurs on the surface of the white dwarf. This causes the brightness of the star to increase thousands of times, forming a nova. A nova will remain bright for a few weeks or months and then return to its original brightness.

▶ Whether a star ends up as a white dwarf, a neutron star, or a black hole depends on mass. If the white dwarf has a mass less than 1.4 solar masses, it will remain as a white dwarf until it uses up all of its fuel. A white dwarf star with a mass between 1.4 and 3.0 solar masses will evolve into a neutron star. If the mass of the white dwarf is over 3.0 solar masses, it will evolve into a black hole.

▶ A very strong candidate for a black hole is A0620-00 located in the binary star system of V616 Monocerotis. It appears to have an accretion disk around it and has a mass of at least 3.8 solar masses. Until this discovery, Cygnus X-1 had been the leading candidate for a black hole.

After the star's core uses up its supply of helium, it contracts even more. If the star has a large mass, its core uses up the carbon and other elements it previously created and produces even heavier elements. As the core of the star runs out of fuel, the outer layers become unstable and begin escaping into space. This leaves behind the hot, dense core. The burned-out core contracts under
3 the force of gravity. At this stage in a star's evolution, it is a **white dwarf.**

What determines whether a star becomes a giant versus a supergiant?

In stars more than ten times more massive than our sun, the stages of evolution occur more quickly and more violently. The core heats up to much higher temperatures. Heavier and heavier elements form by fusion. The star expands into a **supergiant.** Eventually, iron forms in the core. Because fusion can no longer occur, the core collapses violently, sending a shock wave outward through the star. The outer portion of the star explodes, producing a supernova. A supernova can be millions of times brighter than the original star.

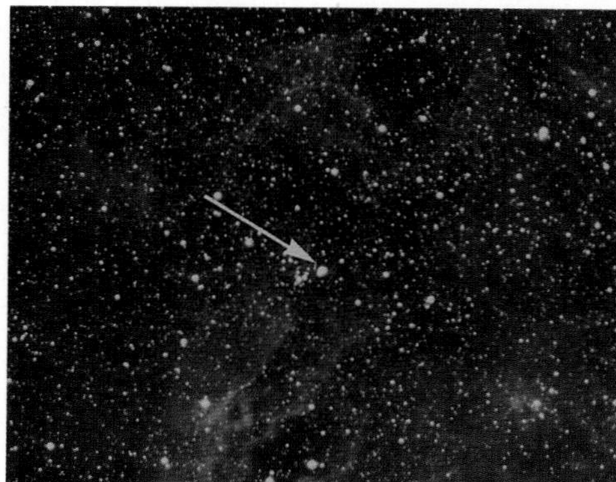

Figure 24-9. The photo on the left shows the star named Sanduleak−69°202 before it evolved into a supernova. The photo on the right was taken in 1987, when Sanduleak −69°202 entered a supernova stage.

The collapsed core shrinks to about the size of a large
4 city. Only neutrons can exist in the dense core, which becomes a **neutron star.**

If the original star is more than 30 times more massive than the sun, probably nothing can stop the core's collapse. It quickly evolves into a **black hole**—an object so dense, nothing can escape its gravity field. In fact, not even light can escape a black hole. If you could shine a flashlight on a black hole, it wouldn't illuminate it. The light would simply disappear into it. As matter and energy are pulled toward a black hole, X rays are given off.

OPTIONS

INQUIRY QUESTIONS

▶ **Why do some stars evolve into giants while others evolve into supergiants?** *Stars that have masses more than ten times that of the sun generate much higher temperatures inside the contracting core. This plus the higher mass cause the star to expand to a much larger size.*

▶ **Why do some stars explode violently, causing a supernova?** *Temperatures inside the star become high enough to produce an iron core. The iron core is so dense that no further fusion can occur. This causes the core to collapse suddenly and to send a shock wave outward that destroys the star.*

▶ **What occurs to cause a black hole?** *The core of a very massive star contracts so much that light can't travel fast enough to leave the object. The gravity associated with a black hole is so great that nothing can leave it.*

▶ **How do astronomers know where black holes might be located?** *It is believed that as matter and energy are pulled into a black hole, X rays are given off into space. Astronomers believe that strong X-ray sources in space may be black holes.*

TECHNOLOGY

Studying Supernovas

Near Cleveland, Ohio, and in Kamioka, Japan, large tanks of water and sensitive radiation-detecting instruments rest underground. The instruments are capable of detecting the radiation given off when subatomic particles called neutrinos strike protons or electrons in the water. In February 1987, the instruments recorded the presence of neutrinos. The records of the neutrinos striking the tanks went unnoticed until astronomers in the southern hemisphere observed a supernova.

Astronomers had previously theorized that neutrinos are emitted when a star evolves into a supernova. When the supernova was spotted, astronomers asked researchers at the underground tanks to check records of activity in the tanks. Records from Cleveland and Kamioka verified that neutrinos had been emitted during the explosion of the star. The neutrinos had traveled at the speed of light and arrived at Earth at about the same time as the visible light from the supernova.

Think Critically: The neutrinos that traveled through Earth in 1987 were created about 163 000 years ago when Sanduleak –69°202 evolved into a supernova. How far away was Sanduleak –69°202?

Astronomers have located X-ray sources around possible black holes. Extremely massive black holes may exist in the centers of galaxies.

A star begins its life as a nebula, but where does the matter in a nebula come from? Nebulas form partly from the matter that was once in other stars. A star ejects enormous amounts of matter during its lifetime. Millions or billions of years after a star dies, this matter condenses to form new nebulas, which then evolve into new stars. The matter in stars is recycled many times.

What about the matter created in the cores of stars? Are elements like carbon and iron recycled also? Some of these elements do become parts of new stars. In fact, spectrographs have shown that our sun contains carbon, iron,

Why haven't black holes been directly observed?

TECHNOLOGY

Think Critically: Sanduleak –69°202 is 163 000 light-years away. It's located in one of the two small irregular galaxies, called the Megallanic Clouds, that orbit the Milky Way Galaxy.

CHECK FOR UNDERSTANDING

Use the Mini Quiz to check for understanding.

MINI QUIZ

Use the Mini Quiz to check students' recall of chapter content.

1. **A star begins as a large cloud of gas and dust called a(n) ___.** *nebula*
2. **When the hydrogen in the core of a star is exhausted and the outer layers of the star expand outward, the star evolves into a(n) _____.** *giant*
3. **Once the outer layers of a star like our sun escape into space, a(n) ______ is left behind.** *white dwarf*
4. **The collapsed core of a star, composed of only neutrons, is called a(n) ______.** *neutron star*

RETEACH

Obtain a series of slides or pictures of many different types of nebulas. Show slides or pictures of nebulas with dark globules contained in them (the Eagle, Lagoon, and Trifid Nebulas are good examples). Explain that these dark globules are thought to be places where stars are presently forming. Show slides or pictures of the Crab Nebula and other supernova remnants. Ask students what they look like. Students should recognize evidence of massive explosions.

EXTENSION

For students who have mastered this section, use the **Reinforcement** and **Enrichment** masters or other OPTIONS provided.

ENRICHMENT

▶Have students use a chemistry book to research the formation and detection of neutrinos. Neutrinos are subatomic particles that are produced when atomic nuclei are struck by high-energy particles. They are detected by a neutrino "telescope" as they strike protons in water, producing a flash of light. Solar neutrinos are detected when they pass through layers of rock and reach detection tanks deep underground.

PROGRAM RESOURCES

From the **Teacher Resource Package** use:

Concept Mapping, pages 53-54.

Use **Laboratory Manual,** pages 191-192, Star Colors.

3 CLOSE

▶Ask a volunteer to describe how the temperature of a star is related to its color. Elicit help from other students, if needed.

▶Ask questions 1-4 and the **Apply** Question in the Section Review.

SECTION REVIEW ANSWERS

1. Giants are very large but relatively cool stars. Their temperatures compare to small main sequence stars but their absolute magnitudes compare to the larger main sequence stars.

2. Because the blue star is hotter and gives off more energy, its absolute magnitude would be brighter than that of the yellow star.

3.
- I. Begins as nebula
  - A. cloud contracts
  - B. heated to 10 000 000°C
  - C. fusion in cloud center
- II. Main sequence star
  - A. energy of fusion balances gravity
  - B. hydrogen fuel exhausted
- III. Giant
  - A. fuses helium in core
  - B. outer layers begin to escape
- IV. White dwarf
  - A. exhausts fuel supply
  - B. becomes a dead star

4. A star must be very high in mass to evolve into a neutron star. Generally, stars with a mass greater than ten times our sun will evolve into neutron stars.

5. Apply: The sun still has a supply of hydrogen for fusion. This keeps the core from collapsing and temperatures from rising. Currently, the sun's core is not hot enough to fuse significant amounts of helium.

Skill Builder

black hole, neutron star, white dwarf, giant, main sequence star

Figure 24-10. A thick collection of gas and dust makes up the Horsehead nebula. There's evidence that new stars are evolving from the matter and energy contained within this nebula.

What evidence is there that our sun evolved from material from a previous star?

and other such elements. Because the sun is a main sequence star, it is too young to have created these elements itself. Our sun condensed from material that was created in stars that died many billions of years ago.

Some elements condense to form planets and other bodies rather than stars. In fact, your body contains many atoms that were fused in the cores of ancient stars. Most scientists believe that the early universe contained only hydrogen and helium. The first stars formed from these two elements, and all other elements have formed in the cores of stars.

SECTION REVIEW

1. Explain why giants are not in the main sequence on the H-R diagram. How do their temperature and absolute magnitude compare to main sequence stars?
2. What can be said about the absolute magnitudes of two equal-sized stars whose colors are blue and yellow?
3. Outline the history and probable future of our sun, a main sequence star.
4. Why do some stars evolve into neutron stars but others do not?
5. **Apply:** Why doesn't the helium currently in the sun's core undergo fusion?

Skill Builder — **Sequencing**

Sequence these stars in order of most evolved to least evolved: *white dwarf, main sequence star, giant, neutron star,* and *black hole*. If you need help, refer to Sequencing in the **Skill Handbook** on page 680.

OPTIONS

INQUIRY QUESTIONS

▶**Why do some scientists say that our bodies are made of star stuff?** *Astronomers think that heavy atoms are generated in the centers of stars and then travel into space during supernovas. Materials made of heavy atoms, such as your body, must be made of the material from stars. Many scientists theorize that all atoms heavier than hydrogen and helium have been formed in the cores of stars.*

▶**Are there any atoms in your body that weren't fused in the core of a star?** *It's likely that the hydrogen and helium atoms in our bodies were not formed by stellar fusion.*

▶**How do we know the iron in our sun was not produced inside the sun?** *The sun's interior is not hot enough to fuse carbon into iron. The iron must have been formed elsewhere and become part of the nebula that formed the sun.*

ACTIVITY 24-2
Sunspots

Problem: *How can you trace the movement of sunspots?*

Materials 

- several books
- clipboard
- small tripod
- small refracting telescope
- cardboard
- drawing paper
- scissors

Procedure

1. Find a location where the sun may be viewed at the same time of day for a minimum of five days. **CAUTION:** *Do not look directly at the sun. Do not look through the telescope at the sun. You could damage your eyes.*
2. Set up the telescope with the eyepiece facing away from the sun as shown. Set up the clipboard with the drawing paper attached.
3. Use the books to prop the clipboard upright. Point the eyepiece at the drawing paper.
4. Arrange a shield of heavy cardboard with the center cut out.
5. Move the clipboard back and forth until you have the largest possible image of the sun on the paper. Adjust the telescope to form a clear image.
6. Trace the outline of the sun on the paper.
7. Trace any sunspots that appear as dark areas on the sun's image. At the same time each day for a week, check the sun's image and trace the position of the sunspots.
8. Using the sun's diameter as approximately 1 400 000 km, estimate the size of the largest sunspots that are observed.
9. Calculate how many kilometers any observed sunspots appear to move each day.
10. At the rate determined in Step 9, predict how many days it will take for the same group of sunspots to return to about the same position in which you first observed them.

Analyze

1. Which part of the sun showed up in your image?
2. What are solar flares, and how can they be related to sunspots?
3. What was the average number of sunspots observed each day during this investigation?

Conclude and Apply

4. How can the movement of sunspots be traced?
5. How can sunspots be used to determine that the sun's surface is not solid like Earth's?

Data and Observations

Sample Data

Date of observation	Number of sunspot groups (approx.)	Estimated average sunspot diam. (km)	Approximate actual movement (km)	Predicted return time (Earth days)
Answers will d	epend on level of sunspot	activity. Estimates for sun	spot diameter range from	several thousand km to
30 000 km.	Sunspots average about	5000 km of movement ea	ch Earth day and take 25	to 34 days to rotate.

ACTIVITY 24-2
10 minutes

OBJECTIVE: Observe sunspots and **estimate** their size and rate of motion across the sun's photosphere.

PROCESS SKILLS applied in this activity:
▶ **Observing** in Procedure Steps 5-7.
▶ **Estimating** in Procedure Steps 8 and 10.
▶ **Interpreting Data** in Analyze Questions 1 and 3.
▶ **Using Numbers** in Procedure Step 9.

TEACHING THE ACTIVITY

Troubleshooting: To ensure correct alignment in the event the apparatus must be taken down or moved for any reason, mark the exact position of the telescope, books, and clipboard. Only in this way will students be able to accurately record the changing positions of the sunspots.

Alternate Materials: If a telescope isn't available, use binoculars set on the window ledge with one of the eyepieces covered.

▶ If no sunspots are visible, keep the setup in place until some are sighted. Students should observe that sunspots are transitory features of the sun's surface, moving across the sun and disappearing within a relatively short period of time.

PROGRAM RESOURCES

From the **Teacher Resource Package** use:

Activity Worksheets, pages 218-219, Activity 24-2: Sunspots.

ANSWERS TO QUESTIONS

1. the photosphere

2. Solar flares are increases in brightness of the chromosphere in the area of sunspots. When sunspot activity is high, solar flare activity is greater.

3. Student answers will vary depending on solar activity. All answers should be approximately the same, however.

4. by using a telescope and projecting the image of the sun onto a sheet of paper

5. When viewed over a number of days, equatorial sunspots require less time to return to their original position (about 25 days) than those that occur near the solar poles (35 days). This couldn't occur if the photosphere were solid.

SECTION 24-3

PREPARATION

SECTION BACKGROUND

▶ The sun is composed of 74% hydrogen, 25% helium, and 1% other elements.

▶ The Solar Max satellite, which monitored solar activity, crashed to Earth on December 2, 1989. Expansion of Earth's atmosphere caused by high levels of activity on the sun caused Solar Max's orbit to decay.

▶ One theory to explain the formation of sunspots deals with magnetic force lines that stretch from the sun's north pole to its south pole. The faster rotation of the sun's equator causes the magnetic force lines to wrap around the sun. They become twisted, and where they dip into and come out of the sun, sunspots form.

▶ The *Ulysses* spacecraft was launched by the space shuttle *Discovery* in October 1990. Also called the Solar Polar Explorer, *Ulysses* was designed to study the sun's solar wind, magnetic field, and X rays and radio waves given off by the sun.

1 MOTIVATE

FLEX Your Brain

Use the Flex Your Brain activity to have students explore SUNSPOTS.

Cooperative Learning: Using the Paired Partners strategy, have students compare and contrast the sun with Earth. Students might consider size, shape, rotation, layers, and composition.

PROGRAM RESOURCES

From the **Teacher Resource Package** use:

Activity Worksheets, page 5, Flex Your Brain.

24-3 The Sun

New Science Words

photosphere
chromosphere
corona
sunspots
binary system

Objectives

- ▶ Describe how energy is produced in the sun.
- ▶ Recognize that sunspots, prominences, and solar flares are related.
- ▶ Explain why our sun is considered an average star and how it differs from stars in binary systems.

The Layers of the Sun

More than 99 percent of all of the matter in our solar system is in the sun. It is the center of our solar system, and it makes life possible on Earth. To you and everyone else on Earth, the sun is a special object in the sky and one of the most important objects in your life. Nevertheless, our sun is just an average star.

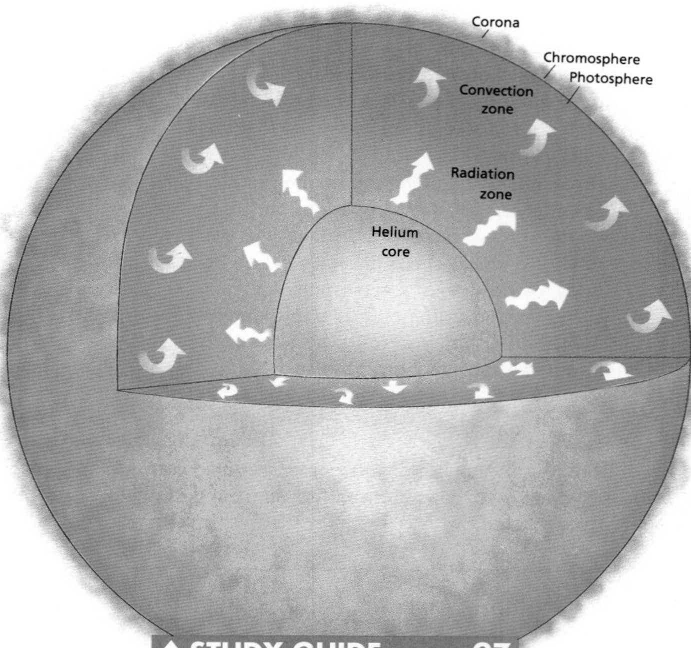

Figure 24-11. Energy produced by fusion in the sun's core travels outward by radiation and convection. The sun's atmosphere, composed of the photosphere, chromosphere, and corona, is illuminated by the energy produced in the core.

OPTIONS

Meeting Different Ability Levels

For Section 24-3, use the following **Teacher Resource Masters** depending upon individual students' needs.

◆ **Study Guide Master** for all students.

● **Reinforcement Master** for students of average and above average ability levels.

▲ **Enrichment Master** for above average students.

Additional Teacher Resource Package masters are listed in the OPTIONS box throughout the section. The additional masters are appropriate for all students.

◆ STUDY GUIDE 97

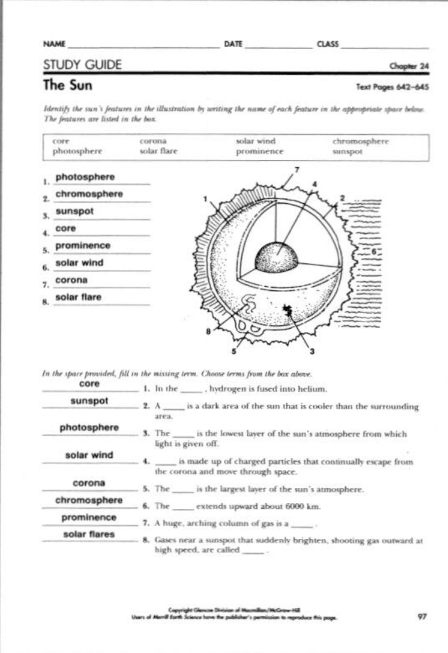

NAME ______ DATE ______ CLASS ______

STUDY GUIDE — Chapter 24

The Sun — Text Pages 642–645

Identify the sun's features in the illustration by writing the name of each feature in the appropriate space below. The features are listed in the box.

core	corona	solar wind	chromosphere
photosphere	solar flare	prominence	sunspot

1. photosphere
2. chromosphere
3. sunspot
4. core
5. prominence
6. solar wind
7. corona
8. solar flare

In the space provided, fill in the missing term. Choose terms from the box above.

core — 1. In the _____, hydrogen is fused into helium.

sunspot — 2. A _____ is a dark area of the sun that is cooler than the surrounding area.

photosphere — 3. The _____ is the lowest layer of the sun's atmosphere from which light is given off.

solar wind — 4. _____ is made up of charged particles that continually escape from the corona and move through space.

corona — 5. The _____ is the largest layer of the sun's atmosphere.

chromosphere — 6. The _____ extends upward about 6000 km.

prominence — 7. A huge, arching column of gas is a _____.

solar flares — 8. Gases near a sunspot that suddenly brighten, shooting gas outward at high speed, are called _____.

97

The sun is a main sequence star on the H-R diagram. Its absolute magnitude is about average and it shines with a yellow light. The sun is an enormous ball of gas, fusing hydrogen into helium in its core. Figure 24-11 is a model of the sun's interior.

The lowest layer of the sun's atmosphere and the layer from which light is given off is the **photosphere.** 1 Temperatures there are around 6000°C. Above the photosphere is the **chromosphere.** This layer extends upward about 6000 km. Above the chromosphere is the **corona.** 2 This is the largest layer of the sun's atmosphere and extends millions of kilometers into space. Temperatures in the corona are as high as 2 000 000°C. Charged particles continually escape from the corona and move through space as the solar wind.

Did You Know?

Betelgeuse is a supergiant. If our sun were replaced by Betelgeuse, its surface would extend beyond Earth's orbit—Earth would be engulfed by its new sun!

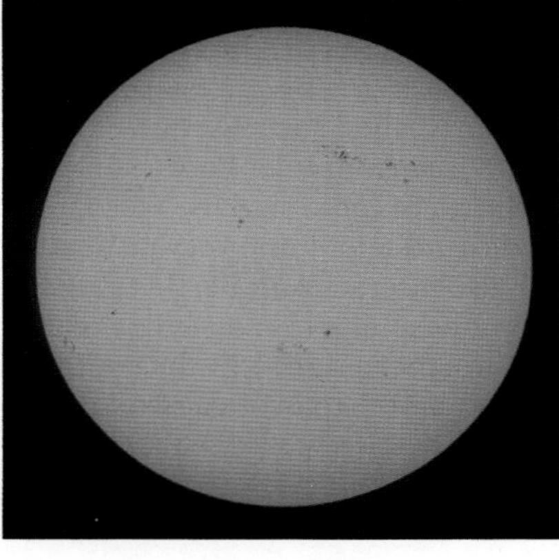

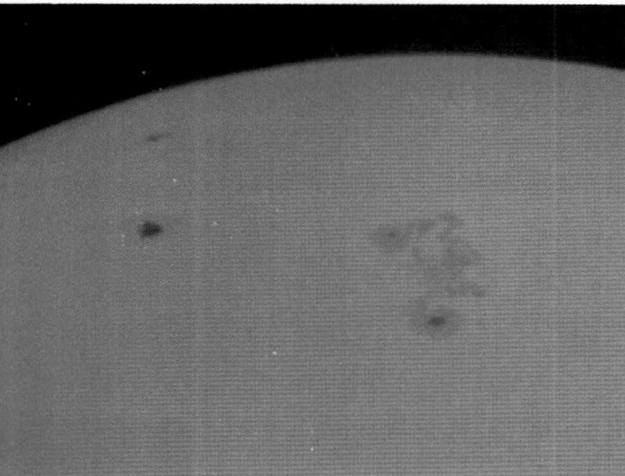

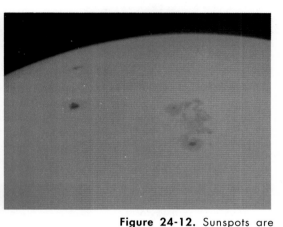

Figure 24-12. Sunspots are brighter than a full moon, but seen against the rest of the photosphere, they appear dark.

Sunspots

The sun's surface is not a smooth layer of gas. There are many features that can be studied. Dark areas of the sun's surface, which are cooler than surrounding areas, are called **sunspots.** 3 Ever since Galileo first identified sunspots, scientists have been studying them. One thing we've learned by studying sunspots is that the sun rotates. We can observe individual sunspots moving across the surface as they are carried by the sun's rotation. The sun doesn't rotate as a solid body, as does Earth. It rotates faster at its equator than at its poles. Sunspots near the equator take about 25 days to go around the sun; at higher latitudes, they take a day or two longer.

● REINFORCEMENT 97

NAME ____________ DATE ________ CLASS ________

REINFORCEMENT Chapter 24

The Sun Text Pages 642–645

The diagram shows interior and outer features of the sun. Write the name of each feature on the lines provided in the diagram.

core
photoshere
chromosphere
solar wind
sunspot
corona
prominence

Answer the questions in complete sentences.

1. How can the sun be classified? **The sun is a yellow main sequence star.**
2. How is the energy of the sun produced? **The energy of the sun is produced by the fusion of hydrogen, which becomes helium.**
3. How does our sun differ from most other main sequence stars? **Most main sequence stars are in a binary system or cluster in which two or more stars orbit one another. The sun is not in a binary system or cluster.**
4. How do solar flares affect Earth? **Solar flares can disrupt radio signals and interact with Earth's magnetic field, causing the aurora borealis and aurora australis.**
5. How are sunspots related to prominences and solar flares? **The intense magnetic field of sunspots can cause prominences that erupt from the sun. The gases near sunspots sometimes brighten up suddenly, causing eruptions known as solar flares.**
6. What is the solar wind? **The solar wind is charged particles that have escaped from the sun's corona and stream outward into the solar system.**

 97

▲ ENRICHMENT 97

NAME ____________ DATE ________ CLASS ________

ENRICHMENT Chapter 24

The Sun Text Pages 642–645

SUNSPOT ACTIVITY

Use the information about sunspot activity to answer the questions.

Year	Number of observed sunspots	Year	Number of observed sunspots
1728	135	1766	20
1732	7	1770	130
1739	125	1775	5
1743	6	1778	165
1750	90	1784	18
1756	15	1788	140
1761	80	1797	6

1. In the list underline in red all the entries that include at least 80 sunspots.
2. Which years did you underline in red? These are years of sunspot maximum. **1728, 1739, 1750, 1761, 1770, 1778, 1788**
3. Which years are NOT underlined? These are years of sunspot minimum. **1732, 1743, 1756, 1766, 1775, 1784, 1797**
4. How many years are between 1728 and 1739? 1739 and 1750? 1750 and 1761? 1761 and 1770? 1770 and 1778? 1778 and 1788? **11 years, 11 years, 11 years, 9 years, 8 years, 10 years**
5. Do sunspot maximums always occur every 11 years? **No, but most often the maximums occur in 11-year cycles.**
6. How many years are between 1732 and 1743? 1743 and 1756? 1756 and 1766? 1766 and 1775? 1775 and 1784? 1784 and 1797? **11 years, 13 years, 10 years, 9 years, 9 years, 13 years**
7. Scientists think the sunspot minimums are also on an 11-year cycle. Do your data support this theory? **Yes, the data indicate that the sunspot minimums occur, on average, every 11 years.**
8. If the last sunspot maximum was in 1990, when will the next two maximums most likely occur? **2001, 2012**
9. If the last sunspot minimum occurred in 1986, when might the next minimum occur? **1997**

 97

TYING TO PREVIOUS KNOWLEDGE: Help students recall from Chapter 10 that the sun affects our weather. Remind them that interactions of air, water, and the sun cause Earth's weather. Have students explain what role the sun plays in the formation of clouds.

OBJECTIVES AND SCIENCE WORDS: Have students review the objectives and science words to become familiar with this section.

2 TEACH

Key Concepts are highlighted.

REVEALING MISCONCEPTIONS

▶ Ask students why the sun is so bright and hot. Some students will think the sun burns gas similar to the way in which a range burns gas. Explain that the sun is a ball of hot glowing gas because fusion of hydrogen into helium at the core releases tremendous amounts of energy that heats gases in the outer layers of the sun. The gases glow when heated.

TEACHER F.Y.I.

▶ Energy from the sun's core takes two million years to radiate out to the surface but only 8.3 minutes to reach Earth once it has radiated from the surface.

CROSS CURRICULUM

▶ **Meteorology:** Have students research the relationship between sunspot activity and Earth's weather and climate. Have interested students research the Maunder Minimum, a period from 1645 through 1715 when very few sunspots were observed. During this time, Europe experienced record low temperatures and severe droughts occurred in the western United States.

MINI-Lab

Materials: string (125 cm in length), chalk, meterstick

Teaching Tips: Help students conceptualize the diameter of the sun compared to that of Earth. The sun's diameter is about 110 times greater than Earth's. Draw a circle with a diameter of 1 cm to represent Earth. Using a string with a length of 55 cm, draw a circle with a diameter of 110 cm to represent the sun. The following table gives the diameters (km) of some observable stars:

Star	Diameter (km)
Betelgeuse	450 000 000
Vega	7 700 000
Sirius	4 800 000
The sun	1 390 000
LP 327-16 (white dwarf)	1 700

Answers to Questions: The large circle represents a supergiant. The two circles representing our sun and a white dwarf can be any diameter as long as the large circle is approximately 100 times larger than the smaller.

CONCEPT DEVELOPMENT

Cooperative Learning: Form Science Investigation groups with three students per group. Assign the roles of materials handler, reporter, and organizer. Using the list of data presented below, have the groups plot a graph showing the number of sunspots that have occurred over time. When completed, have the reporter describe any trend his or her group notices from the plotted data.

YEAR	SUN SPOTS	YEAR	SUN SPOTS
1964	11	1977	28
1965	18	1978	93
1966	53	1979	155
1967	91	1980	155
1968	106	1981	140
1969	105	1982	116
1970	104	1983	67
1971	67	1984	46
1972	69	1985	18
1973	38	1986	14
1974	35	1987	29
1975	16	1988	100
1976	13	1989	159

MINI-Lab

What are the relative sizes of stars?

Find an area where you can make a chalk mark on pavement or other surface. Tie a piece of chalk to one end of a string that's 125 cm long. Hold the other end of the string to the pavement. Have a friend pull the string tight and walk around you, leaving a mark on the pavement as he or she circles you. Draw a circle with a 1 cm diameter in the middle of the large circle. The small circle represents a star the size of our sun. What type of star is represented by the large circle? Now draw two new circles to represent our sun and a white dwarf. Our sun is about 100 times larger than a white dwarf. What are the diameters of your two new circles?

Sunspots aren't permanent features on the sun. They appear and disappear over a period of several days or months. Also, there are times when there are many large sunspots—a sunspot maximum—and times when there are only a few small sunspots or none at all—a sunspot minimum. Sunspot maximums occur about every 11 years. The last maximum was in 1990. The next is expected in 2001.

Prominences and Flares

Sunspots are related to several features on the sun's surface. The intense magnetic field associated with sunspots may cause prominences, huge arching columns 4
of gas. Some prominences are so eruptive that material from the sun is blasted into space at speeds approaching 1000 km/s. Others form into loops through which matter flows into and out of the corona.

Gases near a sunspot sometimes brighten up suddenly, shooting gas outward at high speed. These violent eruptions from the sun are called solar flares.

Ultraviolet light and X rays from solar flares can reach Earth and cause disruption of radio signals. This makes communication by radio and telephone very difficult at times. Solar flares can also interact with Earth's magnetic field, causing Earth's atmosphere to radiate light called the aurora borealis, or northern lights. In the southern hemisphere this light is called the aurora australis.

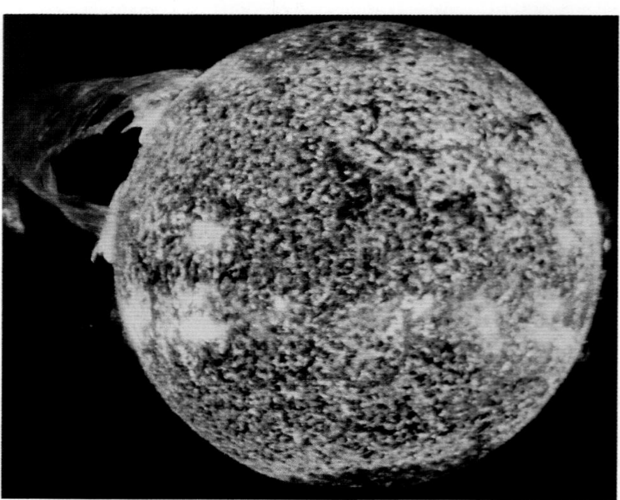

Figure 24-13. This photograph of a huge prominence was taken by astronauts on board *Skylab* in 1973. The prominence arches hundreds of thousands of kilometers into space and is large enough to contain several Earths.

OPTIONS

ENRICHMENT

► Have students research our solar system's nearest neighbor, the Alpha Centauri star system. To the naked eye, Alpha Centauri appears as a single star in the southern hemisphere. However, Alpha Centauri is really two stars revolving around each other. A third star, Proxima Centauri, seems to orbit them. This group of three stars, 4.2 to 4.3 light-years from our sun, is a trinary system. Refer students to "Does Alpha Centauri Have Intelligent Life?" by K. Coswell, *Astronomy*, April 1991, pp. 28-37.

PROGRAM RESOURCES

From the **Teacher Resource Package** use:

Activity Worksheets, page 222, Mini-Lab: What are the relative sizes of stars?

Transparency Masters, pages 99-100, Evolution of a Main Sequence Star.

Use **Color Transparency** number 50, Evolution of a Main Sequence Star.

Our Sun: A Typical Star?

Although our sun is a main sequence star, it is somewhat unusual in one way. Most stars are in systems in which two or more stars orbit each other. When two stars orbit each other, it is called a **binary system.** In some cases, astronomers can detect binary systems because one star occasionally eclipses the other. The total amount of light from the star system becomes dim and then bright again, on a regular cycle.

In many cases, stars move through space together as a cluster. In a star cluster, many stars are relatively close to one another and are gravitationally attracted to each other. The Pleiades star cluster can be seen in the constellation of Taurus in the winter sky. On a clear, dark night, you may be able to make out seven of the stars of this cluster. Most star clusters are far from our solar system, and appear as a fuzzy patch in the night sky.

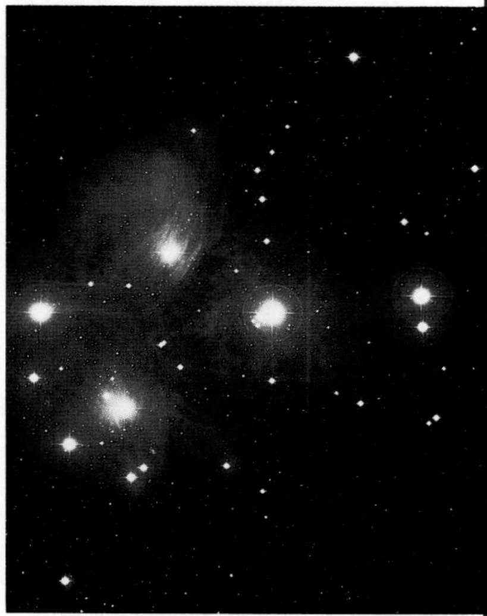

Figure 24-14. Pleiades is a cluster of stars gravitationally bound to each other. All of the stars in this cluster have only recently begun fusing hydrogen in their cores—becoming main sequence stars.

SECTION REVIEW

1. How does the sun generate energy? What will happen to the sun when it exhausts its supply of hydrogen?
2. How are sunspots, prominences, and solar flares related?
3. What properties of the sun make it a typical star? What property makes it different from most other stars?
4. **Apply:** In approximately 5 billion years, our sun's surface may expand beyond the orbit of Earth, engulfing Mercury, Venus, and Earth in its fiery gases. What evolutionary stage will the sun be in at this point? What type of star will it become after that?

☑ Interpreting Scientific Illustrations — Skill Builder

Use Figure 24-11 to answer the questions below. If you need help, refer to Interpreting Scientific Illustrations in the **Skill Handbook** on page 693.

1. Compare Figure 24-11 with Figure 22-8 on page 587, showing a total solar eclipse. What part of the sun is visible in Figure 22-8?
2. Which layers make up the sun's atmosphere?
3. How does the diameter of the sun's core compare to the diameter of the core of a supergiant?

Skill Builder

1. the corona
2. photosphere, chromosphere, and corona
3. The diameter of the sun's core is greater than the diameter of a super giant's core.

CHECK FOR UNDERSTANDING

Use the Mini Quiz to check for understanding.

MINI QUIZ

Use the Mini Quiz to check students' recall of chapter content.

1. **Light is given off from the sun's ____, the lowest layer of the sun's atmosphere.** *photosphere*
2. **Temperatures in the outer layer of the sun's atmosphere, or ____, can reach 2 000 000°C.** *corona*
3. **____ are cooler, dark areas on the sun's surface.** *Sunspots*
4. **The intense magnetic field associated with sunspots may cause ____, huge arching columns of gas.** *prominences*

RETEACH

Refer students to the figures in Section 24-3. Have students use these illustrations and photographs to draw a cross section of the sun's interior.

EXTENSION

For students who have mastered this section, use the **Reinforcement** and **Enrichment** masters or other OPTIONS.

3 CLOSE

▶ Invite a ham radio operator in to class to discuss how solar activity affects his or her hobby.

▶ Ask questions 1-3 and the **Apply Question** from the Section Review.

SECTION REVIEW ANSWERS

1. Fusion reactions in the sun's core change hydrogen into helium with some matter being converted into energy. When it exhausts its hydrogen supply, the sun will begin to fuse helium in its core and will become a giant.
2. Magnetic fields near a sunspot can cause huge arching columns of gas called prominences. Gases near sunspots can also become very concentrated and shoot outward from the sun as a solar flare.
3. The sun's size, temperature, and absolute magnitude make it a main sequence star. The sun is unlike most stars because it's not a member of a binary system or star cluster.
4. Apply: a giant, a white dwarf

SECTION 24-4

PREPLANNING

SECTION BACKGROUND

▶ The largest galaxy presently known is in the midst of the galaxy cluster Abell 2029 in the constellation Virgo. Its outer halo is more than 8 million light-years across. The entire Local Group of galaxies is contained within a space only 3 million light-years across.

▶ Clusters of galaxies are grouped into even larger associations called superclusters. Superclusters contain dozens of individual clusters spread over 100 million light-years of space.

▶ Recent evidence suggests that matter isn't evenly distributed in the universe. Large voids in which very little matter is found contrast sharply with the presence of the Great Wall—a dense chain of galaxies stretching across 500 billion light-years of space. This discovery indicates that matter began condensing into clumps early in the evolution of the universe. This fact can't be explained by the big bang theory as it presently stands. Because the big bang theory can't explain these recent observations, many scientists are having to modify their theories of the origin and evolution of the universe.

▶ Extremely large concentrations of matter interrupted by voids within the structure of the universe indicate the presence of gravitational forces from unseen cold, dark matter. This as yet undetected, theoretical dark matter could possibly account for 90 percent of the universe's mass. If this matter exists, the universe could eventually stop expanding and begin to contract in upon itself.

24-4 Galaxies and the Expanding Universe

New Science Words

galaxy
big bang theory

Objectives

- ▶ Describe a galaxy and list the three main types of galaxies.
- ▶ Identify several characteristics of the Milky Way Galaxy.
- ▶ Explain how the big bang theory explains observed Doppler shifts.

Galaxies

One reason to study astronomy is to learn about your place in the universe. Long ago, people thought they were at the center of the universe and everything revolved around Earth. Today, you know this isn't the case. But do you know where you are in the universe?

You are on Earth, and Earth orbits the sun. But does the sun orbit anything? How does it interact with other objects in the universe? The sun is one star in the Milky
1 Way Galaxy. A **galaxy** is a large group of stars, gas, and dust held together by gravity. Our galaxy, the Milky Way,

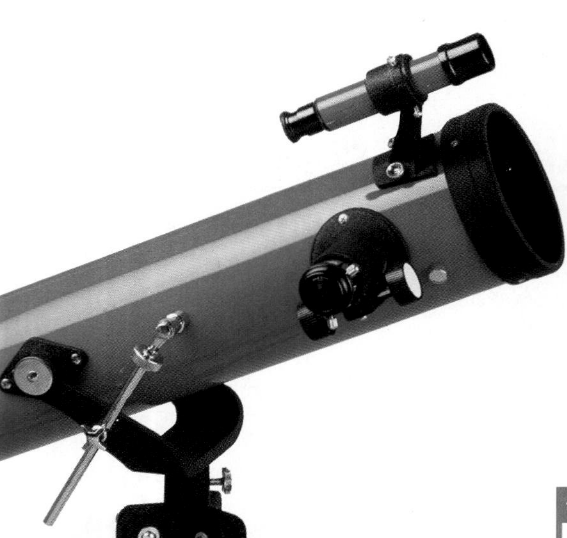

Figure 24-15. Centaurus A is a peculiar elliptical galaxy16 million light-years away.

OPTIONS

Meeting Different Ability Levels

For Section 24-4, use the following **Teacher Resource Masters** depending upon individual students' needs.

◆ **Study Guide Master** for all students.

● **Reinforcement Master** for students of average and above average ability levels.

▲ **Enrichment Master** for above average students.

Additional Teacher Resource Package masters are listed in the OPTIONS box throughout the section. The additional masters are appropriate for all students.

◆ STUDY GUIDE 98

NAME ________ DATE ________ CLASS ________

STUDY GUIDE — Chapter 24

Galaxies and the Expanding Universe — Text Pages 646–651

Write the term that matches each description in the spaces provided. Place one letter in each space. One letter has been given for each answer.

1. M I L K Y W [A] Y
2. U N I V E R [S] E
3. L O C A L [G] R O U P
4. B I G B [A] N G T H E O R Y
5. E L L I P T I C A L G A L A [X] I E S
6. I R R [E] G U L A R S
7. S P [I] R A L S
8. D O P P [L] E R S H I F T

1. This is the name of the galaxy in which you live.
2. Scientists determined this was expanding by using the spectrograph.
3. This cluster of galaxies is made up of about twenty-five galaxies including the Milky Way.
4. According to this theory, billions of years ago the universe began expanding out of an enormous explosion.
5. This class of galaxies includes football-shaped galaxies.
6. These galaxies are usually small and have many different shapes.
7. These galaxies have arms winding outward from inner regions.
8. This is the change of color on the spectrograph as objects move toward or away from other objects.

Write the clue letters that were given in the answers: ASGAXEIL

Rearrange the letters to form a word for the groups of stars, dust, and gas held together by gravity.
galaxies

98

contains about 200 billion stars. Galaxies are separated by huge distances—often millions of light-years.

Just as stars are grouped together within galaxies, galaxies are grouped into clusters. The cluster the Milky Way
2 belongs to is called the Local Group. It contains about 25 galaxies of various types and sizes.

What is the Local Group?

There are three major classifications of galaxies: ellip-
3 tical, spiral, and irregular. The most common type of galaxy is the elliptical galaxy. These galaxies are shaped
4 like large, three-dimensional ellipses. Many are football-shaped. Some elliptical galaxies are quite small, while others are so large that the entire Local Group of galaxies would fit inside one of them.

Spiral galaxies have spiral arms winding outward from inner regions. These spiral arms are made up of stars and dust. In between the arms, there are fewer stars. The fuzzy patch you can see in the constellation of Andromeda is actually a spiral galaxy. It's so far away that you can't see its individual stars. Instead, it appears as a hazy spot in our sky. The Andromeda galaxy is a member of the Local Group and is about 2 million light-years away.

In what ways are the Andromeda galaxy and the Milky Way related?

Arms in a normal spiral start close to the center of the galaxy. Barred spirals have two spiral arms extending from a large bar that passes through the center of the galaxy. Figure 24-18 shows a barred spiral galaxy.

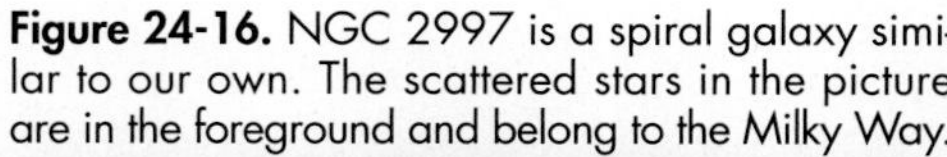

Figure 24-16. NGC 2997 is a spiral galaxy similar to our own. The scattered stars in the picture are in the foreground and belong to the Milky Way.

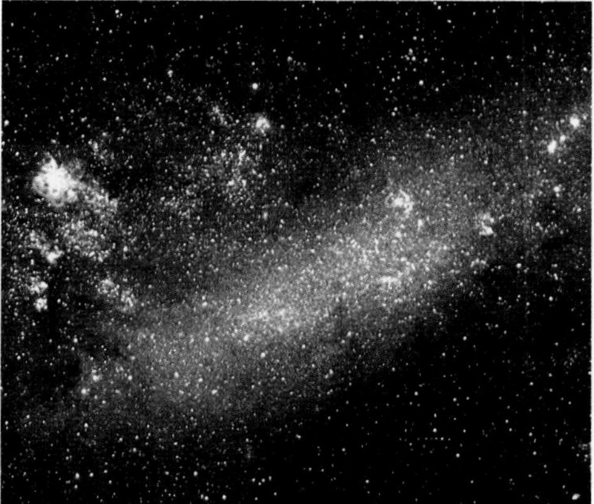

Figure 24-17. The Large Magellanic Cloud is an irregular galaxy. It's a member of the Local Group, and it orbits our own galaxy.

● REINFORCEMENT 98

NAME ______ DATE ______ CLASS ______

REINFORCEMENT — Chapter 24

Galaxies and the Expanding Universe — Text Pages 646–651

Use the terms in the box to complete the following sentences.

Milky Way	200 billion stars	Andromeda	Local Group
galaxy	cluster	Doppler shifts	big bang theory
irregular	spiral	elliptical	Clouds of Magellan

1. A **galaxy** is a large group of stars, gas, and dust held together by gravity.
2. A **cluster** is a group of galaxies.
3. **Irregular** galaxies have many different shapes and are usually smaller and less common than other types of galaxies.
4. The two types of **spiral** galaxies are barred and normal.
5. Galaxies shaped like footballs are **elliptical** galaxies.
6. The **Clouds of Magellan** are two irregular galaxies about 170 000 light-years away from Earth.
7. The solar system in which we live is in the **Milky Way** Galaxy.
8. The **big bang theory** is an explanation for the formation of the universe.
9. A spiral galaxy about 2 million light-years away is in the constellation of **Andromeda**.
10. The Milky Way Galaxy contains more than **200 billion stars**.
11. Both the Milky Way and Andromeda galaxies are members of the cluster named the **Local Group**.
12. **Doppler shifts** show that outside galaxies are moving away from the Local Group.

98

▲ ENRICHMENT 98

NAME ______ DATE ______ CLASS ______

ENRICHMENT — Chapter 24

Galaxies and the Expanding Universe — Text Pages 646–651

REVOLVING ABOUT THE MILKY WAY

Every 250 million years, our sun revolves once about the center of the Milky Way Galaxy. Find how many revolutions or parts of a revolution have occurred since the following events in Earth's history. Show your work for each event.

1. Earth formed 4600 million years ago.
   4600 million ÷ 250 million = 18.4 revolutions
2. Oceans of water began forming 3800 million years ago.
   3800 million ÷ 250 million = 15.2 revolutions
3. Animals with shells and skeletons first appeared 570 million years ago.
   570 million ÷ 250 million = 2.28 revolutions
4. The Appalachian Mountains began forming 500 million years ago.
   500 million ÷ 250 million = 2 revolutions
5. The first mammals appeared 225 million years ago.
   225 million ÷ 250 million = 0.9 revolution
6. The Atlantic Ocean basin began forming as Africa, Eurasia, and the Americas began separating 190 million years ago.
   190 million ÷ 250 million = 0.76 revolution
7. The last dinosaurs died 65 million years ago.
   65 million ÷ 250 million = 0.26 revolution
8. The Himalaya Mountains began forming 53 million years ago.
   53 million ÷ 250 million = 0.21 revolution
9. The light we now see from the Andromeda galaxy began traveling through space 2.4 million years ago.
   2.4 million ÷ 250 million = 0.0096 revolution
10. The last ice age ended 10 000 years ago.
   10 000 ÷ 250 million = 0.000 04 revolution
11. The Apollo astronauts first landed on the moon in 1969.
   1993 (year will vary) – 1969 = 24
   24 ÷ 250 million = 0.000 000 09 revolution

98

1 MOTIVATE

FLEX Your Brain

Have students use the Flex Your Brain activity to explore THE STRUCTURE OF THE MILKY WAY GALAXY or THE LOCATION OF THE SUN IN THE GALAXY. Students should discover that they are inhabitants of a spiral galaxy. There is some debate over whether it's a normal or a barred spiral. The sun is about two-thirds the total diameter from the nucleus.

▶ Obtain a set of astronomy slides showing several galaxies. Demonstrate the different types of galaxies by showing slides of each type. Show a slide of the galaxy M31 in the Andromeda constellation. This is the closest large galaxy to the Milky Way.

TYING TO PREVIOUS KNOWLEDGE: Help students recall the electromagnetic spectrum from Chapter 21. Remind them that radiant energy is given off by stars. Have students review the types of radiant energy that are part of the electromagnetic spectrum.

OBJECTIVES AND SCIENCE WORDS: Have students review the objectives and science words.

2 TEACH

Key Concepts are highlighted.

CONCEPT DEVELOPMENT

Cooperative Learning: Using the Paired Partners strategy, have students make flash cards of the types of galaxies. Have them draw the galaxy type on one side and write its name on the reverse. Partners can then test each other using the flash cards. Next have the partners draw 10 to 20 images of the Milky Way Galaxy on separate cards. Have them place the sun at slightly different positions around the galaxy on each card. When finished, partners can demonstrate movement of the sun around the galaxy by flipping the cards.

TEACHER F.Y.I.

▶ A supermassive black hole with a mass equal to 10 million suns may lie at the center of the Milky Way Galaxy. Some astronomers theorize that the black hole is the mass of only 100 suns. Still other astronomers don't think a black hole exists there at all.

CONCEPT DEVELOPMENT

▶ Have students outline Section 24-4: Galaxies and the Expanding Universe.

Cooperative Learning: Form Expert Teams with four students in each team. Have students answer the following four questions. **What are the Clouds of Magellan?** *irregular galaxies orbiting the Milky Way* **How does the Milky Way Galaxy compare in size and type with the galaxy M31 in the constellation of Andromeda?** *They are both spiral galaxies, but the Andromeda galaxy is a little larger than the Milky Way.* **Recent evidence indicates that the Milky Way may be what type of galaxy?** *a barred spiral* **Why was our galaxy named the Milky Way?** *To the unaided eye, the thick band of stars lying in the plane of the spiral Milky Way Galaxy looks like a hazy, milky area of the sky.*

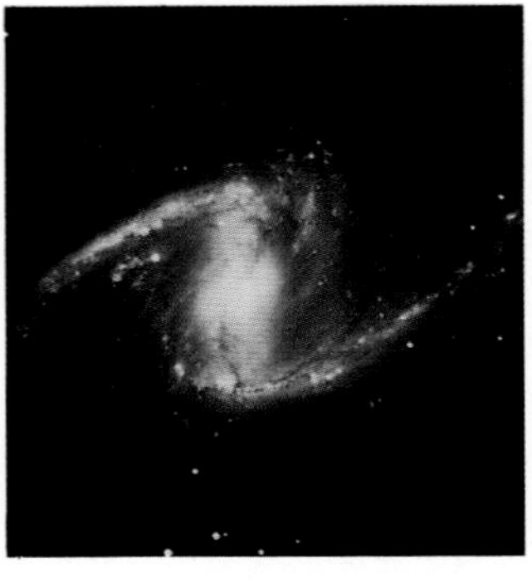

Figure 24-18. In a barred spiral, the spiral arms originate at the ends of a bar passing through the nucleus. This galaxy is named NGC 1365.

Figure 24-19. The Milky Way Galaxy is probably a normal spiral galaxy. Its spiral arms, composed of stars and gas, radiate out from an area of densely packed stars, the nucleus. Clusters of stars lie above and below the plane of the spiral arms.

The third class of galaxies, irregulars, includes most of those galaxies that don't fit into the other classifications. Irregular galaxies have many different shapes and are smaller and less common than the other types. Two irregular galaxies called the Clouds of Magellan orbit the Milky Way Galaxy at a distance of about 170 000 light-years.

The Milky Way Galaxy

The Milky Way contains more than 200 billion stars. It's about 100 000 light-years across, and the sun is located about 30 000 light-years out from its center. In our galaxy, all stars orbit around a central region. The sun orbits around the center of the Milky Way once every 200 million years.

A diagram of our galaxy is shown in Figure 24-19. The Milky Way is usually classified as a normal spiral galaxy. However, recent evidence suggests that it might be a barred spiral. It is difficult to know for sure because we can never see our galaxy from the "outside."

You can't see the normal spiral or barred shape of the Milky Way because you are located within one of its spiral arms. You can see the Milky Way stretching across the sky as a faint band of light. All of the stars you can see in the night sky belong to the Milky Way Galaxy.

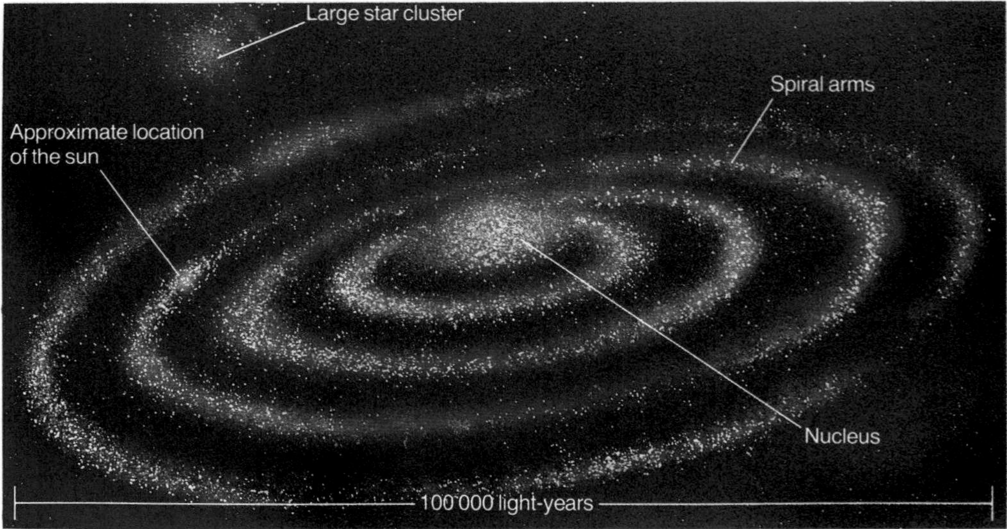

OPTIONS

INQUIRY QUESTIONS

▶ **Why are some galaxies classified as irregular in shape?** *Irregular galaxies don't have the regular shape that spirals and elliptical galaxies have.*

▶ **Why can't you see the spiral shape of the Milky Way Galaxy?** *In order to see the spiral shape of the Milky Way, you would have to be above or below the plane of the galaxy. Earth, in orbit around the sun, is located in one of the spiral arms.*

▶ **Why are dark lines in a spectrum shifted toward the red end when an object is moving away from you?** *Each dark line represents a wavelength of light. As objects move away, the wavelengths of light are stretched out, making them longer, and thus appear toward the red end of the spectrum.*

▶ **Why do we not observe a red shift in the light of the galaxies of the Local Group?** *All galaxies in the Local Group are gravitationally affecting each other and move through space together.*

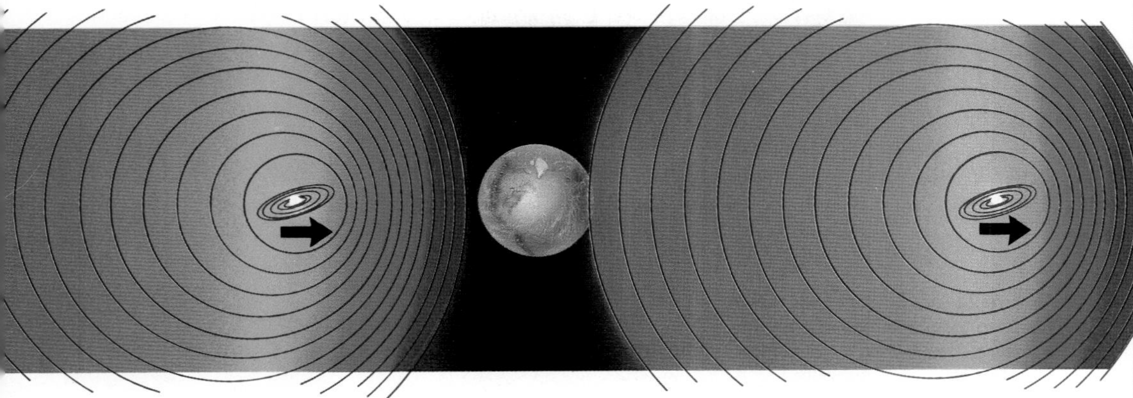

Figure 24-20. The Doppler effect causes the wavelengths of light coming from galaxies to be compressed or stretched. When a galaxy is moving toward Earth, the wavelengths are forced together and the light shifts toward the blue-violet end of the spectrum. A galaxy shows a red shift when moving away from Earth.

Expansion of the Universe

What does it sound like when a car is blowing its horn while it drives past you? The horn has a high pitch as the car approaches you, then the horn seems to change to a low pitch as the car drives away. This effect is called the Doppler shift. The Doppler shift occurs with light as well as with sound.

Look at the spectrum of a star containing sodium in Figure 24-21a. Note the position of the dark lines. How do they compare with the lines in Figures 24-21b and c? They have shifted in position. What caused this shift? When a star is moving toward you, its wavelengths of light are pushed together, just as the sound waves from the car's horn are. The dark lines in the spectrum shift toward the blue-violet. A red shift in the spectrum occurs when an object is moving away from you. In a red shift, the dark lines shift toward the longer wavelength, red end of the spectrum.

In 1924, Edwin Hubble noticed an interesting fact about the light coming from most galaxies. When a spectrograph is used to study light from galaxies beyond the Local Group, there is a red shift in the light. What does this red shift tell you about the universe?

5 Because all galaxies beyond the Local Group show a red shift in their spectra, they must be moving away from Earth. If all galaxies outside the Local Group are moving away from you, the entire universe must be expanding. Think of the Find Out activity at the beginning of the chapter. The dots on the balloon moved apart as the

EcoTip

Viewing the stars and galaxies is possible only when the sky is unpolluted by artificial lights. Help keep the sky dark and save energy by turning off unnecessary outdoor lights.

ENRICHMENT

▶ Have students research the work of Margaret Geller and John Huchra, of the Harvard-Smithsonian Center for Astrophysics, on mapping the universe. The work of these two astronomers has led to the realization that great voids and large concentrations of galaxies alternate throughout the universe. They discovered that many galaxies lie in an enormous sheet now called the "Great Wall." For more information, refer students to "A Cross Section of the Universe," by Jeff Kanipe, *Astronomy*, November 1989, p. 44.

▶ Provide students with drawings of Hubble's classification of galaxies. Have students hypothesize how the classification of elliptical and spiral galaxies may be related to the evolution of galaxies. Show students how elliptical galaxies become more elliptical as the classification goes from E0 to E7.

CONCEPT DEVELOPMENT

▶ **Demonstration:** Ask students if they have ever experienced the Doppler shift of sound waves. Remind them of train whistles from approaching and receding trains, and the siren of a fire truck as it drives by. Securely tie an alarm clock to a cord and gently twirl the clock around as the alarm is sounding. Students will hear the changing pitch as the clock first approaches them and then recedes.

CHECK FOR UNDERSTANDING

Use the Mini-Quiz to check for understanding.

MINI QUIZ

Use the Mini Quiz to check students' recall of chapter content.

1. **A large group of stars, gas, and dust held together by gravity is a(n) _____.** *galaxy*
2. **The Milky Way is usually classified as a spiral galaxy and belongs to the _____.** *Local Group*
3. **What are the three major classifications of galaxies?** *elliptical, spiral, irregular*
4. **The most common type of galaxy is the _____ galaxy.** *elliptical*
5. **The dark lines in the spectrum of light from galaxies outside the Local Group show a(n) _____, which indicates the galaxies are moving away.** *red shift*

RETEACH

Demonstration: Show students one loaf of raisin bread before baking. Have students measure the distance between the raisins in the bread. Send the loaf to the home economics or domestic arts department and have them bake it. When the loaf is returned, have students measure the distance between the raisins again. Have students explain why the raisins are farther apart after baking and relate this to the expansion of the universe. Each raisin represents a galaxy cluster.

EXTENSION

For students who have mastered this section, use the **Reinforcement** and **Enrichment** masters or other OPTIONS provided.

MINI-Lab

Materials: large sheet of paper, metric ruler or meterstick

Teaching Tips

▶ Help students conceptualize the scale of their model. If our sun were represented by a dot on their drawing, Proxima Centauri would be contained within that same dot.

▶ Discuss the significance of the circle representing the distance to Deneb. Remind students that every star that they can observe with the naked eye is located within that circle. Telescopes must be used to see any star outside of the sun-Deneb radius.

Answers to Questions: The 1400 light-year radius circle represents the farthest distance from which an observer on Earth can observe a star without the aid of a telescope. The scale distance to the Andromeda galaxy will depend on the size of the student's model Milky Way. Whatever the scale used, the distance to the Andromeda galaxy would be about 20 times the diameter of the student's Milky Way model. This can be determined by dividing the distance to the Andromeda galaxy (2 000 000 light-years) by the diameter of the Milky Way (100 000 light-years).

CONCEPT DEVELOPMENT

▶ Have students write a brief paragraph that answers the following question. **Why don't galaxies within the Local Group show a red shift in their spectra like galaxies outside the Local Group do?** *Galaxies within the Local Group are gravitationally attracted to each other. Because of this, they travel through space together. Galaxies outside the Local Group are expanding outward through space.*

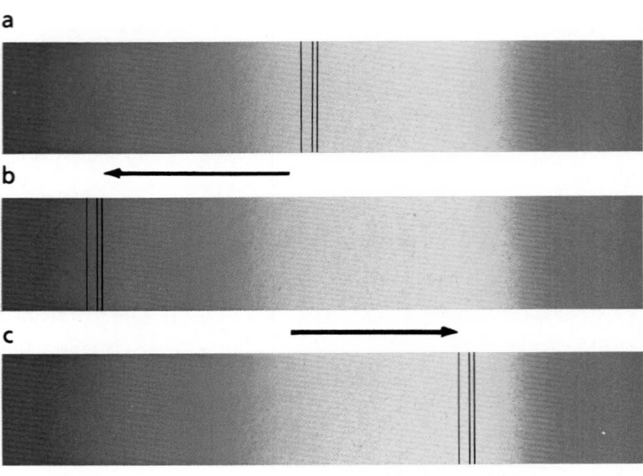

Figure 24-21. The dark lines in the spectra (a) are shifted toward the blue-violet end when a star is moving toward Earth (b). A red shift (c) indicates a star is moving away from Earth.

MINI-Lab

How far into space do we "see"? On a large sheet of paper, make a diagram of the Milky Way Galaxy as it would appear looking down on it from somewhere out in space. Mark the approximate location of the solar system, about 2/3 of the way out one of the spiral arms. Indicate the approximate location of the next closest star to the sun, Proxima Centuri, at a distance of 4.2 light-years. The most distant star that can be seen on a clear night without the aid of a telescope is Deneb in the constellation Cygnus at a distance of 1400 light-years. On your diagram, draw a circle with a radius of about 1400 light-years with the sun at the center. What does this circle represent? At this scale, how far away would the Andromeda galaxy (the next closest spiral galaxy) be located?

"universe" expanded. Regardless of which dot you picked, all the other dots moved away from it. Galaxies beyond the Local Group move away from us just as the dots moved apart on the balloon.

When scientists determined that the universe was expanding, they realized that galaxies must have been closer together in the past. The leading theory about the formation of the universe is based on this fact. The **big bang theory** states that between 15 and 20 billion years ago, the universe began expanding out of an enormous explosion.

At the beginning of the explosion, all matter in the universe was concentrated in a state of infinite density. The explosion of the big bang sent all matter moving apart. As matter cooled, hydrogen and helium gas formed. Matter began collecting in clumps and eventually formed into galaxies. There is evidence to support the big bang theory. Scientists have discovered radiation in space they believe was created by the explosion of the big bang.

Will the universe expand forever? Some scientists think that it will. Others think that the expansion will stop. Whether the universe expands forever or stops depends on how dense the matter is in the universe. All matter exerts a gravitational force. If there's enough matter, gravity will halt the expansion. In that case, the universe would contract until everything came to one point—a "big crunch" would result. It's not known if the universe is dense enough for this to happen.

OPTIONS

INQUIRY QUESTIONS

▶ **Why do astronomers think that galaxies must have been much closer in the past?** *If galaxies outside the Local Group are presently expanding outward, they must have been closer together at some time in the past.*

▶ **What evidence is there that the universe began with an explosion called the big bang?** *Doppler shifts toward the red end of the spectrum indicate that the universe is expanding. Scientists have detected background radiation of the type expected from an explosion of this type.*

▶ **What will determine if the universe keeps on expanding or begins to contract?** *The determining factor is mass. If enough mass exists in the universe, it will eventually slow its rate of expansion, stop, and begin to contract again.*

Astronomers continue to study the structure of the known universe in hopes of learning its exact age, how it has evolved, and how it might end. You will learn in the next section that astronomers also search the galaxy in hopes of finding evidence that life exists elsewhere in our solar system and galaxy.

Figure 24-22. This 305-m dish at Arecibo, Puerto Rico is the world's largest telescope. On page 661 in the Science and Art feature, you will read how this telescope was used in an attempt to communicate with extraterrestrial life.

SECTION REVIEW

1. List the three major classifications of galaxies. What do they all have in common?
2. What is the name of the galaxy that you live in? What motion do the stars in this galaxy exhibit?
3. How does the big bang theory explain observations of galaxies made with spectrographs?
4. **Apply:** All galaxies outside the Local Group show a red shift in their spectra. What does this tell you about the galaxies in the Local Group?

Recognizing Cause and Effect — Skill Builder

Current measurements and calculated densities of the universe show it's not dense enough to collapse on itself. Scientists are trying to prove the existence of so-called "dark matter," which is not directly observable. If the universe contains an abundance of dark matter, what could you infer about the true density and the future of the universe? If you need help, refer to Recognizing Cause and Effect in the **Skill Handbook** on page 683.

PROGRAM RESOURCES

From the **Teacher Resource Package** use:

Activity Worksheets, page 223, Mini-Lab: How far into space do we "see"?

3 CLOSE

▶ Ask a student to read the objectives for the lesson. Ask a volunteer to explain how the objectives were attained. If students are unsure as to whether or not objectives were attained, show photographs of the three main types of galaxies. Ask a volunteer to draw a representation of the Milky Way Galaxy on the chalkboard. Call on another student to present a review of the big bang theory. Elicit help from other students as needed.

Cooperative Learning: Form Numbered Heads Together groups with four students per group. Have students brainstorm and come up with an original idea they can use to demonstrate the big bang theory to their classmates. If needed, remind students of the Find Out activity in the chapter introduction. Reward points based on the originality of the group's idea.

▶ Ask questions 1-3 and the **Apply Question** from the Section Review.

SECTION REVIEW ANSWERS

1. Shapes are elliptical, spiral (regular and barred), and irregular. All galaxies are large groups of stars, gas, and dust held together by gravity; they are grouped in clusters.

2. the Milky Way Galaxy; stars orbit its nucleus

3. Red shifts, observed in the spectra of galaxies outside the Local Group, indicate galaxies are moving away from us as they would be if the universe were expanding from a big bang.

4. Apply: All galaxies within the Local Group travel through space together, and galaxies outside the Local Group are moving apart.

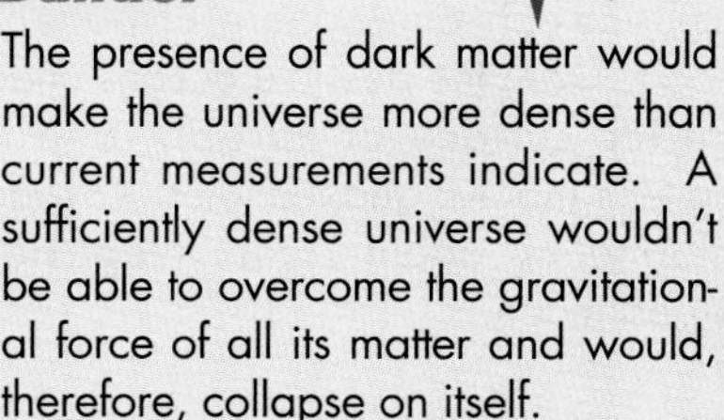

Skill Builder

The presence of dark matter would make the universe more dense than current measurements indicate. A sufficiently dense universe wouldn't be able to overcome the gravitational force of all its matter and would, therefore, collapse on itself.

SECTION 24-5

PREPARATION

SECTION BACKGROUND

▶ When searching for life elsewhere in space, scientists search for the presence of organic molecules. These are the molecules that contain the element carbon. Life as we know it is made of organic molecules.

▶ Certain meteorites called carbonaceous chondrites are often found to contain organic substances. Interstellar clouds, nebulae, contain many organic compounds. This is not proof that life exists elsewhere in space; rather, it's an indication that the precursors of life are relatively abundant. From 1992 to 1998, radio telescopes will be used to study all sunlike stars within a distance of 82 light-years of Earth.

1 MOTIVATE

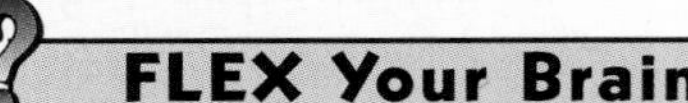

FLEX Your Brain

Use the Flex Your Brain activity to have students explore THE ENVIRONMENT ON MARS. Students should discover that the Martian environment contains air that's 95 percent carbon dioxide, polar ice caps of frozen carbon dioxide and water, evidence that water may have flowed on the surface during Mars' past, and soil with high concentrations of iron.

TYING TO PREVIOUS KNOWLEDGE: Help students recall conditions on some of the moons of the gaseous giant planets as described in Chapter 23. Remind them of the methane-rich atmosphere of Saturn's moon, Titan; the possible oceans under the ice surface of Europa, one of Jupiter's moons; and the latest *Voyager* information about Triton, Neptune's largest moon.

24-5 The Search for Extraterrestrial Life

New Science Words

extraterrestrial life

Objectives

- ▶ Name locations in our solar system where life may have existed in the past or could exist now.
- ▶ Describe methods used by astronomers to search for extraterrestrial life within and beyond our solar system.
- ▶ Decide if methods used by scientists might cause contamination of other worlds.

Can NASA Safely Explore Other Worlds?

On July 20, 1976, the first *Viking* probe landed on Mars. It conducted three different types of tests on Martian soil in searching for evidence of extraterrestrial life. **Extraterrestrial life** is life that exists beyond Earth. It could be microorganisms living in the rocks of a barren world or intelligent life living on a planet orbiting a distant star.

Figure 24-23. The *Viking* probes failed to find evidence of life on Mars.

OPTIONS

Meeting Different Ability Levels

For Section 24-5, use the following **Teacher Resource Masters** depending upon individual students' needs.

◆ **Study Guide Master** for all students.

● **Reinforcement Master** for students of average and above average ability levels.

▲ **Enrichment Master** for above average students.

Additional Teacher Resource Package masters are listed in the OPTIONS box throughout the section. The additional masters are appropriate for all students.

◆ STUDY GUIDE 99

NAME ____________ DATE ________ CLASS ________

STUDY GUIDE — Chapter 24

The Search for Extraterrestrial Life — Text Pages 652–654

Match the description in Column I with the correct terms in Column II. Write the letter of the correct term in the space provided.

Column I	Column II
d 1. Program that searches for extraterrestrial life	a. Triton
c 2. Showed no evidence of the kind of molecules that seem necessary for life	b. extraterrestrial life
b 3. Life that exists beyond Earth	c. Martian soil
a 4. A satellite of Neptune that contains molecules that resemble those from which life on Earth probably evolved.	d. SETI
g 5. A moon of Jupiter that may possibly receive sunlight on its ocean.	e. *Viking*
e 6. Sterilized so it wouldn't contaminate soil on Mars	f. organic molecules
h 7. Scheduled to send a probe into Jupiter's clouds	g. Europa
f 8. Molecules from which life evolved	h. *Galileo*

Unscramble the following words to reveal what SETI stands for.

eth — the
chears — search
orf — for
xtttrrrreeeaails — extraterrestrial
elligtennice — intelligence

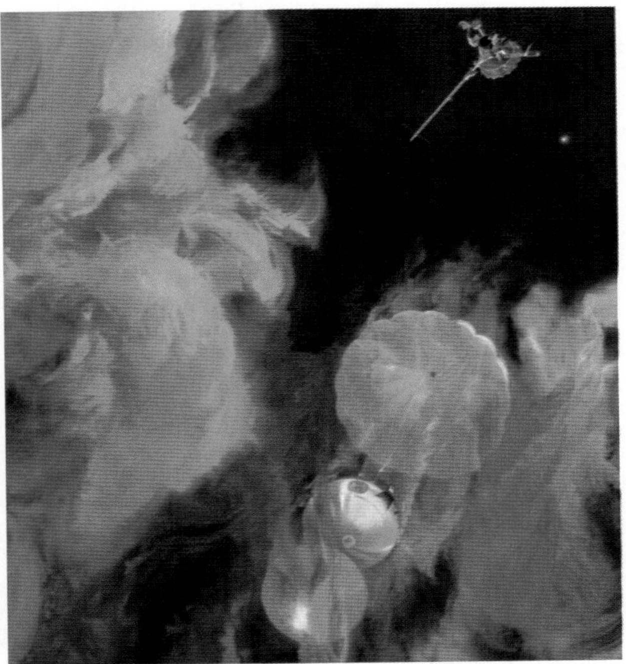

Figure 24-24. The *Galileo* probe will send a small probe parachuting into Jupiter's atmosphere. It will transmit data back to the orbiter above. Should the probe have been sterilized prior to launch?

Each test made by the *Viking* probes gave results that could have been caused by life or by chemical reactions with the Martian soil. However, analysis of the soil showed it lacked the types of molecules that appear to be necessary for life. It appears Mars doesn't contain life or the remains of life.

The *Viking* spacecrafts were carefully sterilized so the Martian soil would not be contaminated. The *Galileo* spacecraft, which should arrive at Jupiter in 1995, will send a probe down into the clouds of the planet. It was not sterilized before being launched. Is there a danger that microbes from Earth could contaminate the environment of Jupiter's clouds? NASA doesn't think so. *Galileo's* probe will be crushed and sterilized in the depths of Jupiter's atmosphere. Project scientists don't believe there is any chance for planetary contamination.

Triton, one of the satellites of Neptune, contains organic molecules. The molecules themselves aren't considered to be life, but they are thought to resemble the molecules from which life evolved on Earth. Given enough time, millions or billions of years, it's possible that the molecules

Why would Triton be a good place to look for extraterrestrial life?

● REINFORCEMENT 99

NAME ________ DATE ________ CLASS ________

REINFORCEMENT — Chapter 24

The Search for Extraterrestrial Life — Text Pages 652-654

Answer the following questions in complete sentences.

1. Why were the *Viking* spacecraft sterilized before they were launched? **The spacecraft were sterilized to prevent the Martian soil from being contaminated by life-forms from Earth.**
2. Why does it appear that life never existed on Mars? **Soil analysis indicated that the Martian soil lacks the molecules considered necessary for life.**
3. Why wasn't *Galileo* sterilized before it was launched? **It is believed that *Galileo* will be crushed and sterilized in Jupiter's atmosphere, so sterilizing it beforehand wasn't necessary.**
4. Why is there a possibility that life may evolve on Triton in the distant future? **Triton has organic molecules which are similar to those from which life on Earth evolved.**
5. What does SETI listen for? **SETI listens for radio signals that may have been sent by intelligent life somewhere else in the universe.**
6. How long will it be before we know whether intelligent life responds to the SETI message sent in 1974 to a star cluster over 26 000 light-years away? **A response to the message could not arrive until 52 000 years in the future.**
7. Why do scientists want to send a probe to Triton? Should the probe be sterilized? **Scientists want to send a probe to Triton to study the organic molecules there. The probe should probably be sterilized since there may be a chance that the probe would contaminate the environment there.**
8. Why might life evolve on Europa, one of Jupiter's moons? **Cracks in Europa's icy crust may allow sunlight into the ocean underneath the crust. The sunlight could help start biological activity.**
9. Is there a safe way to search for intelligent life, a way that cannot contaminate the environment? **Radio signals cannot contaminate an environment and so are considered a safe, but generally impractical, way.**

 99

▲ ENRICHMENT 99

NAME ________ DATE ________ CLASS ________

ENRICHMENT — Chapter 24

The Search for Extraterrestrial Life — Text Pages 652-654

SEARCHING FOR INTELLIGENT LIFE

Is there extraterrestrial intelligent life in our galaxy? Are there intelligent societies trying to contact us? Scientists are trying to answer these questions.

Based on findings from the space programs and astronomy studies, scientists have concluded that intelligent life does not exist anywhere in our solar system except on Earth. They think the best place to look for intelligent life would be around stars in the Milky Way that have orbiting satellites similar to Earth.

If intelligent beings do exist on satellites around stars, how can we contact them? Because it would take a spacecraft hundreds of thousands of years to travel to distant stars, scientists think the radio telescope is the best way to establish contact. However, scientists can only speculate that an advanced society would be sending or receiving radio signals. If the society does transmit radio signals, what is the frequency of the transmission? Would scientists recognize the transmission if received? Scientists can only hypothesize answers to these questions.

Some scientists developed a formula to determine the probability of extraterrestrial intelligent life. The formula is

$$N = R^* \times f_p \times n_e \times f_l \times f_i \times f_c \times L$$

where N = the number of societies in the Milky Way capable of interstellar communication
R^* = the average rate that stars develop in the galaxy
f_p = the fraction of stars with planets
n_e = the average number of a star's planets able to sustain life
f_l = the fraction of planets with any form of life
f_i = the fraction of planets with intelligent life
f_c = the fraction of planets with intelligent life with the capability for interstellar communications
L = the average lifetime of a society with the capability for interstellar communications

Can numbers be assigned to the formula? Only the rate of development of stars in the galaxy is a number that scientists can determine with any certainty. Scientists would have to guess all the other variables. Scientists have used the formula to estimate that there might be 1000 societies capable of interstellar communication. It's possible that there're many more or fewer societies capable of this communication. No one knows for sure.

1. Why do you think people continue to think extraterrestrial intelligent life exists even when no contact has been made with this life? **Answers will vary; students may note that the vastness of the universe indicates that conditions similar to Earth's must have a good chance of existing, thus intelligent life must exist beyond Earth.**
2. Why do you think scientists developed the formula given even though numbers for the variables can only be guessed at? **Answers will vary. Students may conclude that the formula does help scientists determine the probability of extraterrestrial intelligent life in our galaxy for a variety of conditions.**

 99

OBJECTIVES AND SCIENCE WORDS: Have students review the objectives and science words to become familiar with this section.

2 TEACH

Key Concepts are highlighted.

CONCEPT DEVELOPMENT

▶ **Library Research:** Have students research the tests for life conducted by the *Viking* lander on Mars. Ask them to include a description of the tests and possible conclusions that have been drawn. Refer students to the following article: "The Case for Life on Mars," by Andrew Chaikin, *Air and Space*, v. 5, March 1991, pp. 63-71.

Cooperative Learning: Form Science Investigation groups with four students per group. Assign each group a different planet or moon located within our solar system. Have each group devise a plan to search for life on their particular world. Students must include methods to be used in the search and safeguards to be followed that would avoid contaminating their assigned world.

▶ Direct students to the photograph on page 661 in the Unit Review material. This photograph illustrates the message sent by the Arecibo telescope. Prior to reading the Science and Art feature, have students interpret the photograph. Ask why one planet is offset from the plane in which the rest of the planets lie. Some students should realize that the offset planet is third from the sun and that it represents Earth. It's closer to the figure of a human to indicate that this is the planet where humans live.

PROGRAM RESOURCES

From the **Teacher Resource Package** use:

Activity Worksheets, page 5, Flex Your Brain.

Cross-Curricular Connections, page 28, The Martians are Coming! The Martians are Coming!

Science and Society, page 28, UFO Encounters.

TEACHER F.Y.I.

▶All of the energy that has been received by radio telescopes since they were first used is less than the energy contained in a single falling snowflake!

CHECK FOR UNDERSTANDING

Ask questions 1-3 in the Section Review.

RETEACH

Cooperative Learning: Using the Numbered Heads Together strategy, have students discuss whether it is appropriate to spend tax dollars to send probes to search for life on other worlds. Students should discuss the fact that the chance of finding life is relatively remote. However, if life is found, it could tell us a great deal about how life evolved on Earth. Students may wish to stage a debate after they have researched the topic.

EXTENSION

For students who have mastered this use the **Reinforcement** and **Enrichment** masters or other OPTIONS provided.

3 CLOSE

SECTION REVIEW ANSWERS

1. Earth; Triton and Europa

2. SETI, the *S*earch for *E*xtra*t*errestrial *I*ntelligence

3. The *Viking* lander was sterilized so the Martian soil would not be contaminated. NASA believes the *Galileo* probe will be crushed and sterilized in the depths of Jupiter's atmosphere. Its route to Jupiter carries it close to the sun. Therefore, it may be sterilized long before reaching Jupiter.

will evolve into life as they did on Earth. Scientists hope to send a probe to Triton to further investigate the organic molecules there.

Cracks in the icy crust of Europa, one of Jupiter's moons, may allow sunlight into the ocean underneath. The sunlight could have helped start biological activity. If this is even remotely possible, what types of precautions should be taken before a probe is sent to Europa?

Are there perfectly safe ways to search for life? One method is to search the universe for sources of radio signals from intelligent life. This program is called SETI, the *S*earch for *E*xtra*t*errestrial *I*ntelligence. In 1974, astronomers used the large radio telescope in Arecibo, Puerto Rico, to beam a radio message to a star cluster more than 26 000 light-years away. Although more than 52 000 years will pass before a reply from intelligent life in the star cluster could arrive at Earth, the attempt was still made.

Maybe the wait won't be that long. Perhaps life elsewhere has already sent out a message. The program called SETI continues to listen for signs of intelligence in radio signals from space.

SECTION REVIEW

1. Where is life known to exist in the solar system? Name two other places in the solar system where life might be evolving.
2. Which program searches for evidence of intelligent life using radio telescopes?
3. The *Viking* probes were sterilized, but the *Galileo* probe wasn't? Why?

You Decide!

Scientists believe life could now exist or could someday evolve on several planets and moons in our solar system. A spacecraft from Earth studying these planets could carry organisms with it. Is it acceptable to sterilize only those probes going to Triton and other moons or planets felt to have a relatively good chance of having life on them? It's possible we could contaminate other worlds with microorganisms and organic molecules from Earth. Should we avoid going to those worlds where life may be evolving? Would it be better to search for intelligent life with radio telescopes only?

YOU DECIDE!

Students will have various answers to the questions posed here. It's always a possibility that we will contaminate other worlds by sending probes to them. However, the chance is small, and some students will feel that we should visit these worlds in search of extraterrestrial life. Searching for life with radio telescopes seriously limits the possibility of finding life in the universe. Only technologically advanced, intelligent life-forms can send radio signals. Also, the signals must travel astronomical distances to reach Earth. Radio telescopes are useless for finding life within our solar system.

CHAPTER

REVIEW

SUMMARY

24-1: Stars

1. The constellations seem to move because Earth rotates on its axis and revolves around the sun.
2. The magnitude of a star is a measure of the star's brightness. Absolute magnitude is a measure of the light emitted. Apparent magnitude is the amount of light received on Earth.
3. Parallax is the apparent shift in the position of an object when viewed from two different positions. The closer an object is to the observer, the greater its parallax.

24-2: Evolution of Stars

1. The H-R diagram illustrates the relationship between a star's temperature and its absolute magnitude.
2. Blue-white stars are very hot and bright. Red stars are relatively dim and cool. Yellow stars have brightnesses and temperatures in between those of blue and red stars.
3. A main sequence star uses hydrogen as fuel. When the hydrogen is used up, the core collapses and the star's temperature increases. The star becomes a giant or a supergiant, which use helium as fuel. As the star evolves, the outer layers escape into space. The core has no fuel left and the star becomes a white dwarf. Depending on the original mass of the star, it can evolve into a neutron star or a black hole.

24-3: The Sun

1. The sun produces energy by fusing hydrogen into helium in its core.
2. Sunspots, prominences, and flares are all probably caused by the intense magnetic field of the sun.
3. The sun is a main sequence star. Yet it's somewhat unusual because it isn't part of a binary system, which forms when two stars orbit each other.

24-4: Galaxies and the Expanding Universe

1. A galaxy is a large group of stars, gas, and dust held together by gravity. Galaxies can be elliptical, spiral, or irregular in shape.
2. The Milky Way is a spiral galaxy and contains over 200 billion stars. The sun is located about 30 000 light-years from the center of the galaxy.
3. Shifts toward red light suggest that all galaxies beyond the Local Group are moving away from our galaxy. This fact supports the big bang theory, which states that the universe began expanding out of an explosion 15 to 20 billion years ago.

24-5: Science and Society: The Search for Extraterrestrial Life

1. Organic molecules, similar to those that evolved into life on Earth, have been found on Triton, a satellite of Neptune.
2. Space probes and radio telescopes are used to determine whether or not life exists in other parts of the universe.
3. Spacecraft sent to other planets might contaminate the planets with organisms from Earth. Sterilization of spacecraft may eliminate the contamination.

CHAPTER

REVIEW

SUMMARY

Have students read the summary statements to review the major concepts of the chapter.

ASSESSMENT

To assess student understanding of material in this chapter, use the resources listed

COOPERATIVE LEARNING

Consider using cooperative learning in the THINK AND WRITE CRITICALLY, APPLY, and MORE SKILL BUILDERS sections of the Chapter Review.

PROGRAM RESOURCES

From the **Teacher Resource Package** use:

Chapter Review, pages 51-52.

Chapter and Unit Tests, pages 158-161, Chapter Test.

Chapter and Unit Tests, pages 162-163, Unit Test.

CHAPTER
REVIEW

UNDERSTANDING VOCABULARY

1. g
2. a
3. l
4. n
5. k
6. e
7. m
8. q
9. d
10. c

CHECKING CONCEPTS

1. d
2. b
3. c
4. c
5. d
6. d
7. d
8. a
9. b
10. a

UNDERSTANDING CONCEPTS

11. apparent
12. light-years
13. corona
14. big bang
15. Sunspots

THINK AND WRITE CRITICALLY

16. The closer star will have a greater parallax.

17. absolute magnitude and surface temperature

18. All are solar features that seem to be related to the sun's intense magnetic field. Sunspots are relatively cool areas on the surface. Flares and prominences are eruptive features in which matter is violently spewed from the sun's surface.

19. The big bang theory states that all matter began expanding from a single point billions of years ago. Because red shifts indicate that matter is expanding, they support the big bang theory.

20. Probes are able to get close to their targets but pose the problem of contamination. Radio telescopes don't contaminate other worlds, but they can search only for intelligent life that may have sent a radio broadcast.

CHAPTER
REVIEW

KEY SCIENCE WORDS

a. **absolute magnitude**
b. **apparent magnitude**
c. **big bang theory**
d. **binary system**
e. **black hole**
f. **chromosphere**
g. **constellations**
h. **corona**
i. **extraterrestrial life**
j. **galaxy**
k. **giant**
l. **light-year**
m. **main sequence**
n. **nebula**
o. **neutron star**
p. **parallax**
q. **photosphere**
r. **sunspots**
s. **supergiant**
t. **white dwarf**

UNDERSTANDING VOCABULARY

Match each phrase with the correct term from the list of Key Science Words.

1. groups of stars that resemble objects, animals, or mythological characters
2. amount of light given off by a star
3. distance light travels in one year
4. the beginning of a star's life cycle
5. star that uses helium as fuel
6. dense object that allows nothing to escape its field of gravity
7. our sun belongs to this group of stars
8. layer of the sun's atmosphere that emits light
9. formed when two stars orbit each other
10. supported by observed red shifts in the spectra of galaxies

CHECKING CONCEPTS

Choose the word or phrase that completes the sentence.

1. The stars of a constellation are ______.
   a. in the same cluster **c.** equally bright
   b. all giants **d.** none of these
2. ______ is a measure of the amount of a star's light received on Earth.
   a. Absolute magnitude **c.** Fusion
   b. Apparent magnitude **d.** Parallax
3. The closer an object is to an observer, the greater its ______.
   a. absolute magnitude **c.** parallax
   b. red shift **d.** all of these
4. As a nebula contracts, ______ begins.
   a. main sequencing **c.** fusion
   b. supernova **d.** a white dwarf
5. A ______ is about the size of a city.
   a. giant **c.** black hole
   b. white dwarf **d.** neutron star
6. Our sun ______.
   a. fuses hydrogen **c.** emits yellow light
   b. is an average star **d.** all of these
7. Loops of matter flowing from the sun are ______.
   a. sunspots **c.** coronas
   b. auroras **d.** prominences
8. Groups of galaxies are called ______.
   a. clusters **c.** giants
   b. supergiants **d.** binary systems
9. ______ galaxies are sometimes shaped like footballs.
   a. Spiral **c.** Barred
   b. Elliptical **d.** Irregular
10. A shift toward the ______ end of the spectra of stars indicates that galaxies are moving away from the Local Group.
    a. red **c.** either a or b
    b. blue-violet **d.** none of these

APPLY

21. Because the universe is expanding, these initial galaxies are far out in space. Present instruments are not able to detect the galaxies because of the vast distances involved.

22. Astronomers are able to use instruments to detect the X rays possibly originating from sources surrounding black holes.

UNDERSTANDING CONCEPTS

Complete each sentence.

11. The _______ magnitude of a star depends on its distance from Earth.

12. Because they are so large, distances in space are measured in _______.

13. Temperatures in the sun's _______ are greater than those in the chromosphere.

14. Evidence indicates that the universe has been expanding ever since the _______.

15. _______ prove that the sun rotates.

THINK AND WRITE CRITICALLY

16. How can parallax be used to determine which of two stars is closer to Earth?

17. What variables determine a star's position on the H-R diagram?

18. Compare and contrast sunspots, solar flares, and prominences.

19. How do red shifts support the big bang theory?

20. What are the advantages and disadvantages of using radio telescopes and probes to search for life in the universe?

APPLY

21. Why have the first galaxies that formed not yet been observed by astronomers?

22. How do scientists know that black holes exist if these objects don't emit any visible light?

23. Use the autumn star chart in Appendix J to determine which constellation is directly overhead at 8 P.M. on November 21 for an observer in North America.

24. How are radio waves used to detect objects in space?

25. What kinds of reactions produce the energy emitted by stars?

MORE SKILL BUILDERS

1. Making and Using Tables: Astronomical objects are given numbers to represent their absolute and apparent magnitudes. The lower the number, the greater the object's brightness. What object listed in the table below has the brightest absolute magnitude? What object is the brightest as seen from Earth?

2. Making and Using Tables: How does the table show that apparent magnitude is dependent on both absolute magnitude and distance from an observer?

Star	Absolute Magnitude	Apparent Magnitude	Light-years from Earth
The sun	4.9	–26.7	0.000 002
Sirius	1.5	–1.5	8.70
Arcturus	–0.3	–0.1	35.86
Alpha Centauri	4.4	0.0	4.34
Betelgeuse	–5.5	0.8	489.0
Deneb	–6.9	1.3	1401.80

3. Concept Mapping: Make a concept map that shows the evolution of a main sequence star with a mass similar to that of the sun.

4. Comparing and Contrasting: Compare and contrast the sun with other stars on the H-R diagram.

5. Measuring in SI: The Milky Way is 100 000 light-years in diameter. What scale would you use if you were to construct a scale model of the Milky Way with a diameter of 20 cm?

PROJECTS

1. Design and construct scale models of a spiral and a barred Milky Way. Show the approximate position of the sun in each.

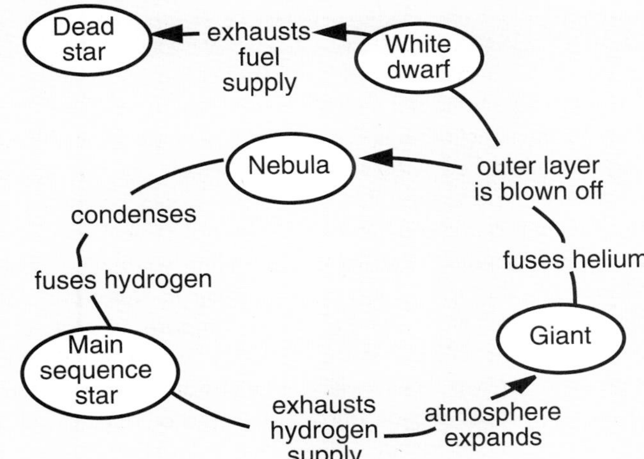

23. Pegasus is almost directly overhead at this time.
24. Any object at a temperature above absolute zero emits radio waves. The sun, other stars, and even people give off radio waves. These waves can be gathered by the antenna of radio telescopes and then analyzed to determine what type of object is emitting them.
25. Stars produce energy by fusion. Hydrogen is converted into helium in main sequence stars. Helium then fuses to produce heavier elements. As nuclei are fused, mass is converted into energy.

MORE SKILL BUILDERS

1. Making and Using Tables: Deneb, the sun
2. Making and Using Tables: The absolute magnitudes of some nearby objects are relatively low, but their apparent magnitudes are high. For example, the sun is the brightest object as seen from Earth, but its absolute magnitude is dim compared to Betelgeuse, 489 light-years away.
3. Concept Mapping: The map should trace the evolution of a star beginning with a nebula. The nebula contracts and fusion begins. The main sequence star fuses hydrogen until its core collapses and its outer surface expands. The giant fuses helium in its core. When it uses up its helium supply, it contracts to form a white dwarf. White dwarfs use up their fuel and die. One possible solution is shown at left.
4. Comparing and Contrasting: The sun is an average star in terms of mass, temperature, and its place in it evolutionary cycle. The sun differs from more massive stars in that they have higher temperatures and are further along in their evolutionary cycle. Other stars, such as white dwarfs, are hotter than the sun but don't emit as much light.
5. Measuring in SI: 1 cm = 5000 light-years

UNIT 8 GLOBAL CONNECTIONS

Objective

In this unit ending feature, the unit topic, "Astronomy," is extended into other disciplines. Students will see how the study of astronomical objects and events is important to understanding observed phenomena in other disciplines.

Motivate

Cooperative Learning: Assign one Connection to each group of students. Using the Expert Teams strategy have each group research to find out more about the geographic location of the Connection—its climate, culture, flora and fauna, and ecological issues.

Wrap-Up

After students have reviewed all the boxes on these pages, ask them to form a hypothesis about how latitude affects climate.

METEOROLOGY

Background: Scientists think the sunspot cycle is like a magnetic dynamo whose fields are increased about every 11 years. This change is accompanied by a magnetic polarity reversal. The magnetic polarity in the sunspot cycle is a 22-year cycle, in which for 11 years the spots have north magnetic polarity in the northern hemisphere and south magnetic polarity in the southern hemisphere. This polarity is reversed for both hemispheres during the following 11 years.
Discussion: Discuss how records show a strong correlation between the rainfall cycle and the double sunspot cycle. It is not clear why this is so, but point out that such correlations often lead to important discoveries.
Answer to Question: Trees need water in order to grow, so the more rain, the greater the growth.
Extension: Have students make a bar graph that shows the amount of rainfall in your area during the past 22 years.

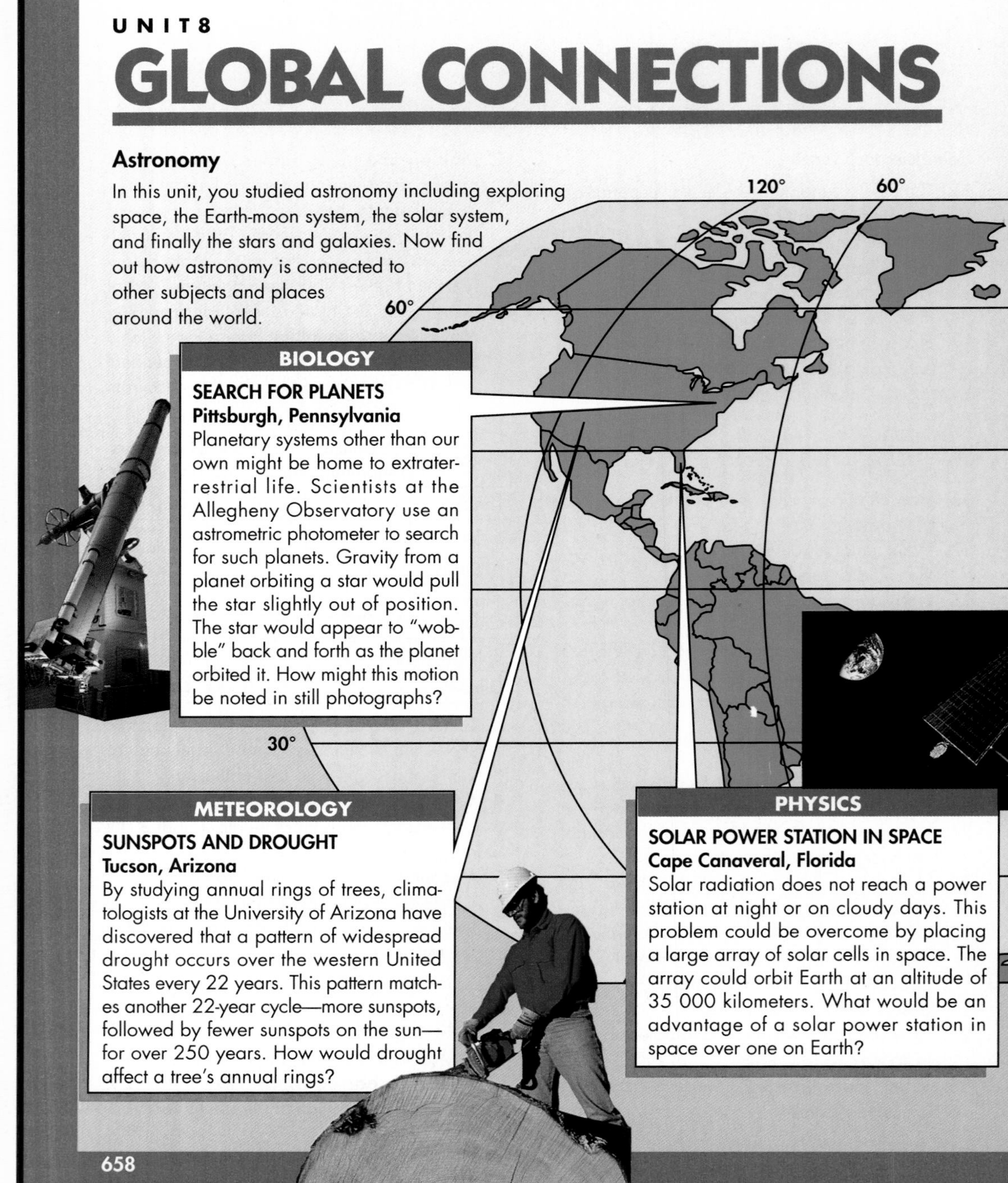

UNIT 8
GLOBAL CONNECTIONS
Astronomy
In this unit, you studied astronomy including exploring space, the Earth-moon system, the solar system, and finally the stars and galaxies. Now find out how astronomy is connected to other subjects and places around the world.
120°
60°
60°
30°
BIOLOGY
SEARCH FOR PLANETS
Pittsburgh, Pennsylvania
Planetary systems other than our own might be home to extraterrestrial life. Scientists at the Allegheny Observatory use an astrometric photometer to search for such planets. Gravity from a planet orbiting a star would pull the star slightly out of position. The star would appear to "wobble" back and forth as the planet orbited it. How might this motion be noted in still photographs?
METEOROLOGY
SUNSPOTS AND DROUGHT
Tucson, Arizona
By studying annual rings of trees, climatologists at the University of Arizona have discovered that a pattern of widespread drought occurs over the western United States every 22 years. This pattern matches another 22-year cycle—more sunspots, followed by fewer sunspots on the sun—for over 250 years. How would drought affect a tree's annual rings?
PHYSICS
SOLAR POWER STATION IN SPACE
Cape Canaveral, Florida
Solar radiation does not reach a power station at night or on cloudy days. This problem could be overcome by placing a large array of solar cells in space. The array could orbit Earth at an altitude of 35 000 kilometers. What would be an advantage of a solar power station in space over one on Earth?
658

BIOLOGY

Background: The gravitational attraction of a planet can pull on a star, causing the star's position to change slightly as the planet orbits it. One device for detecting planet-induced wiggles in star positions is the astrometric photometer that is mounted on a 30-inch refracting telescope at the Allegheny Observatory in Pittsburgh. It can look at 12 stars simultaneously through separate fiberoptic light pipes. At the same time, a grid of 4 lines per millimeter moves smoothly across the field. A star photographed for two weeks with the photometer reveals its proper motion and also any wiggle that indicates a companion.

Discussion: Ask students to imagine that there are planets with intelligent observers orbiting the nearby star Alpha Centauri. To the observers, our sun would be quite bright, and Earth would be lost in its glare. Discuss how those observers might overcome this difficulty and finally recognize that Earth is a planet.
Answer to Question: Astronomers would have to compare several successive photographic plates over several days to detect the motion.
Extension: Have students imagine and draw life-forms on another Earth-like world containing only half of Earth's water supply.

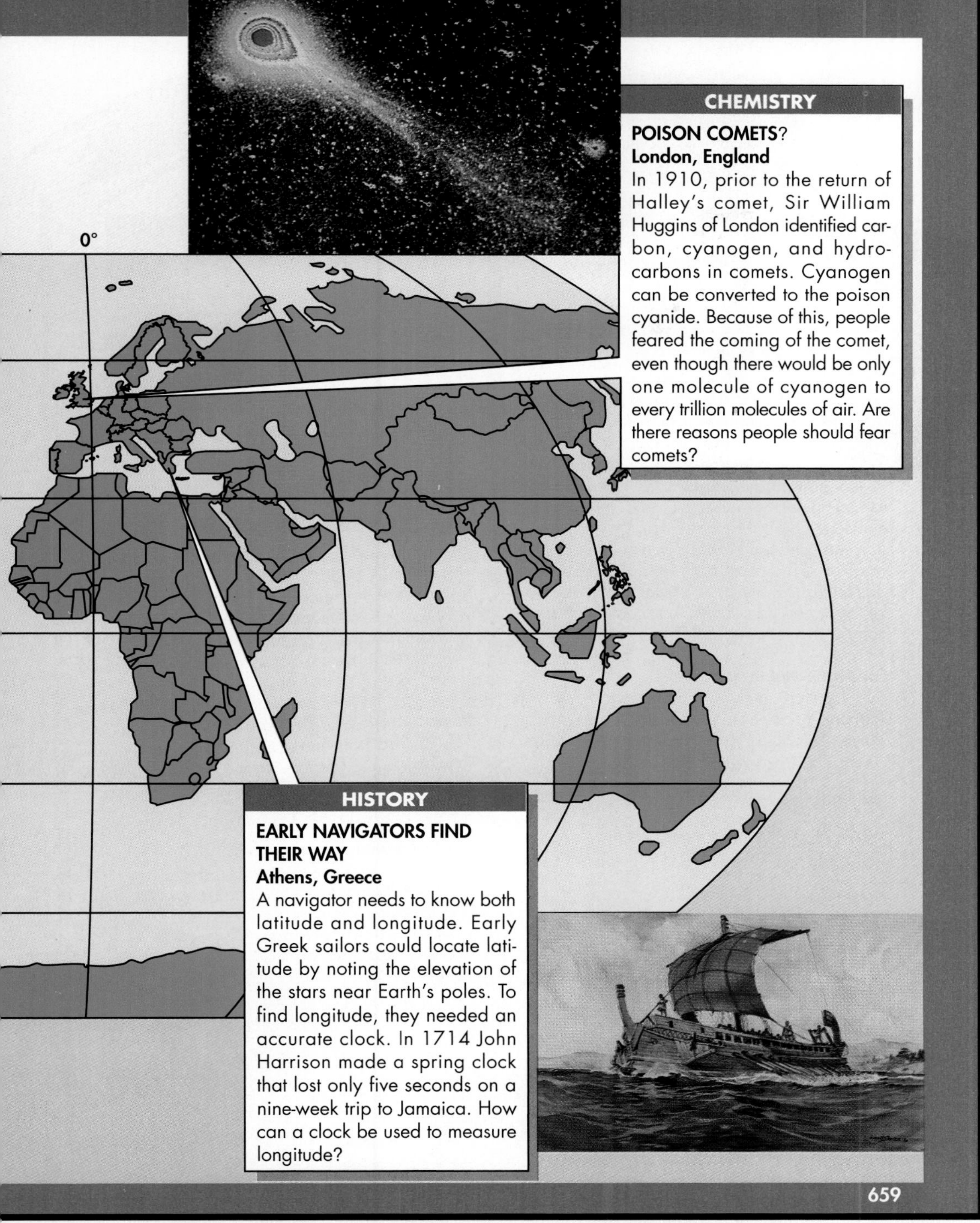

CHEMISTRY

POISON COMETS?
London, England

In 1910, prior to the return of Halley's comet, Sir William Huggins of London identified carbon, cyanogen, and hydrocarbons in comets. Cyanogen can be converted to the poison cyanide. Because of this, people feared the coming of the comet, even though there would be only one molecule of cyanogen to every trillion molecules of air. Are there reasons people should fear comets?

HISTORY

EARLY NAVIGATORS FIND THEIR WAY
Athens, Greece

A navigator needs to know both latitude and longitude. Early Greek sailors could locate latitude by noting the elevation of the stars near Earth's poles. To find longitude, they needed an accurate clock. In 1714 John Harrison made a spring clock that lost only five seconds on a nine-week trip to Jamaica. How can a clock be used to measure longitude?

PHYSICS

Background: A possible power system may consist of several collectors, each about 5 kilometers by 10 kilometers spread around Earth. Microwaves or lasers would transmit the energy from the power station to Earth. It would be more efficient than an Earth-based system, but the initial cost would be enormous.

Discussion: Discuss the problem of cost in starting up a new system such as an orbiting solar-power station. Also discuss the possible environmental hazards from the microwaves that would beam the energy to Earth.

Answer to Question: An orbiting solar power station would receive solar radiation day and night and even when it is cloudy on Earth.

Extension: Have students make a pie graph showing how energy from other sources compares with solar energy use in the United States.

CHEMISTRY

Background: The molecules identified in the comets so far are similar but simpler than the molecules in interstellar space. The most abundant atoms in comets are hydrogen, oxygen, carbon, nitrogen, silicon, and sulfur.

Discussion: Discuss how Halley's Comet has been sighted 32 times since 239 B.C. Every 76 years it reappears—its most recent visit being in 1986. Edmund Halley saw the comet in 1682. He predicted its return in 1758 but was not still living to see it again.

Answer to Question: Comets do not come very close to Earth, so they can do little harm to Earth.

Extension: Have students discuss what might happen if Earth traveled through a comet's tail such as possibly occurred in 1910.

HISTORY

Background: Before an accurate seafaring clock was devised, a navigator had to be a trained mathematician. Mathematics was needed to find longitude at sea. Precise observations of the moon required refined instruments and careful calculations. Few navigators were prepared for the task. An error of 5′ in observing the moon could mean an error of 2.5 degrees of longitude, or as much as 150 nautical miles.

Discussion: Discuss how ignorance of a way to calculate longitude caused many shipwrecks during ancient and medieval times. It also delayed the discovery of the New World.

Answer to Question: To locate east-west position while sailing, the navigator had to measure the difference between the time when the sun was at noon in two different places.

Extension: Using a globe of Earth, have students determine how many degrees of longitude are equal to one hour.

ASTRONOMER

Background: Many astronomers teach at universities or colleges. Some lecture at planetariums or work at national observatories. Knowing a foreign language helps an astronomer communicate with foreign astronomers.

Related Career	Education
Astronomy Librarian	college
Planetarium Guide	high school
Astronomy assistant	associate degree
Planetologist	college

Career Issue: Any space project is very expensive. To lower costs, joint efforts are becoming widespread. The European Space Agency is a cooperative space program among the nations of Western Europe. The ESA built *Spacelab,* a crewed laboratory which is part of the United States Space Shuttle Program. *Spacelab* has traveled into space in the cargo bay of space shuttles.

What do you think? Have students discuss ways in which amateur astronomers help professional astronomers.

AEROSPACE WORKER

Background: Aerospace workers may work on production lines, in machine shops, or at space centers. Usually an aerospace worker specializes in a particular kind of machine. A worker who switches to a different kind of machine must take courses in preparation for the new work.

Related Career	Education
Laser Cutter	trade school
Electron Beam Machinist	trade school
Aerospace Engineer	college

Career Issue: When the space shuttle has a problem before launching, aerospace workers may have to work long hours seven days a week until the problem is resolved. Each worker bears a tremendous responsibility toward the success of the mission.

What do you think? Have students design an experimental satellite that is to be placed into orbit by the space shuttle.

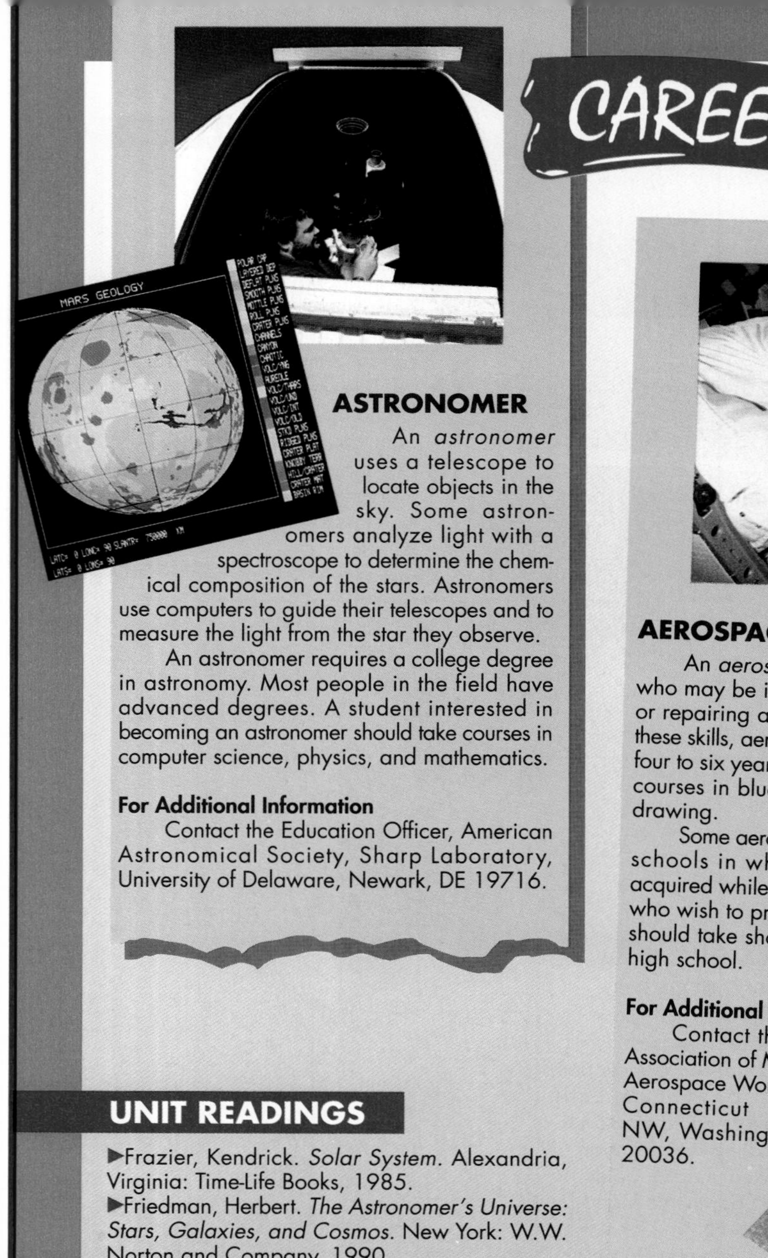

CAREERS

ASTRONOMER

An *astronomer* uses a telescope to locate objects in the sky. Some astronomers analyze light with a spectroscope to determine the chemical composition of the stars. Astronomers use computers to guide their telescopes and to measure the light from the star they observe.

An astronomer requires a college degree in astronomy. Most people in the field have advanced degrees. A student interested in becoming an astronomer should take courses in computer science, physics, and mathematics.

For Additional Information

Contact the Education Officer, American Astronomical Society, Sharp Laboratory, University of Delaware, Newark, DE 19716.

AEROSPACE WORKER

An *aerospace worker* is a skilled worker who may be involved in making, assembling, or repairing aircraft or spacecraft. To acquire these skills, aerospace workers may spend from four to six years as apprentices. They also take courses in blueprint reading and mechanical drawing.

Some aerospace manufacturers have trade schools in which the necessary skills are acquired while the student is working. Students who wish to prepare for the aerospace trades should take shop and mathematics courses in high school.

For Additional Information

Contact the International Association of Machinists and Aerospace Workers, 1300 Connecticut Avenue NW, Washington, DC 20036.

UNIT READINGS

►Frazier, Kendrick. *Solar System.* Alexandria, Virginia: Time-Life Books, 1985.

►Friedman, Herbert. *The Astronomer's Universe: Stars, Galaxies, and Cosmos.* New York: W.W. Norton and Company, 1990.

►Sagan, Carl and Ann Druyan. *Comet.* New York: Random House, 1985.

660

UNIT READINGS

Background

► *Solar System* is one volume of the *Planet Earth* series. It has striking illustrations, accompanied by fascinating text.

► *The Astronomer's Universe* answers many questions a reader may have about the universe, besides providing interesting vignettes of famous astronomers.

► *Comet* is written in the easy style readers expect from Carl Sagan and Ann Druyan. It provides many interesting anecdotes about the discovery of comets.

More Readings

1. Asimov, Issac. *Exploring the Earth and the Cosmos.* New York: Crown Publishers, Inc., 1982. This book tells of the quest for knowledge about the universe.

2. Smolders, Peter. *Living in Space: A Handbook for Space Travellers.* Blue Ridge Summit, Pennsylvania: Tab/Aero, 1986. The author begins by describing life on the space shuttle, then describes future living on a space station, in a space colony, and even on Mars and Venus.

Message to the Stars

In this unit, you were introduced to radio telescopes as tools for learning about the universe that lies beyond Earth. But one radio telescope, the largest in the world, has been used for another purpose. Read about how we used a tool of astronomy in an attempt to communicate with life among the stars.

In the hope that some stars have planets revolving around them and that those planets might harbor intelligent beings, the Arecibo radio telescope in Puerto Rico was used to send this artistic interstellar message to the star cluster named M13. Cluster M13 is located in the Milky Way Galaxy, 26 000 light-years from Earth. It probably consists of about 100 000 stars.

Much information is crammed into each row of design. The top row sets down the rules for counting in the message. It states that all numbers are in the binary number system, using just 0 and 1. The second row states the atomic numbers of the elements hydrogen, carbon, nitrogen, oxygen, and phosphorus, the elements that all known living things are made of. The rows of green blocks and blue blocks stand for substances in DNA—molecules in the cells of living things that carry genetic information. The vertical white design gives information about human genes. The red figure is that of a human being. The white design to the left shows how many people are on the planet Earth. The yellow figures represent our solar system, with the sun and nine planets. The purple design is the radio telescope in Arecibo.

The art of this message had to be rigidly controlled by the kind of radio signal being used. Words couldn't be used in the signal going to another planet because an intelligent being would not understand what was being transmitted.

In Your Own Words

▶ Write an essay describing what you would like any intelligent beings in the M13 cluster to know about you and your planet.

Source: Carl Sagan. *Cosmos.* New York: Random House, 1980.

Biography: Carl Sagan is a popular American Astronomer who is the Director of the Laboratory for Planetary Studies at Cornell University. He was a consultant for the *Mariner, Viking, and Voyager* expeditions to the planets. He wrote and narrated the television series "Cosmos." His books and television appearances have helped make astronomy better understood.

TEACHING STRATEGY

▶ Mention to students that the art in the work shown consists not only in the design but in the creative messages that are conveyed.

▶ Ask students why they think it was important to convey the message of what a human looks like, and is composed of, and what the structure of DNA is.

Cooperative Learning: Have groups of students work together on a message from their group to interstellar teenagers. Remind them that they have to overcome the language barrier.

Cooperative Learning: You may want to bind all the messages into a booklet. Each group should illustrate its message.

Other Works

▶ Other works on communication with extraterrestrials:

Morrison, David and Jane Samz. "Voyager's Greetings to the Universe." *Voyage to Jupiter.* Washington, DC, NASA, 1980, pp. 28-29.

Sagan, Carl. *Contact.* New York: Random House.

Classics

▶ Verne, Jules. *From the Earth to the Moon* (1865). This science fiction story about a trip to the moon predated the actual trips to the moon by over 100 years.

▶ Wells, H.G. *The War of the Worlds* (1898). A story about an invasion from Mars had people conjecturing about whether there is life on Mars for quite some time.

APPENDIX A

International System of Units

The International System (SI) of Measurement is accepted as the standard for measurement throughout most of the world. Three base units in SI are the meter, kilogram, and second. Frequently used SI units are listed below.

Table A-1

FREQUENTLY USED SI UNITS	
LENGTH	1 millimeter (mm) = 1000 micrometers (µm) 1 centimeter (cm) = 10 millimeters (mm) 1 meter (m) = 100 centimeters (cm) 1 kilometer (km) = 1000 meters (m) 1 light-year = 9 460 000 000 000 kilometers (km)
AREA	1 square meter (m^2) = 10 000 square centimeters (cm^2) 1 square kilometer (km^2) = 1 000 000 square meters (m^2)
VOLUME	1 milliliter (mL) = 1 cubic centimeter (cc) (cm^3) 1 liter (L) = 1000 milliliters (mL)
MASS	1 gram (g) = 1000 milligrams (mg) 1 kilogram (kg) = 1000 grams (g) 1 metric ton = 1000 kilograms (kg)
TIME	1 s = 1 second

Temperature measurements in SI are often made in degrees Celsius. Celsius temperature is a supplementary unit derived from the base unit kelvin. The Celsius scale (°C) has 100 equal graduations between the freezing temperature (0°C) and the boiling temperatue of water (100°C). The following relationship exists between the Celsius and kelvin temperature scales:

$$K = °C + 273$$

Several other supplementary SI units are listed below.

Table A-2

SUPPLEMENTARY SI UNITS			
Measurement	**Unit**	**Symbol**	**Expressed in base units**
Energy	Joule	J	$kg \bullet m^2/s^2$ or $N \bullet m$
Force	Newton	N	$kg \bullet m/s^2$
Power	Watt	W	$kg \bullet m^2/s^3$ (J/s)
Pressure	Pascal	Pa	$kg/(m \bullet s^2)$ ($N \bullet m$)

APPENDIX B

Table B-1

SI/METRIC TO ENGLISH CONVERSIONS			
	When you want to convert:	**Multiply by:**	**To find:**
Length	inches	2.54	centimeters
	centimeters	0.39	inches
	feet	0.30	meters
	meters	3.28	feet
	yards	0.91	meters
	meters	1.09	yards
	miles	1.61	kilometers
	kilometers	0.62	miles
Mass and Weight*	ounces	28.35	grams
	grams	0.04	ounces
	pounds	0.45	kilograms
	kilograms	2.20	pounds
	tons	0.91	tonnes (metric tons)
	tonnes (metric tons)	1.10	tons
	pounds	4.45	newtons
	newtons	0.23	pounds
Volume	cubic inches	16.39	cubic centimeters
	cubic centimeters	0.06	cubic inches
	cubic feet	0.03	cubic meters
	cubic meters	35.31	cubic feet
	liters	1.06	quarts
	liters	0.26	gallons
	gallons	3.78	liters
Area	square inches	6.45	square centimeters
	square centimeters	0.16	square inches
	square feet	0.09	square meters
	square meters	10.76	square feet
	square miles	2.59	square kilometers
	square kilometers	0.39	square miles
	hectares	2.47	acres
	acres	0.40	hectares
Temperature	Fahrenheit	5/9 (°F – 32)	Celsius
	Celsius	9/5 °C + 32	Fahrenheit

*Weight as measured in standard Earth gravity

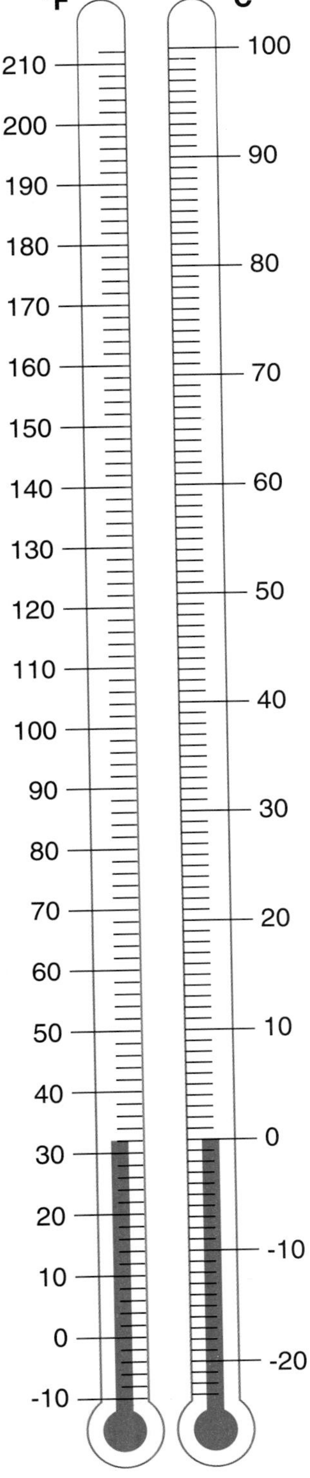

APPENDIX C

Safety in the Science Classroom

1. Always obtain your teacher's permission to begin an investigation.
2. Study the procedure. If you have questions, ask your teacher. Understand any safety symbols shown on the page.
3. Use the safety equipment provided for you. Goggles and a safety apron should be worn when any investigation calls for using chemicals.
4. Always slant test tubes away from yourself and others when heating them.
5. Never eat or drink in the lab, and never use lab glassware as food or drink containers. Never inhale chemicals. Do not taste any substances or draw any material into a tube with your mouth.
6. If you spill any chemical, wash it off immediately with water. Report the spill immediately to your teacher.
7. Know the location and proper use of the fire extinguisher, safety shower, fire blanket, first aid kit, and fire alarm.
8. Keep materials away from flames. Tie back hair and loose clothing.
9. If a fire should break out in the classroom, or if your clothing should catch fire, smother it with the fire blanket or a coat, or get under a safety shower. **NEVER RUN.**
10. Report any accident or injury, no matter how small, to your teacher.

Follow these procedures as you clean up your work area.

1. Turn off the water and gas. Disconnect electrical devices.
2. Return all materials to their proper places.
3. Dispose of chemicals and other materials as directed by your teacher. Place broken glass and solid substances in the proper containers. Never discard materials in the sink.
4. Clean your work area.
5. Wash your hands thoroughly after working in the laboratory.

Table C-1

FIRST AID	
Injury	**Safe response**
Burns	Apply cold water. Call your teacher immediately.
Cuts and bruises	Stop any bleeding by applying direct pressure. Cover cuts with a clean dressing. Apply cold compresses to bruises. Call your teacher immediately.
Fainting	Leave the person lying down. Loosen any tight clothing and keep crowds away. Call your teacher immediately.
Foreign matter in eye	Flush with plenty of water. Use eyewash bottle or fountain.
Poisoning	Note the suspected poisoning agent and call your teacher immediately.
Any spills on skin	Flush with large amounts of water or use safety shower. Call your teacher immediately.

APPENDIX D

Safety Symbols

Table D-1

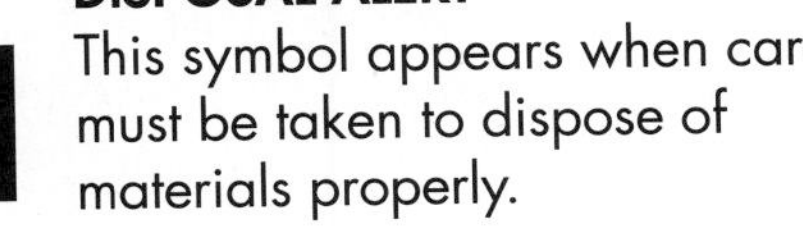 **DISPOSAL ALERT** This symbol appears when care must be taken to dispose of materials properly.	 **ANIMAL SAFETY** This symbol appears whenever live animals are studied and the safety of the animals and the students must be ensured.
 **BIOLOGICAL HAZARD** This symbol appears when there is danger involving bacteria, fungi, or protists.	 **RADIOACTIVE SAFETY** This symbol appears when radioactive materials are used.
 **OPEN FLAME ALERT** This symbol appears when use of an open flame could cause a fire or an explosion.	 **CLOTHING PROTECTION SAFETY** This symbol appears when substances used could stain or burn clothing.
 **THERMAL SAFETY** This symbol appears as a reminder to use caution when handling hot objects.	 **FIRE SAFETY** This symbol appears when care should be taken around open flames.
 **SHARP OBJECT SAFETY** This symbol appears when a danger of cuts or punctures caused by the use of sharp objects exists.	 **EXPLOSION SAFETY** This symbol appears when the misuse of chemicals could cause an explosion.
 **FUME SAFETY** This symbol appears when chemicals or chemical reactions could cause dangerous fumes.	 **EYE SAFETY** This symbol appears when a danger to the eyes exists. Safety goggles should be worn when this symbol appears.
 **ELECTRICAL SAFETY** This symbol appears when care should be taken when using electrical equipment.	 **POISON SAFETY** This symbol appears when poisonous substances are used.
 **PLANT SAFETY** This symbol appears when poisonous plants or plants with thorns are handled.	 **CHEMICAL SAFETY** This symbol appears when chemicals used can cause burns or are poisonous if absorbed through the skin.

APPENDIX E

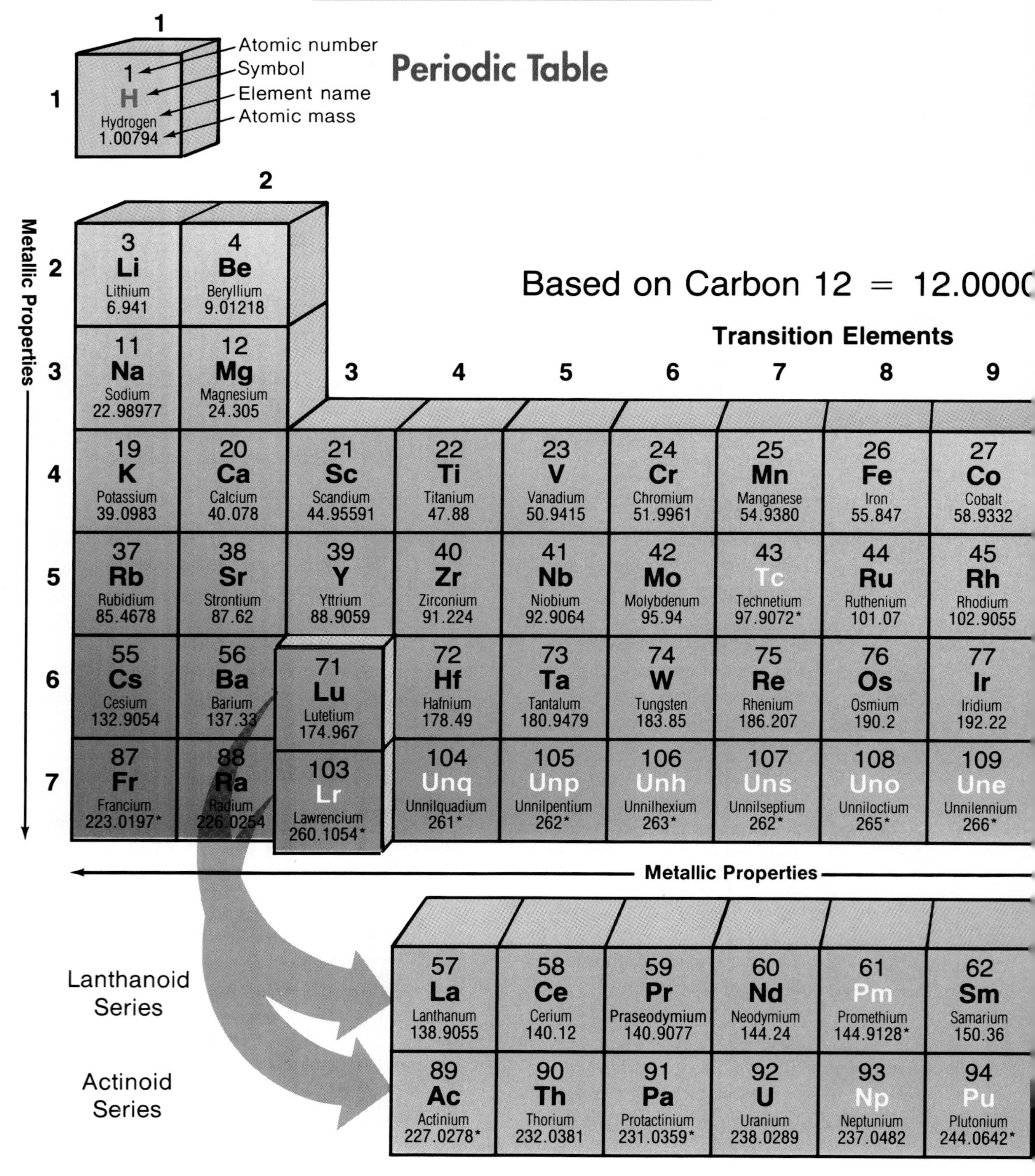

*Mass of isotope with longest half-life, that is, the most stable isotope of the element

666

Noble Gases

10	11	12	13	14	15	16	17	18
								2 He Helium 4.002602
			5 B Boron 10.811	6 C Carbon 12.011	7 N Nitrogen 14.0067	8 O Oxygen 15.9994	9 F Fluorine 18.998403	10 Ne Neon 20.179
			13 Al Aluminum 26.98154	14 Si Silicon 28.0855	15 P Phosphorus 30.97376	16 S Sulfur 32.06	17 Cl Chlorine 35.453	18 Ar Argon 39.948
28 Ni Nickel 58.69	29 Cu Copper 63.546	30 Zn Zinc 65.39	31 Ga Gallium 69.723	32 Ge Germanium 72.59	33 As Arsenic 74.9216	34 Se Selenium 78.96	35 Br Bromine 79.904	36 Kr Krypton 83.80
46 Pd Palladium 106.42	47 Ag Silver 107.8682	48 Cd Cadmium 112.41	49 In Indium 114.82	50 Sn Tin 118.710	51 Sb Antimony 121.75	52 Te Tellurium 127.60	53 I Iodine 126.9045	54 Xe Xenon 131.29
78 Pt Platinum 195.08	79 Au Gold 196.9665	80 Hg Mercury 200.59	81 Tl Thallium 204.383	82 Pb Lead 207.2	83 Bi Bismuth 208.9804	84 Po Polonium 208.9824*	85 At Astatine 209.98712*	86 Rn Radon 222.017*

Nonmetallic Properties

Metallic Properties
Nonmetallic Properties
Metalloids
Synthetic Elements

State at Room Temperature: and Solid Liquid Gas

63 Eu Europium 151.96	64 Gd Gadolinium 157.25	65 Tb Terbium 158.9254	66 Dy Dysprosium 162.50	67 Ho Holmium 164.9304	68 Er Erbium 167.26	69 Tm Thulium 168.9342	70 Yb Ytterbium 173.04
95 Am Americium 243.0614*	96 Cm Curium 247.0703*	97 Bk Berkelium 247.0703*	98 Cf Californium 251.0796*	99 Es Einsteinium 252.0828*	100 Fm Fermium 257.0951*	101 Md Mendelevium 258.986*	102 No Nobelium 259.1009*

APPENDIX F

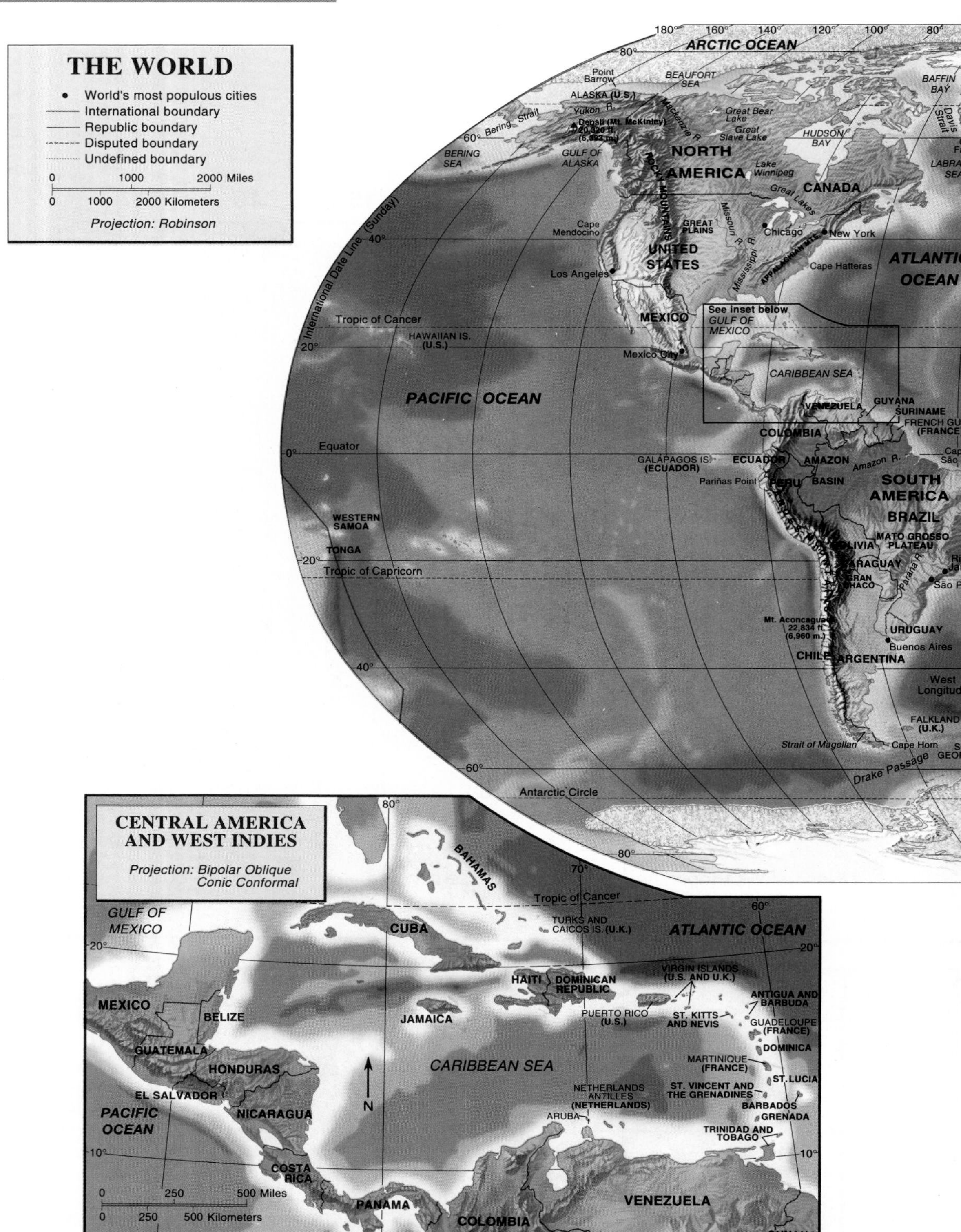

THE WORLD
World's most populous cities
International boundary
Republic boundary
Disputed boundary
Undefined boundary
0 1000 2000 Miles
0 1000 2000 Kilometers
Projection: Robinson
ARCTIC OCEAN
PACIFIC OCEAN
ATLANTIC OCEAN
NORTH AMERICA
CANADA
UNITED STATES
MEXICO
SOUTH AMERICA
BRAZIL
Equator
Tropic of Cancer
Tropic of Capricorn
Antarctic Circle
CENTRAL AMERICA AND WEST INDIES
Projection: Bipolar Oblique Conic Conformal
GULF OF MEXICO
CARIBBEAN SEA
CUBA
JAMAICA
HAITI
DOMINICAN REPUBLIC
BELIZE
GUATEMALA
HONDURAS
EL SALVADOR
NICARAGUA
COSTA RICA
PANAMA
COLOMBIA
VENEZUELA
GUYANA
0 250 500 Miles
0 250 500 Kilometers

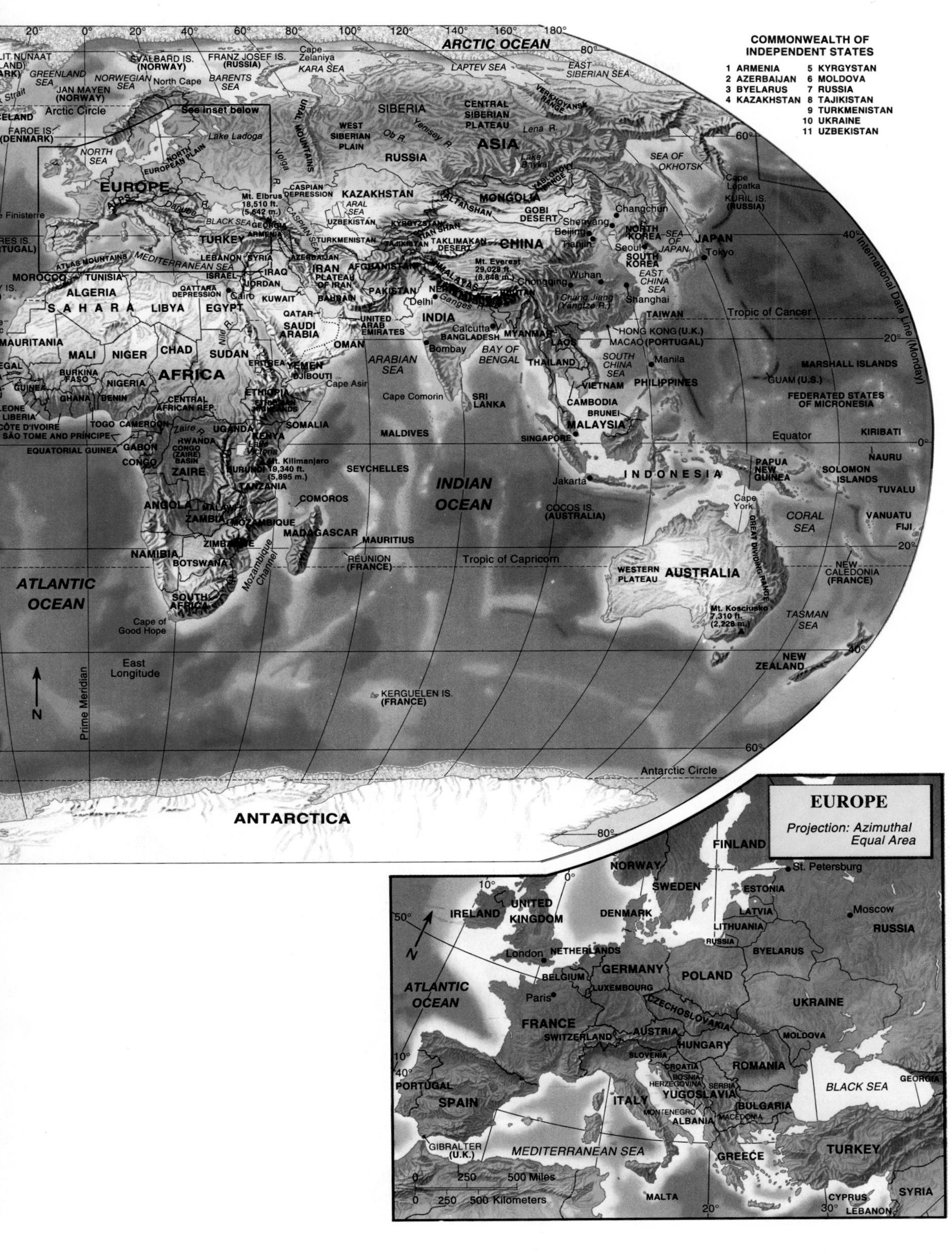

COMMONWEALTH OF INDEPENDENT STATES
1 ARMENIA
2 AZERBAIJAN
3 BYELARUS
4 KAZAKHSTAN
5 KYRGYSTAN
6 MOLDOVA
7 RUSSIA
8 TAJIKISTAN
9 TURKMENISTAN
10 UKRAINE
11 UZBEKISTAN
ARCTIC OCEAN
SVALBARD IS. (NORWAY)
FRANZ JOSEF IS. (RUSSIA)
Cape Zelaniya
KARA SEA
LAPTEV SEA
EAST SIBERIAN SEA
GREENLAND SEA
NORWEGIAN SEA
North Cape
BARENTS SEA
JAN MAYEN (NORWAY)
Arctic Circle
FAROE IS. (DENMARK)
See inset below
Lake Ladoga
NORTH SEA
NORTH EUROPEAN PLAIN
EUROPE
ALPS
URAL MOUNTAINS
Volga R.
SIBERIA
WEST SIBERIAN PLAIN
CENTRAL SIBERIAN PLATEAU
Ob R.
Yenisey R.
Lena R.
ASIA
RUSSIA
VERKHOYANSK RANGE
Lake Baykal
SEA OF OKHOTSK
Cape Lopatka
KURIL IS. (RUSSIA)
CASPIAN DEPRESSION
Mt. Elbrus 18,510 ft. (5,642 m.)
KAZAKHSTAN
ARAL SEA
BLACK SEA
CASPIAN SEA
GEORGIA
ARMENIA
UZBEKISTAN
KYRGYZSTAN
TURKMENISTAN
TAJIKISTAN
TAKLIMAKAN DESERT
MONGOLIA
GOBI DESERT
ALTAI SHAN
TIAN SHAN
CHINA
Changchun
Shenyang
Beijing
Tianjin
NORTH KOREA
SOUTH KOREA
Seoul
SEA OF JAPAN
JAPAN
Tokyo
Finisterre
TURKEY
LEBANON
SYRIA
ISRAEL
JORDAN
IRAQ
IRAN
PLATEAU OF IRAN
AZERBAIJAN
AFGHANISTAN
MEDITERRANEAN SEA
ATLAS MOUNTAINS
MOROCCO
TUNISIA
ALGERIA
QATTARA DEPRESSION
Cairo
KUWAIT
BAHRAIN
PAKISTAN
Mt. Everest 29,028 ft. (8,848 m.)
HIMALAYAS
NEPAL
BHUTAN
Delhi
Ganges
Wuhan
Chongqing
Chang Jiang (Yangtze R.)
EAST CHINA SEA
Shanghai
TAIWAN
Tropic of Cancer
International Date Line (Monday)
SAHARA
LIBYA
EGYPT
QATAR
SAUDI ARABIA
UNITED ARAB EMIRATES
OMAN
INDIA
Calcutta
BANGLADESH
MYANMAR
HONG KONG (U.K.)
MACAO (PORTUGAL)
Nile R.
MAURITANIA
MALI
NIGER
CHAD
SUDAN
ERITREA
YEMEN
DJIBOUTI
Cape Asir
ARABIAN SEA
Bombay
BAY OF BENGAL
LAOS
THAILAND
SOUTH CHINA SEA
Manila
PHILIPPINES
MARSHALL ISLANDS
GUAM (U.S.)
FEDERATED STATES OF MICRONESIA
BURKINA FASO
GUINEA
NIGERIA
AFRICA
GHANA
BENIN
CENTRAL AFRICAN REP.
ETHIOPIA
Cape Comorin
SRI LANKA
VIETNAM
CAMBODIA
BRUNEI
MALAYSIA
LIBERIA
CÔTE D'IVOIRE
TOGO
CAMEROON
SÃO TOME AND PRINCIPE
EQUATORIAL GUINEA
GABON
CONGO
Zaire R.
UGANDA
KENYA
RWANDA
CONGO (ZAIRE) BASIN
SOMALIA
MALDIVES
SINGAPORE
Equator
KIRIBATI
NAURU
ZAIRE
BURUNDI
Lake Victoria
Mt. Kilimanjaro 19,340 ft. (5,895 m.)
TANZANIA
SEYCHELLES
INDIAN OCEAN
Jakarta
INDONESIA
PAPUA NEW GUINEA
SOLOMON ISLANDS
TUVALU
COMOROS
ANGOLA
MALAWI
ZAMBIA
MOZAMBIQUE
MADAGASCAR
COCOS IS. (AUSTRALIA)
Cape York
CORAL SEA
VANUATU
FIJI
MAURITIUS
ZIMBABWE
NAMIBIA
BOTSWANA
Mozambique Channel
RÉUNION (FRANCE)
Tropic of Capricorn
GREAT DIVIDING RANGE
WESTERN PLATEAU
AUSTRALIA
NEW CALEDONIA (FRANCE)
ATLANTIC OCEAN
SOUTH AFRICA
Cape of Good Hope
Mt. Kosciusko 7,310 ft. (2,228 m.)
TASMAN SEA
NEW ZEALAND
East Longitude
N
Prime Meridian
KERGUELEN IS. (FRANCE)
Antarctic Circle
ANTARCTICA
EUROPE
Projection: Azimuthal Equal Area
FINLAND
NORWAY
St. Petersburg
SWEDEN
ESTONIA
IRELAND
UNITED KINGDOM
DENMARK
LATVIA
Moscow
RUSSIA
LITHUANIA
London
NETHERLANDS
BYELARUS
BELGIUM
GERMANY
POLAND
ATLANTIC OCEAN
Paris
LUXEMBOURG
CZECHOSLOVAKIA
UKRAINE
FRANCE
SWITZERLAND
AUSTRIA
MOLDOVA
HUNGARY
SLOVENIA
CROATIA
BOSNIA HERZEGOVINA
SERBIA
ROMANIA
PORTUGAL
SPAIN
ITALY
YUGOSLAVIA
MONTENEGRO
BULGARIA
MACEDONIA
ALBANIA
BLACK SEA
GEORGIA
GIBRALTER (U.K.)
MEDITERRANEAN SEA
GREECE
TURKEY
0 250 500 Miles
0 250 500 Kilometers
MALTA
CYPRUS
LEBANON
SYRIA

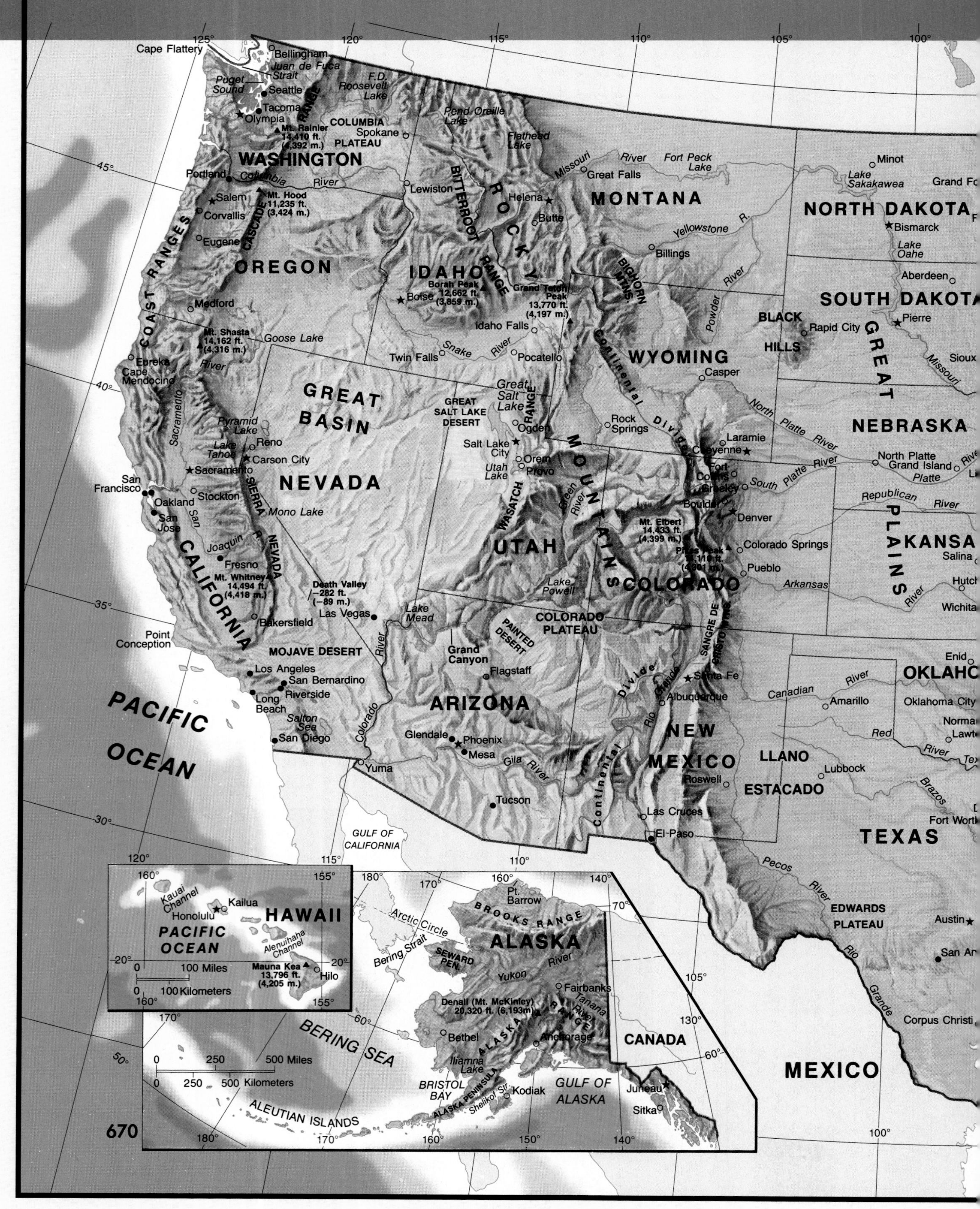

Cape Flattery
Bellingham
Juan de Fuca Strait
Puget Sound
Seattle
Tacoma
Olympia
F.D. Roosevelt Lake
Mt. Rainier 14,410 ft. (4,392 m.)
COLUMBIA PLATEAU
Spokane
Pend Oreille Lake
Flathead Lake
WASHINGTON
Portland
Columbia River
Lewiston
Salem
Mt. Hood 11,235 ft. (3,424 m.)
Corvallis
Eugene
CASCADE RANGE
COAST RANGES
OREGON
BITTERROOT RANGE
ROCKY MOUNTAINS
Missouri River
Great Falls
Fort Peck Lake
Helena
Butte
MONTANA
Yellowstone R.
Billings
IDAHO
Borah Peak 12,662 ft. (3,859 m.)
Boise
Grand Teton Peak 13,770 ft. (4,197 m.)
Idaho Falls
BIGHORN MTNS.
Powder River
Medford
Mt. Shasta 14,162 ft. (4,316 m.)
Goose Lake
Snake River
Twin Falls
Pocatello
Eureka
Cape Mendocino
River
Sacramento
GREAT BASIN
GREAT SALT LAKE DESERT
Great Salt Lake
Ogden
Salt Lake City
Utah Lake
Orem
Provo
WASATCH RANGE
Continental Divide
WYOMING
Casper
Rock Springs
Laramie
Cheyenne
Fort Collins
Greeley
Boulder
Denver
Pyramid Lake
Lake Tahoe
Reno
Carson City
Sacramento
SIERRA NEVADA
NEVADA
Mono Lake
San Francisco
Oakland
Stockton
San Jose
San Joaquin R.
Fresno
Mt. Whitney 14,494 ft. (4,418 m.)
CALIFORNIA
Death Valley −282 ft. (−89 m.)
Las Vegas
Bakersfield
Point Conception
MOJAVE DESERT
Los Angeles
San Bernardino
Riverside
Long Beach
Salton Sea
San Diego
PACIFIC OCEAN
UTAH
Green River
Lake Powell
Lake Mead
Mt. Elbert 14,433 ft. (4,399 m.)
Pikes Peak 14,110 ft. (4,301 m.)
Colorado Springs
Pueblo
COLORADO
Arkansas River
COLORADO PLATEAU
PAINTED DESERT
Grand Canyon
Flagstaff
SANGRE DE CRISTO MTS.
Santa Fe
Albuquerque
ARIZONA
Glendale
Phoenix
Mesa
Gila River
Colorado River
Yuma
Tucson
Rio Grande
NEW MEXICO
Roswell
Las Cruces
El Paso
GULF OF CALIFORNIA
Minot
Lake Sakakawea
NORTH DAKOTA
Bismarck
Lake Oahe
Aberdeen
SOUTH DAKOTA
BLACK HILLS
Rapid City
Pierre
GREAT PLAINS
Sioux
North Platte River
NEBRASKA
North Platte
Grand Island
South Platte River
Republican River
KANSAS
Salina
Wichita
OKLAHOMA
Canadian River
Amarillo
Oklahoma City
Red River
LLANO ESTACADO
Lubbock
Brazos
Fort Worth
TEXAS
Pecos River
EDWARDS PLATEAU
Austin
San Antonio
Corpus Christi
MEXICO
Kauai Channel
Kailua
Honolulu
HAWAII
PACIFIC OCEAN
Alenuihaha Channel
Mauna Kea 13,796 ft. (4,205 m.)
Hilo
0 100 Miles
0 100 Kilometers
Pt. Barrow
BROOKS RANGE
Arctic Circle
ALASKA
Bering Strait
SEWARD PEN.
Yukon River
Fairbanks
Denali (Mt. McKinley) 20,320 ft. (6,193 m)
Tanana River
ALASKA RANGE
Bethel
Anchorage
CANADA
BERING SEA
Iliamna Lake
BRISTOL BAY
ALASKA PENINSULA
Shelikof Str.
Kodiak
GULF OF ALASKA
Juneau
Sitka
ALEUTIAN ISLANDS
0 250 500 Miles
0 250 500 Kilometers
670

APPENDIX G

UNITED STATES
National capital
State capital
Major city
Other city
International boundary
State boundary
0 100 200 Miles
0 100 200 Kilometers
Projection: Albers Equal Area
CANADA
ATLANTIC OCEAN
GULF OF MEXICO
THE BAHAMAS
Strait of Florida
MAINE
N.H.
VT.
MASS.
R.I.
CONN.
NEW YORK
N.J.
PENNSYLVANIA
MD.
DEL.
WEST VIRGINIA
VIRGINIA
NORTH CAROLINA
SOUTH CAROLINA
GEORGIA
FLORIDA
ALABAMA
MISSISSIPPI
LOUISIANA
ARKANSAS
TENNESSEE
KENTUCKY
OHIO
INDIANA
ILLINOIS
MICHIGAN
WISCONSIN
IOWA
MISSOURI
CENTRAL LOWLAND
APPALACHIAN MOUNTAINS
CUMBERLAND PLATEAU
COASTAL PLAIN
OZARK PLATEAU
ADIRONDACK MTNS.
Lake Superior
Lake Michigan
Lake Huron
Lake Erie
Lake Ontario
Lake Champlain
Lake of the Woods
Red Lake
Moosehead Lake
Lake Okeechobee
Lake Pontchartrain
St. Lawrence River
Mississippi River
Ohio River
Cumberland River
Tennessee R.
Wabash R.
Hudson R.
Susquehanna River
Roanoke River
Chattahoochee R.
Alabama R.
DELAWARE BAY
CHESAPEAKE BAY
Mt. Washington 6,288 ft. (1,905 m.)
Mt. Mitchell 6,684 ft. (2,037 m.)
Washington D.C.
Augusta
Bangor
Lewiston
Portland
Burlington
Montpelier
Concord
Manchester
Boston
Worcester
Springfield
Cape Cod
Providence
Hartford
New Haven
Albany
Utica
Syracuse
Rochester
Buffalo
Niagara Falls
Binghamton
Yonkers
New York
Newark
Allentown
Trenton
Philadelphia
Camden
Wilmington
Dover
Harrisburg
Pittsburgh
Erie
Baltimore
Annapolis
Arlington
Richmond
Newport News
Norfolk
Roanoke
Charleston
Huntington
Wheeling
Parkersburg
Youngstown
Cleveland
Akron
Canton
Toledo
Columbus
Dayton
Cincinnati
Fort Wayne
Muncie
Indianapolis
Evansville
Louisville
Lexington
Frankfort
Owensboro
Detroit
Ann Arbor
Lansing
Flint
Grand Rapids
South Bend
Gary
Hammond
Chicago
Joliet
Aurora
Rockford
Peoria
Springfield
Decatur
East St. Louis
St. Louis
Milwaukee
Racine
Madison
Green Bay
Appleton
Duluth
St. Paul
Rochester
Dubuque
Cedar Rapids
Davenport
Des Moines
Kansas City
Independence
Jefferson City
Harry S. Truman Res.
Springfield
Greensboro
Winston-Salem
Durham
Raleigh
Charlotte
Cape Hatteras
Knoxville
Nashville
Chattanooga
Memphis
Spartanburg
Greenville
Columbia
Augusta
Charleston
Savannah
Atlanta
Macon
Columbus
Albany
Huntsville
Birmingham
Tuscaloosa
Montgomery
Mobile
Pensacola
Tallahassee
Jacksonville
Orlando
Cape Canaveral
Tampa
St. Petersburg
Palm Beach
Miami Beach
Miami
Cape Sable
Key West
Meridian
Jackson
Hattiesburg
Biloxi
Greenville
Baton Rouge
Lafayette
Lake Charles
New Orleans
Houston
Shreveport
Toledo Bend Res.
Little Rock
North Little Rock
Hot Springs
Pine Bluff
Fort Smith
R.S. Kerr Res.
Copyright © by Glencoe Division of Macmillan/McGraw-Hill Publishing Company. All rights reserved.
N

APPENDIX H

Topographic Map Symbols

Primary highway, hard surface
Secondary highway, hard surface
Light-duty road, hard or improved surface
Unimproved road
Railroad: single track and multiple track
Railroads in juxtaposition

Buildings
School, church, and cemetery — cem
Buildings (barn, warehouse, etc.)
Wells other than water (labeled as to type) — o oil o gas
Tanks: oil, water, etc. (labeled only if water) — water
Located or landmark object; windmill
Open pit, mine, or quarry; prospect

Marsh (swamp)
Wooded marsh
Woods or brushwood
Vineyard
Land subject to controlled inundation
Submerged marsh
Mangrove
Orchard
Scrub
Urban area

Spot elevation — ×7369
Water elevation — 670

Index contour
Supplementary contour
Intermediate contour
Depression contours

Boundaries: National
State
County, parish, minicipio
Civil township, precinct, town, barrio
Incorporated city, village, town, hamlet
Reservation, National or State
Small park, cemetary, airport, etc.
Land grant
Township or range line, United States land survey
Township or range line, approximate location

Perennial streams
Elevated aqueduct
Water well and spring
Small rapids
Large rapids
Intermittent lake
Intermittent streams
Aqueduct tunnel
Glacier
Small falls
Large falls
Dry lake bed

672

APPENDIX I

Solar System Information

Planet	Mercury	Venus	Earth	Mars	Jupiter	Saturn	Uranus	Neptune	Pluto
Diameter (km)	4878	12104	12756	6794	142796	120660	51118	49528	2290
Diameter (E = 1.0)*	0.38	0.95	1.00	0.53	11.19	9.46	4.01	3.88	0.18
Mass (E = 1.0)*	0.06	0.82	1.00	0.11	317.83	95.15	14.54	17.23	0.002
Density (g/cm³)	5.42	5.24	5.50	3.94	1.31	0.70	1.30	1.66	2.03
Period of Rotation days hours minutes R = retrograde	58 15 28	243 00 14_R	00 23 56	00 24 37	00 09 55	00 10 39	00 17 14_R	00 16 03	06 09 17
Surface gravity (E = 1.0)*	0.38	0.90	1.00	0.38	2.53	1.07	0.92	1.12	0.06
Average distance to sun (AU)	0.387	0.723	1.000	1.524	5.203	9.529	19.191	30.061	39.529
Period of revolution	87.97d	224.70d	365.26d	686.98d	11.86y	29.46y	84.04y	164.79y	248.53y
Eccentricity of orbit	0.206	0.007	0.017	0.093	0.048	0.056	0.046	0.010	0.248
Average orbital speed (km/s)	47.89	35.03	29.79	24.13	13.06	9.64	6.81	5.43	4.74
Number of known satellites	0	0	1	2	16	18	15	8	1
Known rings	0	0	0	0	1	thou-sands	11	4	0

*Earth = 1.0

APPENDIX J

Star Charts

Shown here are star charts for viewing stars in the Northern Hemisphere during the four different seasons. These charts are drawn from the night sky at about 35° North Latitude, but they can be used for most locations in the Northern Hemisphere. The lines on the charts outline major constellations. The dense band of stars is the Milky Way. To use, hold the chart vertically, with the direction you are facing at the bottom of the map.

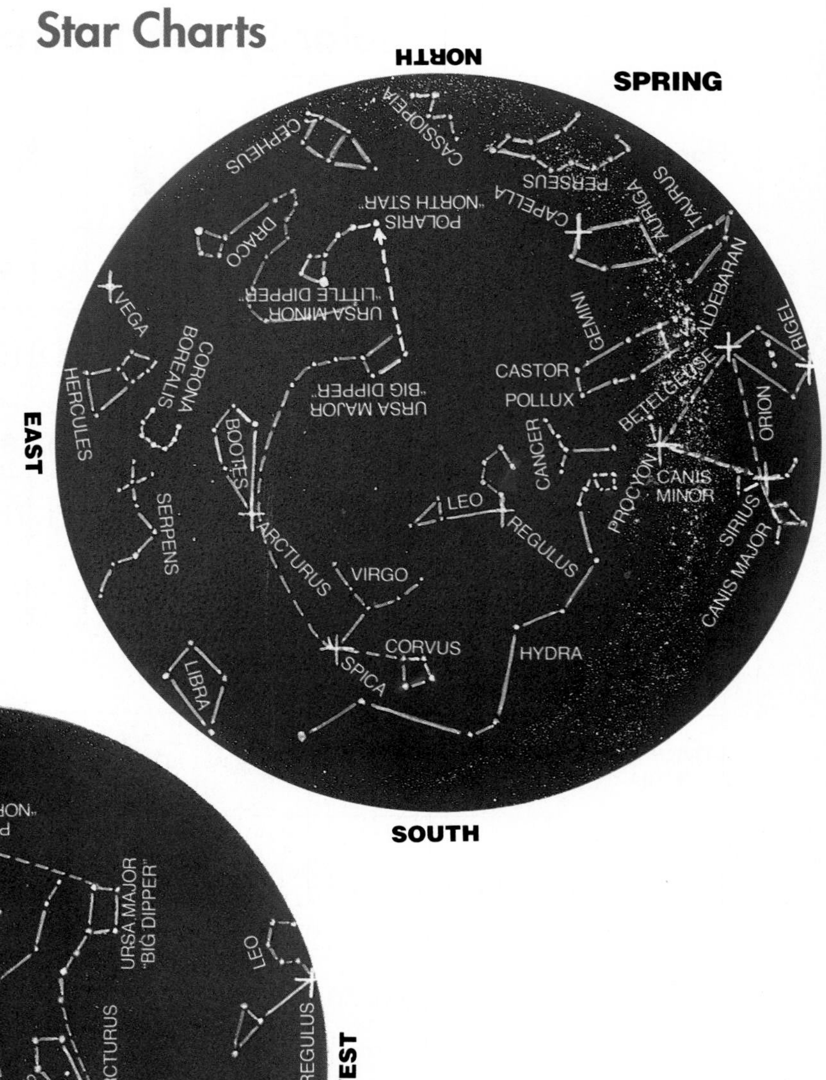

NORTH
SUMMER
CASSIOPEIA
POLARIS
"NORTH STAR"
CEPHEUS
URSA MINOR "LITTLE DIPPER"
URSA MAJOR
"BIG DIPPER"
DENEB
CYGNUS
"NORTHERN CROSS"
DRACO
LEO
PEGASUS
CORONA BOREALIS
REGULUS
VEGA
EAST
WEST
ARCTURUS
DELPHINUS
ALTAIR
LYRA
BOOTES
AQUARIUS
HERCULES
OPHIUCHUS
SAGITTA
VIRGO
CORVUS
CAPRICORNUS
AQUILA
SERPENS
SPICA
ANTARES
LIBRA
SAGITTARIUS
SCORPIUS
SOUTH

674

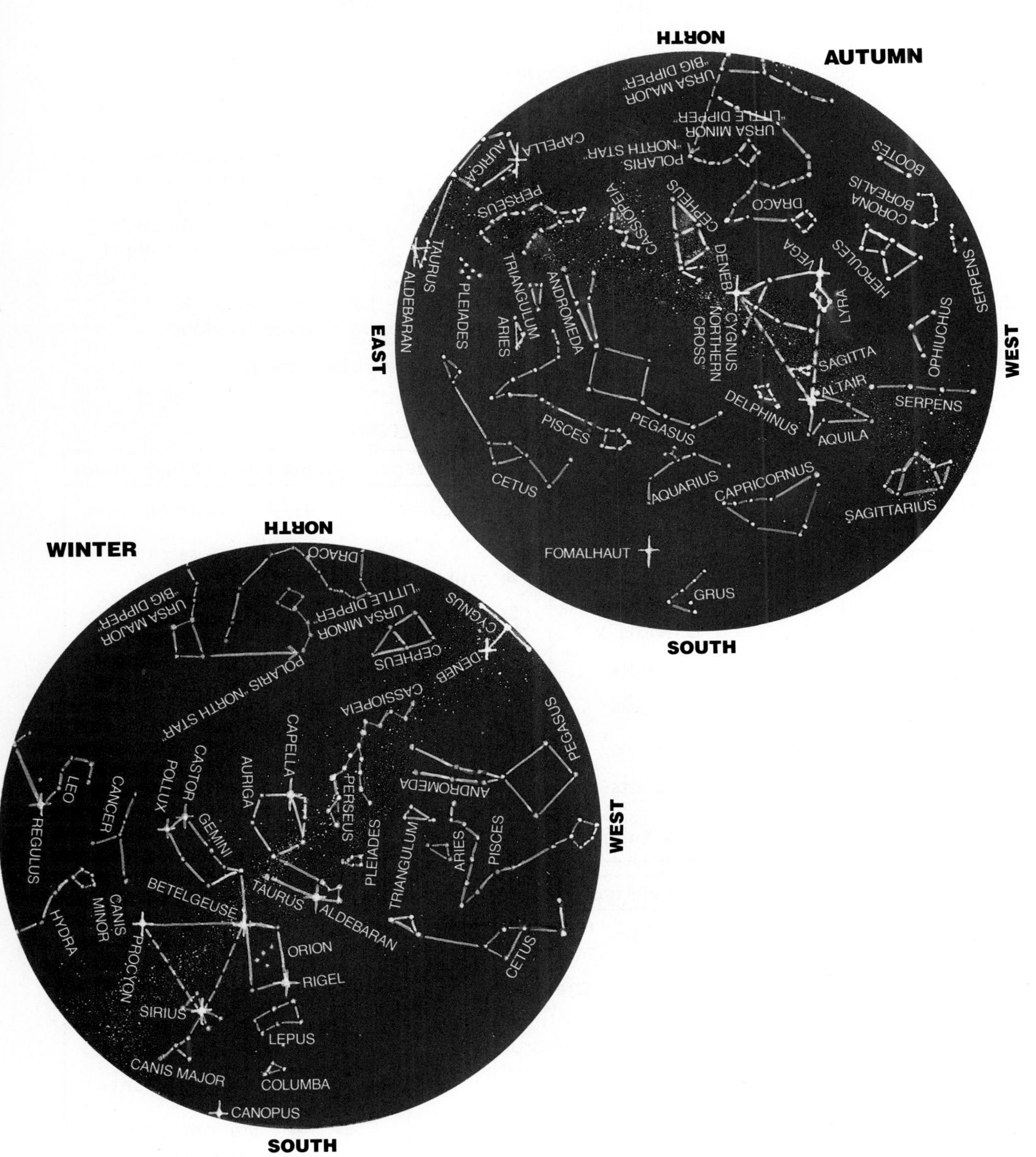
AUTUMN
NORTH
URSA MAJOR
"BIG DIPPER"
URSA MINOR
"LITTLE DIPPER"
POLARIS
"NORTH STAR"
CAPELLA
AURIGA
PERSEUS
CASSIOPEIA
CEPHEUS
DRACO
BOÖTES
CORONA BOREALIS
HERCULES
SERPENS
VEGA
LYRA
DENEB
CYGNUS
NORTHERN "CROSS"
TAURUS
ALDEBARAN
PLEIADES
TRIANGULUM
ARIES
ANDROMEDA
EAST
WEST
OPHIUCHUS
SAGITTA
ALTAIR
SERPENS
DELPHINUS
AQUILA
PEGASUS
PISCES
CETUS
AQUARIUS
CAPRICORNUS
SAGITTARIUS
FOMALHAUT
GRUS
SOUTH
WINTER
NORTH
DRACO
URSA MAJOR
"BIG DIPPER"
URSA MINOR
"LITTLE DIPPER"
CYGNUS
CEPHEUS
DENEB
POLARIS "NORTH STAR"
CASSIOPEIA
PEGASUS
ANDROMEDA
CAPELLA
AURIGA
CASTOR
POLLUX
GEMINI
LEO
CANCER
REGULUS
PERSEUS
PLEIADES
TRIANGULUM
ARIES
PISCES
WEST
BETELGEUSE
TAURUS
ALDEBARAN
CANIS MINOR
HYDRA
PROCYON
ORION
RIGEL
CETUS
SIRIUS
LEPUS
CANIS MAJOR
COLUMBA
CANOPUS
SOUTH

675

APPENDIX K

Weather Map Symbols

SAMPLE PLOTTED REPORT AT EACH STATION

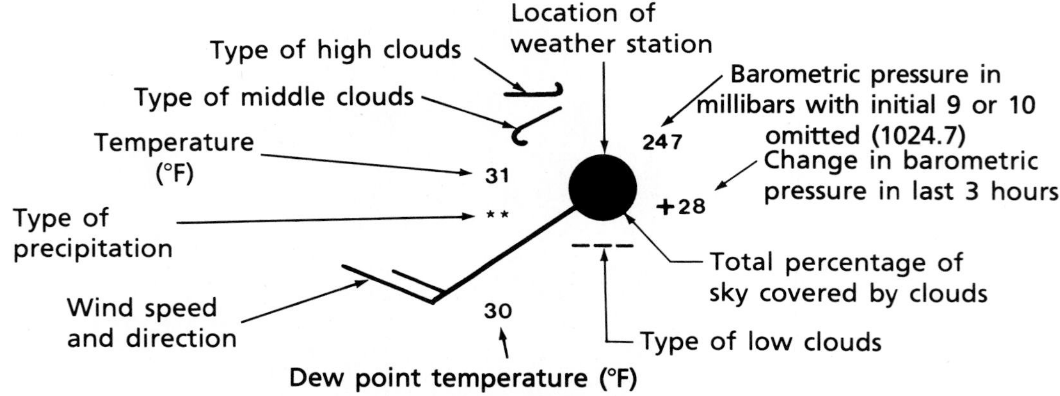

SYMBOLS USED IN PLOTTING REPORT

Precipitation	Wind speed and direction	Sky coverage	Some types of high clouds
Fog	0 calm	No cover	Scattered cirrus
Snow	1–2 knots	1/10 or less	Dense cirrus in patches
Rain	3–7 knots	2/10 to 3/10	Veil of cirrus covering entire sky
Thunder-storm	8–12 knots	4/10	Cirrus not covering entire sky
Drizzle	13–17 knots	½	
Showers	18–22 knots	6/10	
	23-27 knots	7/10	
	48-52 knots	Overcast with openings	
	1 knot = 1.852 km/h	Complete overcast	

Some types of middle clouds	Some types of low clouds	Fronts and pressure systems	
Thin altostratus layer	Cumulus of fair weather	(H) or High (L) or Low	Center of high or low pressure system
Thick altostratus layer	Stratocumulus		Cold front
Thin altostratus in patches	Fractocumulus of bad weather		Warm front
Thin altostratus in bands	Stratus of fair weather		Occluded front
			Stationary front

APPENDIX L

Minerals with Metallic Luster

Mineral (formula)	Color	Streak	Hardness	Specific gravity	Crystal system	Breakage pattern	Uses and other properties
graphite (C)	black to gray	black to gray	1-2	2.3	hexagonal	basal cleavage (scales)	pencil lead, lubricants for locks, rods to control some small nuclear reactions, battery poles
silver (Ag)	silvery white, tarnishes to black	light gray to silver	2.5	10-12	cubic	hackly	coins, fillings for teeth, jewelry, silverplate, wires; malleable and ductile
galena (Pbs)	gray	gray to black	2.5	7.5	cubic	cubic cleavage perfect	source of lead, used in pipes, shields for X rays, fishing equipment sinkers
gold (Au)	pale to golden yellow	yellow	2.5-3	19.3	cubic	hackly	jewelry, money, gold leaf, fillings for teeth, medicines; does not tarnish
bornite (Cu_5FeS_4)	bronze, tarnishes to dark blue, purple	gray-black	3	4.9-5.4	tetragonal	uneven fracture	source of copper; called "peacock ore" because of the purple shine when it tarnishes
copper (Cu)	copper red	copper red	3	8.5-9	cubic	hackly	coins, pipes, gutters, wire, cooking utensils, jewelry, decorative plaques; malleable and ductile
chalcopyrite ($CuFeS_2$)	brassy to golden yellow	greenish black	3.5-4	4.2	tetragonal	uneven fracture	main ore of copper
chromite ($FeCr_2O_4$)	black or brown	brown to black	5.5	4.6	cubic	irregular fracture	ore of chromium, stainless steel, metallurgical bricks
pyrrhotite (FeS)	bronze	gray-black	4	4.6	hexagonal	uneven fracture	often found with pentlandite, an ore of nickel; may be magnetic
hematite (specular) (Fe_2O_3)	black or reddish brown	red or reddish brown	6	5.3	hexagonal	irregular fracture	source of iron; roasted in a blast furnace, converted to "pig" iron, made into steel
magnetite (Fe_3O_4)	black	black	6	5.2	cubic	conchoidal fracture	source of iron, naturally magnetic, called lodestone
pyrite (FeS_2)	light, brassy, yellow	greenish black	6.5	5.0	cubic	uneven fracture	source of iron, "fool's gold," alters to limonite

APPENDIX M

Minerals with Nonmetallic Luster

Mineral (formula)	Color	Streak	Hardness	Specific gravity	Crystal system	Breakage pattern	Uses and other properties
talc ($Mg_3(OH)_2$ Si_4O_{10})	white, greenish	white	1	2.8	monoclinic	cleavage in one direction	easily cut with fingernail; used for talcum powder; soapstone; is used in paper and for table tops
bauxite (hydrous aluminum compound)	gray, red, white, brown	gray	1-3	2.0-2.5	—	—	source of aluminum; used in paints, aluminum foil, and airplane parts
kaolinite ($Al_4Si_2O_5$ $(OH)_4$)	white, red, reddish brown, black	white	2	2.6	triclinic	basal cleavage	clays; used in ceramics and in china dishes; common in most soils; often microscopic-sized particles
gypsum ($CaSO_4$ $\cdot$ $2H_2O$)	colorless, gray, white, brown	white	2	2.3	monoclinic	basal cleavage	used extensively in the preparation of plaster of paris, alabaster, and dry wall for building construction
sphalerite (ZnS)	brown	pale yellow	3.5-4	4	cubic	cleavage in six directions	main ore of zinc; used in paints, dyes, and medicine
sulfur (S)	yellow	yellow to white	2	2.0	ortho-rhombic	conchoidal fracture	used in medicine, fungicides for plants, vulcanization of rubber, production of sulfuric acid
muscovite ($KAl_3Si_3O_{10}$ $(OH)_2$)	white, light gray, yellow, rose, green	colorless	2.5	2.8	monoclinic	basal cleavage	occurs in large flexible plates; used as an insulator in electrical equipment, lubricant
biotite ($K(Mg, Fe)_3$ $AlSi_3O_{10}$ $(OH)_2$)	black to dark brown	colorless	2.5	2.8-3.4	monoclinic	basal cleavage	occurs in large fexible plates
halite (NaCl)	colorless, red, white, blue	colorless	2.5	2.1	cubic	cubic cleavage	salt; very soluble in water; a preservative
calcite ($CaCO_3$)	colorless, white, pale, blue	colorless, white	3	2.7	hexagonal	cleavage in three directions	fizzes when HCl is added; used in cements and other building materials
dolomite ($CaMg$ $(CO_3)_2$)	colorless, white, pink, green, gray, black	white	3.5-4	2.8	hexagonal	cleavage in three directions	concrete and cement, used as an ornamental building stone

Mineral (formula)	Color	Streak	Hardness	Specific gravity	Crystal system	Breakage pattern	Uses and other properties
fluorite (CaF_2)	colorless, white, blue, green, red, yellow, purple	colorless	4	3-3.2	cubic	cleavage	used in the manufacture of optical equipment; glows under ultraviolet light
limonite (hydrous iron oxides)	yellow, brown, black	yellow, brown	5.5	2.7-4.3	—	conchoidal fracture	source of iron; weathers easily, coloring matter of soils
hornblende ($CaNa(Mg, Al, Fe)_5(Al,Si)_2 Si_6O_{22}(OH)_2$)	green to black	gray to white	5-6	3.4	monoclinic	cleavage in two directions	will transmit light on thin edges; 6-sided cross section
feldspar (orthoclase) ($KAlSi_3O_8$)	colorless, white to gray, green and yellow	colorless	6	2.5	monoclinic	two cleavage planes meet at 90° angle	insoluble in acids; used in the manufacture of porcelain
feldspar (plagioclase) ($NaAlSi_3O_8$) ($CaAl_2Si_2O_8$)	gray, green, white	colorless	6	2.5	triclinic	two cleavage planes meet at 86° angle	used in ceramics; striations present on some faces
augite ($(Ca, Na)(Mg, Fe, Al)(Al, Si)_2 O_6$)	black	colorless	6	3.3	monoclinic	2-directional cleavage	square or 8-sided cross section
olivine ($(Mg, Fe)_2SiO_4$)	olive green	colorless	6.5	3.5	ortho-rhombic	conchoidal fracture	gemstones, refractory sand
quartz (SiO_2)	colorless, various colors	colorless	7	2.6	hexagonal	conchoidal fracture	used in glass manufacture, electronic equipment, radios, computers, watches, gemstones
garnet ($(Mg, Fe, Ca)_3(Al_2Si_3O_{12})$)	deep yellow-red green, black	colorless	7.5	3.5	cubic	conchoidal fracture	used in jewelry, also used as an abrasive
topaz ($Al_2SiO_4(F, OH)_2$)	white, pink yellow, pale blue, colorless	colorless	8	3.5	ortho-rhombic	basal cleavage	valuable gemstone
corundum (Al_2O_3)	colorless, blue, brown, green, white, pink, red	colorless	9	4.0	hexagonal	fracture	gemstones: ruby is red, sapphire is blue; industrial abrasive

Organizing Information

Classifying

You may not realize it, but you make things orderly in the world around you. If your shirts hang in the closet together, your socks take up a particular corner of a dresser drawer, or your favorite cassette tapes are stacked together, you have used the skill of classifying.

Classifying is sorting objects or events into groups based on common features. When classifying, you first make observations of the objects or events to be classified. Then, you select one feature that is shared by some members in the group but not by others. Those members that share the feature are placed in a subgroup. You can classify members into smaller and smaller subgroups based on characteristics.

How would you classify a collection of cassette tapes?

You might classify cassettes you like to dance to in one subgroup and cassettes you like to listen to in another. The cassettes you like to dance to could be subdivided into a rap subgroup and a rock subgroup. Note that for each feature selected, each cassette only fits into one subgroup. Keep selecting features until all the cassettes are classified. The chart shows one possible classification.

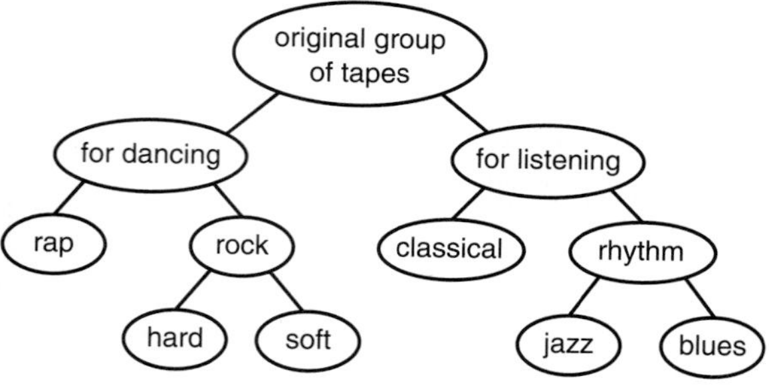

Remember when you classify, you are grouping objects or events for a purpose. Select common features to form groups and subgroups with your purpose in mind.

Sequencing

A common sequence with which you are familiar is students sitting in alphabetical order. Another use of a sequence would be the steps in a cookie recipe. Think about baking chocolate chip cookies. The steps in the recipe have to be followed in order for the cookies to taste good. A sequence is an arrangement of things or events in a particular order.

When you are asked to sequence objects or events, first identify what comes first, then what should come second. Continue to choose objects or events until they are all in order. Then, go back over the sequence to make sure each thing or event logically leads to the next.

Suppose you wanted to watch a movie that just came out on videotape. What sequence of events would you have to follow to watch the movie? You would first turn the television set to Channel 3 or 4. You would then turn the videotape player on and insert the tape. Once the tape has started playing, you would adjust the sound and picture. Then, when the movie is over, you would rewind the tape and return it to the store.

Outlining

Have you ever wondered why teachers ask students to outline what they read? The purpose of outlining is to show the relationships among main ideas and information about the main ideas. By doing this, outlining can help you organize, remember, and review written material.

When you are asked to outline, you must first find a group of words that summarizes the main idea. This group of words corresponds to the Roman numerals in an outline. Next, determine what is said about the main idea. Ideas of equal importance are grouped together and are given capital letters. These ideas are further broken down and given numbers and letters.

To familiarize yourself with outlines, compare the following outline with Chapter 10 of your textbook.

Weather and Climate

I. What Is Weather?
  A. Factors of Weather
    1. What weather is
      a. present state of atmosphere
      b. current conditions
    2. Important factors are
      a. air pressure
      b. wind
      c. temperature
      d. amount of moisture in air
    3. Humidity is amount of water vapor in air
      a. amount of water vapor held depends on temperature
      b. warm air holds more water vapor
  B. Clouds and Precipitation
    1. Clouds are made when cooled air condenses
    2. When air condenses into large water droplets, the droplets may fall as precipitation

Notice that the outline shows the pattern of organization of the written material. The boldfaced title is the main idea and corresponds with I. The letters A and B and the numbers and letters that follow divide the rest of the text into supporting ideas.

681

Thinking Critically

Observing and Inferring

Imagine that you and your friends have just finished a volleyball game. You hurry home to get a cold drink. Opening the refrigerator, you see a jug of orange juice on the back of the top shelf. The jug feels cold as you grasp it. "Ah, just what I need," you think. When you quickly drink the juice, you smell the oranges and enjoy the tart taste in your mouth.

As you imagined yourself in the story, you used your senses to make observations. You used your sense of touch to feel the cold jug, your hearing to listen as the liquid filled the glass, your sense of smell and taste to enjoy the odor and tartness, and you used your sight to find the jug in the refrigerator. The basis of all scientific investigation is observation. Scientists are careful to make accurate observations. When possible, they use instruments, like microscopes, to extend their senses.

Often they use instruments to make measurements. Because measurements are easy to communicate and provide a concrete means of comparing collected data, scientists use them whenever possible.

When you make observations in science, you may find it helpful to first examine the entire object or situation. Then, look carefully for details. Write down everything you observe before using other senses to make additional observations.

Scientists often make inferences based on their observations. An inference is an attempt to explain or interpret observations or to determine what caused what you observed. For example, if you observed a CLOSED sign in a store window around noon, you might infer the owner is taking a lunch break. But, it's possible that the owner has a doctor's appointment or has taken the day off to go fishing. The only way to be sure your inference is correct is to investigate further.

When making an inference, be certain to make accurate observations and to record them carefully. Analyze all of the data that you've collected. Then, based on everything you know, try to explain or interpret what you've observed. If possible, investigate further to determine if your inference is correct.

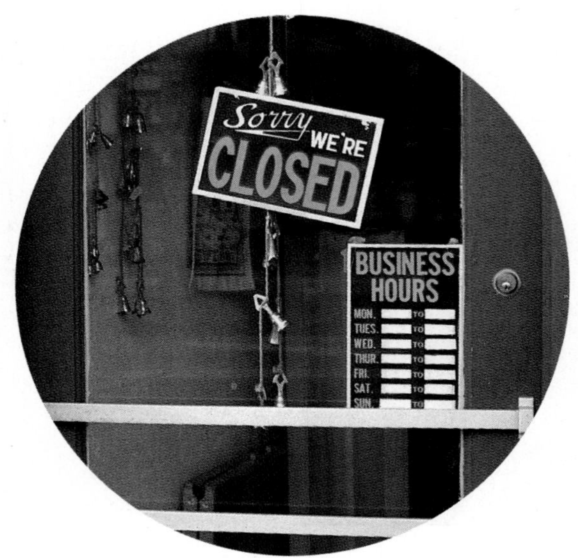

Comparing and Contrasting

Observations can be analyzed and then organized by noting the similarities and differences between two or more objects or events. When you examine objects or events to determine similarities, you are comparing. Contrasting is looking for differences in similar objects or events.

Properties	Earth	Venus
Diameter (km)	12 756	12 104
Average density (g/cm^3)	5.5	5.3
Percentage of sunlight reflected	39	76
Daytime surface temperature (K)	300	750
Number of satellites	1	0

Suppose you were asked to compare and contrast the planets Venus and Earth. You would start by examining observations made of these planets. You would then divide a piece of paper into two columns. List ways the planets are similar in one column and ways they are different in the other. Then report your findings in a table or in a paragraph.

Similarities you might point out are that both are similar in size, shape, and mass. Differences include Venus having hotter surface temperatures, a dense cloudy atmosphere, and an intense greenhouse effect.

Recognizing Cause and Effect

Have you ever observed something happen and then tried to figure out why or how it might have happened? If so, you have observed an event and inferred a reason for its occurrence. The event is an effect, and the reason for the event is the cause.

Suppose that every time your teacher fed fish in a classroom aquarium, she tapped the food container on the edge. Then, one day she tapped the edge of the aquarium to make a point about an ecology lesson. You observe the fish swim to the surface of the aquarium to feed.

What is the effect and what would you infer would be the cause? The effect is the fish swimming to the surface of the aquarium. You might infer the cause to be the teacher tapping on the edge of the aquarium. In determining cause and effect, you have made a logical inference based on careful observations.

Perhaps, the fish swam to the surface because they reacted to the teacher's waving hand or for some other reason. When scientists are unsure of the cause for a certain event, they often design controlled experiments to determine what caused their observations. Although you have made a sound judgment, you would have to perform an experiment to be certain that it was the tapping that caused the effect you observed.

Experimentation Skills

Measuring in SI

The metric system is a uniform system of measurement developed by a group of scientists in 1795. The development of the metric system helped scientists avoid problems with different units of measurement by providing an international standard of comparison for measurements. A modern form of the metric system called the International System, or SI, was adopted for worldwide use in 1960.

Your text uses metric units in most of its measurements. In the activities and experiments you will be doing, you will use the metric system of measurement.

The metric system is easy to use because it has a systematic naming of units and a decimal base. For example, meter is the base unit for measuring length, gram for measuring mass, and liter for measuring volume. Unit sizes vary by powers of ten. When changing from smaller units to larger, you divide by ten or a power of ten. When changing from larger units to smaller, you multiply by ten or a power of ten. Prefixes are used to name larger and smaller units. Look at the following table for some common metric prefixes and their meanings.

METRIC PREFIXES			
Prefix	**Symbol**	**Meaning**	
kilo-	k	1000	thousand
hecto-	h	100	hundred
deka	da	10	ten
deci-	d	0.1	tenth
centi	c	0.01	hundredth
milli-	m	0.001	thousandth

Do you see how the prefix *kilo-* attached to the unit *gram* is *kilogram* or 1000 grams? The prefix *deci-* attached to the unit *meter* is *decimeter* or one tenth (0.1) of a meter.

You have probably measured distance many times. The meter is the SI unit used to measure distance. To visualize the length of a meter, think of a baseball bat. A baseball bat is about one meter long. When measuring smaller distances, the meter is divided into smaller units called centimeters and millimeters. A centimeter is one hundredth (0.01) of a meter which is about the size of the width of the fingernail on your ring finger. A millimeter is one thousandth of a meter (0.001), about the thickness of a dime.

Most metersticks and metric rulers have lines indicating centimeters and millimeters. Look at the illustration. The centimeter lines are the longer numbered lines and the shorter lines between the centimeter lines are millimeter lines.

When using a metric ruler, you must first decide on a unit of measurement. You then line up the zero centimeter mark with the end of the object being measured, and read the number where the object ends.

Units of length are also used to measure surface area. The standard unit of area is the square meter (m^2). A square that's one meter long on each side has a surface area of one square meter. Similarly, a square centimeter (cm^2) is a square one centimeter long on each side. The surface area of an object is determined by multiplying the number of units in length times the number of units in width.

The volume of rectangular solids is also calculated using units of length. The cubic meter (m^3) is the standard SI unit of volume. A cubic meter is a cube one meter on a side. You can determine the volume of rectangular solids by multiplying length times width times height.

Liquid volume is measured using a unit called a liter. A liter has the volume of 1000 cubic centimeters. Since the prefix *milli-* means thousandth (0.001), a milliliter equals one cubic centimeter. One milliliter of liquid would completely fill a cube measuring one centimeter on each side.

During science activities you will measure liquids using beakers and graduated cylinders marked in milliliters. A graduated cylinder is a tall cylindrical container marked with lines from bottom to top.

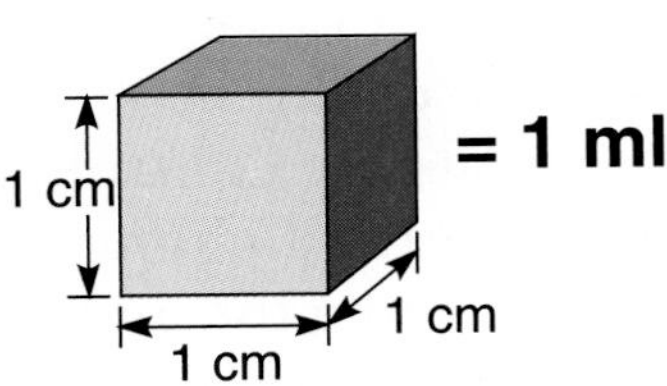

Scientists use a balance to find the mass of an object in grams. You will likely use a beam balance similar to the one illustrated. Notice that on one side of the beam balance is a pan and on the other side is a set of beams. Each beam has an object of a known mass called a rider that slides on the beam.

Before you find the mass of an object, you must set the balance to zero by sliding all the riders back to the zero point. Check the pointer to make sure it swings an equal distance above and below the zero point on the scale. If the swing is unequal, find and turn the adjusting screw until you have an equal swing.

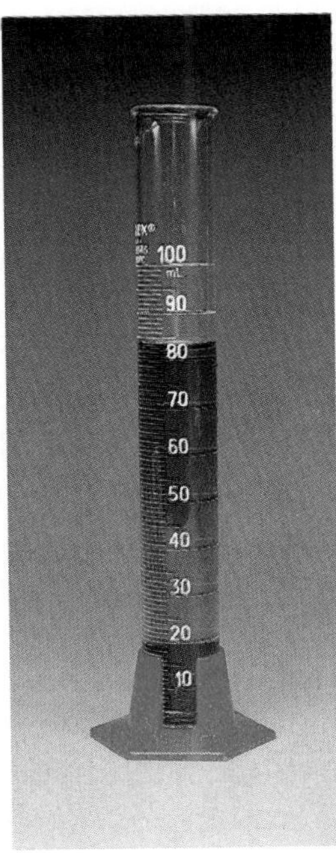

You are now ready to use the balance to find the mass of the object. Place the object on the pan. Slide the rider with the largest mass along the beams until the pointer drops below the zero point. Then move it back one notch. Repeat the process on each beam until the pointer swings an equal distance above and below the zero point. Read the masses indicated on the beams. The sum of the masses is the mass of the object.

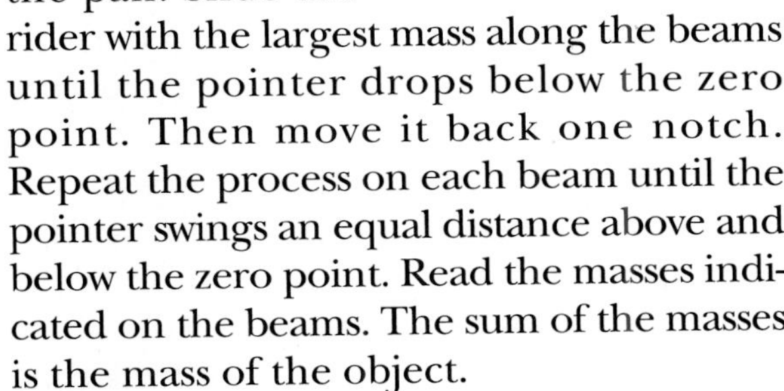

Never place a hot object or pour chemicals directly on the pan. Determine the mass of a suitable container and place dry or liquid chemicals into the container. Then determine the mass of the container and the chemicals. Finally, calculate the mass of the chemicals by subtracting the mass of the empty container.

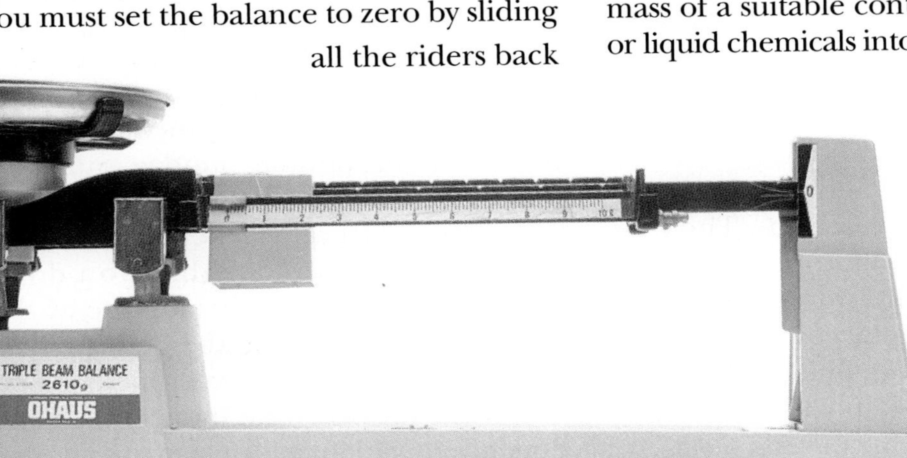

Hypothesizing

What would you do if the combination lock on your locker didn't work? Would you try the combination again? Would you check to make sure you had the right locker? You would likely try several possible solutions until you managed to open the locker.

Scientists generally use experiments to solve problems and answer questions. An experiment is a method of solving a problem in which scientists use an organized process to attempt to answer a question.

Experimentation involves defining a problem and formulating and testing hypotheses. A hypothesis is a testable prediction. Each hypothesis is tested during an experiment which includes making careful observations and collecting data. After analysis of the collected data, a conclusion is formed and compared to the hypothesis.

Imagine it's after school, and you are changing clothes. You notice a brownish-black spot on a favorite shirt. You problem is how to remove the stain from the shirt without damaging the shirt. You think that soap and water will remove the stain. You have made a hypothesis, or a prediction. But, making a prediction is not enough, the hypothesis must be tested. You try soap and water, but the stain doesn't budge.

You then observe the stain more carefully and decide that you will need to use a solvent. You have revised your hypothesis based on your observations. The new hypothesis is still only a proposed prediction until you test it and examine the results. If the solvent removes the stain, the hypothesis is supported. But, if the solvent doesn't remove the stain,you will have to revise and refine the hypothesis.

Using Variables, Constants, and Controls

When scientists do experiments, they are careful to manipulate or change only one condition and keep all other conditions in the experiment the same. The condition that is manipulated is called the independent variable. The conditions that are kept the same during an experiment are called constants. The dependent variable is any change that results from manipulating the independent variable.

Scientists can only know that the independent variable caused the change in the dependent variable if they keep all other factors constant in the experiment. Scientists use controls to be certain that the observed changes were a result of manipulating the independent variable. A control is a sample that is treated exactly like the experimental group except that the independent variable is not applied to the control. After the experiment, the change in the dependent variable of the control sample is compared to the change observed in the experimental group. Any observed differences may be the effect of application of the independent variable.

Suppose you were asked to bring your portable compact disc player on a weekend camping trip. You put in fresh dry cell batteries so that you and your friends can play CDs all weekend. But, the player loses volume about midday Sunday and soon won't play at all. You expected the dry cell batteries to last all weekend. Since you played the CDs louder than you do at home, you wonder if the volume of the player affects how long the batteries last and decide to design an experiment to find out. What would be your independent and dependent variables, constants, and control in your experiment?

This is how you might set up your experiment. You decide to compare the amount of time the player will operate at different volume settings. You purchase enough fresh dry cell batteries to operate the player at number 6, your normal listening volume, and for lower and higher volume settings. You first set the volume at number 6 and operate the player until you can no longer hear the music. You then repeat the experiment two more times using volume settings of 3 and 9. You record the amount of time the player operates for each volume setting in a data table. Your data table might look like this:

DURATION MUSIC IS HEARD	
Volume	**Amount of Time**
3	23 h, 46 min
6	18 h, 13 min
9	14 h, 53 min

What are the independent and dependent variables in the experiment? Because you are changing the volume setting of the compact disc player, the independent variable is the volume setting. Since the dependent variable is any change that results from the independent variable, the dependent variable is the number of hours and minutes music is heard on the player.

What factors are constants in the experiment? The constants are using identical dry cell batteries, playing the same compact disc, and keeping the compact disc player in the same environment for each test. What was the purpose of playing the compact disc player at your normal setting? The normal setting of the player is the control. The duration that music is heard for the normal volume setting will be used to compare the durations of lower and higher volume settings.

Interpreting Data

After doing a controlled experiment, you must analyze and interpret the collected data, form a conclusion, and compare the conclusion to your hypothesis. Analyze and interpret the data in the table. On which volume setting did the dry cell batteries last the longest? The batteries lasted the longest on number 3, the lowest setting. On which volume setting did the dry cell batteries last the shortest duration? The batteries lasted the shortest duration on volume setting number 9. What conclusion did you form? The data indicate that as the volume increases the dry cell batteries last for a shorter duration. How does the conclusion compare with your hypothesis for this experiment? Was your hypothesis supported by the experiment or not?

Graphic Organizers

Concept Mapping

If you were taking an automobile trip, you would likely take along a road map. The road map shows your location, your destination, and cities along the way. By examining the map, you can know where you are in relation to other locations on the map.

A concept map is similar to a road map. But, a concept map shows the relationship among ideas rather than cities. A concept map is a diagram that visually represents how science concepts are related. Because the concept map shows the relationships among science ideas, it can clarify the meaning of the ideas and terms and help you to understand what you are studying.

Look at the construction of a simple concept map called a network tree. Notice how some words are circled while others are written on the lines. The circled words are science ideas or terms called concepts. The lines in the map show related concepts, and the words written on them describe relationships between the concepts.

A concept map can also show more complex relationships between the concepts. For example, a line labeled "affected by" could be drawn from "weather" to "plants" or "animals," because plants and animals are affected by the weather. Another example of a relationship that crosses branches would be a line connecting "Earth changes" and "matter and energy" labeled "caused by interactions of." Earth changes are caused by interactions of matter and energy.

When you are asked to construct a concept map, state the topic and select the major concepts. Find related concepts and put them in order from general to specific. Branch the related concepts from the major concept and describe the relationships on the lines. Continue to write the more specific concepts. Write the relationships between the concepts on the lines until all concepts are mapped. Examine the concept map for relationships that cross branches, and add them to the concept map.

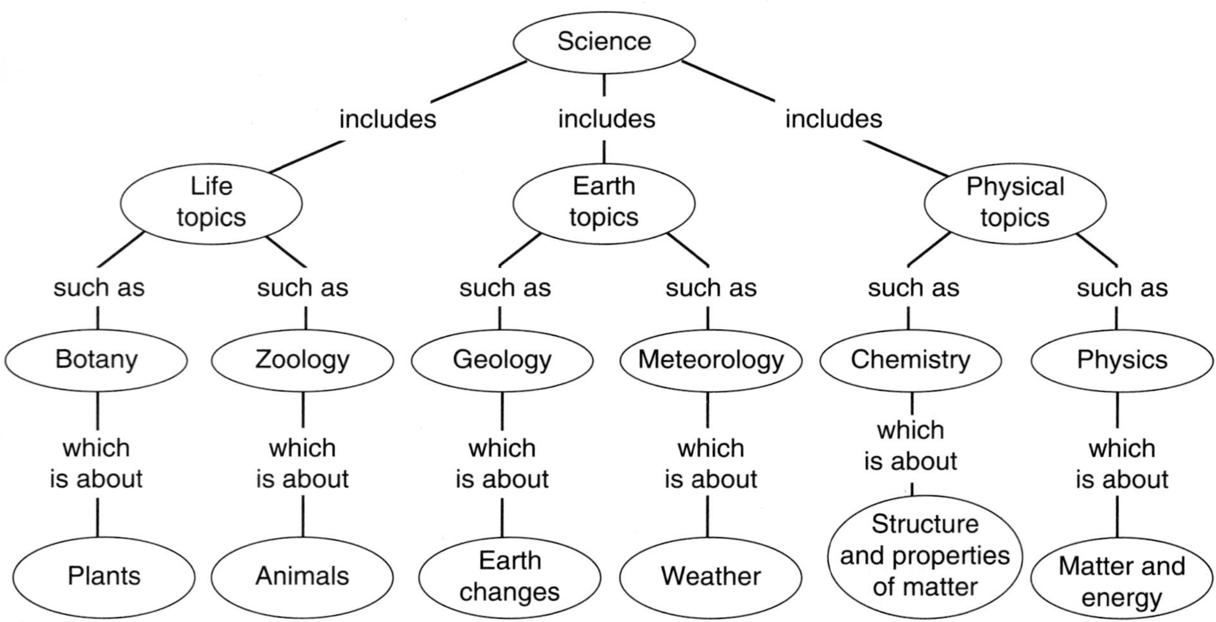

An **events chain** is another type of concept map. An events chain map is used to describe ideas in order. In science, an events chain can be used to describe a sequence of events, the steps in a procedure, or the stages of a process.

When making an events chain, you first must find the one event that starts the chain. This event is called the initiating event. You then find the next event in the chain and continue until you reach an outcome. Suppose your mother asked you to wash the dinner dishes. An events chain map might look like the one below. Notice that connecting words may not be necessary.

Initiating event:
Mother asks you to wash dishes.
↓
Event 2:
You clear the table.
↓
Event 3:
You wash the dishes in soapy water.
↓
Event 4:
You rinse the dishes in hot water.
↓
Event 5:
You dry the dishes.
↓
Final outcome:
You put the dishes away.

A **cycle concept map** is a special type of events chain map. In a cycle concept map, the series of events do not produce a final outcome. There is no beginning and no end to a cycle concept map.

To construct a cycle map, you first decide on a starting point and then list each important event in order. Since there is no outcome and the last event relates back to the first event, the cycle repeats itself. Look at the cycle map of physical changes of water:

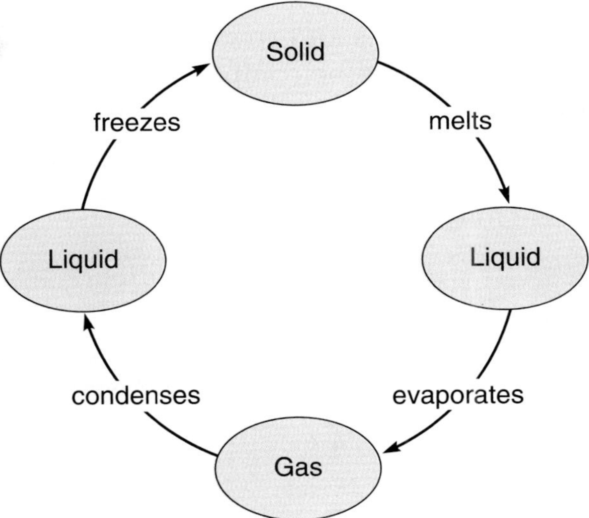

There is usually not one correct way to create a concept map. As you are constructing a map, you may discover other ways to construct the map that show the relationships among concepts better. If you do discover what you think is a better way to create a concept map, don't hesitate to change it.

Concept maps are useful in understanding the ideas you have read about. As you construct a map, you are constructing knowledge and learning. Once concept maps are constructed, you can use them again to review and study and to test your knowledge.

Making and Using Tables

Browse through your textbook, and you will notice many tables both in the text and in the activities. The tables in the text arrange information in such a way that it's easier for you to understand. Also, many activities in your text have tables to complete as you do the activity. Activity tables will help you organize the data you collect during the activity so that it can be interpreted easily.

Most tables have a title telling you what is being presented. The table itself is divided into columns and rows. The column titles list items to be compared. The rows headings list the specific characteristics being compared. Within the grid of the table, the collected data is recorded. Look at the following table:

EARTHQUAKE MAGNITUDE

Magnitude at focus	Distance from epicenters that tremors are felt	Average number expected per year
1.0 to 3.9	24 km	> 100 000
4.0 to 4.9	48 km	6 200
5.0 to 5.9	112 km	800
6.0 to 6.9	200 km	120
7.0 to 7.9	400 km	20
8.0 to 8.9	720 km	< 1

What is the title of this table? The title is "Earthquake Magnitude." What is being compared? The distance away from the epicenter that tremors are felt and the average number of earthquakes expected per year are being compared for different magnitudes on the Richter scale.

What is the average number of earthquakes expected per year for an earthquake with a magnitude of 5.5 at the focus? To find the answer you must locate the column labeled "Average number expected per year" and the row "5.0 to 5.9." The data contained in the box where the column and row intersect is the answer. Did you answer "800?" What is the distance away from the epicenter that tremors are felt for an earthquake with a magnitude of 8.1 on the Richter scale? If you answered "720 km," you have an understanding of how to use a table.

RECYCLED MATERIALS

Day of Week	Paper (kg)	Aluminum (kg)	Plastic (kg)
Mon.	4	2	0.5
Wed.	3.5	1.5	0.5
Fri.	3	1	1.5

To make a table, you simply list the items compared in columns and the characteristics compared in rows. Make a table and record the data comparing the mass of recycled materials collected by a class. On Monday, students turned in 4 kg of paper, 2 kg of aluminum, and 0.5 kg of plastic. Wednesday, they turned in 3.5 kg of paper, 1.5 kg of aluminum, and 0.5 kg of plastic. On Friday, the totals were 3 kg of paper, 1 kg of aluminum, and 1.5 kg of plastic. If your table looks like the one shown, you should be able to make tables to organize data.

Making and Using Graphs

After scientists organize data in tables, they often display the data in graphs. A graph is a diagram that shows a comparison between variables. Since graphs show a picture of collected data, they make interpretation and analysis of the data easier. The three basic types of graphs used in science are the line graph, bar graph, and pie graph.

A line graph is used to show the relationship between two variables. The variables being compared go on two axes of the graph. The independent variable always goes on the horizontal axis, called the *x*-axis. The dependent variable always goes on the vertical axis or *y*-axis.

Suppose a school started a peer study program with a class of students to see how it affected their science grades.

AVERAGE GRADES OF STUDENTS IN STUDY PROGRAM	
Grading Period	**Average Science Grade**
First	81
Second	85
Third	86
Fourth	89

You could make a graph of the grades of students in the program over a period of time. The grading period is the independent variable and should be placed on the *x*-axis of your graph. The average grade of the students in the program is the dependent variable and would go on the *y*-axis.

After drawing your axes, you would label each axis with a scale. The *x*-axis simply lists the grading periods. To make a scale of grades on the *y*-axis, you must look at the data values. Since the lowest grade was 81 and the highest was 89, you know that you will have to start numbering at least at 81 and go through 89. You decide to start numbering at 80 and number by twos through 90.

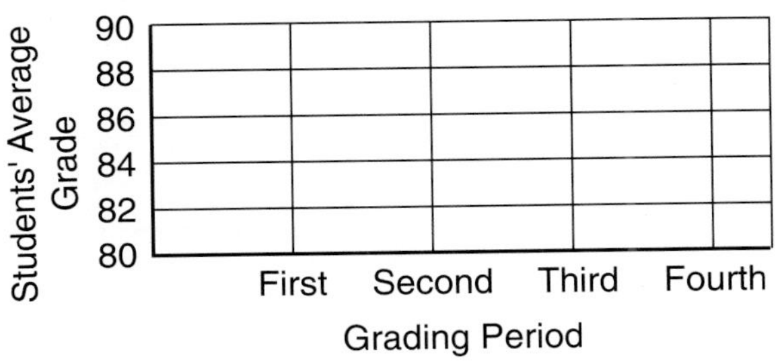

You next must plot the data points. The first pair of data you want to plot is the first grading period and 81. Locate "First" on the *x*-axis and "81" on the *y*-axis. Where an imaginary vertical line from the *x*-axis and an imaginary horizontal line from the *y*-axis would meet, place the first data point. Place the other data points the same way. After all the points are plotted, connect them with a smooth line.

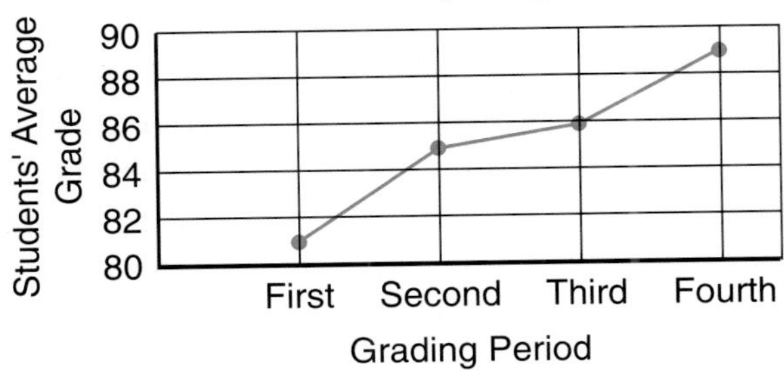

What if you wanted to compare the average grades of the class in the study group with the grades of another science class? The data of the other class can be plotted on the same graph to make the comparison. You must include a key with two different lines, each indicating a different set of data. Also change the title of the new graph to represent the data you are comparing.

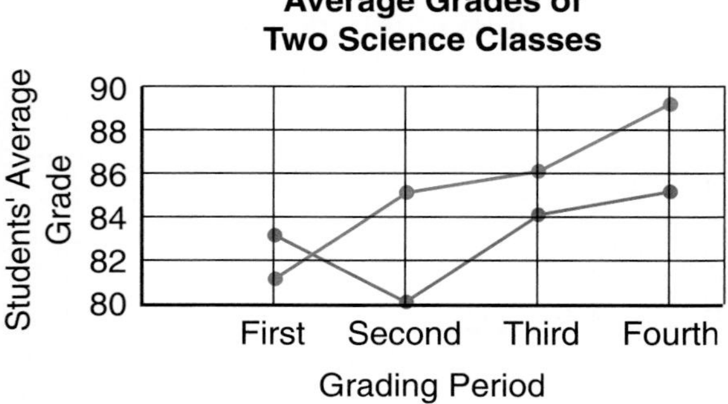

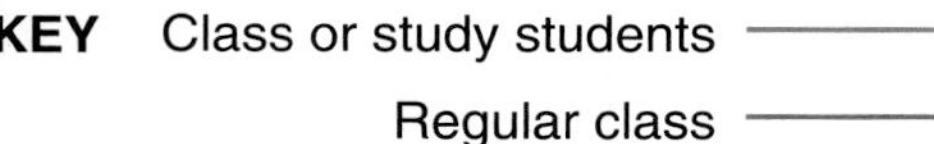

Bar graphs are similar to line graphs, except they are used to compare or display data that does not continuously change. In a bar graph, thick bars, rather than data points, show the relationships among data.

To make a bar graph, set up the x-axis and y-axis as you did for the line graph. The data is plotted by drawing thick bars from the x-axis up to an imaginary point where the y-axis would intersect the bar if it was extended.

Look at the bar graph comparing the amounts of the most abundant dissolved elements in a kilogram sample of seawater. The independent variable is the type of element, and the dependent variable is the number of grams in the sample. The amounts of different elements are being compared.

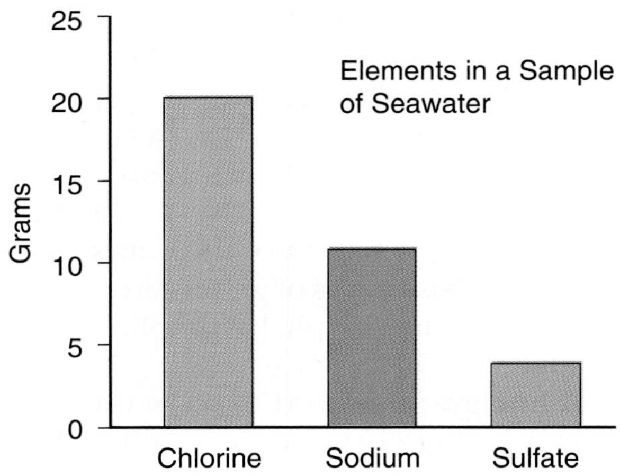

A pie graph uses a circle divided into sections to display data. Each section represents part of the whole. When all the sections are placed together, they equal 100 percent of the whole.

Suppose you had a rock collection and wanted to make a pie graph to show the percentage of rocks that are igneous, sedimentary, and metamorphic. You would have to determine the total number of rocks and the number of rocks of each type. You count the rocks and find that you have 25 rocks in the collection. Therefore, the whole pie will represent this amount.

You then place the igneous rocks in one group, the sedimentary in another, and the metamorphic in the last group. After counting the rocks in each group, you find you have 8 igneous rocks, 5 sedimentary rocks, and 12 metamorphic rocks.

To find out how much of the pie each section should take, you must divide the number of rocks in each group by the total number of rocks. You then multiply your answer by 360, the number of degrees in a circle. Round your answer to the nearest whole number. The percentage of igneous rocks would be determined as follows:

$$\frac{8}{25} \times 360° = 115.2° \text{ or } 115 \text{ degrees}$$

Use the formula to compute how much of the circle sedimentary and metamorphic rocks would take up. Sedimentary rocks would take up 72 degrees, and metamorphic rocks would take up 173 degrees.

To plot the groups on the pie graph, you need a compass and protractor. Use the compass to draw a circle. Then, draw a straight line from the center to the edge of the circle. Place your protractor on this line and use it to mark a point on the edge of the circle at 115 degrees. Connect this point with a straight line to the center of the circle. This is the part of the circle representing igneous rocks. Place your protractor on the line you just made and use it to mark a point on the edge of the circle at 72 degrees. Again draw a straight line from this point to the center of the circle. This part represents sedimentary rocks. The remaining part of the circle represents the percentage of metamorphic rocks. Complete the graph by labeling the sections of your graph and giving the graph a title. What title would you give the pie graph shown below?

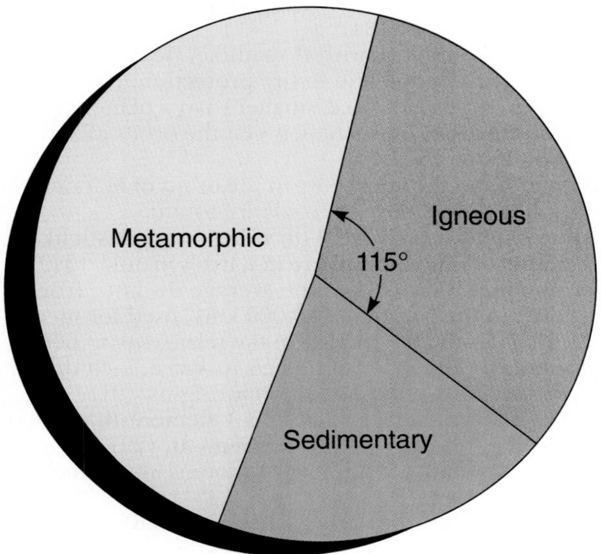

Interpreting Scientific Illustrations

Your science textbook contains many scientific illustrations to help you understand, interpret, and remember what you read. When you are reading the text and encounter an illustration, examine it carefully and relate it to the text you have just read. Also read the caption for the illustration. The caption is a brief comment that explains or identifies the illustration.

Some illustrations are designed to show you how the internal parts of a structure are arranged. Look at Figure 15-13 on page 406. The purpose of this illustration and the text it accompanies is to help you understand how calderas form. Notice that the caption of the illustrations identifies the location of this caldera and briefly describes the illustrations.

The illustrations of the caldera show what is called a cross section. A cross section is a section that is formed by cutting through an object. The illustration of the caldera is formed by cutting at right angles to the horizontal axis of the volcano.

You will notice many maps as you read the text. The map helps you understand your reading by showing you the locations of places described in the text.

Scientific illustrations similar to maps are two dimensional. A two-dimensional illustration has height and width. However, many of the illustrations in this text are three-dimensional. The illustration of the caldera is three dimensional. Notice that the illustration has not only height and width but also depth. Since an illustration in three dimensions is similar to the way you see the world, it is even more useful to help you understand the science ideas you are reading about.

GLOSSARY

This glossary defines each key term that appears in **bold type** in the text. It also shows the page number where you can find the word used. Some other terms that you may need to look up are included, too. We also show how to pronounce some of the words. A key to pronunciation is in the table below.

PRONUNCIATION KEY		
a . . . b**a**ck (bak)	oh . . . g**o** (goh)	sh . . . **sh**elf (shelf)
ay . . . d**ay** (day)	aw . . . s**o**ft (sawft)	ch . . . na**t**ure (nay chur)
ah . . . f**a**ther (fahth ur)	or . . . **or**bit (or but)	g . . . **g**ift (gihft)
ow . . . fl**ow**er (flow ur)	oy . . . c**oi**n (coyn)	j . . . **g**em (jem)
ar . . . c**ar** (car)	oo . . . f**oo**t (foot)	ing . . . s**ing** (sing)
e . . . l**e**ss (les)	ew . . . f**oo**d (fewd)	zh . . . vi**s**ion (vihzh un)
ee . . . l**ea**f (leef)	yoo . . . p**u**re (pyoor)	k . . . ca**k**e (kayk)
ih . . . tr**i**p (trihp)	yew . . . f**ew** (fyew)	s . . . **s**eed, **c**ent (seed, sent)
i (i + con + e) . . . **i**dea (i dee uh), l**i**fe (life)	uh . . . comm**a** (cahm uh)	z . . . **z**one, rai**s**e (zohn, rayz)
	u (+ con) . . . flow**er** (flow ur)	

abrasion: a type of erosion caused when windblown or waterborne sand grains strike other sand grains and rocks, breaking off small fragments. (163)

absolute dating: determining the age of rocks using the radioactive decay of atoms in them. (436)

absolute magnitude: a measure of the amount of light a star or other space object gives off. (630)

abyssal (a BIHS uhl) **plain:** the flat seafloor in the deep ocean. (313)

acid: any substance with a pH lower than seven; the lower the pH number, the stronger the acid. (526)

acid rain: precipitation that is very acidic because it contains sulfuric acid (from coal-burning power plants) and nitric acid (from car exhausts). (526)

air mass: a large body of air that has the properties of the surface over which it formed. (262)

alluvial fan: a deposit of sediment that occurs when water rushing down a slope abruptly slows at the bottom, depositing its sediment load. (150)

amphibians (am FIHB ee unz)**:** vertebrate animals adapted to living both on land and in water; they return to water to reproduce. (459)

angular unconformity: a type of unconformity where tilted rock layers meet horizontal rock layers; this indicates that layers are missing and causes a gap in the time record.

anthracite: the hardest, cleanest burning coal, contains about 90 percent carbon. (482)

apparent magnitude: a measure of light received on Earth from an object in space. (630)

aquifer: a layer of permeable rock that has connecting pores and transmits water freely. (183)

arête (uh RAYT): a sharp-edged mountain ridge carved by glaciers.

artesian (ahr TEE zhun) **well:** a well in which water under natural pressure rises to the surface without being pumped. (184)

asbestos: a mineral with threadlike, flexible fibers used as insulation and in fire protection. (78)

asteroid: a piece of rock, smaller than a planet, that orbits the sun; most are between the orbits of Mars and Jupiter. (622)

asteroid belt: the area between the orbits of Mars and Jupiter where most asteroids are found.

asthenosphere (as THEN uh sfihr)**:** the plasticlike layer below the lithosphere in Earth's mantle. (349)

astronomical unit (AU): the average distance from Earth to the sun (150 000 000 km), used for measuring distances to objects in the solar system. (608)

astronomy: the study of objects in space, including stars, planets, comets, and their origins. (9)

atom: the smallest particle of an element that still has all the properties of that element. (29)

atomic number: the number of protons in the nucleus of an atom.

Australopithecus: the earliest animals to have distinct humanlike characteristics; now extinct.

axis: an imaginary line around which an object spins; for example, Earth spins around its axis. (577)

B

barred spiral galaxy: a galaxy having two spiral arms extending from a large bar.

barrier island: a sand deposit that parallels the shore but is separated from the mainland. (310)

basaltic: dark-colored igneous rocks that form from magma rich in iron and magnesium. (93)

base: any substance with a pH above seven; the higher the pH number, the stronger the base. (526)

basin: a low area that contains an ocean. (283)

batholith: a large body of intrusive igneous rock that forms when magma cools underground and stops rising toward the surface. (404)

beach: a deposit of sediment that runs parallel to a seashore. (308)

benthos (BEN thohs)**:** animals that live on the ocean bottom, such as corals, snails, clams, sea urchins, and bottom-dwelling fish. (320)

big bang theory: the leading theory of the origin of the universe. (650)

binary system: a system of two stars orbiting one another. (645)

biomass fuel: organic matter used as fuel, such as firewood. (491)

bituminous coal: commonly used coal, contains 50 to 75 percent carbon; also called soft coal. (481)

black hole: the final stage in the life cycle of some stars; the remnant of a star that is so dense that not even light can escape its gravity field. (638)

brachiopods (BRAY kee uh pahdz): fan-shaped marine invertebrate animals commonly found as fossils in Paleozoic Era rocks.

breaker: an ocean wave that tumbles forward and breaks up as it approaches the shore, because its top is moving faster than the bottom. (293)

buoyancy (BOY un see): the lifting effect on an object immersed in water.

C

caldera (kal DARE uh)**:** the large opening formed at the top of a volcano when the crater collapses into the vent following an eruption. (406)

carbonic acid: a weak acid formed when water mixes with carbon dioxide from air.

carbonaceous film: a fossil impression in a rock, consisting only of a thin carbon deposit. (421)

cast: a type of fossil formed when an earlier fossil in rock is dissolved away, leaving behind the impression of that fossil (a mold), and new sediments or minerals enter the mold. (421)

cave: an large underground opening formed when groundwater gradually dissolves rock. (186)

cementation: a sedimentary rock-forming process in which sediments are glued together by minerals deposited between the sediments. (101)

Cenozoic (sen uh ZOH ihk) **Era:** the most recent era of Earth's geologic history; spans 65 million years ago to the present time. (466)

chemical properties: characteristics of an element or compound that determine how it will react with other elements or compounds. (35)

chemical weathering: the breaking up of rocks due to a change in chemical composition; occurs when water, air, and other substances react with the minerals in rocks. (124)

chemosynthesis (kee moh SIHN thuh sihs)**:** a process used by bacteria to produce food and oxygen by using dissolved sulfur compounds. (318)

chlorofluorocarbons (CFCs): a group of chemicals used as refrigerants and aerosol spray propellants. CFCs destroy the atmosphere's ozone layer. (237)

chromosphere: the intermediate layer of the three layers of the sun's atmosphere, lying between the photosphere and the corona. (643)

cinder cone: a type of volcano in which tephra (cinders) piles up into a steep-sided cone. (399)

circumpolar constellation: a constellation that appears to circle Polaris as Earth rotates.

cirque (SURK): a bowl-shaped basin carved by a glacier at the glacier's place of origin.

clay: sediment particle less than 0.004 mm in size.

Clean Air Act: this 1990 U.S. law sets maximum levels for major air pollutants. (529)

Clean Water Act: this 1987 U.S. law gives money to the states for building sewage and wastewater treatment facilities. (537)

cleavage: the physical property of a mineral that causes it to break along smooth, flat surfaces. (71)

climate: the pattern of weather in an area.

coal: a sedimentary rock formed from compacted, decayed plants; burned as a fossil fuel.

coastal plain: a landform that is a broad, flat area along a coastline; also called a lowland.

cold front: the boundary that develops when a cold air mass invades a warm air mass.

comet: a mass of frozen gases and rock particles that orbits the sun, often developing a bright tail when it passes near the sun. (618)

compaction: a sedimentary rock-forming process that occurs when layers of sediment become compressed by the weight of layers above them. (101)

composite volcano: a type of volcano built of lava and ash layers that accumulate from repeated cycles of tephra eruptions and lava eruptions. (400)

composting: the piling up of grass clippings, dead leaves, and other organic matter, so they can gradually decompose. (514)

compound: a substance containing two or more chemically combined elements and having properties different from those elements. (34)

compression: squeezing forces that compress rocks together at convergent plate boundaries, causing them to rumple, fold, and sometimes break.

conduction: the transfer of energy that occurs when molecules collide. (241)

conic projection: a map projection made by projecting locations and lines from a globe onto a cone; it produces accurate maps of areas smaller than the whole Earth, such as a nation or state. (207)

conservation: the careful use of resources to avoid wasting them and damaging the environment; includes reusing and recycling resources. (513)

constellation: a grouping of stars that has a shape resembling an animal, mythological character, or other object and thus is named for it. (628)

container law: a law requiring you to pay a refundable deposit each time you buy a container of beverage. (518)

continental drift: a hypothesis that continents have moved around the globe thousands of kilometers over millions of years to reach their current locations. (340)

continental glacier: a type of glacier in Earth's polar regions that covers a vast area; existing now only in Greenland and Antarctica.

continental shelf: the part of every continent that extends out under the ocean. (312)

continental slope: a part of the continental shelf that dips steeply down to the seafloor. (312)

contour interval: the difference in elevation between two contour lines on a topographic map. (209)

contour line: a line on a topographic map that connects points of equal elevation. (209)

control: in an experiment, the standard for comparison. (17)

convection: the transfer of heat due to movement caused by density differences in fluids like water or air. (241)

convection current: a circular current in a fluid like air, water, or molten rock; caused when the fluid is unevenly heated, so that part of it rises, and then cools and sinks, causing a circular movement. (352)

convergent boundary: in plate tectonics, the boundary between two plates that are converging, or moving toward each other. (350)

Copernicus, Nicholas: Polish astronomer (1473-1543) who hypothesized a sun-centered solar system.

Coriolis (kohr ee OH lus) **effect:** the effect of Earth's rotation on the movement of air masses. (245)

corona: the outermost and largest of the three layers of the sun's atmosphere, extending from the chromosphere outward millions of kilometers into space. (643)

crater: the opening at the top of a volcano. (389)

creep: a type of mass movement in which sediments move down a hill very slowly, sometimes causing posts to lean. (144)

crest: the highest point of a wave. (292)

crinoids (KRI noyds): marine invertebrate animals that resemble plants, commonly found as fossils in Paleozoic Era rocks and still a living animal group.

crust: the outermost layer of Earth. (338)

crystal: a solid having a distinctive shape because its atoms are arranged in repeating patterns. (63)

crystal system: the pattern that atoms form in a crystal.

cyanobacteria: bacteria thought to be one of the earliest life-forms on Earth. (458)

data gloves: electronic gloves worn by a person controlling a robot; the gloves sense every movement the person makes and command the robot to perform identical moves. (611)

deflation: erosion caused by wind as it wears away sediments such as clay, silt, and sand. (162)

deforestation: the removal of forests, mostly by people who are clearing land for farming or construction. (275)

delta: a triangular deposit of sediment that occurs when a stream or river slows as it empties into an ocean, gulf, or lake. (150)

density: how tightly packed a substance's molecules are; expressed as the mass of an object divided by its volume, in g/cm^3. (41)

density current: an ocean current that occurs when denser seawater moves toward an area of less dense seawater. (289)

deposition (dep uh ZIHSH un)**:** the dropping of sediments by running water, wind, gravity, or glaciers as their energy of motion decreases. (143)

desertification: the formation of a desert when livestock overgraze an area that receives little rain. (135)

dew point: the temperature at which air becomes saturated with water and condensation begins. (256)

dike: igneous rock that forms when magma is squeezed into a vertical crack and solidifies. (405)

disconformity: a type of unconformity in which the top rock layer is eroded before the next layer can be deposited, causing a gap in the time record.

divergent boundary: in plate tectonics, the boundary between two plates that are diverging, or spreading apart. (350)

doldrums: a zone at the equator where heated air rises vertically, so there appears to be no wind. (246)

Doppler shift: the change in wavelength that occurs in any kind of wave energy (light, radio, sound) as the source of the energy moves toward you (the wavelength shortens) or away from you (the wavelength lengthens).

drainage basin: the land area drained by a river system. (177)

dust bowl: the Great Plains area of the United States in the 1930s, when it was struck by devastating drought and dust storms.

Earth: in our solar system, the third planet from the sun; the only planet known to support life. (608)

earthquake: the movement of the ground, caused by waves from energy released as rocks move along faults. (360)

electromagnetic spectrum: the classification of electromagnetic waves, either by wavelength or frequency. (553)

electron: one of the three sub-atomic particles; orbits the atom's nucleus; has a negative electric charge. (31)

element: a substance that contains only one kind of atom; cannot be broken down into simpler substances. (29)

ellipse: an elongated, closed curve; the shape of planetary orbits. (579)

elliptical galaxy: the most common type of galaxy, shaped like a large, three-dimensional ellipse.

endangered: describes a species that has a small number living and thus is in danger of dying out. (454)

energy: the ability to do work. (480)

epicenter: the point on Earth's surface directly above an earthquake's focus. (367)

epochs: subdivisions of periods on the geologic time scale. (449)

equator: an imaginary line that circles Earth halfway between the North and South Poles. (202)

equinox: two times each year that the sun is directly over Earth's equator and the day and night are of equal length, the start of spring or fall. (581)

eras: the four largest subdivisions of the geologic time scale—Precambrian, Paleozoic, Mesozoic, Cenozoic. (449)

erosion (ih ROH zhun)**:** the process that moves weathered rocks from one location to another. (142)

esker: a winding ridge of sand and gravel formed by streams flowing beneath a glacier.

extinct: describes an organism species that no longer lives anywhere on Earth. (426)

extraterrestrial life: life that may exist in the universe outside of Earth. (652)

extrusive igneous rocks: igneous rocks that form when magma extrudes onto Earth's surface and cools as lava. (92)

F

fault: a large fracture in rocks, from several meters to many kilometers long, where rocks not only crack but also move along either side of the break. (360)

fault-block mountains: mountains formed from huge, tilted blocks of rock. (200)

first quarter: the moon phase halfway between new moon and full moon, when half of the side facing Earth is lighted. (585)

fission: the splitting of the nuclei of atoms to release energy. (494)

floodplain: the broad, flat valley floor carved by a meandering stream and often covered with water when the stream floods. (179)

focus: in an earthquake, the point in Earth's interior where movement releases energy to cause the earthquake. (366)

fog: a stratus cloud that forms on or near the ground when air is cooled to its dew point. (257)

folded mountains: mountains created when forces cause rock layers to fold. (199)

foliated: a texture of metamorphic rock, created when mineral grains flatten and line up in parallel bands. (97)

fossil: the remains or traces of a once-living organism; usually preserved in rock. (419)

fossil fuel: a fuel made of the decayed remains of ancient plants and animals; includes coal, oil, and natural gas. (480)

fracture: the physical property of a mineral that causes it to break with rough or jagged edges. (71)

front: in weather systems, the moving boundary between two colliding air masses. (263)

full moon: the moon phase when the side facing Earth is completely lighted, because Earth is between the sun and the moon. (585)

fusion: the process that powers our sun and other stars; hydrogen fusion occurs when great temperatures and pressures fuse hydrogen atoms to form helium atoms and energy is released.

galaxy: a massive grouping of gas, dust, and stars in space, held together by gravity. (646)

Galileo: Italian astronomer (1564-1642) who supported a sun-centered solar system by discovering that Venus has phases similar to our moon.

gamma rays: electromagnetic waves having very short wavelengths and high energy.

Ganymede: one of Jupiter's four largest moons; the largest satellite in the solar system.

gasohol: a biomass fuel that is about 90 percent gasoline and 10 percent alcohol; used in cars and trucks.

gem: a mineral highly prized because it is rare and beautiful. (74)

geologic time scale: a chart of Earth's history showing events, time units, and ages. (447)

geology: the study of Earth and its matter, processes, and history. (8)

geothermal energy: thermal energy from the magma underneath volcanoes. (394)

geyser: a hot spring of groundwater that erupts periodically, shooting water and steam into the air. (186)

giant: a late stage in a star's life cycle where the core has contracted and grown hotter, causing its outer layers to expand. (637)

glacier: a moving mass of snow that has compacted into ice and is moving downhill. (154)

Glossopteris (glah SAHP tuhr ihs): a fossil fern providing evidence that continents once were joined.

granitic: light-colored igneous rocks, form from magma rich in silicon and oxygen. (93)
gravitational force: an attractive force that exists between all objects. (19)
Great Red Spot: a giant storm in Jupiter's atmosphere. (613)
greenhouse effect: the process by which heat radiated from Earth's surface is trapped and reflected back to Earth by gases in the atmosphere. (275)
groundwater: water that soaks into the ground and collects in the pore spaces between particles of rock and soil. (182)
Gulf Stream: an ocean current that flows out of the Gulf of Mexico, then northward along the East Coast of the United States, and then toward Europe.
gully erosion: a type of erosion in which water swiftly running down a slope creates large channels in the soil or rock. (149)

H

habitat: any place where organisms live, grow, and interact. (455)
hachures (ha SHOORZ): lines drawn at right angles to contour lines on a topographic map; they indicate depressions.
half-life: the time it takes for half of the atoms of an isotope in an object to decay. (437)
hardness: a measure of how easily a mineral can be scratched. (69)
hazardous waste: waste that is dangerous to organisms because it is poisonous, cancer causing, or radioactive. (510)
Hess, Harry: a Princeton University scientist who proposed the theory of sea-floor spreading in the 1960s.
high pressure system: an air mass with densely packed air molecules, where cold air descends and rotates clockwise (in the Northern Hemisphere).
Homo erectus: an ancestor of modern *Homo sapiens,* this extinct primate lived in Africa and Asia from 1.7 million to 250 000 years ago. (466)
Homo habilis: the earliest species to have fully human characteristics, this extinct primate evolved from *Australopithecus,* lived in Africa 1.5 to 2 million years ago, and regularly used tools. (466)
Homo sapiens: our modern human species, primates having large brains, use of language, and use of complex tools; evolved from *Homo erectus* about half a million years ago. (466)
horizon: a soil layer; most areas of Earth have three, called the A horizon (topsoil), B horizon, and C horizon. (129)
horn: a sharp mountain peak, pointed like an animal's horn, carved by glaciers.
hot spots: areas in Earth's mantle that are hotter than neighboring areas, forming magma that rises toward the crust. (392)
hot spring: a spring of warm groundwater, caused when the water is heated by rocks that contact magma under Earth's surface. (186)
humidity: the amount of water vapor in the air.
humus: dark-colored organic matter made of decaying plants and animals. (129)
hurricane: a large, swirling, low-pressure system with winds of at least 120 km/hour that forms over tropical oceans. (268)
hydroelectric energy: electricity produced by the energy of running water. (490)
hypothesis: a testable prediction for a problem. (16)

I

ice wedging: the breaking of rocks when water in cracks freezes and expands. (124)
igneous rock: rock formed from magma or lava when it cools. (90)
impermeable: rock or soil that has very small pores, preventing water from passing through. (183)
index fossil: a fossil of a species that existed briefly and was widespread geographically, used in determining the relative ages of rock layers. (424)
infrared waves: electromagnetic waves that are the heat waves that we feel.
inner core: the solid center of Earth. (336)
inner planets: the four solid, rocky planets closest to the sun—Mercury, Venus, Earth, and Mars. (602)
International Date Line: the 180° meridian, on the other side of Earth from the prime meridian; an imaginary line in the Pacific Ocean where we change calendar days. (205)
International System of Units (SI): the standard worldwide system of measurement; a modern version of the metric system. (18)
intrusive igneous rocks: igneous rocks that form below Earth's surface. (92)
invertebrates: animals without backbones.
ion: an atom with an electric charge. (36)
ionosphere: a high layer of Earth's atmosphere, made up of ions that reflect radio waves. (231)
irregular galaxies: galaxies having irregular shapes.
isobar: on a weather map, a line connecting points of equal atmospheric pressure. (271)
isotherm: on a weather map, a line connecting points of equal temperature. (271)
isotopes: atoms of the same element that have the same number of protons in their nuclei, but different numbers of neutrons. (32)

J

jet stream: narrow wind belts occurring near the top of the troposphere where trade winds and polar easterlies meet prevailing westerlies. (246)

Jupiter: in our solar system, the fifth planet from the sun; the largest planet, mostly gas and liquid. (612)

K

Kepler, Johannes: German mathematician (1571-1630) who discovered that the planets travel at different speeds and in orbits around the sun.

L

laccolith: a dome-shaped body of igneous rock created when the magma that forms a sill continues to push the rock layers upward. (405)

land breeze: wind blowing from land to sea at night because the land cools faster and cool air over the land flows over the sea. (248)

landfill: an area of land that is excavated and filled with waste. (510)

landforms: features that make up the shape of the land at Earth's surface, such as plains, plateaus, and mountains.

latitude: a distance north or south of the equator, expressed in degrees. (203)

lava: molten rock from a volcano flowing on Earth's surface. (91)

law: a "rule of nature" that describes the behavior of something in nature. (17)

law of superposition: a law stating that, in layers of undisturbed rock, the oldest are on the bottom, and rocks become younger toward the top. (430)

leaching: when minerals are dissolved in water and carried down through a soil profile. (131)

legend: a list of symbols used on a map that explains their meaning.

light pollution: the glow in the night sky caused by city lights. (558)

light-year: a unit used to measure distance in space; the distance that light travels in one year (about 10 trillion km). (631)

lignite: soft, brown coal that is about 30 percent carbon; smoky and polluting when burned. (481)

lithosphere (LITH uh sfihr): the rigid, outermost layer of Earth, about 100 km thick and including the crust and part of the mantle. (349)

Local Group: the cluster of about 25 galaxies that includes our galaxy (the Milky Way).

loess (LES): a thick deposit of very fine, wind-eroded sediments. (164)

longitude: a distance east or west of the prime meridian, expressed in degrees. (203)

longshore current: an ocean current that runs parallel to the shore, caused by waves hitting the shore at a slight angle. (307)

low pressure system: in weather systems, an area where warm air rises and rotates counterclockwise (in the Northern Hemisphere).

lunar eclipse: the passing of Earth between the sun and moon, so that Earth blocks sunlight from reaching all or part of the moon. (588)

luster: the physical property of a mineral that describes how light is reflected from its surface. (70)

M

magma: molten rock beneath Earth's surface. (64)

magnetometer: an instrument that measures the strength of Earth's magnetic field. (346)

magnitude: in earthquake studies, a measure of the energy released by an earthquake; the Richter scale is used to describe earthquake magnitude. (375)

main sequence: on a Hertzsprung-Russell diagram, the diagonal band that includes 90 percent of all stars. (634)

mammals: warm-blooded vertebrates.

mantle: the thickest layer inside Earth; it lies between the outer core and the crust and is solid. (337)

map scale: the relationship between the distances drawn on a map and actual distances on Earth. (210)

maria: dark, flat regions of ancient lava on the moon; viewed from Earth, they resemble oceans, the Latin word for which is *maria.* (589)

market: the people or businesses that want to purchase a product. (517)

Mars: in our solar system, the fourth planet from the sun. (608)

mass: the amount of matter in an object; SI unit is the gram. (18)

mass movement: the sliding of a volume of loose material down a slope, caused by gravity.

mass number: the sum of the protons and neutrons in the nucleus of each atom of an element.

matter: anything that takes up space and has mass. (28)

meander: a curve in a mature stream. (179)

mechanical weathering: the breaking up of rocks without changing their chemical composition. (123)

Mercator (mur KAYT ur) **projection:** a map projection method using parallel longitude lines; continent shapes are accurate, but areas are distorted. (207)

Mercury: in our solar system, the first planet from the sun; the second-smallest planet, it has a cratered surface like our moon. (606)

Mesosaurus (mes oh SAR uhs): a fossil reptile found in both South America and Africa, providing evidence that these continents once were joined.

Mesozoic (mez uh ZOH ihk) **Era:** the middle era of Earth's geologic history; spans 225-65 million years ago. (462)

metallic luster: the physical property of any mineral that has a shiny appearance resembling metal.

metamorphic rock: rock formed from existing rock when the temperature or pressure changes. (95)

meteor: a meteoroid that enters Earth's atmosphere and burns up as it falls. (620)

meteorite: a meteor that reaches Earth's surface. (621)

meteoroid: small pieces of rock that orbit the sun, resulting from the breakup of comets.

meteorologist: a scientist who studies weather conditions, draws weather maps, forecasts weather, and warns of severe weather. (270)

meteorology: the study of Earth's atmosphere, its processes, and weather. (8)

microwaves: electromagnetic waves that are shorter than radio waves, but longer than light waves; we use them for radar and transmitting voice, music, video, and data.

mid-ocean ridge: an underwater mountain range that extends through the middle of most oceans, formed when forces within Earth spread the seafloor apart, causing it to buckle. (313)

mineral: a naturally occurring, nonliving solid with a definite structure and chemical composition. (62)

mixture: a combination of different substances that keep their own physical and chemical properties despite being mixed. (36)

Moho discontinuity: the boundary between Earth's crust and the upper mantle; seismic waves travel slower above the Moho and faster below it. (370)

Mohs' Scale of Hardness: a list of common minerals and their hardnesses, developed by German mineralogist Friedrich Mohs.

mold: a cavity in a rock that has the shape of a fossil that was trapped there; water dissolved the fossil away, leaving its imprint. (421)

molecule: the smallest particle of a compound that still keeps all the properties of the compound; it is made of atoms. (34)

moon colony: a permanent structure on the moon in which people could live and work. (592)

moon phases: the changes in appearance of the moon as it orbits Earth every 29-1/2 days; for example, full moon and new moon. (585)

moraine: a ridge of rock and soil bulldozed ahead of a glacier and along its sides; left behind when the glacier melts.

N

natural gas: a mixture of gases formed as ancient plants and animals decayed; burned as a fossil fuel.

natural selection: the natural process by which some organisms survive and reproduce because they have traits favorable to survival in an environment, while others die out because they lack those traits. (450)

neap tide: a tide that is lower than normal because the sun, Earth, and moon form a right angle.

nebula: a large cloud of gas and dust in space that is the beginning of a star. (637)

nekton (NEK tuhn): sea-dwelling animals that swim, such as fish, turtles, whales, and seals. (319)

Neptune: in our solar system, the eighth planet from the sun; it is large and gaseous. (615)

neutron: one of the two particles that make up the nucleus of an atom; it has no electric charge. (31)

neutron star: the final stage in the life cycle of some stars, where the core collapses and becomes so dense that only neutrons can exist there. (638)

new moon: the moon phase when the side facing Earth is completely dark, because the moon is between Earth and the sun. (585)

nonfoliated: a texture of metamorphic rock, created when mineral grains change, grow, and rearrange but don't form bands. (97)

nonmetallic luster: a physical property of a mineral that does not resemble metal.

nonrenewable energy resources: energy resources (coal, oil, and natural gas) that we are using up faster than natural processes can replace them. (483)

normal fault: a pull-apart (tension) fracture in rocks, where rocks that are above the fault surface drop downward in relation to rocks that are below the fault surface, like this: $\leftarrow_{normal}/^{fault}\rightarrow$. (361)

nuclear energy: energy produced by the fission (splitting) of the nuclei of uranium atoms. (494)

nuclear reactor: a device in which uranium atoms fission to release energy, used to generate electricity.

O

observatory: a building that contains a telescope for observing objects in space. (554)

occluded front: in weather systems, the boundary that results when two cool air masses merge and force warmer air to rise between them.

oceanography: the study of Earth's oceans, their processes, and life within them. (9)

ocean trench: a deep trench in the ocean, caused when one piece of seafloor is pushed beneath another piece. (314)

oil: a liquid formed as ancient plants and animals decay; burned as a fossil fuel and used to make lubricants and plastics.

old stream: a stream that flows very slowly down a gradual slope, through a broad floodplain that it has made, often meandering.

Olympus Mons: the largest volcano in the solar system—on Mars.

Oort Cloud: a cloud of comets surrounding the solar system outside Pluto's orbit; it may be the source of most comets. (619)

orbit: the curved path followed by a satellite as it travels around a star, planet, or other object. (561)

ore: minerals or rocks that contain a useful substance, such as a metal, that can be mined at a profit. (75)

organic evolution: the gradual change in life-forms through time. (449)

organic matter: any material that originated as plant or animal tissue; decaying animals or plants that become sediment and a part of soils.

outer core: a liquid layer of Earth's core that surrounds the solid inner core. (337)

outer planets: the five planets farthest from the sun—Jupiter, Saturn, Uranus, Neptune, and Pluto. (602)

outwash: a glacial deposit left by streams flowing from a melting glacier. (159)

overgrazing: occurs when too many livestock graze too small an area and eat all the grass off the land.

oxidation: chemical weathering that occurs when a substance is exposed to oxygen and water. (126)

ozone layer: a layer of the stratosphere that contains ozone; absorbs ultraviolet radiation from the sun. (236)

P

Pacific Ring of Fire: the area around the Pacific tectonic plate where volcanoes and earthquakes are common due to tectonic movement. (391)

Paleozoic (pay lee uh ZOH ihk) **Era:** the second-oldest era of Earth's geologic history; began when organisms developed hard parts; spans 570 to 225 million years ago. (458)

Pangaea (pan JEE uh): the name Alfred Wegener gave to the landmass that he believed existed before it split apart to form the present continents. (340)

parallax: the apparent shift in position of an object when viewed from two different points, such as your left eye and right eye. (631)

peat: a low-grade, smoky fossil fuel made of decaying plants; the first stage in the development of coal. (481)

pebble: a sediment particle measuring 2.0 mm to 64 mm in size.

penumbra: during an eclipse, the lighter outer portion of the shadow.

periods: subdivisions of eras on the geologic time scale. (449)

permeable: describes rock or soil that has connecting pores that allow water to pass through easily. (183)

petrified remains: plant or animal remains that have been petrified, or "turned to rock"; this happens when minerals carried in groundwater replace the original materials. (420)

photochemical smog: a brown-colored air pollution that forms when sunlight chemically changes the pollutants released by burning fossil fuels. (524)

photosphere: the innermost of the three layers of the sun's atmosphere; radiates the light we see. (643)

photosynthesis (foh toh SIHN thuh sihs): the process that plants use to make food, using light energy and oxygen. (318)

pH scale: a number scale used to describe how acidic or how basic a solution is; an abbreviation of *p*otential of *H*ydrogen. (526)

physical properties: characteristics of an element or compound that affect weight, color, density, and such, but don't affect how it will react with other elements or compounds. (40)

plain: a landform that is a large, relatively flat area. (196)

plankton (PLANK tuhn): plants and animals that drift in seawater; most are microscopic. (319)

plateau: a landform created when forces within Earth raise a flat area of nearly horizontal rocks. (198)

plates: in plate tectonics, sections of Earth's lithosphere (crust and upper mantle). (348)

plate tectonics: the theory that Earth's crust and upper mantle (lithosphere) exist in sections called plates and that these plates slowly move around on the mantle. (348)

plucking: a type of glacial erosion in which rock fragments from sand size to boulders are broken off and carried by the glacier. (156)

Pluto: in our solar system, the ninth and last planet from the sun. (616)

polar easterlies: winds caused by cold polar air. (246)

pollutants: substances that cause harmful changes in the environment; they are produced by both human activities and natural processes.

pollution: the addition of harmful substances to an environment. (322)

population: the number of individuals of a particular species that exists in a specific area. (502)

population explosion: a large increase in the population of a species, due to a rapid reproduction, or a sharply reduced death rate, or both. (503)

Precambrian (pree KAM bree un) **Era:** the oldest and longest era of geologic time, including about 90 percent of Earth's history; spans 4.6 billion to 570 million years ago. (457)

precipitation: water or ice that condenses in the air and falls to the ground as rain, snow, sleet, or hail. (259)

prevailing westerlies: winds between 30° and 60° north and south of the equator that blow opposite to the trade winds and cause much of our weather. (246)

primary waves: waves of energy, released during an earthquake, that travel through Earth by compressing particles in rocks in the same direction the wave is traveling. (367)

prime meridian: an imaginary line running from the North Pole to the South Pole, passing through Greenwich, England; the 0° reference line for longitude. (203)

Project Apollo: a project of the U.S. space program in which astronauts first traveled to the moon in the spacecraft *Apollo 11*. (564)

Project Gemini: an early project of the U.S. space program in which two crewed *Gemini* spacecraft successfully linked in orbit. (563)

Project Mercury: an early project of the U.S. space program in which a crewed spacecraft orbited Earth and returned safely. (563)

prominence: a huge, arching column of gas extending above the sun's surface; associated with sunspots.

proton: one of the two particles that make up the nucleus of an atom; it has a positive electric charge. (31)

psychrometer (si KRAH muh tur): a device used by meteorologists to measure relative humidity.

radiation: the transfer of energy by electromagnetic waves that can travel through space and some materials. (239)

radioactive decay: the decay of an atom of one element to form another element, occurring when an alpha particle or beta particle is expelled from the original atom. (437)

radiometric dating: an absolute dating method that uses the rate of decay of radioactive isotopes in rocks. (438)

radio telescope: an instrument that uses a large antenna to gather radio waves from space, for use in studying space objects and communicating with artificial satellites and probes. (554)

radio waves: electromagnetic waves having long wavelengths; we use them to transmit voice, music, video, and data over distances.

recyclable: describes a product that can be reprocessed into the same product or a similar one; for example, an aluminum can might be recycled to make other aluminum cans or foil. (516)

red shift: a kind of Doppler shift in which light from a star that is moving away from us has its wavelength shifted toward the red end of the spectrum.

reef: in the ocean, a large underwater colony of coral animals that have become cemented together. (321)

reflecting telescope: an optical instrument that uses a concave mirror, a flat mirror, and a convex lens to magnify distant objects. (554)

refracting telescope: an optical instrument that uses two convex lenses to magnify distant objects. (554)

relative dating: determining the order of events and the relative age of rocks (older or younger) by examining the positions of rocks in layers. (431)

relative humidity: the amount of water vapor actually in the air, compared to the maximum it can hold; it varies with temperature and is between 0 percent and 100 percent. (256)

renewable energy resources: energy resources (sun, wind, and water power) that are constantly being replenished. (486)

reptiles: vertebrate animals having dry, scaly skin that prevents loss of body fluids so they can survive out of the water on dry land. (460)

respiration (res pur AY shun): the process used by all organisms to combine oxygen with food so that the energy in food can be used. (318)

reverse fault: a compression fracture in rocks, where rocks that are above the fault surface are forced up over rocks that are below the fault surface, like this: $\rightarrow^{\text{reverse}}/_{\text{fault}}\leftarrow$. (362)

revolution: the orbiting of one object around another, like Earth revolving around the sun. (579)

Richter (RIHK tur) scale: describes how much energy is released by an earthquake.

rift zone: an area in the middle of some oceans that contains a system of cracks where the seafloor is rifting, or spreading apart. (313)

rill erosion: a type of erosion in which water swiftly running down a slope creates small channels in the soil; these channels can enlarge into gullies. (149)

Robinson projection: a map projection method using curved longitude lines; continent shapes and land areas are accurate, with little distortion. (207)

rock: Earth material made of one or more minerals. (87)

rock cycle: the processes by which, over many years, Earth materials change back and forth among magma, igneous rocks, sedimentary rocks, and metamorphic rocks. (87)

rock-forming minerals: a group of minerals that make up most of the rocks in Earth's crust.

rotation: the spinning of an object around its axis. (577)

runoff: water that neither soaks into the ground nor evaporates, but instead flows across Earth's surface and eventually into streams, lakes, or oceans. (174)

Safe Drinking Water Act: this 1986 law sets safety standards for drinking water in the U.S. (536)

salinity: a measure of the amount of solids (mostly salts) dissolved in seawater. (284)

salt marsh: a saltwater marsh by the ocean that is a breeding ground for many ocean organisms. (300)

sand: a sediment particle measuring 0.06 mm to 2.0 mm in size.

sanitary landfill: a waste-disposal area that is excavated, lined with leakproof material, and filled with layers of waste and dirt. (510)

satellite: any object that revolves around another object; planets and human-made satellites are examples. (560)

saturated (SACH uh rayt id): condition when all the spaces in a solid, liquid, or gas are filled with another substance: air is saturated with water when the relative humidity is 100 percent; a saltwater solution is saturated when it can dissolve no more salt; a rock or soil is saturated with water when it can hold no more. (256)

Saturn: in our solar system, the sixth planet from the sun; it is the second-largest planet, is mostly gas and liquid, and has prominent rings. (613)

science: the process of observing, explaining, and understanding our world; means "having knowledge." (7)

scientific methods: the problem-solving procedures used by scientists that may or may not include the following basic steps: define the problem, make a hypothesis, test the hypothesis, analyze the results, and draw conclusions. (16)

scrubber: a device that "scrubs" the exhaust from coal-burning power plants to reduce the amount of sulfur gases released into the air. (531)

Sea Beam: a system of 16 sonar (sound echo) devices on a ship to measure the depth of the seafloor. (215)

sea breeze: wind blowing from sea to land during the day when the sun warms the land faster and cool air from above the water forces the warm air above the land to rise. (247)

sea-floor spreading: the theory that magma from Earth's mantle rises to the surface at the mid-ocean ridge and cools to form new seafloor, which new magma slowly pushes away from the ridge. (344)

seamount: an underwater volcano.

secondary waves: waves of energy, released during an earthquake, that travel through Earth by moving particles in rocks at right angles to the direction the wave is traveling. (367)

sediment: loose materials such as rock fragments and mineral grains that have been transported by wind, water, or glaciers. (100)

sedimentary rock: rock formed when sediments become pressed or cemented together. (100)

seismic-safe: describes structures that are resistant to movements from an earthquake. (380)

seismic waves: the energy waves that make the ground quake during an earthquake. (366)

seismograph: an instrument that records earthquake waves. (375)

seismologist: a scientist who studies earthquakes and seismic waves. (375)

shadow zone: the area where seismic waves cannot reach because Earth's liquid outer core bends primary waves and stops secondary waves.

shearing forces: along strike-slip faults, forces that push on rocks from various directions, causing them to twist and break.

sheet erosion: a type of erosion in which water flowing over a gentle slope slowly removes sediment from the entire surface. (149)

shield volcano: a broad volcano with gently sloping sides, built by quiet eruptions of runny basaltic lava, which spreads out in flat layers; example: the Hawaiian Islands. (399)

shore zone: the land area at the ocean's edge between high tide and low tide. (306)

silicate: a mineral containing silicon and oxygen (often with other elements); the largest group of minerals. (66)

sill: a small body of igneous rock that forms when magma is squeezed into a horizontal crack and then solidifies. (405)

silt: a sediment particle measuring 0.004 mm to 0.06 mm in size.

sinkhole: a depression in the ground caused when groundwater dissolves limestone beneath the hole, causing the ground to collapse.

slump: a type of mass movement in which loose material slowly moves downhill a short distance, leaving a curved scar. (144)

smog: air pollution seen around cities, resulting from burning fossil fuels.

soil: a mixture of weathered rock and decaying organic matter (plants and animals). (128)

soil profile: a vertical section of soil layers (horizons). (129)

solar cell: a device that collects solar energy and converts it into electricity. (488)

solar eclipse: the passing of the moon directly between Earth and the sun, so that the moon blocks sunlight from reaching Earth. (587)

solar energy: energy from the sun. (488)

solar flare: an intense bright spot in the sun's chromosphere, associated with sunspots and radio interference on Earth.

solar system: a system of nine planets and many other objects that orbit our sun. (601)

solstice: the two times each year that Earth's tilt makes the sun reach its greatest angle north or south of the equator, marking the start of summer or winter. (582)

solution: a mixture of different substances, occurring without chemical reaction. Usually one substance is dissolved in another.

sonar: the use of sound wave echoes to detect the size and shape of structures found under water. (215)

space probe: an instrument that travels through space to probe for information and transmit it back to Earth. (561)

space shuttle: a reusable spacecraft that transports astronauts, satellites, and other material between Earth and space. (568)

space station: a facility in space with living quarters, workspace, and its own environmental control and power generation equipment. (569)

species: a group of organisms that are similar to each other and that typically reproduce only with each other. (449)

sphere: a round, three-dimensional object whose surface at all points is the same distance from its center. (576)

spiral galaxy: a galaxy having spiral arms.

spring: the point at which the water table meets Earth's surface, causing water to flow from the ground. (184)

spring tide: a tide level greater than normal because the moon, Earth, and sun are aligned.

stalactite: an icicle-like deposit of calcite hanging from the ceiling of a cave.

stationary front: in weather systems, a warm front or cold front that has stopped moving.

station model: in weather forecasting, a group of meteorological symbols that depict weather information for a location on a weather map. (271)

streak: the color of a mineral when it is powdered, usually observed by rubbing the mineral on a ceramic streak plate. (70)

striations (stri AY shunz): long, parallel scars in rocks, caused by rock fragments being dragged across them, often by a glacier.

strike-slip fault: a break in rocks where rocks on either side of the fault move past each other (instead of above or below each other). (363)

strip mine: mine in which resources such as coal or iron ore are removed by digging at Earth's surface, instead of through underground tunnels. (108)

subduction zone: in plate tectonics, a boundary where an ocean plate collides with a continental plate, and the denser ocean plate slides beneath the less-dense continental plate. (350)

sulfurous smog: a gray-colored air pollution created when power plants and home furnaces burn fossil fuels, releasing sulfur compounds and smoke particles. (525)

sunspot: a dark spot on the sun's surface that shows up because it is cooler than surrounding areas. (643)

superconductor: a material that allows electricity to pass through it without resistance. (48)

supergiant: a late stage in the life cycle of a very large star, when the core reaches high temperatures, heavy elements form by fusion, and the star's outer layers expand. (638)

supernova: a late stage in the life cycle of some stars where the core collapses, causing the outer portion to explode.

surface current: an ocean current found in the upper few hundred meters of seawater. (288)

surface waves: waves of energy, released during an earthquake, that reach Earth's surface and travel outward from the epicenter in all directions. (367)

synfuel: a human-made energy source, usually involving conversion of a fossil fuel into a different form (*syn*thetic + *fuel*). (491)

T

technology: the useful application of scientific knowledge. (10)

temperate zones: the two areas of moderate, seasonal weather that exist between the tropics and the polar regions. (272)

tension: stretching forces that can be strong enough to pull rocks apart at divergent plate boundaries.

tephra: lava that is blasted into the air by violent volcanic eruptions and solidifies as it falls to the ground as ash, cinders, and volcanic bombs. (399)

terraces: broad, steplike cuts in the side of a slope. (152)

theory: an explanation backed by results from repeated tests, experiments, or observations. (17)

thermal pollution: the addition of heat to a lake, stream, or ocean by power plants and other industries, which kills organisms that cannot quickly adapt to the warmer water. (324)

third quarter: the moon phase halfway between full moon and new moon, when half of the side facing Earth is lighted. (586)

tidal energy: electricity generated by the ocean tides.

tidal range: the vertical distance between high tide and low tide. (294)

tide: the periodic change in the surface level of the oceans due to the gravitational force of the sun and moon on Earth. (294)

till: a mixture of boulders, sand, silt, and clay left by a melting glacier. (159)

Titan: Saturn's largest moon.

topographic map: a map that uses contour lines to show the varying elevations of Earth's surface. (208)

topsoil: the top layer of soil, also called the A horizon; usually contains humus and is dark in color.

tornado: a small, violent, whirling, funnel-shaped, low pressure windstorm that moves in a narrow path over land. (266)

trace fossils: footprints, worm holes, burrows, and other traces of animal activity preserved in rock.

trade winds: steady winds, about 15° north and south of the equator, caused by cool descending air. (246)

transform fault: in plate tectonics, a boundary between two plates that are sliding past one another. (352)

trilobites (TRI luh bites): shield-shaped marine invertebrate animals commonly found as fossils in Paleozoic Era rocks but are now extinct.

Triton: Neptune's largest moon.

troposphere: the lowest layer of Earth's atmosphere, in which we live, and where clouds and weather occur. (231)

trough: the lowest part of a wave. (292)

tsunami (soo NAHM ee): an ocean wave caused by an earthquake. (377)

turbine: a machine with fan blades that spin when water or air pushes on them; it turns a generator to produce electricity. (299)

ultraviolet radiation: a type of energy that comes to Earth from the sun and is mostly absorbed in the ozone layer. (236)

ultraviolet waves: electromagnetic waves that are a little shorter than light waves; they cause sunburn and skin cancer.

umbra: during an eclipse, the darker central portion of the shadow

unconformity: one or more missing layers in a sequence of rocks; this causes a gap in the time record. (432)

uniformitarianism: a basic principle of geology stating that Earth processes occurring today are similar to those that occurred in the past. (439)

upwarped mountains: landforms created when forces within Earth push up the crust. (200)

upwelling: the rising of cold, nutrient-rich water from deep in the ocean to the surface. (291)

Uranus: in our solar system, the seventh planet from the sun; it is large, gaseous, and is the only planet that "lays on its side" in orbit. (614)

Valles Marineris: a huge rift on Mars that is more than 4000 km long.

valley glacier: the commonest type of glacier, occurring locally in mountain valleys where the average temperature allows snow to accumulate faster than it can melt.

variable: in an experiment, the factor that you change to see what will happen. (17)

vent: in volcanic regions, an opening in Earth's surface through which flow lava, ash, and steam. (389)

Venus: in our solar system, the second planet from the sun; it is very similar in size to Earth, is blanketed with dense clouds, and is very hot. (607)

vertebrates: animals with backbones; evolved during the Ordovician Period.

visible light: electromagnetic waves having short wavelengths; the only part of the electromagnetic spectrum that we can see.

volcanic mountains: mountains created when magma within Earth escapes to the surface, building cones of lava and ash. (201)

volcanic neck: the core of a volcano's vent that remains after the outer layers of lava and tephra have been eroded away from an extinct volcano. (405)

volcano: a mountain built of lava and volcanic ash, which erupt from a vent over rising magma. (388)

volume: the amount of space occupied by an object; SI unit is the cubic meter (m^3).

waning: describes the moon as its visible lighted area grows smaller during the lunar cycle. (586)

waning crescent: the shrinking slice of lighted moon when the visible lighted area is decreasing from third quarter to new moon.

waning gibbous: the shrinking area of moon as the visible lighted area is decreasing from full moon to third quarter.

warm front: the moving boundary that develops when a warm air mass meets a cold air mass.

water cycle: the continual worldwide movement of water evaporating from the ocean into the atmosphere as water vapor, then to the ground as precipitation, and then back into the ocean through runoff. (173)

water diversion: changing the natural flow of water to another location by using dams, canals, or pipelines. (189)

water table: the top of the zone of saturation (the area where all of the pores in a rock are completely filled with water). (183)

wave height: the vertical distance between the crest and trough of a wave. (292)

wavelength: the distance between a point on one wave and the identical point on the next wave; for example, the distance between two crests. (292)

waxing: describes the moon as its visible lighted area grows larger during the lunar cycle. (585)

waxing crescent: the growing slice of moon when the visible lighted area is increasing from new moon to first quarter.

waxing gibbous: the growing area of visible lighted moon as the lighted area is increasing from first quarter to full moon.

weather: the behavior of the atmosphere—wind, temperature, pressure, precipitation—at a particular place and time. (254)

weathering: the breaking of rocks into smaller pieces, either mechanically or chemically. (123)

Wegener, Alfred: a German scientist who proposed the idea of continental drift in 1915.

weight: a measure of the force of gravity on an object. (19)

white dwarf: a late stage in a star's life cycle where its core runs out of fuel and its unstable outer layers escape into space, leaving the white-hot core. (638)

wind farm: a place having steady winds where windmills are installed to generate electricity. (490)

X rays: electromagnetic waves having very short wavelengths; they can penetrate many materials; we use them to see inside our bodies and some materials.

young stream: a stream that flows swiftly down a steep slope or a valley with steep sides, causing rapid erosion.

zone of saturation: an area where all the pores in a rock are completely filled with water, usually near the ground surface. (183)

INDEX

The Index for *Merrill Earth Science* will help you locate major topics in the book quickly and easily. Each entry in the index is followed by the numbers of the pages on which the entry is discussed. A page number given in **boldface type** indicates the page on which that entry is defined. A page number given in *italic type* indicates a page on which the entry is used in an illustration or photograph. The abbreviation *act.* indicates a page on which the entry is used in an Activity.

PHOTO CREDITS

Cover, Galen Rowell/Mountain Light; **iv,** Tim Courlas; **v,** (l) Smithsonian Institution, (r) Jack S. Grove/Tom Stack & Associates; **vi,** (t) courtesy GeoGraphix, Inc., (b) Floyd Holdman/The Stock Solution; **vii,** (t) Studiohio, (b) Science Source/Photo Researchers; **viii,** (t) Studiohio, (b) courtesy Dr. Adam Dziewonski, Harvard University; **ix,** © Chip Clark; **x,** (t) Tim Courlas, (b) Studiohio; **xi,** (l) NASA, (r) Studiohio; **xii,** NASA; **xiii,** Doug Martin; **xv,** Tim Courlas; **xvi,** (t) Elaine Comer Shay, (b) Doug Martin; **xviii,** Studiohio; **xx,** Doug Martin; **2-3,** Steve Lissau; **4,** Tom Sanders/Adventure Photo; **5,** Kenji Kerins; **6,** Tim Courlas; **7,** (t) Hickson-Bender Photography, (bl) A. B. Dowsett/Science Photo Library/Photo Researchers, (br) Tim Courlas; **8,** (t) Krafft/Explorer/Photo Researchers, (b) Dan McCoy from Rainbow; **10,** (l) Hickson & Associates, (r) Milepost Corporation; **11,** (t) Merrill photo, (b) Tim Courlas; **12,** Bob Daemmrich Photography; **13,** Todd Powell/ProFiles West; **14, 16, 18,** Milepost Corporation; **19,** Hickson & Associates; **20,** (l) Milepost Corporation, (r) Doug Martin; **21,** Tim Courlas; **22,** Doug Martin; **25,** First Image; **26,** Milepost Corporation; **27,** Studiohio; **28,** Steve Lissau; **29,** Studiohio; **30,** (brc) Kenji Kerins, (others) Doug Martin; **31,** Animals Animals/Donald Specker; **32,** Studiohio; **33, 34,** Tim Courlas; **35,** courtesy IBM Corporation; **36,** First Image; **37,** Doug Martin; **38,** First Image; **40,** (l) Studiohio, (r) Tim Courlas; **41,** Gary Braasch/Woodfin Camp & Associates; **42, 43,** Studiohio; **44,** (t) Doug Martin, (b) Gary Ladd; **45,** Cameramann Internat'l. Ltd./The Image Works; **46,** Larry Ulrich/DRK Photo; **47,** NASA; **48,** Rich Brommer; **49,** Runk/Schoenberger from Grant Heilman; **52,** Hickson-Bender Photography; **54,** (t) Center for Astrophysics/Harvard-Smithsonian Astrophysical Laboratory, (b) courtesy Dr. Julian G. Rosenmann, Department of Radiation Oncology, University of North Carolina at Chapel Hill; **55,** (t) David Parker/Science Photo Library/Photo Researchers, (c) courtesy Bridgestone Corporation, Japan, (b) Allen Russell/ProFiles West; **56,** (tl, br) Doug Martin, (tr) Kenji Kerins, (bl) courtesy Corning Glass; **57,** "Nora, 1979," © David Em/Represented by Spieckerman Associates, San Francisco; **58-59,** Karen Kasmauski/Woodfin Camp & Associates, (inset) NASA; **60,** courtesy Akzo Salt, Inc.; **61,** Studiohio; **62,** (t) file photo, (others) Studiohio; **63, 64, 65, 67,** Doug Martin; **68,** (tl) Roger K. Burnard, (trc) Smithsonian Institution, (others) Craig Kramer; **69, 70,** Doug Martin; **71,** (t) First Image, (b) Doug Martin; **72,** Craig Kramer; **73,** Doug Martin; **74,** (l, r) Ward's Natural Science, (lc) Field Museum of Natural History, (rc) D.C.H. Plowes; **75,** (t) E. Alan McGee/FPG, (bl) Doug Martin, (br) Studiohio; **76,** courtesy Dr. Andrzej Badzian, Pennsylvania State University; **77,** Paolo Koch/Photo Researchers; **78,** (t) Craig Kramer, (b) Bob Daemmrich/The Image Works; **79,** Gold Information Center; **80,** John Chiasson/Gamma-Liaison; **82,** Elaine Comer Shay; **84,** P. & G. Bowater/The Image Bank; **85,** Studiohio; **86,** (b) Linda Young, (others) Doug Martin; **87, 88, 90, 91,** Doug Martin; **92,** (t) Doug Martin, (b) Soames Summerhays/Photo Researchers; **94,** (l) Doug Martin, (r) Earth Scenes/Breck P. Kent; **95,** Doug Martin; **96,** Michael Kreisler Photography, Fairfield, IA/courtesy Granitech Corp.; **97,** (l) Phil Degginger/Color-Pic, Inc., (r) Earth Scenes/E. R. Degginger; **98,** Alpha/FPG; 99, **100,** Doug Martin; **102,** G. R. Roberts; **103,** (t) Craig Kramer, (b) Tim Cairns; **104,** (t) Elaine Comer Shay, (b) Tom Bean; **105,** Aaron Haupt; **106,** (l) Studiohio, (r) Kevin Schafer/Tom Stack & Associates; **108,** Chris Niedenthal/Black Star; **110,** ODNR, Division of Reclamation; **113,** Ward's Natural Science; **114,** (t) Merrill photo, (b) Kennecott Explorations; **115,** (t) Tracy I. Borland, (b) Giraudon/Art Resource; **116,** (tl) Kenji Kerins, (tr) Hickson & Associates, (b) Doug Martin; **117,** SuperStock; **118-119,** Tom Bean, (inset) G. R. Roberts; **120,** Jack S. Grove/Tom Stack & Associates; **121,** Studiohio; **122,** (l) Bill Ross/Woodfin Camp & Associates, (r) Dale Jorgenson/Tom Stack & Associates; **123,** Studiohio; **124,** Bud Fowle; **125,** Doug Martin; **126,** Tom Bean; **127,** Weldon King/FPG; **129,** Studiohio; **130,** Doug Martin; **131,** William E. Ferguson; **132,** (t) Tim Courlas, (b) Doug Martin; **133,** (l) file photo, (r) Larry Koons; **134,** (tl) Studiohio, (tc) Tim Cairns, (tr) Tom Hollyman/Photo Researchers, (b) Studiohio; **135,** Library of Congress; **136,** Kenneth W. Fink/Photo Researchers; **138,** Studiohio; **140,** Ron Thomas/FPG; **141,** Studiohio; **142,** Grant Heilman from Grant Heilman Photography; **143,** Studiohio; **144,** Thomas G. Rampton from Grant Heilman; **146,** Lawrence S. Burr/Sygma; **147,** Curt Schieber; **149,** Tom Till/DRK Photo; **151,** NASA; **153,** SuperStock; **155,** (l) Wolfgang Kaehler, (r) Roger K. Burnard; **156,** Thomas Kitchin/Tom Stack & Associates; **157,** James Westwater; **158,** William D. Popejoy; **160,** John Barger; **161,** Doug Martin; **162,** (l) Debbie Dean, (r) Earth Scenes/M. J. Coe; **163,** Floyd Holdman/The Stock Solution; **164,** Michael Collier; **165,** Steve Lissau; **166,** Doug Martin; **168,** Studiohio; **170,** Doug Lee/Tom Stack & Associates; **171,** Studiohio; **172,** NASA; **174,** (l) Doug Martin, (r) Lindsay Gerard/Merrill; **175,** Grant Heilman Photography; **176,** Larry Hamill; **178,** (t) Pictures Unlimited, (b) First Image; **179,** Larry Hamill; **180,** Doug Martin; **181,** Wendy Shattil & Bob Rozinski/Tom Stack & Associates; **182,** Studiohio; **185,** Doug Martin; **187,** (l) M. Timothy O'Keefe/Tom Stack & Associates, (r) Steve Lissau; **188,** Tim Cairns; **189,** (t) Byron Augustin/Tom Stack & Associates, (b) Len Rue Jr./DRK Photo; **190,** (l) Gary Milburn/Tom Stack & Associates, (r) Joe Sohn/The Image Works; **194,** NASA; **195,** Studiohio; **196,** Wayne Lynch/DRK Photo; **198,** Peter French/DRK Photo; **199,** Earth Scenes/Jim Tuten; **200,** (t) Tom Till/DRK Photo, (b) Robert Frerck/Woodfin Camp & Associates; **201,** Michael Giannechini/Photo Researchers; **208,** USGS; **209,** courtesy of GeoGraphix, Inc.; **211, 212,** USGS; **213,** Doug Martin; **214,** NOAA; **216,** Doug Martin; **220,** (t) Allen Russell/ProFiles West, (b) David M. Dennis; **221,** (t) Ed Nagele/FPG, (b) NASA; **222,** (tl) Bob Daemmrich Photography, (tr) David R. Frazier/The Stock Solution, (bl) Studiohio, (br) Doug Martin; **223,** Mark E. Gibson; **224-225,** NASA/Science Source/Photo Researchers, (inset) Walter Stricklin/Stock South; **226,** SuperStock; **227,** Mary Lou Uttermohlen; **228,** Morgan Photos; **229,** Tony Freeman/PhotoEdit; **233,** Doug Martin; **240,** Earth Scenes/Doug Wechsler; **243,** Doug Martin; **251,** Studiohio; **252,** A. & J. Verkaik/The Stock Market; **253,** Mary Lou Uttermohlen; **254,** Robert Brenner/PhotoEdit; **256,** (t) Mary Lou Uttermohlen, (b) Doug Martin; **257,** SuperStock; **258,** (l to r, t to b) file photo, William D. Popejoy, Betty Crowell, David M. Dennis, Betty Crowell, William Tucker/Uniphoto, Betty Crowell, James Fullmer, David R. Frazier, David M. Dennis; **259, 261,** Doug Martin; **265,** Keith Kent/Science Photo Library/Photo Researchers; **266,** Larry Miller/Photo Researchers; **267,** NOAA; **269,** SuperStock; **271,** Bill Bachman/Photo Researchers; **275,** Jacques Jangoux/Peter Arnold, Inc.; **278, 279,** Science Source/Photo Researchers; **280,** Brian Parker/Tom Stack & Associates; **281,** Doug Martin; **282,** (l) Steve Ogden/Tom Stack & Associates, (r) SuperStock; **285,** Dan McCoy from Rainbow; **286,** Doug Martin; **287,** NOAA; **289,** O. Brown, R. Evans, and J. Brown/University of Miami/RSMAS; **290,** Studiohio;

713

293, Doug Martin; **294,** Steve Lissau; **295,** Travelpix/FPG; **297,** Doug Martin; **298,** Cameramann Internat'l Ltd.; **300,** Animals Animals/Alfred B. Thomas; **304,** Al Satterwhite/The Image Bank; **305,** Kenji Kerins; **306,** SuperStock; **308,** Larry Ulrich/DRK Photo; **309,** Studiohio; **310,** G. R. Roberts; **313,** "The Floor of the Oceans," Bruce C. Heezen and Marie Tharp, © 1980 by Marie Tharp. Reproduced by permission of Marie Tharp; **316,** Thomas Kitchin/Tom Stack & Associates; **317,** Emory Kristof/National Geographic Society; **318,** Wood's Hole Oceanographic Institute; **319,** Animals Animals/Mickey Gibson; **320,** Norbert Wu/Peter Arnold, Inc.; **321,** Charles Seaborn/Woodfin Camp & Associates; **323,** SuperStock; **324,** Randy Brandon/Peter Arnold, Inc.; **326-327,** David Hall/The Image Works; **328,** (t) SuperStock, (b) Dr. Robert Hessler, Scripps Institution of Oceanography; **329,** Robert Holland/DRK Photo; **330,** (tl) Steve Lissau, (tr) Cobalt Productions, (bl) Ken Frick, (br) file photo; **331,** Pictorial Parade; **332-333,** Dennis Oda/Photo Resource Hawaii, (inset) © Brookhouse Associates 1988/The Travel Image; **334,** Tom Van Sant/GeoSphere Project; **335,** First Image; **338,** courtesy Dr. Adam Dziewonski, Harvard University; **339,** Scripps Institute of Oceanography; **341,** courtesy Sageware Corp.; **342,** Ullstein Bilderdienst; **344,** First Image; **347,** Doug Martin; **356,** Chip Isenhort/Tom Stack & Associates; **358,** Robert Parker/Black Star; **359,** Studiohio; **362,** (t) Greg Vaughn/Tom Stack & Associates, (b) Earth Scenes/Mike Andrews; **363,** Kevin Schafer/Tom Stack & Associates; **364,** © Click the Photo Connection; **368,** David Parker/Science Photo Library/Photo Researchers; **371,** Studiohio; **374,** Wernher Krutein/Gamma-Liaison; **376,** courtesy Waverly Person, Nat'l. Earthquake Info. Center/USGS; **378,** © 1989 *San Francisco Chronicle,* All Rights Reserved. Used by permission; **380,** James Stanfield, © National Geographic Society; **381,** Francois Gohier/Photo Researchers; **386,** Steve Kaufman/Peter Arnold, Inc.; **387,** Doug Martin; **389,** K. & M. Krafft/Photo Researchers; **390,** SuperStock; **395,** Franco Salmoiraghi/Photo Resource Hawaii; **396-397,** Keith Ronnholm; **398,** © Ministry of Construction for Osumi/Fujifotos/The Image Works; **399,** Earth Scenes/Breck P. Kent; **400,** (t) Tom Bean/DRK Photo, (b) David Weintraub/Photo Researchers; **401, 403,** Doug Martin; **404,** Earth Scenes/L.L.T. Rhodes; **406,** Greg Vaughn; **408,** SuperStock; **410,** (t) Luana George/Black Star, (b) © MacDonald *et al.,* "Nature," 1988; **411,** (t) Field Museum of Natural History, (b) from a painting by Heinrich Berann, courtesy Aluminum Company of America; **412,** (tl) David R. Frazier Photolibrary, (tr) David Parker/Science Photo Library/Photo Researchers, (bl) National Park Service, (br) Skip Comer Photography; **413,** The Metropolitan Museum of Art, Henry L. Phillips Collection, Bequest of Henry L. Phillips, 1939 (JP 2986); **414-415,** Bildarchiv Okapia 1989/Photo Researchers, (inset) Barry L. Runk from Grant Heilman; **416,** John Cancalosi/Peter Arnold, Inc.; **417,** Studiohio; **420,** Tom Algire/Tom Stack & Associates; **421,** Gerard/Shay Photography; **422,** Museum of Comparative Zoology/Dr. Paul A. Zahl/Photo Researchers; **424,** Stephen Trimble/DRK Photo; **427,** © Chip Clark; **428,** Steve Elmore/TSW; **430,** Kenji Kerins; **443,** John Cancalosi/Peter Arnold, Inc.; **445,** Kenji Kerins; **449,** (l) Animals Animals/Barbara J. Wright, (c) Robert Barclay from Grant Heilman, (r) Gerard Lacz/Peter Arnold, Inc.; **450,** Animals Animals/Breck P. Kent; **453,** Ben Simmons/The Stock Market; **454,** Zoological Museum, Tring; **455,** © Boyd Norton; **456,** Kenji Kerins; **458,** Fred Bavendam/Peter Arnold, Inc.; **459,** Field Museum of Natural History; **460,** Doug Martin; **461,** Animals Animals/Zig Leszczynski; **464,** Michael Collier; **465,** Runk/Schoenberger from Grant Heilman; **470,** Jonathan Blair/Woodfin Camp & Associates; **472,** David M. Stone, Photo/Nats; **473,** Stephen Green-Armytage/The Stock Market; **474,** (tl) First Image, (tr) Kenji Kerins, (bl) Roger K. Burnard, (br) Smithsonian Institution; **475,** by permission of the Syndics of Cambridge University Library; **476-477,** Photo by John B. Carnett © 1990 *Popular Science,* (inset) NASA; **478,** The Image Bank; **479,** Kenji Kerins; **480,** (l) Tim Courlas, (r) Allen Zak; **482,** (t) John Colwell from Grant Heilman, (b) Elaine Comer Shay; **484,** Tim Courlas; **486,** SuperStock; **487,** Ken Frick; **488,** NASA; **489,** (t) Greg Vaughn/Tom Stack & Associates, (b) SuperStock; **490,** T. J. Florian/Rainbow; **491,** SuperStock; **492,** Merrill photo; **493,** Doug Martin; **496,** V. Zufarov/TASS/Sovfoto; **499,** Mark Antman/The Image Works; **500,** Thomas Kitchin/Tom Stack & Associates; **501,** Milepost Corporation; **502,** SuperStock; **505,** Milepost Corporation; **507,** Grant Heilman Photography; **508,** (t) Fred Ward/Black Star, (b) Doug Wilson/The Stock Solution; **511,** Milepost Corporation; **512,** © John Fowler; **513,** Milepost Corporation; **515,** Doug Martin; **517,** Kenji Kerins; **520,** Studiohio; **522,** © James Randklev/AllStock; **523,** Milepost Corporation; **524,** SuperStock; **526,** John Shaw/Tom Stack & Associates; **531,** Milepost Corporation; **532,** Graham Finlayson/TSW; **534,** (l) Kenji Kerins, (r) Barbara Pfeiffer/Peter Arnold, Inc.; **535,** (l) courtesy City of San Diego Dept. of Water Utilities, (r) Earth Scenes/E. R. Degginger; **536,** Hanson Carroll/FPG; **542,** Kenji Kerins; **544,** (t) Grant Heilman Photography, (bl) John Cancalosi/Tom Stack & Associates, (br) courtesy Society of Automotive Engineers; **545,** (t) Farrell Grehan/Photo Researchers, (b) Gary I. Rothstein; **546,** (tl) Jack D. Swenson/Tom Stack & Associates, (tr) Kenji Kerins, (bl) Mark Burnett/Merrill photo, (br) Doug Martin; **547,** Erich Hartmann/Magnum; **548-549,** NASA, (inset) file photo; **550,** Earth Scenes/Breck P. Kent; **551,** Doug Martin; **552,** (l) file photo, (r) Kenji Kerins; **553,** Kenji Kerins; **555, 556,** NASA; **559,** NOOA; **564,** Studiohio; **565,** NASA; **566, 567,** Ken Frick; **568, 570,** NASA; **574,** Alan Kearney/FPG; **575,** Tim Courlas; **578,** Latent Image; **580, 583,** Doug Martin; **587,** NASA; **588,** Hansen Planetarium; **590, 592,** NASA; **594,** *World Book Encyclopedia;* **596, 598,** NASA; **599,** Milepost Corporation; **600,** (l) courtesy the Patrick Moore Collection, (r) courtesy The Royal Society, London; **604,** Scala/Art Resource; **606, 607,** NASA; **608,** (l) NASA, (r) NASA/USGS, Flagstaff; **611,** © VPL Research 1991, Sydney Stein; **612, 613, 615, 616,** NASA; **619,** European Space Agency; **620,** (t) James M. Baker, (b) John Sanford/Science Photo Library/Photo Researchers; **624,** JPL; **626,** file photo; **627,** Tim Courlas; **629,** Bill Belknap/Photo Researchers; **630,** Tim Courlas; **632,** Michael Tcherevkoff/The Image Bank; **633,** Kenji Kerins; **638,** David F. Malin/Anglo-Australian Observatory; **639,** Joe Stancampiano & Karl Luttrell/IMB Collaboration; **640,** Royal Observatory, Edinburgh; **641,** Milepost Corporation; **643,** (l) Tersch, (r) file photo; **644,** NASA; **645,** California Institute of Technology and Carnegie Institute of Washington; **646,** (l) Studiohio, (r) National Optical Astronomy Observatories; **647,** (l) file photo, (r) Dennis di Cicco/Sky & Telescope; **648,** David Malin/Anglo-Australian Telescope Board; **651,** Dan McCoy from Rainbow; **652,** NASA; **653,** JPL; **655,** AURA, Inc.; **658,** (t) © Herbert K. Barnett, (bl) David R. Frazier, (br) NASA; **659,** (t) R. E. Schmidt, U.S. Naval Observatory, (b) Mary Evans Picture Library; **660,** (tl) Dan McCoy from Rainbow, (others) NASA; **661,** "The Arecibo Observatory is part of the National Astronomy and Ionosphere Center which is operated by Cornell University under a cooperative agreement with the National Science Foundation"; **680,** Ken Frick; **681,** (t) Hurricane Research Division, Atlantic Oceanic Meteorological Laboratory, (b) Tracy I. Borland; **682,** (t) Ken Frick, (b) Lloyd Lemmermann; **683,** Janet L. Adams; **684,** Ken Frick; **685,** Doug Martin; **687, 689, 690,** Ken Frick.